Contents

Foreword by Cellnet 5

Introduction 11

How to Use this Guide 14

Starred Restaurants wit[h] 16

De Luxe Hotels 19

1993 Awards

Hotel of the Year 20
Restaurant of the Year 21
Chef of the Year 22
Dessert of the Year 23
British Cheeseboard of the Year 28
Cellar of the Year 32
California Cellar of the Year 36
Hosts of the Year 42

Cellnet

New tariff opportunities 44

London

Hotels and Restaurants 49

Serviced Apartments 182

Places of Interest 200

Quick Reference Lists
(London)

Hotels under £80 for 2 204
Restaurants under £40 for 2 204
Town House Hotels 205
Private House Hotels 205
Hotels with Sporting Facilities 205
Restaurants with Non-Smoking Areas 206
Romantic Dinners 206
Open Air Eating 206
Early Evening Eating 207
Late Night Eating 208
Sunday Eating 211
National Cuisines 213
Seafood Restaurants 216
Outstanding Desserts 216
Outstanding Cheeseboards 217
Outstanding Wine Lists 218
California Wines 218
Wines by the Glass 218

Cellnet

Primetime information 220

England 225

Cellnet
Lifetime information 634

Scotland 639

Wales 719

Channel Islands
& The Isle of Man 751

Northern Ireland 763

Republic of Ireland 771

Quick Reference Lists (Outside London)		
	Hotels under £65 for 2	822
	15 Minutes off the Motorway	825
	Restaurants with Rooms	827
	Town House Hotels	829
	Private House Hotels	830
	Country House Hotels	830
	Beautifully Situated Hotels	831
	Hotels with Sporting Facilities	833
	Establishments Accessible to Wheelchairs	847
	Restaurants with Non-Smoking Areas	848
	Sunday Eating	851
	Seafood Restaurants	855
	Outstanding Desserts	855
	Outstanding Cheeseboards	856
	Outstanding Wine Lists	860
	California Wines	861
	Wines by the Glass	862

Hotel Groups and Hotels with Conference and Banqueting Facilities 865

Special Features

Chefs' British Pork Competition 934

The Highs and Lows of Wine List Pricing 948

Maps 951

Index 977

Readers' Comments Tear-Out Pages 1001

Cellnet. Making more of the cellphone.

With the technological expertise and financial support of our parent companies - BT & Securicor - Cellnet has played a

key role in developing the UK mobile telecommunications market ever since the launch of cellular systems in the mid-1980s.

Today, we are acknowledged industry leaders with an unrivalled record of innovation.

With the most comprehensive range of relevant and proven services Cellnet enables business users to be more responsive, and more competitive - wherever business takes them.

Now, we're about to make portable communications affordable for lower users such as smaller businesses and private individuals - with the introduction of the 'Lifetime' tariff.

Welcome to the 1993 edition of Egon Ronay's Cellnet Guide to Hotels and Restaurants.

Cellnet has been associated with the Guide for six years so I know that it can be relied upon to offer impartial advice and information about the thousands of establishments qualifying for an entry, to the business traveller and personal user alike.

The Guide has long been an authority trusted by business customers as well as playing a key

role as a point of reference for hotels and restaurants to achieve higher standards, greater choice and better value. But dining out and staying in good hotels is no longer just the preserve of people on business, and the everyday traveller can make as much – if not more – use of the Guide.

Indeed, we at Cellnet share the same philosophy when it comes to mobile phones. Once seen as something only people in business would use, the mobile phone is set to become an essential part of everyone's, everyday life. With the launch of Lifetime, we aim to bring the benefits of mobile phones to thousands of households to enable family and friends to stay in touch while out and about whether it is just for the evening at a restaurant or away for the weekend. For the best in quality and value at hotels and restaurants, and for staying in touch on the move, all you have to do to get the message is simply read on.

Stafford Taylor, Managing Director, Cellnet.

The siting of our
transceivers and aerials
is critical, if we're to
ensure the best possible
radio reception for
Cellnet users.

The higher, the better -
is the rule for cellular
equipment. To this end
we sometimes take
advantage of the most
unlikely sites - Ely
Cathedral, for example,
and even Manchester
City's football stadium.

Altogether there are
over 800 cellular
stations nationwide all
regularly tuned by a
dedicated team of over
400 Cellnet engineers.

Better coverage - nationwide.

The locations of Cellnet radio antennae ensure better coverage and uninterrupted service as cellphone users travel from one part of the country to another.

Optimum cellsite positions are determined using ANET, the advanced networking engineering tool licensed exclusively to Cellnet in the UK.

Our entire network is subject to a continuous network tuning programme we call NEPTUNE. This embraces every single element of the Cellnet network nationwide ensuring the best possible signal quality.

Cellnet's national network includes exclusive coverage of the Channel Islands and the Isle of Man and enables our mobile service to embrace over 98% of the UK population.

And monitored by a unique management resource.

Controlling a network of this size and sophistication and monitoring its usage 24 hours a day, 365 days a year, demands advanced management systems. At the hub of the network - the nerve centre - is Cellnet's unique Network Management Centre.

From here, our engineers can respond immediately to events as they occur resolving problems long before they can affect service to our customers.

(In the unlikely event of experiencing any difficulty with the network, corporate customers with Direct Access links can, with the agreement of their Service Provider, phone directly into Cellnet. No other mobile communications network offers UK businesses service and support on this scale).

A real commitment to business - today and for the future.

Proof of Cellnet's commitment to delivering a communications service, second to none, the Network Management Centre also symbolizes our technology leadership, the resources with which we are able to put advanced ideas into practice, and our ability to meet your needs today and in the future.

BRITANNIA FOOD SAFETY SERVICE LTD

NEW RECIPE FOR HYGIENE

Britannia Food Safety Service Ltd, with the support of Egon Ronay's Guide, has launched a new Award Scheme for the food industry which aims to help raise standards of hygiene and create greater consumer confidence in catering establishments.

When you see the Britannia Food Safety and Hygiene Award Certificate displayed, you know that the premises operate to high standards of hygiene and food safety.

The Dorchester leads the way
The Dorchester Hotel, Park Lane, London was the first establishment to receive the Britannia Food Safety Award.
Egon Ronay makes the presentation to general manager Ricci Obertelli.

Food Minister, the Hon. Nicholas Soames at the launch of the Britannia Food Safety and Hygiene Award Scheme said "I welcome this initiative It will heighten awareness among both providers and consumers of the importance of high standards of hygiene in the food industry."

Introduction by Managing Editor Andrew Eliel

During a recession the hotel and catering industry is perhaps as good a barometer as there is of what's happening throughout the land – not so many people eat out, there are fewer travellers and tourists about so beds remain empty, occupancy levels fall, staff numbers are cut and planned improvements are shelved.

Gravy Trains Axed

Established hoteliers and restaurateurs, of course, survive better than those new to the industry and there's always someone who bucks the trend, but sadly there are fewer and fewer of these around, as the moneymen take over. Less and less are hotels run by hoteliers and restaurants by restaurateurs, and more and more by teams of accountants and boards of shareholders who make their decisions purely on financial considerations, with little thought of the effect it will have on customers, management and staff. Cost savings in hard times are indeed a necessity – we can all survive without eating foie gras, caviar, truffles or best butter from Normandy, and we can sleep easily without decanters of sherry, goodnight chocolates on the pillow or luxurious bathrobes. Even if we can't afford the luxuries on the menus there's no excuse for poor quality, especially meat, nor should we put up with threadbare sheets or thin towels. Hotel bedrooms, still often in excess of £100 per night per person, should be more comfortable, at least as well decorated, and as well serviced as bedrooms at home. Restaurant menus should offer food that is not only expertly cooked, but generally involves more complexity in preparation than dishes cooked at home.

Trendsetters

Unsurprisingly, little has happened this last year to awaken our taste buds – outside London hardly a new restaurant of note has opened, and for the most part the style of cooking has not followed that set by a rash of new restaurants in the capital, which has probably suffered deeper from the recession than elsewhere. There are occasional attempts to change from the established cooking format of provincial and country restaurants which, good that they might be, remain straightjacketed by the demands of their customers; many are continuing the trend of fixed-price meals, albeit with a choice, thus dictating the price the customer has to pay. The problem is that few of these restaurants are busy mid-week, most barely survive, and yet they all struggle on to satisfy Friday and Saturday night diners, and are left twiddling their thumbs for the rest of the week. Regrettably, it's a Catch 22 situation – if restaurants cut back when they're quiet, they can't cope when they're busy, so in effect prices are determined when a restaurant is full, subsidising empty chairs at other times. Despite the proliferation of newspaper and magazine articles on the subject of food and cooking, the general public do not offer enough support to local restaurants that really set out to succeed, hence the lack of friendly and reasonably cheap neighbourhood places to meet and eat in, unlike in the rest of Europe. How much better it would be for all concerned if there were a steady stream of customers – ultimately it's up to us, but at the same time restaurateurs must realise they are now competing against not only each other, but also decent ready-prepared meals from the supermarket eaten at home. It can, and is being done – outside London witness the success of the Pierre Victoire outlets in Scotland, Franc's at Chester, Café Fleur in Harrogate and No.24 at Wymondham – all restaurants where value-for-money and quality are paramount. And take heed of new-wave cooking at places such as Brasserie 44 in Leeds, the Olive Tree in Bath, Leadon's Brasserie, Chepstow and the remarkable Heathcote's at Longridge. In London, too, it's not quite all doom and gloom, with a succession of new restaurants bursting on the scene, their chefs spawned by familiar starred names such as Raymond Blanc and Marco Pierre White. The proof of the pudding will be if they are still around next year, but the omens are good for the likes of L'Accento Italiano, Nico Central, Olivo, Pied à Terre, La Sémillante, Snow's on the Green, The Square and Antony Worrall-Thompson's large and busy Dell'Ugo, with White's (again) Harveys Canteen in Chelsea Harbour and the seafood bistro at 190 Queen's Gate (AW-T again!) just happening. Belgo bucks all the trends by being themed on a Belgian brewery hall!

Even so, many well known restaurants are in the doldrums, and the same can equally be said of hotels. Rumours abound of who is up for sale and at what price, how badly so-and-so is doing, whose occupancy levels are down by 30% (and falling!) etc. Yet new hotels are still opening at a fast pace, mostly (and sensibly) in the lower price bracket, though who's going to fill them is anyone's guess. Surely we have reached saturation point, but the optimists continue to build – again in London: King's Cross Holiday Inn, London International, The Milestone and the soon-to-open Wilshire on Marylebone Road.

The hotel price war continues with the customer as the certain winner. Chain hotels are aggressively marketing their special offers, and at weekends a room at a 'business' hotel can be up to 50% cheaper. Quite right too if they want to attract families – staying just off a motorway junction hardly means a room with a view!

Best of British

The purpose of this Guide has always been to select hotels and restaurants which consistently strive to maintain and improve their standards, but at the same time to support the best of British, and this year is no exception. Cellnet, now into their 7th year as our main sponsors, have entered into a long-term association which will comfortably make it the longest sponsorship involvement the guide has enjoyed over its 35 years. The Meat and Livestock Commission continues to promote British meat through the chefs' competition – this year, British Pork (see Special Features) and the Ilchester Cheese Co do likewise for British cheese, often a neglected component of a good meal.

Wine Pricing and Service Charges: Perennial Grumbles

The marriage of wine with food is an endless topic of debate, and we comment on more restaurant wine lists than ever before, taking particular note of prices. With the benefit of assembling so many lists, we asked Robin Young (see Special Features) to delve into the pricing policy on mark-ups, and to try to understand why Grand Marque champagne costs up to three times what you pay in a supermarket or wine shop. This is not an 'expose the rip-off brigade', but a genuine attempt to increase restaurant wine sales throughout the country.

And once again we feel obliged to comment on the service charge. Why oh why can't we pay an inclusive price for a meal, as on the Continent? 10%, 12.5%, 15%, optional, automatically added, gratuities at your discretion, etc, have no place on bills. The customer is not interested in how restaurant staff are paid, only in what he or she is going to pay. For goodness sake, we have even encountered restaurants that add a service charge and still print on the bill that gratuities are left at the customer's discretion! The 'tip' of the iceberg perhaps? More power to the likes of The Savoy, Nico at Ninety, Chewton Glen and many, many others where all prices include the service charge.

How to use this guide

As well as our recommended
establishments this Guide includes many
interesting features and a wealth of useful
quick reference lists designed to help you
select the hotel or restaurant that best suits
your requirements. New for 1993 is a list
by county of hotels offering conference
and banqueting facilities. This will enable
organisers to see at a glance what is
available in any area, with the maximum
capacity for banquets and theatre–style
conferences. Extended this year are the
places of interest, which are listed after
the London gazetteer and under the
nearest relevant location throughout the
Guide. For details of all listings consult
the contents pages.

Order of Entries

London appears first in alphabetical
order by **establishment name**. Listings
outside London are in alphabetical
order by **location** within England,
Scotland, Wales, Channel Islands, Isle
of Man, Northern Ireland and the
Republic of Ireland. See contents page
for specific page numbers, and the
index for individual entries. London
Airports hotels are now listed under
their locations in the England section.

Map References

Map references alongside each hotel
or restaurant entry are to the map
section at the back of the book. Use this
section to help select establishments in
areas you wish to visit.

Hotels

Hotel entries are identified by the letter
'**H**'.

Percentage ratings

According to their percentage rating,
hotels are classified as:

De luxe 80% and over

Grade 1   70-79%

Grade 2   50-69%

Prices

These are based on high-season rates
at the time of going to press and
include VAT (also service if applicable),
for a *double room for two occupants
with private bath and cooked breakfast.*

The Percentage shown on a hotel entry
is an individual rating arrived at after
careful testing, inspection and
calculation according to our unique
grading system.

We assess hotels on 23 factors, which
include the public rooms – their
cleanliness, comfort, state of repair and
general impression. Bedrooms are
looked at for size, comfort, cleanliness
and decor. The exterior of the building,
efficiency of reception, conduct and
appearance of the staff, quality of
service and leisure facilities are among
other factors. The percentage is arrived
at by comparing the total marks given
for the 23 factors with the maximum the
hotel could have achieved.

The Size of a hotel and the prices
charged are not considered in the
grading. **The standard of food is also
taken into account in the grading
calculation, and if we recommend
meals in a hotel a separate entry is
made for its restaurant.**

A new category of chain hotels offering
cheap, practical accommodation and
not much else is denoted by the letter
'**L**'.

Certain other hotels are ungraded.
These may be private house hotels
('**PH**') which are de luxe 'bed and
breakfast' hotels offering comfortable,
often luxurious accommodation and
personal service, but do not have a
restaurant or public rooms - although
some have a drawing room.

Inns, identified by the letter '**I**', are
ungraded, being distinguished from
hotels proper by their more modest
nature, usually with respect to the day
rooms. For our purposes an inn is
normally either a pub with hotel-style

accommodation or a small hotel with a bar and the atmosphere of a pub.

Also ungraded are some of the more modest London hotels and hotels undergoing major construction or refurbishment programmes at the time of research, and those which opened too late for the fullest inspection.

The major characteristics of the leading hotel groups are covered in a special section at the back of the Guide.

Bargain breaks. Almost all hotels now offer bargain breaks of some kind. Specific details regarding the availability and price of such breaks should be checked with individual establishments. In addition to bargain breaks many hotels are offering price reductions more or less throughout their range. Phone the hotels in the area you're visiting and see what they have to offer.

Restaurants

Restaurants are identified by the letter '**R**'.

★★★ ★★ ★

We award one to three stars for excellence of cooking. One star represents cooking much above average, two consistently outstanding cooking, and three the best in the land.

↑ beside stars indicates a restaurant at the top of its star range.
by itself indicates a restaurant approaching star status.

The symbol '**RR**' denotes a restaurant with rooms, a category based on *restaurant avec chambres* in France. Food is the main attraction, but overnight accommodation is also available. A list of these restaurants appears at the back of the Guide.

We only include restaurants where the cooking comes up to our minimum standards, however attractive the place may be in other respects. We take into account how well the restaurant achieves what it sets out to do as

reflected in the menu, decor, prices, publicity, atmosphere - factors that add up to some sort of expectation.

Crowns are awarded to restaurants offering a degree of traditional luxury ♛ or some striking modern features. ♛ They have nothing to do with the quality of the cooking.

🍾 This symbol represents a wine list that is outstanding.

✹ Signifies a wine list featuring good-quality Californian wines.

🍷 Signifies a restaurant serving a selection of good-quality wines by the glass.

🍓 Signifies a restaurant serving notable desserts.

🧀 Signifies a restaurant serving good British cheeses.

🫖 Signifies an establishment serving quality tea to a standard set by The Tea Council.

Restaurant prices, correct at the time of going to press, are for a *three-course meal for two including one of the least expensive bottles of wine, coffee, service and VAT*.

Set-price menus. Prices quoted will often not include service and usually exclude wine. They are not necessarily for three courses. Where two prices are given thus - £14.50/£17.75 - it indicates that there is a 2 or 3-course option; prices given thus - £17.95 & £24.95 - indicates that there are two different set-price menus. A great number of restaurants around the country now *only* offer a set-price menu (although this will usually include a choice).

Many restaurants offer at least one main course for vegetarians; tell them your requirements when you book. There is a list of restaurants with non-smoking areas in the Quick Reference List section, as well as a list of hotels and restaurants with wheelchair access.

Starred Restaurants

London ★★★

Nico at Ninety **W1** ↑
La Tante Claire **SW3** ↑

Le Gavroche **W1**
Harveys **SW17**

England ★★★

Bray-on-Thames Waterside Inn
Great Milton Le Manoir aux
Quat'Saisons
Shinfield L'Ortolan

London ★★

Alastair Little **W1**
L'Arlequin **SW8**
Bibendum **SW3**
The Capital **SW3**
The Connaught **W1**
The Dorchester, Terrace Restaurant **W1**
Inn on the Park, Four Seasons **W1**
Hotel Inter-Continental, Le Soufflé **W1**
The Savoy, Grill Room **WC2**

England ★★

Chagford Gidleigh Park
Dartmouth Carved Angel

Scotland ★★

Ullapool Altnaharrie Inn

Wales ★★

Abergavenny Walnut Tree Inn

London ★

Halkin Hotel, Gualtiero Marchesi **SW1** ↑
Hilaire **SW7** ↑
Le Meridien, Oak Room **W1** ↑
Les Saveurs **W1** ↑

Moycullen ●

Ahakista ●

Guernsey

CHANNEL
ISLANDS

Jersey

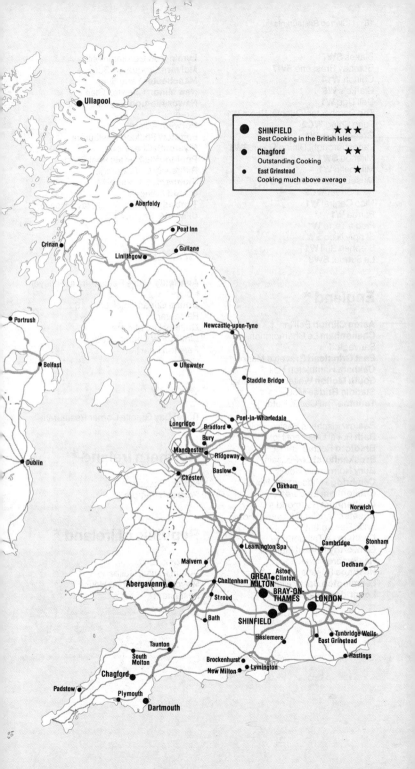

● **SHINFIELD** Best Cooking in the British Isles		★ ★ ★
● Chagford Outstanding Cooking		★ ★
● East Grinstead Cooking much above average		★

Ullapool

Aberfeldy

Peat Inn
Crinan
Linlithgow
Gullane

Portrush
Belfast

Newcastle-upon-Tyne

Dublin

Ullswater

Staddle Bridge

Pool-in-Wharfedale
Longridge
Bradford
Bury
Manchester
Ridgeway
Chester
Baslow

Oakham

Norwich

Leamington Spa
Cambridge
Stonham
Malvern
Dedham

Abergavenny
Cheltenham
GREAT
Aston
MILTON
Clinton
Stroud
BRAY-ON-
THAMES
LONDON
Bath
SHINFIELD
Tunbridge Wells
Haslemere
East Grinstead
Taunton
Hastings
South
Molton
Brockenhurst
Chagford
New Milton
Lymington
Padstow
Plymouth
Dartmouth

© Leading Guides Ltd.

Blakes **SW7**
Bombay Brasserie **SW7**
Chinon **W14**
Clarke's **W8**
Dell'Ugo **W1**
The Dorchester, Oriental Room **W1**
Fung Shing **WC2**
Greenhouse **W1**
Lanesborough, Dining Room **SW1**
Mijanou **SW1**
Mirabelle **W1**
Museum Street Café **WC1**
Neal Street **WC2**
Nico Central **W1**
Panda **W1**
Pied à Terre **W1**
Simply Nico **SW1**
Stephen Bull **W1**
Le Suquet **SW3**

England *

Aston Clinton Bell Inn ↑
Cheltenham Le Champignon
Sauvage ↑
East Grinstead Gravetye Manor ↑
Oakham Hambleton Hall ↑
South Molton Whitechapel Manor ↑
Staddle Bridge McCoy's ↑
Taunton The Castle Hotel ↑

Baslow Fischer's Baslow Hall
Bath Royal Crescent Hotel
Bradford Restaurant 19
Brockenhurst Le Poussin
Bury Normandie Hotel
Cambridge Midsummer House
Cheltenham Epicurean
Cheltenham Redmond's
Chester Chester Grosvenor Hotel,
Arkle Restaurant
Dedham Le Talbooth
Gulworthy Horn of Plenty
Haslemere Morel's
Hastings Röser's
Leamington Spa Mallory Court
Longridge Heathcote's

Lymington Gordleton Mill
Malvern Croque-en-Bouche
Manchester Yang Sing
New Milton Chewton Glen
Newcastle-upon-Tyne 21 Queen
Street
Norwich Adlard's
Padstow Seafood Restaurant
Plymouth Chez Nous
Pool-in-Wharfedale Pool Court
Ridgeway Old Vicarage
Stonham Mr Underhill's
Stroud Oakes
Tunbridge Wells Thackeray's House
Ullswater Sharrow Bay

Scotland *

Aberfeldy Atkins Restaurant at Farleyer
House
Crinan Crinan Hotel, Lock 16
Restaurant
Gullane La Potinière
Linlithgow Champany Inn
Peat Inn Peat Inn

Jersey *

Rozel Bay Granite Corner Restaurant

Northern Ireland *

Belfast Roscoff
Portrush Ramore

Republic of Ireland *

Ahakista Shiro
Dublin Patrick Guilbaud
Moycullen Drimcong House
Restaurant

De Luxe Hotels

London

91%	The Connaught **W1**
	The Dorchester **W1**
90%	The Savoy **WC2**
89%	Inn on the Park Hotel **W1**
	The Lanesborough **SW1**
88%	Claridge's **W1**
	Hyatt Carlton Tower **SW1**
86%	The Berkeley **SW1**
	47 Park Street **W1**
	Halkin Hotel **SW1**
	The Ritz **W1**
85%	Hotel Conrad **SW10**
84%	Inter-Continental Hotel **W1**
	Le Meridien **W1**
83%	Grosvenor House **W1**
82%	Hyde Park Hotel **SW1**
81%	The Howard **WC2**
80%	The Capital **SW3**
	The Churchill **W1**
	Royal Garden Hotel **W8**

England

90%	**Taplow** Cliveden
89%	**New Milton** Chewton Glen
87%	**Bath** Bath Spa Hotel
	Ston Easton Ston Easton Park
86%	**Aylesbury** Hartwell House
	Stapleford Stapleford Park
85%	**Great Milton** Le Manoir aux Quat'Saisons
84%	**Chester** Chester Grosvenor
	East Grinstead Gravetye Manor
	Oakham Hambleton Hall
83%	**Bath** Royal Crescent Hotel
	Colerne Lucknam Park
82%	**Ashford** Eastwell Manor
	Chagford Gidleigh Park
	Hintlesham Hintlesham Hall
	Thornbury Thornbury Castle
81%	**Amberley** Amberley Castle
	Bath Priory Hotel
	Thundridge Hanbury Manor
	Torquay Imperial Hotel
	Ullswater Sharrow Bay
80%	**Cheltenham** The Greenway
	Leamington Spa Mallory Court
	Linton Wood Hall

Scotland

90%	**Fort William** Inverlochy Castle
86%	**Auchterarder** Gleneagles Hotel
84%	**Turnberry** Turnberry Hotel
83%	**Edinburgh** The Balmoral
82%	**Dunblane** Cromlix House
	Glasgow One Devonshire Gardens
	St Andrews St Andrews Old Course Hotel
81%	**Alexandria** Cameron House

Wales

80%	**Llyswen** Llangoed Hall

Channel Islands

80%	**St Saviour** Longueville Manor

Republic of Ireland

86%	**Cong** Ashford Castle
	Kenmare Sheen Falls Lodge
	Straffan Kildare Hotel
85%	**Kenmare** Park Hotel
81%	**Gorey** Marfield House
	Thomastown Mount Juliet Hotel
80%	**Waterford** Waterford Castle

Hotel of the Year

The Chester Grosvenor
Chester, Cheshire

"Tired and a little jaded" in the mid-eighties, the hotel now ranks alongside city greats after careful rebuilding, restoration and renovation. No expense has been spared in the refurbishment - handcrafted furniture, marble from Italy, silks and the finest fabrics from France and America - which has transformed the hotel into a tasteful and luxurious haven of discreet charm, with a quality of service and cooking rarely found in town hotels outside the capital.

The hotel receives a unique handpainted Wedgwood plate

Previous Winners

1992   **The Dorchester**
London

1991   **Longueville Manor**
St Saviour, Jersey

1990   **Gidleigh Park**
Chagford

1989   **The Savoy**
London

1988   **Park Hotel**
Kenmare

1987   **Homewood Park**
Freshford

Restaurant of the Year

The Carved Angel
Dartmouth, Devon

The Carved Angel serves some of the best food in the West Country, and the views of the harbour are a bonus. Since 1975 Joyce Molyneux has been putting her skills on the line, working in full view of diners in her tiny kitchen. The Mediterranean influence arrived here many years ago, and Joyce has given it her personal stamp, so the dishes you find here appear nowhere else. Sunday lunch is a particular delight, but any meal here is a treat.

The restaurant receives a unique handpainted Wedgwood plate

Previous Winners

1992 **Bibendum**
London

1991 **L'Ortolan**
Shinfield

1990 **Waterside Inn**
Bray-on-Thames

1989 **L'Arlequin**
London

1988 **Morels**
Haslemere

1987 **Walnut Tree Inn**
Abergavenny

Chef of the Year

Shaun Hill
Gidleigh Park, Chagford, Devon

An intelligent man, Shaun is an eloquent speaker with forthright views on cooking and *real* produce, and a passionate supporter of local suppliers. He's also an outstanding chef, innovative, adventurous, bold without being outrageous, with a hunger for knowledge and new ideas that takes him to restaurants the length and breadth of the country.

Shaun receives a unique handpainted Wedgwood plate

Previous Winner

1992   Marco Pierre White, Harveys
London

Profile

PROFILE MANAGEMENT & SPECIALIST RECRUITMENT LTD

Dessert of the Year

Le Provence at Gordleton Mill
Lymington, Hampshire

This year's clear winner is Jean-Christophe Novelli. His exuberant energy is focused on outstandingly artistic presentation and this is best exemplified by his fantastical desserts. His Fabergé-like *boite surprise aux noisettes* ranks among the most elaborate and visually exciting desserts we have ever seen: a brittle nougatine box filled with a light, bitter chocolate mousse, accompanied by glazed roasted hazelnuts and a cocoa sauce with caramel springs bursting out of the opened lid.

Previous Winner

1992   Roger Pizey, Harveys
London

FRESH CREAM *Ice Cream*

In order to remain as

CLOSE

to perfection as humanly
possible only prime
ingredients come into

CONTACT

with our ice cream.

Häagen-Dazs

FRESH CREAM ICE CREAM.

Dedicated to Pleasure.

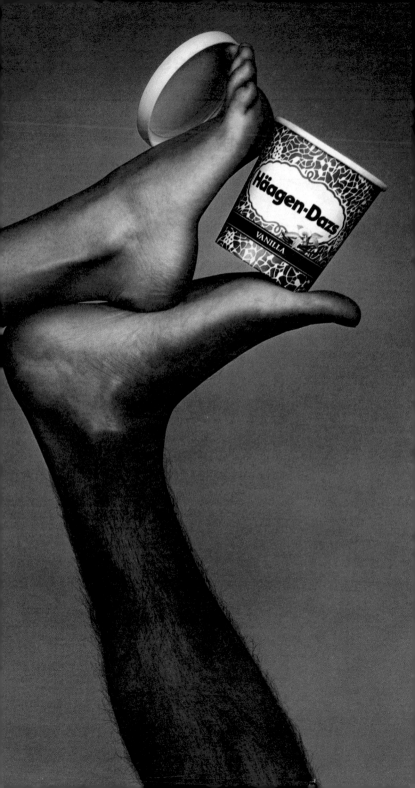

Outstanding Desserts

Les Saveurs
London W1

Millefeuille à la réglisse

Heathcote's
Longridge

Chocolate terrine with honey ice cream

Regional Selection of Favourite Desserts

In the interests of promoting appreciation of good desserts and puddings, Häagen-Dazs has sponsored a special award. Its symbol 🍓 appears against selected restaurants throughout the gazetteer, signifying the availability of outstanding desserts at these establishments. Of these, Jean-Christophe Novelli's was judged the best with Heathcote's and Les Saveurs highly commended (see previous pages). The following were particularly enjoyed this year:

London

Chinon **W14**
Halkin Hotel Gualtiero Marchesi **SW1**
Mirabelle **W1**

Home Counties

Bray-on-Thames The Waterside Inn
Great Milton Le Manoir aux Quat'Saisons
Shinfield L'Ortolan

South of England

Battle Netherfield Place
Eastbourne Grand Hotel, Mirabelle Restaurant
Storrington Manley's

West Country

Bath Bath Spa Hotel
South Molton Whitechapel Manor
Taunton Castle Hotel

East of England

Felsted Rumbles Cottage
Morston Morston Hall
Oakham Hambleton Hall

Midlands/Heart of England

Aston Clinton Bell Inn
Baslow Fischer's Baslow Hall
Cheltenham Le Champignon Sauvage

North of England

Chester Chester Grosvenor
Hawkshead Tarn Hows Hotel
Pool-in-Wharfedale Pool Court

Scotland

Arisaig Arisaig House
Cupar Ostlers Close
Gullane Greywalls Hotel

Wales

Abergavenny Walnut Tree Inn
Llandudno St Tudno Hotel
Reynoldston Fairyhill

Northern Ireland

Belfast Roscoff
Portrush Ramore

Republic of Ireland

Dun Laoghaire Digby's

New Award

British Cheeseboard of the Year

Old Vicarage
Witherslack, Cumbria.

Apart from the Colston Bassett Stilton, Roger Burrington-Brown's excellent cheese selection comes from the North of England or just over the border into Scotland. Prime condition is ensured by sensibly limiting the selection to just seven or eight at any one time. Whenever possible Roger buys direct from the producer thus tracking down the likes of 12-month-matured Lancashire from Singleton Dairy's herd of pedigree Friesians (who also provide a very creamy low-salt butter) and a rare Cumberland smoked farmhouse cheese. Old-fashioned varieties of apple, home-made oatcakes and special Cumberland molasses bread accompany.

Ilchester

Great British Cheeses

Innovative, intriguing . . . delicious.

British Cheeseboard of the Year Regional Winners

London

The Lanesborough SW1

A few Continentals are allowed, but the majority of the cheese on the dining room trolley (a plated selection is served in the Conservatory) are from around the British Isles, supplied in prime condition by Neal's Yard Dairy and served with home-made walnut and apricot bread. Try the Golden Cross, a goat's cheese, or Montgomery, a mature Cheddar.

Home Counties

The Bell Aston Clinton, Buckinghamshire

The extensive selection of well-kept British cheeses is a new attraction here. Displayed on a trolley, strategically placed by the entrance to attract the eye, the range of some 20 cheeses - most from the Cheese Cellar Co - looks as tempting as any comparable French board: Tiverdale, a ewe's milk; Chesbit, 6-months-old cow's milk; or Little Rydings from Slate Farm, Bath, a month-old goat's cheese.

South of England

Grand Hotel - Mirabelle Restaurant Eastbourne, East Sussex

Cheese merchant James Aldridge, rapidly becoming the English *Philippe Olivier*, supplies many of the unusual British cheeses that find their way into the selection here: local Sussex goat's cheese from Greenacre Farm (plain or mature 'Ash-log'), Sussex Slipcote (soft and herby with garlic, a bit like Boursin), Doddeswell (Cheddar style) and Gospel Green. Just three British cheeses (plus a similar number of Continental ones) are offered at any one time and arrive on your own marble cheese board along with a little bunch of grapes and some home-made walnut and raisin bread.

West Country

Danescombe Valley Hotel Calstock, Cornwall

Choosing between cheese and a dessert to end a meal can sometimes be a problem, but not here, for the cheese course comes before the dessert, in Continental style, though the cheeses themselves are exclusively West Country unpasteurised produce - Sharpham, a double cream Jersey cow cheese; Tornegus, a Somerset Caerphilly aged by James Aldridge; or a Devon Tomme from Robin Congden.

East of England

Bell Inn Stilton, Cambridgeshire

It was from the Bell that the original Stilton cheese was first sold to travellers on the old Great North Road in the 1720s, so where better to sample England's most famous cheese today? Served in the bar or restaurant with plum bread or by the pound to take away.

Midlands/Heart of England

Old Vicarage Worfield, Shropshire

Cheeses from around Britain, usually about eight, are helpfully described on the menu: Wedmore from Somerset, Cornish Yarg, local Shropshire Blue. Pencarreg and Teifi are organically produced in Wales using vegetarian rennet.

North of England

Victor's Restaurant Darlington, Co Durham

Very much a local list with cheeses coming from surrounding farms and creameries; a goat's cheese from Liestons Farm, Whitby Jet from Littlebeck Dairies in Whitby, Ashes Farm in Ribblesdale provides goat's and sheep's cheese in addition to hand-made Wensleydale, a smoked Tyndale from High Skeghill Farm. Usually some 10 or 12 cheeses on the list at any one time.

Scotland

Riverside Inn Canonbie, Dumfries & Galloway

Mr Appleby's cloth-wrapped farmhouse Cheshire, smoked Westmorland, Somerset Brie and Wensleydale are amongst the fine cheeses one is likely to find here served with a selection of breads including olive bread and unbleached, white French country loaf.

Wales

Llangoed Hall Llyswen, Powys

There are half-a-dozen or so Welsh cheeses on offer here - Pant-Ysgawn, St Illtyd, Pencarreg and a local farmhouse Cheddar - along with Mark Salter's home-made wheat and celery biscuits, oatcakes and bread.

Cellar of the Year

There is a problem with a Cellar of the Year Award. The same names crop up time and again. Because they are assembled by enthusiasts, some might say fanatics, the best cellars tend to get better with each passing vintage.

This year's winner, the Croque-en-Bouche, has won the title before. The White Horse Inn at Chilgrove is another regular collector of gongs. It is a tiny club, and the danger is that other restaurants will throw in the towel if they believe they cannot join it, and so will not bother to improve their selection of wines. This would be sad, because what matters to most of us, most of the time, is the general standard of wines in the restaurants that we use every week, every day.

Happily, this standard has been improving steadily over the years. There is of course no excuse for a poor wine list. Britain is recognised as having the best wine trade in the world, and the restaurant trade should reflect this excellence.

A good list need not be long, and it certainly need not be full of grand names at high prices. There is, in other words, no need for a restaurateur to spend huge sums of money stocking a vast cellar. The Croque-en-Bouche cellar, as it happens, is very big. But it didn't win merely because it has a lot of bottles. It won because it observed a few simple principles, which are valid for any restaurant, at whatever level it operates.

Firstly, mark-ups should be reasonable. That may mean adding a fixed margin rather than simply doubling or tripling the cost price. At a stroke this would bring many fine bottles within reach of more customers, and increase turnover. Nobody loses.

Secondly, there should be ample choice at modest price levels. If we can buy good wines for under a fiver in a supermarket, why can we not buy equally good wines for less than £10 in a restaurant? At Croque-en-Bouche, and at most of our regional winners, we can. *Vins de pays*, eastern Europe, Chile, California, Iberia and Australasia are all sources of good but inexpensive bottles.

Thirdly, there should be a good choice of wines available by the glass. Customers may want to drink modest quantities, or perhaps pair each course with a different wine. Simple technology is now able to preserve opened bottles for a few days if necessary, to save on costs, so again there is no excuse for not offering quality wines by the glass.

Fourthly, wine service should not be shrouded in intimidating mystery. As Robin Jones puts it in his introduction to the Croque-en-Bouche list: "We have strong, unorthodox opinions on the service of wine; that it is bugged by too much rigmarole and ritual. Here wine is simply placed on the table." What! No bucket, no linen cloth, no smirk from the bow-tied wine waiter, no incessant pouring of tiny drops every few minutes to try to justify the high mark-up? No, just matter-of-fact, as it should be.

Lastly, the wines should be clearly presented. You should not have to be an expert to choose wisely and appropriately. A good list helps with a few sensible and intelligent words, and so does the wine waiter, if called upon to do so. The list may be arranged by country and region, or by style, but details of who made the wine, and when, are essential. If the bottle is not the one advertised, then we should be told before the cork is drawn, and be given the opportunity to change our minds.

Croque-en-Bouche does all this and much, much more. Wines constantly change, to reflect developments in New Zealand, Spain, or Italy. They also reflect something of the obsession that grips wine buffs like Robin Jones: red Rhones are his passion. And above all they encourage us to try new wines, to broaden our repertoire, to learn as we drink, and to enjoy the immense variety of styles that help to make eating out such a pleasure.

Jim Ainsworth *Author of the Mitchell Beazley Red and White Wine Guides*

The judging panel decides (left to right): Jim Ainsworth, Andrew Ellel (standing), Managing Editor Egon Ronay's Guides, Robin Young, The Times, Andrew Montague, UK Director The Wine Institute of California

Cellar of the Year

Croque-en-Bouche
Malvern, Hereford & Worcester

The restaurant receives a unique handpainted Wedgwood plate

Recent Winners

The Cross
Kingussie, Highland

White Horse Inn
Chilgrove, West Sussex

La Potinière
Gullane, Lothian

Old Bridge Hotel
Huntingdon, Cambridgeshire

Champany Inn
Linlithgow, Lothian

Cellar of the Year Regional Winners

London

Le Pont de la Tour Butlers Wharf, SE1

This wide-ranging list takes in some of the finest wines and best producers anywhere, including Australia and California. Top wines are generally at a premium, but careful selection is second nature to the buyers, and the choice of good bottles under £20 is impressive, providing you can manage without claret and burgundy. Italy is a treasure house, sweet wines a *forte*.

Home Counties

Gravetye Manor East Grinstead, West Sussex

A patrician list that parades lots of interesting wines and tempting vintages. There is very little under £20 from France, but a good new Italian section, and the German, Australasian, and fine Californian wines are especially welcome. It also has a very commendable selection of half bottles. Don't forget to add VAT (at 17.5%) to list prices.

South of England

Chewton Glen New Milton, Hampshire

That Chewton Glen is head and shoulders above the competition is due in large part to the professional skills of award-winning sommelier Gerard Basset. Big spenders are indulged with the best champagne and a dozen vintages of Ch Latour, but so are ordinary drinkers with Beaujolais, Rhone and Alsace, and an intriguing selection that takes in Luxembourg and Moldavia. There are no notes, but it is clearly indexed; and advice, freely given, cannot be bettered.

West Country

Castle Hotel Taunton, Somerset

The Castle has assembled a lot of claret over the years, but not at the expense of other regions; southern Burgundy, Rhone, the Loire and Alsace add a dash of spice. It lists over thirty house wines, mostly under £12 a bottle, and is also one of the few places to treat sherry with the respect that it deserves.

East of England

The Crown Southwold, Suffolk

A delightful list, very sensibly priced, with a catholic selection from around the world to encourage adventurous drinking. Close association with Adnams, the wine merchant, pays dividends. There is an intelligent choice of sweet wines, claret vintages, Italians and Californians. Clear layout and neat short tasting notes are as helpful as can be.

Midlands/Heart of England
Sir Charles Napier Inn Chinnor, Oxfordshire

Pub wine lists are generally lamentable. Here, by contrast, is a fine example for all: enterprising, well-balanced, fairly priced, and helpfully annotated. It offers a good variety of styles, but is put together economically, and is kind to anybody looking for wines from Australia and California, or for half bottles.

North of England
Crabwall Manor Chester, Cheshire

Any restaurant, given the money, can stock an impressive range of fine claret and burgundy, but the skill lies in backing this up with good wines from elsewhere that most diners can afford. Here, Beaujolais, Loire and Alsace perform this valuable service, helped by a peppering of French provincial wines. Australia and California are good too, and there are stacks and stacks of half bottles.

Scotland
The Ubiquitous Chip Glasgow, Strathclyde

Scotland is well served for excellent wine lists, so the competition is stiff. A good spread of prices helps to give this list wide appeal, and although there are no tasting notes or comments, there is plenty of interest around the French regions, and in Italy. Single malt whiskies are outstanding.

Wales
Plas Bodegroes Pwllheli, Gwynedd

An enterprising list, well chosen, with a sharp eye for what is most exciting and best value in the wine world today. This leads naturally to a good selection from Alsace, Rhone, Italy, Australia and California, but even mature and venerable claret vintages are reasonably priced. White wines are helpfully numbered 1-9 according to sweetness, and the house selection is impeccable.

Ireland
Park Hotel Kenmare, Co Kerry

Wine lists in Ireland tend to specialise in claret and other classic French wines, often at steep prices. This list is in the same mould. Vintages and producers are classic too, and are as sound as a bell. The Park explores further afield than most, with good Australians and impressive Californians.

California Cellar of the Year

Gravetye Manor
East Grinstead, West Sussex

Napa Valley is the main strength of this 40-bottle California cellar. Excellent Chardonnays from Cuvaison, and from Acacia's Marina Vineyard in Carneros, complement a spread of Cabernet Sauvignons (Heitz, Mondavi, Jordan, Clos du Bois) back to 1977. But there are also gems from further afield: Ridge Zinfandel and half a dozen Pinot Noirs, including Sanford and Edna Valley. Sweet Johannisberg Rieslings – from Ch St Jean and Phelps – are among California's unsung classics.

Previous Winners

1992 **190 Queen's Gate**
London
1991 **Croque-en-Bouche**
Malvern
1990 **Gidleigh Park**
Chagford

Photograph by kind permission of Martin Brigdale - Good Housekeeping.

For an even more favourable view
of Californian wines,
just ask the wine waiter.

Wines of the Californias

COULD THIS BE THE / MOST PERFECT PLACE ON / EARTH TO MAKE WINE?

California FOOD

I was sitting in a restaurant in Napa Valley toying with the deep-fried spinach that came with my spatch-cooked quail covered in sesame seeds. The smart restaurant had opened only a few days before, yet it was buzzing with casually but elegantly dressed and animated customers having the time of their lives.

Pony-tailed waiters worked the tables with panache and good humour, while impressive whooshing noises and much steam issued from the open-plan kitchen. The owner/chef - who had previously run restaurants in New York and London - moved among us and chatted to all and sundry. Occasionally a winemaker

would stroll across to another table and splash a drop of something interesting into a colleague's glass. Everybody was happy and enjoying the good clean fun.

A few days later I was telling somebody about it, saying how delightful it was to see a brand new restaurant so full and busy, it wouldn't happen in England, aren't you lucky ..."Oh!" she interrupted. "They had a bunch of shils in."

Excuse me? Shils?

A shil, apparently is a restaurant's version of rent-a-crowd. Pack the place out with friends, and friends of friends, give them a free meal and a bottle of wine, and you have instant atmosphere, a sort of spray-on glamour that attracts punters like me, who pay for their food.

I only felt like a sucker for a few moments. Although naturally disappointed that I hadn't been wise to the shil trick and a buddy of the owner. I was, on reflection, grateful for the lively cheer-leading razzamatazz that made this a memorable and enjoyable evening.

In this respect, the restaurant was indistinguishable from any other in Napa Valley or San Francisco. They are all buzzing and jumping from the word go. That is one of the joys of eating in California. The quality of the food is remarkably high, but nobody sits there glumly and self-consciously chewing it because some critic has told them to. People go to a restaurant for the fun of eating out.

What they eat mostly is California cuisine. I asked quite a few people in the business if they could tell me what was meant by the term, because it seemed to be bandied about a lot. Nobody could. Most, on reflection, said there was no such thing. Yet eating in California - or in a London restaurant with Californian connections - is undeniably different from eating anywhere else, and it has a lot to do with a simple feeling of all-round pleasure and enjoyment.

In order to achieve this, the requirements, as far as I can make out, are as follows. People should have enough money to spend, without feeling guilty about it. In California, prices are generally reasonable by British standards, so there is no need to think of a meal as a quick way of blowing a week's housekeeping. Three-course meals are not thrust upon you when just a Reuben sandwich or Caesar salad will do the job.

Service is part of the enjoyment too: everybody recognises the brief and artificial nature of the relationship between waiting staff and customers, but that doesn't cause any more resentment than say, an evening at the theatre, to which dinner in a Californian restaurant can bear a striking resemblance. All parties manage to live comfortably with the role-playing.

Then, Californian restaurants are thankfully not run by purists. There is nobody to breathe down anybody else's neck and say "This is how it should be done." As long as there is no right or wrong way of cooking, no textbook recipe to follow.

If California cuisine does exist, then one of its most conspicuous attributes is eclecticism. It draws together strands from Asian (including Chinese, Thai and Japanese), European (Italian, French, and broadly Mediterranean) and American (largely Mexican) cuisine. The Mediterranean-Italian thread equates roughly to what we in Britain have chosen to call New Wave Italian.

Squeaky spinach and arugula salads dressed up to the nines, home-made ravioli with shaved (not grated) parmesan, bresaola and charred carpaccio, polenta, balsamic vinegar, oil-dipped focaccia bread with sun-dried tomatoes and grilled red peppers, and risotto with porcini mushrooms, are all part of the repertoire. And all are crying out for a bottle of Californian wine.

But Italians export more than just ingredients and a few classic dishes. The package, as exhibited in somewhere like Tra Vigne in St Helena, includes designer flair: a large box of a dining room is transformed into a stylish meeting place (that you have to twist arms to get into) by a singular drape of brightly coloured material across an otherwise featureless expanse of wall, and an outrageously bold splash of gold paint. Hams and strings of red chilli peppers dangle dramatically from the high ceiling. An air of organised confusion reigns.

Another part of the Italian package concerns food's role as a fashion accessory. The main business of eating is to talk and relish the company of friends. Food and drink function like an Armani suit and a pair of Gucci shoes; they have to be noticed, but must not be the centre of attention. They are there to make you appear in your best light.

When all this has passed through Californian hands it ceases to be purely Italian and becomes Italifornian. Then it joins up with wilted greens, pickled beets, re-fried pinto beans, fudge brownie sundae, butterscotch pudding with shortbread cookies and other strands, to weave the uniquely Californian coat of many colours.

In Mustard's Grill in Napa Valley you can (provided you remember to book well in advance) enjoy far-flung Thai curry lamb shank stew, or Mongolian pork chop, alongside more local smoked Long Island duck with one hundred almond onion sauce, or grilled Sonoma rabbit with red peppers, saffron and fennel. In Brava Terrace further up the road, Hawaiian fish meets Italian pasta meets Provençal herbs meets Oregon clams meets Parisian duck (an Alan Senderens recipe) meets cassoulet in glorious profusion.

The global village kitchen is stocked with New Zealand rock oysters and Maine lobster, while fresh Pacific fish - grilled tuna is a favourite - make the running in any restaurant with even half an ounce of swank. If there is no tuna, you might get opah, sand dabs or swordfish, perhaps with red onion marmalade, ginger lime butter, or warm chanterelle vinaigrette. Boring it is not.

Neither is the spectacle. At lunch you might laze outside in dappled sunlight. At dinner, you sit in what seems like an extension of the kitchen. Whether they want to prove that the food is not being micro-waved, or whether it is so that the chef can keep an eye on us, I don't know. But the old-fashioned idea of maintaining a distance between cooker and cookee has vanished. The steamy, greasy, smoky, lively, sweaty reality of kitchen life is exposed for better or for worse.

The language, meanwhile passes through a mangle of its own. Juggling with so many foreign influences creates a rich tapestry of words, most of them adjectives. Trying to work out what is on the menu often means waiting until the end of a very long phrase.

Thus you might need to plough through "fire-roasted, whole, sweet, locally-grown, organic, pink," before you discover that the objects they are queuing up to qualify are onions. This is because the kitchen is just bubbling over with enthusiasm to tell you everything about the ingredients. Unless you know that the burger you are eating is a "Julie's Must-Have Neman-Schell All-Natural" one, how on earth can you enjoy it properly?

Sometimes, a menu will remain inscrutable even after prolonged study. "Grilled pasilla pepper with tamale stuffing" sounds too good to miss, whatever it turns out to be. And "lima-bean succotash" can only be understood by seeing it, poking it, smelling and eating it.

Waiting staff are very much at home with all this; some even develop their own idiosyncratic expressions in tandem, instead of asking, "Is everything all right?" the question put to me over a mouthful of buckwheat hotcakes with sweet pecan butter was, "Is this something that you're liking?"

But I shall not mock Californian waitpersons. Most of them put most of ours in the shade. They may look as if they are filling in time between modelling or acting jobs - an illusion to which the stage set decor can contribute significantly - but they are invariably good-natured, smiling, helpful and patient.

If the welcoming, "Hi, how are you today?" from a complete stranger unsettlingly implies that they had some idea of how you were yesterday, then so what? It is merely the oil that sets the machine in motion. "I'm fine thanks, how are you?" "Oh, just great. Can I get you guys anything?" And off you go as if you've known each other since you were at school. Now isn't that better than being ignored?

And if you ask what lima-bean succotash is when it's at home, you don't get a resigned sigh and a pre-recorded message, you get a straight look and a straight answer. If I wanted to become a professional waiter I wouldn't go to hotel school in Europe to learn, I'd go to San Francisco.

Somewhere like Zuni Cafe and Grill would suit me fine. Above the long, glass-fronted bar is a restaurant that even the owner describes as "weird". It looks perfectly normal, with starched white cloths and a warren of small inter-connecting dining rooms, but is makes some attempt to get away from the "fillay" syndrome.

Most restaurants serve fillay: of beef, perhaps, or grilled Ahi tuna. In California cuisine you rarely come across bones, bits of insides or extremities. It is all prime cuts that can be sliced through with dentures or a spoon. Californians are "safe" eaters and drinkers, which is odd because what they seem to enjoy drinking most is something with a government health warning slapped on it. Anyway, if they are going to try anything unusual in San Francisco, Zuni is probably where they will give it a go.

Zuni serves manageable dishes too - duck sausages with chanterells, baked ricotta and roasted figs with rosemary focaccia, even fresh home-cured anchovies, tasting of fish rather than salt and oil - but it also cooks ox-tail brilliantly. Apart from that, calf liver and bacon, or veal sweetbreads in the more avant-garde places, are the nearest you are likely to get to what Americans call "variety meats". Offal, traditionally, is for poor people, and nobody I saw in a restaurant in California ever looked remotely poor.

But no lunch or dinner can be as sumptuous as brunch. Of all edible American exports, from the streamlined, precision-weighed, mass-produced burger, to blueberry muffins when you can find them, the ensemble and institution that is brunch has to be the most lavish, indulgent and relaxing way to spend a morning, especially Sunday, especially in San Francisco.

Whole families come out to play, dressed better than a lettuce at Chez Panisse, the birthplace of California cuisine. If they eat a lot of food, it may be because they view it as two meals rolled into one, and therefore reasonable. But brunch is not about being reasonable. It is, in hotels at any rate, about combining an awesome number of dishes from a great diversity of cooking styles in any order you please, and taking as long as you like.

Two items are essential. Eggs Benedict and a good Californian sparkling wine. The fizz, which can be Buck's, must be dispensed liberally. It helps if you have already read the papers and don't have anything planned for the afternoon, except a doze in a hammock.

Some places in San Francisco, such as Washington Square Bar & Grill, just provide the basics. A bit like Soho's Coach & Horses pub, it is somewhere for arty-media folk to practise their favourite hobby: idle chatter. Washbag throws in piano jazz too. Other places, such as the Sheraton Palace Hotel, go in more for string quartets, but ones that play Jerome Kern, Irving Berlin and Harold Arlen rather than Britten, Stravinsky and Bartok.

The Sheraton Palace brunch is a massive display of oysters, crab claws, half a dozen different kinds of grilled sausage, green salads wilted before your very eyes, omelettes prepared under your nose, hunks of roast beef and lamb, sushi, sashimi, dim-sum, eggs Benedict of course, waffles, muffins, and cakes, cakes, and more cakes. It is profligacy on a grand scale, and all it costs is a few dollars. Brilliant.

To sum up, Californian cuisine is more a set of attitudes than a list of dishes or a doctrinaire collection of recipes. You can recognise a Californian restaurant, wherever in the world it happens to be, by its phenomenally good service, by colourful plates of food that cross cultural boundaries, gastronomic disciplines and national frontiers, by the poetic licence of the menu, and by its generally good value. It will also be bursting at the seams. If it is less than a week old, make sure you're one of the shils and not one of the schmucks.

Jim Ainsworth

Hosts of the Year

Peter and Nita Hauser
Stock Hill House
Gillingham, Dorset

The Hausers' own particular brand of hospitality has made their Victorian house one of the most relaxing and peaceful hotels in the land. Keeping the guests happy should be every hotelier's aim, and here they do it with unflagging energy and good humour, just as they did on Sark a few years ago. Customer satisfaction includes the inner man, and the breakfasts, the afternoon teas and the full meals all keep the smiles wide.

Previous Winner

1992 **Woodhayes**
Whimple, Devon

FOR BUSINESS

FOR LEISURE

FOR DINERS CLUB
LOOK FOR THE
SYMBOL IN THIS GUIDE

Diners Club International, Diners Club House, Kingsmead,
Farnborough, Hampshire, GU14 7SR.

primetime ™

Wherever business takes you.

Dedicated to the needs of the business user
for whom the telephone is a vital productivity
tool, Primetime offers a comprehensive range
of relevant services - including information
lines - many of them exclusive to Cellnet.

A number of messaging services are also
available for use with the Cellnet network.

The nearest phone.

For further details call Cellnet on
0800 424 323

lifetime™

In touch. Whatever life holds in store.

Giving you more flexibility to juggle business commitments, social responsibilities and your leisure pursuits, Cellnet's exciting new service 'Lifetime' makes mobile communications more affordable for the lower user.

If the majority of your calls can be made outside peak business hours, Cellnet Lifetime is the service for you.

With Cellnet you have a choice.

cellnet

PUT YOUR DINERS CLUB CARD INTO ACTION
AND BENEFIT FROM
100 BONUS DIVIDENDS POINTS

Each time you charge over £50 to your Diners Club Card, in any one of the recommended establishments featured in this guide, you can claim 100 Bonus Dividends Points*. Our special 'thank you' for using your Diners Club Card.

We normally award you one point for every £5 you spend on your Card. You can then collect your Points and use them to claim quality gifts and activities from our latest Dividends Brochure.

The more Points collected - the bigger and better the thank you.

And with 100 Bonus Dividends Points everytime you spend over £50 you will soon be eligible for some very big thank you's indeed.

HOW TO CLAIM

To claim your 100 Bonus Dividends Points, please write to us, giving the following details:- Card Number, Cardholder Name, Name of Establishment, Town of Establishment, Value of Charge, Date of Charge and send to:-

Dividends Department, FREEPOST, The Diners Club Limited, Diners Club House, Kingsmead, Farnborough, Hampshire, GU14 7BR.

Apply for a Diners Club Card today and start earning Dividends Points. Dial 0252 513500 and our Customer Service Staff will be pleased to help you.

*All claims must be made before 1st January 1994. This offer applies to Personal Card Members only.

London

W2	**Abbey Court**		£136

Tel 071-221 7518   Fax 071-792 0858

PH

20 Pembridge Gardens W2 4DU

Map 21 D3

Efficient staff, good-quality furniture and eye-catching flower arrangements are the hallmarks of good hotel-keeping in this friendly establishment. It's a five-storey Victorian town house in a quiet street only a few minutes from Notting Hill Gate. Public rooms are limited to a smart reception area and a conservatory where cooked breakfast is served. The 22 individually styled and decorated bedrooms have Italian marble whirlpool baths and towelling robes. *Rooms 22. Access, Amex, Visa,* 🄳

W2	**L'Accento Italiano**	↑ NEW	£60

Tel 071-243 2201

R

16 Garway Road W2 4NH

Map 22 C1

Near enough to Westbourne Grove to be easy to find but just far enough into the side street to be away from the hubbub. Behind an all-glass frontage it's a simply appointed room with plain wooden tables (set with excellent cakey bread, olive oil); one wall is plain white, the other curved and the colour of wet sand. It's been a great success since its opening late in 1991 with its blend of regional Italian cooking and kind prices. Many locals are already regulars, and it's not possible to get a table without booking. This is Italian cooking unlike the normal British product, and Andrea Beltrami offers particularly good value on his 2-course set menu, where you could find rice salad, excellent croquettes of aubergine and pecorino, polenta with gorgonzola, a hearty pork casserole making use of cheaper bits, beef in Barolo, grilled swordfish with olive oil, lemon and oregano. From the carte could come risotto in black cuttlefish sauce, gratin of spinach noodles with artichokes and ham, fillet of brill with roast onions, pan-fried calf's liver with balsamic vinegar sauce. On the pudding list are ice creams and sorbets, vin santo and cantucci, chilled mixed berries marinated in Marsala. They really care about their customers, take evident pains with the food and look to have a rosy future; they will need all the extra table space planned. *Seats 42. Parties 12. L 12.30-2.30 D 6.30-11.30. Closed L Sat, all Sun. Set meals from £10.50. Access, Visa.*

W12	**Adam's Café**		£25

Tel 081-743 0572

R

77 Askew Road W12 9AH

Map 21 D4

Jekyll and Hyde in W12. By day this is an English café, by night a modest restaurant serving Mediterranean cuisine and Tunisian specialities. Couscous is *the* speciality – a bed of steamed durum wheat with a spicy bouillon sauce and a choice of vegetarian, lamb, royale (lamb, chicken and merguez) and impériale (all those plus beef). Lamb soup, briks or rolls of filo pastry filled with minced beef to start, patisserie or hot lemon pancake to round things off. *Seats 36. Parties 36. D only 7.30-10.30. Closed Sun, Bank Holidays. No credit cards.*

SW7	**Adelphi Hotel**	62%	£122

Tel 071-373 7177   Fax 071-373 7720

H

127 Cromwell Road SW7 4DT

Map 23 E1

Recently totally refurbished, white-painted period-style hotel on a busy corner of Cromwell Road, with its main entrance in Courtfield Gardens. Three conference suites hold up to 80. Charges by the hour for departures after 11am. *Rooms 68. Access, Amex, Visa,* 🄳

WC2   Ajimura
Tel 071-240 0178

£60

R

51 Shelton Street WC2H 9HE

Map 25 B1

Sushi and sashimi are the specialities at a popular Japanese restaurant which sticks mainly to familiar dishes with a healthy slant. Zensai are either starters or a good accompaniment to drinks. *Seats 54. Parties 25. Private Room. L 12-3 D 6-11. Closed L Sat, all Sun, Bank Holidays. Set L from £7.50. Access, Amex, Visa,*

W8   Al Basha
Tel 071-938 1794

£70

R

Troy Court 222 Kensington High Street W8 7RG

Map 23 D1

Lebanese restaurant with the accent on comfort and good service. Plenty of tables outside in summer. *Seats 80. Parties 60. Private Room. Meals 12-11.30. Set L from £12.50. Access, Amex, Visa,*

SW1   Al Bustan
Tel 071-235 8277

£60

R

27 Motcomb Street SW1X 8JU

Map 23 D4

One of the prettiest and best of London's growing number of Lebanese restaurants. A generous plateful of salad items is as crisp and fresh as the summery decor. A robust selection of hot and cold hors d'oeuvre accounts for more than half the menu; aubergine dip, spicy mini-sausages, minced meat-filled samosas and falafel are all excellent. Main-course grills include boneless chicken with garlic sauce. Good choice of honey-rich sweets. *Seats 65. Meals noon-11pm (Sun to 10pm). Closed 25 Dec, 1 Jan. Access, Amex, Visa,*

W1   Al Hamra
Tel 071-493 1954

£50

R

31 Shepherd Market W1Y 7RJ

Map 22 C3

One of London's best-known and most popular Lebanese restaurants, with close-set tables and outside eating in fine weather. Munch on crunchy salad, olives and bread while awaiting your meal – typically a selection of hot and cold hors d'oeuvre, something from the charcoal grill and, if you're still not replete, a honey-sticky sweet or two. *Seats 70. Parties 30. Meals 12-12. Closed 25 Dec, 1 Jan. Access, Amex, Visa,*

W2   Al San Vincenzo   NEW
Tel 071-262 9623

£75

R

30 Connaught Street W2 2AS

Map 22 C2

Vincenzo Borgonzolo is adept at Italian cooking that's quite unburdened by the usual traditions and stereotypes. Neither is it outlandish, but each high-quality ingredient makes its full contribution in dishes like tagliolini with sun-dried tomatoes and basil, octopus cooked in its own juices with a piquant sauce, calf's liver pan-fried with onions, or pigeon casseroled with white and red cabbage. The wine list includes a number of luscious pudding wines and grappa available by the glass to accompany desserts such as pancakes with a sauce of blood oranges and bitter orange liqueur. The decor is as unfussy as the food: white walls, lightwood floors, simple table settings, good linen, modern crystal. The opening of the basement room has almost doubled the capacity. One house champagne, otherwise a concise, all-Italian wine list. *Seats 36. Parties 16. Private Room. L 12.30-2.30 D 7-10.30. Closed L Sat, all Sun, 2 weeks Xmas. Access, Visa,*

W1   Alastair Little   ★★   £85

Tel 071-734 5183	**R**

49 Frith Street W1V 5TE   Map 25 A2

Alastair Little's highly individual cooking continues to evolve in a style
that is particularly distinctive. His creations are invariably a mixture of
superbly fresh ingredients and stunning visual presentation, to say nothing
of the wizardry that Alastair conjures up in between. Dishes such as
Chinese-style glazed Bresse pigeon with crispy vegetables or spring green
and sauerkraut soup with sour cream and paprika show that his influences
come from far and wide – even the vegetables served with main courses
(and charged for separately) are away from the norm: celeriac purée, rösti
potatoes and sautéed spinach with five spices can hardly be termed run-of-
the-mill. Starters always offer a wider choice than main courses: a range of
up to ten might include charcuterie, sautéed squid with ink sauce, trio of
terrines with various relishes and French bean salad, pissaladière,
bouillabaisse and carpaccio with rocket, Parmesan and truffle oil. Main
courses are often simply described, cheekily underselling the headline act
(but not the prices which help top up the bill): roast baby brill with cèpes,
red mullet fillets with parsley and grilled vegetable salads, tournedos with
polenta and pesto, calf's liver with sage. The intelligent creativity doesn't
stop there, though, continuing into 'expresso' granita and whipped cream,
dark and white truffle cake with ginger sauce, or lemon and goat's cheese
tart. A typical fixed-price lunch menu offers white-cooked sliced pork with
spicy Chinese dressing, followed by salt cod and saffron potato fishcakes
with tomato sauce and sautéed spinach, and cheeses or dessert. Hand-
written menus are decorated with modern graphics that complement
bright paintings and the general monochrome of decor and fittings; the
wine list is short but well chosen, accurately matching the eclectic
influences of the extraordinary cooking. *Seats 35. Parties 15. L 12-3
D 6-11.30. Closed L Sat & Xmas/New Year, all Sun, Bank Holidays.
Set L £18. Access, Amex, Visa.*

EC1   Alba   £60

Tel 071-588 1798	**R**

107 Whitecross Street EC1Y 8JD   Map 20 C1

A friendly Italian restaurant very close to the Barbican Centre. Cooking
puts the emphasis on good honest flavours throughout a menu which
mixes familiar favourites such as minestrone, *risi e bisi* and *saltimbocca alla
romana* with some much more unusual offerings, notably thinly sliced raw
veal with parmesan, rocket and truffle olive oil, and bresaola using not
only beef but also horse and deer. *Seats 50. Parties 25. L 12-3 D 7-11.
Closed Sat & Sun, Bank Holidays, 2 weeks Xmas. Access, Amex, Visa,*
Diners Club International

SW7   Alexander Hotel   69%   £116

Tel 071-581 1591 Fax 071-581 0824	**H**

9 Sumner Place SW7 3EE   Map 23 E1

Behind the elegant town-house facade is a modern hotel in country-house
style. The lounge/reception area is furnished with a mixture of antique and
reproduction pieces, and personal touches abound in the choice of pictures,
posters, cartoons and flowers. Decent-sized bedrooms include several with
four-posters and a suite with its own patio. 24hr room and valet service.
No dogs. *Rooms 37. Garden. Access, Amex, Visa,* Diners Club International

W11   L'Altro   £70

Tel 071-792 1066	**R**

210 Kensington Park Road W11   Map 20 C3

Sister to *Cibo*, L'Altro is decorated in a clever indoor courtyard style.
Essentially a seafood restaurant although one meat dish is always offered
and a good vegetarian selection. Lobster and artichoke heart salad dressed

with balsamic vinegar, olive oil and lemon or red mullet with black cuttlefish risotto are typical of the modern Italian style. Pasta dishes are unusually good – try the gnocchi with langoustine and asparagus if it's on the regularly–changing menu. *Seats 43. Parties 40. L 12-2.30 (Sun 12.30-3) D 7-11 (Fri & Sat to 11.30). Closed L Bank Holidays, D Sun, all Mon. Set L £14.95/£17.95. Access, Visa,*

N1   Anna's Place   £44
Tel 071-249 9379   R
90 Mildmay Park Newington Green N1 4PR   Map 20 B1

Chatty Anna Hegarty is a constant presence in her tiny and noisy place with its close-set tables and summer conservatory. Her native Sweden is the main inspiration for the menu, which includes home-cured herring served in dill and light curry sauces, broccoli and lemon soup, gravlax or a hefty Janssen's Temptation (a creamy mixture of baked potatoes, anchovies and onions). Salmon fishcakes with sorrel sauce, a daily special fish dish, game in season and hotpots are typical of the style. *Seats 45. Parties 30. L 12.15-2.15 D 7.15-10.45. Closed Sun, Mon, 2 weeks Xmas, 2 weeks Easter, Aug. No credit cards.*

W8   Apollo Hotel   £62
Tel 071-835 1133   Fax 071-370 4853   H
18-22 Lexham Gardens W8 5JE   Map 23 E1

Long-established bed and breakfast hotel off Cromwell Road, offering value-for-money accommodation with few frills. Most rooms have private facilities, all have TVs and dial-out phones. *Rooms 59. Closed Xmas/New Year. Access, Amex, Visa,*

SW3   The Argyll   NEW   £70
Tel 071-352 0025   R
316 King's Road SW3   Map 23 E2

Chef Anand Sastry (who has worked with some of the best chefs in the country) has teamed up with Christian Arden (formerly at *Sutherlands*, now closed) and restaurant manager John Keating to bring chic eating to Chelsea. The restaurant is barely decorated (not quite trendily minimalist) and one of its greatest assets is the front that opens up on sunny days to give a little more light to the otherwise windowless room. Time will tell whether the King's Road set are prepared to pay the prices asked (somewhat higher than average for the type of establishment), but there can be little argument as to the *quality* of the cooking or the modish repertoire of dishes – foie gras with braised beans and lentils or wild mushroom ravioli with a herb and watercress sauce to start, followed by pot-roasted poussin with roasted potatoes, morels and lardons, or chump end of lamb with garlic and mashed potato. Annoyingly, vegetables are charged extra. Faultless desserts might include a tangy fruit terrine or a divine chocolate marquise and it's worth waiting for the hot caramel soufflé served with caramel ice cream. Good-value, 2- or 3-course fixed-price lunches deserve to attract a crowd. Good British cheeses might incude Mr Gould's Cheddar, Mendip goat and Shropshire Blue. Sensibly concise wine list has lots of good bottles from around the world at under £20. *Seats 50. Parties 8. L 12-2.30 D 7-10.15. Closed L Mon, all Sun, Bank Holidays. Set L £12/£15.75. Access, Amex, Visa,*

W1   Arirang Korean Restaurant   £50
Tel 071-437 6633   R
31 Poland Street W1V 3DB   Map 22 B3

Pleasant service accompanies the fiery flavours of Korean cuisine on the fringes of Soho. Bulgogi – thinly sliced marinated beef – is the national dish, while among the more intriguing items are bracken stalks, a pizza made of ground green peas and wings of skate in a hot chili sauce. *Seats 100. Parties 120. Private Room. L 12-3 D 6-11. Closed Sun, 25 Dec, 1 Jan, L Bank Holidays. Set meals from £16.50. Access, Amex, Visa,*

W1   Arisugawa   £60

Tel 071-636 8913   **R**

27 Percy Street W1   **Map 22 B3**

The first choice of many Japanese diners, this smart modern restaurant in a
basement has a menu of more than usual interest. Western palates can play
safe with familiar favourites, or venture into unknown territory with sliced
liver stir-fried with wild garlic, sea-urchin roe sashimi, desiccated gourd,
burdock root rolled sushi or pungent fermented soya beans with raw egg.
Seats 100. *Private Room. Parties* 100. *L 12.30-2.30 D 6-10. Closed L Sat, all
Sun, Bank Holidays, Xmas/New Year. Set L from £6.50 Set D from £15.
Access, Amex, Visa,*

SW8   L'Arlequin   ★★   £110

Tel 071-622 0555   **R**

123 Queenstown Road SW8 3RH   **Map 21 E2**

Charming Geneviève Delteil leads the smooth, professional service in this
comfortable and thoroughly stylish establishment, a fine home south of the
river for Christian Delteil's superb French cooking. Gimmickry and
showmanship have no place here – the menu says it all, with simple dish
titles and none of the flowery descriptions that appear on many more
pretentious establishments' menus around the country. The good-value 2-
or 3-course fixed-price lunch might offer *pistou provençale* or *terrine de
lapereau* followed by *dorade poelée sauce corail* or *pieds de porc farcis*, and
fromages, opéra chocolat café or *chaud froid fruits rouges* to finish; the
simplicity of the menu belies the true value on offer and the real skills at
work in the kitchen. Even the à la carte dinner menu is hard pushed to
escape from such laconicism – perhaps *persillé de homard et ris de veau* and
petit chou farci à l'ancienne among the seven or so starters, with *pièce de boeuf
à la moelle, méli-mélo de foie gras* or *selle de lapereau à la graine de moutarde*
following. Daily plats du marché reflect the very freshest ingredients: *loup
poelé à la vinaigrette, saumon "gros sel", blanc de turbot au champagne, gigot
d'agneau des Pyrénées.* The sensational mixed plate of desserts should not be
missed. An improved wine list with several good good regional French bottles
under £20. Smart surroundings and serious bourgeois French cooking to
match. *Seats* 45. *Parties* 60. *L 12.30-2 D 7-10.30. Closed Sat & Sun, Bank
Holidays, 1 week Xmas. Set L £18.50/£20.50 & £28 Set D £28. Access,
Amex, Visa,* ⬥ *Diners Club International*

WC2   Arts Theatre Café   £46

Tel 071-497 8014   **R**

6 Great Newport Street WC2   **Map 25 B2**

Tucked away in the basement of the theatre, the café's unassuming,
utilitarian decor belies Italian cooking that's considerably above average.
The menu changes every day: typical choices run from rocket and
chickpea soup to bollito misto by way of skewered minced lamb with
home-baked flat bread; baked halibut with mussel sauce; and spinach,
salami and Parmesan cakes. Everything has the robust and comforting taste
of healthy home cooking. Exclusively Italian, sensibly-priced wine list to
match. *Seats* 25. *Parties* 25. *Meals 12-10. Closed Sat & Sun, Bank Holidays,
1 week Xmas/New Year. Set D from £10.50. No credit cards.*

SW7   Aster House   £70

Tel 071-581 5888   Fax 071-584 4925   **H**

3 Sumner Place SW7 3EE   **Map 23 E1**

A charming home-from-home at the end of an early-Victorian terrace. Bed
and breakfast is offered with rooms ranging from small singles to a four-
poster studio suite, all with private bath/shower, TVs, dial-out phones,
fridges and mini-safes. A health-conscious buffet breakfast is served in a

sunny first-floor conservatory. No smoking. Unlicensed. No dogs.
Minimum booking for two nights. *Rooms 12. Access, Amex, Visa,*

NW1　　　Asuka

£70

Tel 071-486 5026

R

209a Baker Street NW1 6AD

Map 22 B2

In an arcade at the northern end of Baker Street, Asuka is also the name of
a traditional ten-course feast of two soups, seven dishes and fruit. That's at
the top of the price range, but there's plenty more to choose from,
including some items daintily prepared at the table by waitresses in
kimonos. *Seats 34. Parties 34. Private Room. L 12-3 D 6-11. Closed L Sat, all
Sun, Bank Holidays. Set L from £11.50 Set D from £30. Access, Amex, Visa,*

W1　　　The Athenaeum　　78%

£222

Tel 071-499 3464   Fax 071-493 1860

HR

116 Piccadilly W1V 0BJ

Map 22 C3

A peaceful and luxurious hotel near Hyde Park Corner, overlooking Green
Park. Public rooms are limited for the size and location of the hotel but
what rooms there are have an intimate atmosphere, if lacking in daylight;
the Windsor Lounge is an attractive room with a mix of elegant
furnishings – comfortable, striped sofas and soft lighting enhanced by table
lamps; the clubby cocktail bar is similarly relaxing with mahogany
panelling and a choice of 56 single malt whiskies. Bedrooms are
exceptionally well appointed with co-ordinated fabrics and bathrooms clad
in Italian marble. A choice of four meeting rooms caters for gatherings of
up to 44 people. Valet car parking. 34 apartments are in town houses next
door to the hotel – see Serviced Apartments section for further details.
Rooms 144. Access, Amex, Visa,

Restaurant

£80

Elegant, intimate surroundings and attentive service are complemented by
carefully prepared dishes from the mainstream of classic and current
fashion: Parma ham with melon or figs, sausage of vegetables with a broad
bean sauce; pan-fried red mullet with Chinese-style vegetables and a hoi-sin
vinaigrette, steamed salmon and turbot with pastis and fennel, plus more
simple grills, savouries and a small choice of desserts. *Seats 60. Parties 65.
Private Room. L 12.30-2.30 (Sun 11.30-1.30) D 6-10.30. Closed L Sat. Set L
& D £23.50*

W8　　　Atlas Hotel

£62

Tel 071-835 1155   Fax 071-370 4853

H

24-30 Lexham Gardens W8 5JE

Map 23 E1

Neighbour of the Apollo Hotel (see above), in the same ownership, with
the same long-serving manager, Mr Monina, and offering the same
services. *Rooms 64. Closed Xmas/New Year. Access, Amex, Visa,*

SW3　　　Au Bon Accueil

£45

Tel 071-589 3718

R

19 Elystan Street SW3 3NT

Map 23 E2

Everyday French cooking in an enduring local with outside eating in
summer. Onion soup, garlic snails, chicken with tarragon, prawns
provençale, steak au poivre. *Seats 80. Parties 35. L 12.30-2.30 D 7-11.30.
Closed L Sat, all Sun, Bank Holidays. Access, Amex, Visa,*

W1   Au Jardin des Gourmets

£75

Tel 071-437 1816   Fax 071-437 0043

R

5 Greek Street W1V 5LA

Map 25 A2

Established in 1931 and still going strong, this Soho stalwart is a bastion of
traditional French cooking. Saucisson with lentils, vichyssoise, quenelles de
brochet with sorrel sauce, kidneys with Meaux mustard and sirloin steak
béarnaise show the style. More remarkable than the food is the exceptional
wine list where there is only a brief mention of non-French wines; classics
are reasonably priced (plenty of pre-'70 clarets) and there's a fine selection
of armagnacs. 15% service charge is added to the bill. *Seats 85. Parties 55.
Private Rooms. L 12.15-2.30 D 6.15-11.15. Closed L Sat, all Sun, Bank
Holidays. Set meals £17.50. Access, Amex, Visa,* ⓘ Diners Club International

NW8   L'Aventure

£65

Tel 071-624 6232

R

3 Blenheim Terrace NW8 0EH

Map 20 C3

Owner Catherine Parisot's personality is stamped all over this delightful
little French restaurant with a terrace for summer eating. In a friendly,
intimate atmosphere regulars and newcomers enjoy a short, innovative
selection of dishes typified by coquilles St. Jacques florentine, clafoutis of
leeks beurre blanc, roast guinea fowl with honey and cabbage, and rack of
lamb with garlic 'en chemise'. *Seats 40. Parties 40. L 12.30-2.30 D 7.30-11
(Sun to 10). Closed L Sat, Bank Holidays, 1 week Xmas, 4 days Easter.
Set L £17.25 Set D £23.50. Access, Amex, Visa.*

SW7   Bacco

£50

Tel 071-589 4142   Fax 071-835 2145

R

30 Old Brompton Road SW7 3DL

Map 23 E1

Bright basement restaurant with a safe, mainly modern Italian menu:
mussels in black pepper with fresh tomato, bresaola with rocket and
Parmesan cheese, pennette with leeks and pancetta, fillet of sole in lemon
sauce and pan-fried lamb with fresh rosemary. *Seats 45. Parties 50. L 12-3
D 6-11.30. Closed L Sat & Sun, Bank Holidays ex Good Friday. Access,
Amex, Visa,* ⓘ Diners Club International

W1   Bahn Thai

£60

Tel 071-437 8504

R

21a Frith Street W1V 5TS

Map 25 A2

The menu at one of London's first authentic Thai restaurants is full of
helpful advice, including "temperature gauge" symbols. Less welcome is the
health warning..."It is impossible always to guarantee that all seafood, in
particular, is always fit to eat. There can be occasions when shellfish appear
fresh but may cause an upset stomach." Diners deterred from prawns, crab,
mussels and scallops will still find plenty in the way of choice, including
perch, pomfret, pork, chicken, duck and beef. There's also a good
vegetarian selection. The restaurant has recently been refurbished and a
new private dining room opened. *Seats 110. Parties 45. Private Room.
L 12-2.45 (Sun 12.30-2.30) D 6-11.15 (Sun 6.30-10.30). Closed some Bank
Holidays. Access, Amex, Visa,* ⓘ Diners Club International

W12   Balzac Restaurant

£50

Tel 081-743 5370

R

4 Wood Lane W12 7DT

Map 21 D3

For many years a haunt of BBC staff, the restaurant has recently undergone
a change of ownership but the style is still mainly old-fashioned bistro
French (onion and fish soups, lapin à la moutarde, carré d'agneau persillé,
boeuf bourguignon, crème renversée) with a few Italian touches (wild
mushrooms with polenta, Parma ham with melon). Good value wines;
staff are friendly and switched-on, and the place is much lighter and

roomier than it was in the 70s and 80s. A la carte lunch, fixed-price only evening meals. **Seats 80.** *L 12-2.30 D 7-11. Closed L Sat, all Sun, Bank Holidays, 2 weeks Xmas. Set D £13.90 & £15.90. Access, Amex, Visa,*

SW7   Bangkok £36

Tel 071-584 8529   Fax 071-823 7883

R

9 Bute Street SW7 3EY

Map 23 E1

One of the area's first Thai restaurants, the sparsely appointed Bangkok has been run by the same family since its opening in 1967. The short menu includes beef and pork satay, fried prawns, spare ribs, beef and chicken curry and Thai rice-noodle. **Seats 60.** *Parties 24. L 12.15-2.15 D 7-11.15. Closed Sun, Bank Holidays. Set L from £12.50. Access, Visa.*

SE3   Bardon Lodge   60% £74

Tel 081-853 4051   Fax 081-858 7387

H

15 Stratheden Road SE3 7TH

Map 21 E1

In a residential area of Blackheath, a privately-owned and family-run hotel with a friendly, English atmosphere. Three Victorian houses have a few period features and modern bedrooms. Two new four-poster beds have recently been added. The open-plan lounge leads through to a cocktail bar and on to the patio overlooking the garden. Convenient for those visiting the Greenwich area. **Rooms 37.** *Garden. Access, Amex, Visa.*

SW3   Basil Street Hotel   71% £170

Tel 071-581 3311   Fax 071-581 3693

H

Basil Street SW3 1AH

Map 23 D2

An Edwardian English atmosphere pervades a privately-owned hotel just 191 steps (according to their publicity) from Harrods. Public areas have a country house feel, from the antique-lined corridor leading to the dining room and a spacious lounge in sunny yellow with rug-covered polished parquet floor. Up a broad staircase are well-kept bedrooms, which are of a good size, usually with a sitting area, traditionally furnished and decorated with understated good taste. Most have equally roomy private bathrooms. It's been under the same management for more than 30 years, and old-fashioned standards of courteous and obliging service include shoe cleaning, servicing of rooms in the evenings and 24hr room service. Children under 16 stay free in parents' room. **Rooms 92.** *Access, Amex, Visa,*

SW3   The Beaufort £175

Tel 071-584 5252   Fax 071-589 2834

PH

33 Beaufort Gardens SW3 1PP

Map 23 D2

In a tree-lined Knightsbridge square, the Beaufort offers personal service and almost rural peace (though Harrods is only 100 yards away). Guests are given front door keys, as there's no reception, and terms include VAT, service, drinks from the drawing room bar, Continental breakfast (served in the room only), room service snacks, personal laundry and membership of a local health club. Air-conditioned, pastel-decorated bedrooms – full of extras large and small – range from a single with shower/WC only to a junior suite. A wonderful collection of over 400 English floral watercolours graces the walls. No children under ten except babes in arms. No dogs. **Rooms 28.** *Closed 22 Dec-2 Jan. Access, Amex, Visa,*

W4   Bedlington Café £25

Tel 081-994 1965

R

24 Faulconberg Road W4 3JY

Map 21 D4

Bacon butties are a daytime staple, but in the evening the Bedlington becomes a budget Thai restaurant. Beef, pork, chicken and seafood appear several ways, and the noodle dishes are popular one-plate choices. Unlicensed (bring your own from the off-licence a few doors down). No

credit cards or cheques. *Seats 28. Parties 30.* D only 6.30-10 (Sun 6-9.30).
Café meals 9-2.

NW1   Belgo   NEW   £40

Tel 071-267 0718   **R**

72 Chalk Farm Road NW1 8AN   Map 20 C2

A remarkable example of post-modern design, with a flat concrete
frontage, a high-tech wheel and pulley design for the stairs, a bar made of
latex rubber, an environment-friendly heating and air system using huge
chrome pipes, and a restaurant area conceived as a brewery eating hall. Its
walls are also concrete, with a frieze inlaid with Rabelais-inspired names of
obscure fish. Tables are refectory-style (for four), topped with ash, chairs
are minimalist, with wooden axe handle seats which deliver more comfort
and support than looks likely. Waiters are dressed in monk's habits, a
practical garb for serving the hefty portions of mussels that are the most
popular order. These and other marginally more refined Belgian dishes –
wild boar sausage, croquettes, chicken waterzooi – are washed down with
Belgian beer, some of it monastery-brewed, some fruit-fermented, one sour
and lemony, one as strong as wine! A big hit from the moment it opened,
Belgo is a place for tucking into simple, sustaining food, for drinking beer
and talking – but definitely not in a whisper. It's very busy in the evenings,
and bookings are taken on the day from 11am. Open all day at weekends.
Seats 70. Parties 25. L 12-3 D 6-11.30 (Sat & Sun 12-11.30). Set menu
£8.95. Access, Amex, Visa.

W8   Belvedere in Holland Park   £55

Tel 071-602 1238   **R**

Holland House off Abbotsbury Road W8 6LU   Map 21 D3

A delightful setting for this airy restaurant in the heart of Holland Park
that has had a chequered history over many years. It was refurbished in
contemporary style eighteen months ago, utilising inlaid wood tables,
smart lighting and stylish glassware. Once the summer ballroom of
Holland House, it is now a home to contemporary cooking along the lines
of char-grilled breast of chicken with marinated vegetables, salad of roast
tomatoes, rocket, asparagus and warm shiitake mushrooms, and pan-fried
Scottish salmon with home-made noodles and a creamy cucumber and dill
sauce. For once, parking is easy (in the nearby pay and display car park)
and there's al fresco dining on a small balcony in fine weather. *Seats 120.*
L 12-3 D 7-11. Closed 25, 26 Dec & 1 Jan. Access, Amex, Visa, *Diners Club International*

NW3   Benihana   £75

Tel 071-586 9508   **R**

100 Avenue Road NW3 3HF   Map 20 C3

American-style Japanese teppanyaki griddle cooking in large and often
lively basement surroundings, next to the Hampstead Theatre. Surf'n'turf is
served with showbiz flair by knife-flailing chefs at hibachi tables. Great
value week-day lunches and children's menu (with entertainment on
Sundays). Branches around the world, from Beverly Hills to Seoul.
Seats120. L 12.30-3 (Sat & Sun from 1) D 6.30-12. Closed L Mon, 25 Dec.
Set L from £6.75. Access, Amex, Visa, *Diners Club International*

W1   Bentley's   £85

Tel 071-287 5025   **R**

11 Swallow Street W1R 7HD   Map 22 C3

Simple and classical seafood dishes (moules marinière, lobster bisque, scampi
provençale, Dover sole meunière) are served in the club-like surroundings
of a London landmark founded in 1916. Oysters are a speciality. *Seats 100.*
Parties 20. Private Room. L 12-3 D 6-10.45. Closed Sun, some Bank Holidays.
Set meals from £19.50. Access, Amex, Visa, *Diners Club International*

SW1   The Berkeley   86%

£277

Tel 071-235 6000   Fax 071-235 4330

Wilton Place SW1X 7RL

Map 23 D2

Just off Knightsbridge, close to Hyde Park Corner, The Berkeley gives off an air of timeless beauty from the minute one walks into the spacious, marble-floored foyer with its open fire, gilt mirror and panelled ceiling. Other public areas make good use of light or pickled oak panelling. Many of the staff are long-serving, enabling returning guests to feel at home. Bedrooms are decorated in a friendly, restrained style that perfectly matches the mood of the hotel – a mix of classical and modern with stylish fabrics, lots of scatter cushions, desks, dressing tables, armchairs and useful extras; some rooms have adjoining open-air terraces and others overlook Hyde Park. Slippers and luxurious bathrobes are provided in the bathrooms. The Wellington Suite is a delightful set of top-floor rooms with a light and sunny conservatory, plus a roof terrace. Two distinctly unusual features are the cinema and a fine roof-top swimming pool, whose roof opens back in good weather. Five banqueting rooms cater for private parties and meetings of up to 200 people. Certain areas of the hotel – notably the corridors – are looking a little dowdy. No dogs. *Rooms 160. Indoor swimming pool, sauna, solarium, gymnasium, beauty & hair salon, valeting, cinema, coffee shop (7am-11.30pm Mon-Sat). Access, Amex, Visa,*

Restaurant

£90

A luxurious restaurant with a traditional French menu, tail-coated waiting staff and a head chef (Clement Schmidl) of over 20 years standing. First-rate raw materials and confident cooking are evident in dishes like quenelles of sole with champagne, parfait of foie gras with port jelly, braised turbot with orange and grapefruit, calf's liver with mango and green peppercorns, and veal steak with morel cream sauce, apples and leeks. Lighter meals are available in the Perroquet brasserie which offers menus with a Mediterranean leaning. *Seats 80. Parties 34. Private Room. L 12.30-2.30 (Sun 12.45-2.15) D 6.30-10.45 (Sun 7-10.15). Closed Sat, 2 weeks Aug. Set L £19.50 Set D £21.*

♛

☕

W1   Berkshire Hotel   72%

£230

Tel 071-629 7474   Fax 071-629 8156

H

350 Oxford Street W1N 0BY

Map 22 B3

Occupying its own small triangular block on the north side of Oxford Street, almost facing the top of New Bond Street, the Berkshire possesses comfortable though not extensive public rooms, with a chintzy, panelled drawing room and the intimate Ascot Bar. Bedrooms, including 30 designated non-smoking, are attractively appointed, much use being made of rich, colourful fabrics and darkwood furniture. Executive rooms are bigger and have more accessories; suites have whirlpool baths. Edwardian Hotels. *Rooms 147. Access, Amex, Visa,*

W1   Berners Park Plaza   72%

£150

Tel 071-636 1629   Fax 071-580 3972

H

10 Berners Street W1A 3BE

Map 22 B3

Turn-of-the-century splendour survives in the marble columns and intricate moulded ceilings at the former *Ramada Hotel* a few steps from Oxford Street. The traditional atmosphere extends to afternoon tea and the cocktail hour. Bedrooms are of a good size, well laid-out, smartly furnished and double-glazed. Tiled bathrooms all have showers as well as tubs. Children up to 12 stay free in parents' room. Conference facilities for up to 160 delegates. *Rooms 235. Coffee shop (9am-11pm). Access, Amex, Visa,*

WC2   Bhatti   £50

Tel 071-831 0817   **R**

37 Great Queen Street WC2   **Map 22 B4**

A listed 17th-century building now sees service as a very good Indian
restaurant particularly well-placed for theatregoers (there's a special pre-
theatre menu at £8.95). The main menu offers all the usual variations on
lamb, chicken and prawns, plus tandoori quail and pomfret. Chef's
recommendations include the pomfret, lamb chops, chicken drumsticks and
chicken tikka masala. 12.5% service charge is automatically added to your
bill. *Seats 80. Parties 35. Private Room. L 12-3 D 5.45-11.30. Closed 25 &*
26 Dec. Set L & D £12.75. Access, Amex, Visa, 💳 *Diners Club International*

SW3   Bibendum   ★ ★   £130

Tel 071-581 5817   Fax 071-623 7925   **R**

81 Fulham Road SW3 6RD   **Map 23 E2**

The Michelin building at Brompton Cross makes the most superb setting
for a restaurant that since its opening has been one of the capital's most
fashionable eating places. The room itself, the creation of Sir Terence
Conran, is a triumph of light and design, with much more space than
London is used to. But cooking always comes top of our list, and also on
the priorities of Simon Hopkinson, who is supported admirably in the field
of decor, service and wine. With Simon the most important values of taste,
texture and flavour take their rightful leading places in a dish, with no
place for fuss or undue elaboration. His inspiration is a mix of English,
French and the Mediterranean; some dishes are traditional – escargots de
Bourgogne, chateaubriand béarnaise, steak au poivre, deep-fried lemon sole
with tartare sauce, raie au beurre noir. Others are in the forefront of
contemporary style like marinated grilled squid with coriander dressing
and Oriental salad, or grilled rabbit with olive oil mash. There's a smashing
cellar of wine with lots of half bottles and a good balance between lesser-
priced wines and the more luxurious selection. 15% service charge is added
to an already hefty bill. *Seats 70. Parties 8. L 12.30-2.30 (Sat & Sun to 3)*
D 7-11.30 (Sun to 10.30). Closed 4 days Xmas, Easter Monday. Set L from
£24.50. Access, Visa.

SW3   Bibendum Oyster Bar   £60

Tel 071-589 1480   **R**

Michelin House 81 Fulham Road SW3 6RD   **Map 23 E2**

Fronting the marvellous Michelin building, this is a chic daytime meeting
place in Brompton Cross, with room for about two dozen diners and more
who spill out on to the foyer of the Conran shop. Native and rock oysters,
clams, crab, langoustines and lobster appear on the menu alongside brasserie
snacks and designer salads. Mainly cold food, but of high quality with a
few daily specials (pea and ham soup with crème fraiche, grilled squid with
roasted red peppers and apricot or treacle tart with Jersey cream). *Seats 26.*
Meals Mon-Sat 12-10.30pm, Sun L 12-2 & D 7-10.30. Access, Visa.

SW7   Bistrot 190   ↑   £45

Tel 071-581 5666   **R**

190 Queen's Gate SW7 5EU   **Map 23 D1**

Open from breakfast until late, the bistro is the square, lofty front room of
the Gore Hotel (see entry). It's been a huge success from the day Antony
Worrall-Thompson opened it in 1990, and, at peak times, you're unlikely
to get a table without a wait (no bookings are taken). It remains a model
of what a restaurant should offer – decent (sometimes first-class) food
served long hours at sensible prices. Marble-topped tables are set with top-
quality French butter and bottles of olive oil. The Mediterranean sun shines
through many dishes in the dinner menu: country bread with tapénade
and olives, hand-rolled mozzarella with figs and Parmesan crostini,
chargrilled squid with arugula, salsas and frites, chicken with peperonata

and pesto potatoes. One of the most popular dishes is the AWT chargrilled pizza with tomato, olives and Roquefort, while for cooler evenings braised lamb shank is a guaranteed warmer. The wine list is assembled by a new supplier every couple of months. Downstairs, replacing the starred restaurant, a seafood bistro was due to open after we went to press. *Seats 50. Parties 12. Meals 7am-12.30am (Sun to 11.30pm). Access, Amex, Visa,*

SW6   Bitter Lemons Taverna   £40

Tel 071-381 1069   **R**

98 Lillie Road SW6 7SR   Map 21 B5

Friendly, family-run restaurant serving Greek food of a consistently good standard. The menu now extends to more 'continental' delights such as pasta and crepes suzette. Stick to the good-value meze (for two or more) and Greek dishes for best value. *Seats 80. Parties 100. L 12-2.30 D 6-12. Closed L Sat, all Sun, 2 weeks Aug. Access, Visa.*

SW7   Blakes Hotel   78%   £180

Tel 071-370 6701   Fax 071-373 0442   **HR**

33 Roland Gardens SW7 3PF   Map 23 E1

A dark green exterior sets the scene for the drama within this most individual of hotels, created from a series of late-Victorian town houses. The small foyer/lounge area is papered black yet warmed by the browns of wood and leather seating piled high with plumped-up cushions. The overall effect is Oriental, a theme carried through to the Chinese Room that leads off the smart basement restaurant where an intimate bar is also to be found. Bedrooms vary widely in decor – from the opulence of one containing the Empress Josephine's day bed to the contrived simplicity of an all-white room with white-painted floorboards and trompe l'oeil wall paintings. The more expensive rooms are singular in design with masses of heavily swagged drapes in unusual fabrics and polished wood floors; furnished with antiques, objets d'art and a profusion of framed prints along with delicate Venetian glassware. Mostly beautiful bathrooms with marble surrounds, though standard rooms have small modern white-tiled ones. Standard bedrooms are generally small and much plainer, decorated in grey and white. An intimate, unusual and exotic hotel with friendly and helpful staff. 24hr room service. *Rooms 52. Access, Amex, Visa,*

Blakes Restaurant   ★   £150

As stylish and distinctive as the rest of the hotel, the restaurant is done out dramatically in black and white. Thai warrior costumes in perspex cases provide the main decorative feature. New chef Peter Thornley follows the traditions of his predecessors by offering a short but stunningly original blend of modern Western and Far Eastern cuisines. Dishes are well researched, the disparate flavours and textures combining to excite and captivate: a cold dish of green tea-simmered noodles mixed with Japanese pickled ginger, toasted sesame seeds and three different seaweeds; lava-grilled peppers and sun-dried tomatoes with olive caviar; a hot, meringue rising like Ayers Rock from a pool of rich, sticky caramel sauce and topped with vanilla ice cream. There's a very short list of good wines with very little under £20. *Seats 32. L 12.30-2.30 D 7.30-11.30. Set L from £28*

NW11   Bloom's   £38

Tel 081-455 1338   **R**

130 Golders Green Road NW11 8HB   Map 20 A3

This offshoot of the Whitechapel branch opened in 1965 and offers the same menu of strictly controlled kosher food. Note the additional opening Saturday evening late into the night. *Seats 80. Meals 11.30-11 (Fri to sunset, Sat sunset-3am). Closed D Fri, L Sat, Jewish Holidays, Xmas. Access, Amex, Visa,*

E1   Bloom's   £38

| Tel 071-247 6001 |
| R |

90 Whitechapel High Street E1 7RA   Map 20 C1

Morris Bloom set the ball rolling in 1920, opening a small restaurant in
Brick Lane and quickly establishing a reputation for serving fine kosher
food. The Whitechapel premises opened in 1952 and operate under the
same strict kosher rules – a rabbi and a religious supervisor on the premises
every day. Salt beef is the star of the show, best enjoyed with latkes and
pickled cucumber, but gedempte meatballs, viennas, roast chicken and
bloomburgers all have their fans. Start with chopped liver, egg and onion
or gefilte fish and – if you've got room – finish with lockshen pudding.
*Seats 150. Meals 11.30-9.30 (Fri to sunset). Closed D Fri, all Sat, Jewish
Holidays, Xmas. Access, Amex, Visa,* Diners Club International

SW6   Blue Elephant   £70

| Tel 071-385 6595   Fax 071-386 7665 |
| R |

4-6 Fulham Broadway SW6 1AA   Map 21 E3

Verdant decor incorporating a waterfall, a bridge over a stream and a
veritable jungle of greenery – an exotic setting in which to enjoy
luxurious, MSG-free Thai cooking. If you really want to push the boat out
try the 17-dish Royal Thai banquet menu (from £25). Sister restaurants in
Brussels, Copenhagen and Paris. *Seats 250. Parties 250. Private Room.
L 12-2.30 D 7-12.30 (Sun to 10.30). Closed L Sat, 24-27 Dec, 1 Jan. Access,
Amex, Visa,* Diners Club International

SE1   Blueprint Café   £60

| Tel 071-378 7031 |
| R |

Design Museum Shad Thames Butlers Wharf SE1 2YD   Map 24 D3

A stylish Sir Terence Conran-owned restaurant on top of the Design
Museum with views overlooking the Thames; chefs Lucy Crabb and Rod
Eggleston cook an archetypal modern menu that changes daily. The Med
might be represented by grilled goat's cheese with roquette and roasted
peppers or avocado with anchovy salad; spinach and ricotta gnocchi or
black trenette with mussels, cream and gremolata; Portuguese fish stew and
roast chicken with lentils, pancetta and garlic. Britain gets a look in with
celery soup with meatballs, calf's liver with black pudding and bubble and
squeak and the ubiquitous sticky toffee pudding. Summer eating on the
outside balcony tables has the added benefit of wonderful views of Tower
Bridge. Italian wines dominate the short wine list. *Seats 80. Parties 100.
L 12-3 D 7-11 Meals. Closed D Sun, Bank Holidays. Access, Visa.*

SW7   Bombay Brasserie   ★   £70

| Tel 071-370 4040 |
| R |

Courtfield Close Courtfield Road SW7 4UH   Map 23 E1

The handsome room, with its Raj pictures and paddle fans, is from a time
past, evoking a grand hotel of a century ago. Entrance is to a roomy bar
area where mango Bellini is a popular cocktail. One part of the restaurant
proper is a large and flowery conservatory which despite its lack of views
manages to convey a garden feel. Staff are smart, polite, well-informed and
abundant. The kitchen garners its recipes from all parts of the sub-
continent; snacks from Bombay, tandoori specialities from the North-West
Frontier, mild Parsi fare, spicy-hot dishes from Goa and Southern India.
The menu is the most alluring in town and cooking is generally first-class,
but the odd disappointment can come from dishes being slightly dried out
(from waiting too long after final preparation?). House specialities include
lobster peri peri (hot with chilis) and dum ka biryani (chicken and Basmati
rice cooked in a sealed pot). Buffet at lunchtime. Owned by Taj
International Hotels. *Seats 200. Parties 200. Private Room. L 12.30-3
D 7.30-12 (Sun to 11.30). Closed 26 & 27 Dec. Set L from £13.50. Access,
Visa,* Diners Club International

SE24   Bon Ton Roulet

£35

R

Tel 071-733 8701

127 Dulwich Road SE24 0NG

Map 21 F1

"Let the good times roll" is what the name means, and that's what they do in this lively little place. The menu changes every six to eight weeks, with half a dozen choices for each course: moules marinière, tempura vegetables, roast guinea fowl, kidneys turbigo and beef olives show the range. No credit cards. *Seats 50. Parties 35. Private Room. L Sun only 12.30-2.30 D 7-10.30 (Sat to 11). Closed D Sun, Bank Holidays, 1 week Xmas. Set L £7.95.*

WC1   Bonnington Hotel   61%

£116

H

Tel 071-242 2828   Fax 071-831 9170

92 Southampton Row WC1B 4BH

Map 22 B4

In the same family ownership for 80 years, the Bonnington is just south of Russell Square – close to the British Museum and within easy walking distance of the Oxford Street shops and the City. Extensive public areas include a lounge bar, breakfast room and many meeting/function rooms for up to 100 delegates. Bedrooms with all the usual accessories include 56 designated non-smoking. Rooms on Southampton Row are double-glazed. *Rooms 215. Brasserie 10am-midnight. Access, Amex, Visa,*

WC2   Boulestin

£100

R

Tel 071-836 7061   Fax 071-836 1283

Garden Entrance 1a Henrietta Street WC2E 8PS

Map 25 B2

A small, glass entrance on the south side of Covent Garden piazza leads down to one of London's grandest and most traditional dining rooms. Since opening in 1926 Boulestin has been a bastion of French cuisine. Kevin Kennedy's cooking has a sound classical base and old-fashioned dishes like saddle of venison with red cabbage, roast saddle of hare or lamb shank braised with red wine, onions, mushrooms and bacon fulfil a growing demand for big flavours and simplicity. Other choices are from the contemporary repertoire, like *osso buco de lotte de mer* (monkfish braised with a salpicon of vegetables, tomatoes and citrus zest). The two- or three-course, fixed-price and gentler-priced à la carte lunch menus reflect their positive reaction to the recessionary times, but the evening carte is considerably more expensive; nevertheless, both the comfort and cooking make this a splendid setting for a special occasion. A long list of wines with some of the highest prices seen; mostly French, though other countries (notably America) are represented. *Seats 75. Parties 75. Private Room. L 12-2.30 D 7.30-11.15. Closed L Sat, all Sun, Bank Holidays, 1 week Xmas, 3 weeks Aug. Set L £16.50. Access, Amex, Visa,*

W8   Boyd's

£70

R

Tel 071-727 5452

135 Kensington Church Street W8 7LP

Map 21 D3

Almost opposite *Clarke's* and just up the road from *Kensington Place* (and a *Café Flo* has recently opened a few doors up), Boyd Gilmour's neat little conservatory restaurant continues to thrive. A good-value 2-course lunch (perhaps cucumber, mint and yoghurt soup plus fresh tagliatelle with roasted peppers, pine nuts and basil) offers no choice, but the 3-course lunch might extend to duck fillets, grilled halibut with vermouth sauce, chargrilled chicken with goat's cheese and almond parfait with caramel and Armagnac sauce. At dinner dishes become more involved: chargrilled scallops with smoked bacon, mangetout, spring onions and ginger; warm salad of fresh foie gras with sherry vinegar sauce and brioche; casserole of assorted fish and shellfish with croutons and rouille; honey-roasted quail stuffed with spinach, bacon and pine nuts and Chardonnay sauce. "Boyd's choice" of desserts is a selection in miniature; coffee and rum soufflé with rum and raisin ice cream is worth the 20-minute wait. Lots of wines under

£20. *Seats 40. Parties 35. L 12.30-2.30 D 7-11. Closed 1 week Xmas. Set L £8.50 & £14.95. Access, Amex, Visa.*

W6   The Brackenbury   ↑

£30

R

Tel 081-748 0107

129-131 Brackenbury Road W6

Map 21 D4

Adam and Katie Robinson's new venture is a shining example of a well-run restaurant that knows its market and sticks to it. Sensible, realistic pricing is one of its strongest points, along with straightforward cooking that can look deceptively simple. Transformed from an indifferent, U-shaped wine bar formed from two adjacent shops, the decor is warm salmon pink and green paintwork; wooden pew seating remains. Adam Robinson cooks a short menu that changes at each session and manages to encompass much of what is best in London's current simple, modern cooking style; always an interesting soup, often a signature dish of potato pancake with salmon caviar and crème fraiche and an Italian-inspired vegetarian dish like mushroom risotto or spinach gnocchi with a tomato sauce. Main dishes might range from roast whiting with braised cabbage and coriander seeds (or brill with a herb dressing) to roast chump of lamb with flageolet beans and rosemary or poached rump of beef with carrots and horseradish; vegetables are always an integral component of each dish. The interesting plate of mixed savouries (sufficient for four diners) that always starts the menu is a clever way of charging for amuse-gueule, but customers are unlikely to complain. Cheeses are always immaculately kept (the emphasis is firmly on quality not quantity) and served with home-made biscuits. Puddings seem the poor relation, but rarely fail to please; tarte tatin, prune and armagnac ice cream, pecan pie are all well executed. Over twenty wines are offered by the glass from a wine list that is broadly based and concisely described. *Seats 55. Parties 12. L 12.30-2.45 D 7-10.45. Closed L Sat, D Sun, all Mon, Xmas, Easter. Access, Visa*

SW14   Le Braconnier

£60

R

Tel 081-878 2853

467 Upper Richmond Road West SW14 7PU

Map 21 E4

The menu of French regional dishes is always of interest in this splendid little restaurant. *Menu de Champagne* for instance features flamiche aux poireaux (a leek and olive tartlet), trout with ham and cream sauce and chicken cooked in beer. Cassoulet de Toulouse is a regular favourite, particularly good on a cold winter's night. *Seats 30. Parties 24. L 12.30-2.30 Sun Oct-Mar only D 7-11. Closed Bank Holidays, 5 days Xmas. Set L from £13.50 Set D from £11.50. Access, Visa,* **◑** Diners Club International

SW3   La Brasserie

£45

R

Tel 071-581 3089

272 Brompton Road SW3 2AW

Map 23 E2

A little piece of France opposite the splendid Michelin building. All-day, middle-of-the-road French food – from a quiet 8am breakfast with the papers to omelettes, grillades and predictable desserts amid the evening din. *Seats 150. Meals 8am-11.30pm (Sun 10am-11pm). Closed 25 & 26 Dec. Access, Amex, Visa,* **◑** Diners Club International

SW8   Brasserie Faubourg

£55

R

Tel 071-622 6245

28 Queenstown Road SW8 3RX

Map 21 E2

A sunny little spot over Chelsea Bridge, just south of the river. The all-French menu includes soupe de pecheur, vegetable and poultry terrine, duck breast with raspberry sauce, salads, cheeses and desserts like crème brulée, tarte citron and upside-down pear gateau. Simple, straightforward stuff. *Seats 28. Parties 36. L 12-2.30 D 7-11. Closed L Mon & Sat, all Sun, Bank Holidays, 10 days Aug. Set L £9.50. Access, Visa.*

SW3   Brasserie Lott   NEW
| Tel 071-584 4484 |
£58
R

27 Basil Street SW3 1BB   Map 23 D2

Just behind Harrods, this is the former *Sud-Ouest* with new owners and a
new name but, regrettably, the same old decor which is looking rather
tired. Fortunately the cooking outshines the surroundings with perhaps
gravad lax and blinis with crème fraiche or a perfectly made *omelette fines
herbes* before a brochette of salmon and peppers or roast rump of lamb
with mint pesto and couscous from the short monthly-changing menu. The
main restaurant is not really a brasserie at all, but a small, separate café
serving the likes of steak sandwich and chips or tomato and mozzarella
bruschetta throughout the afternoon. **Seats 60.** *Parties 70, Private Room.
L 12-3 (Sat to 3.30) D 7-10.30. Closed D Mon & Tue, all Sun, Bank
Holidays. Access, Visa.*

W10   Brasserie du Marché aux Puces
| Tel 081-968 5828 |
£45
R

349 Portobello Road W10 5SA   Map 20 C3

A bright, informal brasserie with large windows, plain wooden tables and
long mahogany bar. The menu is short with no clear distinction between
starters and main-course dishes; vegetables are charged separately. Snails
with hazelnuts and bacon, goat's cheese in filo with papaya salsa, mushroom
ravioli with mussel sauce and spring onions; potato blinis with ratatouille
and crème fraiche, grilled mackerel fillets with green lentil and tarragon
purée, Caribbean-style chicken breast with coconut, pineapple, rice and
pumpkin – an imaginative menu of eclectic ingredients, reflecting the
ethnic mix of Portobello's populace. Water melon and cassis jelly,
Beaujolais granita, banana and amaretto parfait with saffron coulis among
the desserts. Sunday brunch. **Seats 60.** *Parties 40. Private Room. Meals
10am-11pm (Sun 11-4). Closed D Sun, all Mon, Bank Holidays.
No credit cards.*

W1   Britannia Inter-Continental Hotel   77%
| Tel 071-629 9400   Fax 071-629 7736 |
£233
H

Grosvenor Square W1A 3AN   Map 22 C3

Behind the grand, colonnaded frontage of three Georgian houses
overlooking the Mayfair square is an appropriately elegant interior. The
luxurious, chandeliered lobby sets the civilised tone, which the cocktail
lounge and bar follow. Air-conditioned bedrooms range from standards
(decent size, with reproduction furniture) to de luxe, with desks, seating
areas and bars, and the top-of-the-range suites which offer many extras and
luxury touches. Conference/banqueting facilities for 100/80, supported by
24hr business services. Car parking below the hotel. Children under 14
stay free in parents' room. No dogs. See also entry under *Shogun* for details
of their Japanese restaurant. **Rooms 317.** *Valeting, baby-sitting, shopping
arcade (inc news kiosk & hairdressing), cocktail lounge (7am-11pm). Access,
Amex, Visa,*

W1   Brown's Hotel   74%
| Tel 071-493 6020   Fax 071-493 9381 |
£218
H

Albermarle Street W1A 4SW   Map 22 C3

James Brown, a retired gentleman's gentleman, opened a hotel in
fashionable Mayfair in 1837, the year Queen Victoria came to the throne.
Now a Forte flagship and long favoured as a meeting place for afternoon
tea, it retains great period style and elegance in fine furnishings, richly
panelled woods and original moulded ceilings. Individually decorated
bedrooms offer guests a complementary mixture of the old and the
modern, with high-quality fabrics, bright patterns and bold designs. Neat
bathrooms and assiduous housekeeping. No dogs. **Rooms 133.**
Access, Amex, Visa,

W1   Bryanston Court   61%   £104

Tel 071-262 3141   Fax 071-262 7248   **H**

56 Great Cumberland Place W1H 7FD   Map 22 B2

One minute away from Marble Arch and Oxford Street, the family-run
Bryanston Court is well situated for shopping and sightseeing. Day rooms
and bedrooms offer home-from-home comfort. En-suite facilities are
mainly shower/WC. *Rooms 54. Access, Amex, Visa,*

EC1   Bubb's   £70

Tel 071-236 2435   **R**

329 Central Markets EC1A 9NB   Map 24 A1

The name of this popular lunchtime City rendezvous by Smithfield
Market (at the junction of Snow Hill and Farringdon Street) gives no clue
to its origins as the style is strongly French. The à la carte offers such
familiar dishes as moules marinière or soupe à l'oignon to start, cotelettes
d'agneau or entrecote au roquefort for main and perhaps oeufs à la neige
for dessert. There is also a daily specials menu which includes a fish dish.
Non-smoking section. 15% service charge is added to the bill automatically.
*Seats 70. Parties 15. L only 12-2.30. Closed Sat, Sun, Bank Holidays, 2 weeks
Xmas, 2 weeks Aug. No credit cards.*

SW11   Buchan's   £50

Tel 071-228 0888   **R**

62-64 Battersea Bridge Road SW11 3AG   Map 21 E3

An informal restaurant with a Scottish accent to the decor and the cooking.
Cullen skink, Invergarry crab soufflé, venison paté with oatcakes, fillet
steak flambéed with whisky, Drambuie soufflé. 39 wines; 39 malts. Special
2- or 3-course Sunday lunch menu. Good Scottish and French cheeses.
*Seats 65. Parties 50. L 12.30-2.45 D 6.30-10.45 (Sun 7-10.30). Closed some
Bank Holidays (usually Mondays). Set L (Sun) £8.50/£10.50. Access, Amex,
Visa,*

SW15   Buzkash   £40

Tel 081-788 0599   **R**

4 Chelverton Road SW15 1RH   Map 21 E3

A friendly Afghan restaurant off Putney High Street with the same menus
and prices as *Caravanserai*. Specialities include the national dish *ashak* (pasta
filled with freshly chopped leek served with minced fillet of lamb and
seasoned yoghurt), *poorshuda* (delicately spiced stuffed poussin) and *lugary*
(pan-fried king prawns). *Seats 70. Parties 65. L 12-2.30 D 6-11 (Sun to
10.30). Closed L Sun, 25 & 26 Dec, Muslim Holidays. Set L from £9.95.
Access, Amex, Visa,*

SW1   Cadogan Hotel   £250

Tel 071-235 7141   Fax 071-245 0994   **H**

75 Sloane Street SW1X 9SG   Map 23 D2

Historic House Hotels acquired the Cadogan in 1990, and this former
house of Lillie Langtry is the subject of a major refurbishment programme
now due to start early in 1993. *Rooms 75. Access, Amex, Visa,*

NW1   Café Delancey   £36

Tel 071-387 1985   Fax 071-383 5314   **R**

3 Delancey Street NW1 7NN   Map 20 C2

Every item on the menu is available throughout opening hours at this
popular Continental-style café just off Camden High Street. This could be
anything from a croissant with coffee to croque monsieur, an omelette,

rack of lamb or superior sausages served with fried onions and rösti. Tables outside in summer. *Also at:* 32 Proctor Street, Red Lion Square, WC1 Tel 071-242 6691 Map 22 B4. *Seats 160. Parties 12. Meals 8am-midnight. Closed Bank Holidays, Xmas. Access, Visa.*

EC1 **Café du Marché**	£40
Tel 071-608 1609	**R**
22 Charterhouse Square Charterhouse Mews EC1M 6AH	**Map 20 C1**

Tucked away in a mews between Smithfield Market and the Barbican, this former meat warehouse has the feel of a converted country barn. The appealing set menus offer French regional cooking made with fresh products and commendable care to detail. Interesting specialities include salade de champignons sauvages, boudin blanc sauce bordelaise and crépinette de porc aux huitres. Upstairs, *Le Grenier du Café* is open only for lunch and specialises in grills. Both floors are extremely popular – booking is advisable at lunchtime. *Seats 65. Parties 60. Private Room. L 12-2.30 D 6-10. Closed L Sat, all Sun, Bank Holidays, Xmas/New Year. Set meals from £11. Access, Visa.*

SW1 **Café Fish**	£55
Tel 071-930 3999	**R**
39 Panton Street SW1Y 4EA	**Map 25 A3**

Informal café-restaurant just off Haymarket with a French atmopshere. An all-fish menu ranging from oysters and moules marinière to bouillabaisse, plateau de fruits de mer and fish cakes, plus daily specials. Downstairs is a wine bar with a shorter menu of fishy offerings plus the addition of club and steak sandwiches. Convenient for Haymarket theatres and Leicester Square. *Seats 90. Parties 100. L 12-3 D 5.45-11.30. Closed L Sat, all Sun, 25 & 26 Dec, 1 Jan. Access, Amex, Visa,* 🌀 Diners Club International

---

WC2 **Café Pelican**	£55
Tel 071-379 0309 Fax 071-379 0782	**R**
45 St Martin's Lane WC2N 4EJ	**Map 25 B3**

Parisian-style bar-brasserie with a wiggly wooden counter and tables on the thronging pavement outside. The bar is open all day for good strong coffee with baguettes, tartines and pastries, salads and platters of meat, and steaks with excellent little chips. Also a more elaborate menu served in the large restaurant to the rear, where live music keeps diners happy into the wee small hours. French staff cope amiably with the crowds at this really useful pre- and post-theatre spot. *Seats 125. Parties 125. Meals 12 noon-11.45pm (closed for meals 5-5.30pm only). Closed 24-26 Dec. Set L £9.95 Set D £16.95. Access, Amex, Visa,* 🌀 Diners Club International

---

W1 **Café Royal Grill Room**	£110
Tel 071-439 6320	**R**
68 Regent Street W1R 6EL	**Map 22 C3**

One of the most extravagantly ornate restaurants in the land, its decor providing more to talk about in recent years than the food. Herbert Berger has come to change that, and first indications are that he could succeed. *Seats 55. Parties 30. L 12.30-3 D 6-10.30. Closed L Sat, all Sun, Bank Holidays. Set L from £25. Access, Amex, Visa,* 🌀 Diners Club International

---

W1 **California Pizza Company**	£35
Tel 071-486 7878	**R**
6 Blandford Street W1	**Map 22 B2**

Unusual, designer pizzas ("the signature dish of New Age Cuisine") cooked in a wood-fired oven; plus grills and foot-long barbecue ribs. Up to two children under 12 can choose a child-size pizza before 5pm when an accompanying adult takes a main course. During "happy time" (5-7pm) all

main courses are £3.80 (for all sizes of diner). Opposite *Stephen Bull* (qv).
Seats 80. *Parties 80. Meals 11.30am–midnight. Closed Sun, Bank Holidays,
Xmas. Access, Amex, Visa,* 🌐 *Diners Club International*

NW1	Camden Brasserie	£53
Tel 071-482 2114		**R**
216 Camden High Street NW1 8QR		**Map 20 C2**

Busy brasserie with a short menu based around charcoal-grilled meats (all
served with terrific little chips) and fresh pasta. Spicy chicken wings,
artichoke, pepper and potato salad with coriander dressing, and gravad lax
with dill mustard sauce are among the starters; good salads (avocado,
spinach, shiitake mushrooms and walnut salad), corn-fed chicken, fish of
the day, calf's liver, beef brochette teriyaki and rib-eye steak among the
main dishes. The pommes frites are included, but vegetables are charged
extra. **Seats 110.** *Parties 20. L 12-3 (Sun 12.30-3.30) D 6.30-11.30 (Sun
5-10.30). Closed 24-26 & 31 Dec. Access, Visa.*

W10	Canal Brasserie	£50
Tel 081-960 2732		**R**
Canalot Studios 222 Kensal Road W10 5BN		**Map 20 C3**

Originally a chocolate factory, this modern restaurant overlooking the
Grand Union Canal keeps the locals happy with an all-day selection of
snacks. At meal times proper there's a fashionable menu typified by
carpaccio of tuna and scallops, confit of salmon with rocket salad, and
gammon steak with a herbed brioche crust. **Seats 60.** *Parties 60.
L 12.30-3.30 D 7.30-11 (open all day from 9 for snacks). Closed Sat, Sun &
Bank Holidays. Access, Visa.*

SW19	Cannizaro House	76%	£138
Tel 081-879 1464 Fax 081-879 7338			**H**
West Side Wimbledon Common SW19 4UF			**Map 21 F3**

On the edge of Wimbledon Common, a Georgian mansion where the tone
is set by stately lawned gardens and the bay-windowed drawing room,
which boasts giant flower arrangements, antique furniture, oil paintings
and sumptuous seating. Similar elegance is to be found in the cocktail bar,
with its cream, pale green and pink colour scheme, crystal chandelier,
draped curtains and ornate gilt mirror. The bedrooms, each with its own
character, are superbly appointed, with top-quality reproduction furniture
and bathrooms featuring marble fittings, radio/TV speakers, phones and
bathrobes. New-wing rooms are smaller, their views inferior. Reduced
rates at weekends; higher rates during the All England Lawn Tennis
Championships at the end of June. No children under 8. No dogs. Mount
Charlotte Thistle. **Rooms 45.** *Garden. Access, Amex, Visa,* 🌐 *Diners Club International*

SW3	The Capital	80%	£220
Tel 071-589 5171 Fax 071-225 0011			**HR**
22-24 Basil Street SW3 1AT			**Map 23 D2**

Self-styled as a grand hotel in miniature, David Levin's immaculately run
establishment between Sloane Street and Harrods is a real joy. Perfection
with flair extends all the way from the white marble foyer through to the
day rooms (designed by Nina Campbell) and into the comfortable, air-
conditioned bedrooms that Margaret Levin has furnished in a restrained,
classic style with highly polished darkwood furniture that includes a
writing desk in each room; interesting paintings and soft, subtle lighting
complete the picture. Super king-size beds (with top-notch Egyptian cotton
sheets) feature in the double rooms; eight suites are also available. Fresh
fruit, mini-bars and umbrellas are provided, and there are luxurious
appointments in the marble-floored bathrooms. The fact that the Levins
have a day-to-day involvement guarantees exceptional service here, and the
staff have always been (and are) first-class. The Eaton and Cadogan private

dining/meeting rooms cater for up to 24/20. *Rooms 48. Access, Amex, Visa,* ① *Diners Club International*

Capital Restaurant ★★ £120

Philip Britten's love of fish is evident in all his menus: a choice of three-course lunch menus, an evening carte and table d'hote, plus last year's 21st birthday menu. The first might feature crab mousse with ginger and spring onion, emincé of liver and field mushrooms glazed with port or steamed langoustines and cod with a butter sauce and a coffee parfait with praline sauce or selection of cheeses. The introduction of a fixed-price, three-course dinner was intended to attract diners "other than fat-cat, expense account executives" and has been successful – perhaps because it's easier than fathoming out the charges on a carte where, most unusually, *every* dish carries a supplement to the minimum £25 charge. Dishes such as tartlet of scallops, langoustines, morels and salmon or Armagnac-basted, pot-roasted, milk-fed pigeon with leeks and celery are invariably well executed, but, typically, it was the seven-course, all-fish 21st birthday menu where Britten excelled last year: petite marmite of salmon and beetroot, lobster salad with beans and orange, mussel and saffron mousse; tartlet of scallops, langoustines and morels, baked sea bass with tomatoes and pasta, followed by champagne sorbet, lemon soufflé and home-made petits fours to finish. A predominantly French wine list features exceptional clarets, some of which are keenly priced. There's a good half-bottle selection and useful house suggestions. *Seats 35. Parties 24. Private Room.L 12-2.30 D 7-11. Set L £20 & £23 Set D £25 & £37.50.*

SW1 Le Caprice ↑ £70
R
Tel 071-629 2239   Fax 071-493 9040
Arlington House Arlington Street SW1A 1RT Map 22 C3

A cool, fashionable restaurant in black and white, with David Bailey's classic photographs on the walls. Mark Hix's dishes are sometimes as trendy as the clientele: tomato and basil galette, roasted baby artichokes, risotto nero, baked salmon with treviso, grilled rabbit with rosemary. Others are nostalgic, like deep-fried cod, Lancashire hotpot or eggs Benedict. Sunday brunch pitches off with pitchers of Bucks Fizz or Bloody Mary and swaggers onwards with foie gras, fried egg and wild mushrooms. Booking essential. *Seats 80. Parties 8. L 12-3 (Sun to 3.30) D 6-12. Closed D 24 Dec-2 Jan (open L 2 Jan). Access, Amex, Visa,* ①

W1 Caravan Serai £40
R
Tel 071-935 1208
50 Paddington Street W1M 3RQ Map 22 B2

A sister restaurant to *Buzkash* in Putney, with the same menu and prices. Caravan Serai is a cheerful, relaxed place with authentic Afghan cooking that puts the emphasis more on subtle spices than fiery chili. Among the house recommendations is the national dish *ashak* – pasta filled with leeks served with minced lamb and yoghurt. Note also *istaliffee* – veal on the bone, fresh tomatoes; *poorshuda* – stuffed poussin; and *lugary* – king prawns dipped in a delicate sauce and pan-fried. *Seats 55. Parties 55. Private Room. L 12-3 D 6-11 (Sun to 10.30). Closed L Sun, 25 & 26 Dec. Set L £9.95. Access, Amex, Visa,* ①

SW8 Carraro's £45
R
Tel 071-720 5986
32 Queenstown Road SW8 3RX Map 21 E2

Frescoed walls give a sunny Tuscan feel to this high-quality Italian restaurant. Dishes could be familiar – spaghetti bolognese, seafood risotto, liver veneziana with polenta – or a little less usual, like wild boar ham or grilled grey mullet served with peppers and leeks in balsamic vinegar. Live music Friday and Saturday nights. *Seats 90. Parties 100. Private Room. L 12-2.30 (Sun to 3) D 7-11 (Sat to 11.30). Closed L Sat, D Sun, all Mon, 25 & 26 Dec. Set meals from £10.95. Access, Amex, Visa,* ①

SE6   Casa Cominetti

Tel 081-697 2314

129 Rushey Green SE6 4AA

£50

R

Map 21 F1

Italian restaurant with exceptional staying power (it dates back to 1916!).
The menu rarely departs from standard dishes, but cooking is consistently
enjoyable. *Seats 50. Parties 60. Private Room. L 12-2.30 D 6.30-11. Closed
L Sat, all Sun, 25 & 26 Dec. Access, Amex, Visa,* Diners Club International

N1   Casale Franco

Tel 071-226 8994

134 Upper Street N1 1PQ

£55

R

Map 20 C2

Authentic regional Italian food, cooked simply and honestly, is served in
this convivial brick-walled restaurant/pizzeria off Upper Street (look for an
illuminated Citroën chevron sign to find the courtyard entrance). There's a
no-booking policy in the evening, so arrive early or expect a short wait.
Huge bubbling pizzas (not served at lunch or as a one-course meal after
8pm) come with a familiar range of toppings, and there's a good choice of
pasta. Several of the main courses (cuttlefish in ink sauce, liver with onions,
spicy Italian sausages) are served with polenta. Accompanying vegetables
are excellent, so, too, the plate of antipasto. *Seats 100. Parties 40. L 12.30-
2.30 D 6.30-11.30. Closed L Tue-Thu, all Mon, Bank Holidays, 2 weeks Aug,
2 weeks Dec. Access, Visa,* Diners Club International

SW16   Caterino's

Tel 081-764 6022

1540 London Road Norbury SW16 4EU

£45

R

Map 21 F2

Very much a family affair, with a daughter and two nieces helping
Giovanni at front of house and Maria-Grazia in the kitchen of this smart
south London restaurant which is home to good, authentic Italian cooking.
The menu is extensive, with seafood and shellfish (skate, halibut, prawns,
Dover sole), a particular speciality on the carte and simpler, but equally
well executed dishes (escalope of veal with Marsala or lemon sauce, fillet of
sole with spinach, prawns, cream and cheese sauce) on a choice of
economical fixed-price menus. Uno Plus is an integral wine bar next door
serving a wide range of simpler fare – from Mediterranean tapas to pasta,
pizze and panini. *Seats 70. Parties 70. L 12-3 D 6-11.30. Closed L Sat, all
Sun, Bank Holidays. Set meals £9.50 & £11.95 Access, Amex, Visa,* Diners Club International

SW10   Chapter 11

Tel 071-351 1683

47 Hollywood Road SW10

£50

R

Map 23 E1

An informal, busy brasserie off Fulham Road serving a menu that mixes
traditional and modern elements: Caesar salad, bruschetta with plum
tomatoes, stir-fried beef, Toulouse sausages with far-from-authentic
bubble'n'squeak (where was the squeak?), warm chicken salad with rice
wine vinaigrette. *Seats 60. Parties 60. L 12-3 D 6.45-12. Closed Sun, some
Bank Holidays, 3 days Xmas. Access, Amex, Visa.*

NW3   Charles Bernard Hotel   60%

Tel 071-794 0101   Fax 071-794 0100

5 Frognal Hampstead NW3 6AL

£65

H

Map 20 B3

Just off Finchley Road and well connected by public transport to the West
End, this is a 70s' hotel with open-plan day rooms and practical overnight
accommodation. Children up to 12 stay free in parents' room. No dogs.
Rooms 57. Access, Amex, Visa, Diners Club International

W5   Charlotte's Place

£50

R

Tel 081-567 7541

16 St Matthew's Road W5 3JT

Map 21 D4

Intimate pink and green bistro on the edge of Ealing Common serving
unpretentious, mainly English fare – from haddock smokie to beef
Wellington – plus a few French touches. Easy parking. **Seats 40.** *Parties 25.*
Private Room. L 12.30-2 D 7.30-10. Closed L Sat, all Sun, Bank Holidays,
1 week Xmas/New Year. Set L from £14.50. Access, Visa.

SW1   Chelsea Hotel   63%

£168

H

Tel 071-235 4377   Fax 071-235 3705

17-25 Sloane Street SW1X 9NU

Map 23 D2

A modern Sarova Group hotel in Knightsbridge. Chief feature of the
public areas is a glass-roofed atrium with a polished steel spiral staircase;
this runs up to a restaurant and bar whose dominant black decor gives a
rather stark look. Food and drink are available at all hours in the lounge.
Bedrooms are generally not very roomy, but the expected modern
accessories are provided and there's 24hr room service and porterage. One
floor of rooms is designated non-smoking. The Chelsea is showing some
signs of wear and tear but still retains its individuality. No dogs.
Rooms 225. *Hairdressing, coffee shop (7am-2am). Access, Amex, Visa,*
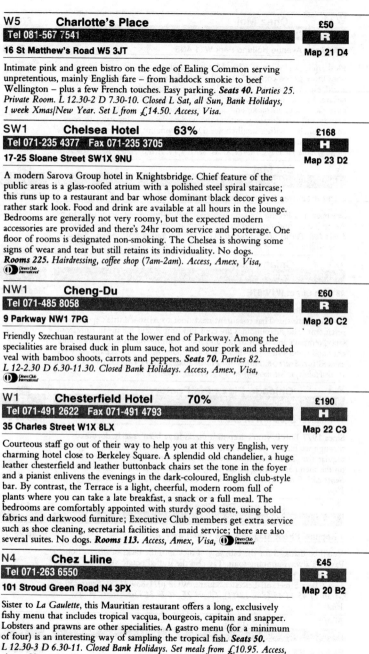 *Diners Club International*

NW1   Cheng-Du

£60

R

Tel 071-485 8058

9 Parkway NW1 7PG

Map 20 C2

Friendly Szechuan restaurant at the lower end of Parkway. Among the
specialities are braised duck in plum sauce, hot and sour pork and shredded
veal with bamboo shoots, carrots and peppers. **Seats 70.** *Parties 82.*
L 12-2.30 D 6.30-11.30. Closed Bank Holidays. Access, Amex, Visa,
Diners Club International

W1   Chesterfield Hotel   70%

£190

H

Tel 071-491 2622   Fax 071-491 4793

35 Charles Street W1X 8LX

Map 22 C3

Courteous staff go out of their way to help you at this very English, very
charming hotel close to Berkeley Square. A splendid old chandelier, a huge
leather chesterfield and leather buttonback chairs set the tone in the foyer
and a pianist enlivens the evenings in the dark-coloured, English club-style
bar. By contrast, the Terrace is a light, cheerful, modern room full of
plants where you can take a late breakfast, a snack or a full meal. The
bedrooms are comfortably appointed with sturdy good taste, using bold
fabrics and darkwood furniture; Executive Club members get extra service
such as shoe cleaning, secretarial facilities and maid service; there are also
several suites. No dogs. **Rooms 113.** *Access, Amex, Visa,* *Diners Club International*

N4   Chez Liline

£45

R

Tel 071-263 6550

101 Stroud Green Road N4 3PX

Map 20 B2

Sister to *La Gaulette*, this Mauritian restaurant offers a long, exclusively
fishy menu that includes tropical vacqua, bourgeois, capitain and snapper.
Lobsters and prawns are other specialities. A gastro menu (for a minimum
of four) is an interesting way of sampling the tropical fish. **Seats 50.**
L 12.30-3 D 6.30-11. Closed Bank Holidays. Set meals from £10.95. Access,
Amex, Visa.

W11   Chez Moi   £70
Tel 071-603 8267   R

1 Addison Avenue Holland Park W11 4QS   Map 21 D3

Plush, quiet and discreet, Chez Moi has stood the test of time. The menu,
once more or less confined to the French classics, now ventures further
afield, especially on the short set lunch menu (gazpacho, Thai-style salmon
tartare, Moroccan lamb tagine). Traditionalists might opt for *sole meunière,
carré d'agneau* or *tournedos béarnaise*. Chocolate truffle cake made with
brandy and Benedictine is among the wicked desserts. Fine value three-
course lunches, with a small choice. Decent wine list at fair price with
plenty of half bottles. *Seats 45. Parties 15. L 12.30-2 D 7-11. Closed L Sat,
all Sun, Bank Holidays, 1 week Xmas. Set L £14. Access, Amex, Visa,* Diners Club International

W3   Chi Mai   £35
Tel 081-992 3160   R

2 The Broadway Gunnersbury Lane W3   Map 21 D4

Szechuan and Peking cooking in a cool, tall-ceilinged restaurant next to
Acton Town underground station. Sizzling dishes among the specialities.
*Seats 100. Parties 60. L 12-2.30 D 6-12. Set L from £8.50. Access, Amex,
Visa,* Diners Club International

W1   Chiang Mai   £40
Tel 071-437 7444   R

48 Frith Street W1V 5TE   Map 25 A2

Vatcharin Bhumichitr, author of *The Taste of Thailand* and *Thai Vegetarian
Cooking*, runs this Thai restaurant next door to Alastair Little's eponymous
restaurant. The surroundings are cool and simple, and the menu runs from
satay, tempura and soups to hot and sour salads flavoured with lemon and
chili and good-value, one-dish rice and noodle dishes. Vegetarians are well
catered for. *Seats 56. Parties 50. Private Room. L 12-3 D 6-11. Closed L Sun,
Bank Holidays. Set meals from £17. Access, Amex, Visa.*

W1   Chicago Pizza Pie Factory   £30
Tel 071-629 2669   R

17 Hanover Square W1R 9AJ   Map 22 C3

Since 1977 Bob Payton's deep-dish pizzas have been eagerly devoured
throughout Europe in restaurants with the look and sound of Chicago. The
regular size feeds two, while the large will keep three or four happy. Also
on the menu are burgers, chili, lasagne, salads and half a dozen desserts.
*Seats 230. Private Room. Meals 11.45-11.30 (Sun 12-10.30). Access, Amex,
Visa.*

SW7   Chicago Rib Shack   £30
Tel 071-581 5595   R

1 Raphael Street Knightsbridge Green SW7 1DL   Map 23 D2

You'll be thankful for the bibs as you tuck into the racks of ribs in Bob
Payton's always-jumping joint. Try also the stuffed potato skins, the onion
loaf and the pecan pie. Valet parking. Newer outlet *Chicago Rib Shack II* at
13-17 Bear Street, off Leicester Square, WC2 (071-839 4188). *Seats 230.
Meals 11.45-11.45 (Sun 12-11). Closed 25, 26 & 31 Dec. Access, Amex,
Visa.*

NW1   China Jazz   £60
Tel 071-482 3940   R

Parkway NW1   Map 20 C2

Drumsticks meet chopsticks in a cool, contemporary setting on busy
Parkway. Jazz (live every evening, late at weekends) accompanies fairly
expensive Chinese food cooked without additives, preservatives, artifical

colouring or much finesse. Valet parking. *Seats 90. Parties 90. L 12.30-3 D 6.30-12 (Fri & Sat 7.30pm to 2am) (Sun 1pm-10pm). Closed L Sat. Access, Amex, Visa.*

W14 Chinon ★ £90

Tel 071-602 5968 **R**

25 Richmond Way W14 0AS Map 21 D3

Chinon's appeal to all as a dining experience is unquestionable, as it has its own allure for those of refined yet adventurous taste. Jonathan Hayes's food exudes as forthright a personality as does Barbara Deane's presence at the front of house, though absolute confidence in the product remains firmly behind the kitchen door. Flavours are as bold as each dish is imaginative, their balance and combination carefully conceived. Baked whole squid with a punchy pesto and warm aubergine gateau; breast of duck with a crispy purse of vegetables and port sauce; scallops (a great favourite with the chef) toasted with garlic, spring onions and ginger and served with sugar peas, regularly excite more than their understated menu descriptions suggest. Yet, in so small a kitchen, time is not wasted on unnecessary frippery and this is wholly to be applauded. To follow, the plate of half a dozen miniature desserts, amongst which the delicate lemon tart is quite memorable, and the selection of out-of-the-ordinary cheeses served with a bowl of fruit show equal dedication to their cause. In the almost romantic atmosphere afforded by a fabric-draped ceiling, candle-lit tables and a highly personal choice of incidental music, up to two dozen diners can comfortably allow this thoughtful creative cookery to speak for itself. Barbara likes to chat to lone diners, convinced that they are restaurant inspectors! *Seats 24. Parties 36. L 12-2 D 7-10.30. Closed L Sat, all Sun & Mon, some Bank Holidays. Access, Amex, Visa.*

W4 Christian's £60

Tel 081-995 0382 **R**

Station Parade Burlington Lane W4 3HD Map 21 D4

A charming neighbourhood restaurant with attractive decor, informal, friendly service and the cheerful presence and talented cooking of Christian Gustin. The modern menu is short and changes monthly, and offers plenty of interest. The wine list is equally short, showing total allegiance to France, unlike the cooking, which generally has greater depth and wider influences. *Seats 40. Parties 10. L (Sun only) 12.30-3 D 7.30-10.30. Closed D Sun, Bank Holidays. Set L from £15.25 Set D £18.75. Access, Visa.*

WC2 Christopher's NEW £70

Tel 071-240 4222 **R**

18 Wellington Street Covent Garden WC2 Map 22 C4

Christopher Gilmour's busy American Grill is set on the first floor of an impressive building at the corner of Wellington Street and Exeter Street (opposite *Orso* – see entry). All-American favourites like oysters Rockefeller, Maine lobster Newburg, 10oz New York strip steak and Key Lime pie come with few frills, disorganised service and little excitement in the execution. The clientele is Covent Garden stylish, as is the decor of the ground-floor bar. *Seats 100. Parties 26. Private Room. L 12-3 D 6-11.30. Closed L Sat, all Sun, Bank Holidays. Access, Amex, Visa,* ⓪ *Diners Club International*

W1 Chuen Cheng Ku £35

Tel 071-734 3281 **R**

17 Wardour Street W1V 3HD Map 25 A2

Vast Chinese restaurant on several floors serving a long selection of Cantonese dishes. The popular daytime choice is dim sum, served by taciturn waitresses from little wagons which ply between the kitchen and the tables. *Seats 400. Meals 11am-11.45pm. Closed 24 & 25 Dec. Set meals from £18 for 2. Access, Amex, Visa,* ⓪ *Diners Club International*

W1   Churchill Hotel   80%   £242
Tel 071-486 5800   Fax 071-486 1255   HR
30 Seymour Street Portman Square W1A 4ZX   Map 22 B2

Just a few minutes from Marble Arch, overlooking Portman Square, the
Churchill projects an English image and nowhere is this more evident than
in the club-like Churchill bar with wood-panelled walls, rug-strewn
parquet floor and deep, comfortable armchairs. Behind the bar, spirits are
kept in cut-glass decanters. A spacious lobby features crystal chandeliers and
a marble floor. Matching floral bedcovers and curtains give colour to
otherwise plainly decorated, but good-sized, bedrooms which offer every
modern comfort from air-conditioning to mini-bars and multi-channel
TVs. The Executive 8th floor has similarly decorated rooms but with
extended check-out time, complimentary breakfast and use of a meeting
room and free pressing of two items of clothing. Guests have free
membership to off-site David Lloyd tennis/health clubs in Finchley, Raynes
Park and Heston, near Heathrow Airport; plus tennis courts in Portman
Square. Garage parking for 48 cars. *Rooms 448. Portman Square garden,
business centre (9am-6pm Mon-Fri), hairdressing, beauty salon, coffee shop
(7am-1am), news kiosk, theatre desk, children's play area, garage. Access, Amex,
Visa,*

Restaurant   £100

Housing an extensive collection of the best in contemporary British art, the
restaurant is certainly different, and not just in its decor. A marble floor is
inlaid in parts with herring-bone oak; tables are set in an unconventional
triangular formation and different crockery is set for every place setting –
stylish, yes, but different for the sake of being different? The cooking by
executive chef David Wilson (formerly at *Blakes* hotel) is in a self-styled
"New British" mode, using a wide range of cosmopolitan ingredients in a
healthy style – perhaps a salad of toasted goat's cheese with thyme
vinaigrette followed by seared calf's liver with honey-glazed apple and
calvados sauce. His menus change daily and often show many oriental
influences: typically, tempura king prawns on black bean ginger sauce and
crispy leek or grilled coriander chicken with basmati rice and mango
chutney. There's usually an additional buffet selection to start at lunchtime
and always a good selection of vegetarian dishes. Puddings range from tarte
tatin or tiramisu to pecan pie and raspberry crème brulée. English breakfast
is served all day, from 7am. There's an interesting Sunday brunch (£17.95,
£10.95 for children, plus 15% service – reservations on 071-935 9050)
from noon to 3pm that starts with an antipasti and tapas bar, followed by
an à la carte main course and choice from the dessert table. *Seats 104.
Parties 20. L 12-3 D 6-11 (Sun from 7.30). Set L £17.50.*

SW10   Chutney Mary   ↑   £60
Tel 071-351 3113   R
535 King's Road SW10 0SZ   Map 23 F1

Almost on the corner of King's Road and Lots Road, Chutney Mary
describes itself as the world's first Anglo-Indian restaurant. Behind a
nondescript modern facade, it's a roomy, attractive place with Raj pictures
on pale walls, mirrored alcoves and a jungly glazed conservatory. The
menu is like no other, reflecting the fusion of cultures and cuisines:
vegetarian kebabs with lentils, cottage cheese, spinach and crushed
vegetables; spicy crab cakes; green chicken curry from Goa; Bangalore
bangers and mash; roast duck with apricots; tandoori ginger lamb chops
served with wilted greens. Everything is home-made, and the food is miles
away from standard Indian – not necessarily miles better (some dishes are
on the bland side), but a great deal more interesting. Desserts include a
spicy 'Hill Station' version of bread and butter pudding with pistachio and
cashew nuts and Madeira. The same à la carte menu is offered at lunchtime,
but at considerably kinder prices. Sunday sees a grand buffet at both lunch
and dinner. The colonial-style Verandah Bar at street level serves drinks,

snacks and light meals. **Seats 106.** *Parties 10. L 12.30-2.30 (Sun to 3.30)
D 7-11.30 (Sun to 10). Closed Sun for bar food. Set L £12.95. Access, Amex,
Visa,* (O) *Diners Club International*

SW6	Ciao		£40
Tel 071-381 6137			**R**
222 Munster Road SW6 6AY			**Map 21 E3**

Neighbourhood restaurant serving decent food at reasonable prices. The
menu divides into starter, fresh pasta, main-course salads, brasserie-style
dishes (often with hints of the East) and desserts. Sister to *Gavin's* in Putney
and *The Depot* in Barnes. **Seats 85.** *Parties 35. L 12-3.30 D 6-11 (Sun to
10.30). Closed Sun before Bank Holidays Mon, 3 days Xmas. Access, Amex,
Visa,* (O) *Diners Club International*

W14	Cibo		£75
Tel 071-371 6271			**R**
3 Russell Gardens W14 8EZ			**Map 21 D3**

Cibo means food in Italian, and here it's served on huge, colourful plates
which match the paintings for exuberance. Italian regional cuisine finds a
contemporary expression in dishes like tagliolini in a leek, scallop and
saffron sauce, grilled lamb cutlets with sautéed broad beans and goat's
cheese, and red mullet with endives and radicchio in a basil sauce. Apart
from champagne, the wine list is exclusively Italian. **Seats 65.** *Parties 65.
L 12-2.30 D 7-11. Closed D Sun, Bank Holidays. Set L from £17.95. Access,
Amex, Visa,* (O) *Diners Club International*

W1	Claridge's	88%	£289
Tel 071-629 8860 Fax 071-499 2210			**HR**
Brook Street W1A 9JQ			**Map 22 C3**

Grand home from home to kings and presidents, Claridge's is a charming
mixture of nostalgia, period style and modern comforts which now include
air-conditioning. Staff, who behave more like old family retainers, offer
unrivalled levels of service and are immaculately attired in pin-striped
trousers and morning coat; there are still lift attendants here and a touch of
the appropriate button in your apartment will summon waiter, valet or
maid. Extensive, 24hr room service runs the gamut from boiled eggs for
breakfast in bed to lobster lunches, afternoon teas and fillet of plaice with
brioche crumbs and Muscat grapes in the wee small hours. The elegant
public rooms include Oswald Milne's famous ballroom that holds up to
350 for a reception, 210 for dinner; the drawing room is in 18th-century
style, with marble fireplace and crystal chandeliers; leading from it, the
French Salon has superb moulded cornices and ceilings, marble fireplace
and silver-based crystal chandeliers. Liveried footmen serve guests in the
magnificent colonnaded foyer, while a Hungarian quartet entertains. A
grand staircase leads up to the bedroom floors where real fires can be lit in
the sitting-rooms of suites and some 'ordinary' bedrooms – which, of
course, are anything but ordinary. Decor ranges from the traditional with
veneer panelled walls and antiques to art deco; one suite has Sir Arthur
Sullivan's piano, another has a collector's William and Mary chair.
Bathrooms feature huge tubs and wonderful deluge shower heads. A new
terrace and exquisite mirrored mural are recent additions to the beautiful
art deco restaurant. Breakfasts are as good as you'll find anywhere – from a
health-conscious version to a full à la carte that includes everything from
freshly-baked brioches, Danish pastries and pancakes with maple syrup to
poached Finnan haddock, kedgeree, eggs Benedict and scrambled eggs with
smoked salmon. Guests have the use of Mark Birley's Bath and Racquets
Club in nearby Brook's Mews; two squash courts and hi-tech gymnasium
equipment are the main attractions and almost all clothing is provided –
guests are asked to bring their own trainers. Savoy Group. **Rooms 190.**
Valeting, hair salon. Access, Amex, Visa, (O) *Diners Club International*

Restaurant   £130

Yugoslavia-born *maitre chef des cuisines* Marjan Lesnik presides over the
kitchen, with the assistance of head chef John Williams. The grand
surroundings of one of London's most elegant dining rooms seem to
outclass the cooking, however, which is a mix of expensive ingredients,
classic techniques and a few modern touches. Fillet steak with oyster
mushrooms and balsamic vinegar sauce, calf's sweetbreads with truffles and
goose liver ravioli, poached egg with creamed mussels under a puff pastry
dome. Good cheeses. Fixed-price menus offer the best value. The levy of a
£1 cover charge seems incongruous when all but one main course costs
over £20 and vegetables are charged for separately (£6). *Seats 110. Parties
20. Private Room. L 12.30-3 D 7-11. Set L £26.50 & £42.*

The Causerie   £85

The fixed-price lunchtime smörgåsbord is still the main attraction here.
Simple pre- and post-theatre suppers are served from 5.30-7.30pm and
10.15-11pm. A la carte dinner is offered throughout the evening, ranging
from spinach salad with warm chicken livers or glazed quail eggs in
creamed smoked haddock to a medley of seafood with broad beans and
chervil, straightforward grills and lamb cutlets Reform. *Seats 40. Parties 8.
L 12-3 D 5.30-11 (Sun from 7). Closed Sat. Set meals from £16.*

W8   Clarke's   ★   £80

Tel 071-221 9225   Fax 071-229 4564   **R**

124 Kensington Church Street W8 4H   **Map 21 D3**

The chargrill is still the most important aspect of Sally Clarke's kitchen,
where the mix of influences ranges from the Mediterranean to California,
off to the Far East and back, producing wonderful dishes – perhaps thinly
sliced salmon that has been marinated in soy, sesame and coriander
followed by apple, raisin and cider-glazed breast of guinea fowl served
with braised celery heart, watercress and potato crisps, or red wine-glazed
pigeon breasts served with red cabbage, dates and walnuts. Typical of her
attention to detail is a dish of boned saddle of rabbit marinated in sage and
honey and accompanied by baby potatoes in truffle butter and various root
vegetables baked in a paper parcel – involved, but interesting and well
balanced. Both menus and dishes are always carefully thought out, perfectly
presented and rarely, if ever, repeated. Lunchtime sees a two- or three-
course menu with a choice of three dishes per course, while a no-choice,
four-course affair is offered in the evening. Cheeses are served in prime
condition with home-made oatmeal biscuits. Puddings, typically, might be
apple Brown Betty with clotted cream, warm lemon pudding with plum
sauce, rhubarb, pear and apple crumble or raspberry and almond tart. Sally
Clarke and Elizabeth Payne's praiseworthy cooking is invariably interesting
and inventive, but, although constantly changing, intentionally limited on
a day-to-day basis, thus keeping her standards consistently high. Dinner
menus change daily but are advertised by the week; however, Clarke's'
popularity makes it essential to book and almost impossible to choose a
fancied menu with only a few days' notice. The ground-floor dining room
is more formal, while downstairs (where the kitchen is open to view) is
more vibrant, particularly when full; an open, airy feel belies the fact that
it is a basement room. Vegetarians should advise in advance. & Clarke's,
next door, provides all the superb baking. A no-nonsense wine list,
naturally strong in Californian wines, has something for everyone; good
choice of wines by the glass. *Seats 90. Parties 10. L 12.30-2 D 7-10. Closed
Sat & Sun, Bank Holidays, 2 weeks Aug, 1 week Xmas, 4 days Easter.
Set L £20 Set D £34. Access, Visa.*

W1   The Clifton-Ford   72%   £200

Tel 071-486 6600   Fax 071-486 7492   **H**

47 Welbeck Street W1M 8DN   **Map 22 B3**

60s-built hotel with conference facilities (max 180) and a handy location
for the West End shops. Day rooms are particularly good, especially the
lounge, which has almost a country house atmosphere. The bar feels more

masculine and clubby. Bedrooms, each floor with its own colour scheme, include some roomy studio suites. The two lowest floors were the last to be refurbished. *Rooms 212. Access, Amex, Visa,*

NW3 Clive Hotel 64%	£64

Tel 071-586 2233   Fax 071-586 1659

Primrose Hill Road NW3 3NA   **Map 20 C2**

Modern Hilton-owned (former Ladbroke) hotel on the fringes of Hampstead, between Swiss Cottage and Chalk Farm. Free car park. Versatile conference facilities. *Rooms 96. Access, Amex, Visa,*

W2 Coburg Hotel 53%	£129

Tel 071-221 2217   Fax 071-229 0557

129 Bayswater Road W2 4RJ   **Map 22 C1**

A 1905 red-brick building by Queensway underground station with a distinctive domed exterior. Within is a rather average hotel showing poor attention to repair, despite recent renovation. *Rooms 132. Access, Amex, Visa,*

SW1 Collin House	£54

Tel 071-730 8031

104 Ebury Street SW1W 9QD   **Map 23 E3**

Privately-owned bed and breakfast hotel in Victorian town house just minutes from Victoria railway and coach stations. Most rooms have their own shower and WC. Good cooked breakfasts. No dogs. *Rooms 13. Closed 2 weeks Xmas. No credit cards.*

W9 Colonnade Hotel 60%	£80

Tel 071-286 1052   Fax 071-286 1057

2 Warrington Crescent W9 1ER   **Map 22 B1**

A Victorian Grade II listed building in residential Little Venice, close to Warwick Avenue underground. The whole hotel has been recently refurbished and 19 rooms are now air-conditioned. Under the same ownership for over 40 years, the style is straightforward with a variety of bedrooms – from singles to suites and four-poster rooms, some with whirlpool baths. Families are well catered for. *Rooms 49. Access, Amex, Visa,*

W2 Columbia Hotel	£66

Tel 071-402 0021   Fax 071-706 4691

95 Lancaster Gate W2 3NS   **Map 22 C1**

Returning guests provide much of the business at a privately-owned hotel overlooking Kensington Gardens. Simply appointed bedrooms, roomy lounge and cocktail bar. Several function rooms, maximum capacity 300 for banquets, 200 for conferences. *Rooms 102. Coffee shop (10am-midnight). Access, Amex, Visa.*

SW5 Concord Hotel	£55

Tel 071-370 4151

155 Cromwell Road SW5 0TQ   **Map 23 E1**

Budget bed and breakfast hotel with some family-size bedrooms. Handy for Earls Court, Olympia and the South Kensington museums. Unlicensed. No dogs. *Rooms 40. Access, Amex, Visa.*

W1	**The Connaught**	91%	£270

Tel 071-499 7070

HR

Carlos Place W1Y 6AL

Map 22 C3

Built in 1897, the Connaught was opened as a London home for the
landed gentry; today's guests may be more cosmopolitan but the
gentlemanly atmosphere remains. You will never be asked for an imprint
of your credit card on arrival, for example, or to sign for anything – a less
risky policy than it may sound as 85% of guests at any one time will have
stayed here before and most will be known by name to the long-serving
staff. It's just one of the things that makes this a very special hotel. Day
rooms, from which business meetings are banned in the interests of
tranquillity, are grand in style but not in scale, with a clubby, oak-panelled,
leather-seated bar and elegant lounges. Traditionally furnished bedrooms,
some with antiques, are individually decorated in an English country style
with a variety of fine fabrics from floral chintzes to restrained damasks.
Rooms are not cluttered with such things as fax machines or mini-bars
(although each of the 24 sitting rooms has an antique chinoiserie cocktail
cabinet), but these, and anything else within reason, are available on request
and the next time you stay here you will find that they will have
remembered such requirements and any other personal preferences. A guest
who is known to have failing eyesight, for example, may not be
consciously aware that the light bulbs have been changed for brighter ones.
Only 30 or so rooms have air-conditioning (all the other top London
hotels, apart from the Ritz, have full air-conditioning in all rooms) and
consommé is the only hot food on the overnight room service menu; but
major pluses are the luxurious bathrobes, fine linen bedding and exemplary
service throughout. No printed brochure or tariff is produced. A fine,
grand hotel with commendable old-fashioned values. *Rooms 90. Access,
Visa.*

Restaurant & Grill Room   ★★

£160

Not one restaurant, but two, sharing an identical à la carte menu. Highly
polished panelling features in the formal restaurant, while the sage-green
Grill Room is warmer and more intimate. That a large portrait of Auguste
Escoffier hangs in the kitchen is the clue to the classical French carte,
printed in French without translations; there are a few exceptions,
including regular daily-changing luncheon dishes like boiled silverside or
chicken pie. The genius of chef Michel Bourdin is the way in which he
interprets the dishes with lighter, more refined sauces without changing
their essential, unashamedly old-fashioned character. Service is very
traditional with a myriad of waiters organised in an elaborate hierarchy
but tempered by an innate and entirely appropriate friendliness. The way
fresh tablecloths are put on the tables after the main course, without
causing so much as a ripple in the conversation around the table, is a minor
miracle, performed nightly. This is *ancien régime* par excellence, an
experience not to be missed. Only France (many classic names), Germany
and Italy are represented on the wine list, and for such a grand
establishment prices are not too outrageous; "15% service charge is
excluded" from the prices quoted. *Seats 75. Parties 20. Private Room.
L 12.30-2 D 6.30-10.30.*

SW10	**Hotel Conrad**	85%	£225

Tel 071-823 3000   Fax 071-351 6525

H

Chelsea Harbour SW10 OXG

Map 23 F1

The design of this purpose-built, curving building puts one in mind of a
great ocean liner of the 1930s, especially with its long deck-like terrace
(where an outdoor barbecue is set up in summer) overlooking the boats
and distinctive apartment block of Chelsea Harbour Marina. Free from
traffic noise, the suites (there are no ordinary rooms here) all have a lobby
insulating them from the corridor and this makes them even more peaceful
than one might expect, given the setting. Designed by David Hicks, with

limed-oak furniture and soft colour schemes, the air-conditioned suite
rooms offer every modern comfort: three telephones with two lines;
multi-channel TVs with videos in both bedrooms and sitting room; a
mini-bar that includes caviar, a small wine cellar and lead crystal glasses,
plus many little extras – from fresh fruit and flowers to magazines and
even an umbrella in the wardrobe. Marble bathrooms are particularly
luxurious with shower cubicles in addition to deep tubs, twin wash basins,
bidets and separate loos. Many suites also have a guest loo off the lobby and
many boast a terrace with table and chairs (the best have views of the
Marina). Marble-floored public areas have a cool, spacious feel and
numerous smartly-dressed staff offer a high standard of service throughout.
A brasserie-style restaurant offers particularly good value at lunchtimes.
Drake's Bar has a terrace overlooking the yachts in the marina. Newly
arrived as the General Manager, Doreen Boulding brings a reputation as
one of the leaders of her profession. Modern conference facilities for up to
150, banqueting to 200. *Rooms 160. Indoor swimming pool, sauna, solarium,
steam room, gymnasium, business centre. Access, Amex, Visa,* (1) Diners Club International

W8	**Copthorne Tara**	69%	£132

Tel 071-937 7211   Fax 071-937 7100
    H

Scarsdale Place Wrights Lane W8 5SR   Map 23 D1

Modern 12-storey hotel close enough to Kensington High Street for easy
shopping but just far enough away to be reasonably peaceful. It's a bustling,
cheerful place with extensive banqueting/conference facilities (for up to
600) and bedrooms that range from "Classic" singles to apartments and
suites, plus rooms for disabled guests and non-smokers. *Rooms 829. 24hr
room service, business centre, coffee shop (22 hrs a day), car rental, theatre
reservation desk. Access, Amex, Visa,* (1) Diners Club International

EC2	**Corney & Barrow**	£55

Tel 071-638 9308
    R

109 Old Broad Street EC2N 1AP   Map 24 C1

All the qualities of a private eating club here: decor, service, intimacy,
hushed tones and City business. A basement sombreness decked in dark
green is lightened by gilt-framed oil paintings. Staff are pleasant,
professional and unobtrusive, the cooking reliable and capable. The seasonal
menu is full of interest, with such out-of-the-ordinary dishes as a warm
soft-boiled egg with creamed sweetbreads, guinea fowl wrapped in a vine
leaf with foie gras and grapes, or ox tongue braised with vegetables. There
are not many bargains on a sound wine list. For those pressed for time a
one-hour turn-round is guaranteed. *Also at:* 44 Cannon Street EC4 Tel
071-248 1700, 19 Broadgate Circle EC2 Tel 071-628 1251, 118 Moorgate
EC2 Tel 071-628 2898. *Seats 28. Parties 28. L only 11.30-3. Closed Sat &
Sun, Bank Holidays. Set L from £19.95. Access, Amex, Visa,* (1) Diners Club International

W8	**Costa's Grill**	£20

Tel 071-229 3794
    R

12-14 Hillgate Street W8 7SR   Map 21 D3

Attic food at basement prices. Moussaka, stifado and kleftiko typify the
robust Greek fare that has kept Costa's Grill so popular for 40 years. Also
grilled fish. A few outside tables on a rear patio in summer. Almost next
door is Costa's fish and chip shop. *Seats 70. Private Room. L 12-2.30
D 5-10.30. Closed Sun, Bank Holidays, 4 weeks Aug/Sep. No credit cards.*

W2	**Craven Gardens Hotel**	£66

Tel 071-262 3167   Fax 071-262 2083
    H

16 Leinster Terrace W2 3ES   Map 22 C1

Comfortable, well-kept bed and breakfast hotel just off Bayswater Road,
handy for Kensington Gardens, Paddington Station and the cosmopolitan
appeal of Queensway. No dogs. *Rooms 43. Access, Amex, Visa,*

SW10   La Croisette ↑   £80
Tel 071-373 3694   R
168 Ifield Road SW10 9AF   Map 23 F1

Once you have negotiated the tricky spiral staircase down to the dining
room you can soak in the evocative South of France decor. Consistency is
the watchword here, with little changing over the years. The fixed-price
menu still represents unusually good value for money, providing a glass of
kir, nibbles, two fish courses, Stilton and salad, plus dessert and coffee.
Highlights of the carte remain the seafood platter – a cornucopia of crab,
oysters, mussels, clams, langoustines and winkles – and fish served plain-
grilled or with classic sauces. A handful of lamb and contrefilet dishes
complete the picture. One of Pierre Martin's group of small, tip-top fish
restaurants; see also entries for *Le Suquet* and *Le Quai St Pierre*. **Seats 55.**
*Parties 55. L 1-2.30 D 7-11.30. Closed L Tue-Sat, all Mon. Set menu £26.
Access, Amex, Visa,* **(1)** Diners Club International

SW14   Crowthers   £65
Tel 081-876 6372   R
481 Upper Richmond Road West SW14 7PU   Map 21 E4

A pretty little restaurant on the busy South Circular Road where Philip
Crowther runs the kitchen and his wife Shirley the front of house. Menus
are fixed price, two- or three-course affairs. Lunch offers a small choice and
might see Gruyère cheese ramekin with tomato and chervil followed by
rib of beef and then sticky toffee pudding with hot butterscotch sauce.
Dinner menus extend to around six dishes per course: perhaps duck breast
salad with an onion and kumquat chutney, followed by steamed fillet of
cod wrapped in Chinese leaves with Noilly Prat and sorrel sauce, and
millefeuille of pear with crème anglaise and caramel to finish. **Seats 32.**
*Parties 32. L 12-2 D 7-10.45. Closed L Mon & Sat, all Sun, Bank Holidays.
Set L £12/£14.50 Set D £14.50/£19. Access, Amex, Visa,* **(1)** Diners Club International

W1   Cumberland Hotel   69%   £150
Tel 071-262 1234   Fax 071-724 4621   H
Marble Arch W1A 4RF   Map 22 C2

London's second largest hotel is at the Marble Arch end of Oxford Street,
overlooking Speakers' Corner. An impressive octagonal central lobby has
bright red columns, white marble and a large floral display as its focal
point, from where four restaurants (including a carvery – where children
under 5 eat free – and *Mon* Japanese restaurant) and three bars lead off.
Bedrooms, though not quite luxurious, are spacious, well maintained and
attractive with pleasant matching fabrics and good darkwood furniture;
200 are classified as Executive. A variety of conference and banqueting
suites cater for 475/560. Children under 16 free in their parents' room. No
dogs. Forte. **Rooms 894.** *News kiosk, coffee shop (6.30am-midnight). Access,
Amex, Visa,* **(1)** Diners Club International

SW3   Dan's   £80
Tel 071-352 2718   R
119 Sydney Street SW3 6NR   Map 23 E2

A bright, informal restaurant with a large garden that's a boon in summer.
Dishes are generally unelaborate, typified by parfait of chicken livers; crab
and avocado; salmon with a chive butter sauce; or roast rib of beef with
sauce béarnaise (this dish for two or more). **Seats 52.** *Parties 35. Private
Room. L 12.30-2.30 D 7-10.45 (Sat to 10.30). Closed L Sat, all Sun, Bank
Holidays, 1 week Xmas. Set D £19.50. Access, Amex, Visa,* **(1)** Diners Club International

NW1   Daphne

£40

Tel 071-267 7322

R

83 Bayham Street NW1

Map 20 C2

In a part of town where Greek restaurants abound, Daphne has the edge over most of them. Its menu of traditional favourites is given a boost by numerous daily specials with an emphasis on fish: charcoal-grilled bream, cod croquettes, even a fish meze. Choice is also generous for meat-eaters and vegetarians. On two floors, plus a roof garden. *Seats 70. Parties 80. L 12-2.30 D 6-11.30. Closed Sun, L Bank Holidays, 25 Dec, 1 Jan. Set L from £7.95. Access, Visa.*

W1   Defune

£80

Tel 071-935 8311   Fax 071-487 3762

R

61 Blandford Street W1H 3AJ

Map 22 B2

Book to be sure of a table, as this is a popular (and very small) Japanese restaurant. Otherwise you can sit at the counter and see your sushi and sashimi being prepared. The à la carte spans a fairly familiar Japanese range, from soups and noodle dishes to barbecued beef, pork and fish, and specialities such as *shabu-shabu* and *yosenabe*. *Seats 30. Parties 8. Private Room. L 12-2.30 D 6-10.30. Closed Sun, Bank Holidays, 1 week Xmas. Set L from £13. Access, Amex, Visa,*

W1   Dell'Ugo   ★ NEW

£40

Tel 071-734 8300

R

56 Frith Street Soho W1

Map 25 A2

Tony Worrall-Thompson – innovator at *Ménage à Trois* (which closed last year) some years ago and more recently one-starred chef at *190 Queen's Gate* (transforming into a seafood bistro as we go to press) and the thriving *Bistrot 190* (see entry) which he continues to oversee – has embarked on yet another fashionable operation which will set the style and trends for other London restaurants to follow in the 90s. This Guide may be criticised in some quarters for rewarding quality so soon after opening, when perhaps the service is not always spot on and inconsistency occasionally occurs in some dishes, but this is seriously good cooking at a price that customers appear to want to pay – judging by the numbers that already flock to the three levels: the ground floor has a bar and is casual; upstairs, especially the top floor, more formal. To pigeon-hole the food as eclectic, Mediterranean or anything else misses the point – AW-T thrives on good new ideas, where braised beef or wild mushroom risotto rests happily alongside marinated duck with beans and chili potatoes or a house pizza. There are bruschetta and crostini, carpaccios and salads, and one-priced puddings such as Granny Smith tart with cinnamon ice cream or ginger brulée with caramel sauce. There is something for everyone, and a sensible wine list with affordable quality, available either by the pichet or the bottle, and a further page of wines priced from £10 to £22.50. As we write the place is buzzing, so book. *Seats 170. Parties 65. Private Room. L 1st floor: 11.30-3, 2nd floor: 12.30-3 D 1st floor: 5.30-11.30, 2nd floor: 7.30-11.30 Ground floor café: 11am-12.30am. Closed Sun. Access, Amex, Visa,*

SW14   The Depot

£40

Tel 081-878 9462

R

Tideway Yard Mortlake High Street SW14 8SN

Map 21 E4

A delightful stable courtyard setting with bare pine tables and floorboards. Sister to *Ciao* and *Gavin's* (see entries), the menu here is also based around fresh pasta with a few brasserie-style dishes (beef stir-fry, veal escalope milanese, buckwheat pancakes with salmon, cod, broccoli, mushrooms and cream cheese) and salads to supplement them. Sensibly-priced wines. Bustling atmosphere and very popular; book well ahead for the best tables that overlook a bend in the Thames. *Seats 80. Parties 30. L 12-3 D 6-11*

*(Sun 7-10.30). Open all day from 11am for light meals. Closed 25 & 26 Dec.
Access, Amex, Visa,* 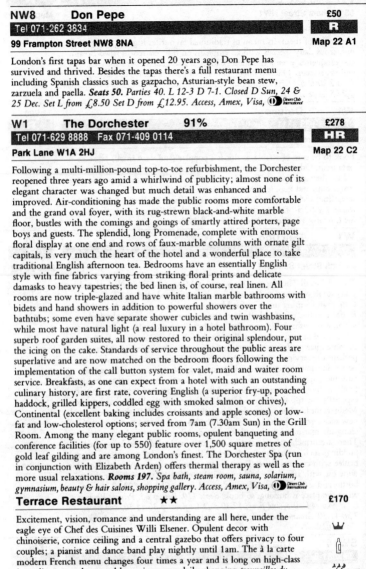 *Diners Club International*

NW8　Don Pepe　　　　　　　　　　£50

Tel 071-262 3834　　　　　　　　　　**R**

99 Frampton Street NW8 8NA　　　Map 22 A1

London's first tapas bar when it opened 20 years ago, Don Pepe has
survived and thrived. Besides the tapas there's a full restaurant menu
including Spanish classics such as gazpacho, Asturian-style bean stew,
zarzuela and paella. **Seats 50.** *Parties 40. L 12-3 D 7-1. Closed D Sun, 24 &
25 Dec. Set L from £8.50 Set D from £12.95. Access, Amex, Visa,* Diners Club International

---

W1　The Dorchester　91%　　　£278

Tel 071-629 8888　Fax 071-409 0114　　**HR**

Park Lane W1A 2HJ　　　　　　　Map 22 C2

Following a multi-million-pound top-to-toe refurbishment, the Dorchester
reopened three years ago amid a whirlwind of publicity; almost none of its
elegant character was changed but much detail was enhanced and
improved. Air-conditioning has made the public rooms more comfortable
and the grand oval foyer, with its rug-strewn black-and-white marble
floor, bustles with the comings and goings of smartly attired porters, page
boys and guests. The splendid, long Promenade, complete with enormous
floral display at one end and rows of faux-marble columns with ornate gilt
capitals, is very much the heart of the hotel and a wonderful place to take
traditional English afternoon tea. Bedrooms have an essentially English
style with fine fabrics varying from striking floral prints and delicate
damasks to heavy tapestries; the bed linen is, of course, real linen. All
rooms are now triple-glazed and have white Italian marble bathrooms with
bidets and hand showers in addition to powerful showers over the
bathtubs; some even have separate shower cubicles and twin washbasins,
while most have natural light (a real luxury in a hotel bathroom). Four
superb roof garden suites, all now restored to their original splendour, put
the icing on the cake. Standards of service throughout the public areas are
superlative and are now matched on the bedroom floors following the
implementation of the call button system for valet, maid and waiter room
service. Breakfasts, as one can expect from a hotel with such an outstanding
culinary history, are first rate, covering English (a superior fry-up, poached
haddock, grilled kippers, coddled egg with smoked salmon or chives),
Continental (excellent baking includes croissants and apple scones) or low-
fat and low-cholesterol options; served from 7am (7.30am Sun) in the Grill
Room. Among the many elegant public rooms, opulent banqueting and
conference facilities (for up to 550) feature over 1,500 square metres of
gold leaf gilding and are among London's finest. The Dorchester Spa (run
in conjunction with Elizabeth Arden) offers thermal therapy as well as the
more usual relaxations. **Rooms 197.** *Spa bath, steam room, sauna, solarium,
gymnasium, beauty & hair salons, shopping gallery. Access, Amex, Visa,* Diners Club International

Terrace Restaurant　★★　　　　£170

Excitement, vision, romance and understanding are all here, under the
eagle eye of Chef des Cuisines Willi Elsener. Opulent decor with
chinoiserie, cornice ceiling and a central gazebo that offers privacy to four
couples; a pianist and dance band play nightly until 1am. The à la carte
modern French menu changes four times a year and is long on high-class
ingredients, supplemented by a six-course daily-changing *trouvailles du
marché* menu; the majority of dishes triumph as they utilise the highest of
well-executed techniques – mousseline of Scottish salmon with caviar, pan-
fried goose liver on a warm salad of French beans scented with truffles, pot
au feu of chicken and beef with marrow; lasagne of lobster and spinach
with tarragon sauce, confit and roast breast of Barbary duck with an
essence of blueberry and kumquat, blue cheese terrine served with poached
pear. Elsener's alternative no-choice *menu léger* also combines basic
traditions with modern influences, taking note of the nutritional content

and using, for instance, low fat and wholemeal ingredients as in a dish of poached fillets of lamb and rabbit on a ragout of grilled courgettes and tomatoes. Desserts, however, are indulgent and picturesque, with a small choice ranging from tiramisu to orange tart with almond ice cream and chocolate millefeuille; a short selection of dessert wines is served by the glass. Fine French and British cheeses served from a wagon that bears a remarkable resemblance to a Jules Verne rocket. Service, under maitre d'hotel Peter Buderath, is as one expects – well-informed, smart, discreet and attentive, but never obtrusive. An extensive list of wines from all parts of the world, though there's little of note under £20; decent half bottles are equally pricy. *Seats 80. Parties 14. D only 7-11. Closed Sun & Mon, Bank Holidays. Set D £30 & £48.*

Grill Room   £130

The lofty gilt-decorated room with its grand Spanish theme remains a very stylish setting for elegant carving trolleys from which smoked salmon, roast rib of Angus beef with Yorkshire pudding and stuffed roast saddle of lamb are served. Other favourite British classics include Cornish dressed crab, Glamorgan sausages (soft cheese deep-fried in breadcrumbs with a leek sauce), cock-a-leekie soup, shepherd's pie and boiled silverside with caraway dumplings. A low cholesterol menu includes skinless meats and salads prepared with low-fat dressings and a minimum of soya oil. Meatless options might inlcude a steamed ragout of scallops and Dublin Bay prawns or a gratin of aubergine and beans. The English cheeseboard is splendid, but the dessert trolley holds a few disappointments. Smart and attentive staff provide high standards of service. Sound, straightforward cooking. *Seats 81. Parties 12. Private Room. L 12.30-2.30 D 6-11 (Sun 7-10.30). Set L £27 Set D £20/£25 & £28.*

Oriental Room   ★   £120

London's most exclusive Chinese restaurant and almost certainly the most expensive, too. On the evidence of recent visits the cooking is just starworthy rather than unreservedly so. The sweet and sour sauce seemed closer to sticky mediocrity than before, a touch too vinegary, and it didn't really work when served with decoratively-cut salmon and needlessly adorned with fruit. A dip looking like soy but unashamedly declared to be Worcester sauce appeared not only with an amuse-bouche of chicken samosa but also with the appetisers. Other dips, one based on yellow beans, one featuring dried fish, were excellent and many of the dishes were resounding successes, including soya chicken, mixed mushrooms in a bean curd case, bites of beef in a very peppy pepper sauce, and fried egg yolk sponge dumplings – a dessert with a homely taste of hard-fried egg and a drizzle of honey. But staff are still smart, charming and knowledgable under a suave and accomplished manager. Lovely private rooms. *Seats 77. Parties 20. Private Room. L 12-2.30 D 7-11. Closed L Sat, all Sun. Set L £20 Set D £28 & £35.*

W4   La Dordogne   £50
Tel 081-747 1836   **R**

5 Devonshire Road W4 2EU   Map 21 D4

"A corner of France in west London" with a short menu of traditional French dishes now supplemented by oysters and good seafood. Boudin blanc with foie gras sauce, sole roulade with aïoli, escalope of monkfish with ginger or basil sauce typify the style. Try the *assiette gourmande* selection from the dozen or so desserts. *Seats 80. Parties 50. Private Room. L 12-2.30 D 7-11. Closed L Sat & Sun, Bank Holidays. Access, Amex, Visa,*

Diners Club International

NW1   Dorset Square Hotel   74%   £129

Tel 071-723 7874   Fax 071-724 3328   **HR**

39 Dorset Square NW1 6QN   Map 22 B2

A charming, elegant house almost unnoticed in the white Georgian facade
of Dorset Square buildings. An attractive combination of hand-painted
woodwork, gilt-framed paintings, tapestry cushions and antique furniture
gives a warm, refined atmosphere to the public rooms on the ground floor.
The guest lounge is furnished with colourful armchairs, a 19th-century
rolltop desk and an antique cabinet which holds an honesty bar. Each
bedroom has its own personality, artistically blending patterns and
materials. Rooms on the first and second floor are particularly large and
lofty, and two of them boast grand pianos. Most rooms are air-conditioned,
and all have satellite TV, books and magazines. Marble and mahogany
bathrooms enjoy natural daylight. Careful thinking has gone into every
detail, making one feel a guest in a friend's home. A chauffeur-driven
Bentley Continental is available by prior arrangement. *Rooms 37. Access,
Amex, Visa,* ![Diners Club International]

Restaurant   £70

A seasonal menu promises much but fails to achieve the same level of
distinction as the hotel. The fixed-price menu is augmented by the
automatic addition of 15% service. Sliced pig's trotter with caramelised
apple and creamed potatoes, asparagus and ricotta ravioli with
marjoram butter, simply-grilled Dover sole or rolled brill and lobster with
a lemon and chive sauce are typical of chef Trevor Baines's style. *Seats 40.
L 12-3 D 6-10.30. Closed L Sun, all Sat. Set L & D from £19.95.*

W1   Dragon Inn   £30

Tel 071-494 0870   **R**

12 Gerrard Street W12 7LJ   Map 25 A2

Set on three floors, an unsophisticated Cantonese restaurant with a
staggeringly long menu covering everything from chicken with cashew
nuts to spiced belly pork with yam served in a clay pot. Dim sum are
always popular. *Seats 150. Parties 12. Meals 12-11.30 (dim sum 12-4.45).
Closed 25-26 Dec & from 8pm 24 Dec. Set meals from £10. Access, Amex,
Visa.*

W1   Dragon's Nest   £45

Tel 071-437 3119   **R**

58 Shaftesbury Avenue W1V 7DE   Map 25 A2

A change of direction at this smarter-than-average Chinese restaurant has
reduced prices and rationalised the menu, although a few unusual dishes
remain (jelly fish with shredded duck, sizzling frogs' legs, tripe with
preserved vegetable, ox tendon simmered in soya sauce). *Seats 150. Parties
40. Private Room. L 12-2.45 D 5-11.15 (Sat 12-11.15, Sun 12-10.45).
Closed 24 & 25 Dec. Set meals from £11.50. Access, Amex, Visa,* ![Diners Club International]

SW3   The Draycott   £235

Tel 071-730 6466   Fax 071-730 0236   **PH**

24-26 Cadogan Gardens SW3 2RP   Map 23 E2

Formed from a pair of redbrick Victorian town houses, a discreet little
brass plate on the door announces the Draycott's residential 'club' status.
One is admitted to a yellow drag-painted entrance hall beyond which is an
appealing drawing room where Victorian paintings, objets d'art, fresh
flowers and a mix of sofas and armchairs creates a certain old-fashioned
elegance enhanced by views of (and access to) Cadogan Gardens, one of
London's most peaceful garden squares. Bedroom size varies considerably
and all are individually decorated in a non-hotel town-house style with
antiques, porcelain ornaments and paintings of rural scenes contrasting with
noisy air-conditioning units and mini-bars. Good bathrooms with

Penhaligon toiletries. The numerous stairs and landings are looking a bit
tired and housekeeping generally needs attention (the new owners may
have this in hand), but overall the Draycott offers a charming and
romantic alternative to more conventional hotels. 24hr room service makes
up for the lack of a restaurant. Guests have free use of the nearby Synergy
Centre Health Centre. **Rooms 25.** *Access, Amex, Visa,* ()

SW1	**Dukes Hotel**	79%	£238

Tel 071-491 4840   Fax 071-493 1264   **HR**

35 St James's Place SW1A 1NY   Map 22 C3

In a quiet cul-de-sac off St James's Street, a charming and secluded hotel in
a tranquil setting. The elegant Edwardian building is conservatively and
tastefully furnished in a club-like fashion, with a cosy sitting room and
splendid cocktail bar; public rooms reflect the traditional qualities aimed
for by the management and the smartly uniformed staff. Bedrooms have
fine antiques and period furniture complemented by chintzy floral fabrics.
While there is no air-conditioning, there are ceiling fans for sultry days.
Bathrooms are not large but have smart marble tiling and a range of
luxurious toiletries. 26 of the rooms are suites with homely sitting rooms;
some have small kitchens. No children under seven. No dogs. **Rooms 64.**
Access, Amex, Visa, ()

Restaurant   £95

An intimate, elegant restaurant offering a mix of classical and modern, but
mainly French-inspired dishes, all competently prepared. Seasonal game,
daily roasts served from a trolley and desserts that include traditional
favourites. *Seats 30. Parties 60. Private Room. L 12.30-2 D 6-10 (Sun from
7). Closed L Sat. Set L £17.75 Set D £28.50.*

SW1	**Durley House**	74%	£271

Tel 071-235 5537   Fax 071-259 6977   **H**

115 Sloane Street SW1X 9PJ   Map 23 D2

A finely furnished residence comprising eleven self-contained one- and
two-bedroom suites, Durley House commends itself to clients seeking the
quiet life in central London. Indeed, its Sloane Street location is handy as a
pied-à-terre for Knightsbridge stores, yet guests can step literally across the
road for a game of tennis in Cadogan Park. Each of its spacious apartments
is individually designed and furnished with antiques and original oil
paintings. Some fine architectural features, carved wooden mantels and
curved panelling are embellished with flamboyant drapes; king-size beds
have crown canopies and matching covers in bold colours. The lounges
include polished mahogany dining tables and, in some cases, grand pianos.
There's a level of service to match: a full room service breakfast arrives by
way of a traditional service lift. Under the same ownership as *Dorset Square*
and *Pelham* hotels. **Rooms 11.** *Access, Amex, Visa.*

W1	**Durrants Hotel**	65%	£106

Tel 071-935 8131   Fax 071-487 3510   **H**

George Street W1H 6BJ   Map 22 B2

A stone's throw from Oxford Street, between Baker Street and
Marylebone High Street and close to the Wallace Collection, Durrants
comprises four creeper-clad Georgian houses. Its appeal is traditional and
club-like with wood panelling in the foyer, a clubby bar, authentic
smoking room and cosy, but not large, bedrooms. Marble bathrooms have
quality fittings. Seven rooms are not en suite. **Rooms 96.** *Access, Amex,
Visa.*

EC1   The Eagle   £30
Tel 071-837 1353   R
159 Farringdon Road EC1R 3AL   Map 20 C2

Converted bare-boards pub transformed lunchtime and evening into an
excellent restaurant serving new-wave Mediterranean dishes from a blackboard
menu. It remains a pub even during meal time, so the fairly cramped
seating area is shared between drinkers and eaters. No booking, but a wait
with a pint is well worth while. Typical dishes: Portuguese soup of spring
cabbage, potatoes and chorizo sausage; linguine with scallops, parsley, chili
and garlic; grilled mackerel with coriander and lime salsa, marinated roast
loin of pork with roast potatoes and braised sweet red onions. *Seats 45.*
L 12.30-2.30 D 6.30-10.30. Closed Sat & Sun, Bank Holidays, 3 weeks Xmas.
Diners Club International

SW6   Earls Court Park Inn International   69%   £114
Tel 071-385 1255   Fax 071-381 4450   H
47 Lillie Road SW6 1UQ   Map 21 E3

Formerly the Ramada Inn West London. Tour parties are big business, so
too conferences, with up to 1750 delegates accommodated theatre-style in
the huge Thames Suite. Just by the side entrance to Earls Court Exhibition
Centre. Children up to 16 free in parents' room. No dogs. *Rooms 501.*
Business centre, coffee shop (6.30am-1am). Access, Amex, Visa, Diners Club International

SE22   Eastern Eye   £30
Tel 081-693 7584   R
44 Lordship Lane East Dulwich SE22 8HJ   Map 21 F1

Friendly staff and careful cooking in an Indian restaurant whose menu
covers all the usual favourites plus tandoori duck and trout. *Seats 70.*
Parties 40. L 12-3 D 6-12 (Sun 12-12). Closed 25 & 26 Dec. Set meals from
£7.95. Access, Amex, Visa, Diners Club International

SW1   Ebury Court   59%   £125
Tel 071-730 8147   Fax 071-823 5966   HR
26 Ebury Street SW1W 0LU   Map 23 D3

In the same family ownership for more than half a century, Ebury Court
offers old-fashioned courtesy and charm in a central location three minutes
walk from Victoria station. Accommodation ranges from singles without
en-suite facilities to luxury four-poster/triple rooms with bath. All are
equipped with hair-dryers and satellite TVs. The hotel owns an adjacent
mews house which is available for rental with full hotel services.
Rooms 46. Closed 2 weeks Xmas/New Year. Access, Amex, Visa, Diners Club International

Tophams   £50

Three elegantly appointed rooms, their walls adorned with paintings by
the owners' ancestors, are the setting for meals that combine traditional and
modern elements. Chicken liver paté, grilled Dover sole and roast leg of
pork with apple sauce represent the school of old favourites, while more
contemporary inspiration is behind beetroot pasta tossed with crispy
duckling and spring onions, or medallions of monkfish sautéed with garlic
and mango. Good value for both food and wine. *Seats 45. Parties 24.*
Private Room. L 12-2.30 D 6.30-10.45 (Sat to 11).

SW7   Eden Plaza Hotel   £72
Tel 071-370 6111   Fax 071-370 0932   H
68-69 Queen's Gate SW7 5JT   Map 23 E1

Neatly kept bed and breakfast hotel a short walk from the South
Kensington museums. Accommodation ranges from singles to quadruples.
Children up to 14 stay free in their parents' room. No dogs. *Rooms 63.*
Access, Amex, Visa, Diners Club International

W1   Efes Kebab House   £40

Tel 071-636 1953   **R**

80 Great Titchfield Street W1N 5FD   Map 22 B3

Brothers Khazim and Ibrahim opened their Turkish restaurant in 1974 and
it's remained popular ever since, even spawning a branch in Great Portland
Street (with music and belly-dancing). Lamb and chicken kebabs are the
principal attraction, preceded by a wide selection of hors d'oeuvre
including stuffed vine leaves, houmus, white cheese with chili and parsley,
walnut-sauced chicken and carrots with yoghurt. Syrupy sweets from the
trolley. *Also at:* Efes Kebab House II 175 Great Portland Street W1 Tel
071-436 0600 Map 22B3. *Seats 160. Parties 100. Meals 12-12. Closed Sun,
Xmas, 1 Jan, Good Friday. Set meals from £15. Access, Amex, Visa,*

SW3   Egerton House   £160

Tel 071-589 2412   Fax 071-584 6540   **PH**

17-19 Egerton Terrace London SW3 2BX   Map 23 D2

In a quiet location off the Brompton Road, close to Harrods, this handsome
Victorian redbrick town house opened as a privately owned hotel in
September 1990. Bedrooms (on four floors, all served by a lift) are
individually decorated with traditional fabrics, antiques and oil paintings
and there's a luxurious look and feel to the marble bathrooms. Some rooms
have four-posters and the majority overlook gardens. Excellent breakfasts
are served in the rooms or in the bright, basement breakfast room.
Concierge, valet. No children under eight. No dogs. *Rooms 30. Access,
Amex, Visa,*

SW10   Eleven Park Walk   £60

Tel 071-352 3449   Fax 071-351 6576   **R**

11 Park Walk SW10 0AJ   Map 23 F1

Regional Italian cooking with modern touches in a smart, lively restaurant
hosting many loyal regulars. Bagna cauda is a favourite starter, while the
likes of spaghetti with lobster, wild boar bresaola and warm goose
carpaccio are more unusual options. Main dishes run from plain-grilled
Dover sole or cod with paprika to veal milanese, liver and bacon or bollito
misto – a dish guaranteed to provide an extra lining in winter. Tiramisu
will complete the weather-proofing. *Seats 90. Parties 25. L 12.30-3 D 7-12.
Closed D Sun, all Bank Holidays. Access, Amex, Visa,*

SW1   Elizabeth Hotel   £65

Tel 071-828 6812   **H**

37 Eccleston Square SW1V 1PB   Map 23 E3

Friendly privately-owned bed and breakfast hotel in a garden square near
Victoria station. Bedrooms range from singles to family-size; a few are
without private facilities. No dogs. *Rooms 40. No credit cards.*

SW7   Embassy House Hotel   59%   £106

Tel 071-584 7222   Fax 071-589 8193   **H**

31 Queen's Gate SW7 5JA   Map 23 D1

Modern comfort in a late-Victorian building near Hyde Park, the Royal
Albert Hall and the Kensington Museums. Children under 16 can stay free
in their parents' room; in their own room they pay 50% of the adult rate.
Jarvis. *Rooms 69. Access, Amex, Visa,*

SW3   English Garden

Tel 071-584 7272   Fax 071-581 2848

10 Lincoln Street SW3 2TS

£65

R

Map 23 E2

English cooking in a stylishly converted Chelsea terrace house. The menu
changes with the seasons: typical spring options include salmon and scallop
terrine with green herb sauce, halibut roulade with crab, ginger and
coriander, roast rack of lamb and ragoo of beef and Guinness topped with
horseradish dumplings. Puddings read just as temptingly with the likes of
rhubarb and cardamom ice cream or honey and orange curd tart. The
room has an attractive conservatory at the back. *Seats 50. Parties 50.
Private Room. L 12.30-2.30 (Sun to 2) D 7.30-11.30 (Sun to 10.30). Closed
25 & 26 Dec. Set L from £14.95. Access, Amex, Visa,*

SW3   English House

Tel 071-584 3002   Fax 071-581 2848

3 Milner Street SW3 2QA

£85

R

Map 23 E2

English cooking in a homely Victorian setting just off King's Road. From
the spring menu come red pepper and ginger soup, chicken roulade with
lemon stuffing, fillet of beef with grated horseradish pancake and port
sauce, rhubarb and cinnamon burnt cream. *Seats 33. Parties 20. Private
Room. L 12.30-2.30 D 7.30-11.30 (Sun to 10.30). Closed 25 & 26 Dec.
Set L £14.75 Set D £19.75. Access, Amex, Visa,*

SW15   Enoteca

Tel 081-785 4449

28 Putney High Street SW15 1SQ

£45

R

Map 21 E3

High street corner site with little in the way of decor, but a lot to like
about the Italian cooking. The menu is strong on pasta (always three or
four plus a daily special), and main courses could include grilled swordfish
with a pistachio and tomato coulis, or medallions of beef fillet with wild
mushroom ravioli in a red wine sauce. Suitable wines are helpfully noted
against each dish. *Seats 35. Parties 45. Private Room. L 12.30-3 D 7-11.30.
Closed Sun, Bank Holidays, 1 week Xmas. Access, Amex, Visa,*

W1   L'Escargot

Tel 071-437 2679

48 Greek Street W1V 5LR

£80

R

Map 25 A2

Ground-floor brasserie, restaurant above, serving an eclectic modern menu
that covers the range from baked filo pastry-wrapped Surrey snails in garlic
butter to bresaola, chargrilled tiger prawns with coriander and chili, and
calf's liver with grilled polenta and Parmesan. *Seats 95. Parties 95. Private
Room. L 12-3 D 5.30-11.15. Closed L Sat, all Sun, Bank Holidays. Set L &
D £12.50. Access, Amex, Visa,*

W8   L'Escargot Doré

Tel 071-937 8508

2 Thackeray Street W8 5ET

£60

R

Map 23 D1

New chef Simon Scrutton (formerly chef-patron at *Byrons* in Eastbourne)
cooks an intrinsically French menu (scallops with celeriac, veal medallions
with ceps, breast of duck with ginger and honey, French cheeses) at this
cool subterranean restaurant. Snails are offered in puff pastry with basil and
capers or in the traditional manner wuth garlic butter, parsley and white
wine. The carte is complemented by a fixed-price, three-course menu for
both lunch and dinner. The ground-floor bar-brasserie offers a daily
blackboard menu and a short carte with simple dishes like *potage de saison,
poulet grillé avec pommes frites* and *crème brulée. Seats 50. Parties 30.
L 12-2.30 D 6.30-11.30. Closed L Sat, all Sun, Bank Holidays, 2 weeks Aug.
Set L & D £14.90. Access, Amex, Visa,*

W1   Est
Tel 071-437 0666
£40
R

54 Frith Street W1V 5TE   Map 25 A2

A Soho media restaurant with large windows looking on to Frith Street.
The menu is very much in the modern Mediterranean mode, with simple
straightforward dishes often using the chargrill: polenta with salsa,
asparagus with Parmesan shavings and garlic butter, chicken with artichoke
trifolate and zucchini fritters, spring lamb with mustard pesto, mixed
leaves and baked potato. **Seats 40.** Parties 24. Meals 12-11 (Sat 6-11.30).
Closed L Sat, all Sun, Bank Holidays. Access, Amex, Visa,

WC2   L'Estaminet   NEW
Tel 071-379 1432
£60
R

14 Garrick Street WC2   Map 25 B2

On the former site of *Inigo Jones*, an attractive French brasserie on the
fringe of Covent Garden with a basement wine bar (*La Tartine*). The menu
covers snails to chateaubriand and oeufs à la neige. **Seats 60.** Parties 20.
L 12-2.30 D 6.30-11.30. Closed Sun, Bank Holidays. Access, Amex, Visa.

W1   L'Etoile
Tel 071-636 7189
£80
R

30 Charlotte Street W1P 1HJ   Map 22 B3

One of the most traditional bastions of French cooking, l'Etoile has been in
business for almost 90 years. Turbot à la monégasque, frogs' legs and paté
to start, fish or onion soup, goujons of sole, sautéed veal kidneys, tripes à la
mode de Caen, pigeon with petits pois, chateaubriand for two. **Seats 60.**
Parties 30. Private Room. L 12.30-2.30 D 6.30-11. Closed L Sat, all Sun,
Bank Holidays. Access, Amex, Visa,

SW10   La Famiglia
Tel 071-351 0761 Fax 071-351 2409
£70
R

7 Langton Street SW10   Map 23 F1

In a wide side street off King's Road, boasting the largest outdoor eating
area of any London restaurant, with extra seating for 125. Outside or in,
you can enjoy Italian cooking with a Tuscan slant. Minimum charge £12
Saturday, Sunday lunchtimes and every evening. **Seats 90.** Parties 10.
Private Room. L 12-2.45 D 7-11.45. Closed Bank Holidays. Access, Amex,
Visa,

NW1   Fanari
Tel 071-586 1969
£28
R

40 Chalcot Road NW1   Map 20 C2

A very friendly and unpretentious Greek restaurant where a meal is like a
family supper. Portions are generous, flavours robust, prices very
reasonable. Dinner ends with a plateful of fresh fruit. **Seats 95.** Parties 20.
Private Room. D only 6-12 (Fri & Sat to 1). Closed Sun, Bank Holidays
except 25 Dec & 1 Jan. Set D from £7.80. Access, Visa,

E8   Faulkners
Tel 071-254 6152
£22
R

424 Kingsland Road E8 4AA   Map 20 B1

Busy fish'n'chip restaurant with an even busier takeaway section.
Groundnut oil is used to fry generous portions of fresh fish from cockney
favourites like cod and rock salmon to more patrician halibut and Dover
sole. Special value children's menu (£2.95). **Seats 60.** Parties 6. Private
Room. L 12-2 D 5-10 (Sat 11.30-10). Closed Sun, Bank Holidays, 10 days
Xmas. No credit cards.

SW3 The Fenja £156

PH

Tel 071-589 7333 Fax 071-581 4958

69 Cadogan Gardens SW3 2RB Map 23 E2

A handsome private residence turned into a home-from-home hotel of town house character with thirteen bedrooms ranging from a single to superior twins and doubles. Antiques, fresh flowers and English prints and paintings of the 18th and 19th centuries are a feature, and both towels and bedding are of high quality. Breakfast (served until 2pm for late risers!) and light meals from room service; drinks on a tray in the room or in the cosy drawing room with an open fire. Guests have access to Cadogan Gardens. No dogs. **Rooms 13.** Garden. Access, Amex, Visa,

N16 La Fin de la Chasse £60

R

Tel 071-254 5975

176 Stoke Newington Church Street N16 0JL Map 20 B1

A long, narrow restaurant with a small garden to the rear and a menu of largely familiar modern dishes given a slight twist (breast of duck with lemon compote and raspberry juice, fillet of salmon with a seaweed mousse on a glazed mushroom sauce, cider syllabub with *langues du chat*). **Seats 40.** Parties 18. Private Room. L 12.30-2 D 7-10.30. Closed Sun & Mon, Bank Holidays, 2 weeks Xmas, 2 weeks Sep. Set D £14.50. Access, Amex, Visa,

N8 Florians £50

R

Tel 081-348 8348

4 Topsfield Parade Middle Lane Crouch End N8 8RP Map 20 A2

A mix of bar and restaurant both serving new-wave Italian food. Snacks include ciabatta steak sandwich with oregano and shallots and a good-value 2-course blackboard menu. The main carte extends from tuna carpaccio with balsamic vinegar and tomato, basil and rocket salad to filo pastry parcels with vegetables, artichokes, sun-dried tomatoes and radicchio pesto. Ricotta and amaretti mousse and Italian bread-and-butter pudding with mascarpone custard among the desserts. **Seats 60.** Parties 42. Private Room. L 12-3 (Sat & Sun to 4) D 7-11 (Sun to 10.30) (wine bar 12-11). Closed Bank Holidays. Set L (bar) £5.95. Access, Visa.

WC1 Forte Crest Bloomsbury 65% £116

H

Tel 071-837 1200 Fax 071-833 2290

Coram Street WC1N 1HT Map 22 A4

Spacious foyer, more bedrooms refurbished, banqueting/conference facilities for 700/550. No dogs. **Rooms 284.** Coffee shop (9am-11pm Mon-Sat). Access, Amex, Visa,

W1 Forte Crest Regent's Park 64% £116

H

Tel 071-388 2300 Fax 071-387 2806

Carburton Street W1P 8EE Map 22 B3

Several categories of accommodation, with much refurbishment recently completed. Conference facilities for up to 650. No dogs. **Rooms 320.** Coffee shop (6.30am-11pm, from 7am Sun) Access, Amex, Visa,

SW1 Forte Crest St James's 68% £116

H

Tel 071-930 2111 Fax 071-839 2125

80 Jermyn Street SW1Y 6JF Map 22 C3

Formerly the Cavendish hotel, built in 1966, conveniently located in the heart of Piccadilly, by the corner of Jermyn Street. Marble floors and modern wood panelling set the tone in the foyer and there's a clubby bar. Bedrooms are to the usual Crest standard (the majority have been recently refurbished), but not large; the Executive 15th floor rooms have a lounge

area and jacuzzi baths. 80-space basement car park. 24hr room and valet
services. Conference facilities for up to 90, banqueting to 75. *Rooms 256.*
Business centre. Access, Amex, Visa,

NW3   Forte Posthouse   65%   £64

H

Tel 071-794 8121   Fax 071-435 5586

215 Haverstock Hill NW3 4RB   Map 20 B3

Close to Belsize Park underground station and a short walk from
Hampstead. Standardised bedrooms, with splendid views from the top-
floor rooms; one floor is being converted into superior rooms. Banqueting
and conference facilities for up to 25. Ample free parking. Brasserie with
outdoor seating. No dogs. *Rooms 138. Access, Amex, Visa,*

W1   47 Park Street   86%   £295

HR

Tel 071-491 7282   Fax 071-491 7281

47 Park Street W1Y 4EB   Map 22 C2

In the heart of Mayfair, a block away from the American Embassy in
Grosvenor Square and close to Hyde Park, this elegant Edwardian town
house offers sumptuous accommodation in its luxuriously appointed and
air-conditioned suites, designed by Monique Roux (the wife of Albert
Roux who oversees his son Michel's cooking in the kitchens at the
celebrated *Le Gavroche* downstairs). Much refurbishment has been
implemented this year, improving the air of graciousness throughout. The
suites comprise one or two bedrooms, an elegant and spacious
lounge/dining area and exquisite bathrooms, are tastefully furnished with
antiques, comfortable sofas and armchairs, beautiful fabrics, many objets
d'art and paintings. All have triple glazing, air-conditioning and fully
equipped kitchens, though these are rarely needed since an extensive 24hr
room service is provided, including continental and English breakfast.
Other services are exemplary, too, from your arrival at the impressive
entrance and oak-panelled lounge to the concierge, business centre (9am-
5pm) and housekeeping: linen sheets and duvets, nightly bed turn-down
and daily changing of fresh flowers. Guests are welcomed with champagne
and bowls of fresh fruit; the triple-glazed rooms have personal safes, private
baths and satellite TV (videos can be installed on request). Bathrooms
provide all the extras that one might expect, including power showers
(some have separate shower rooms) and bathrobes. There are good leisure
facilities (gymnasium, sauna, swimming pool, solarium) a short walk from
Park Street. The third-floor private dining or meeting room (from 8 to 20
people) has a separate lounge; no room charge is made when used as a
dining room. *Rooms 52. Hotel limousine, valeting (8am-5pm), baby-sitting,
hairdressing, shopping service. Access, Amex, Visa,*

Le Gavroche Restaurant   ★★★   £200

Tel 071-408 0881 Fax 071-409 0939

43 Upper Brook Street W1Y 1PF

The low-ceilinged basement setting has a private house intimacy and a
clutter of elegant accoutrements, with flashes of colour from the paintings
breaking up the sea-green card room velours. The digestif trolley and
ceremonial raising of the largest silver cloches in London neatly foster the
illusion of being exiled from reality. The kitchen, under Albert Roux's son
Michel, has discovered more purpose of late and a new incarnation of the
family philosophy is making itself felt. The Gavroche's reputation goes
before it, remaining a superlative restaurant; the weight of the bill (which
is serious) matches the results. Albert Roux's son Michel continues the
traditions set in stone by his father, offering an involved menu of classical
French dishes given the Gavroche touch like *terrine de foie gras d'oie aux
poivres verts, le marmite bretonne, daube de boeuf à la bourgeoise* and *caneton
Gavroche en pot-au-feu.* Michel's personal touch includes *huitres Francine* – a
dish of warm oysters with salmon quenelles, diced cucumber and tomato
and a butter sauce. The main, à la carte menu of Roux classic dishes is
exclusively written in French – *soufflé suissesse, sablé aux fraises, crème de*

cresson, mousseline de homard au champagne, nage de turbotin au Chardonnay –
and has a minimum charge of £50; it is supplemented by daily extras and
a *menu exceptionnel* for a minimum of two diners.

Lunchtime sees an extremely good value fixed-price menu option with
alternative dishes at each course – perhaps *consommé de canard parfumé aux
truffes* or *saucisson de foie gras aux champignons sauvages*, followed by *pavé de
turbot roti au jus de homard* or *fricassée de pintadeau aux olives*; *fromages,
sorbets du jour* or *tarte chibouste chocolat aux abricots* for dessert and coffee
with petits fours to finish the meal. The *menu exceptionel* offers a well-priced
(equal to the cost of around three courses chosen from the carte) six-course,
no-choice menu of delights (perhaps *charlotte d'asperges aux deux caviars*,
followed by *pavé de truite saumonée à la provençale*, then *sorbet à la mandarine
Napoléon* and *supreme de canette aux morilles et sauce madère*; finish with a
plateau de fromages and *tarte aux poires bordaloue*. Staff are constantly
attentive, exuding a smooth professionalism.

Tip-top breads and canapés are all made on the premises and are
exceptional. Spain, California and Italy rate only a brief mention on the
outstanding French wine list with a range of classics that will surely satisfy
every connoisseur (over 800 wines are listed), though most are expensive;
the choice of 70 half bottles, however, can help ease the pocket a little.
Consistently good coffee is accompanied by petits fours that almost give
the wonderful desserts a run for their money! *Seats 60.* Parties 20. Private
Room. L 12-2 D 7-11. Closed Sat & Sun, Bank Holidays, 23 Dec-2 Jan. Set L
£29.50 Set D £59. Access, Amex, Visa, Diners

W2   Four Seasons   £50
Tel 071-229 4320   **R**
84 Queensway W2 3RL   Map 22 C1

In an area thronged with Chinese restaurants, this is one of the most upmarket in terms of both decor and price. Service is friendly and attentive,
and the predominantly Cantonese menu runs the gamut of familiar dishes.
Chef's specialities include shredded beef with crispy rice noodles, stuffed
bean curd in a hotpot and fried prawn cake with vegetables. Lovers of
chicken, prawn and sizzling dishes are particularly well catered for.
Seats 80. Parties 12. Meals 12-11. Closed 25 & 26 Dec. Set D from £10.50.
Access, Amex, Visa, Diners

SW3   Foxtrot Oscar   £50
Tel 081-352 7179   **R**
79 Royal Hospital Road SW3 4HN   Map 23 E2

Popular neighbourhood restaurant offering simple fare – from satay to fish
cakes, omelettes, hamburgers and cottage pie. Long list of cocktails.
Seats 50. Parties 35. L 12.30-2.30 (Sat & Sun to 3.30) D 7.30-11.30. Closed
D Sun, Bank Holidays, 24 Dec-1 Jan. Access, Visa, Diners

N1   Frederick's   £65
Tel 071-359 2888   Fax 071-359 5173   **R**
Camden Passage Islington N1 8EG   Map 20 C1

Smart conservatory restaurant, established in 1969, offering mostly safe,
classical French food on a fortnightly-changing menu: creamy crab soup
laced with cognac, wild rabbit grandmère, paupiettes of sole with smoked
salmon and a dill and prawn sauce, grilled rib steak with Provence herbs
and béarnaise sauce. Non-smoking area. Note early evening opening times
for pre-theatre dinner and drinks. The garden patio opens for outdoor
eating in summer. Some keen prices on the decent wine list. *Seats 140.*
Parties 30. Private Room. L 12-2.30 D 6-11.30. Closed Sun, Bank Holidays.
Set L £14.95 Set D £16.95. Access, Amex, Visa, Diners

W1   Fuji
Tel 071-734 0957

R

36 Brewer Street W1R 3HD   **£70**

Map 22 C3

Well-prepared selection of Japanese standards (yakitori, sushi, sashimi and tempura) served by charming waitresses in rather dark, sombre surroundings. *Seats 50. Parties 16. L 12.30-2.30 D 6-10.30 (Sun to 10.15). Closed L Sun, Bank Holidays, 2 weeks Xmas. Set L from £8.50 Set D from £14. Access, Amex, Visa,*

WC2   Fung Shing   ★
Tel 071-437 1539

R

15 Lisle Street WC2   **£52**

Map 25 A2

In the very top flight of London's Chinese restaurants, Fung Shing presents a relatively well-scrubbed face in a distinctly unkempt Soho Street. Dishes on the long Cantonese-themed menu read fairly similarly to their Chinatown neighbours, but what arrives on the plate is, quite simply, better. Deep-fried oysters in batter, baked quail with chili and salt, stir-fried eel with garlic, venison with yellow bean sauce and stewed belly pork with yam are dishes that continue to please, and in the luxury stakes the chef specials include baked lobster, double-boiled fluffy supreme shark's fin and braised whole abalone with oyster sauce. *Seats 85. Parties 50. Private Room. Meals 12-11.30. Closed 24-26 Dec. Set D from £11. Access, Amex, Visa,*

W1   La Gaulette
Tel 071-580 7608

R

53 Cleveland Street W1P 5PQ   **£65**

Map 22 B3

The ocean blues of the decor complement an exclusively seafood menu on which familiar brill, scallops and sea bass are joined by Indian ocean exotics like parrot fish, red snapper, capitain and vacqua. Sylvain and Shirley Ho Wing Cheong add subtle Mauritian and Eastern spicing to a classical French base: try a feuilleté of lobster and spinach, bouillabaisse, spicy fish casserole mauricienne, king prawns with ginger and spring onion or assiette créole (a selection of tropical fish with tomatoes, chili and herbs). Downstairs is a bistro with the same opening hours and a fixed-price menu (£10.95) offering a good choice of equally fishy dishes. Especially good vintage Armagnacs and Calvados on the short wine list. *Seats 32. Parties 35. Private Room. L 12-3 D 6.30-11.30. Closed L Sat, D Sun, Bank Holidays. Set meals £16.95. Access, Amex, Visa,*

SW15   Gavin's
Tel 081-785 9151

R

5 Lacy Road SW15 1HN   **£35**

Map 21 E3

Just off Putney High Street, sister restaurant to the Depot in Barnes and Ciao in Fulham, serving similar menus of over a dozen fresh pasta and brasserie-style dishes. Lunchtime special (£4.95): pasta, side salad and garlic bread. Sensibly-priced wines. *Seats 80. Parties 25. L 12-3.30 D 6-11.30. Closed Sun before Bank Holiday Mon, 24-27 Dec. Access, Amex, Visa,*

SW1   Gavver's
Tel 071-730 5983

R

61 Lower Sloane Street SW1W 8DH   **£55**

Map 23 E2

Kir, three courses, coffee and petits fours are included in the set price of a dinner at one the Roux brothers' less exalted outlets, and another fiver gets you half a bottle of wine. Chef Pascal Perou copes well with a range of dishes typified by pistachio-studded duck paté, Madeira-sauced chicken vol-au-vents, pan-fried red mullet with stuffed artichoke and sauté of lamb with four different garnishes. 2- or 3-course lunches are simpler, but still offer excellent value. *Seats 65. Parties 65. L 12-2.30 D 7-11. Closed L Sat, all Sun, Bank Holidays. Set L £12.50/£14.75 Set D £22.65. Access, Visa,*

W1   Gay Hussar   £60

Tel 071-437 0973   **R**

2 Greek Street W1V 6NB   Map 25 A1

A Soho institution offering hearty portions of traditional Hungarian food.
Try the chilled wild cherry soup, veal goulash, chicken paprikash or
Transylvanian stuffed cabbage. *Seats 70. Parties 22. Private Room.
L 12.30-2.30 D 5.30-11. Closed Sun, Bank Holidays. Set L from £15. Amex.*

W8   Geale's   £30

Tel 071-727 7969   **R**

2 Farmer Street W8 7SN   Map 21 D3

Behind the Gate cinema stands one of London's oldest and best-loved fish
restaurants. For 52 years they've been serving traditional fish and chips, the
fish cooked in beef dripping, the chips in vegetable fat. English favourites –
from cod to halibut – are joined by more unusual offerings like deep-fried
clams and parrot fish. Nearly always busy, and no bookings, but you can
wait upstairs with a drink for a table. *Seats 100. Private Room. L 12-3
D 6-11. Closed Sun & Mon, Tues after Bank Hol Mons, 2 weeks Xmas,
1 week Easter, 2 weeks Aug. Set L £6.95 (not Sat). Access, Visa.*

WC1   George Hotel   £43

Tel 071-387 8777   Fax 071-383 5044   **H**

58 Cartwright Gardens WC1H 9EL   Map 22 A4

In a crescent near the British Museum, the George and its neighbour the
Euro offer very reasonably priced accommodation, with children up to 13
staying free in parents' room. Unlicensed. No dogs. *Rooms 75. Access, Visa,*
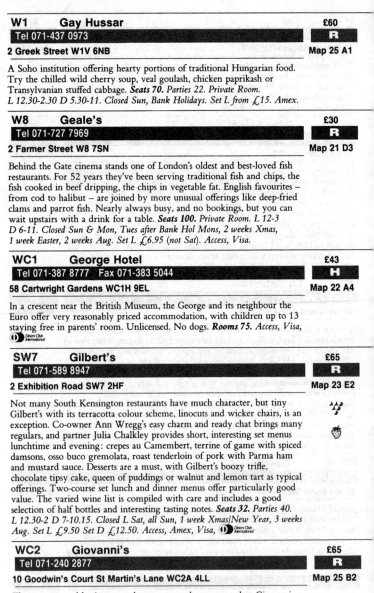 *Diners Club International*

SW7   Gilbert's   £65

Tel 071-589 8947   **R**

2 Exhibition Road SW7 2HF   Map 23 E2

Not many South Kensington restaurants have much character, but tiny
Gilbert's with its terracotta colour scheme, linocuts and wicker chairs, is an
exception. Co-owner Ann Wregg's easy charm and ready chat brings many
regulars, and partner Julia Chalkley provides short, interesting set menus
lunchtime and evening: crepes au Camembert, terrine of game with spiced
damsons, osso buco gremolata, roast tenderloin of pork with Parma ham
and mustard sauce. Desserts are a must, with Gilbert's boozy trifle,
chocolate tipsy cake, queen of puddings or walnut and lemon tart as typical
offerings. Two-course set lunch and dinner menus offer particularly good
value. The varied wine list is compiled with care and includes a good
selection of half bottles and interesting tasting notes. *Seats 32. Parties 40.
L 12.30-2 D 7-10.15. Closed L Sat, all Sun, 1 week Xmas/New Year, 3 weeks
Aug. Set L £9.50 Set D £12.50. Access, Amex, Visa,* Diners Club International

WC2   Giovanni's   £65

Tel 071-240 2877   **R**

10 Goodwin's Court St Martin's Lane WC2A 4LL   Map 25 B2

Theatregoers and business people are among those attracted to Giovanni
Colla's long-established Italian restaurant off St. Martin's Lane. The menu is
familiar Italian, with variations on pasta, meat, poultry and fish dishes.
*Seats 38. Closed L Sat, all Sun, Bank Holidays. L 12.30-2.30, D 6.30-11. 38
seats. Access, Amex, Visa. Parties 10. L 12.30-3 D 6-11.30. Closed L Sat, all
Sun, Bank Holidays. Access, Amex, Visa,* Diners Club International

SW10   Glaister's

£40
R

Tel 071-352 0352

4 Hollywood Road SW10 9HW

Map 23 F1

Restaurant, café-bar and garden. The bistro-style menu flips around the world with dishes like moules marinière, chicken satay, tagliatelle, burgers, beef Wellington and chicken stuffed with Emmenthal on a grain mustard sauce. The three-course, fixed-price menu offers a small choice, perhaps mozzarella crostini on a basil and tomato sauce followed by grilled spatchcocked poussin créole, pudding and coffee. Traditional roast sirloin of beef is served all day on Sundays. *Seats 80. Parties 40. Private Room. L 12.30-4.30 D 7-11.45 (Sun to 10.30). Closed Bank Holidays, 2 weeks Xmas. Set L & D £12.95. Access, Visa.*

SW7   The Gloucester   74%

£170
H

Tel 071-373 6030   Fax 071-373 0409

4 Harrington Gardens SW7 4LH

Map 23 E1

High standards of housekeeping, pleasant staff and good accommodation are among the strengths of this tall modern hotel close to Gloucester Road underground station. A lot of money has recently been spent on 100 Reserve Club bedrooms, with their own lift service, check-in facilities and private lounge area. Even the standard rooms are of a decent size, light, double-glazed and air-conditioned plus all the expected accessories; all rooms have small dressing areas and there is good desk space, plus plenty of shelf space in the tiled bathrooms. Children up to 12 stay free in parents' room. There is an up-to-the-minute business centre and banqueting/conference space for 400. The restaurant serves grill and standard fare, but with a little more style and effort than most. *Rooms 550. News kiosk, coffee shop (6.30am-11.30pm). Access, Amex, Visa,*

WC1   Gonbei

£45
R

Tel 071-278 0619

151 Kings Cross Road WC1X 9BN

Map 22 A4

A mixture of imitation wood, metallic chairs, Japanese lamps and rush-covered benches provides a simple setting for an introduction to Japanese culinary art. Sashimi, beautifully fresh, is fresh with shredded radish and shiso leaf – a puzzling taste from the mint family. Tempura is coated in the lightest, crispest batter. A choice of four speciality dishes based on beef, chicken and fish is prepared at the table. *Seats 26. Parties 24. Private Room. D only 6-10.30. Closed Sun, Bank Holidays, 1 week Aug, 1 week Jan. Set D from £16. Access, Visa,*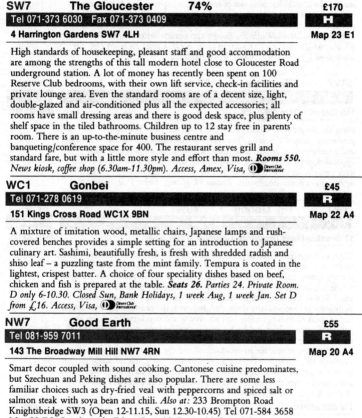

NW7   Good Earth

£55
R

Tel 081-959 7011

143 The Broadway Mill Hill NW7 4RN

Map 20 A4

Smart decor coupled with sound cooking. Cantonese cuisine predominates, but Szechuan and Peking dishes are also popular. There are some less familiar choices such as dry-fried veal with peppercorns and spiced salt or salmon steak with soya bean and chili. *Also at:* 233 Brompton Road Knightsbridge SW3 (Open 12-11.15, Sun 12.30-10.45) Tel 071-584 3658 Map 23 D2. *See also under Esher. Parties 80. Private Room. L 12-2.30 (Sun 12.30-2.45) D 6-11.15 (Sun to 10.45). Closed 24-27 Dec. Set meals from £16.75. Access, Amex, Visa,*

E14   Good Friends

£38
R

Tel 071-987 5541

139 Salmon Lane E14 7PG

Map 24 D2

Little has changed at this 60s' institution. Dishes on the predominantly Cantonese menu can be ordered in any of three sizes (a common exercise in China); a 'small' portion is still adequate for at least four people when combined with other dishes. A few fashionable Peking and Szechuan dishes also appear, but the very best (lobster with ginger and spring onions, stuffed crab claws, whole suckling pig and Peking duck) all require an unnecessarily long two days' notice. **Seats 100.** Parties 100. L 12-4 D 5-11. Closed 24-26 Dec. Set L from £13 Set D from £14. Access, Amex, Visa, ⓪ *Diners Club International*

W1   Gopal's of Soho   £40
Tel 071-434 0840   **R**
12 Bateman Street W1V 5TD   **Map 25 A2**

Head chef and co-owner N P Pittal, known to his friends as Gopal, runs one of the capital's best Indian restaurants. Little is likely to disappoint on a menu which includes some out-of-the-ordinary specialities: king prawns with spring onions, chicken steamed in a sealed pot with Hyderabadi herbs and spices, mutton xacutti (a Goan dish of lamb with coconut, vinegar and "rare spices"). David Wolfe has chosen appropriate wines. **Seats 45.** Parties 65. Private Room. L 12-3 D 6-11.30 (Sun to 11). Closed 25 & 26 Dec. Set meals from £9.75. Access, Amex, Visa, ⓪ *Diners Club International*

SW7   The Gore   65%   £146
Tel 071-584 6601   Fax 071-589 8127   **H**
189 Queen's Gate SW7 5EX   **Map 23 D1**

Near the Royal Albert Hall and Hyde Park, the Gore is a hotel of pleasantly mellow character. The striking bar-lounge has dark green walls and comfortably arranged sofas. Best bedrooms are elegant and well appointed, with small sitting areas; among them is the fine Tudor room, dark and atmospheric. The hotel houses the successful *Bistrot 190* (qv) and a new seafood bistro downstairs. **Rooms 58.** Access, Amex, Visa, ⓪ *Diners Club International*

SW1   The Goring   79%   £190
Tel 071-834 8211   Fax 071-834 4393   **HR**
17 Beeston Place Grosvenor Gardens SW1W 0JW   **Map 23 D1**

Close to Victoria Station and Buckingham Palace, but in an enviably quiet location, a very English hotel in the old style, "loved and nurtured" by the Goring family since it was built in 1910. Behind the impressive Edwardian facade is a high level of service and elegant, busy day rooms that make a good first impression with polished marble, paintings and leather sofas. Bedrooms are individually decorated, but with the unanimously traditional feel of solid furnishings using various woods and comfortable settees. Brass bedsteads often feature and bathrooms are particularly good, mostly fitted out in marble; 24hr room and evening maid turn-down services are offered. Many rooms are air-conditioned and the best have balconies that overlook the manicured Goring garden (which, sadly, has no access for guests); similarly, the Garden lounge and Garden bar have delightful outlooks. Private dining rooms cater for up to 70. **Rooms 82.** Valeting. Access, Amex, Visa, ⓪ *Diners Club International*

Restaurant   £85

A traditionally elegant dining room (with service to match), where chef John Elliott is beginning to make his mark. There's a good choice of dishes on both the table d'hote and à la carte menus, ranging from the classical roast leg of English lamb with onion sauce or braised oxtail to the more modern (mousseline of guinea fowl and sweet pepper with cranberry chutney or baked fillet of salmon with sorrel butter sauce). Desserts come from the trolley. Proprietor George Goring provides laconic comments on the good all-round wine list (which features several classics at fair prices) as well as recommending wines on the daily menu. **Seats 75.** Parties 52. Private Room. L 12.30-2.30 D 6-10. Closed L Sat. Set L £15.50/£18.50 Set D £24.

W1   Grafton Hotel   63%   £160
Tel 071-388 4131   Fax 071-387 7394   **H**

130 Tottenham Court Road W1P 9HP   Map 22 A3

Edwardian Hotels own the Grafton, built in 1908 and still showing some
style of the period. Bedrooms have recently been augmented by nearly
100. Children under 12 stay free in parents' room. The hotel is at the top
end of Tottenham Court Road, not far from Madame Tussaud's and
Regent's Park. *Rooms 323. Access, Amex, Visa,*

SW4   Grafton Français   £65
Tel 071-627 1048   **R**

45 Old Town Clapham Common SW4 0JL   Map 21 E2

Traditional French cooking in Clapham's oldest building. Cream of mussel
soup with saffron, terrine of duck and foie gras with pistachio nuts, breast
of duck with fruity Calvados sauce. *Seats 72. Parties 28. Private Room.*
L 12.30-3 (Sun from 12) D 7.30-11.30. Closed L Sat, D Sun & Mon, Bank
Holidays, 3 weeks Aug, 1 week Xmas. Set L from £12. Access, Amex, Visa,

W1   Grahame's Seafare   £40
Tel 071-437 3788   **R**

38 Poland Street W1V 3DA   Map 22 B3

In clean, simple, green and white surroundings, fish is served deep-fried,
grilled, steamed or cooked in milk and butter, according to the customer's
mood. The deep-fried fish has a light matzo meal crust. Gefilte fish,
chopped herring, egg and onion, borsht, potato latkes and cheese blintzes
have their place on the menu. Service is extremely attentive. The food is
guaranteed kosher. *Seats 86. L 12-2.45 D 5.30-9 (Fri & Sat to 8). Closed*
Sun, Bank Holidays, Jewish New Year. Access, Amex, Visa,

NW1   Great Nepalese   £30
Tel 071-388 6737   **R**

48 Eversholt Street NW1   Map 22 A4

Pork and duck are added to a large variety of more familiar Indian dishes
in a durable restaurant near Euston station. Other out-of-the-ordinary
dishes include black lentils, steam-cooked pastries and a Tibetan dry
vegetable curry. *Seats 50. Parties 35. L 12-2.45 D 6-11.45. Closed 25 & 26*
Dec. Set meals from £9.95. Access, Amex, Visa,

N1   Great Northern Hotel   62%   £93
Tel 071-837 5454   Fax 071-278 5270   **H**

King's Cross N1 9AN   Map 22 A4

Being just moments from both King's Cross and St Pancras stations (with
Euston also nearby), London's first purpose-built hotel, opened in 1854, is a
convenient pausing point for northbound travellers. Accommodation spans
singles, doubles, twins and family rooms, all but ten with en-suite facilities.
Meeting rooms and suites provide conference/function facilities for 100+.
No dogs. *Rooms 89. Closed 25-27 Dec. Access, Amex, Visa,*

NW8   Greek Valley   £40
Tel 071-624 3217   **R**

130 Boundary Road NW8   Map 20 C3

Many of the dishes are taken from the familiar Greek/Cypriot repertoire,
but the cooking at Greek Valley is much above average. Spicy pork or
minced lamb sausages, stuffed vine leaves, kleftiko and grilled baby chicken
are all excellent, and vegetarians have their own versions of moussaka and
souvlaki. Reasonable prices, friendly owners who really put their hearts
into the job, and always a convivial party atmosphere. *Seats 70. Parties 75.*
Private Room. L 12-2.30 D 6-11.30. Closed L Sat, all Sun. Access, Visa.

NW3	**Green Cottage**	£40

Tel 071-722 5305 · **R**

9 New College Parade Finchley Road NW3 5EP · Map 20 B3

A Cantonese restaurant that is seemingly the most popular Chinese
restaurant of the half dozen in the area (*Mr Ke* is nearly next door). Old
favourites like roasted duck and pork, barbecued spare ribs, outstanding
baked crab with ginger and spring onion, steamed fish and stir-fried
everything are all on offer, crispy fragrant duck, dry shredded beef with
chili, stuffed green peppers in gravy and fried beancurd with mushrooms
are also better than average. The adventurous should try soyed mixed
meats (liver, gizzard, squid and duck wings). Unusual vegetarian Zhai
duckling is formed from deep-fried soy bean sheets. *Seats 90. Parties 30.
Meals 12-11. Closed 25-26 Dec. Set D £11.50. Access, Visa.*

W1	**Green Park Hotel**	70%	£163

Tel 071-629 7522   Fax 071-491 8971 · **H**

Half Moon Street W1Y 8BP · Map 22 C3

Half Moon Street is as good an address as Mayfair offers and this Sarova
hotel created from a terrace of Georgian town houses tries hard to combine
old-fashioned values and modern amenities. There are several meeting
rooms (capacity 66), a conservatory and a cocktail bar (the Half Moon)
with intimate alcoves. Grey-wood fitted units furnish the bedrooms, their
marble-floored bathrooms traditionally resplendent with white suites, some
including bidets and spa baths. Children up to 12 stay free in parents'
room. *Rooms 161. Access, Amex, Visa, Diners Club International*

SW11	**The Green Room**	NEW	£50

Tel 071-223 4618 · **R**

62 Lavender Hill SW11 5RQ · Map 21 E2

At the Queenstown Road end of Lavender Hill, an organically and
ecologically sound restaurant that copes creditably with an over-long menu
(from many vegetarian offerings to steaks, snails and sesame salmon).
Unpretentiously comfortable surroundings. *Seats 40. Parties 45. L 12-4
D 7-11.45. Access, Amex, Visa, Diners Club International*

SW1	**Green's Restaurant & Oyster Bar**	£66

Tel 071-930 4566   Fax 071-930 1383 · **R**

36 Duke Street St James's SW1Y 6DF · Map 22 C3

Green's restaurants and Oyster bars represent unashamed tradition, old-
fashioned simplicity and nursery values. The St James's branch is more
horse-racing and champagne, while Marsham Street, on the division bell, is
more political. The menu is pinstripe English: 'Green's Standards' include
native oysters (Sept to Apr), smoked salmon, fish cakes, omelette Arnold
Bennett, bangers and mash, kippers with poached eggs, lamb cutlets and
steaks. Daily menus and special dishes (boiled beef with carrots and
dumplings on Tuesdays) increase the choice considerably. All the meat is
organically produced. Sunday brunch always includes roast Scotch rib of
beef. Concise wine list with good house selections. *Seats 75. Parties 35.
Private Room. L 11.30-3 (Sun 12-3.30) D 5.30-11. Closed D Sun, 25 & 26
Dec, 1 Jan. Access, Amex, Visa, Diners Club International*
Also at: Marsham Court, Marsham Street SW1 Tel 071-834 9552 Map 23
E4. *Closed all Sat & L Sun.*

W1   Greenhouse   ★   £80

| Tel 071-499 3331 | R |

27a Hays Mews W1X 7RJ   Map 22 C3

One of the most attractive approaches to a London restaurant – a paved,
plant-filled courtyard with a trellised canopy leading to the front entrance.
Inside, the decor is all creams and beiges, the dining chairs a merry
mixture. Empty, the impression might be of a country house dining room
with its richly patterned carpets and walls covered with flower paintings.
But empty it never is, for this is one of the capital's most fashionable eating
spots, and one of the liveliest – the floor of the Stock Exchange can rarely
be noisier than the Greenhouse at full throttle. Gary Rhodes is the man at
the helm in the kitchen, a young champion of hearty British cooking, the
man who gave faggots back their dignity. His faggots, brawny but elegant
enough for the Mayfair set, are a signature dish, along with oxtail, salmon
fish cakes and boiled bacon with parsley sauce. Some dishes are further
from the English mainstream, such as beef carpaccio with Parmesan, or
grilled sea bass with noodles and ratatouille sauce. The kitchen feeds a lot
of mouths both lunchtime and evening, and not everything is always up to
the mark, either in execution or in the balance of flavours. Service, too,
will find its critics in those who prefer the personal touch. But on a good
day the Greenhouse takes a lot of beating for its combination of sustaining
food and atmospheric setting. The small selection of wines, though
carefully chosen and reasonably priced, doesn't quite do justice to the
generally superior cooking. *Seats 100. Parties 16. L 12-2.30 (Sun to 3)
D 7-11. Closed L Sat, D Sun, Bank Holidays. Access, Amex, Visa.*

SW3   Grill St Quentin   £55

| Tel 071-581 8377   Fax 071-584 6064 | R |

2 Yeoman's Row SW3 2AL   Map 23 D2

Large, bright basement restaurant in the style of a classic Parisian brasserie.
The chargrill provides most of the main courses, which are served with
very good chips. Oysters, neatly composed salads, fish soup and goose paté
among the starters, excellent pastries and desserts from Patisserie St
Quentin. Dependable cooking, realistic prices and agreeable service from
young French staff make this a splendid place for a luxury snack or a
leisurely full meal. *Seats 140. Parties 40. Meals noon-midnight. Closed Sun,
1 week Xmas. Set L £12.50. Access, Amex, Visa,*

W1   Grosvenor House   83%   £219

| Tel 071-499 6363   Fax 071-493 3341 | H |

90 Park Lane W1A 3AA   Map 22 D2

Last summer saw the completion of a major refurbishment programme at
the Grosvenor House. Built in 1929 on the site of old Grosvenor House,
home of the Duke of Westminster. Some of the most spacious day rooms
in London are to be found at Grosvenor House. The vast lounge has
recently been refurbished and the elegant, intimate bar has a Japanese
theme; there's also a stylish café with views over Hyde Park. All bedrooms
have a lobby and even single rooms have double beds. Solid furniture and
soft colours please the eye and the bathrooms are splendid, with marble
floors and excellent toiletries. The fifth floor is the Crown Club, with
separate executive check-in and a small lounge and boardroom for
executive guests only. Space, comfort, service and state-of-the-art facilities
for business people and conference organisers (up to 1500 delegates theatre-
style). The main restaurant is now Nico Ladenis's new flagship – see entry
under Nico at Ninety. No dogs. Forte Exclusive. *Rooms 454. Indoor
swimming pool, sauna, solarium, spa bath, gymnasium, beauty & hair salon,
valeting, coffee shop (6.30am-10pm). Access, Amex, Visa,*

SW1   Grosvenor Thistle Hotel   64%   £138
`Tel 071-834 9494   Fax 071-630 1978`   **H**

101 Buckingham Palace Road SW1W 0SJ   Map 23 D3

Built in the 1850s, the Grosvenor Thistle still boasts some handsome
Victorian touches, notably in the splendid foyer with pillars and fine tile
work. The stylish Harvard Bar has mahogany panelling, mottled green
walls and brown leather sofas. Bedrooms are spacious, with a sitting area
and desk space, and bathrooms, too, are more than adequate in size.
Banqueting/conference facilities for 150/200. Direct access from Victoria
railway station. Children up to 12 stay free in parents' room. No dogs.
24hr lounge service. *Rooms 366. Access, Amex, Visa,* (Ⅰ)Diners Club

W11   The Halcyon   79%   £260
`Tel 071-727 7288   Fax 071-229 8516`   **HR**

81 Holland Park W11 3RZ   Map 21 D3

The conversion of two Victorian town houses on the corner of Holland
Park Avenue and Holland Park has been done most sympathetically,
leaving not only lovely architectural features like ornate plaster cornices
and fireplaces, but also the original proportions. Needless to say, the
preserved period charm is enhanced by quality antiques. The
accommodation varies from quite opulent suites (the best has its own
conservatory) to single bedrooms that are modest but attractive. Marble
bathrooms, whirlpool baths, bidets and night safes are added luxuries.
Residents have temporary membership to the exclusive, and expensive,
Vanderbilt tennis club close by. An elegant, homely hotel with panache.
Rooms 43. Access, Amex, Visa, (Ⅰ)Diners Club

Restaurant   £70

The views of an ornamental garden and patio through the large French
windows are reflected by a garden theme in the decor with a green theme,
trellis work, murals and large French windows. The accent is on
informality with contemporary cooking competently handled. Sunday
brunch (£18.25) served from midday to 4pm. *Seats 80. Private Room.
L 12-2.30 D 7-11.*

W2   Halepi   £50
`Tel 071-262 1070`   **R**

18 Leinster Terrace W2 3ET   Map 22 C1

Greek favourites, including dips, salads, charcoal grills, afelia and moussaka,
are served throughout the day in one of London's most cheerful and
bustling tavernas. Meze at £14 a head is a popular choice that should
satisfy the hungriest customer. *Seats 68. Meals Noon-12.30am. Closed 25 &
26 Dec. Set L £10. Access, Amex, Visa,* (Ⅰ)Diners Club

SW1   Halkin Hotel   86%   £237
`Tel 071-333 1000   Fax 071-333 1100`   **HR**

5 Halkin Street SW1X 7DJ   Map 22 D3

Set in a peaceful side street, between the rear of Buckingham Palace and
Belgrave Square, the neo-Georgian facade of this modern, five-storey
purpose-built luxury hotel blends happily with surrounding Belgravia, in
contrast with the interior which is strikingly contemporary Italian in style.
The marble terrazzo and mosaic floor of the lobby takes its design from
Michelangelo's Campidoglio piazza in Rome and smart staff uniforms were
designed by Giorgio Armani. Public areas are rather limited in extent with
a few sofas and blue leather seating around coffee tables in the lobby
serving as both lounge and bar. In curved bedroom corridors doors merge
imperceptibly into black-ribbed panelling and, while the bedrooms all
share a similar style, each floor has a subtly different colour scheme based
on the Elements: earth, fire and water. Beautiful wood-veneer panelling
blends with glass and marble surfaces and clever use is made of mirrors,

adding a feeling of spaciousness. The occasional antique-style Korean chest or small Oriental statuette only serves to point up the essentially modernist style. Bathrooms, in coloured marble to match the room colour scheme, are particularly stunning and luxurious. With the business person very much in mind, the state-of-the-art technology not only includes touch-activated panels to control lights and air-conditioning but two telephone lines with three phones (all with speaker and conference-call facilities) and a direct-line fax machine in each room. Push-button butler service, room safes, mini-bars and video recorders are all provided in every room. A strikingly different hotel concept, bearing all the hallmarks of the very best in contemporary Italian design from Laboratorio Associati in Milan. Only the lack of any real public rooms holds our grading back from being one of the highest in London. Private meeting room for up to 30. *Rooms 41.* *Access, Amex, Visa,* ⓘ Diners Club International

Gualtiero Marchesi ★ ↑ £100

A cool, modern, ultra-chic restaurant whose Roman arched windows overlook a wild, verdant garden complete with wooden pagoda. Tables are well spaced, fashionably set with a single flower; lighting is by recessed halogen spots. Gualtiero Marchesi comes over from his eponymous Milan restaurant every few weeks and chef Stefano Cavallini, who worked with him there, offers a menu that's largely Milan-inspired. True to current trends in Italian cooking the emphasis is on the use of top-quality ingredients treated with deliberate simplicity, an exercise in manipulating peasant food to create highly sophisticated dishes. Wild boar is prepared here as bresaola – sliced paper-thin on a bed of rocket and liberally sprinkled with finely sliced artichoke and shavings of Reggiano Parmesan, the whole dribbled with Oneglia Imperia olive oil. Classics from the Milan menu include saffron risotto (adorned with a square of gold leaf) and veal cutlet in breadcrumbs. The simple approach is epitomised in a superb dish of fillets of red mullet, lightly pan-fried and accompanied by a mixture of puréed and chopped fresh plum tomatoes and strips of basil. Desserts such as chocolate bombe with a delicate apricot purée provide a magnificent end to a fine meal served by staff who are as well trained as they are well dressed. Service is included in all menu prices – viva! There are almost no half bottles on a wine list which is predominantly Italian, backed up by some expensive French bottles. *Seats 50. Parties 30. Private Room.* L 12.30-2.30 D 7.30-11. Closed Sun. Set L £16.50 Set D £24.50/£28.50.

WC2	Hampshire Hotel	77%	£230
Tel 071-839 9399 Fax 071-930 8122			**H**
31 Leicester Square WC2 7LH			Map 25 A3

There's no site more central than Leicester Square, and the Hampshire offers a pristine haven to overnight guests. It retains the solidity of an ex-Royal Dental Hospital with none of the anguish. Both finish and fittings are impressive. An overall Oriental theme is embellished with redwood panelling, hand-woven Thai carpets and Chinese furnishings, although low ceilings give a confined air to public areas. Afternoon tea is served in the intimate drawing room decorated with cosy sofas and low tables around a fireplace; Celebrities Bar is smart but creates an impression of enforced cosiness. Accommodation ranges from standard bedrooms to studios and suites. All are spacious and well appointed, with attractive (yet compact) bathrooms lined with Sicilian marble and mahogany. Conference and banqueting facilities for up to 120; the Penthouse conference room has views over Trafalgar Square and Westminster. No dogs. Chef Colin Button's "food from heart" in Celebrities Restaurant doesn't match the standards set in other parts of the hotel. Edwardian Hotels. *Rooms 124.* *Business centre, Oscars wine bar. Access, Amex, Visa,* ⓘ Diners Club International

SW17   Harveys   ★★★   £150
Tel 081-672 0114   R
2 Bellevue Road SW17 7EG   Map 21 F2

An apposite quote from Oscar Wilde is printed on Harveys menu: "To get
into society nowadays, one has either to feed people, amuse people or shock
people". Marco, of course, famously does all three, but it's the first that
brings diners on a culinary pilgrimage to his stylish restaurant facing
Wandsworth Common. He continues to develop and introduce new dishes,
among them the sensational sea bass with caviar (this one attracts a hefty
£25 supplement). Others have become classics, including braised pig's
trotter (originally Pierre Koffmann's classic), Bresse pigeon with braised
cabbage, ravioli of wild mushrooms, confit of garlic and thyme jus and an
unrivalled tarte tatin. The supercharged Marco handles the finest (often
luxury) raw materials with complete assurance, putting his personal stamp
on remarkable dishes which are at once elaborate (hard work)and
straightforward. A perfect example is galette of red mullet with
langoustines, deep-fried leeks, salad of herbs, pomme fondant and white
truffle oil. Lunchtime's set menu is rather simpler in concept, with dishes
like scrambled eggs with wild mushrooms and roast rump of lamb with
Provençal vegetables. His new venture, a 'canteen' at Chelsea Harbour, was
due to open after we went to press. If it causes as many waves as Harveys,
Chelsea could well and truly be in the flood danger zone. *Seats 44. Parties
20. L 12.30-2.15 D 7.30-11.15. Closed D Sun, all Mon, Bank Holidays,
2 weeks Aug/Sep, 2 weeks Xmas. Access, Amex, Visa.*

SW10   Harveys Café   NEW   £30
Tel 071-352 0625   R
The Black Bull 358 Fulham Road SW10 9UU   Map 23 F1

A bright restaurant above the the *Black Bull* pub (on the corner next to
Wilds restaurant), with huge modern paintings on the walls and simple
decor in Mediterranean blue and pine. Chef Harvey Smallbrook prepares a
regularly changing menu of Mediterranean and Californian-inspired dishes:
red pepper soup, bruschetta with aubergine compote, cassoulet with duck
confit, fresh pasta with mixed wild mushrooms are typical dishes. Pizzas
come with interesting toppings like walnut and blue cheese or smoked
salmon with Boursin and salmon caviar. Modern food, friendly prices.
*Seats 60. Parties 35. L 12-3 D 7.30-11. Closed D Sun, all Mon, Bank
Holidays, Aug, 1 week Xmas. Set L £6.95. No credit cards.*

NW1   Hellas   £30
Tel 071-267 8110   R
158 Royal College Street NW1 0TA   Map 20 C2

Good Greek food at very reasonable prices, with a larger-than-usual menu.
Chef's specialities include kioftedes (minced lamb grilled or skewered) and
chicken grill. *Seats 60. Parties 60. L 12-3 D 6-12. Closed L Sat, all Sun,
Bank Holidays. Access, Amex, Visa,* Diners Club International

NW4   Hendon Hall   63%   £105
Tel 081-203 3341   Fax 081-203 9709   H
Ashley Lane NW4 1HE   Map 20 A3

Once the home of actor/manager David Garrick, this is now a comfortably
modernised hotel catering for private guests, banquets and conferences (up
to 300). Near A1 and M1, but the setting is peaceful. No dogs. Mount
Charlotte Thistle. *Rooms 52. Garden. Access, Amex, Visa,* Diners Club International

| SW7 | **Hilaire** | ★↑ | £95 |

Tel 071-584 8993

R

68 Old Brompton Road SW7 3LQ

Map 23 E1

British and French influences combine in Bryan Webb's kitchen to make
Hilaire a very good restaurant indeed. There's no hint of fussiness or even
elaboration in the cooking, and service is in keeping – smart, relaxed and
never pushy. Flavours are very much to the fore in well-conceived dishes
like crispy crab pancake with Thai dip, oysters au gratin with laverbread
and Stilton, roast guinea fowl with wild mushrooms or fillet steak au
poivre. Rhubarb sorbet, gratin of summer fruits and crème brulée keep
things simple through to the sweets. The restaurant is at ground level and
in the basement. A sensible wine list presented by style and price, with
plenty of good drinking under £20. *Seats 40. Parties 30. Private Room.
L 12.30-2.30 D 7-11.30. Closed L Sat, all Sun, Bank Holidays, 1 week Xmas,
1 week Easter,2 weeks Aug.Set L £20 Set D £26.50.Access,Amex,Visa,*

| W11 | **Hilton International Kensington** | 67% | £180 |

Tel 071-603 3355   Fax 071-602 9397

HR

179 Holland Park Avenue W11 4UL

Map 21 D3

Large, busy, modern hotel next to Shepherds Bush roundabout. The
Executive Floor has superior bedrooms and business facilities. The coffee
shop is open 24 hours every day of the week. Banqueting and conference
amenities for up to 250. *Rooms 603. Car hire desk, news kiosk, beauty and
hair salons. Access, Amex, Visa,*

Hiroko Restaurant   £80

Smartly clad staff are on hand to give advice in a high-quality Japanese
restaurant reached either from the street or through the hotel. Cooking and
presentation are both of a high standard, and the menu spans a wide range,
including all the familiar dishes plus specialities such as sankaiyaki (beef,
pork, chicken, prawns, scallops, oysters and vegetables cooked at the table
and served with a soy-flavour sauce) or queen roll, with prawns, cucumber
and mayonnaise. *Seats 76. Parties 20. L 12-2.15 D 6-10.15. Closed Mon.
Set L from £15 Set D from £30.*

| W14 | **Hilton International Olympia** | 66% | £157 |

Tel 071-603 3333   Fax 071-603 4846

H

380 Kensington High Street W14 8NL

Map 21 D3

The closest hotel to the Olympia exhibition halls, a busy conference and
tour group hotel with a choice of standard or superior Plaza rooms. New
air-conditioning system in all rooms. *Rooms 406. Coffee shop
(7am-10.30pm, 7 days). Access, Amex, Visa,*

| NW8 | **Hilton International Regent's Park** | 73% | £148 |

Tel 081-722 7722   Fax 081-483 2408

HR

18 Lodge Road St John's Wood NW8 7JT

Map 22 A2

Close to London Zoo and Lord's cricket ground, this Hilton International
numbers free parking and 24hr room service among its facilities. There are
three restaurants (one Japanese, one modelled on a New York deli), a
lounge bar with nightly music, a well-equipped business centre and several
conference suites catering for up to 150 delegates. Bedrooms, some with
balconies, include Executive rooms and three-bedded rooms for family
occupation. High-pressure showers are a good feature. No dogs.
Rooms 377. Coffee shop (8.30am-11.45pm). Access, Amex, Visa,

Kashi Noki Restaurant   £70

Sister restaurant to Hiroko (at the Hilton International Kensington),
offering classic Japanese food, from a long sushi list (cuttlefish, sea urchin,
sea eel, surf and giant clams, mackerel, tuna, salmon roe...) to beef teriyaki
and shabu shabu. Unusual red bean, green tea and chestnut ice creams.

Choice of à la carte and interesting set menus. **Seats 42.** Parties 10. L 12-2
D 6-10. Closed Mon, 25 & 26 Dec, 1-3 Jan. Set L from £14 Set D from
£29.

W1	L'Hippocampe ↑	£75
Tel 071-734 4545		**R**
63 Frith Street W1V 5TA		Map 25 A2

All the seaside colours are here in a witty amalgam – sea green, sea blue,
sand, even the surf with the sparkling white tablecloths. Fish is the main
medium in Pierre Condou's specialist restaurant, with only an occasional
meat dish muscling in on the menu. Produce is gleaned from many sources
– Billingsgate, the West Country, oysters from Brittany, langoustines from
Scotland, bouillabaisse fish from the Mediterranean – and plenty of care
goes into both the recipes and the presentation. Recent highlights include
deep-fried crab pakora with lemon and cucumber yoghurt, roast zander on
bacon choucroute with a red wine sauce and blackened turbot served with
herb and vegetable polenta. Set dinner (the same as the set lunch) is only
served pre-theatre. **Seats 45.** Parties 15. L 12-2.30 D 6.15-11.15. Closed
L Sat, all Sun, Bank Holidays, 1 week Xmas. Set meals from £17.50.
Access, Amex, Visa, **Diners Club International**

SW5	Hogarth Hotel	59%	£92
Tel 071-370 6831 Fax 071-373 6179			**H**
Hogarth Road SW5 0QQ			Map 23 E1

Recent refurbishment has improved the bedrooms at a 20-year-old,
privately-owned tourist hotel close to Earls Court and Olympia. Book in
advance for a space in the basement car park. Families are well catered for,
with children up to 16 accommodated free in parents' room. **Rooms 86.**
Access, Amex, Visa, **Diners Club International**

SW7	Holiday Inn Kensington	68%	£160
Tel 071-373 2222 Fax 071-373 0559			**H**
94-106 Cromwell Road SW7 4ER			Map 23 E1

Right on Cromwell Road, opposite Gloucester Road underground station,
a stylishly modern hotel behind an Edwardian facade with double or triple
glazing for all bedrooms. There's one floor each of Executive and non-
smoking rooms, plus 19 Duplex suites with spiral staircases leading up to
their bedroom areas. Restaurant, café-bar, 24hr lounge service. Versatile
conference and meeting facilities. **Rooms 162.** Sauna, spa bath, steam room,
keep-fit equipment. Access, Amex, Visa, **Diners Club International**

WC1	Holiday Inn Kings Cross/Bloomsbury	69% NEW	£130
Tel 071-833 3900 Fax 071-917 6163			**H**
1 Kings Cross Road WC1X 9DF			Map 22 A4

The capital's newest Holiday Inn, just around the corner from Kings Cross
station. A large floral display takes pride of place in the cool (the whole
hotel is air-conditioned), marble-floored lobby and the lounge, decorated in
autumnal shades, is restful with plenty of deep settees and armchairs.
Bedrooms have all the Holiday Inn hallmarks: large beds (even single
rooms get double beds), open clothes-hanging space and powerful showers
over short tubs in the bathrooms. Extensive room service can run to a
choice of hot dishes around the clock. Conference-room facilities for up to
250. Children under 19 stay free in parents' room. Very limited parking.
Unusually, the leisure facilities include a squash court. **Rooms 405.** Indoor
swimming pool, steam room, spa bath, sauna, solarium, beauty & hair salon,
squash, gymnasium. Access, Amex, Visa, **Diners Club International**

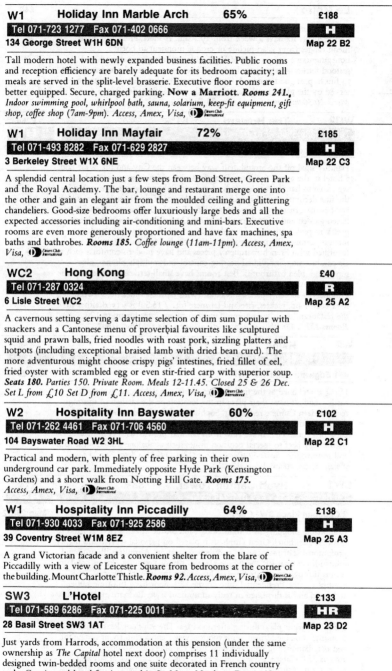

| W1 | **Holiday Inn Marble Arch** | 65% | £188 |

Tel 071-723 1277   Fax 071-402 0666

H

134 George Street W1H 6DN

Map 22 B2

Tall modern hotel with newly expanded business facilities. Public rooms and reception efficiency are barely adequate for its bedroom capacity; all meals are served in the split-level brasserie. Executive floor rooms are better equipped. Secure, charged parking. **Now a Marriott.** *Rooms 241., Indoor swimming pool, whirlpool bath, sauna, solarium, keep-fit equipment, gift shop, coffee shop (7am-9pm). Access, Amex, Visa,* Diners Club International

| W1 | **Holiday Inn Mayfair** | 72% | £185 |

Tel 071-493 8282   Fax 071-629 2827

H

3 Berkeley Street W1X 6NE

Map 22 C3

A splendid central location just a few steps from Bond Street, Green Park and the Royal Academy. The bar, lounge and restaurant merge one into the other and gain an elegant air from the moulded ceiling and glittering chandeliers. Good-size bedrooms offer luxuriously large beds and all the expected accessories including air-conditioning and mini-bars. Executive rooms are even more generously proportioned and have fax machines, spa baths and bathrobes. **Rooms 185.** *Coffee lounge (11am-11pm). Access, Amex, Visa,* Diners Club International

| WC2 | **Hong Kong** | | £40 |

Tel 071-287 0324

R

6 Lisle Street WC2

Map 25 A2

A cavernous setting serving a daytime selection of dim sum popular with snackers and a Cantonese menu of proverbial favourites like sculptured squid and prawn balls, fried noodles with roast pork, sizzling platters and hotpots (including exceptional braised lamb with dried bean curd). The more adventurous might choose crispy pigs' intestines, fried fillet of eel, fried oyster with scrambled egg or even stir-fried carp with superior soup. *Seats 180. Parties 150. Private Room. Meals 12-11.45. Closed 25 & 26 Dec. Set L from £10 Set D from £11. Access, Amex, Visa,* Diners Club International

| W2 | **Hospitality Inn Bayswater** | 60% | £102 |

Tel 071-262 4461   Fax 071-706 4560

H

104 Bayswater Road W2 3HL

Map 22 C1

Practical and modern, with plenty of free parking in their own underground car park. Immediately opposite Hyde Park (Kensington Gardens) and a short walk from Notting Hill Gate. **Rooms 175.** *Access, Amex, Visa,* Diners Club International

| W1 | **Hospitality Inn Piccadilly** | 64% | £138 |

Tel 071-930 4033   Fax 071-925 2586

H

39 Coventry Street W1M 8EZ

Map 25 A3

A grand Victorian facade and a convenient shelter from the blare of Piccadilly with a view of Leicester Square from bedrooms at the corner of the building. Mount Charlotte Thistle. **Rooms 92.** *Access, Amex, Visa,* Diners Club International

| SW3 | **L'Hotel** | | £133 |

Tel 071-589 6286   Fax 071-225 0011

HR

28 Basil Street SW3 1AT

Map 23 D2

Just yards from Harrods, accommodation at this pension (under the same ownership as *The Capital* hotel next door) comprises 11 individually designed twin-bedded rooms and one suite decorated in French country style. Continental breakfast is served in *Le Metro*. No dogs. **Rooms 12.** *Access, Amex, Visa,* Diners Club International

Le Metro   £40

A bistro-cum-wine bar in the basement of the building serving food to
non-residents six days a week from 10.30am. A short, French-inspired
menu ranges from salad niçoise or croque monsieur to boeuf
bourguignonne and navarin of lamb, although bangers and mash and
seafood fettuccine also get a look in. Chocolate mousse cake and apple tart
to finish, plus good coffee. A Cruover machine allow fine wines to be
served by the glass; bottles are also fairly priced. *Seats 50. Parties 6.*
Meals 10.30am-11pm. Closed Sun, 25 & 26 Dec.

WC2   The Howard   81%   £254
Tel 071-836 3555   Fax 071-379 4547   H

Temple Place Strand WC2R 2PR   Map 24 A2

Handily sited off the Strand, half way between the City and the West End,
a hotel in the grand tradition. Reception staff and porterage are first-rate,
well able to handle the demands of visitors. Public areas are dominated by
the fine decorations and Italian marble columns of the foyer-lounge, which
typifies the ornate tone throughout. The Temple Bar has views over the
tiered garden and leads through into the Quai d'Or restaurant; both are
pretty in pink with ruched window drapes, plush green chairs and
intricate ceilings. Bedrooms are mainly twin-bedded and classically
furnished with French marquetry pieces and have modern comforts such as
air-conditioning, individual heating control and multiple phones, plus
superb marbled bathrooms. Best rooms have small terraces with panoramic
views over the river Thames – from St Paul's to Westminster. No dogs.
Uniquely, a special Japanese breakfast (with Japanese omelette, seaweed,
soya bean soup, pickles, rice and Japanese tea: £15.50) is served either in
the restaurant or in your room. Function rooms cater for up to 120.
Rooms 137. 24hr lobby service, valeting. Access, Amex, Visa, ①💳 *Diners Club International*

W2   Hsing   £50
Tel 071-402 0904   R

451 Edgware Road W2 1TH   Map 22 A1

Hsing is reckoned as the five essences of life – metal, wood, water, fire,
earth – and all have their place in the location or the kitchen of this high-
tech modern Chinese restaurant. Sophisticated food and stylish, friendly
service are the order of the day, and the booklet-style menu represents most
parts of China. The choice runs from familiar prawns with chili or deep-
fried crispy beef to special occasion dishes such as abalone stuffed with ham
and mushrooms. *Seats 60. Parties 12. L 12-3 D 6-11. Closed Sun, 3 days*
Xmas. Access, Amex, Visa, ①💳 *Diners Club International*

SW1   Hyatt Carlton Tower   88%   £245
Tel 071-235 5411   Fax 071-245 6570   HR

2 Cadogan Place SW1X 9PY   Map 23 D2

Fashionable shopping in Knightsbridge and Sloane Street is close at hand to
this first-class hotel. Great emphasis is placed on personal service and highly
professional staff maintain an excellent reputation. A multi-million pound
refurbishment has left the whole place in tip-top condition. From standard
rooms through to the spacious de luxe suites the level of decor is
exemplary; the Presidential suite on the 18th floor has a full-time butler
and maid and is furnished in truly sumptuous style. Beds are extravagantly
large and furnishings lavish and luxurious. The gracious Chinoiserie lounge
still holds its place as one of *the* London venues for exchanging smart
gossip; a harpist plays during afternoon tea. The 9th-floor Peak health club
is another notable feature, with rooftop views and a club room restaurant
and bar. Banqueting/conference facilities for 300/150. No dogs.
Rooms 224. Garden, gymnasium, sauna, steam bath, solarium, beauty and hair
salon, tennis, valeting, Chinoiserie (7am-11pm). Access, Amex, Visa, ①💳 *Diners Club International*

Chelsea Room   ↑   £110

A luxurious restaurant with limed-wood panelling and abundant greenery
in a conservatory overlooking Cadogan Gardens. Jean Quéro, manager for
30 years, has now moved elsewhere, but Bernard Gaume still holds
the reins in the kitchen. His classic cooking skills and sense of adventure are
well illustrated by specialities (denoted by a toque on the menu) such as
warm crab sausages with a mustard and chervil sauce, celeriac lasagne with
lobster, fillets of duck topped with duck liver served on a polenta pancake,
and two fillets of beef with shallot and bordelaise sauces. The second
restaurant is the club-like Rib Room, renowned for traditional roasts and
English fare. *Seats 60. Parties 40. Private Room. L 12.30-2.45 D 7-10.45
(Sun to 10). Set L £21.50 Set D £29.50.*

SW1   Hyde Park Hotel   82%   £253
Tel 071-235 2000   Fax 071-235 4552   **H**
66 Knightsbridge SW1Y 7LA   Map 23 D2

Commanding an unrivalled position in Knightsbridge, opposite Harvey
Nichols department store, with a suitably imposing Edwardian frontage
and interior to match. The reception foyer and central lobby are
particularly impressive, with marble walls and floors of eight different
colours, pilasters with Corinthian capitals picked out in gold, ornate
ceilings and glittering chandeliers. The Park Room lounge, with a discreet
bar in the corner, is elegantly comfortable, and there's a panelled bar.
Bedrooms are individually and charmingly decorated, with quality
matching fabrics, traditional polished wood furniture and good armchairs
and settees; bathrooms have loudspeaker extensions, telephones and bidets.
Service is good, with numerous smart and attentive staff. 19 elegant suites
are decorated with antiques and overlook the Serpentine in Hyde Park.
Valet parking. A new fitness centre is on line to open as we went to press.
Function and banqueting rooms cater for up to 250. Forte Exclusive.
Rooms 185. Valeting. Access, Amex, Visa, Diners Club International

---

SW10   I Sardi   NEW   £50
Tel 071-352 7534   **R**
112 Cheyne Walk SW10   Map 23 F1

Ignore the rather unprepossessing exterior and inside you will find a clean
and light room with white-tiled floors, lightwood furniture and crisp
white linen. Sardinia is the main influence and the menu is written in the
Latin-like language of that country with English translations. The
refinement shown in the new wave of Italian restaurants is not in evidence
here, merely generous portions and robust Italian dishes with an emphasis
on fish. Fresh pasta with grated grey mullet roe (bottarga), broad beans

with pancetta and onions, spaghettini with fresh clams, cassoba mediterranea (fish stew with tomato, garlic and chili), fresh tuna with onions and olives, calf's liver with sage, wild boar chops in red wine and herbs, deep-fried sand eels, smoked swordfish, cuttlefish, turbot and more. The cover charge brings crisp, paper-thin mazzamuru Sardinian bread with marinated olives and ciabatta throughout the meal. The dessert trolley still holds sway here, staggering under the weight of tiramisu, caramelised oranges, fresh figs and sebadas (pastry encasing cheese and drizzled with honey, the whole with a hint of lemon). Nearly 30 Sardinian wines on the list. Tables in a trellised garden during good weather. *Seats 100. Parties 25. L 12-2.45 D 7-11.45. Closed Bank Holidays. Access, Amex, Visa,* (**DC**) *Diners Club International*

W1 **Ikeda**	£100
Tel 071-629 2730	**R**
30 Brook Street W1Y 1AG	Map 22 C3

Traditional Japanese cooking in a popular little West End restaurant. A place at the bar gets you a ringside seat to the sushi show, while the tables are all close enough to the kitchen to make you feel part of the action. The daily-changing chef's specials are the choice of many, or you can venture round an à la carte selection that runs from salmon roe with grated white radish or crab meat with fermented rice and soya bean paste to chicken yakitori (grilled on skewers) and assorted tempura and sushi. *Seats 30. Parties 10. Private Room. L 12.30-2.30 D 6.30-10.30 (Sat 6-10). Closed L Sat, all Sun, Bank Holidays. Set L from £12 Set D from £30. Access, Amex, Visa,* (**DC**) *Diners Club International*

W1 **Ikkyu**	£50
Tel 071-636 9280	**R**
67a Tottenham Court Road W1	Map 22 B3

Busy basement Japanese restaurant by Goodge Street underground station offering fine home-style cooking (robatayaki) including yakitori, sushi, grilled fish and pot dishes. Finish off with fresh fruit. *Seats 65. Parties 30. Private Room. L 12.30-2.30 D 6-11. Closed L Sun, all Sat, 10 days Xmas. Set L from £6 Set D from £8. Access, Amex, Visa,* (**DC**) *Diners Club International*

SW1 **L'Incontro**	£100
Tel 071-730 3663 Fax 071-730 5062	**R**
87 Pimlico Road SW1 8PH	Map 23 E3

Venetian dishes feature on the menu at this stylishly modern, up-market Italian restaurant in the same stable as *Santini*. Some typical dishes: tagliolini in a fresh crab sauce, grilled langoustines with lime, roast quail with polenta and wild mushrooms, entrecote with radicchio. Pranzo (lunch) is an altogether lighter affair with a short list of simpler dishes (bresaola, risotto, daily fish with polenta). Some expensive clarets accompany mostly Italian bottles on the good wine list. *Seats 65. Parties 30. Private Room. L 12.30-2.30 D 7-11.30 (Sun to 10.30). Closed L Sun, Bank Holidays. Access, Amex, Visa,* (**DC**) *Diners Club International*

W1 **Inn on the Park Hotel** 89%	£272
Tel 071-499 0888 Fax 071-493 6629	**HR**
Hamilton Place Park Lane W1A 1AZ	Map 22 C3

The bland modernity of a purpose-built high-rise block belies the elegant, individual interior of this luxurious hotel. This is grandness on a modern scale: marble floors, lush plant and flower displays and smartly liveried porters set the tone in the spacious foyer and the chandeliered lounge and panelled bar live up to expectations. The superb bedrooms are large and are decorated in the same quiet good taste as the public areas. All have writing bureaux, numerous telephones, sofas, huge beds, video players, teletext and Reuters; robes and thick towels in the bathrooms. Conservatory rooms are the best, offering glazed, plant-filled sitting areas off the bedrooms; the 27 suites are quite outstanding and even include humidifiers and stereo systems. Children up to 18 stay free in parents' room; baby-listening and baby-sitting service available. Two bedrooms have been specially adapted for disabled guests. Tea is served in the Lobby Lounge to the strains of piano or harp music. Banqueting facilities for up to 400, theatre-style conferences of up to 500 delegates. The Pine Room, featuring original carved panels from the 18th-century town house that once stood on the site, is a magnificent setting for private dining. Valet parking, twice-daily maid service, one-hour pressing service around the clock plus both English (with cholesterol-free eggs) and Japanese-style breakfasts are all examples of the attention to detail that puts the Inn on The Park in the top echelon of London hotels. *Rooms 228.* **Now called Four Seasons Hotel.** *Access, Amex, Visa,*

Four Seasons Restaurant ★★ £120

A grand hotel dining room with tall windows overlooking the hotel's private garden – a theme reflected within by stone urns on pedestals containing potted palms and plants. The mix of well-spaced tables and curved banquette booth seating gives a spacious air, on which the discreet service almost floats. Born near Bordeaux, chef de cuisine Bruno Loubet's passion for cooking is clear for all to see; now in his fifth year here, his distinctive *Cuisine du Terroir* style is unencumbered by the banqueting duties that many chefs at other major London hotels have to oversee. Thus, given full rein, Loubet produces dishes that reflect his Gallic earthiness but are carefully attuned to the world-wise clientele; so, *délices du Sud-Ouest* includes rillettes and both tartare and foie gras of duck with mushroom pickles, and a spit-roasted free-range chicken is served (for two) with hot smoked white pudding and a morel stew. Other indications that his appreciative audience are happy to try out new flavour combinations are shown in a salad of sautéed crayfish, courgette flowers and grilled salmon; lasagne of langoustines and artichoke flavoured with lovage; a light chervil and oyster soup; veal sweetbreads coated with hazelnuts and pistachios with a black truffle sauce; and iced aniseed parfait accompanied by red fruits flavoured with liquorice. Seafood and desserts are particularly strong points – the former typified by fillet of turbot braised with clams and leeks and served with sour fennel; the latter by a savarin soaked in Amaretto syrup and accompanied by pistachio mousse and poached apricot. A typical daily fixed-price lunch might commence with Scottish salmon (smoked or en tartare) or crayfish soup with nutmeg, followed by sautéed John Dory with potatoes and spinach and a veal jus or duck confit with wild mushrooms and a seasonal salad; desserts of the day and coffee with fine petits fours to finish. Unless you have deep pockets stick to the house wines – the wine list is indeed splendid, but pitched at prices they think that the clientele should be able to afford. *Seats 60. L 12.30-3 D 7-11 (lounge: 9am-2am, Sun 9am-1am). Set L £25 (Sun £28) Set D £40.*

Lanes Restaurant £80

One of London's smartest late-night restaurants, with last orders at midnight – ideal for the light post-theatre menu (after 11pm) if you've got the stamina. The Queen Anne-style decor is a fitting setting for the grand buffet-style display of hors d'oeuvre (and breakfast), a central feature of the windowless room. The choice of fixed-price lunch menus all include wine, a self-service selection from the hors d'oeuvre table and desserts from a trolley. Dinner includes a choice of grills and dishes as varied as couscous with raisins and cumin, and crab cakes with grilled monkfish, saffron and ginger. *Seats 75. L 12-3 D 6-12. Set L from £24.75 Set D £29 (£25 post-theatre).*

W1   Inter-Continental Hotel   84%   £212

Tel 071-409 3131   Fax 071-409 7460   **HR**

1 Hamilton Place Hyde Park Corner W1V 1QY   Map 23 D3

On Hyde Park Corner, this luxury monolith is popular with Americans both on business and on holiday. The vast, elegant foyer leads to a stylish lounge decorated in blues and golds and well provided with supremely comfortable seating. Discreet panelled meeting rooms with paintings and fireplaces are features of a business centre that is noticeably more civilised and appealing than most. Bedrooms are sleek and airy with seating areas, air-conditioning, double-glazing and mini-bars. Conference and banqueting facilities for 800. *Rooms 467. Plunge pool, spa bath, sauna, solarium, beauty salon, gymnasium, coffee shop (7am-11pm, 11.30 Sat). Access, Amex, Visa,* Diners Club International

Le Soufflé Restaurant   ★ ★   £140

Right in the top flight of London hotel restaurants, Le Soufflé has been fortunate enough to have the services of Peter Kromberg for the best part of 10 years. He's equally at home with the classics as with modern trends, and his soufflés still rise to every occasion: oyster and shallot accompanying Irish rock oysters, asparagus and smoked salmon served with caviar and chive butter sauce, broccoli in a crisp filo shell, rich curd cheese with rum-marinated berries, chocolate and candied kumquats with a light whipped cream. Main courses, beautifully cooked and presented, run from roast venison Saint Hubert to grilled lobster or red mullet fillets sautéed with sliced potatoes to veal with mushroom sauce and fillet of beef with fresh goose liver and truffle sauce. Classic wines, strong on half bottles and vintage ports. *Seats 70. Parties 12. L 12.30-3 (Sun Brunch 12-3) D 7-10.30 (Sat to 11.15). Closed L Sat, 26 Dec, Good Friday. Set L £25 Set D £45.*

SW1   Isohama   £55

Tel 071-834 2145   **R**

312 Vauxhall Bridge Road SW1V 1AA   Map 23 D3

Whitewashed walls, bare darkwood tables and purple velvet chairs add up to a simply decorated little restaurant just a few steps from Victoria station. Japanese dishes both familiar and less so make up an interesting menu which staff will happily explain to you (some of it's in Japanese). Good cooking, unfussy presentation, and it's open early enough for a meal before *Starlight Express*. Lunchtime sees simpler fare, but using equally good-quality ingredients. *Seats 30. L 12-2.30 D 6-10.30. Closed L Sat, all Sun, Bank Holidays. Set L from £6.50 Set D from £25. Access, Amex, Visa,* Diners Club International

N16   Istanbul Iskembecisi   £20

Tel 071-254 7291   **R**

9 Stoke Newington Road N16 8BH   Map 20 B1

Now trebled in size, on the opposite side of the road from the original café site. Authentic Turkish peasant food in a busy, lively environment. Mezze, kebabs, plus unusual offal specialities – tripe soup, oven-roasted lamb's head, boiled brain with salad, lamb's intestines cooked over charcoal. Book a couple of days ahead for Fri and Sat eves. *Seats 80. Parties 40. Meals noon-5am. No credit cards.*

WC2   The Ivy   ↑   £70

Tel 071-836 4751   Fax 071-497 3644   **R**

1 West Street WC2H 9NE   Map 25 B2

Sister restaurant to *Le Caprice* (which has a similarly upmarket brasserie menu), the design-conscious Ivy has mirrored wood panelling, stained-glass diamond lattice windows and art all around. Following along the lines of its glamorous heyday in the 30s, the customers are still the suave, fashion-conscious, theatre-going crowd who are nowadays attracted by the long opening hours and eclectic menu assembled by Nigel Davis: soupe au pistou, grilled squid and bacon, classic Dover sole served elegantly off the bone from a designer trolley, tagliatelle of lobster and scallops, steak and kidney pie. Puddings are equally diverse, from prune and Armagnac mousse to tarte aux pommes Chantilly and rhubarb fool. The signature dish of salmon fishcake with sorrel sauce also appears on the Sunday brunch menu, alongside bagels with smoked salmon and cream cheese, blueberry muffins and corned beef hash with fried eggs. A choice of coffees, teas and tisanes (from Fauchon) completes the picture, alongside a helpful and concise wine list that has been carefully compiled. *Seats 100. Parties 8. Private Room. L 12-3 D 5.30-12. Closed 25 & 26 Dec, 1 Jan. Access, Amex, Visa,* ⏺ *Diners Club International*

W1 **Jade Garden**	£35
Tel 071-437 5065	**R**
15 Wardour Street W1V 3HA	**Map 25 A2**

The dim sum are among the best in town and they serve them until 4.30. Sunday morning queues start early for everything from freshly-steamed *cheung fun* (slippery rice flour rolls) to succulent chicken's feet or fragrant glutinous rice. The extensive menu is predominantly Cantonese, but one of the set menus features Peking cuisine. *Seats 150. Parties 70. Private Room. Meals 12-11.45 (Sat from 11.30, Sun 11.30-10.45). Closed 25 & 26 Dec. Set meals from £9.50. Access, Amex, Visa,* ⏺ *Diners Club International*

WC2 **Joe Allen**	£40
Tel 071-836 0651	**R**
13 Exeter Street WC2E 7DT	**Map 22 C4**

A brash, resiliently American basement restaurant with a menu that runs from potato, broad bean and bacon soup to chopped chicken liver, spinach and blue cheese omelet, salmon teriyaki and rib-eye steak. Also main-course salads. Two sittings in the evening, the second post-theatre from 10pm. *Seats 150. Parties 8. Meals 12-12.45 (Sun to 11.45). Closed 24 & 25 Dec. No credit cards.*

SW3 **Joe's Café**	£70
Tel 071-225 2217	**R**
126 Draycott Avenue SW3 3AH	**Map 23 E2**

At fashion man Joseph Ettedgui's cool monochrome restaurant, some customers are content with just one dish, say artichoke, asparagus and French bean salad with foie gras, while others will happily work through three, perhaps roast peppers on olive bread, chopped steak with pommes frites and apple tart with vanilla ice cream. From 3.30 to 4.30 Mon-Fri they serve only desserts. *Seats 95. Parties 14. L 12-3.30 (Sun 11-3.30) D 7.30-11.30. Closed D Sun, 25 & 26 Dec, 1 Jan. Access, Amex, Visa,* ⏺ *Diners Club International*

W2 **Kalamaras**	£40
Tel 071-727 9122	**R**
76-78 Inverness Mews W2 3JQ	**Map 22 C1**

One of the best loved, busiest and liveliest of London's Greek restaurants, largely because it's also one of the best. In the same ownership since 1979, it's genuinely Greek, as opposed to the usual Cypriot, and its menu extends far beyond familiar dishes like *taramasalata, dolmades* and *moussaka*. Try *horta* (wild greens with lemon juice), *kavouropites* (filo pastry with crab), *varkoula thalassini* (baked courgettes topped with fresh salmon and bechamel sauce), *moskharaki stifado* (veal cooked with shallots, wine and tomatoes). The speciality sweet is *bouyatsa* (a sweetmeat with eggs, semolina and cinnamon, served hot). The restaurant is located at the end of a mews running parallel to Queensway. *Kalamaras Micro*, an unlicensed sibling, is at no. 66 (Tel 071-727 5082). *Seats 92. Parties 14. Private Room. D only 7-12. Closed Sun, Bank Holidays. Set D from £14.50. Access, Amex, Visa,* ⏺ *Diners Club International*

W2   Kam's   £35

Tel 071-727 8859   R

52 Westbourne Grove W2   Map 22 B1

Simply appointed Chinese restaurant whose standard menu is boosted by a
long list of excellent dim sum available, unusually, throughout the opening
hours. **Seats 100.** Meals 12-11. Set meals from £9.50.

W1   Kaya   £70

Tel 071-437 6630   R

22 Dean Street W1V 5AL   Map 25 A2

Korean food, not as varied as Chinese nor as "pretty" as Japanese, finds a
friendly home in Soho. Some items, including squid, pork fillet, venison
and marinated steak for the national dish *bulgogi*, are prepared at the table.
15% service is added to your bill. **Seats 70.** Parties 40. Private Room. L 12-3
D 6-11. Closed L Sun, also Xmas/New Year. Set D £38. Access, Amex, Visa,

SW1   Ken Lo's Memories of China   £75

Tel 071-730 7734   R

67 Ebury Street SW1W 0NZ   Map 23 D3

London's serious Chinese eating is largely concentrated in Soho, but Ken
Lo's long-established restaurant is outside that area, just moments from
Victoria coach and railway stations. It's much more comfortable and
sophisticated (and, it must be said, rather more expensive) than its Soho
counterparts, and chef Kam-Po But continues to produce fine dishes such as
siu mai (steamed dumplings), pomegranate prawn balls, iron-plate sizzling
dishes and Mongolian barbecued lamb in lettuce puffs. 'Old family
favourites and specialities' include Szechuan double-cooked pork and
Peking mu shu rou (quick-fried sliced pork with eggs and tree-ear
mushrooms). Pre-arranged banquets are often outstanding and set menus –
like the eleven-dish menu for four – also worthy of consideration. **Seats
110.** Parties 105. Private Room. L 12-2.30 D 7-10.45. Closed Sun, Bank
Holidays. Set L from £18.50 Set D from £24. Access, Amex, Visa,

SW10   Ken Lo's Memories of China   £60

Tel 071-352 4953 Fax 071-351 2096   R

Harbour Yard Chelsea Harbour SW10   Map 23 F1

Airy modern restaurant with views of Chelsea Harbour marina but
without the buzz of Ken Lo's Ebury Street original site. The cooking is
generally sound, nothing more, and best value is provided by the bar snack
menu (including excellent crisp-fried dim sum) available at lunchtimes
from Monday to Friday. **Seats 200.** Parties 12. Private Room. L 12-2.30
D 7-10.45 (Sun 12.30-10). Closed Mon, 25 & 26 Dec, 1 Jan. Set L from
£10.85 Set D from £24. Access, Amex, Visa,

WC1   Kenilworth Hotel   63%   £172

Tel 071-637 3477 Fax 071-631 3133   H

97 Great Russell Street WC1B 3LB   Map 25 B1

A handsome red-brick building near the British Museum. The foyer gives
a good impression, decorated in warm colours, with plenty of seating.
Carpets in the bar get replaced every two years. Bedrooms are quite pretty
in floral pinks and green, though some of the top-floor rooms are a bit
over the top, with four-posters and quite a lot of clutter. All are double-
glazed, with two armchairs and a desk. In the bedrooms are plenty of
shelves and good towels and toiletries. No dogs. Edwardian Hotels.
Rooms 192. Access, Amex, Visa,

NW1   Kennedy Hotel   63%

£102

H

Tel 071-387 4400   Fax 071-387 5122

Cardington Street NW1 2LP

Map 22 A3

Conveniently situated near to the west side of Euston station, a modern
hotel with simply decorated rooms. Close to Drummond Street where
there's a fine choice of Indian restaurants. Conference facilities for up to
100, banqueting to 85. Mount Charlotte Thistle. *Rooms 360.*
Access, Amex, Visa,

SW5   Kensington Court Hotel

£74

H

Tel 071-370 5151   Fax 071-370 3499

33 Nevern Place SW5 9NP

Map 21 D3

A budget hotel with bright, open-plan reception area and good-sized
bedrooms, all with en-suite facilities. *Rooms 35. Access, Amex, Visa,* (I) *Diners Club International*

SW7   Kensington Manor

£80

H

Tel 071-370 7516   Fax 071-373 3163

8 Emperor's Gate SW7 4HH

Map 23 D1

Small bed and breakfast hotel just moments from Gloucester Road tube
station and handy for the South Kensington museums. 24hr private bar.
Extensive buffet breakfast. Children up to 12 share parents' room free of
charge. *Rooms 15. Access, Amex, Visa,* (I) *Diners Club International*

W8   Kensington Palace Thistle   67%

£130

H

Tel 071-937 8121   Fax 071-937 2816

De Vere Gardens W8 5AP

Map 23 D1

Well-equipped bedrooms, two bars, conference rooms (for up to 250) and
an all-day restaurant serving dishes from around the world. It's just across
the road from Kensington Gardens and close to the Albert Hall and high-
street shops. *Rooms 298. News kiosk, coffee shop (7am-11pm). Access, Amex,
Visa,* (I) *Diners Club International*

W8   Kensington Park Hotel   67%

£148

H

Tel 071-937 8080   Fax 071-937 7616

16-32 De Vere Gardens W8 5AG

Map 23 D1

Quiet, comfortable and fairly roomy Mount Charlotte Thistle hotel
opposite Kensington Gardens, although lacking in facilities that many other
big hotels offer. The Cairngorm Grill serves interesting food prepared by
Rolf Amberge. *Rooms 323. Access, Amex, Visa,* (I) *Diners Club International*

W8   Kensington Place   ↑

£60

R

Tel 071-727 3184

205 Kensington Church Street W8 7LX

Map 21 D3

One of the capital's culinary hot spots, busy from the day it opened in
1987, and a front-runner in a modern style of cooking that puts the
emphasis on simple techniques and fresh, rugged flavours. Rowley Leigh
takes his inspiration from near and far on a menu that concentrates more
on starters and desserts than on main courses. Foie gras served on a
sweetcorn pancake is *the* luxury starter: soft, slippery and seductive. Celery
and tomato risotto, smoked eel salad with bacon, boar's head terrine, grilled
sole with beetroot purée and spiced shoulder of lamb with couscous and
harissa show the eclectic range. There's always an interesting choice of
dessert wines by the glass to complement the likes of poached pears with
red wine and cinnamon ice cream, tarte tatin or exotic fruit salad with
tamarillo sorbet. It's a place of noisy, lively conversation, with a definite
lack of plush in the stark modern furnishings. At one end is a glitzy bar, at
the other a vast mural depicting an eating scene in gay pastel shades. The

view through the all-glass frontage is mainly of heavy traffic, and the interest remains firmly on the inside. Sensible, short list of inexpensive worldwide wines. *Seats 90. Parties 90. L 12-3 (Sat & Sun to 3.45) D 6.30-11.45 (Sun to 10.15). Closed 3 days Xmas, 3 days Aug. Set L from £12.50. Access, Visa.*

SW7   Khan's of Kensington   NEW   £50

Tel 071-584 4114   **R**

3 Harrington Road SW7 3ES   **Map 23 E1**

Light green is the main colour of the stylish modern decor, and the greens and pinks of the chairs are taken up in the waiters' waistcoats. Tiny lights are hung from tramline wires, and a silk banana plant stands in one corner. Downstairs is a colonial-style lounge bar. The menu includes familiar items from the lexicon of Indian cuisine and some less usual choices such as lotus leaves rolled with herbs and sesame seeds, fried pomfret, tandoori salmon (marinated in yoghurt, dill and spices) and *sabzi kofta* – balls of assorted grated vegetables in a mild kashmiri sauce. Besides the à la carte there are meat and vegetarian set menus for one, a set lunch (Mon-Fri) and a Sunday lunchtime buffet (£8.95). *Seats 70. Parties 70. Private Room. L 12-2.30 (Sun 1-3.30) D 5.30-11.30 (Sun from 6.30). Closed 25 & 26 Dec. Set L from £7.50 Set D from £12.50. Access, Amex, Visa,* Diners Club International

SW7   Khyber Pass   £30

Tel 071-589 7311   **R**

21 Bute Street SW7 3EY   **Map 23 E1**

Popular little Indian restaurant with a loyal local following. Run-of-the-mill menu climbs up the thermometer all the way to Bangalore phal (phew! what a scorcher). *Seats 36. L 12-2.45 D 6-11.30. Closed 25 & 26 Dec. Access, Amex, Visa,* Diners Club International

SW1   Knightsbridge Green Hotel   £117

Tel 071-584 6274   Fax 071-225 1635   **PH**

159 Knightsbridge SW1X 7PD   **Map 23 D2**

A family-run private hotel in the heart of Knightsbridge offering comfortable, spotlessly-kept accommodation with double-glazing and the usual conveniences – except, that is, for a restaurant or bar as the hotel is unlicensed; however, this is hardly an inconvenience given the location. Breakfast (English or Continental) is served in the bedrooms and tea/coffee and cakes are available all day long in the Club Room. No dogs. *Rooms 24. Closed 4 days Xmas. Access, Amex, Visa.*

NW1   Koto   £60

Tel 071-482 2036   **R**

75 Parkway NW1 7AH   **Map 20 C2**

Unpretentious dinner-only Japanese restaurant serving good sushi. *Seats 24. Parties 18. Private Room. D 6-10.30. Closed Sun, Bank Holidays. Set D from £18.50. Access, Amex, Visa,* Diners Club International

SW1   Kundan   £50

Tel 071-834 3434   **R**

3 Horseferry Road SW1P 2AN   **Map 23 D4**

Politician-spotting comes as a free side order with a meal in this comfortable and roomy basement restaurant on the division bell circuit. All parties are agreed on the quality of the Mogul-inspired Indian cooking. Yakhni (chicken consommé) is a light prelude to dishes which are both rich and fragrant: chicken or lamb jalfrezi, chicken makhani, boiled eggs coated with marinated minced meat. Note also dishes from the tandoor, the day's dal and very good vegetable patties. A service charge of 15% is levied on all bills. *Seats 130. Parties 180. Private Room. L 12-3 D 7-11.30. Closed Sun, Bank Holidays. Set meals from £13.50. Access, Amex, Visa,* Diners Club International

W1   Lal Qila   £40

Tel 071-387 4570   **R**

117 Tottenham Court Road W1P 9HN   Map 22 B3

A serious, elegant restaurant in a busy location. The comparatively short
North Indian menu covers mainstream tandoori offerings and lamb and
chicken curries, plus specials that include lamb brain masala, tandoori trout,
fish curry and thalis. Fresh mangoes to finish when in season. Cocktails that
will "blow your trunk off". 15% service is added to the final bill. *Seats 78.*
Parties 85. L 12-3 D 6-11.30. Closed 25 & 26 Dec. Set L £9.95 (Sun buffet).
Access, Amex, Visa, Diners

SW1   The Lanesborough   89%   £290

Tel 071-259 5599   Fax 071-259 5606   **H**

1 Lanesborough Place Hyde Park Corner SW1X 7TA   Map 22 D3

Originally Lanesborough House, a private residence demolished in the
1820s and replaced by St George's Hospital which in turn was gutted in
1987 but with most of the original Georgian facade kept intact. Now
transformed into London's newest grand hotel and a sister to Caroline Rose
Hunt's *Mansion on Turtle Creek* in Dallas, the Lanesborough enjoys a fine
location overlooking Hyde Park Corner. Great care has been taken to
meticulously restore some of the original Regency-era designs and
furnishings. Enormous and exotic flower arrangements abound
complementing the polished marble floors and the colourful and stylish
neo-Georgian furniture and furnishings. The hotel's bar – The Library –
has rich mahogany panelling inset with bookshelves which, along with
leather upholstered seating, creates a deeply civilised effect. Next door is
The Withdrawing Room, a sumptuously elegant room with a striking old-
gold colour scheme. Public rooms have many quiet corners and a general
level of intimacy is to be found here that one might more usually associate
with country house hotels in deepest rural England. Very effective triple
soundproofed glazing throughout the hotel ensures that outside noises
appear as no more than a distant murmur. On arrival, guests are issued
with their own personalised stationery, while each of the 95 bedrooms
(which include 46 suites) has two direct access telephone lines as well as a
fax line (their system allows for 1000 numbers with 200 reserved
permanently for repeat guests). Security, too, is given a very high priority
with 35 surveillance cameras, window sensors and alarms that include the
sophisticated door-key system. Upon being shown to their rooms, guests
are introduced to a butler who, in terms of service and information, is their
only point of contact; all the butlers have been trained in the traditional
manner and will unpack, pack, iron, and even run baths as required.
Bedrooms are equipped to a high-tech standard as well as having exquisite
decor, with comfort being paramount. Each has a VCR, CD and tape decks
– all fully remote and secreted in attractive pieces of furniture, together
with the TVs. Bathrooms are lined with white marble and have every
conceivable amenity including, in most, steam showers and spa baths.
Rooms 95. Car hire desk, news kiosk, coffee shop (7am-midnight). Access,
Amex, Visa,

The Dining Room   ★   £110

The plush setting includes dramatic pink columns and walls, rich red, gold
and bottle green fabrics with Napoleonic flourishes on the chairs,
handsome mahogany furniture and spectacular flower arrangements. Paul
Gayler's menu includes some intriguing flavour combinations: two of his
most popular dishes are mousseline soufflé of Arbroath smokies with a
garnish of langoustines, and rosettes of lamb – trimmed, rolled slices of loin
topped with an aubergine purée and accompanied by sautéed slices of
aubergine and a basil leaf, all wrapped in caul, crépinette-style. Sharing mid
plate with the lamb is a crisp pastry parcel of spinach, tomatoes, strongly
flavoured goat's cheese and a touch of tapénade. The goat's cheese parcel

tends to dominate the flavours of this intricate dish and is perhaps more appropriate in its other appearance as a starter with salad. This is skilled, elaborate cooking by a perfectionist, and his updating of traditional British methods has found a worthy home in this truly grand room. *Seats 66. Parties 30. Private Room. L 12.30-2.30 D 7-10.30. Set L from £24 Set D from £43.50.*

The Conservatory   £80

The decor is Chinese-inspired under a high glass cupola housing giant potted palms; however, by late evening candle-light and the sound of splashing fountains and tinkling piano keys turn the mood into pure New Orleans. Paul Gayler's menus are equally international, with forceful flavourings (grilled calf's liver with cracked pepper, sage and garlic mashed potatoes) and presentation in the modern idiom. Salmon tartare with sweetcorn blinis and guacamole; stracci of spring vegetables with lentil bolognese; chicken breast with Thai spices and lemon sag (spinach); Cajun-grilled quail with almond and raisin tabouleh – all criss-cross the globe for inspiration. The choice is wide, the menu descriptions almost unbelievable and the results mixed. Dull lemon tart and disappointing sweetmeats ("sweet temptations"), though, are firmly rooted in English tradition; good tea blancmange and spicy apple and walnut crumble with rhubarb ice cream help redress the balance. A recent set dinner started with a salad of smoked duckling carpaccio and sweet ginger crisps, followed by herby basmati risotto with seafood, then rack of lamb with tomato and courgette tart, garlic fritters and a rosemary sauce, finishing with crunchy Napoleon of caramelised bananas. Service can be distinctly below par. Breakfast (if you want huevos rancheros with chorizo sausage and guacamole and spicy red salsa you can have it) and tea are also served in the Conservatory. *Seats 66. Parties 30. Private Room. L 12.30-2.30 D 7-10.30. Set D £26.50*

W1 Langan's Bistro	£65
Tel 071-935 4531	R
26 Devonshire Street W1N 1RJ	Map 22 B3

Photographs and paintings line the walls of one of London's best-known bistros, which lie next to its big brother Odin's just off Marylebone High Street. The short menu makes the occasional diversion from standard bistro fare with dishes such as fillet of tuna with mango salsa. *Seats 30. Parties 12. L 12.30-2.30 D 7-11.30. Closed L Sat, all Sun, Bank Holidays. Access, Amex, Visa,*

W1 Langan's Brasserie	£85
Tel 071-491 8822	R
Stratton Street W1X 5FD	Map 22 C3

An enormous brasserie on two floors, its walls are covered in modern art. Downstairs is the place to see and be seen, but the Venetian room above has its own quieter charm and a speciality – roast beef from the trolley. The long menu offers all-time brasserie favourites (garlic quails, veal cordon bleu, steak béarnaise), traditional English dishes (cod and chips, liver and bacon, bubble and squeak, rice pudding) and some more eclectic choices (grilled medallions of pork with ginger sauce, baked fillet of swordfish with Pommery mustard). *Seats 275. Parties 12. L 12.30-3 D 7-11.45 (Sat 8-12.45). Closed L Sat, all Sun, Bank Holidays. Access, Amex, Visa,*

W1 The Langham 75%	£243
Tel 071-636 1000 Fax 071-323 2340	HR
Portland Place W1N 3AA	Map 22 B3

The Langham was recently lavishly refurbished, recreating a grand hotel very much in the mould of the first 1865 building. Standing across the road from the BBC's Broadcasting House (a monument to the 30s), the exterior is what can only be described as a huge Victorian pile. Smart

doormen in Tsarist uniforms set the tone for the stylish interior which has been transformed into a sophisticated modern hotel retaining many of the original features. The Grand Entrance Hall with polished marble, oriental rug-strewn floors and thick Portland stone pillars leads to a light yet fairly intimate Palm Court, where afternoon tea is served (to the accompaniment of a pianist) and food is available all day and all night. Heavy burgundy velvet drapes divide this from Tsar's – a vodka, champagne and caviar bar. The Chukkha Bar is very much in the gentleman's club tradition with polo memorabilia decorating the walls. Bedrooms, furnished in solid, traditional style have all the expected extras but the suites, of which there are 50, also have video recorders and hi-fi units. Bathrooms throughout are in white marble and, while all have good showers, only some have bidets. Conference facilities for up to 320, banqueting to 280.
Rooms 411. Gymnasium. Access, Amex, Visa, Ⓓ Diners Club International

The King's Room   £100

Two huge brass lanterns hang from a lofty ceiling painted with a trompe l'oeil of palms, tropical plants and swallows. Tables are large, well spaced and beautifully appointed, but the refined tone of the surroundings is somewhat diminished by the clatter coming from the main restaurant next door (Memories of the Empire, where Ken Hom is consultant chef). Executive chef Anthony Marshall offers a short menu of dishes that are sound rather than scintillating, showing competence but not much creativity. Seafood is favoured, as in langoustines and crab with a good rice wine and coriander dressing, or halibut on a bed of spring vegetables accompanied by a well-made hollandaise. Service is friendly and generally attentive, but as with the cooking it lacks a few revs. Quite a helpful wine list with a good choice from the New World. *Seats 25. Parties 6. Private Room. L 12-3 D 6-10.45. Closed Sun & Bank Hols.*

W8   Launceston Place   £65
Tel 071-937 6912   Fax 071-938 2412   **R**

1a Launceston Place W8 5RL   Map 23 D1

Nick Smallwood and Simon Slater may have made more waves at their fashionable Kensington Place, but this quieter, more comfortable amd more elegant restaurant off the tourist track has also proved a considerable success. Charles Mumford is the chef, and his modern British cooking appeals to the traditional palates of loyal locals as well as to the slightly more adventurous. The set menu (available lunchtime and till 8pm in the evening) tends to cater for the former (black pudding with apple sauce, skate with capers and brown butter, Lancashire hotpot, rhubarb fool) while the carte strikes a more contemporary note with griddled scallops with red onion salsa, breast of duck with salsify fritters or crépinette of lamb with stuffed button mushrooms. Always a good selection of dessert wines offered by the glass. *Seats 70. Parties 80. Private Room. L 12.30-2.30 (Sun to 3) D 7-11.30. Closed L Sat, D Sun, Bank Holidays. Set L £12.50/£15.50, £16.50 (Sun). Access, Visa.*

NW2   Laurent   £28
Tel 071-794 3603   **R**

428 Finchley Road NW2 2HY   Map 20 B3

In surroundings as simple as the menu Laurent Farrugia prepares couscous and very little else. This excellent North African dish of steamed semolina grain comes in three forms: *vegetarian* with basic vegetables, *complet* with added lamb and merguez, and *royal* boosted to festive proportions by lamb chop and brochette. The only starter is brique à l'oeuf, a deep-fried thin pastry parcel with a soft egg inside – fun but tricky to eat. Algerian or Moroccan wine stands up well to the hearty food. *Seats 36. Parties 40. L 12-2 D 6-11. Closed Sun, Bank Holidays, 3 weeks Aug. Access, Visa.*

W11   Leith's

Tel 071-229 4481

92 Kensington Park Road W11 2PN

£110

R

Map 21 D3

Prue Leith's flagship restaurant continues along the same path trodden since 1969. Occupying the ground floors of three Victorian houses in Notting Hill, it has always managed to combine formal and efficient service with a relaxed atmosphere. Head chef for three years Alex Floyd is still only in his mid-20s. The dinner menu is a fixed-price affair ranging from two to four courses; the vegetarian alternative is £10 less, also offering two to four courses. First courses (perhaps chicken consommé with herb quenelles or marinated and grilled red mullet and squid with gazpacho sauce among the selection of four), cheeses (all British) and desserts are still wheeled around the dining room on trolleys. Leith's famous crisply-roasted duckling, cooked with celery and almonds, is always popular among main courses which might also feature lasagne of cod and spinach glazed with cheese and basil or feuilleté of rabbit with watercress, horseradish and rosemary. Baked Alaska with pear and warm passion fruit sauce was worth the 15 minutes' wait on a spring menu. "Wines of the month" (including half bottles) is an enterprising idea on a sound list that spreads its wings worldwide. *Seats 80. Parties 38. Private Room. D only 7.30-11.30. Closed 2 days Aug Bank Holiday, 4 days Xmas. Set D £36.50-£47.50. Access, Amex, Visa,*

NW1   Lemonia

Tel 071-586 7454

89 Regent's Park Road NW1 8XN

£28

R

Map 20 C2

A move across the road has almost doubled the capacity of this splendid Greek restaurant, but it's still full to bursting at peak evening times. Outside and in there's a Mediterranean air, with lots of light and masses of hanging flower baskets. Table settings are very simple, so too the main menu, but Lemonia scores through reliability and the lovely relaxed atmosphere. The speciality is the meze selection at £8.25 (plus extra for pitta bread), which should satisfy even the biggest appetite. *Seats 85. Parties 16. Private Room. L 12-3 D 6-11.30. Closed L Sat, D Sun, Bank Holidays, 2 weeks Aug. Access, Visa.*

SW11   Lena's

Tel 071-228 3735

196 Lavender Hill SW11 1JA

£40

R

Map 21 E2

Thai staff, Thai decor and Thai music, but above all very good Thai cooking. On a menu where seafood provides the widest choice the chef's specialities include soft-shell crab stewed with chili sauce and lemon, or stir-fried with ginger and mushrooms; beef or chicken in red curry paste and citrus leaves; and rice with pork and pineapple. *Seats 50. Parties 50. D 6.30-11 (Sun from 7). Closed Xmas, Easter, 1 Jan. Access, Amex, Visa,*

W8   Hotel Lexham

Tel 071-373 6471   Fax 071-244 7827

32 Lexham Gardens W8 5JU

£63

H

Map 23 D1

In a surprisingly peaceful garden square within walking distance of Kensington's shops and museums, the Lexham has been in the same family ownership since 1956 and provides good-value bed and breakfast accommodation. Cheapest rooms are without private facilities. Children free up to the age of three. No dogs. *Rooms 66. Garden. Access, Visa*

W1   Lido

£35

Tel 071-437 4431

R

41 Gerrard Street W1V 7LP

Map 25 A2

Busy Chinatown location on three floors and lengthy opening hours.
Mainly Cantonese and Peking-style dishes with an emphasis on seafood.
Dim sum at lunch and, usually, quick service in the evening. *Seats 120.*
Parties 50. Meals 11.30am-4.30am. Closed 25 & 26 Dec. Set meals from
£7.50. Access, Amex, Visa,

W11   Lilly's

£75

Tel 071-727 9359

R

6 Clarendon Road W11 3AA

Map 21 D3

There's a very English feel to this delightful little restaurant with greenery
outside and cream-painted brick walls and fresh flowers within. Roger
Jones puts the emphasis on lightness and healthy eating, with alcohol,
cream and butter used only sparingly in his recipes. Fish features
prominently, from sautéed scallops in crisp potato pancakes with a citrus
sauce to grilled Cornish cod with rock salt served with a parsley sauce and
garnished with clams. For something meaty try pan-fried calf's kidneys
presented on tagliatelle with a wild mushroom sauce, or roast rack of lamb
coated in herbs and garlic with a mint-flavoured salad. *Seats 28. Parties 6.*
L 12-2.30 D 7-11. Closed L Sat, all Sun, Bank Holidays. Set L £14.50 Set D
£15.95. Access, Amex, Visa,

W1   Lindsay House

£80

Tel 071-439 0450   Fax 071-581 2848

R

21 Romilly Street W1V 5TG

Map 25 A2

Ring the bell to gain admittance through the heavy front door of the 17th-
century Lindsay House. A comfortable lounge has sofas and armchairs for
drinks, while upstairs the dining room is in country-house style.
Sweetbreads and scallops in pastry, salmon and eel terrine, calf's liver,
kidney and bacon, plainly-grilled meats and fish, chilled sweet soufflé,
Stilton with apple, celery and grapes and buck rarebit indicate the updated
English style. Conveniently situated (and open early enough) for the
Shaftesbury Avenue theatres. Mostly French wines at reasonable prices.
Seats 40. Parties 20. Private Room. L 12.30-2.30 (Sun 12-2) D 6-12 (Sun
7-10.30). Closed 25 & 26 Dec. Set L £14.75. Access, Amex, Visa,

W1   Little Akropolis

£30

Tel 071-636 8198

R

10 Charlotte Street W1P 1HE

Map 22 B3

Stick to the Greek section of the menu at this enduring Soho address:
klefticon, moussaka, kebabs, afelia, stifado and stuffed vegetables. *Seats 30.*
Parties 25. L 12-2.30 D 6-10.30. Closed L Sat, all Sun, Bank Holidays,
2 weeks Aug. Access, Amex, Visa,

W1   Lok Ho Fook

£35

Tel 071-437 2001

R

4 Gerrard Street W1

Map 25 A2

Bare white-painted walls and contemporary artwork with simple white-
clothed tables create a simple feel at this Chinatown restaurant. The menu
covers Cantonese, Peking and Szechuan dishes – from a choice of 16 soups
to sea-spice braised egg plant, fried squid cake with minced meat, belly
pork and yam hot pot, to braised carp with ginger and spring onion, and
all the usual favourites. There's also a pictorially descriptive dim sum menu
for daytime eaters (noon until 6pm). *Seats 100. Parties 40. Private Room.*
Meals 12-11.45 (dim sum 12-6). Closed 25 & 26 Dec. Set L from £6.60.
Access, Amex, Visa,

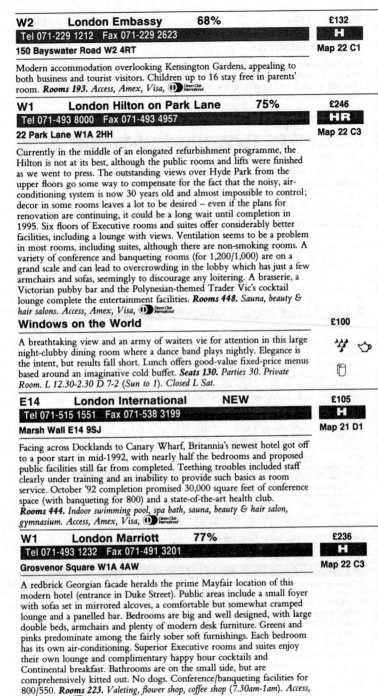

| W2 | London Embassy | 68% | £132 |

H

Tel 071-229 1212   Fax 071-229 2623

150 Bayswater Road W2 4RT

Map 22 C1

Modern accommodation overlooking Kensington Gardens, appealing to both business and tourist visitors. Children up to 16 stay free in parents' room. *Rooms 193. Access, Amex, Visa,* **①** *Diners Club International*

| W1 | London Hilton on Park Lane | 75% | £246 |

HR

Tel 071-493 8000   Fax 071-493 4957

22 Park Lane W1A 2HH

Map 22 C3

Currently in the middle of an elongated refurbishment programme, the Hilton is not at its best, although the public rooms and lifts were finished as we went to press. The outstanding views over Hyde Park from the upper floors go some way to compensate for the fact that the noisy, air-conditioning system is now 30 years old and almost impossible to control; decor in some rooms leaves a lot to be desired – even if the plans for renovation are continuing, it could be a long wait until completion in 1995. Six floors of Executive rooms and suites offer considerably better facilities, including a lounge with views. Ventilation seems to be a problem in most rooms, including suites, although there are non-smoking rooms. A variety of conference and banqueting rooms (for 1,200/1,000) are on a grand scale and can lead to overcrowding in the lobby which has just a few armchairs and sofas, seemingly to discourage any loitering. A brasserie, a Victorian pubby bar and the Polynesian-themed Trader Vic's cocktail lounge complete the entertainment facilities. *Rooms 448. Sauna, beauty & hair salons. Access, Amex, Visa,* **①** *Diners Club International*

Windows on the World   £100

A breathtaking view and an army of waiters vie for attention in this large night-clubby dining room where a dance band plays nightly. Elegance is the intent, but results fall short. Lunch offers good-value fixed-price menus based around an imaginative cold buffet. *Seats 130. Parties 30. Private Room. L 12.30-2.30 D 7-2 (Sun to 1). Closed L Sat.*

| E14 | London International | NEW | £105 |

H

Tel 071-515 1551   Fax 071-538 3199

Marsh Wall E14 9SJ

Map 21 D1

Facing across Docklands to Canary Wharf, Britannia's newest hotel got off to a poor start in mid-1992, with nearly half the bedrooms and proposed public facilities still far from completed. Teething troubles included staff clearly under training and an inability to provide such basics as room service. October '92 completion promised 30,000 square feet of conference space (with banqueting for 800) and a state-of-the-art health club. *Rooms 444. Indoor swimming pool, spa bath, sauna, beauty & hair salon, gymnasium. Access, Amex, Visa,* **①** *Diners Club International*

| W1 | London Marriott | 77% | £236 |

H

Tel 071-493 1232   Fax 071-491 3201

Grosvenor Square W1A 4AW

Map 22 C3

A redbrick Georgian facade heralds the prime Mayfair location of this modern hotel (entrance in Duke Street). Public areas include a small foyer with sofas set in mirrored alcoves, a comfortable but somewhat cramped lounge and a panelled bar. Bedrooms are big and well designed, with large double beds, armchairs and plenty of modern desk furniture. Greens and pinks predominate among the fairly sober soft furnishings. Each bedroom has its own air-conditioning. Superior Executive rooms and suites enjoy their own lounge and complimentary happy hour cocktails and Continental breakfast. Bathrooms are on the small side, but are comprehensively kitted out. No dogs. Conference/banqueting facilities for 800/550. *Rooms 223. Valeting, flower shop, coffee shop (7.30am-1am). Access, Amex, Visa,* **①** *Diners Club International*

W2   London Metropole Hotel   68%   £114

Tel 071-402 4141   Fax 071-724 8866   **H**

Edgware Road W2 1JU   Map 22 B2

Extensive remodelling of grand proportions has turned the Metropole around. From a new entrance on the corner of Praed Street, guests enter a marble, chandeliered foyer from where glass-encased lifts afford a bird's eye view of the first-floor leisure club as they ascend to the latest bedrooms. Here, spacious Crown rooms have work desks and mini-bars and the fully-tiled bathrooms sport separate shower stalls. In the Crown suites a business alcove (with fax point), dressing room and hi-fi system are standard. 19 conference and banqueting areas are purpose-built, from the plush octagonal boardroom (seating 12) to the Palace Suite (seating 1400, banquets 1000). A la carte breakfasts on the 24th floor are a high point. Good, well-designed improvements (with more extension planned in the adjacent empty cinema), but the grading is held down by the older, smaller bedrooms in the 70s' tower block looking down on the busy Westway road. *Rooms 747. Spa bath, sauna, solarium, gymnasium, kiosk, coffee shop (7am-11pm). Access, Amex, Visa,*

W1   London Mews Hilton on Park Lane   67%   £155

Tel 071-493 7222   Fax 071-629 9423   **H**

2 Stanhope Row Park Lane W1Y 7HE   Map 22 C3

Close to Park Lane, tucked away behind the London Hilton. Mainly compact bedrooms. *Rooms 72. Access, Amex, Visa,*

NW1   London Wilshire   NEW

Tel 071-631 8000   Fax 071-631 8080   **H**

222 Marylebone Road NW1 6JQ   Map 22 B2

A 309-room luxury hotel was due to open at the end of 1992 on the site of the old Great Central hotel next to Marylebone Station. Owned by Hazama Corporation and managed by Hong Kong-based Regent International Hotels, the hotel will offer four categories of accommodation (phone for prices), a health club and a large range of banqueting and conference facilities, plus 24 hr concierge and a business centre. **Now the Regent London.** *Rooms 309. Access, Amex, Visa,*

SW5   Lou Pescadou   £50

Tel 071-370 1057   **R**

241 Old Brompton Road SW5 9HP   Map 23 E1

The nautical decor points to the main attraction, which runs from oysters, mussels (marinière and stuffed) or fish soup to daily specials such as red mullet, skate or brandade de morue. Also good are omelettes, pasta, pizza and pissaladière; steaks for the red-blooded. It's quiet at lunchtime, but in the evening it fills up, so arrive early or expect a wait, as they don't take bookings. In 1992 they closed on Sunday in July and August; give them a ring before setting out. Limited choice of wines. An optional 15% service charge is added to the bill. Might close summer Sundays – check before setting out. *Seats 60. Parties 44. Private Room. L 12-3 D 7-12. Closed 25 & 26 Dec. Access, Amex, Visa,*

SW1   The Lowndes   76%   £171

Tel 071-235 6020   Fax 071-235 1154   **H**

Lowndes Street Belgravia SW1X 9ES   Map 23 D2

Following a recent top-to-bottom renovation, the Lowndes is the smaller, more intimate sister hotel to the nearby *Carlton Tower* (where guests may use the Peak Health Club and charge restaurant meals to their room here). Public rooms are limited to a small limed-oak panelled lounge area partly open to the lobby and an all-day brasserie (doubling up as the bar) with pavement tables in summer. Identically furnished bedrooms are appealing with good-quality darkwood furniture, chintzy floral curtains and more masculine check-patterned bedcovers over duvets beneath. All are air-conditioned, but controllably so (and the windows open), and have smart, marble bathrooms with good towelling. Beds are turned down in the evening, but room service ends at midnight. The new wood-panelled Library meeting room overlooks a garden/terrace and holds up to 25 people in theatre-style. No dogs. *Rooms 78. Brasserie (7am-midnight), tennis. Access, Amex, Visa,* **Diners Club International**

EC3   Luc's Restaurant & Brasserie   NEW   £50

Tel 071-621 0666   **R**

17-22 Leadenhall Market EC3V 1LR   Map 24 C2

Well located in the very centre of Leadenhall Market, a busy brasserie on two floors that is only open for lunch on weekdays. Waiters, dressed in black waistcoats and white aprons, skilfully juggle with orders and plates. Atmosphere and menu are those of a Parisian brasserie, but the prices are commensurate with its City setting. Food is well prepared (steak béarnaise a speciality) and baguettes are baked daily in the ground floor sandwich shop. *Seats 50. Parties 20. Private Room. L only 11.30-3. Closed Sat, Sun, Bank Holidays, 5 days Xmas. Access, Amex, Visa,* **Diners Club International**

SE19   Luigi's   £65

Tel 081-670 1843   **R**

129 Gipsy Hill SE19 1QS   Map 21 F1

The standard of cooking here remains reliable and consistent. The long-standing menu offers daily specials to supplement the choice of Italian classics. There are fairly few pasta dishes (linguine with clams and home-made cannelloni are favourites) but a good choice of anitpasti, fish, meat and poultry in generally familiar preparations. *Seats 65. Parties 75. Private Room. L 12-2.30 D 6-11. Closed L Sat, all Sun, Bank Holidays. Set L from £15.90. Access, Amex,Visa,* **Diners Club International**

SW7   Majlis   £35

Tel 071-584 3476   **R**

32 Gloucester Road SW7 4RB   Map 23 D1

Same ownership as Memories of India a few doors away, with a similar menu based around lamb, chicken and prawns (plus a fair vegetarian choice) and a not-so-usual choice of set menus for one. Ask for a fresh mango to finish. *Seats 36. Parties 15. L 12-2.30 D 6-12. Closed 25 & 26 Dec. Set meals from £14.95. Access, Amex, Visa,* **Diners Club International**

W8   Malabar   £40

Tel 071-727 8800   **R**

27 Uxbridge Street W8 7TQ   Map 21 D3

Indian restaurant with a look and style all its own. The look is Mediterranean (an Italian restaurant was on the site previously) but the home-style cooking features unusual dishes like charcoal-grilled chicken livers, venison marinated in tamarind, chicken cooked with cloves and ginger, and a seasonal fish of the day. More everyday items, too, plus a vegetarian thali, a set menu for two and a good-value Sunday buffet lunch. *Seats 56. Parties 15. L 12-3 (Sun from 12.30) D 6-11.15. Closed 4 days Xmas, last week Aug. Set meals from £11.50. Access, Visa.*

W2   Mandarin Kitchen

Tel 071-727 9012

14 Queensway W2 3RX

£32

R

Map 22 C1

Seafood is the speciality at this roomy, air-conditioned restaurant at the top
of Queensway. The range covers crab, lobster, king prawns, sole, eel, sea
bass and exotic yellow croaker. Best to book, as it often gets very busy in
the evening. *Seats 110. Parties 40. Meals 12-11.30. Set meals from £8.95.
Access, Amex, Visa,*

W1   Mandeer

Tel 071-323 0660

21 Hanway Place W1P 9DG

£30

R

Map 22 B4

Indian vegetarian restaurant tucked away in a basement just off the Oxford
Street end of Tottenham Court Road. Good-value set meals include a
vegan thali and a "Wednesday special". Organic wines. *Seats 75. Parties 60.
Private Room. L 12-3 D 5.30-10. Closed Sun, Bank Holidays. Set L from
£4.50 Set D from £7.25. Access, Amex, Visa,*

W1   Mandeville Hotel   62%

Tel 071-935 5599   Fax 071-935 9588

Mandeville Place W1M 6BE

£130

H

Map 22 B3

Sprawling, purely functional hotel behind Wigmore Street with its own
pub, piano bar and all-night drinking lounge. Close to Oxford Street shops.
Rooms 165. Access, Amex, Visa,

E14   Manzi's

Tel 071-538 9615

Turnberry Quay Pepper Street E14 9TS

£50

R

Map 24 D2

Lost in the middle of the Isle of Dogs, a glass-fronted room overlooking
Millwall Dock, busy at lunchtime but less so in the evening. Simple decor
with red check tablecloths; fish, such as simply grilled sardines and skate au
beurre noir, is the main strength on a mixed Italian and French menu.
Wine bar upstairs. Sister to *Manzi's* in Leicester Street, WC2. *Seats 80.
L 12-3 D 6-11. Closed Sat & Sun, Bank Holidays. Access, Amex, Visa,*

WC2   Manzi's

Tel 071-734 0224

1 Leicester Street WC2H 7BL

£70

R

Map 25 A2

London's oldest seafood restaurant offers a largely unchanging menu of fish
and shellfish, usually at its best when prepared in the simplest ways: fried
whitebait, potted shrimps, grilled sardines, skate with black butter, battered
squid, skewers of scallops and bacon. Strawberry tart is the favourite sweet.
Choose the street level room for buzz and banter, upstairs for a more
sedate ambience. The restaurant has sixteen basic letting bedrooms.
*Seats 200. Private Room. L 12-2.30 D 5.30-11.30 (Sun 6.30-10.30) Closed
L Sun, Xmas. Access, Amex, Visa,*

WC1   The Marlborough   69%

Tel 071-636 5601   Fax 071-636 0532

9-14 Bloomsbury Street WC1B 3QD

£184

H

Map 25 B1

In the heart of Bloomsbury, just off New Oxford Street and close to the
British Museum, the restored Edwardian-style facade gives a good
impression of the mix of modern amenity and old-fashioned comfort
within. Liveried porters, fresh flowers and green leather settees greet guests
in the lobby, beyond which there is a mix of both quiet and busy public
rooms. Porcelain and polished brass lamps add a touch of elegance to the
bedrooms. Conference/banqueting facilities for 200/150. Edwardian Hotels.
Rooms 169. Brasserie (7am-10.30pm). Access, Amex, Visa,

W2   Maroush   £60
Tel 071-723 0773   R
21 Edgware Road W2   Map 22 C2

Probably London's most luxurious Lebanese restaurant, serving a standard
range of above-average hot and cold starters and mainly charcoal-grilled
main courses of lamb and chicken. In the evening there's a £5 cover
charge which brings fresh salad and puffy pitta bread as well as music and
dancing. A table anywhere near the entertainment more or less precludes
conversation. Beware a huge minimum charge of £38 after 10pm. No
cheques. *Also at:* **Maroush II** 38 Beauchamp Place, SW3 Tel 071-581
5434 & **Maroush III** 62 Seymour Street, W1 Tel 071-724 5024. *Seats 95.*
Parties 95. Meals 12 noon-2am. Access, Amex, Visa, ⓓ Diners Club International

W1   Masako   £100
Tel 071-935 1579   R
6 St Christopher's Place W1M 5HB   Map 22 B3

Delightful Japanese restaurant with friendly, attentive staff and traditional
decor of black lacquered tables, open screens and red plush chairs. Fine
selection of set meals provide good value, using quality ingredients and
showing delicacy in preparation. Soft-shell crab, deep-fried oysters, fish
bouillon soup and teriyaki fillet steak sit happily alongside the sushi,
sashimi, sukiyaki and kaiseki dinners. £2.50 cover charge per person in the
Japanese private room. *Seats 80. Parties 22. Private Room. L 12-2 D 6-10.*
Closed Sun, Bank Holidays. Set L from £20 Set D from £35. Access, Amex,
Visa, ⓓ Diners Club International

W1   May Fair Inter-Continental   79%   £252
Tel 071-629 7777   Fax 071-629 1459   HR
Stratton Street W1A 2AN   Map 22 C3

For a hotel with so many rooms the public areas have a surprisingly
intimate feel; the small lounge area opposite the reception desk is a little
exposed, perhaps, but a tranquil atmosphere is created by the harpist who
plays there each afternoon. The bars have red leather seating, the smaller
Chateau cocktail bar (open to 2am with live piano music) sporting photos
of many showbiz personalities who have stayed at the hotel. Spacious
bedrooms featuring silk moiré walls come in two different styles, English
or French; the former with green leather armchairs and traditional
darkwood furniture, the latter with velvet soft furnishings and French-style
furniture. Levels of service are high, right from the uniformed doorman to
extensive room service providing hot meals at all hours. There's a
luxurious health club, and the theatre can accommodate 300+ for
conferences. Children up to 14 stay free in parents' room. No dogs.
Rooms 293. Indoor swimming pool, sauna, solarium, keep-fit equipment, beauty
salon, boutique, valeting. Access, Amex, Visa, ⓓ Diners Club International

Le Chateau Restaurant   £75

The setting is stylish and relaxed for Michael Coaker's consistent and
imaginative cooking. His style is contemporary classic (on both à la carte
and fixed-price menus), demonstrated by dishes like marinated king prawns
with a medley of peppers, smoked duck salad with lobster vinaigrette,
baked fillet of sole with minestrone sauce or sautéed loin of lamb with a
panaché of beans, truffle and tarragon. The well-balanced, fixed-price
dinner menu extends to five courses, although no choice is offered. Jazz
brunch on Sundays with buffet-style first-course. Predictable wine list of
French 'names' at hefty prices. *Seats 65. Parties 18. Private Room.*
L 12.30-2.30 D 7-11. Closed L Sat, 25 Dec after lunch to 4 Jan. Set L £22
(£19.50 Sun) Set D £26.50.

SW7   Memories of India

£35

Tel 071-589 6450

R

18 Gloucester Road SW7 4RB

Map 23 D1

Sticking to familiar variations on lamb, chicken and prawns, the glossy menu at this dimly-lit, flock-free, neighbourhood Indian restaurant is helpfully pictorial. A few tables are in a small open-air yard in summer. Sister restaurant to *Majlis*, a few doors away. *Seats 70. Private Room. L 12-2.30 D 5.30-11.30. Closed 25 & 26 Dec. Set L from £6.95 Set D £14.50.* Access, Amex, Visa,

---

W1   Le Meridien   84%

£253

Tel 071-734 8000   Fax 071-437 3574

HR

Piccadilly W1V 0BH

Map 22 C3

In the heart of town, hard by Piccadilly Circus, a haven of peaceful elegance and comfort. A harpist plays under the chandeliers in the grand Lounge during afternoon tea, while a pianist tinkles away in the Burlington bar (open to 1am except Sundays) which evokes the aura of a gentleman's club with its baize-green decor. Bedroom decor is tasteful, with style and quality in equal evidence: pink and turquoise are dominant colours, with flowery quilted bedspreads and reproduction pieces featuring; the marbled bathrooms are nothing short of immaculate; bathrobes are, of course, provided. Impeccable service. Membership of Champneys health-club downstairs is free to guests – the fun-dungeon is a real plus point. Conference & banqueting facilities for 250. *Rooms 263. Indoor swimming pool, plunge pools, Turkish baths & sauna, spa bath, solarium, gymnasium & dance studio, squash, snooker, beauty & hair salons, news kiosk & gift shop, coffee shop (7am-11.30pm).* Access, Amex, Visa,

Oak Room Restaurant   ★ ↑

£135

An opulent dining room with chandeliers hanging from high ceilings, limed oak panelling and gilt abounding. Deep-pile carpets, floral displays, shining glassware and crisp linen help create a luxurious setting for executive chef David Chambers' modern French cooking. Michel Lorain from *La Cote Saint Jacques* in Joigny is his consultant chef and together they produce short cartes of *cuisine créative* and *cuisine traditionelle*. The former might cover gazpacho with warm langoustines and courgette quenelles; fillets of red pandora with chicken oysters, cockscombs and a sweet garlic sauce; or roast Gressingham duck with sautéed endive and arabica coffee sauce. The latter sticks to steamed sea bass on mangetout and celeriac with a truffle butter sauce; panaché of sautéed fresh goose and calf's liver with red wine-poached eggs and confit of onions; and poached squab pigeon in a light beetroot consommé with baby vegetables. The styles of Lorain and Chambers become inextricably intermixed on the 7-course *menu gourmand* with ingredients ranging from rabbit and frog's legs, to turbot and lemon grass, lobster and asparagus, and bitter chocolate with praline and caramel. Lunchtimes offer lighter dishes on a short carte and a 3-course table d'hote: perhaps a light fish soup flavoured with pastis and saffron, followed by courgette flowers stuffed with langoustine mousse and a lobster sauce, plus cheeses. Desserts, served from a trolley, are generally the only weak act in an otherwise superb show. Service is attentive yet suitably discreet. France and California are well represented on the wine list, but the rest of the world is patchily covered; few half bottles. *Seats 40. Parties 8. L 12-2.30 D 7-10. Closed L Sat, all Sun, Bank Holidays. Set L £24.50 Set D £46.*

Terrace Garden Restaurant

£65

Four floors up, overlooking busy Piccadilly, is the lovely, leafy, conservatory-style restaurant, the front, lower section of which is reserved for non-smokers. Open from breakfast until dinner, the menus offer a range from croque monsieur to a club sandwich and crème caramel. Grills, fish, soups and salads complete the picture. The setting is unusual, the food not so. Fine wines by the glass from a Cruvinet machine. Seats 130. Parties 30. Meals 7am-11.30pm. Set meals from £17.

W1   Merryfield House   £46
Tel 071-935 8326   H
42 York Street W1H 1FN   Map 22 B2

Run by the same family for over 20 years and ideally located for the West
End, just off Gloucester Place. Full English breakfast is served in the small
but comfortable and clean bedrooms, all of which have smart bathrooms
en suite. Unlicensed. *Rooms 7. No credit cards.*

EC1   Le Mesurier   £60
Tel 071-251 8117   R
113 Old Street EC1V 9JR   Map 20 C1

Part of a small 18th-century terrace, this little gem of a restaurant is
basically open just for lunch, but evening parties of 15-25 can be arranged.
Gillian Enthoven's modern French-influenced menu is short (three choices
per course) but appealing, typical dishes being Gruyère and Swiss chard
tart, monkfish with mussels and saffron sauce, fried fillet of beef topped
with a marrow and horseradish crust, and (something of a speciality) hot
chocolate soufflé. *Seats 20. Parties 26. Private Room. L only 12-3. Closed Sat
& Sun, Bank Holidays, 1 week Xmas, 3 weeks Aug. Access, Amex, Visa,* ◑ *Diners Club International*

SW6   Le Midi   £53
Tel 071-386 0657   R
488 Fulham Road SW6   Map 21 E3

Fish soup, grilled goat's cheese salad, duck confit casserole, chargrilled
Mediterranean fish, Toulouse sausages, minute steak. Moroccan dishes on
Tuesday evenings. *Seats 38. Parties 14. Private Room. L 12-2.30 (Sun to 3)
D 7-10.30. Closed L Sat, D Sun, L Bank Holidays. Access, Visa,* ◑ *Diners Club International*

SW1   Mijanou   ★   £95
Tel 071-730 4099   Fax 071-823 6402   R
143 Ebury Street SW1W 9QN   Map 23 E3

Sonia and Neville Blech run this intimate and friendly little restaurant
with panache; just one indication of the attention paid to detail is the
'winematch' suggestion listed underneath each dish on the menu – a clever
idea that works because of the helpful classifications on the wine list. Sonia's
cooking style is classical French and dishes are listed in both French and
English: *noisettes d'agneau de lait farcies et sa sauce à la noix de coco et vanille*
(noisettes of lamb stuffed with fresh herbs and served with a coconut and
vanilla sauce). Start perhaps with a terrine of chicken studded with truffles
and foie gras or scallops, crab and chicory glazed with a champagne
sabayon, and then follow with parcels of calf's liver and sweetbreads with a
white port and Fine de Bourgogne sauce or 'lasagne' of veal fillets with
Gruyère cheese and a paprika and Kirsch sauce. Both lunch and dinner
menus are priced on a two- or three-course basis. Daily specials, like grilled
sea bass garnished with wild rice and a ginger and soy sauce, add to the
choice. Good French cheeses and involved desserts – from *l'arlequinade* (of
sorbets) *et ses fruits frais* to pancakes flamed with Strega, Grand Marnier
and Mandarine liqueurs. Neville Blech's quite splendid wine list is laid out
by wine style, with helpful notes. The restaurant also has its own wine
company. *Seats 35. Parties 26. Private Room. L 12.15-2 D 7.15-11. Closed
Sat & Sun, Bank Holidays, 3 weeks Aug, 2 weeks Xmas, 1 week Easter. Set L
£17/£21 Set D £28/£34.50. Access, Visa,* ◑ *Diners Club International*

W8   The Milestone   NEW
Tel 071-917 1000   Fax 071-917 1010
1-2 Kensington Court W8 5DL

£237

H

Map 23 D1

Scheduled to have opened in 1991, the hotel finally became operational in the summer of '92, as the Guide went to press. Situated opposite Kensington Palace, the Victorian mansion has been restored to English Heritage specifications with carved wood panelling, original fireplaces, ornate windows (many overlooking the park) and high ceilings. Luxurious air-conditioned bedrooms – some with private balconies and terraces and several with four-posters – offer guests all modern facilities including 24hr room service, private fax machine, room safe, video and satellite TV. The accent here will be on service, under General Manager James Caetano (previously at the Halcyon), with head chef Frank Rourke in charge of the restaurant and private dining room, originally the oratory. No dogs.
Rooms 56. Sauna, solarium, spa bath, massage, gymnasium. Access, Amex, Visa, Ⓓ ᴰⁱⁿᵉʳˢ ᶜˡᵘᵇ ᴵⁿᵗᵉʳⁿᵃᵗⁱᵒⁿᵃˡ

SW1   Mimmo d'Ischia
Tel 071-730 5406
61 Elizabeth Street Eaton Square SW1

£90

R

Map 23 E3

Sound, straightforward Italian cooking – but at a serious price – in a durable and fashionable restaurant whose walls are adorned with signed photographs of celebrity visitors. Spare ribs a speciality! *Seats 90. Private Room. L 12.30-2.15 D 7.30-11.15. Closed Sun, Bank Holidays. Access, Amex, Visa,* Ⓓ ᴰⁱⁿᵉʳˢ ᶜˡᵘᵇ ᴵⁿᵗᵉʳⁿᵃᵗⁱᵒⁿᵃˡ

W1   Ming
Tel 071-734 2721
35 Greek Street W1V 5LN

£55

R

Map 25 A2

A corner site between Shaftesbury Avenue and Old Compton Street. Specials like aubergine and duck hot pot, fresh spinach with garlic, raw chilis and fermented beancurd sauce and Hong Kong-style king prawns in cheese sauce distinguish Christine and May Yau's Ming from the more everyday establishments nearby in Chinatown. Much of the fish and seafood on the long menu is kept live in their own tank, so freshness is assured; lamb dishes are also good, as are the Oriental pancakes with red bean paste filling. A shorter lunch and pre-theatre menu (starter, soup, main dish, rice, glass of wine and Chinese tea – £13.50) is served between noon and 7pm. Courteous service. The wine list is gradually improving. *Seats 75. Parties 30. Private Room. Meals 12-11.45. Closed Sun (open Chinese New Year), 25 & 26 Dec. Set meals from £12. Access, Amex, Visa,* Ⓓ ᴰⁱⁿᵉʳˢ ᶜˡᵘᵇ ᴵⁿᵗᵉʳⁿᵃᵗⁱᵒⁿᵃˡ

W1   Mirabelle   ★   NEW
Tel 071-499 4636
56 Curzon Street W1

£110

R

Map 22 C3

New Japanese owners have spared no expense in restoring style to Mirabelle, which opened in 1936 and had its heyday in the 60s and 70s. Steps lead down from the street past a huge exotic flower arrangement to an elegant foyer which in turn leads to a cosy bar and a lovely pine-panelled lounge. The dining room, part-panelled in light oak and hung with classical paintings, opens on to a floodlit patio with a waterfall – a perfect setting for fair-weather dining. Michael Croft, formerly at the *Royal Crescent* in Bath, is achieving his true potential, offering a menu that combines modernity with a natural restraint that banishes the outlandish and experimental. The six-course *menu surprise* provides the ideal way of appreciating his skills. A recent dinner included foie gras prepared three ways in a most impressive presentation: pan-fried slices with a light truffled Madeira sauce, chilled terrine with diced Madeira jelly, and a slice marinated in sea salt, sugar, nutmeg and cinnamon served with salad leaves dressed with a walnut vinaigrette and blanched, peeled walnuts; langoustines, eggy noodles and little pools of concentrated minestrone in a simple but stunning marriage of flavours; and tournedos topped with a rich paté of champignons des bois lightly flavoured with tarragon, the meat sitting on a circle of thinly sliced roast potatoes; fine British and French farmhouse cheeses. A warm tart of thinly sliced bananas under a light, crunchy caramelised topping; in the centre, a ball of smooth, creamy coconut ice cream and round it a warm pool of puréed fresh apricots – a stupendous dessert and a wonderful end to an outstanding meal. The Mirabelle also has two two splendid teppan-yaki rooms for parties of up to 8 or 10 diners; the smallest has an adjoining room set aside for the traditional tea ceremony. The wine list is probably one of the most expensive in the country with few bottles under £20. *Seats 120. Parties 90. Private Room. L 12-2.30 D 6.30-10.30. Closed L Sat, all Sun, Bank Holidays. Set L £19 & £25 Set D £45. Access, Amex, Visa,* ⓓ *Diners Club International*

W1	Mr Kai	£50
Tel 071-493 8988		**R**
65 South Audley Street W1Y 5FD		Map 22 C2

An upmarket Chinese restaurant with spotlit tables separated by screens. Service is helpful and polite and cooking above average. And above average it certainly should be given the high prices (with a further 15% service charge added to the bill) and the expectations raised by menu descriptions of some specialities: barbecued Peking duck is "selected duck, basted with magic over flames of expectation till the skin alone is a revelation of taste rivalled only by the meat to follow". All regions of China are represented, but the more elaborate Peking dishes predominate. Minimum charge per person £15. *Seats 100. Parties 50. Private Room. L 12-2.30 D 7-11.30. Closed 25 & 26 Dec. Access, Amex, Visa,* ⓓ *Diners Club International*

NW3	Mr Ke	£42
Tel 071-722 8474		**R**
7 New College Parade Finchley Road NW3 5EP		Map 20 C3

Mr Zhu-Qi Ke was born in a 'land of fish and rice', the Jiangnan region south of the great Yangtse river. He served his apprenticeship in a leading hotel in Peking, where he learned to make fine roast duck and dumplings. Even now, many years later in Finchley Road, amid fierce competition, cooking of these specialities is nothing short of exceptional: the dumplings are poached, or fried on one side then steamed with a crispy base and soft top, known as kuo tish (pot stickers); then they are served with either red chili and garlic oil (Szechuan style) or ginger and vinegar dip sauce (Jiangnan and Peking style). First-rate sea bass soup with fresh coriander, a really good range of seafood. Next door but one to *Green Cottage* (see entry). *Seats 55. Parties 10. L 12-2.30 (Fri-Sun to 3) D 6-11.30. Closed 25 & 26 Dec. Set meals from £13.50. Access, Amex, Visa,* ⓓ *Diners Club International*

SW1	Mitsukoshi	£100
Tel 071-839 6714		**R**
Dorland House 14/16 Regent Street SW1		Map 22 C3

In the basement of a Japanese department store, this is a roomy, comfortable restaurant making stylish use of frosted glass panelling. You can choose from the à la carte selection or plump for one of the many set meals. These range from a fairly simple *hana* – appetiser, tempura, grilled fish, rice, miso soup and pickles – to all sorts of sushi and the *Kaiseki* ten-course feasts. 15% service charge is added to all bills. *Seats 140. Parties 22. Private Room. L 12-2.30 D 6-10.30. Closed Sun, Bank Holidays. Set meals from £25. Access, Amex, Visa,* ⓓ *Diners Club International*

EC4	Miyama	£80

Tel 071-489 1937   Fax 071-329 4225

R

17 Godliman Street EC4V 5BD

Map 24 B2

A stylish operation offering immaculately produced Japanese food in crisp business-like surroundings: a sushi bar upstairs and tables downstairs. As is often the case, the most interesting dishes are on the part of the menu written in Japanese script; it's often worth selecting a few at random, perhaps turning up chopped natto with grated yam, or soft-shell crabs. The main menu holds few surprises (sushi, sashimi, shabushabu, sukiyaki, tempura, teppanyaki) but all dishes are prepared with a high degree of competence and beautifully presented. For a change, why not try grilled eel with a kabayaki sauce, sea urchin sushi or cuttlefish sashimi? 15% service is automatically added to all bills. **Seats 85. Parties 40. Private Room.** L 12-2.30 D 6-10. Closed Sat & Sun, Bank Holidays. Set L from £16 Set D from £30. Access, Amex, Visa, ⓓ *Diners Club International*

W1	Miyama	£80

Tel 071-499 2443

R

38 Clarges Street W1Y 7PJ

Map 22 C3

The West End version of the City branch, stylish and modern, with opaque screens for privacy. Cooking is of a high standard, flavours delicate and refined. Set lunches offer the best value (raw fish, grilled fish, tempura, beef or chicken teriyaki, pork ginger or pork deep-fried). The rest of the menu spans the expected range, from *zen-sai* (hors d'oeuvre) to rice and noodle dishes and *nabemono* specialities prepared at the table. Excellent presentation and service. **Seats 65. Parties 20. Private Room.** L 12.30-2.30 D 6.30-10.30. Closed L Sat, all Sun, Bank Holidays, Xmas/New Year. Set L from £11 Set D from £30. Access, Amex, Visa, ⓓ *Diners Club International*

WC2	Moat House	65%	£177

Tel 071-836 6666   Fax 071-831 1548

H

10 Drury Lane WC2B 5RE

Map 25 B1

High-rise hotel handy for Covent Garden and the West End (just a few steps from *Cats* at the New London theatre). Bedrooms in the new wing are the best. Conference and banqueting facilities for 100 delegates. **Rooms 153.** Access, Amex, Visa, ⓓ *Diners Club International*

W5	Momo	NEW	£50

Tel 081-997 0206

R

14 Queens Parade W5 3HU

Map 21 D4

Cosy Japanese restaurant behind a smoked-glass frontage just off Hanger Lane (by North Ealing underground), catering for the West Acton Japanese community. One-dish lunches served with rice, miso soup, pickles and a piece of fresh fruit offer particularly good value, as does a fine *shokado bento* box with tempura and sashimi; considerably more expensive, but extensive menu in the evenings includes the likes of grilled eel and soft-shell crab. **Seats 24. Parties 25.** L 12-2.30 D 6-10. Closed Mon, Bank Holidays, 1 week Xmas. Set L from £5.35. Set D from £22. Access, Amex, Visa, ⓓ *Diners Club International*

WC2	Mon Plaisir	£50

Tel 071-836 7243   Fax 071-379 0121

R

21 Monmouth Street WC2H 9DD

Map 25 B2

Popular and long-established theatreland restaurant with cooking in classic French bistro style. Go for traditional favourites like onion soup, garlic snails, omelettes, salmon beurre blanc, coq au vin and daube de boeuf, French cheeses. A la carte, plus set menus at lunch and pre-theatre times (6-7.15pm). **Seats 90. Parties 25. Private Room.** L 12-2.15 D 6-11.15. Closed L Sat, all Sun, Bank Holidays. Set L from £13.70. Access, Amex, Visa, ⓓ *Diners Club International*

SW3   Monkeys   £70

Tel 071-352 4711   **R**

1 Cale Street SW3 3QT   Map 23 E2

Pine-panelled walls hung with monkey pictures in an intimate little
restaurant best known for its seasonal game, including grouse, partridge,
pheasant, woodcock and all the wild ducks. Otherwise the menu offers a
selection of English and French dishes, from grilled sardines and foie gras to
sautéed scallops and ginger and chateaubriand béarnaise. *Seats 36. Parties
36. Private Room. L 12.30-2.30 D 7.30-11. Closed Sat & Sun, Bank Holidays,
2 weeks Easter, 3 weeks Aug. Set L £12.50 Set D £22.50. Access, Visa.*

W1   Montcalm Hotel   74%   £220

Tel 071-402 4288   Fax 071-724 9180   **H**

Great Cumberland Place W1A 2LF   Map 22 B2

There's some justification to the Montcalm's claim to be "the best-kept
secret in London": behind a listed Georgian frontage, the hotel stands
discreetly in a tree-lined crescent, yet only two minutes walk from Marble
Arch. The staff – from management to maid service – are among the
friendliest in London. The atmosphere in the day rooms is redolent of a
private club: discreet reception desks, leather armchairs and low coffee
tables set the tone. The Marquis de Montcalm suite can accommodate up
to 80 for meetings. Splendidly appointed bedrooms include 12 duplex
apartments and two penthouse suites. Air-conditioning is first-class, and
bathrooms contain bidets and bathrobes. Children up to 12 stay free in
parents' room. 24hr room service. No dogs. *Rooms 116. Valeting. Access,
Amex, Visa,* (**I**) *Diners Club International*

W2   Mornington Hotel   63%   £92

Tel 071-262 7361   Fax 071-706 1028   **H**

12 Lancaster Gate W2 3LG   Map 22 C1

In a residential area just north of Hyde Park, the Swedish-owned
Mornington scores on housekeeping and efficiency. There's a fresh, bright
look to the place, both in the day rooms (panelled foyer-lounge, library
bar) and in the bedrooms. Rates include a Swedish buffet breakfast – full
English is available at extra cost. Children up to 12 stay free in parents'
room. *Rooms 68. Sauna. Closed 23 Dec-3 Jan. Access, Amex, Visa,* (**I**) *Diners Club International*

W1   Mostyn Hotel   62%   £124

Tel 071-935 2361   Fax 071-487 2759   **H**

Bryanston Street W1H 0DE   Map 22 B2

Tucked away quietly behind Marble Arch, the 18th-century building was
originally the home of Lady Black, a lady-in-waiting to the Court of
George II. Inside, period detail blends with up-to-date amenities, but the
most impressive features – a Georgian staircase, Adam carved ceilings and
fire surrounds – are in the conference areas. Public rooms include the
colonial-style Tea Planter restaurant (where breakfast is served) with its
own street entrance. Bedrooms of various sizes have slate-blue stained
wooden units, desks and small breakfast tables. No dogs. *Rooms 122. Coffee
shop (7am-11pm). Access, Amex, Visa,* (**I**) *Diners Club International*

SW1   Motcomb's   £60

Tel 071-235 9170   **R**

26 Motcomb Street SW1X 8JU   Map 23 D2

Old-established basement restaurant beneath a wine bar. The long menu of
classical French dishes has recently failed to excite, with service to match.
*Seats 70. Parties 18. Private Room. L 12-3 D 7-11. Closed L Sat, all Sun,
Bank Holidays. Set L from £12.95. Access, Amex, Visa,* (**I**) *Diners Club International*

WC2   Mountbatten Hotel   70%   £205

Tel 071-836 4300   Fax 071-240 3540

20 Monmouth Street WC2H 9HD   Map 25 B2

The hotel is themed around the late Lord Louis, with a glass case of
memorabilia in the lobby and photographs and cartoons in both the smart,
wood-panelled Broadlands drawing room and the small Polo Bar. The
marble-floored reception is elegant, as is the tip-top Lord Mountbatten
suite (one of seven). There's a range of function and meeting rooms
catering for up to 70 delegates (who most likely appreciate Larry's
informal wine bar after a hard day's work). Decent bedrooms have
darkwood furniture, mini-bars and remote-control TVs; bathrooms are
marble-tiled and luxuriously large bathrobes are provided. Edwardian
Hotels. *Rooms 127.* *Access, Amex, Visa,*

W1   Mulligans of Mayfair   NEW   £60

Tel 071-409 1370   R

13-14 Cork Street W1X 1PF   Map 22 C3

South of Mayfair, in the basement of a lively pub and oyster bar, an
elegant Irish restaurant is making quite a name for itself. Chef Richard
Corrigan gives a modern touch to traditional Irish cooking, with splendid
results in dishes like black pudding, apples and calvados, boiled corned beef
with ox tongue, sauerkraut and a mustard sauce or Cashel Blue and celery
omelette. Home-pickled crubbeens (pig's trotters) are boiled, boned, shaped
into small croquettes, pan-fried and served with a tartare vinaigrette.
Venison and red-cabbage sausages come with celeriac purée and star anise
sauce. Beef, Guinness and oyster casserole is rich and satisfying, the dark
meat brightened by turned carrots and turnips, the Guinness and oysters in
perfect harmony. The dining rooms are separated by mahogany panels and
frosted glass, which give a quiet, intimate feel to the place. Aperitifs and
after-dinner drinks are served in a clubby little bar. First-rate Sunday
brunch. *Seats 60. Parties 20. L 12.30-2.15 (Sun brunch to 2.30)*
*D 6.15-11.15. Set L £14.50. Closed L Sat, D Sun, Bank Holidays. Access,
Amex, Visa,*

W1   Le Muscadet   £60

Tel 071-935 2883   R

25 Paddington Street W1M 3RF   Map 22 B2

François Bessonard has a new chef at his popular bourgeois bistro. The
handwritten menu changes daily and still offers mainly traditional French
cooking: *oeufs en meurette*, oysters, coquilles St Jacques with lime and
ginger, noisettes of lamb in Madeira sauce and foie gras-stuffed quails with
balsamic vinegar are typical of the style. *Seats 40. Parties 42. L 12.30-2.30
D 7.30-10.45 (Sat to 10). Closed L Sat, all Sun, Bank Holidays, 3 weeks Aug.
Access, Visa.*

WC1   Museum Street Café   ★   £55

Tel 071-405 3211   R

47 Museum Street WC1A 1LY   Map 25 B1

Food is number one here and since space is very limited it's best to book
well in advance. Decor is unfussily spartan, with naive artwork on the
walls. The ambience is informal, nay laid-back: there are no side plates for
the excellent bread and glasses for wine (bring your own – no corkage) are
in school dining room tumbler style. Gail Koerber and Mark Nathan show
a commendable degree of commitment, working in a tiny kitchen to
produce delightfully simple dishes that owe more than a nod to the
Mediterranean. Typical lunchtime choices: salmon and fennel soup, roasted
aubergine and red pepper tart, penne with broccoli, tomato and Parmesan,
chargrilled organic lamb with hazelnut and mustard vinaigrette, tarte tatin

with crème fraiche. Main courses are accompanied by generous salads. Evening set menus are more expensive, but the cooking style stays the same. Cheese comes from Neal's Yard. No smoking. **Seats 22.** L 12.30-2.30 D 7.30-9.15. Closed Sat & Sun, Bank Holidays, 1 week summer. No credit cards.

W1   Nakamura   £50
Tel 071-935 2931   R

31 Marylebone Lane W1M 5FH   Map 22 B3

Just off Wigmore Street, a spiral staircase leads down to a simply-decorated restaurant with white walls, natural wood and screens. The food thus gets centre stage: freshly-made sushi and sashimi, tempura, nabemono specialities prepared at the table (sukiyaki beef or kamo nabe duck) and suimono soups. Try the *tamago-yaki* omelette dish to start, then fillet of cuttlefish, brill or salmon, or even *kaki-fry* deep-fried breadcrumbed oysters. There's a choice of five balanced set meals in the evening. Simpler dishes at lunchtime. **Seats 35. Parties 25. Private Room.** L 12-2.30 D 6-10.30. Closed L Sun, all Sat, 25 & 26 Dec, 1 Jan, Good Friday. Set L from £8 Set D £24-£37.50 Access, Amex, Visa, ◑ Diners Club International

SW1   Nakano   £75
Tel 071-581 3837   R

11 Beauchamp Place SW1   Map 23 D2

A steep flight of stairs leads down from Beauchamp Place to a very simply furnished room with white walls and red-tiled floor. Sweet-mannered waitresses will guide you through a Japanese menu that's longer and more varied than most. Chef's specials, which change every month, could include such comparative rarities as *shirano masago ae* (baby sardines marinated with herring roe), *kinpira gobo* (shredded burdock stir-fried with sesame seeds) and *gyu-tan oil yaki* (grilled tongue with garlic sauce). **Seats 30. Parties 30.** L 12.30-3 D 6.30-11 (Sun from 7). Closed L Sun, all Mon, Bank Holidays, 1 week Aug, Xmas/New Year. Set L from £11 Set D from £26.50. Access, Amex, Visa, ◑ Diners Club International

W6   Nanking   £60
Tel 081-748 7604   R

332 King Street W6   Map 21 D4

In a street bursting with ethnic restaurants Nanking is the best of the Chinese. Decor is cool, staff admirably helpful and friendly. The menu is strong on Szechuan dishes and a warning fire symbol is much in evidence. "Special selections" include crispy chili squid with onions and peppers, double-sautéed string beans with pork mince and a particularly good sizzle-grilled sesame steak with teriyaki sauce. In the same group and with a similar menu are *Cheng-Du* (Parkway NW1) and *Mao Tai* (King's Road SW6). **Seats 60. Parties 60. Private Room.** L 12-2.30 D 6.30-11.30. Set meals from £17.20. Access, Amex, Visa, ◑ Diners Club International

WC2   Neal Street Restaurant   ★   £102
Tel 071-836 8368   R

26 Neal Street WC2H 9PH   Map 25 B2

The decor has changed little over the years – brick walls hung with abstract artwork – but essentially this is a modern Italian restaurant in terms of both appearance and what the menu offers. Two things you come to expect on arrival are the fatherly figure of Antonio Carluccio beaming a welcome, and a magnificent display of all manner of mushrooms. The selection of mushrooms changes almost daily – chanterelles, wild and cultivated horse mushrooms, puffballs the size of rugby balls – and there's often a separate menu for them. A dish that must not be missed (but is not always available) is carpaccio with truffle cheese – a stunningly simple combination of paper-thin beef fillet, scrapings of a cheese made with white truffles, and a liberal dribble of extra virgin olive oil. Tagliolini with a truffle sauce uses the black truffles, the deliciously earthy aroma and flavour making a truly memorable dish. Breads, of which there is a wide selection, include some excellent focaccia – an onion one and a peppery one sprinkled with rosemary – the dough soft and moist with its high olive oil content – far more enjoyable that the rasping coarse dryness of ciabatta found in almost every Italian restaurant these days. On a recent visit, chargrilled halibut steak – the flesh meaty and succulent – was accompanied by a translucently light sauce whose flavour of dill rather overwhelmed that of the saffron. On a side-plate was arranged a very well-cooked selection of spinach, tender sliced French beans and small broccoli heads decorated with fresh ginger and chili – an imaginative treatment that lifted this particular vegetable out of the ordinary. Red and yellow sautéed peppers were a little undercooked but had good flavour. A salad of what seemed 101 leaves was dressed with a very good vinaigrette – the balance of olive oil to wine vinegar being spot on. Lychee and elder sorbet was quite icy but with a good flavour of lychees. Vin Santo with cantuccini is another excellent way to round off a meal with many definite high points. Leave room for the special Amaretti served with the coffee, moist in the centre and much more almondy than the usual variety. 15% service is added to your bill. *Seats 60. Parties 24. Private Room. L 12.30-2.30 D 7.30-11. Closed Sat & Sun, Bank Holidays, 1 week Xmas/New Year. Access, Amex, Visa,*

N1   Neshiko   £90
Tel 071-359 9977   R

265 Upper Street N1 2UQ   Map 20 C1

Named after a southern Japanese fishing village, Neshiko is a bright modern restaurant on two floors (the ground floor has a sushi counter that's also used for lone diners) The varied and interesting menu is clearly laid out in sections, by style of dish: deep-steamed, rice, simmered, deep-fried, grilled and raw. *Seats 55. Parties 25. Private Room. L 12-2.30 D 6.30-11. Closed L Sat, all Sun, Bank Holidays. Set L from £10 Set D from £30. Access, Amex, Visa,*

EC1   New Barbican Hotel   51%   £100
Tel 071-251 1565   H

Central Street Clerkenwell EC1V 8DS   Map 20 C1

Large Mount Charlotte Thistle Hotel close to the City and ten minutes from the Barbican Exhibition Centre. Popular with tour groups and conferences. *Rooms 470. Access, Amex, Visa,*

W1   New Fook Lam Moon   £40
Tel 071-734 7615   R

10 Gerrard Street W1   Map 25 A2

A simply furnished restaurant in Soho's Chinatown where meats hang invitingly in the window. Fast service from a long list of sound Cantonese cooking. Good choice of one-pot, porridge and noodles in soup dishes – stewed spare ribs with pig's liver, duck with yam and Mandarin minced meat with noodles are typical. Order barbecue suckling pig in advance. *Seats 50. Parties 40. Meals 12-11.30. Closed 25 & 26 Dec. Set meals from £10. Access, Amex, Visa,*

W2   New Kam Tong   £35
Tel 071-229 6065   R

59 Queensway W2   Map 22 C1

One of Queensway's longest established and most popular Chinese restaurants. The menu is predominantly Cantonese, with the occasional excursion into other regions, and the 200+ items include good "tim sum" (served until 5.30pm) and a number of sustaining one-plate noodle dishes. *Seats 120. Parties 80. Meals 12-11.15. Set meals from £9.80. Amex.*

W1   New World   £35

Tel 071-434 2508   **R**

1 Gerrard Place W1V 7LL   Map 25 A2

Exceptional value for money is offered at one of Chinatown's biggest and
best-known restaurants. A huge menu provides something for everyone,
including daytime dim sum, "popular provincial dishes", seafood specials
(lobster for under £10) and chef's specialities which include deep-fried
chicken rolled with mango, and sautéed scallops stuffed with minced
cuttlefish. *Seats 600. Parties 250. Private Room. Meals 11am-11.45pm (Fri &*
Sat to 12.15am, Sun 11-11). Closed 25 & 26 Dec. Set meals from £6.60.
Access, Amex, Visa, ⓘ *Diners Club International*

SW4   Newtons   £45

Tel 081-673 0977   **R**

73 Abbeville Road SW4 9LA   Map 21 E2

A popular place with several tables outside on an attractive terrace. The
menu runs a worldwide gamut from bang-bang chicken and seared pepper
and fennel crostini to hamburgers, Thai fish and vegetable curry and duck
confit with poppyseed cabbage and mashed potato. *Seats 82. Parties 25.*
L 12.30-2.30 D 7-11.30 Meals (Sat & Sun 12.30-11.30). Closed 25 & 26
Dec, Easter Sun. Set L £9.95 Set D £11.95. Access, Visa.

NW6   Nichol's   £53

Tel 071-624 3880   **R**

75 Fairfax Road NW6 4EE   Map 20 C3

At a neat and comfortable modern restaurant ten minutes walk from Swiss
Cottage, David Nichol cooks with subtlety and quiet artistry. On a short
menu of English and French pedigree you could find a warm salad of
smoked haddock, onion and Gruyère or a grilled tuna niçoise, boned leg of
lamb with a tarragon and green peppercorn sauce and fresh pasta with
artichoke hearts. *Seats 50. Parties 40. L 12-3 D 7-11. Closed L Sat, D Sun,*
Bank Holidays. Access, Amex, Visa.

W1   Nico Central   ★NEW   £65

Tel 071-436 8846   Fax 071-436 0134   **R**

35 Great Portland Street W1N 5DD   Map 22 B3

Chez Nico has moved to Park Lane and turned into *Nico at Ninety* (qv), to
be replaced in Great Portland Street by this upmarket brasserie. You'll now
find lighter and cheaper eating, but while the style might be easier on the
pocket and the palate, the quality remains high. A shortish menu of
modern classics might commence with a gateau of smoked haddock, the
fish flaked and blended with a featherlight soufflé mixture and gratinated
on a bed of spinach; boudin blanc – a superb and deliciously moist sausage
of foie gras with pork, veal and chicken blended with cream, accompanied
by slightly caramelised apple segments and creamy whole grain mustard
sauce – a magical combination that is genuine plate-licking stuff! Main
courses are typified by fillets of red mullet gently pan-fried in olive oil and
served atop a velvety smooth purée of potatoes coloured pale green by and
flavoured with an infusion of basil. A very plump and moist breast of
chicken wrapped in bacon and stuffed with a morel mixture is served in a
light wild mushroom-studded jus. The pommes frites are second to none,
lightly salted with a golden crisp exterior and just-soft interior. Puddings
are a mixture of classic favourites like a super creamy-soft crème caramel,
its poaching perfectly timed, or an alcoholic sherry trifle and Nico's own
creations such as his outstanding chocolate tart – a fine pastry case filled
with a rich fluffy bitter chocolate mousse. Good breads, like black olive
ciabatta and very nutty walnut bread, precede the meal, while at the end
very fine sugar-coated biscuits are served with excellent tea or coffee.
Service is now in the capable hands of the delightful Marianne Scrutton

who, until recently, was a partner at *Byrons* in Eastbourne. *Seats 62. Parties 14. Private Room. L 12-2.15 D 7-11. Closed L Sat, all Sun, L Bank Holidays, 10 days Xmas. Access, Amex, Visa,* ⓘ Diners Club International

W1   Nico at Ninety   ★★★↑   NEW   £150

| Tel 071-409 1290   Fax 071-355 4877 | R |

90 Park Lane London W1A 3AA   Map 22 D2

The move to 90 Park Lane has provided Nico Ladenis with new inspiration to elevate his brilliant talents to even greater heights. With Paul Flynn, his head chef, he works in a brand new, impressively refurbished kitchen re-defining his classic dishes and lifting them to even more impressive levels of sophistication.

The setting is a beautiful, stylishly appointed room, light and bright where it once was sombre. Honey-coloured panelling framed by mirrors, mirrored columns and well-spaced tables on a beautiful sea-green carpet complement the pastel-coloured deep-cushioned settees and well-upholstered dining chairs. All this together with crisp, white table linen, gleaming silver and long-stemmed glasses creates a formal dining room with a relaxed if not laid-back ambience.

The current menu still features signature dishes such as his stunning *tartine briochée de foie gras chaud* but also includes the simple-sounding but no less marvellous *petite solette de Douvres grillée, sauce aux cèpes* – a grilled small sole trimmed of all bone except the central one which separates from the flesh with incredible ease. The flesh itself remains just firm yet yielding. A rosette of finely sliced rounds of potato is the only accompaniment. The sauce of wild mushrooms possesses an unparalleled delicacy – a light, subtle blend of cream and the true essence of mushrooms. The *jarret de veau braisé au madère, légumes à la 'Printanière'* is a new interpretation. It now comes boned and rolled, cooked as ever to a melting succulence. The meat, topped with a glistening meat glaze, is surrounded by a superbly well-balanced Madeira sauce. Around the plate are asparagus spears, new potatoes, and two mounds looking for all the world like tagliatelle but in fact thin strands of subtly sweet carrot and mooli with cream and parsley – a real touch of magic. Brilliant brill is studded with tiny toasted cubes of bread and set on a bed of sliced potatoes flavoured with lemon, olive oil and oregano. Around the plate are thin slices of beetroot alternated with baby spinach leaves. The colour and slight acidity of the beetroot is a cleverly contrapuntal addition. Cheeses are a plated selection of ten French varieties in peak condition and sweets include a return to the repertoire of classics such as crème caramel, here glamourised by a syrup flavoured with Grand Marnier and a garnish of papaya, mango and lychees. The assiette gourmande is a stunning array of most of the sweets on the menu served in perfect miniature. Nico's wife Dinah-Jane orchestrates splendidly professional staff.

Notable features on an outstanding wine list include classics from the Grosvenor House cellars, French regional wines, the New World and many half bottles. The food, the wine and the service combine to make this currently London's finest restaurant. *Seats 60. Parties 20. Private Room. L 12-2 D 7-11. Closed L Sat, all Sun, Bank Holidays, 10 days Xmas/New Year. Set L £25 Set D £40. Access, Amex, Visa,* ⓘ Diners Club International

SW10   Nikita's   £70

| Tel 071-352 6326 | R |

65 Ifield Road SW10 9AU   Map 23 F1

Conviviality is the name of the game at candle-lit Nikita's, whose owner has been providing a warm welcome for 25 years. The Russian menu includes caviar, smoked fish, coulibiac, shashlik, chicken Kiev and beef stroganoff. The classic accompaniment is of course vodka, available by the glass or carafe in nearly 20 varieties. Parking is difficult, but worth the effort. *Seats 60. Parties 35. Private Room. L by arrangement for 20 or more only D 7.30-11.30. Closed Sun, Bank Holidays, 2 weeks Aug. Set D from £25.50. Access, Amex, Visa,* ⓘ Diners Club International

W1   Ninjin   £60
Tel 071-388 4657   R
244 Great Portland St W1   Map 22 B3

Modest premises beneath its own supermarket. Set lunches include
appetiser, soup, rice, main course (a choice of 13 – from sushi or tempura
to tonkatsu pork steak or kushiyaki skewered meat or fish), pickles and
dessert. Dinner sees a more varied, enterprising menu with kushiyaki
skewered foods a speciality; the faint-hearted might be well advised to
avoid heart or chicken gizzards, but fresh asparagus rolled with sliced
beef or aubergine rolled with sliced belly pork redress the balance. Noodle
dishes with tempura or fried bean curd are good value. Green tea, chestnut
and red bean ice creams to finish. *Seats 54. Parties 20. L 12-2.30 D 6-10.30.
Closed Sun, Bank Holidays. Set L £8.50-£20 Set D £26-£32. Access,
Amex, Visa,* (**①**) Diners Club International

NW1   Nontas   £25
Tel 071-387 4579   R
14 Camden High Street London NW1 0JH   Map 20 C2

A bustling, neighbourhood Greek Cypriot restaurant with a difference –
try the *pasri* fish kebab or the smoked sausage and pork marinated in red
wine and served with *pourgouri* (ground wheat). Particularly good value
complete meals for two or more diners are also offered. Small open-air area
in the rear garden. The separate Ouzerie area serves snacks, teas and coffee
from 8.30am-11.30pm. Overnight accommodation in 12 en-suite
bedrooms (£51 for two). *Seats 50. Parties 24. L 12-2.45 D 6-11.30. Closed
Sun, Bank Holidays. Set meals fron £8.75. Access, Amex, Visa,* (**①**) Diners Club International

SW5   Noor Jahan   £35
Tel 071-373 6522   R
2a Bina Gardens SW5 0LA   Map 23 E1

Durable Indian local opposite the top of Drayton Gardens, off Old
Brompton Road, serving the usual variants on the chicken, lamb and
prawn themes. *Seats 60. Parties 20. L 12-2.45 D 6-11.45. Closed 24-26 Dec.
Access, Amex, Visa,* (**①**) Diners Club International

SW7   Norfolk Hotel   69%   £164
Tel 071-589 8191   Fax 071-581 1874   H
2 Harrington Road South Kensington SW7 3ER   Map 23 E1

Close to the museums and the 'French quarter' of South Kensington. Built
in 1888, the Norfolk retains a certain Victorian air, although the amenities
are up to date. Standard rooms are in soft pastel shades, with attractive
limed wood furntiure. Day rooms include a brasserie, a basement wine bar
and a traditionally-styled English pub. Queens Moat Houses. *Rooms 96.
Keep-fit equipment, sauna, solarium. Access, Amex, Visa,* (**①**) Diners Club International

W6   Novotel   65%   £105
Tel 081-741 1555   Fax 081-741 2120   H
1 Shortlands W6 8DR   Map 21 D3

Very large modern hotel alongside (but not accessible from) Hammersmith
flyover. It's popular for functions (up to 750) and conferences (up to 900
delegates). Continental or buffet breakfast. *Rooms 640. Theatre booking desk,
news kiosk, lounge bar (7am-midnight). Access, Amex, Visa,* (**①**) Diners Club International

WC2   Now & Zen

£75

R

Tel 071-497 0376

Orion House 48 Upper St Martin's Lane WC2

Map 25 B2

High on interior design (by Rick Mather) and handy for theatreland,
Lawrence Leung's stylish, ultra-modern restaurant is on three levels with
minimalist decor behind a sleek glass frontage. Value-for-money is not a
high priority on the expensive menu, which is a mix of modern and classic
Chinese cooking – from dim sum to coriander and cuttlefish cakes, shin of
beef with coconut in a clay pot and tofu almond jelly with fresh fruit.
*Seats 200. Parties 30. Private Room. L 12-3 D 6-11.30 (Sun to 11). Closed 25
& 26 Dec. Access, Amex, Visa,*

SW7   Number Sixteen

£136

PH

Tel 071-589 5232   Fax 071-584 8615

16 Sumner Place SW7 3EG

Map 23 E2

In a terrace of white-painted early-Victorian houses, Number Sixteen offers
style, elegance and seclusion. There's a comfortable informality about the
drawing room, and the conservatory opens onto a walled garden.
Bedrooms are smartly furnished with a combination of antiques and
traditional pieces. A tea and coffee service is available throughout the day.
No children under 12. No dogs. *Rooms 36. Access, Amex, Visa,*

W1   Nusa Dua

£35

R

Tel 071-437 3559

11-12 Dean Street W1

Map 22 B3

Indonesian food is a delightful mixture of tastes and aromas involving
sweet, pungent, hot and spicy. Otto, the manager, who dispenses charm and
information in equal measure, comes from Java, where they like their food
sweet, but his menu spans the whole range. Set meals provide good value,
or you can explore the carte. Chicken, beef, prawn and beancurd satays;
whole fish cooked in banana leaves, lamb chops with chili and sweet soya
sauce, and mixed vegetables cooked in tamarind soup are just a few of the
70+ dishes on offer. The restaurant is on two levels, lighter at street level,
more intimate below. *Seats 50. Parties 30. L 12-2.30 D 6-11.30. Closed
L Sat, all Sun, Bank Holidays. Set L from £7 Set D from £13.50. Access,
Visa,*

NW1   Odette's

£65

R

Tel 071-586 5486

130 Regent's Park Road NW1 8XL

Map 20 C2

A pretty, romantic restaurant in Primrose Hill with a daily-changing menu
that is always interesting and sometimes over-adventurous. Six rock oysters
with spicy Thai-style sausages; scallop, salmon and plaice fishcakes with
wilted rocket sauce; warm salad of lamb's brains and deep-fried capers
show the adventure, although home-smoked fillet of sea bass with fennel or
sautéed calf's liver with mashed potato and onion gravy are more
successful. Straightforward puddings such as crème brulée, bread-and-butter
pudding and rhubarb crumble tart with honey ice cream, plus farmhouse
cheeses. A helpful and fairly-priced wine list is laid out by wine style.
Downstairs is a wine bar with a separate menu. *Seats 55. Parties 30. Private
Room. L 12.30-2.30 (Sun 12-3) D 7-11. Closed L Sat, D Sun, Bank Holidays,
1 week Xmas, 2 weeks Aug. Access, Amex, Visa,*

W1   Odin's Restaurant

£85

R

Tel 071-935 7296

27 Devonshire Street W1N 1RJ

Map 22 B3

The image of Peter Langan still looms large over the outsize menu at this
smart, picture-lined restaurant. Just off Marylebone High Street, it serves
the Harley Street area well, with a singular menu mix that ranges from

calf's brains with onion and gherkins or stewed eels and mash to steamed monkfish with saffron sauce and cottage pie. 15% service and cover charges are added to your bill. *Seats 60. Parties 10. L 12.30-2.30 D 7-11.30. Closed L Sat, all Sun, Bank Holidays. Access, Amex, Visa,*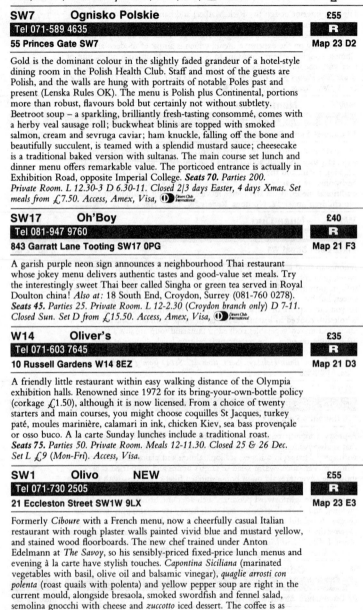

SW7   Ognisko Polskie   £55

Tel 071-589 4635	**R**
55 Princes Gate SW7	**Map 23 D2**

Gold is the dominant colour in the slightly faded grandeur of a hotel-style dining room in the Polish Health Club. Staff and most of the guests are Polish, and the walls are hung with portraits of notable Poles past and present (Lenska Rules OK). The menu is Polish plus Continental, portions more than robust, flavours bold but certainly not without subtlety. Beetroot soup – a sparkling, brilliantly fresh-tasting consommé, comes with a herby veal sausage roll; buckwheat blinis are topped with smoked salmon, cream and sevruga caviar; ham knuckle, falling off the bone and beautifully succulent, is teamed with a splendid mustard sauce; cheesecake is a traditional baked version with sultanas. The main course set lunch and dinner menu offers remarkable value. The porticoed entrance is actually in Exhibition Road, opposite Imperial College. *Seats 70. Parties 200. Private Room. L 12.30-3 D 6.30-11. Closed 2/3 days Easter, 4 days Xmas. Set meals from £7.50. Access, Amex, Visa,*

SW17   Oh'Boy   £40

Tel 081-947 9760	**R**
843 Garratt Lane Tooting SW17 0PG	**Map 21 F3**

A garish purple neon sign announces a neighbourhood Thai restaurant whose jokey menu delivers authentic tastes and good-value set meals. Try the interestingly sweet Thai beer called Singha or green tea served in Royal Doulton china! *Also at:* 18 South End, Croydon, Surrey (081-760 0278). *Seats 45. Parties 25. Private Room. L 12-2.30 (Croydon branch only) D 7-11. Closed Sun. Set D from £15.50. Access, Amex, Visa,*

W14   Oliver's   £35

Tel 071-603 7645	**R**
10 Russell Gardens W14 8EZ	**Map 21 D3**

A friendly little restaurant within easy walking distance of the Olympia exhibition halls. Renowned since 1972 for its bring-your-own-bottle policy (corkage £1.50), although it is now licensed. From a choice of twenty starters and main courses, you might choose coquilles St Jacques, turkey paté, moules marinière, calamari in ink, chicken Kiev, sea bass provençale or osso buco. A la carte Sunday lunches include a traditional roast. *Seats 75. Parties 50. Private Room. Meals 12-11.30. Closed 25 & 26 Dec. Set L £9 (Mon-Fri). Access, Visa.*

SW1   Olivo   NEW   £55

Tel 071-730 2505	**R**
21 Eccleston Street SW1W 9LX	**Map 23 E3**

Formerly *Ciboure* with a French menu, now a cheerfully casual Italian restaurant with rough plaster walls painted vivid blue and mustard yellow, and stained wood floorboards. The new chef trained under Anton Edelmann at *The Savoy*, so his sensibly-priced fixed-price lunch menus and evening à la carte have stylish touches. *Capontina Siciliana* (marinated vegetables with basil, olive oil and balsamic vinegar), *quaglie arrosti con polenta* (roast quails with polenta) and yellow pepper soup are right in the current mould, alongside bresaola, smoked swordfish and fennel salad, semolina gnocchi with cheese and *zuccotto* iced dessert. The coffee is as good as one might expect, and extra virgin olive oil served with the bread is a nice touch. *Seats 45. Parties 6. L 12-2.30 D 7-11. Closed L Sat & D Sun, Bank Holidays, 3 weeks Aug/Sep. Set L £12/£14. Access, Amex, Visa.*

W11   192

Tel 071-229 0482

£54

R

192 Kensington Park Road W11 2JF

Map 21 D3

The wine bar section on the ground floor (the main eating area is
downstairs) sets the informal tone of this restaurant near Portobello Road.
The kitchen has had its ups and downs over the last 10 years (two of the
'ups' were when Alastair Little and later Angela Dwyer were in charge)
but seems to be on the up again under new chef Dan Evans (most recently
at *Odette's* after working under Little). Cooking remains very much in the
modern idiom with the likes of grilled squid with black pasta and salsa
verde, warm goat's cheese with rocket and sour dough bruschetta, roast
plaice with spinach and sun-dried tomatoes, and dressed crab niçoise on the
short menu that changes twice each day. Service is both friendly and
helpful. **Seats 75. Parties 30. Private Room.** *L 12.30-3 (Sun 1-3.30)
D 7.30-11.30 (Sun to 11). Closed L Mon, Bank Holidays except Good Friday.
Access, Amex, Visa.*

E3   1789

Tel 081-980 8233

£55

R

9 Fairfield Road Bow Road E3

Map 20 C1

Nothing revolutionary at this cheerful East End restaurant, but
straightforward dishes from the standard French bistro repertoire. Fish soup
with rouille, crudités with dips, chicken normande, steak au poivre, poire
belle Hélène. **Seats 20. Parties 20.** *L 12-2 D 7.30-10.30.Closed Sun & Mon.
Set L £14.50 Set D £17.50. Access, Amex, Visa.*

SW5   Hotel 167

Tel 071-373 0672   Fax 071-373 3360

£77

H

167 Old Brompton Road SW5 0AN

Map 23 E1

Frank Cheevers has transformed a Victorian private house into a most
delightful little hotel. Each room has its own character, with inspiration
ranging from pine to art deco. Central heating and double-glazing
keep things warm and peaceful. Breakfast is served in the bedrooms or in a
pleasant reception room. Light evening meals also available. Unlicensed.
No dogs. **Rooms 19.** *Access, Amex, Visa,* ◍ Diners Club International.

WC2   Orso

Tel 071-240 5269

£65

R

27 Wellington Street WC2E 7DA

Map 22 B4

A basement restaurant in Covent Garden with a discreet entrance on the
other side of the road from *Christopher's* (see entry). White-tiled walls are
hung with arty black and white photographs and the clientele is stylish and
starry. Wonderful small pizzas with a variety of toppings: sardines, wild
mushrooms, goat's cheese, roasted garlic or artichokes. Grilled scallops with
roasted peppers, a selection of pasta dishes (try risotto with gorgonzola and
spinach), grilled tuna with radicchio, white beans and roasted tomatoes,
veal escalopes stuffed with spinach, mushrooms, fontina and Parma ham,
pecorino cheese with pears and vin santo with cantucci indicate the style.
Easy-to-use list of good Italian wines. **Seats 100. Parties 8.** *Meals 12-12.
Closed Xmas. No credit cards.*

SW11   Osteria Antica Bologna

Tel 071-978 4771

£40

R

23 Northcote Road SW11 1NG

Map 21 F2

Italian cooking at kind prices in friendly, unpretentious surroundings.
That's the Osteria formula, and it works well. The food, which takes its
inspiration from all parts of Italy, is not what you'll find in the usual high-
street Italian restaurant. Bolognese starters are fun to share or can make up
an excellent light meal: olives with garlic and olive oil, cabbage with three

cheeses and pancetta, fried breadcrumbed fennel, raw swordfish marinated in lemon, brown lentils with sun-dried tomatoes and chilis. Pasta comes with interesting sauces and among the mains are grilled sausages, young goat and fresh grilled cuttlefish with artichokes. Lengthy Italian wine list. *Seats 70. Parties 20. Meals 11am-11.30pm (Sat 12-11, Sun 12.30-11). Closed Bank Holidays, 2 weeks Xmas. Access, Amex, Visa.*

SW18   Le P'tit Normand   £45
Tel 081-871 0233   R
185 Merton Road SW18 5EF   Map 21 F3

Neighbourhood restaurant serving French dishes, many with a normand provenance: gambas au Calvados, cote de veau normande, magret de canard Vallée d'Auge. Hearty cooking and if you like, hearty drinking (15 Calvados going back to 1938). *Seats 30. Parties 40. Private Room. L 12-2 D 7-10.30 (Sun to 10). Closed L Sat. Set L from £9.75. Access, Amex, Visa.*

W8   La Paesana   £40
Tel 071-229 4332   R
30 Uxbridge Street W8 7TR   Map 21 D3

Standard Italian fare in a lively Notting Hill restaurant that's been going since the 60s. All the antipasti and pastas are available as either starters or main courses. *Seats 90. Parties 44. Private Room. L 12-2.45 D 6-11.45. Closed L Sat, all Sun, Bank Holidays. Access, Amex, Visa,* Diners Club International

W1   Panda   ★   £45
Tel 071-437 2069   R
56 Old Compton Street W1V 5PA   Map 22 C3

Arguably the most authentic Szechuan restaurant in Britain, now refurbished and with a long menu of classic dishes. Pelmeni (won ton) soups – red chili oil and soya sauce or hot and sour – are interesting choices alongside garlic ribs with spicy salt and chili, bang bang chicken or herb-marinated beef to start. There is a choice of three different duck dishes: Peking, crispy aromatic or tea-smoked; the last two are subtly fragrant and meaty. Sticklers for authenticity might choose stewed croaker fish, red-cooked aubergines or diced pork with cashew nut and chili – all done in Szechuan style. Crispy red bean pancakes are an excellent sweet taste with which to complete a meal. Service is usually attentive and cheerful. Our star is awarded for chef Tsao's cooking which shows that not all Szechuan cooking is richly flavoured and peppery hot; chili and spices are essential ingredients for many of the dishes, but by no means all. To stimulate the palate and create distinctive flavours is the ultimate aim and chef Tsao achieves this admirably. *Seats 60. Parties 14. Private Room. Meals 12-11.30. Closed Sun, 25 & 26 Dec. Set meals from £9.50. Access, Amex, Visa,* Diners Club International

W1   Park Lane Hotel   77%   £195
Tel 071-499 6321   Fax 071-499 1965   HR
Piccadilly W1Y 8EB   Map 25 A4

Built in 1927, the hotel retains some of its distinctive art deco features, although the feel throughout the public rooms and bedrooms is very traditional. The Palm Court lounge, where afternoon teas are served, is brightened by a magnificent vaulted ceiling with arched art deco stained glass. The Bracewells Bar and the Brasserie on the Park are more modern in style. The original art deco ballroom is popular with film makers. Standard bedrooms are well sized but tend to look out on the dark inside courtyard. All rooms have double-glazing, multi-channel TV, mini-bars and bathrobes. The best rooms are the suites: all air-conditioned, they look out on to the central court or Green Park and benefit from private sitting rooms and more luxurious bathrooms. Large-scale banqueting suites (including an art deco ballroom) for up to 600; conference facilities for up to 500. Parking in a covered garage for 180 cars. *Rooms 330. Keep-fit*

equipment, solarium, beauty & hair salons, brasserie noon-11.30pm, garage.
Access, Amex, Visa,

Bracewells   £70

The restaurant atmosphere is traditional. The decor is of dark carved wood,
light flowery panels, mirrors and silver trolleys; jacket and tie are a must.
New chef Jon Tindall plays comfortably with English and French classics
with particular attention to accompanying vegetables. Apple, celery and
Stilton soup coexist with lobster bisque, while calf's liver and bacon could
be an alternative to medallions of venison. Some desserts from the trolley
can be disappointing. The wine list is well constructed and the three-course
luncheon menu offers good value. *Seats 90. Parties 10. L 12.30-2.30*
D 7-10.30 Set L £17.50

W2   Parkwood Hotel   £65
Tel 071-402 2241 Fax 071-402 1574	**H**

4 Stanhope Place W2 2HB   Map 22 C2

Bed and breakfast town house hotel close to Marble Arch and Oxford
Street shops. Special rates for children under 13. Unlicensed. No dogs.
Rooms 18. Access, Visa, **(i)**

SW1   Pearl of Knightsbridge   NEW   £75
Tel 071-225 3888	**R**

22 Brompton Road Knightsbridge Green SW1   Map 23 D2

An unusually stylish Cantonese restaurant overlooking what there is of
Knightsbridge Green, with the inside quite high-tech (note the interesting
lighting) and traditional carved panels and gold Chinese characters on the
exterior. This is a luxurious and expensive Oriental restaurant as far
removed from Chinatown as imaginable. Head chef Felix has cooked in
London before and since he's also trained in Szechuan cooking, there are
influences from various provinces. Try the shark's fin soup, baked lobster
with ginger, crispy roasted chicken marinated in soya sauce, or seasonal
vegetables with Chinese mushrooms in oyster sauce. Dim sum at weekends.
Seats 80. Parties 20. Private Room. L 12-3 D 6-11.30 (Sat 12-11.30, Sun
12-11). Closed 25 & 26 Dec. Set L from £12.50 Set D from £25. Access,
Amex, Visa, **(i)**

W14   Peking Garden   £40
Tel 071-602 0312	**R**

11 Russell Gardens W14   Map 21 A4

Summery basement Chinese restaurant offering a long à la carte plus set
menus. *Seats 80. Parties 14. L 12-2.30 D 6-11.30. Closed 25 & 26 Dec. Set*
meals from £15.20. Access, Amex, Visa, **(i)**

SW7   Pelham Hotel   74%   £136
Tel 071-589 8288 Fax 071-589 8444	**H**

15 Cromwell Place SW7 2LA   Map 23 E1

Friendly, helpful staff and owners Kit and Tim Kemp's flair combine to
create a charmingly intimate hotel in the heart of South Kensington. Day
rooms, like the bar with 18th-century pine panelling and the cosy
Victorian snuggery, are most appealing with deeply comfortable armchairs
and profusion of fresh flowers. Paintings and antique furniture have been
carefully chosen by the owners. Bedrooms vary from small and cosy to
grand and high-ceilinged (on the first floor) but all feature fine fabrics
varying from traditional floral prints to bold black and white stripes.
Practicalities are not forgotten, either, with all rooms having a useful
second telephone by the desk and full air-conditioning. Excellent
bathrooms. Under the same ownership as *Durley House* and *Dorset Square*
hotels. Valet service and 24hr room service. Guests have free use of the
garden and outdoor swimming pool of the hotel's administrative building
opposite. *Rooms 37. Access, Amex, Visa.*

W2   Pembridge Court Hotel   65%   £100
Tel 071-229 9977   Fax 071-727 4982   H
34 Pembridge Gardens W2 4DX   Map 21 D3

Very close to Portobello market, Pembridge Court has personality,
warmth and charm thanks to a delightful, long-serving manager (Valerie
Gilliat) and well-motivated staff. There's an inviting feeling to the town
house as soon as you cross the threshold into the lobby with its exposed
brickwork, a style continued in the downstairs bar. Most of the bedrooms
are luxurious with stylishly co-ordinated fabrics and furnishings and
Victorian prints on the wall. Many of the bathrooms have chic Italian tiles.
Rooms are generously proportioned, with three very spacious top-floor
rooms. Children up to 10 stay free in parents' room. Good breakfasts.
Rooms 21. Access, Amex, Visa,

NW6   Peter's   £60
Tel 071-624 5804   R
65 Fairfax Road NW6 4EE   Map 20 C3

20s' French decor with live piano music, good-value fixed-price meals
(with a choice) and a carte with one-price courses (£3.75 starters, £11.75
mains, £2.50 desserts). Chef-partner Jean Charles's style is traditional:
soupe de poisson, asparagus in puff pastry, snails and wild mushrooms in
filo pastry, salade niçoise, carré d'agneau or cote de boeuf (for two), half a
boneless duck with Calvados and ginger sauce, grilled halibut, panaché de
fruits de mer. Daily market specials such as Dover sole or roulade of sole
and salmon. *Seats 70. Parties 70. Private Room. L 12-3 D 6.30-11.30. Closed
L Sat, D Sun, 26 Dec, 1 Jan. Set L & D £13.95 (except Sat). Access, Amex,
Visa,*

NW5   Le Petit Prince   £30
Tel 071-267 0752   R
5 Holmes Road NW5 3AA   Map 20 B2

Friendly, lively place just off Kentish Town Road. Couscous is the main-
course speciality, running from the basic vegetable version to others with
extras like merguez, spicy meatballs, lamb kebabs and chicken. Chocolate
mousse is the favourite dessert. Drink Algerian red wine or Sans Culottes
beer. *Seats 54. Parties 20. Private Room. L 12.30-2.30 D 7-11.30 (Sat to
11.45, Sun to 11.15). Closed L Sat-Mon, 1 week Xmas, 1 week Aug. No credit
cards.*

W8   Phoenicia   £45
Tel 071-937 0120   R
11-13 Abingdon Road W8 6AH   Map 21 D3

A civilised, family-run Lebanese restaurant just off Kensington High Street.
Hot and cold hors d'oeuvre, from houmus and moutabal to chicken wings
and lamb's liver, precede charcoal-grilled main courses, with deliciously
sticky sweetmeats to finish. Besides the à la carte there are several set
menus, including vegetarian options, and a good-value lunchtime buffet.
*Seats 100. Parties 35. Private Room. Meals 12-11.45. Closed 24 & 25 Dec.
Set L £8.95 Set D £14.30. Access, Amex, Visa,*

W1   Pied à Terre   ★NEW   £105
Tel 071-636 1178   R
34 Charlotte Street W1P 1HJ   Map 22 B3

With more than a little help from their mentor Raymond Blanc, Richard
Neat and David Moore seemed to transform the premises that were
previously *Jamdani* almost overnight. The slate floor, the halogen lighting,
the white plaster walls and the steel chairs create a high-tech, somewhat

spartan look which Neat mirrors with his modern, minimalist approach to presentation. Fancy flourishes play no part in the dishes on his short, fixed-price menu, but the dishes themselves are full of interest: a broth-like casserole of lamb's tongues with cabbage leaves, carrots and turnips (he has a penchant for offal), rare-roasted pigeon with a confit of the leg, roast sea bass with an aniseed and orange beurre blanc, a superb hot chocolate soufflé accompanied by a tiny bitter chocolate tart, topped with a chocolate sorbet. Unafraid of charging prices that reflect the skills involved in producing tagliatelle of langoustines with a bouillon of asparagus, millefeuille of frog's legs, braised pig's head with root vegetables, or roasted veal sweetbreads, creamed parsley and a confit of turnips, the prices were fixed high right from the start. Neat challenges himself with sophisticated and adventurous dishes, and mainly succeeds. This is an important new opening. Concise wine list with few bargains. *Seats 30. Parties 10. L 12.15-2.15 D 7.15-10.15. Closed L Sat, all Sun, Bank Holidays, Xmas/New Year, 2 weeks Aug. Set L £17.50 Set D £36. Access, Visa.*

NW1   Pinocchio's

£60

R

Tel 071-388 7482

160 Eversholt Street NW1 1BL

Map 20 A3

Neat and compact, with an informal atmosphere that suits the light, interesting Italian cooking on offer: antipasto misto (goose salami, smoked venison, duck and quail with eggplant salad), fresh fettuccine with button mushroom and creamed leeks, calf's liver on skewers with mustard cream sauce. Zabaglione, tiramisu, pannacotta and Italian cheeses to finish. *Seats 45. Parties 60. L 12-3 D 6.30-11. Closed L Sat, all Sun, Bank Holidays, 24-31 Dec. Access, Amex, Visa,* Diners Club International

SE1   Pizzeria Castello

£30

R

Tel 071-703 2556

20 Walworth Road SE1 6SP

Map 21 D1

Brash, bustling and very popular pizzeria and basement wine bar on the Elephant and Castle roundabout. Effusive Italian charm, simple decor, tip-top pizzas (try the castellana with baby artichokes, olives, ham and mushrooms), fresh minestrone and a choice of pasta dishes. Sensibly-priced wines. *Seats 100. Parties 30. Meals 12-11 (Sat 5-11). Closed L Sat, all Sun, Bank Holidays, 10 days Xmas. Access, Visa,* Diners Club International

SW3   Poissonnerie de l'Avenue

£80

R

Tel 071-589 2457

82 Sloane Avenue SW3 3DZ

Map 23 E2

Darkwood panelling and marine artefacts give this old-fashioned fish restaurant and oyster bar (opposite Sir Terence Conran's eponymous shop) a relaxed and comfortable atmosphere. Cooking is careful and classic, service solicitous. Vegetables, charged separately, and 15% automatic service bump up the final bill beyond expectation. Unusually short wine list. *Seats 70. Parties 12. Private Room. L 12-3 D 7-12. Closed Sun, Bank Holidays, 10 days Xmas, 4 days Easter. Access, Amex, Visa,* Diners Club International

SW11   Pollyanna's

£72

R

Tel 071-228 0316

2 Battersea Rise SW11 1ED

Map 21 E2

Traditional and modern French cuisine in a comfortable and well-supported upmarket neighbourhood restaurant. Richard Aldridge's dinner menu (two or three courses fixed price) are short but select, with typical dishes such as millefeuille of chicken livers with a Sauternes sauce, fillet of cod topped with a herb crust served on mashed potato with a lemon sauce and roasted guinea fowl, served off the bone with a red wine sauce. Vegetarian dishes are always available. A superb list of French wines (nothing else) and plenty of half bottles; excellent selection under £20.

Seats 35. Parties 35. Private Room. D only 7-12. Closed Sun, 24-28 Dec, 1 Jan. Set L £14.95 Set D £18.50. Access, Visa.

SW1   Pomegranates   £80
Tel 071-828 6560   R

94 Grosvenor Road SW1V 3LE   Map 24 D3

"Variety is the spice of life" could be the motto of this durable basement restaurant, where Patrick Gwynn-Jones takes his customers on a gastronomic tour of the world. Gower oyster soup, taramasalata or borek with Sudanese pepper sauce could be a prelude to lemon sole meunière, English game pie, Cantonese roast duck or West Indian curried goat with plantain. *Seats 50. Parties 60. Private Room. L 12.30-2.15 D 7.30-11.15. Closed L Sat, all Sun, 25 & 26 Dec. Set L from £15. Access, Amex, Visa,* Diners Club International

SE1   Le Pont de la Tour   NEW   £80
Tel 071-403 8403   R

Butlers Wharf Building 36D Shad Thames Butlers Wharf SE1   Map 21 D1

Sir Terence Conran's latest venture is not just a converted Thameside wharf, but a veritable foodie complex, modestly self-styled as The Gastrodome, and includes an all-day Bar & Grill (no bookings or children under 14), bakery, food store and wine merchant in addition to the stylish restaurant. The setting is surely one of the most spectacular in London – right alongside the river at the south end of Tower Bridge, resplendent in its centenary coat of paint. Tables on the terrace (in good weather this must be the best alfresco dining area in London) and those by the many windows of a long, chic room are at a premium. David Burke, once sous-chef at Conran's *Bibendum*, produces evening à la carte menus that bear a similar family resemblance to his previous place of employ; the starting point is France (fish soup with rouille, Gruyère and croutons, homard poché à la nage, lapin grillé au vinaigre) with fashionable trips around the Mediterranean (marinated mozzarella, roast pepper and aubergine salad, grilled red mullet with basil and tomato vinaigrette) and back (roast venison with beetroot, port wine sauce and beetroot crisps, colcannon – mashed potato and cabbage). Much use is made of the open charcoal grill and seafood is generally outstandingly fresh. Vegetarian diners are not well catered for. Lunch is a fixed-price only affair with a reasonable choice. Bread is from their own bakery. The restaurant is approached via the **Bar & Grill**, a separate eating area next to the Crustacea Bar just inside the door, where a menu similar to the Bibendum Oyster Bar is offered: simple starters like egg mayonnaise, Piedmontese peppers, chicken liver paté and scallops ceviche, followed by plateau de fruits de mer (£33.50 for two minimum), oysters, salads (foie gras and French bean), crustacea and grills (calf's liver, entrecote with béarnaise sauce, Dover sole). The wine list wins our London Region 1993 Cellar of the Year award – top wines are at a premium, but the choice is wide and carefully selected. 15% service is added to all bills. *Seats 109. L 12-3 D 6-12 (Sun to 11) Bar & Grill 12-12 daily (Sun to 11). Closed 3 days Xmas. Set L £22.50. Access, Visa.*

WC2   Poons   £20
Tel 071-437 4549   R

27 Lisle Street WC2   Map 25 A2

William Poon's original Cantonese café is unchanged, unmodernised and unlicensed, and the enticing wind-dried meats still hang in the window; it's now run by his sister and her husband, Mr & Mrs Chiu. The decor may be a little shabby for some but the quality of food and value for money are unbeatable. *Seats 40. Parties 8. Private Room. Meals 12-11.30. Closed 25 & 26 Dec. No credit cards.*

WC2 Poons	£30
Tel 071-437 1528	**R**
4 Leicester Street WC2H 7BL	Map 25 A2

Unsophisticated, yet wholesome, mainly Cantonese food served swiftly in simple surroundings; better value than its Covent Garden sister. Wind-dried meats and steamed chicken with Chinese sausage are specialities here. Original rice hot pot and noodle soup dishes make for inexpensive eating out. Hard by *Manzi's* and *Joy King Lau*. **Seats 100.** *Parties 55. Private Room. Meals 12-11.30. Closed 3 days Xmas. Set meals from £9. Access, Amex, Visa,*

WC1 Poons	£50
Tel 071-580 1188	**R**
50 Woburn Place WC1	Map 22 A4

Another outlet in this Chinese chain, but with more than a few out-of-the-ordinary dishes: broad beans sautéed with salt and peppercorns, crispy yam croquettes with roast duck, shredded jellyfish with sesame oil, roasted suckling pig (ordered in advance), abalone various ways, chicken with dried tiger lilies and fungi, wind-dried pork slices with celery. Try the red bean paste pancakes or almond-flavoured bean curd to finish. **Seats 100.** *Parties 50. Private Room. L 12-3 D 5.30-11.30. Closed Bank Holidays, 4 days Xmas. Set meals from £9. Access, Amex, Visa,*

W2 Poons	£55
Tel 071-792 2884	**R**
Unit 205 Whiteleys Queensway W2	Map 22 C1

Located in the food court on the third floor. Cool, black and white decor and varying standards of service depending on how busy they are.
A large range of dim sum, including steamed buns, pot rice and soft rice pasta sheets, is served between noon and 4pm. The long main menu ranges from seaweed to sea bass or sizzling scallops in black bean sauce, crab claws to cuttlefish cakes, sliced duck covered with mashed yam to fried beef with cashew nuts. **Seats 120.** *Parties 120. Private Room. Meals 12-11. Closed 25 & 26 Dec. Set meals from £12. Access, Amex, Visa,*

WC2 Poons	£70
Tel 071-240 1743	**R**
41 King Street WC2E 8JS	Map 25 B2

Just a few moments from the Covent Garden piazza, the smartest and most expensive of the Poons restaurant, to where William Poon expanded after opening his original, small café in Lisle Street (see entry) more than 20 years ago. The unusual greenhouse-style kitchen forms the centrepiece of the interior decor and was designed in the mid-70s to deter customers from believing horror stories about Chinese restaurant kitchens. Nowadays, customers are more certain about what actually goes into an authentic Cantonese menu and choose the house wind-dried specialities such as sausages, duck and bacon. Hot pots and dishes cooked in the style of Mr Poon's home town (typically deep-fried stuffed bean curd and stir-fried beef) are also specialities of the house. Lap Yuck Soom (a starter for two that includes finely chopped, stir-fried wind-dried bacon with bamboo shoots, water chestnuts and lettuce leaves), a three-course duck feast (Kam Ling style) and Buddha's Hand (chicken stuffed with minced pork, water chestnuts and bamboo shoots served with peppercorn salt and sweet and sour sauce) are always popular. **Seats 100.** *Parties 14. Meals 12-12. Closed Sun Jan-Jun, 24-27 Dec. Set L from £13 Set D from £24 (pre-theatre from £17). Access, Amex, Visa,*

W11   Portobello Hotel   60%   £135

Tel 071-727 2777   Fax 071-792 9641   **H**

22 Stanley Gardens W11 2NG   Map 21 D3

Two six-floor houses in an 1850 terrace near Portobello antiques market
converted into a unique hotel decorated in an eclectic mix of styles. There
are singles, doubles, twins and suites, plus some compact cabins. Children
sharing parents' room stay free. The 24hr bar and restaurant in the
basement caters admirably for those guests with nocturnal life styles.
Rooms 25. *Closed 2 weeks Xmas. Access, Amex, Visa,*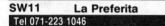

EC2   Le Poulbot   £85

Tel 071-236 4379   **R**

45 Cheapside EC2V 6AR   Map 24 B2

In the heart of the City, a lunchtime-only basement restaurant in the Roux
Brothers' empire. Plush red banquette seating with private booths makes
this an ideal setting for a business lunch. New chef Yves Gautier offers a
fixed-price, three-course French menu inclusive of aperitif of your choice,
coffee and petits fours. The choice is usually around five dishes per course
and might include stuffed courgette flowers, artichoke terrine with goat's
cheese or curried mussels to start, followed by cod with asparagus and an
orange sauce, salmon and sorrel lasagne or medallions of pork with ginger
and a confit of shallots. A brasserie-style operation – *Le Poulbot Pub* – is on
the ground floor (open for breakfast from 7.30-10.30 and lunch 12-3, no
reservations). **Seats 50.** *Parties 7. L only 12-3. Closed Sat & Sun, Bank
Holidays. Set L £31.50. Access, Visa,*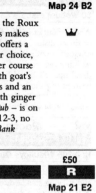

SW11   La Preferita   £50

Tel 071-223 1046   **R**

163 Lavender Hill SW11 5QH   Map 21 E2

Booking is advisable as the closely-packed tables fill up quickly in this
attractive Italian restaurant. The menu features a range of well-prepared
and familiar favourites with a refreshing smattering of more innovative
dishes. Current favourites include grilled vegetables, spaghetti cooked with
seafood in a paper bag, grilled calamari with fresh chili, osso buco.
Seats 45. *L 12-3 D 7-11.30. Closed L Sat, 24-26 Dec. Access, Amex, Visa.*

WC1   President Hotel   £72

Tel 071-837 8844   Fax 071-837 4653   **H**

Russell Square WC1N 1DB   Map 22 B4

Large bed and breakfast hotel next door to the Imperial, on the corner of
Guilford Street and Southampton Row, catering mainly for tour parties
and exhibition delegates from surrounding sister hotels. Close to the British
Museum. **Rooms 447.** *Coffee shop (10.30am-2am). Access, Amex, Visa,*

SW7   Prince Hotel   £71

Tel 071-589 6488   Fax 071-581 0024   **H**

6 Sumner Place SW7 3AB   Map 23 E1

Two houses in an early Victorian terrace provide comfortable bed and
breakfast accommodation near South Kensington underground station.
Some rooms are without private facilities. One family room sleeps four.
Chintzy lounge; plant-filled conservatory. No bar; breakfast is the only
meal served. Under the same ownership as *Alexander Hotel* (see entry) at 9,
Sumner Place. **Rooms 20.** *Garden. Access, Amex, Visa.*

SW7   Pun

£50

Tel 071-225 1609

R

53 Old Brompton Road SW7 3JS

Map 23 E1

Good food served by friendly staff in smart surroundings has kept this
Chinese restaurant near South Kensington station busy since its opening
eight years ago. Seafood is a speciality, typified by sea bass soup with
coriander, crab and lobster with ginger and onion or black beans and green
pepper, Dover sole Kwangtung style and sea-spice-flavoured sautéed
oysters. Szechuan duck and double-cooked pork are other popular classics.
*Seats 72. Parties 28. Private Room. L 12-3 D 6-11.30 Meals (Sat & Sun
12-11.30). Closed 25 & 26 Dec. Access, Amex, Visa,*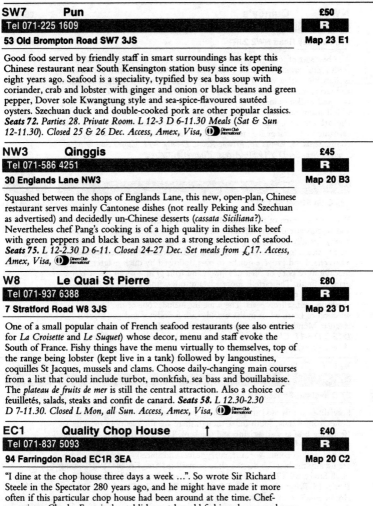

NW3   Qinggis

£45

Tel 071-586 4251

R

30 Englands Lane NW3

Map 20 B3

Squashed between the shops of Englands Lane, this new, open-plan, Chinese
restaurant serves mainly Cantonese dishes (not really Peking and Szechuan
as advertised) and decidedly un-Chinese desserts (*cassata Siciliana?*).
Nevertheless chef Pang's cooking is of a high quality in dishes like beef
with green peppers and black bean sauce and a strong selection of seafood.
*Seats 75. L 12-2.30 D 6-11. Closed 24-27 Dec. Set meals from £17. Access,
Amex, Visa,*

W8   Le Quai St Pierre

£80

Tel 071-937 6388

R

7 Stratford Road W8 3JS

Map 23 D1

One of a small popular chain of French seafood restaurants (see also entries
for *La Croisette* and *Le Suquet*) whose decor, menu and staff evoke the
South of France. Fishy things have the menu virtually to themselves, top of
the range being lobster (kept live in a tank) followed by langoustines,
coquilles St Jacques, mussels and clams. Choose daily-changing main courses
from a list that could include turbot, monkfish, sea bass and bouillabaisse.
The *plateau de fruits de mer* is still the central attraction. Also a choice of
feuilletés, salads, steaks and confit de canard. *Seats 58. L 12.30-2.30
D 7-11.30. Closed L Mon, all Sun. Access, Amex, Visa,*

EC1   Quality Chop House   ↑

£40

Tel 071-837 5093

R

94 Farringdon Road EC1R 3EA

Map 20 C2

"I dine at the chop house three days a week ...". So wrote Sir Richard
Steele in the Spectator 280 years ago, and he might have made it more
often if this particular chop house had been around at the time. Chef-
proprietor Charles Fontaine's establishment has old-fashioned, cramped pew
seats (you'll probably need to share) and a lively, buzzing atmosphere.
Good plain food is served at very reasonable prices in generous quantities.
"Progressive Working Class Caterer" introduces a menu that progresses
from egg, bacon and chips, corned beef hashcake and lamb chops to
linguine with pesto and grilled halibut steak hollandaise. Eight or so dishes
(scrambled eggs with smoked salmon, bang bang chicken, roast lamb and
rocket salad) are dual priced as starters or main courses, inviting one-course
dining, although desserts like tiramisu, pecorino cheese with pear or bread-
and-butter pudding are likely to tempt. No longer open for breakfast.
*Seats 46. Parties 6. L 12-3 (Sun 12-3.30) D 6.30-12. Closed L Sat. No credit
cards.*

NW2   Quincy's   £55
Tel 071-794 8499   R
675 Finchley Road NW2 2JP   Map 20 B3

The best sort of local restaurant – friendly front-of-house, good quality
fresh food, reasonable prices. The menu, of British and French provenance,
is short but varied with dishes such as chicken livers in a tartlet with grapes
and tarragon, smoked haddock on a potato skin, sirloin with a fumet of
ceps and grilled guinea fowl with roast vegetables and Madeira. The fish
dish depends on what's good in the market. Desserts could be traditional –
rhubarb crumble, treacle tart – or more modern like glazed satsumas with
cardamon and orange ice cream, or pistachio charlotte on strawberry
coulis. *Seats 30. Parties 16. Private Room. D only 7-11. Closed Sun & Mon,
2 weeks Sep. Set D £19.50. Access, Visa,* **①** Diners Club International

SE1   RSJ   £63
Tel 071-928 4554   R
13a Coin Street SE1 8YQ   Map 24 A3

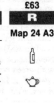

Within easy reach of the South Bank complex, thus a handy spot for pre-
and post-theatre dinners. Modern British cooking with French influences in
a very friendly and relaxing restaurant (upstairs) and brasserie (downstairs).
Fixed-price 2- or 3-course menus might offer tartare of smoked haddock or
Swiss chard and gruyère quiche to start, followed by duck magret,
medallions of pork or fillet of salmon and fruit gratin, pecan pie or coupe
glace to finish. The carte is more adventurous with the likes of Anjou
pigeon salad, maize-fed chicken stuffed with caramelised apples and
chestnuts, and saffron pears. The wine list includes one of the finest
selection of Loire wines in the world – ask for advice and you'll get it.
Regular Monday wine-tasting dinners. *Seats 90. Parties 16. Private Room.
L 12-2 D 6-11. Closed L Sat, all Sun, Bank Holidays. Set meals from £13.75.
Access, Amex, Visa.*

W1   Ragam   £25
Tel 071-636 9098   R
57 Cleveland Street W1P 5PQ   Map 22 B3

Specialities at this modest, yet popular Indian restaurant are vegetarian
dishes from Kerala, South India, though there are also plenty of meat dishes
(featuring beef as well as lamb and chicken). Try dosai (rice and lentil flour
pancakes), vadai (gram flour doughnuts), and avial (mixed vegetables
cooked with coconut, yoghurt, curry leaves and spices) – vegetarian dishes
are usually the best. Under the same ownership: *Sree Krishna*, 192 Tooting
High Street, SW17 (081-672 4250, open later at weekends). *Seats 60.
Parties 15. Private Room. L 12-3 D 6-11.30 (Fri to 12). Closed 25 & 26 Dec.
Access, Amex, Visa,* **①** Diners Club International

W12   Rajput   £26
Tel 081-740 9036   R
144 Goldhawk Road W12 8HH   Map 21 D4

North Indian restaurant with helpful staff, near Goldhawk Road
underground station. Specialities include murgh tikka masala (tandoori-
grilled chicken with creamy sauce) and gosht badam pasanda (slices of
lamb with yoghurt, cream,butter and whole spices). Bangalore phal will
appeal to macho man. Sunday buffet. *Seats 48. Parties 20. L 12-2.30
D 6-11.45. Closed 25 & 26 Dec. Set L from £6.95. Access, Amex, Visa,*
① Diners Club International

N3 Rani

£40
R

Tel 081-349 4386

7 Long Lane N3 2PR

Map 20 A3

Rani may well be the queen of London's Gujerati restaurants – a clean and sparkling diner with a wide frontage and a fine repertoire of vegetarian food. Full use is made of grain flours and various dal combined with fresh, exotic vegetables and delicate spicing. Start perhaps with a choice of spiced lentil soups or bajia, bhel poori, bean papri chat (spicy beans and chopped onions served on crispy pooris with tamarind and yoghurt sauce), or a daily special (perhaps rani tiffin, hachori or stuffed green chili). Similarly, a special curry changes daily (spinach and sweetcorn, gram flour and fenugreek balls or stuffed okra). Chutneys are made on the premises and desserts should not be missed. The children's set menu (£5) serves tomato ketchup with potato bajia followed by poppadum, bean curry, dosa and bhatoora – showing that this is no ordinary Indian restaurant! Prices are extremely reasonable and service is by professional, young and motivated staff who operate a 'no tipping' policy. Equally good-value set meals only all lunchtimes and Monday dinner. Egon Ronay's *Just a Bite* Guide London Restaurant of the Year 1992. *Seats 90. L 12.30-2 D 6-10.30. Closed L Mon, Tue & Sat, 25 Dec. Set meals from £11.50. Access, Visa.*

W1 Rasa Sayang

£40
R

Tel 071-734 8720

10 Frith Street W1

Map 25 A2

Malaysian and South-East Asian food (prepared without using MSG) served in congenial surroundings. Set meals provide a good introduction to an interesting cuisine that includes traditional dishes like orange chicken, special rice dishes and rendang (cutlets of beef in coconut gravy). *Also at:* 38 Queensway W2 Tel 071-229 8417 Map 22C1. *Seats 200. Parties 150. Private Room. L 12-2.45 D 6-11.30 (Sun 1-10). Closed L Sat, Bank Holidays. Set meals from £20.50. Access, Amex, Visa,*

W1 Rathbone Hotel 69%

£142
H

Tel 071-636 2001   Fax 071-636 3882

30 Rathbone Street W1P 1AJ

Map 22 B3

An intimate hotel notable for its location (minutes from Oxford Street) and personal air. Crystal chandeliers, Italian marble and objets d'art adorn the limited public areas. The stylishness is matched in carefully modelled bedrooms, where smoked-glass mirrors add depth and boldly patterned curtains enrich the colour. Brightly lit, marbled bathrooms all have powerful showers. Executive and single-bedroomed suites feature whirlpool baths. Plush, perhaps, but not deluxe; no leisure facilities. *Rooms 72. Access, Amex, Visa,*

NW1 Ravi Shankar

£25
R

Tel 071-388 6458

135 Drummond Street NW1 2H1

Map 22 A3

South Indian vegetarian cooking in friendly, informal surroundings. Prices are very low, and the afternoon buffet lets you eat as much as you like for £3.95. *Also at:* 422 St John Street, EC1 Tel 071-833 5849 Map 20 C1 (open L 12-3.30 D 6-11) *Closed L Sun-Thurs. Seats 58. Parties 30. Private Room. Meals 12-11. Set meals from £2.75. Access, Visa,*

W1 La Reash

£35
R

Tel 071-439 1063

23 Greek Street W1

Map 25 A2

In the heart of Soho, at the junction of Old Compton Street and Greek Street, La Reash specialises in Lebanese and Moroccan cuisine. Mazala (Meze) and kebabs represent the former, couscous the latter. *Seats 60. Meals 12-12. Closed 25 Dec. Set L from £5. Access, Visa.*

W1 Red Fort £50

Tel 071-437 2525 **R**

77 Dean Street W1V 5HA **Map 25 A2**

Opened in 1983 by Amin Ali, the stylish Red Fort takes its name from the red sandstone fort built by Emperor Shah Jahan on the banks of the river Jamuna in Delhi. The chefs are expert in Moghul cuisine; tandoori food is a popular choice and includes not only lamb, chicken and prawns but quail, trout and duck. Elsewhere on the menu hare and pomfret find a place beside more familiar dishes. 15% service charge is added to all bills. ***Seats 150.*** *Parties 75. Private Room. L 12-3 D 6-11.30. Closed 25 Dec. Set L £12.50. Access, Amex, Visa,* Diners Club International

SW7 Regency Hotel 68% £156

Tel 071-370 4595 Fax 071-370 5555 **H**

100 Queen's Gate SW7 5AG **Map 23 E1**

Privately owned hotel near the South Kensington museums and Knightsbridge shopping. Beyond the marble foyer the Terrace (more marble, and natural light) is a pleasant spot for afternoon tea, and there's a cocktail bar, a health spa and several conference rooms (maximum capacity 100). Children up to 12 stay free in parents' room. No dogs. ***Rooms 210.*** *Sauna, solarium, spa bath, keep-fit equipment, steam room, beautician, 24hr lounge service. Access, Amex, Visa,* Diners Club International

NW3 Regent's Park Marriott 73% £178

Tel 071-722 7711 Fax 071-586 5822 **H**

128 King Henry's Road Swiss Cottage NW3 3ST **Map 20 C3**

Formerly a Holiday Inn, this modern hotel has a lot to offer: good-sized rooms with large beds, desks, breakfast tables and easy chairs; free car parking; facilities for up to 400 conference delegates; a well-equipped health and leisure centre. The foyer features marble flooring and pale-wood panelling, a theme which extends to the bar lounge. Children stay free in parents' room. Not far from Swiss Cottage underground station. ***Rooms 303.*** *Garden, indoor swimming pool, sauna, solarium, beauty and hair salon, gift shop. Access, Amex, Visa,* Diners Club International

SW7 Rembrandt Hotel 67% £146

Tel 071-589 8100 Fax 071-225 3363 **H**

11 Thurloe Place SW7 2RS **Map 23 D2**

The Aquilla health and fitness centre, designed along the lines of an ancient Roman Spa, is a notable feature of a well-kept Sarova Group hotel opposite the Victoria and Albert Museum. Best of the stylish day rooms is a marble-pillared bar-lounge with a glass-roofed annexe where a pianist plays. A recent improvement programme has upgraded 62 rooms to Executive standard, with jacuzzis. Conference facilities for up to 250. ***Rooms 195.*** *Gymnasium, exercise room, indoor swimming pool, spa bath, sauna, solarium, beautician. Access, Amex, Visa,* Diners Club International

SW10 La Réserve 62% £80

Tel 071-385 8561 Fax 071-385 7662 **H**

422 Fulham Road SW6 1DU **Map 23 F1**

A strikingly different hotel, created with a keen eye for modern design throughout. Day rooms are virtually non-existent, apart from a small lounge off the lobby. Both this lounge and the cool bar feature modern seating aimed at style rather than comfort. Bedrooms are small with high-tech furniture and contemporary fabrics. ***Rooms 40.*** *Access, Amex, Visa,* Diners Club International

W1   The Ritz   86%

Tel 071-493 8181   Fax 071-493 2687

150 Piccadilly W1V 9DG

£247

HR

Map 22 C3

When César Ritz opened this hotel in 1906 it was his intention to create "the most fashionable hotel in the most fashionable city in the world". Today's management endeavours to keep at least the first part true, and standards of service, comfort and housekeeping are enviably high. Tea at the Ritz is part of our heritage and the Palm Court is one of London's most elegant teatime settings. The rest of the hotel is equally grand: the Long Gallery, the sumptuously beautiful restaurant, the private salons and the bedrooms, with delicate pastels and gold leaf, marble fireplaces, Louis XVI furnishings and lavishly equipped marble bathrooms. Children up to 8 stay free in parents' room. This is the flagship of the Cunard group, owners also of Dukes and Stafford hotels. No dogs. *Rooms 129. Garden, valeting, dinner dance (Fri & Sat). Access, Amex, Visa,*

Ritz Restaurant

£120

One of London's grandest dining rooms, with chandeliers, ornate gilt plasterwork, a beautiful painted ceiling and tapestry-covered chairs. The menus offer a varied mix of classic and modern dishes in the luxury mould. The Italian Garden overlooking Green Park is one of *the* places for alfresco dining. *Seats 100. Parties 80. Private Room. L 12.30-2.30 D 6.30-11. Set L from £22.*

SW13   Riva

Tel 081-748 0434

169 Church Road Barnes SW13 9HR

£60

R

Map 21 E4

Since opening in the summer of 1990, Andrea Riva's small restaurant has been a front-runner in the new wave of Italian cooking and has already built up a large and loyal following. Mirrors, prints on pale walls, high-tech lighting and taped opera provide a backdrop for dishes like grilled endive, radicchio, dandelion and mushrooms with herbed olive oil; potato and spinach dumplings with bitto cheese; duck breast with roasted pumpkins; roast shank of lamb with mashed potatoes and caramelised onions; and zabaglione with almonds and bananas. Not everything scores full marks, but young chef Francesco Zanchetta's unfussy approach produces plenty of robust flavours. Decent Italian wines and a large selection of grappas. *Seats 50. Parties 10. L 12.15-2.30 D 7-11 (Sun to 9.30). Closed L Sat, Bank Holidays, 25 Dec-2 Jan, 4 days Easter, 2 weeks Aug. Access, Visa.*

W6   River Café

Tel 071-381 8824

Thames Wharf Studios Rainville Road W6 9HA

£80

R

Map 21 E3

Very close to the Thames, but not so close as to offer views unless you're sitting outside. Opened in 1987, it instantly made waves with its Italian regional cooking; Ruth Rogers and Rose Gray are leading exponents of a cuisine that puts the emphasis on simple, fresh ingredients, marinades and the chargrill. Pappa pomodoro – a thick peasant soup of Tuscan bread, plum tomatoes and fresh basil – typifies a style that runs throughout the menu: chargrilled squid with fresh chili, calf's sweetbreads with sorrel, pancetta and chicory, bollito misto (using guinea fowl or free-range chicken), marinated leg of lamb with salsa verde, new potatoes, red onions and balsamic vinegar. 12½% service charge is automatically added to your bill. As we went to press, the River Café was still subject to local restrictions which insist that diners must leave the premises by 11pm sharp. *Seats 75. Parties 15. Private Room. L 12.30-3 D 7.30-9.45. Closed D Sat & Sun, 10 days Xmas, 4 days Easter, Bank Holidays. Access, Visa,*

W2   Romantica Taverna   £40

`Tel 071-727 7112`   **R**

10 Moscow Road W2 4BT   Map 22 C1

Enjoyable, straightforward Greek fare in a long-established restaurant just
off Queensway. Kleftiko is always a good bet. *Seats 70. Parties 60. Private
Room. L 12-3 D 5.30-12. Closed L Sat, 3 days Xmas. Access, Amex, Visa,*

W12   The Rotisserie   £40

`Tel 081-743 3028`   **R**

56 Uxbridge Road W12 8LP   Map 21 D3

Friendly and informal eating place next to Shepherds Bush underground
station. Pride of place in the large, airy room goes to the charcoal
grill/rotisserie, where the main courses are prepared: corn-fed chicken,
paper-wrapped salmon, Toulouse sausages, calf's liver, rack of lamb, rib-eye
steaks. It's in the same ownership as the *Camden Brasserie,* and the little
chips are just as good. *Seats 90. Parties 50. L 12-3 D 6.30-11 (Fri to 11.30,
Sat 7-11.30). Closed L Sat & Bank Holidays, all Sun. Access, Visa.*

W2   Royal China   £48

`Tel 071-221 2535`   **R**

13 Queensway W2   Map 22 B2

Striking decor of black lacquered walls, with gold and silver inlaid murals,
spotlights and smartly uniformed staff. This is a very serious Chinese
restaurant serving many dishes that get out of the rut: steamed curried
squid and grilled turnip paste with dried meat in the dim sum selection
(noon-5pm), deep-fried whole quail, spring onion duck and marinated pork
with jellyfish among the specialities. Also of note are hot and spicy veal, six
ways with lobster, Szechuan whole fish and the sizzling dishes. *Seats 100.
Parties 40. Private Room. Meals 12-11.30. Set D from £20. Access, Amex,
Visa,*

SW1   Royal Court Hotel   68%   £164

`Tel 071-730 9191   Fax 071-824 8381`   **H**

Sloane Square SW1W 8EG   Map 23 E2

The reception area, with its panelling and chandeliers, sets an elegant tone
for the Royal Court, which stands on a prime site on Sloane Square. The
Tavern is a traditional English pub serving meals at lunchtime, while
Courts café bar is open from 11am to 11pm. Bedrooms feature limed oak
period-style furniture and soft pastel colour schemes. Queens Moat Houses.
Rooms 102. Access, Amex, Visa,

W8   Royal Garden Hotel   80%   £224

`Tel 071-937 8000   Fax 071-938 4532`   **HR**

Kensington High Street W8 4PT   Map 23 D1

A modern high-rise hotel between the bustle of the high street and the
green expanse of Kensington Gardens. Service under general manager
James Brown is a priority for his polished and professional team. The lofty
marbled lobby is all you'd expect from a hotel of this standard, and above
it is the two-tiered Gallery Bar. The Garden Bar and Lounge overlook the
park, as do the brightest and sometimes balconied bedrooms, all of them
well equipped. Room size is adequate, and bathrooms have good solid
fittings, some gold-plated. The top, Reserve Floor offers more luxurious
rooms and suites with butler service. Banqueting (for up to 640) and
conference facilities (up to 900) are on a grand scale; large underground car
park. Three executive boardrooms hold up to 12. No dogs. Rank Hotels.
*Rooms 398. Valeting, car park, news kiosk, Garden Café (7am-11pm). Access,
Amex, Visa,*

Royal Roof Restaurant £120

Like the hotel, the tenth-floor restaurant has aged well, the views to Kensington Round Pond and beyond are still fabulous and Friday and Saturday nights (when a dance band plays) are always popular. The chef offers both table d'hote and à la carte menus, the latter covering a range from hot soufflé of avocado, smoked salmon and green peppercorns or chilled artichoke filled with seasonal vegetables and orange lentil sauce to sea bass with langoustines and leeks, fillet of lamb with sherry vinegar, celeriac and morels, and fillet of venison on cabbage with roasted goose liver. The prices can hardly be called keen, but the effort is there. The wine list encompasses most regions, albeit at stiffish prices. *Seats 70. Parties 18. L 12.30-2.30 D 7.30-10.30 (Fri & Sat to 11). Closed Sun. Set L £18.95 Set D £33.*

SW1   Royal Horseguards Thistle   71%   £140

Tel 071-839 3400   Fax 071-925 2263

2 Whitehall Court SW1A 2EJ   Map 22 C4

A spacious foyer with beautiful Wedgwood-style moulded ceilings sets the tone of elegant public rooms in a comfortable hotel close to the Thames Embankment. A charming lounge area in cool, pastel lemon shades boasts chandeliers, oil paintings and a country-house style of furniture. Bedrooms range widely from a single overlooking Whitehall Court to the Tower Suite on two floors with a panoramic view of the City. The best are grand, spacious rooms with attractive limed oak furniture, elegant mirrors and colourful chintzy fabrics. Superb marble bathrooms are a stunning feature of some rooms. Excellent range of meeting rooms, catering for conferences up to 750. Children up to the age of 12 are accommodated free in parents' room. *Rooms 376. Coffee shop (7.30am-11pm). Access, Amex, Visa,*

W2   Royal Lancaster Hotel   75%   £156

Tel 071-262 6737   Fax 071-724 3191

Lancaster Terrace W2 2TY   Map 22 C1

Just a few minutes from Marble Arch and the West End, this fine modern hotel enjoys splendid views of Hyde Park from its upper floors. Day rooms show style and quality: the long-hours Pavement Café (6.45am-11pm), the elegant lounge – a favourite spot for afternoon tea, La Rosette restaurant, and several suites with technical facilities for meetings and conferences (up to 1400 delegates). Best of the high-class accommodation is on the Reserve Club floors (15th to 18th) with five luxurious suites and a reserved drawing room, bar and boardroom. No dogs. *Rooms 418. Business centre, hairdressing, news kiosk, car hire desk, garage. Access, Amex, Visa,*

WC2   Royal Trafalgar Thistle   64%   £145

Tel 071-930 4477   Fax 071-925 2149

Whitcomb Street WC2 7HG   Map 25 A3

Modern hotel behind the National Gallery, close to Leicester and Trafalgar Squares. Best rooms are on the top floor; the fourth floor has recently been refurbished. Children up to the age of 12 are accommodated free in parents' room. *Rooms 108. Hamiltons Brasserie (7.30am-11.30pm 7 days). Access, Amex, Visa,*

SW1   Royal Westminster Thistle   71%   £150

Tel 071-834 1821   Fax 071-828 8933

Buckingham Palace Road SW1W 0QT   Map 23 D3

Polished marble and carved wood grace the foyer, where smartly turned-out staff provide a warm and efficient welcome. The Royal Lounge is a stylish venue for afternoon tea, while the Parisian-style Café Saint-Germain provides a relaxed, casual ambience for a drink or snack. Individually air-conditioned bedrooms are of a generally good size and have pickled-pine furnishings and a wide range of accessories. Children up to the age of 14 are accommodated free in parents' room. *Rooms 134. Access, Amex, Visa,* ① *Diners Club International*

SW1 **Rubens Hotel** 66%	£134

Tel 071-834 6600   Fax 071-828 5401 — **H**

Buckingham Palace Road SW1W 0PS — **Map 23 A6**

Opened at the turn of the century, the Rubens stands in a prime position facing the Royal Mews behind Buckingham Palace; it's also conveniently close to Victoria Station and Westminster. Comfortable day rooms in country house style include a library lounge and a cocktail bar with resident pianist. Well-appointed bedrooms (just one suite) offer the usual extras. No dogs. Five conference suites cater for up to 75 delegates. Sarova Hotels. *Rooms 189. Access, Amex, Visa,* ① *Diners Club International*

W1 **Rue St Jacques**	£95

Tel 071-637 0222   Fax 071-637 0224 — **R**

5 Charlotte Street W1P 1HD — **Map 22 B3**

Formal French restaurant comprising a number of small, elegantly appointed rooms. Gunther Schlender's menus are based on the French classics, but modern and exotic influences are apparent in such dishes as light smoked haddock gateau with a fennel jelly or sautéed scallops with a juice of ginger and lemon grass. More traditional renditions of veal and beef, fine sorbets, excellent French cheeseboard and a comprehensive list of mostly French wines, though few are realistically priced. Vintage Bordeaux date back to 1937. *Seats 70. Parties 45. Private Room. L 12.15-2.30 D 7.15-11. Closed L Sat, all Sun, Bank Holidays, 10 days Xmas/New Year. Set L £19.50 Set D £25. Access, Amex, Visa,* ① *Diners Club International*

WC2 **Rules**	£60

Tel 071-836 5314 — **R**

35 Maiden Lane WC2E 7LB — **Map 25 B2**

Coming up for its second centenary, Rules claims itself as the oldest restaurant in London. Its literary and artistic connections are captured in the paintings, cartoons, sketches and theatre bills that cover the walls. Cooking is run-of-the-mill traditional English, with oysters, game, pies and puddings the specialities. *Seats 120. Parties 48. Private Room. Meals 12-12 (Sun 12-10.30). Closed 3/4 days Xmas. Access, Amex, Visa.*

WC1 **Hotel Russell** 68%	£140

Tel 071-837 6470   Fax 071-837 2857 — **H**

Russell Square WC1B 5BE — **Map 23 B4**

An imposing late-Victorian hotel, handy for both the City and the West End, with a hugely impressive marble foyer complete with grand staircase, crystal chandeliers and ornate plasterwork; public areas include a clubby panelled bar. The best of the bedrooms are located on the Executive 7th floor and have extra facilities like the use of a boardroom; the others are up-to-date, with a variety of attractive fabrics and well-maintained bathrooms. Banqueting facilities for 350, conference facilities for 450. No dogs. Forte Grand. *Rooms 326. Brasserie 11am-11pm (from 5pm Sat, Sun, Mon). Access, Amex, Visa,* ① *Diners Club International*

W1   SAS Portman   76%

Tel 071-486 5844   Fax 071-935 0537

22 Portman Square W1H 9FL

£227

H

Map 22 B2

Scandinavian Air Services are the new owners of this stylish hotel dating from the early 1970s and standing just a few blocks from Marble Arch. Bedrooms are all equipped with desks, mini-bar, air-conditioning and a room key-card security system. Top of the range are the two-bedroomed penthouses. Among the day rooms are the Bakery and the Pub, open throughout the day for informal meals and pub lunches. First floor banqueting suites can cater for up to 400 delegates. *Rooms 272. Coffee shop (11am-midnight). Access, Amex, Visa,*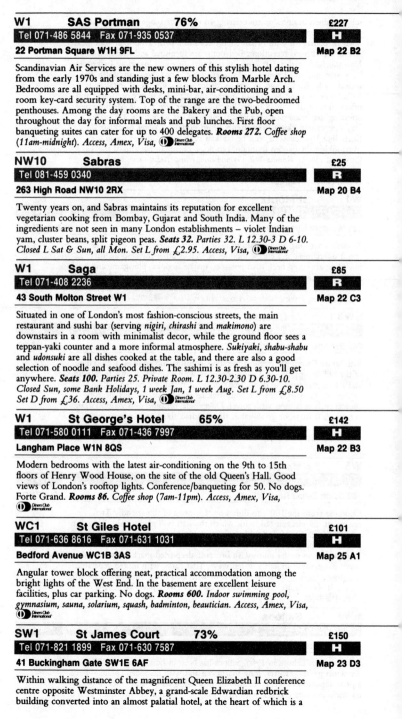

NW10   Sabras

Tel 081-459 0340

263 High Road NW10 2RX

£25

R

Map 20 B4

Twenty years on, and Sabras maintains its reputation for excellent vegetarian cooking from Bombay, Gujarat and South India. Many of the ingredients are not seen in many London establishments – violet Indian yam, cluster beans, split pigeon peas. *Seats 32. Parties 32. L 12.30-3 D 6-10. Closed L Sat & Sun, all Mon. Set L from £2.95. Access, Visa,*

W1   Saga

Tel 071-408 2236

43 South Molton Street W1

£85

R

Map 22 C3

Situated in one of London's most fashion-conscious streets, the main restaurant and sushi bar (serving *nigiri, chirashi* and *makimono*) are downstairs in a room with minimalist decor, while the ground floor sees a teppan-yaki counter and a more informal atmosphere. *Sukiyaki, shabu-shabu* and *udonsuki* are all dishes cooked at the table, and there are also a good selection of noodle and seafood dishes. The sashimi is as fresh as you'll get anywhere. *Seats 100. Parties 25. Private Room. L 12.30-2.30 D 6.30-10. Closed Sun, some Bank Holidays, 1 week Jan, 1 week Aug. Set L from £8.50 Set D from £36. Access, Amex, Visa,*

W1   St George's Hotel   65%

Tel 071-580 0111   Fax 071-436 7997

Langham Place W1N 8QS

£142

H

Map 22 B3

Modern bedrooms with the latest air-conditioning on the 9th to 15th floors of Henry Wood House, on the site of the old Queen's Hall. Good views of London's rooftop lights. Conference/banqueting for 50. No dogs. Forte Grand. *Rooms 86. Coffee shop (7am-11pm). Access, Amex, Visa,*

WC1   St Giles Hotel

Tel 071-636 8616   Fax 071-631 1031

Bedford Avenue WC1B 3AS

£101

H

Map 25 A1

Angular tower block offering neat, practical accommodation among the bright lights of the West End. In the basement are excellent leisure facilities, plus car parking. No dogs. *Rooms 600. Indoor swimming pool, gymnasium, sauna, solarium, squash, badminton, beautician. Access, Amex, Visa,*

SW1   St James Court   73%

Tel 071-821 1899   Fax 071-630 7587

41 Buckingham Gate SW1E 6AF

£150

H

Map 23 D3

Within walking distance of the magnificent Queen Elizabeth II conference centre opposite Westminster Abbey, a grand-scale Edwardian redbrick building converted into an almost palatial hotel, at the heart of which is a self-contained business centre offering an extensive range of rooms and services for up to 250 delegates. At the heart of the hotel stands a fine open-air courtyard with ornamental trees and a period fountain – an ideal setting for alfresco receptions. Bedrooms are furnished and equipped to a high standard, with smart reproduction furniture and luxurious bathrooms. 75 apartments and 19 suites are also available. The Olympian health club includes a health bar and an aerobic dance studio. Choice of restaurants includes French and Szechuan Chinese; the latter is smartly decorated and offers an unusual Sunday buffet lunch (£15 per head); Café Mediterranée offers lighter brasserie-style meals from breakfast to post-theatre snacks. Daytime valet parking (free after 6.30pm Friday). "Power breakfasts" (including Japanese-style) can be booked in the airy Chinese room overlooking the garden fountain. No dogs. European flagship of the Taj Group of Hotels. *Rooms 390. Gymnasium, sauna, steam room, spa bath, solarium, pool table, beauty salon, business centre, brasserie (7am-10.30pm). Access, Amex, Visa,*

W1   St Moritz

	£40
Tel 071-734 3324	**R**
161 Wardour Street W1	Map 22 B3

A small, charming Swiss establishment on two floors whose extensive menu offers meat and cheese fondues as well as other Swiss specialities including air-cured beef, rösti potatoes, spatzle noodles, plus game and wild mushrooms in season. Excellent cheese platter with fine Tete de Moine, Vacherin and Emmenthal. *Seats 45. Private Room. L 12-3 D 6-11.30. Closed L Sat, all Sun, Bank Holidays. Access, Amex, Visa,*

SW3   St Quentin

	£55
Tel 071-581 5131 Fax 071-584 6064	**R**
243 Brompton Road SW3 2EP	Map 23 D2

The Savoy Group has retained the style, comfort and civilised atmosphere of the old Brompton Grill days, complete with chandeliers, ornate mirrors and a long bar running down one side. French staff are on the ball and dressed for the part. French menus stick largely to fairly unadventurous choices such as salmon with sorrel, Dover sole, cassoulet and venison grand veneur. A la carte, or good-value, three-course, fixed-price menus with a small choice. *Seats 70. Parties 25. Private Room. L 12-3 (Sat & Sun to 4) D 7-11.30 (Sat from 6.30). Set L £12.50 Set D £15.25. Access, Amex, Visa,*

W5   Sala Thai

	£30
Tel 081-560 7407	**R**
182 South Ealing Road W5 4RJ	Map 21 D4

Choosing from the 100 plus dishes on the menu of this friendly Thai restaurant is a pleasant task with which the staff will gladly assist. Thai dim sum, fried bean curd skin with crab meat and minced pork, chicken or pork in a pepper and garlic mixture, dried sweet beef with coriander seeds, king prawns in oyster sauce with broccoli, deep-fried mackerel with red curry sauce, squid in half a dozen ways, Thai curry with mixed vegetables and prawns or cod show the flavour of what's on offer. *Seats 60. Parties 60. L 12-2.30 D 6-11.30. Closed L Sat, all Sun, 24 Dec-2 Jan. Access, Amex, Visa,*

SW1   Salloos

	£70
Tel 071-235 4444	**R**
62-64 Kinnerton Street SW1X 8ER	Map 23 D2

Established in Lahore in 1966, Salloos has been in London since 1977. Tandoori grills – fat-free, long marinated and with no added colour – have a great reputation here, especially the little lamb chops, and other dishes to try include soups, chicken with fresh ginger, vegetable kebabs (spicy mixed

vegetables covered with mashed potato and fried like cutlets) and halva
served hot adorned with silver leaf. 15% service charge is added to all bills.
**Seats 70. Parties 65. L 12-2.30 D 7-11.15. Closed Sun, Bank Holidays. Set L
from £18.40 Set D from £28.75. Access, Amex, Visa,** (D) *Diners Club International*

SW3   Sambuca

Tel 071-730 6571

£55

R

6 Symons Street SW3

Map 23 E2

Straightforward Italian cooking in a popular, bustling restaurant by Sloane
Square (opposite the rear door of *Peter Jones*). Oven-braised lamb with
herbs and red wine sauce is a speciality for two. Try also *penne marinara*
with fresh tomato, garlic and crawfish, or *animelle mare e terra* (sweetbreads
with cream, brandy and lobster sauce). **Seats 70. Parties 30. L 12.30-2.30
D 7-11.30. Closed Sun, Bank Holidays. Access, Amex, Visa,** (D) *Diners Club International*

SW3   San Frediano

Tel 071-584 8375   Fax 071-589 8860

£50

R

62 Fulham Road SW3 6HH

Map 23 E2

Buzzing with atmosphere and old-fashioned Italian charm, San Fred is one
of the real survivors among London's trattorias. Honest cooking, decent
wine, ungreedy prices and slick service have provided 24 years of customer
satisfaction and a long list of daily specials always adds interest to the
menu: marinated herrings with beans, crab salad, guinea fowl with wine
and grapes, chicken escalopes with cheese and asparagus tips. **Seats 110.
Parties 40. L 12.30-2.30 D 7-11.30. Closed Sun, Bank Holidays. Access,
Amex, Visa,** (D) *Diners Club International*

SW3   San Lorenzo

Tel 071-584 1074

£100

R

22 Beauchamp Place SW3 1NL

Map 23 D2

Handily placed for a pause in the shopping round and popular for both
chatty lunches and leisurely dinners. Tables are arranged in two distinct
styles, a bright central raised area and a surrounding one with more
subdued lighting. Competently cooked, generally familiar Italian dishes on
the daily-changing menu may include a good spicy fish soup, fritto misto
di mare, guinea fowl with polenta, veal piccata with lemon and bollito
misto salsa verde. Helpings are hearty, but if you reach the desserts go for
the San Lorenzo pancake. Prices mount up with wine at £3.50 per glass,
£2.50 cover charge and £2.50 for a small cup of coffee. **Seats 120. Parties
18. Private Room. L 12.30-3 D 7.30-11.30. Closed Sun, Bank Holidays. No
credit cards.**

SW3   San Martino

Tel 071-589 3833

£60

R

103 Walton Street SW3 2HP

Map 23 C4

One of London's busiest and friendliest Italian restaurants, San Martino
recently expanded into the adjoining property, more than doubling its size.
Costanzo Martinucci and his family are completely involved, the owner
himself growing herbs, vegetables and ingredients for the splendid made-
to-order salads. The seasonal menu provides great variety and three of the
most renowned dishes are fish soup, tagliatelle with hazelnuts and tarragon
and spaghetti cooked with seafood in a paper bag. **Seats 120. Parties 52.
Private Room. L 12-3 D 6.30-11.30. Closed 10 days Xmas, 4 days Easter.
Set L from £10.50. Access, Amex, Visa,** (D) *Diners Club International*

SW3   Sandrini   £60

Tel 071-584 1724   **R**

260 Brompton Road SW3 2AS   Map 23 E2

High marks for comfort and smart modern decor. Above-average marks
for Italian cooking throughout a menu which mixes the traditional and the
modern. *Libaio ruffino* is a very drinkable white wine that goes with most
of the dishes. Tables outside in appropriate weather. *Seats 70. L 12-2.30
(Sun to 3) D 7-11.30. Access, Amex, Visa,*

SW1   Santini   £100

Tel 071-730 4094   Fax 071-730 0544   **R**

29 Ebury Street SW1W 0NZ   Map 23 D3

Business people at lunchtime and theatre-goers in the evening keep things
busy at Santini's close-set tables, and a profusion of waiters provide rapid
service. The menu mixes the familiar (mussels marinara, tortelloni with
ricotta and spinach, devilled baby chicken) with some more original items
like pasta with artichoke sauce, sea bream with olives or hot carpaccio with
matchstick courgettes. Good espresso with a kick. Just a few minutes walk
from Victoria Station. Sister to *L'Incontro* in Pimlico Road, with an equally
upmarket menu. *Seats 60. Parties 10. L 12.30-2.30 D 7-11.30 (Sun to 11).
Closed L Sat & Sun, all Bank Holidays. Set L £16.50. Access, Amex, Visa,* ⓘ *Diners Club International*

N1   Satay Hut   £30

Tel 071-359 4090   Fax 071-482 4513   **R**

287 Upper Street N1 2TZ   Map 20 C1

The surroundings belie the name, as this is a roomy, comfortable restaurant
with air-conditioning. Satay of lamb, beef, chicken or prawns (plus
vegetarian) tops the menu, with four sticks as a starter portion, six for a
main course. Otherwise the menu runs through the cuisines of Singapore,
Malaysia, Indonesia and Thailand. MSG is not used. *Seats 100. Parties 250.
Private Room. L 12.30-3 D 6-12 (Sat & Sun 12-12). Closed 25 & 26 Dec.
Set meals from £9.50. Access, Amex, Visa,* ⓘ *Diners Club International*

W1   Les Saveurs   ★↑ NEW   £120

Tel 071-491 8919   **R**

37a Curzon Street W1Y 8EY   Map 22 C3

After training in France with some of the best chefs (les frères Troisgros,
Joël Robuchon and Marc Meneau), Joël Antunès was appointed chef de
cuisine at *The Oriental* in Bangkok; he now exercises his considerable
talents in this new Mayfair restaurant whose well-proportioned downstairs
dining room has elegant decor and the hushed and relaxing air of a club.
The culinary theme is Niçois, pepped up by the subtle intrusion of spices
and the influence of Oriental experiences, illustrated by dishes such as a
salad of Dublin Bay prawns with aubergine compote and caraway
vinaigrette or slivers of duck served with a compote of figs and Thai spice
sauce; tomatoes stuffed with sautéed frog's legs and snails and a galette of
pig's trotter garnished with pommes Darphin and roquette salad typify
Antunès' unusual style. Desserts can vary from technical feats to a watery
chocolate gateau. Terrine of fresh goat's cheese *à la niçoise* is an unusual
cheese course. Service is formal with orchestrated presentation of dishes
from under silver cloches and different china is used for every dish. The
multi-course *menu gourmand* offers a perfectly balanced meal. Good-value,
fixed-price lunch. *Seats 50. Parties 35. Private Room. L 12-2.30 D 7-10.30.
Closed all Sat & Sun, 10 days Xmas/New Year, 2 weeks Aug. Set L £21
Set D £39.50. Access, Amex, Visa,* ⓘ *Diners Club International*

WC2   The Savoy   90%

£242

Tel 071-836 4343   Fax 071-240 6040

The Strand WC2R 0EU

Map 22 C4

The Savoy has its very own, special atmosphere, right from the harpist
playing in the Thames Foyer during afternoon tea to the superbly-run
banqueting suites on a grand scale. Its long-standing reputation (it opened
in 1889) is justly world-wide and standards of service tip-top. The contrast
between the very English drawing room (which provides a peaceful retreat
from the cosmopolitan bustle of the lobby) and the international American
Bar sums up the hotel well – an ability to cater for so many people in so
personal a manner, making allowances for their guests' differences in both
nationality and personality. The Savoy has always had wonderful staff, no
more so than those of the present day who are charmingly motivated by
General Manager Herbert Striessnig. Bedrooms, including many large
suites, boast such luxuries as real linen bedding and positively vast bath
sheets; the nightly turn-down service and personal maid, valet and waiter
bell service set standards that other hotels strive hard to match. Some
rooms are in original art deco style and the most sought-after offer river
views, particularly the suites. Next to the American Bar is "Upstairs"
where champagne, fine wines from a Cruover machine and seafood are the
specialities. Banqueting (arguably the best in London) and conference
facilities for up to 500. Guests have temporary membership of the
Wentworth Club (one of the world's greatest golf clubs, under the
direction of ex-Savoy General Manager Willy Bauer; proof of handicap
required), which also offers 14 tennis courts and a swimming pool. Leisure
facilities are being incorporated as part of the new Savoy Theatre complex,
currently being rebuilt following the recent fire. No dogs. **Rooms 202.**
*News kiosk, beauty & hair salon, valeting, champagne & seafood bar
(noon-midnight), dinner dancing. Access, Amex, Visa,* Diners Club International

River Restaurant

£130

Indisputably this is one of the busiest restaurants in London and one of the
most comfortable – its setting, with tables that overlook the Thames,
suggests excitement both at lunchtime and in the evening. It is one of the
few places where you can dance in the evening to a live band. And yet...
last year we commented that when *maitre chef des cuisines* Anton Edelmann
was orchestrating the show, then we were talking stars; when not, both
food and service can sometimes be vulnerable. *Plus ça change...* on our most
recent visit (at the end of July) *maitre d'hotel* Luigi Zambon was present, so
service was swift and courteous, albeit lacking in smiles; both the waiter
who recited dishes on the menu and the young man who presented the
sweet trolley were incomprehensible. The food was undeniably good, but
not brilliant – previous visits indicated the same – bread was not offered (it
had to be requested), a pot of tea contained teabags, and an espresso coffee
was particularly minuscule – one sip emptied the cup! At The Savoy you
expect better; you get the feeling that the restaurant is simply going
through the motions; which is a pity, for Edelmann is an outstanding chef
(he's certainly among the best banqueting chefs in town) as well as being
one of the most personable. The à la carte, supported by fixed-price
gastronomic and daily menus (including vegetarian options) offers classical
dishes such as *paté de foie gras* or *coquilles St Jacques* to start, followed by
filets de sole pochés or *noisettes d'agneau aux truffes.* The smoked salmon is
legendary and the trolleys rarely fail to please the eye and deliver the goods
– fine roasts and a selection of desserts. Side plates of vegetables are
exceptional, and yet... even the wine list is good but not great – serious
wine drinkers may be disappointed. **Seats 150.** Parties 60. Private Room.
L 12.30-2.30 D 7.30-11.30 (Sun to 10.30). Set L £25.20 Set D £30.50 &
£39.50.

Grill Room   ★ ★

£120

One of the most handsome of all the great London hotel dining rooms,
with polished yew panels, hushed carpeting and immaculately clad tables.

Long-service medals are due to many of the tail-coated staff, to the trolleys and the silver cloches, and to the speciality menu: a lexicon of classical cuisine, from 'Les potted shrimps', omelette Arnold Bennett and seasonal asparagus to lobster Thermidor, roast saddle of lamb and 'Le mixed grill'. A regular assortment of daily dishes appear at both lunch and dinner – shepherd's pie for Wednesday lunch, roast Norfolk duck with almond and apples for Friday dinner. It may be an institution, but it's not in a time warp. Young waiters are trained under the watchful eye of maitre d'hotel Angelo Maresca. Perhaps there's a pecking order for the 'best' tables, but every table is a good one, and everyone eats the same fine food. The Grill remains one of *the* places for a serious lunch or dinner. A pre-theatre menu (with a reasonable choice) is served between 6 and 7pm, with coffee and pastries served after the show in the Thames Foyer.
Seats 85. Parties 12. L 12.30-2.30 D 6-11.15. Closed L Sat, all Sun, Bank Holidays (open 25 Dec), Aug. Set D (6-7pm) £25.75/£28.75.

WC1   Scandic Crown Euston   65%   £130
Tel 071-383 4105   Fax 071-383 4106   H
17 Upper Woburn Place WC1H 0HT   Map 22 A4

Good-looking Swedish-designed hotel very near Euston mainline railway station. Leafy conservatory-lounge, bar, basement conference facilities. Air-conditioned bedrooms have beds with fibre-filled duvets. Children up to 14 stay free in parents' room. No dogs. *Rooms 150. Coffee bar (10.30am-11pm). Access, Amex, Visa,*

SE16   Scandic Crown Nelson Dock   67%   £156
Tel 071-231 1001   Fax 071-231 0599   H
265 Rotherhithe Street SE16 1EJ   Map 21 D1

On the Surrey Quays peninsula, the hotel is a clever conversion of the 19th-century Columbia Wharf, combining a marvellous new development with glass walkways leading to the three bedroom blocks. An old sailing barque is moored in the dry dock between the buildings and contributes to the nautical theme; the hotel also has its own pier at which the river bus stops. Most of the bedrooms have a river view and include mini-bar, trouser press, hairdryer and security locks. Cheerful and helpful staff. An excellent Scandinavian buffet breakfast is served in the restaurant, which also serves a good evening smörgåsbord spread. Children free up to the age of 14 in parents' room. *Rooms 390. River terrace, indoor swimming pool, sauna, solarium, spa bath, gymnasium, tennis, games room, snooker. Access, Amex, Visa,*

SW1   Scandic Crown Victoria   66%   £160
Tel 071-834 8123   Fax 071-828 1099   H
2 Bridge Place SW1V 1QA   Map 23 E3

As the name implies, everything about this hotel is Scandinavian – the furniture, the staff, even the beer in the bedroom mini-bars! It's just round the corner from Victoria station, which is handy for arrivals from the Continent. Air-conditioned bedrooms are contemporary and smart, with decent bathrooms. Conference and banqueting facilities for up to 200 delegates. Children free up to the age of 14 in parents' room. *Rooms 210. Indoor swimming pool, gymnasium, sauna, solarium, spa bath, coffee shop (11am-10.30pm). Access, Amex, Visa,*

W1   The Selfridge   75%   £220
Tel 071-408 2080   Fax 071-629 8849   H
Orchard Street W1H 0JS   Map 22 B2

A covered porte-cochère with brass lanterns and greenery makes a good first impression at this modern hotel adjacent to the famous department store. Warm cedar panelling lends a traditional English feel to the reception foyer and a smart first-floor lounge with leather wing armchairs. In

complete contrast, Stoves Bar is olde-worlde rustic with wheelback chairs
and genuine old beams and timbers recovered from a medieval barn.
Bedrooms vary in size and are more comfortable than luxurious, with
darkwood units and TV remote controls wired to the bedside; all have air
conditioning and telephones by the bed, at the desk and in the modestly-
sized bathrooms that also offer good towelling and marble vanitory units.
Valetparking. **Rooms 296.** *Access, Amex, Visa,* **(I)** Diners Club International

---

SE22 Sema	£35
Tel 081-693 3213	**R**
57 Lordship Lane SE22	Map 21 F1

A small, informal Thai restaurant with gentle and helpful service. Start
with 'Golden Sema' – a selection of fried dumplings and spring rolls,
follow with green curry or stir-fried beef with chili and onions. The
special Thai noodles (Pub Thai) are a must. **Seats 68.** *Parties 70. Private
Room. L 12-3 D 6-11.30. Closed L Mon-Fri, 25 Dec, 1 Jan. Set meals from
£15. Access, Amex, Visa,* **(I)** Diners Club International

W1 La Sémillante ↑ NEW	£80
Tel 071-499 2121	**R**
3 Mill Street W1R 9TF	Map 22 C3

A disciple of Raymond Blanc and Pierre Koffmann, Patrick Woodside
then teamed up with Marco Pierre White to create wonderful desserts at
Harveys. Today he is happy and confident in his impressive, newly opened
premises between Regent Street and New Bond Street (close to the
Westbury hotel). La Sémillante is an old French word for libertine, one of
whom makes a naked appearance on the gaudy menu. Dashing, sincere,
free and different is how Woodside's novel talents might be described.
Down a theatrical staircase from the ground-floor bar, the restaurant is
non-smoking except for a further split-level lounge where puffers can
indulge and where after-dinner drinks are also served; high-back chairs are
upholstered in lemon yellow and deep blue and tied at the back with huge
contrasting bows. Patrick has extended his talents of pastry chef to savoury
delicacies and beyond. Nothing is left to chance – from the brochette for
amuse-gueule to the flavoured, piping-hot petits pains (raisin and walnut,
spinach, chives or beetroot) or the delightful plate of petits fours. There is a
fixed-price menu for both lunch and dinner. Simply-titled dishes are
explained at some length by the waiting staff on being served, offering the
likes of tarte of sea scallop and caviar or millefeuille of quail's eggs and foie
gras – masterpieces of precision and timing; the explanations are helpful as
all is not what it might seem at first glance – layers of scallops create the
'millefeuille' by being interleaved with the thinly-sliced quail; the use of
five raw quail's egg yolks to garnish this dish is certainly unusual and,
ultimately, superfluous. Roast breasts of pigeon and aubergine or supreme
of red mullet with aromatics are other typical dishes. Desserts, which of
course are a speciality, are also adventurous with a delectable airy soufflé of
crystallised ginger, a skilful nougat of Pear William, and a tagliatelle of
crêpe with peaches in champagne (a poached peach on a bed of shredded
pancake, gratinated under a creamy champagne sabayon). There is a
sensible policy in the pricing of the wines – many under £15 and perhaps
the best-value Louis Roederer Cristal '83 in the country – let's hope it stays
this way! As we went to press, the decor was being remodelled. This is an
intriguing newcomer with serious intent, but it remains to be seen
whether Woodside's off-the-wall approach will catch on. **Seats 40.** *Parties
20. Private Room. L 12.15-2.15 D 7.15-10.45. Closed L Sat, all Sun, last
2 weeks Aug, 2 weeks Dec/Jan. Set L £14.50 Set D £26. Access, Visa,*
(I) Diners Club International

W1   Shampers   £48

Tel 071-437 1692   **R**

4 Kingly Street W1R 5LF   Map 22 C3

Between Regent Street and Carnaby Street, this is one of the West End's
most popular wine bars and has a serious food side, too. A glass or two
from the keenly-priced, descriptive wine list may be enjoyed in the wine
bar with an interesting menu of snacks – from a platter of charcuterie to
salads, ham and cheese pie and sirloin steak. Lunchtime in the small
restaurant downstairs might include anything from half-a-dozen oysters,
guinea fowl terrine or hot mussel tart to grilled duck sausages with braised
red cabbage and mash or strips of chicken breast with oyster mushrooms,
crème fraiche and chives. *Seats 70. Parties 50. Private Room. Restaurant
Mon-Fri 12-3, Wine bar 11-11 (Sat 11-3). Closed D Sat, all Sun, Easter,
Xmas. Access, Amex, Visa,*

W8   Shanghai   £55

Tel 071-938 2501   **R**

38c Kensington Church Street W8 4BX   Map 23 D1

A smart, window-less basement Chinese restaurant with a few tables at
street level. Lettuce-wrapped oysters, cold tossed prawn slices in a Szechuan
marinade, deep-fried crispy eel, sizzling dishes, Tibetan garlic lamb and
moush pork (a Peking speciality) are some of the most interesting offerings.
Shanghai and Peking dumplings (steamed, griddle-fried or steamed) are a
house speciality. A 12½% service charge is added to your bill. *Seats 90.
L 12-2.15 D 6.30-11.15. Closed Bank Holidays. Set meals from £16.50.
Access, Amex, Visa,*

WC2   Sheekey's Restaurant   £65

Tel 071-240 2565   Fax 071-491 2477   **R**

28-32 St Martins Court Leicester Square WC2N 4AL   Map 25 B2

Old-style fish restaurant, convenient for theatreland, serving a wide mix:
from oysters, potted shrimps, mussels, stewed or jellied eels, seafood platter,
fish cakes with parsley sauce, fisherman's pie and flambéed scallops to
Dover sole and lobster thermidor. British farmhouse cheeses and desserts
from a trolley. Pre-theatre dinner served 6-7.30pm; late, post-theatre last
orders. *Seats 110. Parties 90. Private Room. L 12.30-3 D 6-11.15. Closed
L Sat, all Sun, Bank Holidays, 24 Dec-2 Jan. Set L £14.50. Access, Amex,
Visa,*

SW1   Sheraton Belgravia   75%   £250

Tel 071-235 6040   Fax 071-259 6243   **HR**

20 Chesham Place SW1X 8HQ   Map 23 D2

Personal service is high on the list of priorities at this luxurious modern
hotel and quick evidence is provided by the welcoming glass of Bucks Fizz.
Day rooms, including the lobby, split-level lounge and library bar, offer
abundant comfort, and bedrooms sport freestanding yew furniture. All the
rooms are air-conditioned. Children up to 12 stay free in parents' room.
Rooms 89. Access, Amex, Visa,

Chesham's   £70

An attractive restaurant designed in sections – one of them with a palm
tree, glass-domed roof and wall mirrors. Cooking mixes updated classical
French with traditional English cream of asparagus soup, chicken liver
parfait with grilled pain de campagne, grilled Dover sole, sirloin steak
served plain or flambéed with black peppercorn sauce, nage of brill
flavoured with tomato and mint. *Seats 54. Parties 50. L 12.30-2.30
D 6.30-10.30. Closed L Sat & Sun. Set L £21.95.*

SW1   Sheraton Park Tower   79%   £281

Tel 071-235 8050   Fax 071-235 8231   **HR**

101 Knightsbridge SW1X 7RN   Map 23 D2

A distinctive, circular high-rise tower within a stone's throw of Harrods
and with splendid city views from the upper floors. Bedrooms, apart from
the 31 luxury suites, are identical in size and feature rather pleasing burr
walnut-veneered furniture. Thick quilted bedcovers, turned down at night,
match the curtains; TVs and mini-bars are discreetly hidden away. There
are telephones by the bed, on the desk and in the bathrooms, which have
marble-tiled walls, good shelf space, towels and toiletries. Extra services on
Executive floors include valet unpacking, two-hour laundering, a special
check-out service and extra toiletries. Meeting facilities can handle up to 80
people theatre style. *Rooms 295. Beauty & hair salon. Access, Amex, Visa,* ()Diners Club International

Restaurant 101   £75

The attractive, circular street-level conservatory is well isolated from the
Knightsbridge chaos and the built-in glass roofs make it bright and airy.
The second half of the restaurant is recessed inside the building and features
a semi-circular platform with an art nouveau painted-glass ceiling. Chef
Gerd Jacobmeyer has adapted his cooking to modern conceptions of
healthy eating: even salmon cooked in goose fat with stir-fried vegetables
in a tomato butter sauce feels light and dainty. Vegetarians are well catered
for with both special dishes and a wide selection of side-order vegetables.
Specialities include hare medallions on an endive and leek tart with sweet
and sour sauce. The lunch menu offers an extensive buffet of cold starters
and daily selections providing very good value for money. The dessert
trolley needs a kick start. *Seats 80. Parties 20. L 12-3 (Sun to 4) D 6.30-11.
Set L £19.75.*

W1   Sherlock Holmes Hotel   61%   £149

Tel 071-486 6161   Fax 071-486 0884   **H**

108 Baker Street W1M 1LB   Map 22 B2

Conveniently located close to Marylebone Road, a Hilton-owned hotel
with average size but well-equipped rooms. Currently undergoing a
modern Victorian-look facelift. *Rooms 126. Access, Amex, Visa,* ()Diners Club International

---

W1   Shogun   £80

Tel 071-493 1877   **R**

Britannia Hotel Adams Row W1   Map 22 C3

Kimono-clad waitresses serve good-quality Japanese food in an atmospheric
vaulted basement restaurant behind the Britannia Inter-Continental Hotel.
Suits of samurai armour add an interesting touch to the decor. The clearly
set-out menu includes a Japanese-scripted section which the staff are happy
to explain and a range of set menus provides a good introduction to the
uninitiated – one is based on tempura, one on salmon, another on duck, a
fourth on beef. Consistently high standards of cooking and service.
*Seats 55. Parties 12. D only 6-11. Closed Mon, Bank Holidays, 1 week Xmas.
Set D from £30.50. Access, Amex, Visa,* ()Diners Club International

SW1   Signor Sassi   £60
Tel 071-584 2277   R

14 Knightsbridge Green SW1X 7QL   Map 23 D2

Simple Italian close to Harrods. Straightforward menu of classic dishes –
bresaola with mango and rucola salad, chicken broth with tortellini, calf's
liver with butter and sage, ham-stuffed veal escalope and the like. *Seats 70.
Parties 50. L 12-2.30 (Sat to 2.45) D 7-11.30. Closed Sun. Access, Amex,
Visa,* ◐ *Diners Club International*

SE5   Silver Lake   £40
Tel 071-701 9961   R

59 Camberwell Church Street SE5 8TR   Map 21 E1

A busy and homely Chinese restaurant offering a mix of Peking, Cantonese
and Szechuan cooking. 130 dishes cover the range from prawn, beef or
chicken satay sticks and crab meat and seaweed soup to monkfish in black
bean sauce, sizzling dishes and red-braised duck. *Seats 40. L 12-2 D 5.30-12
(Fri & Sat to 12.30). Closed L Sat & Sun. Set L from £4 Set D from £12.
Access, Amex, Visa,* ◐ *Diners Club International*

SW1   Simply Nico   ★   £75
Tel 071-630 8061   R

48A Rochester Row SW1P 1JU   Map 23 E3

The unchanged region of Nicoland, in a part of town with few rivals.
Three-course lunch and dinner menus (the price includes 10% service
charge) display the talents of Andrew Barber, a chef who believes in the
simple, straightforward approach, eschewing undue elaboration and fussy
garnishes. Typical dishes run from spiced marinated salmon with potato
salad and smoked haddock risotto with a poached egg to maize-fed baby
chicken with fresh tomato sauce, quail pie, veal braised with Madeira and
fillets of sole or brill with tartare mousseline. The house aperitif is Cardinal
– chilled Beaujolais with crème de mures. The restaurant's yellow rag-
rolled walls are hung with framed cartoons; chairs are bentwood and
wicker. *Seats 48. Parties 48. L 12-2.15 D 6.45-11.15. Closed L Sat & Bank
Holidays, all Sun, 10 days Xmas, Easter, 3 weeks Aug. Set L £23 Set D £25.
Access, Amex, Visa,* ◐ *Diners Club International*

WC2   Simpson's-in-the-Strand   £74
Tel 071-836 9112   R

100 The Strand WC2R 0EW   Map 22 C4

Decor, service, menu and cooking all seem stuck in a time-warp at this
famous institution under the ownership of the Savoy Group. Silver-domed
trolleys of roast sirloin of beef, saddle of lamb and Aylesbury duck are the
main attraction, trundled around by long-serving staff. The roasts (served
with cabbage and roast potatoes), daily lunch specials (occasionally boiled
silverside of salt beef), potted shrimps, steak and kidney pie, calf's liver with
bacon and sage plus other classic dishes from the lexicon of British cooking
(including nursery puddings like spotted dick and treacle roll) still attract
diners like bees to a honeypot. Fixed-price (£17.50), 3-course menu served
6-7pm and Saturday lunchtime. Now open for Sunday lunch. So-so wine
list on the pricy side. *Seats 300. Parties 135. Private Room. L 12-2.30
D 6-10.45. Closed D Sun, Bank Holidays. Set L £17.50. Access, Amex, Visa,*
◐ *Diners Club International*

W4   Singapore   £35
Tel 081-995 7991   R

94 Chiswick High Road W4 2EF   Map 21 A4

Neat, cool and smart little restaurant serving Chinese and Malaysian food.
Specialities include mango chicken, crab meat with asparagus and quick-

fried veal cutlets in black pepper sauce. *Seats 60. Parties 40. Private Room. L 12-2.30 D 6-11.30. Closed 25 & 26 Dec. Set L from £5 Set D from £15.90. Access, Amex, Visa,*

NW6   Singapore Garden

Tel 071-328 5314

83 Fairfax Road NW6 4DY

£45

R

Map 20 C3

A long Singaporean, Malaysian and Chinese menu with fresh seasonal supplements; crab in the shell is served three ways: with soya bean, ginger or chili; sizzling dishes are good, as are the Malaysian chicken and beef curries. Steamboat table cooking (for two) is a healthy way to spend £56. Tightly-packed tables create a lively atmosphere. 12½% service is added to all bills. *Seats 96. Parties 100. L 12-2.45 D 6-10.45 (Fri & Sat to 11.15). Closed 1 week Xmas. Set D from £14.85. Access, Amex, Visa,*

W6   Snows on the Green   NEW

Tel 071-603 2142

166 Shepherds Bush Road W6 7PB

£62

R

Map 21 D3

Having worked as chef at Antony Worrall-Thompson's successful *190 Queen's Gate*, Sebastian Snow decided to set up on his own in Brook Green. A W-T's Mediterranean influences feature strongly on the modish menu: bruschetta and chargrilled vegetables; foie gras, fried egg and balsamic vinegar; brandade crostini, gnocchi with pesto...and so on. Main courses might range from steak frites or confit of duck with mountain ham, peas, onions and mash to squid ink casserole with saffron risotto and chargrilled calf's liver with pumpkin, brown butter and mint. Simple desserts – lemon tart, prune and almond tart, apple tarte tatin – usually well executed. The good-value, 2- or 3-course set lunch might offer pumpkin risotto or crispy chicken wing salad to start, then skate with black butter or sauté of lamb and aubergine, finishing with strawberry shortbread or apple and pear strudel. Short, unexciting list of fairly-priced wines. *Seats 70. Parties 20. Private Room. L 12-3 D 7-11. Closed L Sat, D Sun, Bank Holidays, last 2 weeks Aug. Set L £10.50/£12.50. Access, Visa,*

W1   Soho Soho

Tel 071-494 3491

11-13 Frith Street W1

£65

R

Map 25 A2

In the heart of Soho, the first-floor restaurant offers a menu of French and Mediterranean influenced dishes from the kitchen of Tony Howorth. Onion soup cooked with cider, tian de sardines, wild mushroom risotto, seafood couscous and breast of chicken niçoise show the range. At street level is the bustling café bar with pavement tables and a brasserie menu. *Seats 110. Parties 60. Private Room. L 12-3 D 6-12. Closed L Sat, all Sun, Bank Holidays. Access, Amex, Visa,*

N1   Sonargaon

Tel 071-226 6499

46 Upper Street N1

£40

R

Map 20 D3

Decent Indian cooking, crisp table settings, sharp service and cheaper than the West End. *Seats 50. L 12-3 D 6-12. Closed Xmas. Access, Amex, Visa,*

SW13   Sonny's

Tel 081-748 0393

94 Church Road SW13 0DQ

£50

R

Map 21 E4

Informal and relaxed: a mix of sparkling clean glassware and cutlery with linen napkins and paper table slips and no side plates for the warm baguette. Great value food and a busy, buzzing atmosphere typical of a successful local restaurant giving its neighbouring competition (*Riva*, in this instance) a good run for its money. A good-value fixed-price menu offers a choice of three dishes at each course (perhaps endive, watercress and walnut salad with blue cheese butter toasts followed by roast cod with polenta and pesto). Bresaola, asparagus with balsamic vinegar and shaved parmesan, spicy aubergine, feta cheese and roasted peppers with ouzo, rolled shoulder of lamb with flageolets, chargrilled calf's liver with tomato salsa and guacamole, confit of duck with orange sauce and tuna with crème fraiche and horseradish are typical offerings. Eclectic wine list includes a good choice of Australian bottles. *Seats 70. Parties 12. L 12.30-2.30 (Sun to 3) D 7.30-11. Closed D Sun, Bank Holidays. Set L & D £11.95 (2-course), Sun £13.95 (3-course). Access, Visa,* Diners Club International

N1	**Soulard Restaurant**	£40
Tel 071-254 1314		**R**
113 Mortimer Road N1 4JY		Map 20 C1

French atmosphere, French staff, French food: snails in pastry with hazelnuts, vegetable pancakes, breast of duck with ginger sauce, grilled fillet of beef with Roquefort sauce, chocolate genoise with rum syrup, walnut cream and ganache. The house apéritif is floc de Gascogne (red or white wine with armagnac). *Seats 28. Parties 28. Private Room. L 12-2 D 7-10.30. Closed L Sat, all Sun & Mon, Bank Holidays, 3 weeks Aug. Set L from £14.50. Access, Amex, Visa,* Diners Club International

SE10	**Spread Eagle Restaurant**	£60
Tel 081-853 2333		**R**
1&2 Stockwell Street SE10 8QQ		Map 21 E1

Opposite the Greenwich theatre, a restaurant plus function rooms on two floors of an old coaching inn. Bone marrow on toasted olive brioche with light Madeira sauce, veal kidneys and sweetbreads with creamy mustard sauce and a hazelnut and candied fruit tart on a carte that changes every month or so. Pre-theatre suppers from 6.30pm. *Seats 85. Parties 85. Private Room. L (Sun only) 12-3.30 D 6.30-10.30. Closed D Sun, Bank Holidays. Set L £12.75 Set D £13.50. Access, Amex, Visa,* Diners Club International

SW1   The Square   ↑ NEW   £65

Tel 071-839 8787   **R**

32 King Street St James's SW1 6RJ   Map 22 C3

Off to a cracking start, The Square has quickly gained ground on other
restaurants that stood still during the recession. A heady combination of
experience in Marco Pierre White's kitchen and an earnest intention to
achieve success off his own bat have helped fuel the fire in Philip Howard's
kitchen. He cooks a voguish menu that is modern (faultless red mullet with
a crisp Provençal tart, carpaccio of tuna with dressed salad and coriander),
strongly influenced by southern France and Italy and given more than a
few twists: warm quail with parsnip; caramelised calf's tongue with pot-
roasted vegetables (plus fried celeriac, radicchio leaves and sage); skate with
carrot and coriander; salad of avocado, smoked eel and bacon. Invention is
never far away, though, as in a sausage of oxtail and pig's trotter, or roasted
figs, toasted pecans and lemon fritters. Ignoring the faddish, however, still
leaves the likes of honey and spice-roasted duck, roast lamb with aubergine,
salmon three ways, shellfish soup with basil, floating islands (which sank on
a recent visit) and definitive tarte tatin; "The Square Meal" is a mixed grill.
New World wines figure prominently on an excellent list, with plenty of
bottles under £20. The U-shaped dining room opens wide on to the street
through large windows from which hang spiral metal mobiles. The centre
of the room is kept simple with parquet floor, electric blue upholstered
chairs and white tablecloth, while the walls are full of decorative touches
like daisy-shaped lamps, square panelling light from behind or bright
fuchsia, blue and gold panels. *Seats 60. Parties 12. L 12-3 D 6-11.45.
Closed L Sat, all Sun, most Bank Holidays. Access, Visa.*

W1   Sri Siam   £53

Tel 071-434 3544   **R**

14 Old Compton Street W1V 5PE   Map 25 A2

Traditional Thai food cooked to order in a lively Soho atmosphere. Good
range of dishes on à la carte and set menus, and a separate vegetarian list.
*Seats 80. Parties 25. L 12-3 D 6-11.15 (Sun to 10.30). Closed L Sun, 25 &
26 Dec, 1 Jan. Set L from £9 Set D from £14.95. Access, Amex, Visa,*

SW1   The Stafford   74%   £224

Tel 071-493 0111   Fax 071-493 7121   **H**

16 St James's Place SW1A 1NJ   Map 22 C3

In keeping with its clubland address the Stafford exudes civilised discretion,
an impression enhanced by long-serving staff looking after long-serving
clients. Pictures line the foyer walls and leather chesterfields create a scene
of cultured calm. Deeper in, a drawing room is made elegant by antiques
and fresh with cut flowers; the American Bar features a collection of
American club and university ties, caps and badges. Accommodation ranges
from singles with queen-size beds through doubles and junior suites in the
Carriage House to the Terrace Garden suite complete with terrace and
fountain. Decor is individual, with fabrics and furniture of a high standard.
Part of the Cunard group. No dogs. *Rooms 74. Access, Amex, Visa,*

SW1   Stakis St Ermin's   71%   £159

Tel 071-222 7888   Fax 071-222 6914   **H**

Caxton Street SW1H OQW   Map 23 D3

Ideally situated, with Westminster Abbey, the Houses of Parliament and
Buckingham Palace only a neighbourly distance away, the Stakis St Ermins
offers a perfect base for tourists. Extensive conference facilities (for up to
200 delegates theatre-style) also make it a primary choice for functions and
banquets. Behind an opulent Edwardian facade day rooms are equally
sumptuous: luxurious furnishings follow a green theme and the elegant
furniture, much of it antique, finds an ideal setting among marble and

ornate plasterwork. A splendid Baroque staircase leads to the five floors of
bedrooms which offer every modern comfort and, despite being rather
compact, are well-appointed and furnished with taste. *Rooms 290. Access,
Amex, Visa,* (◐) *Diners Club International*

| W1 | Stephen Bull | ★ | £65 |

| Tel 071-486 9696 | **R** |

5-7 Blandford Street W1H 3AA   Map 22 B2

Stephen Bull's new bistro (qv) is making the waves, but his original
Blandford Street establishment remains the showcase for his serious talents.
Cooking here is in the new modern, unfussy mode, and prices are not too
high considering the quality. No ingredient is redundant in appealing,
appetising dishes such as soy-glazed duck with roast peppers and pineapple,
fillet of brill with watercress and cider, chicken basquaise with fresh pasta
or noisettes of lamb with a garlic soufflé. Puddings include some possibly
unique to Bull: physalis and pink grapefruit tart, avocado and lime
cheesecake, muscovado meringue with tropical fruits and hot coconut
fudge. The restaurant is bright and clean-lined with monochromatic decor
and tables packed too tightly for keeping secrets. *Seats 60. Parties 14.
L 12.15-2.30 D 6.30-10.30. Closed L Sat, D Sun, Bank Holidays, 10 days
Xmas/New Year. Access, Visa.*

| EC1 | Stephen Bull Bistro | NEW | £60 |

| Tel 071-490 1750 | **R** |

71 St John Street EC1M 4AN   Map 20 C1

Stephen Bull chose the site for his latest venture carefully; just north of
Smithfield market, close enough to City offices, it has been packed since
the day it opened. Two floors of mimimalist decoration give little
indication of the stylish and original cooking on offer. Hand-written
menus change daily and offer a good choice of starters that might range
from hot or cold beetroot soup with apple and pickled cucumber to
tabouleh with orange and pine nuts, a light and fluffy leek and mushroom
tart, and preserved terrine of pickled lamb's tongues with capers and
mustard cream; the choice of main courses can be smaller, but equally
interesting: fried Cornish grey mullet with sun-dried tomato and black
olive sauce; skate wing with spiced lentils and yoghurt; tagine of lamb
with apricots, almonds and white beans; lamb's liver with sweet-sour red
cabbage and smoked bacon. The invention doesn't stop there: lemon and
lime curd pots with lemon crumble finger biscuits, apricot cabinet
pudding, brown sugar meringue with hot fudge sauce. Farmhouse cheeses
served with oat biscuits. Short, carefully-chosen wine list includes a good
selection of wines by the glass and a few unusual beers. *Seats 84. Parties 7.
L 12-2.30 D 6-10.45. Closed L Sat, all Sun, Bank Holidays, 10 days Xmas.
Access, Visa.*

| W6 | Sumos | | £35 |

| Tel 081-741 7916 | **R** |

169 King Street W6   Map 21 D4

An unassuming Japanese snack restaurant on Hammersmith's main
shopping street. Besides sushi and sashimi there's tempura (evenings only),
pork and beef ginger, salted and grilled chicken wings, and yaki, a
vegetarian dish comprising a ground bean pancake with bean sprouts,
carrot, onion and spring onion. *Seats 40. Parties 40. L 12-3 D 6-11. Closed
L Sat, all Sun, Bank Holidays. Set L from £5 Set D from £10. No credit
cards.*

SW1   Suntory

£110

Tel 071-409 0201

R

72 St James's Street SW1A 1PH

Map 22 C3

One of London's longest-established Japanese restaurants, with more of a
Western style than Oriental; the cooking is of a high standard and staff
have an exemplary attitude towards politeness, patience and understanding.
The main dining area is on the ground floor, but there's several teppanyaki tables on the lower ground. The complete teppan-yaki experience
(appetisers, dobin-mushi soup, sashimi, foie gras, mixed seafood, fillet steak,
mixed salad, rice, miso soup, pickled vegetables, dessert and coffee or green
tea) is £64, but alternatives include turbot, lobster, salmon and
chateaubriand with prawns. The traditional side of the menu ranges from
sushi and tempura to shabu-shabu. Prices at lunchtime are considerably less
than in the evening. Suitably stylish for expense-account dining. *Seats 120.
Parties 30. Private Room. L 12-2 D 7-10. Closed Sun, Bank Holidays. Set L
from £20 Set D from £48. Access, Amex, Visa,*

W9   Supan

£30

Tel 081-969-9387

R

4 Fernhead Road W9 3ET

Map 20 C3

Just around the corner from Harrow Road, Supan is a really delightful
Thai restaurant with charming staff and beautifully prepared food. A
mixed starter of chicken satay, fish cake, spring roll, crab-filled pastry and
chicken wings gets the taste buds budding; next try the deliciously spicy
tom yum soup or its creamy equivalent tom kha, then maybe grilled baby
chicken, a thick red curry or a prawn stir-fry with basil, chili, onion and
red pepper. The menu is long on vegetarian dishes, short on desserts.
*Seats 30. Parties 15. L 12-2.30 D 6.30-11.30. Closed L Sat, all Sun, Bank
Holidays, Notting Hill Carnival. Access, Visa.*

SW3   Le Suquet   ★

£80

Tel 071-581 1785

R

104 Draycott Avenue SW3 3AE

Map 23 E2

The most fashionable of Pierre Martin's small group of French seafood
restaurants, and certainly among the best of its kind in London. In
surroundings inspired by the seafront at Cannes, fresh fish and shellfish get
traditional treatment on a menu whose only changing element is the plats
du jour: *feuilleté de saumon* and *petite bouillabaisse* are regulars, and sea bass is
sold by 100 grams. Otherwise the shellfish are the main attraction, coming
together as a star turn in the mighty *plateau de fruits de mer*. Young French
staff have become more amiable down the years. *Seats 70. Parties 18.
Private Room. L 12.30-2.30 D 7-11.30. Access, Amex, Visa,* ①

SW5   Swallow International Hotel   64%

£121

Tel 071-370 4200   Fax 071-244 8194

H

Cromwell Road SW5 0TH

Map 23 E1

Large hotel on busy Cromwell Road (the main route to Heathrow and
points west), close to Gloucester Road underground station. Several
conference rooms and suites (for up to 200), a leisure club and practical
accommodation that includes 12 top-of-the-range suites. *Rooms 417. Indoor
swimming pool, gymnasium, spa bath, sauna, solarium, news kiosk, coffee shop
(7am-midnight). Access, Amex, Visa, Diners*

NW3   Swiss Cottage Hotel   62%

£85

Tel 071-722 2281   Fax 071-483 4588

H

4 Adamson Road NW3 3HP

Map 20 C3

An unusually individual hotel converted from terraced houses in a quiet
residential street a few minutes from Swiss Cottage underground station.
The bedrooms have plenty of character, with some Victorian/Edwardian

pieces of furniture, plush settees and nice old pictures. Some rooms are not all that large, and they're linked by warrens of corridors and stairs. The lounge is very appealing: ornate gold wallpaper under a moulded ceiling; sofas and button-back chairs on bright Oriental rugs, carved antique furniture and oil paintings. The hotel also has self-catered studio, one- and two-bedroom serviced apartments nearby, let by the week. No dogs. *Rooms 82. Garden. Access, Amex, Visa,* 💳

SW3	Sydney Street	↑	£45
Tel 071-352 3433			**R**
4 Sydney Street SW3 6PP			**Map 23 E2**

Where else could an Australian restaurant open but in Sydney Street? An extraordinary menu served down under in a rather stylish oceanic setting; upstairs has an Aboriginal theme with earthy colours. The menu features lemon grass, okra, kohlrabi, yabbie, crocodile, cashew nuts, papaya, coriander, chi-gio, reef fish, green tea rice, kangaroo, Tasmanian crayfish tails, barramundi in lotus leaf – a Pandora's box of Pacific Rim ingredients inventively used by new chef Mary Jane Hayward (voted Australian chef of the year in 1991 by the Sydney Morning Herald). Her unique – to London – style is typified by dishes like crab and vermicelli balls with sweet chili sauce, roast chicken breast with grilled asparagus and pistachio pesto, blackened kangaroo fillet with broad beans, sweet potatoes and crème fraiche. Good, but less interesting desserts. Extensive Australian and New Zealand wine list. *Seats 68. Parties 68. Private Room. L 12-3 D 7-11.30. Closed Sun, 25 & 26 Dec, 1 Jan. Set L £10. Access, Amex, Visa,* 💳

WC2	The Tageen	NEW	£50
Tel 071-836 7272			**R**
12 Upper St Martin's Lane WC2H 9DL			**Map 25 B2**

A new exotic table for Covent Garden – a roomy Moroccan restaurant decorated with traditional tiles, lanterns and cushions. Staff are dressed in Moroccan style and enjoy talking about the wonders of Moroccan cuisine, which mixes sweet, salt and sour. The menu embraces specialities such as *bastela* (crisp, light pastry revealing the savours of chicken, saffron, almonds and cinnamon), *couscous* (made with extra-fine grain imported from Morocco) and of course *tageens* – aromatic stews cooked in the pots that give them their name. Departing guests are presented with a miniature tageen carrying the restaurant's phone number. *Seats 80. Parties 40. L 12.30-3 D 6.30-11.30. Closed L Sat, all Sun, 1 & 2 Jan. Access, Amex, Visa,* 💳

SW6	Tandoori Lane		£35
Tel 071-371 0440			**R**
131a Munster Road SW6 6DD			**Map 21 E3**

East Indian and Bangladeshi cooking in a congenial local restaurant that's much longer that it is wide. *Seats 50. Parties 14. L 12-2.30 D 6-11.15. Closed 25 & 26 Dec. Set meals from £7.95. Access, Visa.*

SW3	La Tante Claire	★★★	£150
Tel 071-352 6045			**R**
68 Royal Hospital Road SW3 4HP			**Map 23 E2**

Last year we said that, while other restaurants go through transformations and bouts of media faddism, Tante Claire glides along on the outside lane of the motorway. Well, one doesn't expect much to change at this level – Pierre Koffmann's small, elegant and predominantly yellow restaurant is still in overdrive. Like the cooking, the room is not overdone, with original paintings or bird's eye maple panelling gracing the walls; service (under the direction of Jean-Pierre Durantet) is cool and impeccable to match. Koffmann's dishes are invariably memorable – once eaten, who can forget his *assiette canardière aux deux sauces*, his *pied de cochon aux morilles*, purée paysanne or his *filet de chevreuil au chocolat amer et vinaigre de framboise*? His imitators can have no better master, his critics no easier target. A dual-track fixed-price lunch offers a choice of balanced meals, covering vichyssoise with oysters and caviar or salmon and potato salad, followed by pan-fried sole with béarnaise or quail stuffed with mushroom risotto and then fine French cheeses, chocolate tart or poire belle Hélène. Minimum charge £45 per person, which just covers two courses. Best value wines are the French country wines and those from the Alsace and Loire; clarets and burgundies are rather pricy; plenty of half bottles. **Seats 42.** Parties 8. L 12.30-2 D 7-11. Closed Sat & Sun, Bank Holidays, 1 week Xmas. Set L £23.50. Access, Amex, Visa, ⓓ Diners Club International

---

SW1   Tate Gallery Restaurant

Tel 071-834 6754

Millbank SW1P 4RG

£50

R

Map 23 E4

A basement, lunchtime-only setting with interesting murals and a non-smoking section. Plain English dishes seem the best bet, plus almost anything from the fine and varied wine list that features a good selection of half bottles and almost unbelievably low prices – in many cases up to 50% lower than you might expect to pay in other restaurants. **Seats 120.** Parties 30. L only 12-3. Closed Sun, most Bank Holidays. Access, Visa.

EC2   Tatsuso   NEW

Tel 071-638 5863

32 Broadgate Circle EC2M 2QS

£105

R

Map 24 C1

Smart City Japanese restaurant near Liverpool Street station. A modern, predominantly black ground-floor room is where chefs expertly griddle-cook seafood and steaks in front of diners at seven teppanyaki tables with marble counters (each table seats eight); downstairs is more traditionally Japanese with more involved food, simpler decor (gold-leafed floral wall hangings, beechwood slatted screens), kimono-clad waitresses and a sushi bar (seating 8). Catering mainly for business folk at expense-account prices, the choice of Japanese dishes is diverse, with freshness of ingredients and attention to presentation obviously a high priority. Polite service and pretty chinaware. Traditional-style tatami room seats 6. Best value at lunch and Monday teppanyaki dinner. 12½% service is added to all menu prices. Minimum lunchtime charge of £15, dinnertime £25. **Seats 54.** Parties 10. Private Room. L 11.30-3 D 6-9.30. Closed Sat & Sun, Bank Holidays, 10 days Xmas/New Year. Set L from £13 Set D from £13.80. Access, Amex, Visa, ⓓ Diners Club International

---

SW5   Terstan Hotel

Tel 071-835 1900   Fax 071-373 9268

29 Nevern Square SW5 9PE

£48

H

Map 21 D3

Family-owned and run, the Terstan bed and breakfast hotel stands in a garden square just south of the A4 Cromwell Road, a couple of minutes from Earls Court underground station and Exhibition Centre. Most bedrooms have private facilities, the exception being some budget singles. Simple accommodation at a low price. **Rooms 50.** Closed 3 days Xmas. Access, Visa.

SE14   Thailand Restaurant

Tel 081-691 4040

15 Lewisham Way SE14 6PP

£35

R

Map 21 F1

North-East Thailand pinpoints the cooking of Mrs Khamkhong Kambungoet in this unpretentious little place. Hot and Sour is a favourite and typical combination, appearing in soups, bamboo shoots with Lao herbs, minced beef, pork or chicken with pounded chilis, pounded toasted rice, lime juice, spring onions and herbs. **Seats 25.** Parties 25. D only 6-10.30. Closed Sun & Mon, Bank Holidays. Access, Amex, Visa, ⓓ Diners Club International

SW3   Thierry's   £60

Tel 071-352 3365   R

342 King's Road SW3 5UR   Map 23 F2

Cosy and romantic French bistro with window booths and red check
tablecloths topped with paper slips. Good choice of fixed-price lunch
menus offering a variety of two- or three-course options from Waldorf
salad and minute steak with green pepper sauce to Bayonne ham with
melon and duck confit. The à la carte extends to snails, *plateau de fruits de
mer*, cheese soufflé with shallot butter, Toulouse cassoulet and *jarret de porc
en choucroute*. Tarte tatin, crème brulée, chocolate or a selection of French
cheeses to finish. Short, all-French wine list. *Seats 70. Parties 35. Private
Room. L 12-2.30 (Sun to 3) D 7.30-11 (Sun to 10.30). Closed Bank Holidays.
Set L £9.90-£16.90 Set D from £13.50. Access, Amex, Visa,*

SE22   Thistells   £45

Tel 081-299 1921   R

65 Lordship Lane SE22   Map 21 F1

Sami Youssef, "the man who taught Nico Ladenis to cook", is building up
a reputation in an ornately tiled former grocer's shop. It's an unusual and
atmospheric place serving good food at reasonable prices. Sami is Egyptian
and many of his dishes are middle eastern: ful medames (Egyptian brown
beans dressed with olive oil and garnished with houmus, egg and salad),
falafel with tahini suace, couscous, calf's liver with coriander, cumin and
lime. Others are soundly prepared renditions of French classics like best end
of lamb with béarnaise sauce, coq au vin and duck cassoulet. Home-made
ices are a speciality dessert. *Seats 30. L Sun only 12-3 D 7-10.30. Closed
D Sun. Set L £10. Access, Visa.*

SW6   Tien Phat   £30

Tel 071-385 7174   R

1 The Arcade Fulham Broadway Station London SW6   Map 21 E3

Vietnamese and Chinese food in café surroundings. Choose à la carte or
house special set dinners (minimum two people). *Seats 40. L 12-2 D 7-10.
Closed Sun, 25 Dec. Access, Amex, Visa,*

SW5   Tiger Lee   £65

Tel 071-370 2323   R

251 Old Brompton Road SW5 9HP   Map 23 E1

Once-starred Chinese restaurant with an emphasis on seafood: lobster, crab,
eel, squid, abalone, scallops, prawns, shrimps and shark's fin; a few token
meat dishes complete the menu. 15% service is added to your bill. *Seats 60.
Parties 40. Private Room. D only 6-11. Closed 25 & 26 Dec, 2 days Easter.
Access, Amex, Visa,* (I) *Diners Club International*

NW11   Tiger under the Table   £40

Tel 081-458 9273   R

643 Finchley Road Golders Green NW11 7RR   Map 20 B3

Singapore cooking in a bright, cheerful restaurant with particularly helpful
staff. Take their advice, or dive at will among the satays and soups, the
king prawns and crispy squid and peppered crab, the chicken and the duck,
the beef rendang and the sweet and sour pork. Daily two-course lunch
platter (Mon-Sat); Sunday buffet (£9.95) with a choice of ten main dishes
and four desserts. *Seats 70. Parties 17. L 12-3 D 6-11.15. Closed 25 & 26
Dec. Set L £5.50 Set D from £12.90. Access, Amex, Visa,* (I) *Diners Club International*

W1   Topkapi   £35
Tel 071-486 1872   **R**

25 Marylebone High Street W1M 3PE   **Map 22 B3**

Turkish cuisine in a 50-seat restaurant that's open all day. Hot and cold
hors d'oeuvre (stuffed vine leaves, meat balls, aubergines, yoghurt, peppers);
main-course kebab grills. Quick lunches, relaxed dinners. *Seats 50. Parties
60. Meals 12-11.30. Closed 25 & 26 Dec. Set meals from £12.50. Access,
Amex, Visa,*

W4   Topsy Tasty   £40
Tel 081-995 3407   **R**

5 Station Parade Burlington Lane Chiswick London W4 **Map 21 D4**

Under the same ownership as the *Bedlington Café* (qv), a busy Thai
restaurant offering good-value, well-spiced Thai, Laotian, Japanese
(tonkatsu, yakitori, beef teriyaki) and Vietnamese dishes. Now licensed, but
still BYO (70p corkage per head). *Seats 45. Parties 40. D only 6.30-11.
Closed Sun, Bank Holidays. No credit cards.*

E1   Tower Thistle   66%   £155
Tel 071-481 2575   Fax 071-488 4106   **H**

St Katharine's Way E1 9LD   **Map 24 D3**

The Tower Thistle enjoys one of the finest settings in the capital, next to
Tower Bridge and the Tower of London, with views of the Thames and St
Katharine's Dock. Behind a strikingly original modern shell there's style
inside, too, notably in the high-ceilinged marbled foyer. The Which Way
West? café has views overlooking the bridge and turns into a video night
club Tuesday to Saturday evenings. The Tower Suite can accommodate up
to 250 delegates theatre-style. All bedrooms are air-conditioned and there
are three floors of Executive rooms with many extra accessories and a
dedicated check-out desk. In general, bedrooms and corridors are in need of
attention and the refurbishment (which only started in mid 1992) will
extend over the next few years. A secure car park for guests' use adjoins the
hotel. Children up to 14 stay free in parents' room. Conference/banqueting
facilities for 250/210. No dogs. *Rooms 808. News kiosk, coffee shop
(7.30am-10pm), dinner dance (Fri & Sat), covered garage. Access, Amex, Visa,*

NW1   Trattoria Lucca   £47
Tel 071-485 6864   **R**

63 Parkway NW1 7PP   **Map 20 C2**

Halfway along Parkway, and just moments from Camden Town station,
this is a popular Italian restaurant run by the same family for more than 20
years. The standard trattoria menu is supplemented by daily specials which
usually include some very good stuffed vegetables. *Seats 65. Parties 30.
L 12-3 D 6-10.45. Closed Sun, Bank Holidays. Access, Amex, Visa,*

SE1   La Truffe Noire   £66
Tel 071-378 0621   **R**

29 Tooley Street SE1 2QF   **Map 24 C3**

French restaurant east of London Bridge (opposite The London Dungeon)
aimed firmly at the City business market, complete with a good-value 2-
or 3-course *menu express* and a 4-course *menu d'affaires*. Fastest lunches for
those arriving before 12.20pm. The former might feature duck terrine
with sweet onion purée followed by roast chicken leg with honey and
French cheeses or peach Melba; the latter menu extends to mussels in a
pastry case with saffron sauce and squid with fresh black pasta or grilled
langoustines with wild rice and lemon butter. Several vintage classics on
the wine list at rather irrational prices. Credit card payment only accepted
for amounts over £50. *Seats 70. Parties 110. Private Room. L 12-2.30*

*D 6.30-10.30. Closed L Sat (except Summer), all Sun, Bank Holidays. Set
meals £13/£17 & £21. Access, Amex, Visa,* ⓘ Diners Club International

SW7   Tui   £42
Tel 071-584 8359   **R**
19 Exhibition Road SW7 2HE   **Map 23 E1**

Tom Yum, a traditional clear spicy soup scented with lemon grass, lime
leaves and fresh chilis and served in a fire pot, is an almost essential element
in a meal at this civilised Thai restaurant in South Kensington. Pork and
water chestnut dumplings with garlic sauce, satay, spare ribs, galangal and
coconut-flavoured soup (*Tomkha Gai*) all feature among the starters; red
(both chicken and duck) and green curries, crab claws, marinated beef with
chilis and basil, deep-fried pomfret, Thai-style sweet and sour prawns are
among the main dishes. *Mee Grob* is typical of the unusual, yet classic Thai
tastes on offer – a dish of crisply-fried rice noodles tossed in a tamarind-
based sauce of pork and shrimps; *Taohoo Tord* – deep-fried beancurd with
plum sauce for dipping – is considered a house speciality. **Seats 60.** *Parties
40. Private Room. L 12-2.30 (Sun to 3) D 6.30-11 (Sun 7-10.30). Closed
Bank Holidays. Access, Amex, Visa,* ⓘ Diners Club International

N1   Tuk Tuk Restaurant   £30
Tel 071-226 0837   **R**
330 Upper Street N1 2XQ   **Map 20 C1**

Small, stylish and informal restaurant, taking its name from the rickshaw-
style taxis that ply the streets of Bangkok. Satay, chicken wings or fish
patties could precede hot and sour soup with prawns and rice, a mild or
chili-hot curry, garlicky fried beef or noodles with mixed seafood.
Customers are invited to share dishes "in the traditional manner". Singha
Thai beer is a good accompaniment. **Seats 80.** *Parties 50. Private Room.
L 12-3 D 6-11.15. Closed L Sat, all Sun, Bank Holidays. Access, Amex, Visa,*
ⓘ Diners Club International

SW3   Turner's   £95
Tel 071-584 6711   **R**
87-89 Walton Street SW3 2HP   **Map 23 E2**

It is easy to think that all is on autopilot here, now that Brian Turner is to
be seen more at front of house and on television than in his kitchen.
Nevertheless, it is his Yorkshire charm – put to good use as order-taker,
waiter and sommelier – that keeps matters on the right rails at his smart,
once-starred Chelsea restaurant. Chef Peter Brennan continues to head the
team in the kitchen, producing fixed-price menus with a few modern
touches: clear red mullet soup, warm quail breast and lentil salad, English
duck with Thai herbs, millefeuille of Dover sole and artichoke with wild
mushroom butter sauce. The smaller-choice, fixed-price menus offer best
value. Modest, all-French wine list. **Seats 52.** *Parties 54. Private Room.
L 12.30-2.30 D 7.30-11 (Sun to 10). Closed L Sat, Bank Holidays, 1 week
Xmas. Set L £15.75 Set D £23.50 & £32/£38.25. Access, Amex, Visa,* ⓘ Diners Club International

SW9   Twenty Trinity Gardens   £45
Tel 071-733 8838   **R**
20 Trinity Gardens SW9 8DP   **Map 21 E2**

In a pretty square off Acre Lane, a cheerful local offering some enjoyably
different dishes like Persian broad beans on spiced rice with apricot and
orange sauce, Cajun lamb with garlic hash brown and yoghurt, or
sweetbreads in sherry vinegar with hollandaise and toasted hazelnuts.
Seats 50. *Parties 50. L 12.30-2.30 (Sun 11.30-4) D 7-10.30. Closed L Sat,
D Sun, 1 week Xmas. Set D from £16.50. Access, Amex, Visa.*

SW1 22 Jermyn Street

Tel 071-734 2353   Fax 071-734 0750

£188

PH

22 Jermyn Street SW1Y 6HL

Map 22 C3

50 yards from Piccadilly, 22 Jermyn Street was established as 'residential chambers' by Anthony Glyka in 1915. The fine Edwardian property has been converted with panache by his grandson, Henry Togna, to a luxurious private hotel. 13 self-contained suites and 5 studios retain their period furniture and objets d'art and are brightened daily with fresh flowers. Business facilities include fax points and a 'speed-dial' phone directory; housekeeping, 24hr room services (including medical and dental support) and continental breakfast are similarly comprehensive. King-size beds, make-up mirrors, bespoke toiletries and monogrammed bathsheets and robes set the tone. Health and sports club facilities available nearby, by arrangement. *Rooms 18. Access, Amex, Visa,* ◐

W2 Veronica's

Tel 071-229 5079

£65

R

3 Hereford Road W2 4AB

Map 22 C1

Overlooking Bayswater's Leinster Square, indefatigable Veronica Shaw's English restaurant has monthly-changing, well-researched culinary themes; recent examples have covered the Tudor and 20s' and 30s' periods, recreating dishes ranging from "Sir Hugh Plat's Polonian Sawsedges" and "Friggasie of chycken and muskels" to herring in oatmeal with bacon and tomato, and fillet of beef cooked between hot oak planks. There's always a good selection of British farmhouse cheeses (from Mendip Hill Goat to Cornish Yarg) – which are probably a better bet than the theme desserts. Not as gimmicky as it might appear; meals, for example, commence with a lovely spicy nut dip with crudités, while starters are presented on a trolley with full descriptions; low-fat, high-fibre and vegan dishes are always indicated on the wordy menus. Outdoor tables in good weather get away from the sometimes intrusive kitchen grill. *Seats 32. Parties 45. L 12-3 D 7-11. Closed L Sat, all Sun, Bank Holidays. Access, Amex, Visa,* ◐

NW6 Vijay

Tel 071-328 1087

£40

R

49 Willesden Lane NW6 7RF

Map 20 C3

This unpretentious Indian restaurant is not exclusively vegetarian (in fact there are extensive meat, chicken and prawn selections) but vegetarian dishes are perhaps what it is best known for. Specialities include dosas (rice and lentil flour pancakes), uppuma (semolina with onions and spices) and avial (vegetables cooked with ground coconut, yoghurt, butter, curry leaves etc). *Seats 70. Parties 30. L 12-2.45 D 6-10.45 (Fri & Sat to 11.45). Closed 25 & 26 Dec. Access, Amex, Visa,* ◐

W1 Villandry Dining Room NEW

Tel 071-224 3799

£45

R

89 Marylebone High Street W1M 3DE

Map 22 B3

Bare tables, old kitchen chairs and linoleum create a simple setting behind a delicatessen filled with freshly baked quiches, cooked hams and free-range eggs. Everything looks really wholesome and that's the way it tastes, too: courgette and coriander soup served in a handsome tureen; salad of Kentish mixed leaves with goat's cheese, lardons, olive croutons and baby tomatoes; brandade de morue; confit de canard; torte di ricotta; poached pears with cinnamon crème anglaise. No smoking. Open occasionally for dinner. *Seats 48. Parties 30. L only 12.30-3 (light snacks 8.30am-5.30pm). Closed Sun, Bank Holidays, 10 days Xmas. Access, Visa*

SW10   Vin Santo

Tel 071-352 6884

2 Hollywood Road SW10

£45

R

Map 23 F1

Smart deco and prices that won't break the bank at this popular Italian restaurant. The length of the printed menu is virtually doubled by the addition of daily specials. The cooking of dishes as varied as *gnocchi*, swordfish steak with lemon and fresh herbs, oxtail and *linguine partenopea* is sound and enjoyable. Service is both genial and efficient and there's a fine Italian wine list. *Seats 80. Parties 100. Private Room. L 12-3 D 7-11.30. Closed Sun, Bank Holidays. Access, Amex, Visa,*

NW3   Wakaba

Tel 071-586 7960

122a Finchley Road NW3 5HT

£70

R

Map 20 B3

Behind curved glass frosted from busy Finchley Road the decor is designer-zero, canteen-style, basically plain white. The menu provides an interesting span of Japanese dishes, and novitiates in this acquired, pretty cuisine would do well to opt for one of the set meals, which offer various choices. Some dishes, including sukiyaki, shabushabu and yosenabe (Japanese-style bouillabaisse) are prepared at the table. *Seats 55. Parties 55. L 12-2.30 D 6.30-11. Closed Sun, 24-27 Dec, Good Friday, Easter Monday, 1 week Aug. Set L from £9.50 Set D from £23.60. Access, Amex, Visa,*

WC2   The Waldorf

Tel 071-836 2400   Fax 071-836 7244

Aldwych WC2B 4DD

£192

H

Map 22 C4

At the time of our going to press the Waldorf was due to reopen after a major renovation by owners Forte. Edwardian splendour is epitomised in the Palm Court lounge, where the Friday, Saturday and Sunday tea dances have become an institution. The Footlights bar has a pub atmosphere, while the Club Bar is rather more refined, with oak panelling, oil paintings, marble fireplaces and leather armchairs. Bedrooms, including many designated non-smoking, are now all air-conditioned. Banqueting/conferences for 400/600. Graded at 72% in our 1992 Guide. *Rooms 292. Access, Amex, Visa,*

SW3   Walton's

Tel 071-584 0204

121 Walton Street SW3 2PH

£100

R

Map 23 E2

Polished service matches the luxuriously comfortable surroundings and in the kitchen Paul Hodgson shows his considerable skills in some highly enjoyable dishes. The menu is traditional English with an international slant. Asparagus with tarragon vinaigrette, lobster and scallop sausage, baked sole and salmon in a pastry lattice, fillet of venison on noodles, noisettes of lamb served pink on a potato and celeriac cake. Bread-and-butter pudding is served with an apricot custard. Traditional Sunday lunch; after-theatre supper; "Simply Walton's" lunch; and an à la carte menu. *Seats 65. Parties 20. Private Room. L 12.30-2.30 (Sun to 2) D 7.30-11.30 (Sun 7-10). Closed 25 & 26 Dec. Set L £14.75 Set D £21. Access, Amex, Visa,*

W1   Washington Hotel   70%

Tel 071-499 7000   Fax 071-495 6172

5 Curzon Street W1Y 8DT

£199

H

Map 22 C3

Between Berkeley Square and Park Lane, in the heart of Mayfair, a smart hotel with elegant public areas – from the marble-floored reception to Madison's lounge-bar with deep carpets, comfortable seating, elaborately-draped curtains and bird's-eye maple panelling. Bedrooms vary in size and

shape but have a distinctive 30s' feel, with striking burr oak furniture in
art deco style matched by agreeable abstract-patterned fabrics. There's a
floor of non-smoking rooms. Bathrooms have particularly good shower
heads over the tubs, plus convenient phone and loudspeaker extensions.
Long beds and a breakfast table, along with all the usual extras, are
standard throughout. Bright, modern meeting rooms for up to 70. No
dogs. Sarova Hotels. **Rooms 173.** *Access, Amex, Visa,*

W1	The Westbury	75%	£193

Tel 071-629 7755   Fax 071-495 1163

Conduit Street W1A 4UH   Map 22 E3

Built in the 1950s as sister hotel to the Westbury in New York, the
London version is just off New Bond Street. Sparkling chandeliers and
smartly liveried porters create a formal impression on first entering the
marble-floored lobby. The pine-panelled Polo Lounge (open 24 hours for
refreshments) and dark green Polo Bar boast polo murals and memorabilia,
inspired by original owners who had a passion for the sport. Bedrooms
vary in size from smallish singles through mini-suites to 13 full suites and a
penthouse; all share the same traditional-style darkwood furniture with
pleasing floral fabrics and many extras like mini-bars. 20 of the rooms are
suitable for families, with cots, funpacks and babysitting available.
Conference facilities for up to 120, but no leisure amenities. Forte Grand.
Rooms 243. *Access, Amex, Visa,*

NW1	White House	71%	£127

Tel 071-387 1200   Fax 071-388 0091

Albany Street NW1 3UP   Map 22 A3

Just off Euston Road, close to Regent's Park and opposite Great Portland
Street underground station. Built as a block of flats in the 1930s, hence the
numerous pillars to be found in the public rooms. There is no separate
lounge in the smart marble-floored reception/foyer, but it does offer some
seating and the sophisticated bar has plenty of lounge-style armchairs.
There's a cocktail lounge, a garden café and the Wine Press wine bar.
Bedrooms vary in size from compact to suites; most have decent
lightwood units, soft colour schemes and matching fabrics. All have
double-glazed windows and American electric sockets as well as British
ones plus mini-bars, security chains and spyholes. Well used by coachloads
of international travellers stopping over briefly in London. One floor,
called the Reserve Floor, has separate check-in and lounge plus lots of
extras. No dogs. Conference and banqueting facilities for 120/100. Rank
Hotels. **Rooms 576.** *News kiosk & gift shop, sauna, keep-fit equipment, coffee
shop (7am-10.30pm). Access, Amex, Visa,*

W1	White Tower		£70

Tel 071-636 8141   R

1 Percy Street W1P 0ET   Map 22 E2

A comfortable, old-fashioned restaurant where a profusion of waiters cater
to even your smallest needs. The verbose menu centres on Greek dishes,
with some middle-Eastern and French influences. Whatever its origin, the
food is tasty and abundant. **Seats 70.** *Private Room. L 12.30-2.15
D 6.45-10.15. Closed Sat & Sun, Bank Holidays, 3 weeks Aug, 1 week Xmas.
Access, Amex, Visa,*

W2	Whites Hotel	77%	£190

Tel 071-262 2711   Fax 071-262 2147

90 Lancaster Gate W2 3NR   Map 22 C1

A cobbled forecourt leads through glass-topped canopies into a Victorian
mansion with a colonnaded facade. There's a feeling of quiet opulence in
day rooms like the graceful reception with a marble fireplace and a rug-
covered marble floor, a bar with tub chairs and a partly-panelled writing

room. Bedrooms have panel-effect walls, good-quality limed furniture, easy chairs, swagged silk drapes and luxurious Italian marble bathrooms. There are two suites, one in Louis XV style, the other with an Oriental inspiration. No dogs. *Rooms 54. Access, Amex, Visa,* (D) Diners Club International

EC4 Whittington's

£70
R

Tel 071-248 5855

21 College Hill EC4 2RP

Map 24 C2

Once owned by Dick Whittington, this busy restaurant/wine bar has Robert Couzens (who trained with the Roux brothers) as head chef. Basil-flavoured bavarois of red and green peppers, spinach-wrapped fresh sardines with tomato concassé, papillote of rump steak filled with braised red cabbage and a red wine sauce flavoured with juniper berries all typify his style. *Seats 53. Parties 50. Private Room. L only 11.45-2.15. Closed Sat & Sun, Bank Holidays. Access, Amex, Visa,* (D) Diners Club International

SW1 Wilbraham Hotel 55%

£86
H

Tel 071-730 8296 Fax 071-730 6815

Wilbraham Place Sloane Street SW1X 9AE

Map 23 E2

Modest Belgravia hotel formed from three Victorian town houses. Bedrooms and bathrooms are generally quite small and spartan, though there are two large suites on the ground floor. *Rooms 52. No credit cards.*

SW1 Willett Hotel

£91
H

Tel 071-824 8415 Fax 071-824 8415

32 Sloane Gardens SW1X 8DT

Map 23 E2

Victorian townhouse in the heart of Chelsea converted into a peaceful hotel offering bed and breakfast accommodation, but limited public rooms. Three bedrooms are not en suite. Friendly staff. *Rooms 18. Access, Amex, Visa,* (D) Diners Club International

W14 Wilson's

£45
R

Tel 071-603 7267

236 Blythe Road W14 0HJ

Map 21 D3

Robert Wilson and his chef present an eclectic menu with some Scottish influence in this agreeable little bare-boarded restaurant on the corner of Shepherds Bush Road. Finnan haddock pudding with a spinach and bacon salad, chicken and mushroom pie, haggis-stuffed roast lamb and sauté of guinea fowl with hazelnuts and Chartreuse are typical dishes. *Seats 40. Parties 30. L 12.30-2.30 (Sun to 3) D 7-10. Closed L Sat, D Sun, Bank Holidays, 2 weeks Xmas, 2 weeks Aug. Access, Amex, Visa,* (D) Diners Club International

SW1 Wilton's

£110
R

Tel 071-629 9955 Fax 071-495 6233

55 Jermyn Street SW1Y 6LX

Map 22 C3

"Noted for the finest oysters (Sept-Apr), fish and game", Wilton's is yet another string to the Savoy Group's bow. The decor is restrained with pictures of the Royal Family and the founders of the restaurant gracing the walls; service is formal, matching the clubby atmosphere to a T. Lobster bisque, potted shrimps, omelette Arnold Bennett, Dover sole (grilled, fried, meunière, Colbert or Walewska), sherry trifle, apple tart, angels on horseback, British cheeses – a menu as traditional as the setting, which celebrated its 250th year as an eating house last year. *Seats 90. Parties 25. Private Room. L 12.30-2.30 D 6.30-10.30. Closed L Sat, all Sun, Bank Holidays. Access, Amex, Visa,* (D) Diners Club International

W5 Wine & Mousaka

£30

Tel 081-998 4373

R

30 & 33 Haven Green W5 2NX

Map 21 D4

A popularly-priced restaurant on two sides of a corner site offering most of the traditional Greek favourites, including meat or vegetarian mou(s)saka, souvla, winy sausages, *tava* (oven-cooked lamb on the bone) and *triada* (courgette, green pepper and vine leaves stuffed with pork mince, rice and herbs). See also entry under Richmond. ***Seats 100.*** *Parties 50. L 12-2.30 D 6-11.30. Closed Sun, Bank Holidays. Set meals from £6.95. Access, Amex, Visa,* Diners Club International

W8 Wodka

£45

Tel 071-937 6513

R

12 St Alban's Grove W8 5PN

Map 23 D1

In a quiet part of Kensington, this is a trendy restaurant/bar done out in simple modern style. The cooking is Polish, big on portions and flavours, typified by smoked eel, blinis, kulebiak, stuffed cabbage, lamb shashlik and hunter's stew. There's a decent wine selection, but wodka is the thing to drink here – it comes plain or in a dozen flavoured varieties including plum, cherry, bison grass and rye. ***Seats 50.*** *Parties 30. Private Room. L 12.30-2.30 D 7-11. Closed L Sat, Bank Holidays. Access, Amex, Visa,* Diners Club International

SE9 Yardley Court

£52

Tel 081-850 1850

H

18 Court Yard SE9 5PZ

Map 21 E1

A neat Victorian house surrounded by attractive gardens. Bed and breakfast accommodation. Children up to the age of 5 free in parents' room. ***Rooms 9.*** *Access, Visa.*

W5 Young's Rendezvous

£40

Tel 081-840 3060

R

13 Bond Street W5

Map 21 D4

Small, smart Chinese restaurant one street down from the Broadway centre, with smooth service from waiters and waitresses in tunics. Good sizzling dishes, sea food and Szechuan dishes; particularly fine lobster feast set menu. Try the special banana, red bean paste or ko-lei pancake or bean-curd in jade with crème de menthe to finish. Short list of dim sum served every day from 12.15 to 2.45pm; choice of business lunches. 12% service is added to all prices. ***Seats 80.*** *Parties 80. Private Room. L 12.15-2.45 D 6.15-11.45 (Sat to 12). Closed 25 & 26 Dec. Set L £7.50 & £9.50 Set D £11.50. Access, Amex, Visa,* Diners Club International

W1 Yumi

£80

Tel 071-935 8320

R

110 George Street W1H 6DJ

Map 22 B2

Decor is simplicity itself, and the menu is scarcely more complicated; set meals (particularly good value for money) and à la carte choices run the gamut of familiar Japanese dishes prepared with skill from carefully chosen ingredients. Owner Yumi Fujii is always on hand with a smile, a bow and advice. Upstairs and in the private rooms you sit cross-legged at very low tables, and it's only downstairs or in the bar that you can adopt a more conventional seat. No children under 10. ***Seats 76.*** *Parties 24. Private Room. L 12-2.30 D 6-10.30. Closed L Sat, all Sun, 1 week Xmas. Set L from £15. Access, Amex, Visa,* Diners Club International

SW3   Zen   £80

`Tel 071-589 1781   Fax 071-437 0641`   **R**

Chelsea Cloisters Sloane Avenue SW3   Map 23 E2

Zen Chelsea has the look of the 70s, but the other restaurants in this
expanding chain are as well known for Rick Mather's stylish and
minimalist interior designs as they are for the quality of the cooking on
their equally modern menus. Elegant curves, bare white surfaces, lots of
glass and playing water are the family characteristics, yet, while the menus
are quite different, the only other universal trait seems to be a lack of any
real distinction (given the price) in the cooking. When they are good they
are great (and smart enough for special occasions), but when they are off
form the inconsistencies are a let down. Service charges, once obligatory,
are now, thankfully, left to the discretion of diners. *Also at:* **ZeNW3** 81
Hampstead High Street NW3 Tel 071-794 7863 Map 20 B3, **Zen
Central** 20-22 Queen Street Mayfair W1 Tel 071-629 8103, Map 22 C3.
See also entry under **Now & Zen**. *Seats 120. Parties 20. Private Room.
L 12-3 D 6-11.30 (Sun to 11). Closed 25 & 26 Dec. Access, Amex, Visa,*
(i) *Diners Club International*

SW3   Ziani   £65

`Tel 071-352 2698`   **R**

45/47 Radnor Walk SW3 4BT   Map 23 E2

A brightly decorated Italian restaurant named after an ancient Venetian
family. Seafood is quite a strength, and assorted fried or grilled fish is a
popular choice, along with trout with almonds and seafood risotto. Daily
specials are always worth a try. *Seats 60. Parties 22. Private Room.
L 12.30-2.45 (Sun to 3.15) D 7-11.30 (Sun to 10.30). Closed 4 days Xmas,
4 days Easter. Access, Amex, Visa,* **(i)** *Diners Club International*

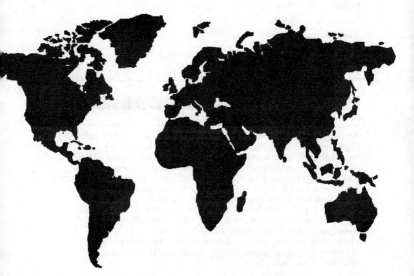

Serviced Apartments in London

Serviced apartments, which are often a preferred alternative for longer visits, have developed into a thriving industry. We recommend only those which have met our minimum high standards. When booking, it is advisable to obtain as many details as possible about the particular apartment as accommodation can vary considerably within the same building in respect of price and other aspects.

In the main, we have quoted weekly prices (incl. VAT unless stated) for the smallest apartment given to us by managements, but these are normally not so hard and fast as those at hotels, and some are known to be negotiable and may be influenced by the length of stay.

In line with our percentage ratings of hotels, each apartment has been similarly graded, and is classified as:

De luxe   80%+
Superior   70-80%
Standard   60-70%

(Map references relate only to the map at the end of this section – see page 199)

W8	Allen House	67%	from £125
Tel 071-938 1346 Fax 071-938 4142			nightly
Allen Street London W8 6BH			Map 1 B2

An Edwardian mansion block situated in a quiet road just off Kensington High Street, offering apartments varying in size and layout (one to three bedrooms), each spacious and airy with high ceilings and large windows, characteristics of buildings of this era. Rooms are pleasantly furnished with good carpets – bedrooms have mostly pine units and brass bedheads, lounge areas, dark furniture and inviting grey-upholstered sofas. Kitchens (some with wash/dryer) and bathrooms are quite modern, and each apartment has its own individual thermostat, a portable radio and useful guest information folders. *Apartments 41. Nearest tube: High Street Kensington. Parking: street (meters) nearby NCP. Maid Service: Monday-Friday. Telephone charge: 14p per unit. Amenities: 24hr porterage, video entryphone, lift, garden, business facilities, laundry services, baby-sitting, cots, highchairs. Credit cards: All.*

NW8	Arabella Court	66%	from £550
Tel 071-328 4498 Fax 071-372 1199			
45 Marlborough Place London NW8 0PX			Map 2 A2

Built in the mid 70s the block is just off Abbey road, close to Lord's Cricket Ground, Regent's Park and the Wellington Humana Hospital. Round the corner in Blenheim Terrace there are two good pubs and L'Aventure, a restaurant recommended in this Guide. There's a goldfish pond in the foyer, and three lifts serve the apartments, ranging from one bedroom suites to the penthouse four bedroom suite with two bathrooms and terrace. Lounge and dining areas are spacious, bedrooms on the small side, and the larger apartments have balconies and a wash/dryer machine. Video and tape hire can be arranged (1 week min). *Apartments 33. Nearest tube: St John's Wood. Parking: own garage. Maid Service: daily (not Sunday) incl. washing-up; linen changed twice a week. Telephone charge: 20p per unit (two phones per apartment). Amenities: 24hr concierge, entryphone, lifts, garden, business facilities, laundry service, cable TV (fixed charge), baby-sitting, cots. Credit cards: All.*

SW1	**Arlington House**	64%	from £490

Tel 071-629 0021   Fax 071-823 9244

Arlington Street London SW1A 1RL   Map 3 B3

A 30s block situated behind The Ritz with views of Green Park from most apartments, grouped around a large grassed courtyard. The excellent Caprice restaurant is on the doorstep. Flats vary in type and style – the largest offering the best quality, but all are comfortably furnished, and the recently redecorated and carpeted corridors are light and welcoming. The two rooftop flats with terraces are particularly inviting with a superior standard of decor and equipment. Porters will deliver groceries and newspapers by arrangement. *Nearest tube: Green Park. Parking: underground car park. Maid Service: Monday-Friday. Telephone Charge: 10p per unit. Amenities: 24hr porterage, lift, baby-sitting, cots, business facilities, satellite TV. Credit cards: Access, Amex, Visa.*

SW7	**Aston's**	75%	from £385 +VAT

Tel 071-370 0737   Fax 071-835 1419

39 Rosary Gardens London SW7 4NQ   Map 4 C2

A row of privately owned Victorian town houses offering a range of excellently run and maintained apartments from budget studios with kitchenette and shared bathrooms (from £25 per night), smart designer studios (sleeping 2-4 guests) to luxury flats furnished in traditional country-house style. The modern designer studios, with bold decor, have been cleverly created, providing remote-control air-conditioning and TV with teletext, video, telephone with answering machine and fax line. Marble-tiled bathrooms have power shower and bathrobes, while the concealed kitchenettes welcome guests with luxury provisions. Minimum length of stay: 3 days. *Apartments 60. Nearest tube: Gloucester Road. Parking: street (meters) nearby NCP. Maid Service: daily. Telephone charge: 16p per unit. Amenities: entryphone, business facilities, laundry services, baby-sitting. Credit cards: Access, Amex, Visa.*

NW1	**Astor Lodge**	64%	from £400 +VAT

Tel 071-723 6677   Fax 071-262 1779

33 Dorset Square London NW1 6Q   Map 5 A3

Dorset Square, close to Baker Street and Regent's Park, was the original site of Lord's cricket ground before it moved up the road to its present site. The surrounding buildings are Georgian, typified by lofty rooms on the ground and first floors with spacious living rooms. Guests staying here – apartments vary in size from studios to three bedrooms with two bathrooms – pay reduced rates after four weeks when the lower VAT tax is passed on. Standards of housekeeping and maintenance are particularly high, furnishings comfortable. Some larger apartments are

RESERVATIONS

0800 243 163

equipped with dishwasher and wash/dryer and the office (notably helpful) can provide a microwave for lazy cooks! *Apartments 25. Nearest tube: Marylebone. Parking: street (meters); NCP nearby. Maid Service: Monday-Friday. Telephone charge: 12p per unit. Amenities: entryphone, lift, garden, laundry service, baby-sitting, cots. Credit cards: None.*

W1	**Athenaeum Apartments**	82%	from £155

Tel 071-499 3464   Fax 071-493 1860   nightly

116 Piccadilly London W1V 0BJ   Map 6 B3

In the heart of Mayfair, just off Piccadilly, these elegant Edwardian apartments adjoin the Athenaeum hotel, thus benefitting from all its facilities, including room service. There are two telephone lines into each apartment, so you can have a separate fax, and other thoughtful touches include portable radios, newspaper and milk delivery, and a shopping service on request. The recently refurbished executive apartments have been redesigned to a high standard in gracious country-house style offering a traditional feel with period furniture, tasteful fabrics and lots of prints and paintings. Super bathrooms and immaculate housekeeping. *Apartments 33. Nearest tube: Green Park/Hyde Park Corner. Parking: nearby NCP. Maid Service: daily. Telephone charge: 55p per unit. Amenities: entryphone, lift, business facilities, cable TV, laundry services, baby-sitting, cots, highchairs. Credit cards: All.*

SW3	**Beaufort House**	73%	from £680

Tel 071-584 2600   Fax 071-584 6532

45 Beaufort Gardens London SW3 1PN   Map 7 B3

With its direct access from Brompton Road, Beaufort Gardens is a remarkably quiet Regency Terrace, yet it's only a short walk from Harrods and Hyde Park. Accommodation ranges from intimate single-bedroom studios to spacious four-bedroom apartments, each with its own electronic security system. Thus privacy and comfort are assured, yet a high level of service is available. In addition to individual private direct lines, Beaufort House provides a switchboard message service. Conversion into serviced apartments has not been achieved without some space problems in achieving a second or third bedroom; most of the marbled bathrooms are small and not all are en suite. Kitchens, however, are fully fitted and well-stocked with quality china and glassware: outside catering can be arranged for parties. *Apartments 24. Nearest tube: Knightsbridge. Parking: meters only. Maid service: Monday-Friday (not Bank Holidays). Telephone: 15p per unit. Amenities: 24hr porterage, video entryphone, lifts, business facilities, same day laundry, video, phone answering service, baby-sitting, cots. Credit cards: All.*

SW3	**Brookman Apartments**	73%	from £525

Tel 071-823 7159   Fax 071-584 3615

20 Ovington Square London SW3 1LR   Map 8 B3

A Georgian house situated in a quiet Knightsbridge square (guests have access to the gardens) has Harrods as its corner shop! The comfortable apartments (ranging from a garden studio to some with three bedrooms) are ideal for business people as each has a state-of-the-art telephone incorporating fax, answering machine and photocopier. Well maintained rooms are light and airy, with quality fabrics, good furniture, and super kitchens that have microwave, dishwasher, and wash/dryer. A provision pack is supplied to guests on arrival. *Apartments 7. Nearest tube: Knightsbridge. Parking: street (meters). Maid Service: twice weekly. Telephone charge: 15p per unit. Amenities: entryphone, garden, laundry service, baby-sitting, cots, highchairs. Credit cards: Amex, Visa.*

RESERVATIONS

0800 243 163

SW1   Carlton Tower Apartments   85%   POA

Tel 071 245 1911   Fax 071-235 8018

Carlton Tower Place Sloane Street London SW1   Map 9 B3

Directly linked to the Hyatt Carlton Tower Hotel, but with a separate,
24hr-manned entrance off Sloane Street, the apartments offer the privacy of
a self-contained *pied à terre* with immediate access to full hotel facilities,
including 24hr room service. The one or two bedroom apartments are
actually all the same size, those with one bedroom enjoying a
compensatingly larger reception/dining area. For longer term lets,
apartments may be taken unfurnished, otherwise they come individually
decorated in considerable style and comfort. All have two bathrooms,
pristine in white marble, and kitchenette with microwave oven and fridge.
The kitchen can be fully stocked and equipped with utensils and tableware
if required, deliveries of milk and shopping can also be arranged.
Flexibility is the keynote here with most things, like a second phone line
for a fax machine for example, available on request Minimum length of
stay: three months. *Apartments 28. Nearest tube: Knightsbridge. Parking:
provided. Maid Service: full hotel service daily. Telephone charge: 24p per unit.
Amenities: All facilities of Carlton Tower Hotel can be cross-charged to
apartments. Credit Cards: None.*

SW3   Cheval Apartments   80%   from £1000

Tel 071-589 7762   Fax 071-581 3701

150 Brompton Road London SW3 1HX   Map 10 B3

Located in the heart of Knightsbridge, the apartments, in four nearby
blocks, are luxuriously furnished and offer high standards of
accommodation. Two at Cheval Place have balconies as do those at
Montpelier Mews, one of which has a spa bath. These flats provide
dishwasher and washing machine, Villeroy and Boch china, and fine
crystal, as well as burglar alarms with panic buttons. The newly built
chalet houses next door have a small patio, and the master bathrooms have
balconies – kitchens are splendid, even equipped with tumble dryer. Free
local health club membership and welcome packs and flowers on arrival.
*Apartments 29. Nearest tube: Knightsbridge. Parking: on site. Maid Service:
Monday-Friday (linen changed weekly). Telephone Charge: 12p per unit.
Amenities: 24hr security, video entryphone, lift, business facilities, cots,
highchairs. Credit cards: None.*

SW3   Clifton Lodge   62%   from £85+VAT nightly

Tel 071-584 0099   Fax 071-823 9194

45 Egerton Gardens London SW3 2DD   Map 11 B3

In a quiet street close to Harrods and Knightsbridge, the building was
originally a Victorian family town house, but is now modernised
providing a choice of one room studios and smallish two room apartments.
The studios can be used as a reception room as the wall beds are hidden
neatly away and can be let down when needed, while the larger apartments
have a separate double bedroom and a reception room with either
concealed beds or sofabeds. Both bathrooms and kitchenettes are neatly
equipped, furnishings smart and colourful. *Apartments 11. Nearest tube:
South Kensington. Parking: street (meters) NCP nearby. Maid Service: daily
(except Sunday). Telephone charge: 20p per unit. Amenities: entryphone, lift,
baby-sitting, cots. Credit cards: Access, Amex, Visa.*

THE APARTMENT SERVICE

RESERVATIONS

0800   243   163

W1   Curzon Plaza   66%   from £85

Tel 071-499 4121   Fax 071-491 7476

56 Curzon Street London W1Y 7PF   Map 12 B3

Originally built as a hotel, this centrally situated Mayfair red-brick block
offers suites with hotel services. A major attraction is its direct access to the
Mirabelle restaurant, which also provides breakfast and room service, and a
small brasserie-style eatery, adjacent to the smart marbled foyer/lounge area,
opened last year. Apartments come in a variety of sizes, styles, and decor,
some have been and are being refurbished, though several have a rather
dated, but comfortable, feel about them. There are another 90 apartments
of similar standard at 39 Hill Street. *Apartments 158. Nearest tube: Green
Park. Parking: nearby NCP. Maid service: daily (twice), turn-down service.
Telephone charge: 16p per unit. Amenities: 24hr porterage, lifts, business
facilities, patio, satellite TV, baby-sitting, cots. Credit cards: All.*

SW1   Dolphin Square   66%   from £450

Tel 071-834 3800   Fax 071-798 8735

London SW1V 3LX   Map 13 C3

A large block of apartments, alongside the Thames Embankment, built in
the 1930s it was then the largest complex of its kind in the world, even
today it remains an impressive structure. Built around a central garden, it
offers some 152 of its apartments to let. These range from one room studio
apartments to the largest with 3 bedrooms and separate lounge. All have
tiled bathrooms and a small, but relatively well equipped kitchens. Premier
rooms on the third and sixth floors have been refurbished in the last couple
of years, and have light decor and modern fittings. Remaining rooms (30)
are more dated, with 70s style furnishings and are discounted by 15% of
the published rate. Residents have use of a well laid out sports club
including a new gym and large swimming pool; a bar and brasserie are
also on site; there's a shopping arcade, too. *Apartments 152. Nearest tube:
Pimlico. Parking: NCP within square, street (meters). Maid Service: daily.
Telephone charge: 18p per unit. Amenities: 24hr reception and porterage,
garden, health club, lifts, shopping arcade, brasserie, launderette, conference rooms,
bar, baby-sitting, cots. Credit cards: All.*

SW3   Draycott House   80%   from £715
                                                       +VAT

Tel 071-584 4659   Fax 071-225 3694

10 Draycott Avenue London SW3 3AA   Map 14 C3

In a quiet tree-lined street, the majority of apartments here have their own
balconies, and one a roof terrace. Full of home comforts, they are
immaculately kept by Linda Coulthard and her team, and the period
building is one of the best run of all those listed in this section. Typically,
the living areas feature period furniture, custom-made sofas, pictures, objets
d'art, books, magazines and flowers while the bedrooms have co-ordinating
fabrics and cosseting extras such as pot-pourri and pomanders. Bathrooms
sparkle and modern fitted kitchens are well stocked with provisions on
arrival, and milk is delivered daily. Answerphones and fax machines can be
installed on request and the remote-control TVs (with video) have fastext.
*Apartments 13. Nearest tube: Sloane Square. Parking: own garage. Maid
Service: Monday-Friday. Telephone charge: 12p per unit. Amenities: video
entryphone, lift, courtyard garden, business services, laundry room, baby-sitting,
cots, highchairs. Credit cards: None.*

R E S E R V A T I O N S

0 8 0 0   2 4 3   1 6 3

SW5   Emperors Gate Apartments   62%

Tel 071-244 8409   Fax 071-373 6455

8 Knaresborough Place London SW5 0TG

from £75
nightly

Map 15 C2

Family-run suites just off the Cromwell road. Prices are per suite, and since there's no lift the higher you go the less you pay. As in all Victorian buildings the larger rooms are on lower floors, but each apartment is pleasantly furnished in contemporary style with compact well-fitted kitchens. A starter pack, comprising tea, coffee, orange juice, cereals and milk is provided on arrival, and guests receive a complimentary daily newspaper and a useful information folder. Minimum 2 nights stay. *Apartments 18. Nearest tube: Earls Court. Parking: by arrangement and street (meters). Maid Service: daily linen change (not Sunday). Telephone charge: payphone in each room. Amenities: reception (Mon-Sat), entryphone, business facilities, laundry room, baby-sitting, cots, highchairs. Credit cards: All.*

W9   Europa House   75%

Tel 071-286 5294   Fax 071-229 3917

79a Randolph Avenue London W9 1DW

£850
+VAT

Map 16 A2

A new block of spacious apartments close to Lord's and a short walk from Little Venice and the canal. There's a stunning penthouse, and several other apartments have their own balconies. Security is particularly good, with not only a member of staff on hand, but also a video entryphone, and each front door has a doorbell and spy hole. The fully fitted kitchens with seating include a dishwasher, wash/dryer and microwave, and would grace any home, and the modern lounges boast state-of-the-art TV and video recorder. Contemporarily furnished bedrooms have trouser press and hairdryer and the sparkling marble bathrooms positively gleam thanks to excellent housekeeping. Complimentary 'welcome pack' of groceries for all guests. *Apartments 14. Nearest tube: Maida Vale/Warwick Avenue. Parking: street (meters). Maid Service: Monday-Friday. Telephone charge: 25p per unit. Amenities: 24hr security, video entryphone, lift, garden, baby-sitting, cots, highchairs. Credit cards: All*

W1   Flemings Apartments   73%

Tel 071-499 2964   Fax 071-491 8866

7 Half Moon Street London W1Y 7RA

from £105
nightly

Map 17 B3

Being part of the Flemings hotel, the apartments here have the best of two worlds – the privacy of an entrance separate from the hotel and the availablity of 24hr room service if required. Rooms are traditionally furnished with elaborately draped curtains and small patterned wallpaper that is pretty rather than stylish. The real luxury is to be found in bathrooms and kitchens, the former in white marble, sometimes with separate shower cubicle, and the latter with polished red granite floor and work surfaces. All mod-cons include microwave oven and wash/dryer. Small details of repair are sometimes missed, and if planning to arrive before the evening check that the apartment is not being used for interviews or some other purpose during that day. *Apartments 11. Nearest tube: Green Park. Parking: street (meters). Maid Service: daily. Telephone charge: 25p/30p per unit. Amenities: entryphone, lift, baby-sitting, cots, highchairs. Credit cards: All.*

THE
APARTMENT
SERVICE

RESERVATIONS

0800 243 163

W2   Fountains   from £1000

Tel 071-286 5294   Fax 071-229 3917

1 Lancaster Terrace London W2   Map 18 B2

Opened as we went to press (and therefore ungraded), these new
apartments offer luxury accommodation just north of Hyde Park. In
addition to the usual amenities, each apartment has an answerphone, fax
machine and stereo equipment, and a video recorder is available on request.
Seven apartments each have 2 bedrooms, 2 bathrooms and 2 reception
rooms while the *pièce de résistance* is the sumptuous 3-bedroom penthouse.
Minimum letting period: one month. **Apartments 17.** *Nearest tube:
Lancaster Gate. Parking: meters. Maid Service: Monday-Friday. Telephone
charge: 25p per unit. Amenities: 24hr concierge, entryphone, lift, satellite TV,
baby-sitting, cots, highchairs. Credit cards: All.*

SW7   Gloucester Park   79%   from £600

Tel 071-373 1444   Fax 071-244 5050

Ashburn Place Kensington London SW4 4LL   Map 19 C2

A brand new luxurious development conveniently located on Cromwell
Rd, near Gloucester Rd. The impressive building is divided into blocks of
three apartments and each block has its own lobby and lift ensuring
maximum privacy. Security is guaranteed by a 24hr concierge controlling
the doors to the different lobbies. A sophisticated video system connected
to the flats' TV screens enable you to acknowledge any visitor in the lobby.
Each of the flats has a small balcony, sometimes two in the larger ones, and
decor is kept simple with unobtrusive colours. Lounge and dining areas are
on the small size and kitchens are stylish and very well fitted with quality
cabinets and Miele appliances. A large complimentary Fortnum & Mason
basket provides tea, jam, biscuits, chocolates and even half a bottle of
champagne. Bedrooms have a separate entrance hall to ensure more privacy
and good size lighted wardrobes. Master bedrooms in 2 and 3 bedroom
flats are larger with king-size beds and master bathrooms have bath and
separate shower as well as extra accessories like scales, robes and slippers.
All flats have beautiful tiled bathrooms with an initial stock of Crabtree &
Evelyn toiletries. Children are not neglected, a special baby toiletry pack
with toys is offered. Bed linen is changed once a week, towels twice. The
flats have two telephone lines with automatic pre-recorded answering
machine and faxes are available for hire. **Apartments 100.** *Nearest tube:
Gloucester Rd. Parking: own. Maid Service: Monday-Friday. Telephone charge
15p per unit. Amenities: 24hr reception/concierge, video entryphone, lift,
secretarial services, laundry services, video, telephone answering service, garden,
hi-tech gym, baby-sitting, cots, highchairs. Credit cards: None.*

W1   Grosvenor House Apartments   87%   from £225

Tel 071-499 6363   Fax 071-493 1552

Park Lane London W1A 3AA   Map 20 B3

As discreet as they are exclusive, the apartments have a separate private
entrance and separate staff from the hotel yet benefit from all its services.
Ranging in size from one to five bedrooms, each is individually
decorated and furnished to a very high standard with antique furniture,
fine fabrics and all the luxuries associated with a leading hotel. Marble-
finished bathrooms are particularly ritzy. Portable air-conditioning units
can be installed on request, as can microwaves in the small kitchenettes,
which are hardly used since there's round-the-clock service. The apartments

can be let on a nightly basis, but are also available for medium term (4 weeks plus) and annual lets. *Apartments 146. Nearest tube: Marble Arch. Parking: own garage. Maid Service: daily. Telephone charge: 22p/35p per unit. Amenities: 24hr reception/porterage, lifts, business centre, satellite TV, health club plus all hotel services. Credit cards: All.*

SW7   Harrington Court   63%

Tel 071-225 0166   Fax 071-581 5752

from £1000
low season

13 Harrington Road London SW7 3ES

Map 21 B3

Light and very spacious apartments, ideal for large families and groups since they range in size from three bedroom maisonettes to ten-bedroomed penthouses (one with its own private lift and sauna). The air-conditioned rooms are massive and have recently been refurbished to a good standard. Huge kitchens are fully equipped and all the apartments have washing machine, tumble dryer and dishwasher. Bathrooms, some with sunken tubs have colourful suites which include bidets. *Apartments 15. Nearest tube: South Kensington. Parking: nearby car park. Maid Service: daily (not Sunday). Telephone charge: 20p per unit. Amenities: 24hr concierge, entryphone, lift, business services, laundry service, baby-sitting, cots. Credit cards: All.*

W1   Hertford Street   60%

Tel 071-409 2373   Fax 071-629 0763

from £500

12 Hertford Street London W1Y 7RE

Map 22 B3

Not at the luxury end of the market but the apartments in this Georgian town house, in the shadow of the London Hilton, benefit from a central location within easy walking distance of Piccadilly Circus – the heart of the West End. Most have kitchenettes open to lounge/ dining rooms, with black stained furniture and decent sofas, but all are well kitted out and include everything one might need including wash/dryers. Bedrooms have pretty floral polycotton duvets with matching curtains and either white painted fitted furniture or inexpensive melamine units. 'Starter packs' of basic provisions are available given prior notice. Newspapers and milk are delivered to the door daily. *Apartments 15. Nearest tube: Hyde Park Corner or Green Park. Parking: street (meters) NCP nearby. Maid service: Monday-Friday. Telephone charge: 18p per unit. Amenities: video entryphone, lift, baby-sitting, cots. Credit cards: All.*

SW5   Huntingdon House   70%

Tel 071-373 4525   Fax 071-373 6676

from £335

200/222 Cromwell Road London SW5 0SW

Map 23 B2

Handy for Earls Court, Olympia and the Cromwell Hospital, there are a variety of modern apartments behind the Edwardian facade of this block. Continuous refurbishment is being carried out in spacious rooms, some contemporary, others in modern Italian style, ensuring guests comfortable accommodation in quiet surroundings (front rooms are double-glazed) and there's the bonus of a delightful country-style garden, accessible from the conservatory. Half the suites, ranging from studio-size to a four-bedroomed penthouse, have a dishwasher and wash/dryer and the penthouses have air-conditioning, stereo equipment and patio areas. Tea, coffee, milk, sugar and bathroom toiletries are provided on arrival. *Apartments 50. Nearest tube: Earls Court. Parking: own spaces available in nearby underground garage. Maid Service: daily. Telephone charge: 18p per unit. Amenities: 24hr reception, lift, garden, business facilities, video hire, laundry service, baby-sitting, cots, highchairs. Credit cards: Access, Amex, Visa.*

THE
APARTMENT
SERVICE

RESERVATIONS

0800 243 163

W1   Hyde Park Residence   76%

from £700
low season
+VAT

Tel 071-409 9000   Fax 071-439 4041

55 Park Lane London W1Y 3DB

Map 24 B3

Across from the park and adjacent to the Dorchester, these apartments offer
elegant accommodation mainly for long-term residents. Planning of repair
and redecoration in the flats is brilliantly handled by the in-house team: an
architect, a decorator, upholsterers, French polishers and carpenters. The
deep and spacious lobby has a 24hr concierge and foyer shop. Security is a
highlight with video surveillance and non-uniformed security guards
touring the corridors. Flats are beautifully maintained but lobby and
corridors could use a new carpet and wall paper. All flats are spacious and
furnished to high standards with attractive bathrooms, mainly tiled or
marbled with a bidet in the most luxurious accommodation. Kitchens are
stylish and well equipped although smaller in one-bedroom flats. Two
luxury penthouse suites are available, with a baby grand piano, a roof
terrace and beautiful views. Facilities are tailored to customers' needs and
length of stay. A fax machine and hiring of office space and secretaries can
easily be arranged. Air-conditioning is provided by mobile units connected
to the walls. *Apartments 120. Nearest tube: Hyde Park Corner. Parking:
own. Maid Service: optional (hourly charged). Telephone charge: 18p per unit.
Amenities: 24hr reception/concierge, entryphone, lifts, secretarial services, laundry
services, foyer shop, video, baby-sitting, cots, highchairs. Credit cards: All.*

SW7   John Howard   67%

from £100
nightly

Tel 071-581 3011   Fax 071-589 8403

4 Queen's Gate London SW7 5EH

Map 25 B2

Adjoining the Regency-built hotel, set in a handsome tree-lined road close
to Hyde Park, the apartments benefit from good security – entry through
the hotel, camera surveillance and entryphone. Guests can make use of all
hotel services, which include a restaurant, conference room and safety
deposit boxes. The traditional elegance of the building carries through to
the apartments which are pleasantly decorated with some good quality
leather sofas and furniture in the lounges, while the bathrooms are practical
and the kitchenettes well equipped. *Apartments 12. Nearest tube: Gloucester
Road/High Street Kensington. Parking: street (meters). Maid Service: daily.
Telephone charge: 25p per unit. Amenities: entryphone, lift, business services,
cable TV, in-house movies, laundry service, safe deposit boxes, baby-sitting, cots,
highchairs. Credit cards: All.*

W8   Kensington Properties   60%

from £610

Tel 071-937 6636   Fax 071-937 5948

70 Abingdon Road London W8 6AP

Map 26 B2

Minutes away from the busy Kensington High St, the four flats in this
Georgian house benefit from a quiet residential location. No concierge or
foyer here, but a warm welcome from the lady owner. Flats are small but
snug and tastefully decorated with comfortable sofas around a gas fireplace.
One ground floor flat has a lovely patio outside the master bedroom.
Bathrooms are simple and partly tiled. Kitchens are well equipped with
wash/dryer, dishwasher, microwave, coffee machine, toaster and even food
processor. Milk and tea are provided on the day of arrival as are fresh
flowers. No lift. Parking tends to be difficult in the area. Bed linen is

THE
APARTMENT
SERVICE

RESERVATIONS

0800   243   163

changed weekly, towels twice a week. *Apartments 4. Nearest tube:
Kensington High Street. Parking: street (meters). Maid Service: Monday-
Friday. Telephone charge: 15p per unit. Amenities: video entryphone, baby-
sitting, cots, highchairs. Credit cards: Visa, Access.*

SW3	Lambs	60%	from £80
Tel 071-589 6297 Fax 071-584 3302			nightly
21 Egerton Gardens London SW3 2DE11			Map 27 C3

In a quiet residential street of terraced Victorian houses, the homely
apartments can accommodate two to four guests in studios (wall bed) or
one bedroomed suites (with additional wall beds hidden by day in the
living room). Comfortably old-fashioned, the building has its own patio
garden and access to Egerton Gardens. Rear ground floor rooms have
balconies. Continental breakfast (included in the price) is left outside the
door each morning; kitchens are quite basic. *Apartments 23. Nearest tube:
South Kensington/Knightsbridge. Parking: street (meters). Maid Service: daily
(excluding Sunday in high season). Telephone charge: 15p per unit. Amenities:
entryphone, garden, sauna, laundry service. Credit cards: Access, Amex, Visa.*

W1	Lodge Park	66%	from £700
Tel 071-436 9981 Fax 071-636 1368			low season
62 Harley Street London W1M 1DD			Map 28 A3

Some of the most spacious apartments in town, handily situated close to the
Oxford Street shops; the brochure has a handy map of the immediate area.
Don't be deceived by the rather tatty front doors to each flat because inside
they are bright and airy with smart bathrooms and splendid kitchens that
include microwaves. Each apartment has a sophisticated view entryphone
and is pleasantly furnished, the decor complementing the architecture –
note the fireplaces and some of the plasterwork in the lofty rooms. Teletext
is available on the large cable-linked remote-control TVs. There are further
apartments (not quite so luxurious) at No 65 and Hertford Street.
*Apartments 6. Nearest tube: Regents Park. Parking: street (meters). Maid
Service: Monday-Friday. Telephone charge: 18p per unit. Amenities: video
entryphone, lift, cable TV (charge for some channels), laundry room. Credit
cards: All.*

THE APARTMENT SERVICE

RESERVATIONS

0800 243 163

London Country Apartments

from £320

Tel 081 660 8167   Fax 081 668 8838

Close to Gatwick airport, and with frequent train service to central
London (12 minutes) these Croydon addresses are handy out-of-town
locations:

Tavistock Gate, Tavistock Road, Croydon   69%

Modern well-furnished and spacious flats with a health studio in the
basement. Each has a double sofa bed in the lounge, a washing machine and
dishwasher and some have an answerphone. 24hr porterage, garden.

28/33 Fleetwood Close Chepstow Rise Park Hill East Croydon CR0 5HD   67%

A 5yr-old block with similar facilities as above, though no health studio,
no garden and no staff on site. Well-equipped kitchens include a
microwave. *Nearest station: BR East Croydon. Parking: good. Maid Service:
weekly (daily at additional cost). Telephone Charge: 14p per unit. Amenities:
entryphone, lift, business facilities, video on request, baby-sitting, highchairs, cots.
Credit cards: Access, Amex, Visa.*

W1   Marble Arch Apartments   65%

from £405
low season

Tel 071-723 8888   Fax 071-724 8828

Map 29 A3

11-13 Harrowby Street London W1H 5YW

A marble-floored entrance foyer with hotel-style reception serves the
newly refurbished apartments ranging from studio size to three bedroomed
suites. Quite sparsely furnished, the rooms are nevertheless smartly
decorated with co-ordinating fabrics and light colour schemes, each flat
having a small well-equipped kitchen (wash/dryer machine in the three-
bedroomed suites) or kitchenette. Good central London location, the redbrick block, made up of several old courts, has its own parking and
security camera system. *Apartments 125. Nearest tube: Edgware Road.
Parking: own and street (meters). Maid Service: daily (not Sunday), linen
changed twice weekly, towels every day. Telephone charge: 15p per unit.
Amenities: 24hr reception, lift, business centre (message service), cable TV,
(nominal charge for some channels), laundry service, baby-sitting, cots. Credit
cards: All.*

SW7   Minds Luxury Apartments   65%

from £300

Tel 071-581 5927   Fax 071-370 2521

88/89 Queen's Gate London SW7 5AA

Map 30 C2

A typical Regency building with a none too imposing entrance, though
this conceals some very nice apartments, independently heated and well
furnished in a traditional style that complements the architecture. Thickly
carpeted rooms are bright and cheerful, the remote-control TVs have
teletext, and the well-equipped kitchens include dishwasher and
wash/dryer. A milkman delivers daily and basic provisions are provided on
arrival, backed up by a shopping service on request. *Apartments 15. Nearest
tube: Gloucester Road. Parking: street (meters). Maid Service: daily (not
Sunday). Telephone charge: 16p per unit. Amenities: 24hr concierge, video
entryphone, lift, cable TV, laundry service, baby-sitting, cots, highchairs, Credit
cards: Amex, Visa, Access.*

THE
APARTMENT
SERVICE

RESERVATIONS

0800 243 163

W8   Monarch House   69%   from £650

Tel 071-376 2038   Fax 071-937 0361

241 Kensington High St W8   Map 31 B2

Set well back from Kensington High Street by a long courtyard with plants, flowers and fountain, Monarch House is part of a new development. The modern and functional accommodation is mainly geared towards corporate lets with a minimum stay of 3 months. Apartments are spacious and neutrally decorated in shades of grey, blue and pink. Some of them look out on a quiet private garden, others benefit from terraces. Kitchens are well equipped with dishwasher, wash/dryer, coffee machine and toaster. Bedrooms are particularly roomy, with plenty of storage and a safe. Master bathrooms have a bidet. Often accommodating families, baby-sitting, cots and highchairs can be arranged as well as newspaper and milk delivery (a provision pack and fresh flowers greet new arrivals). *Apartments 41. Nearest tube: Kensington High Street. Parking: own. Maid Service: Monday-Friday. Telephone charge: 9.5p per unit. Amenities: 24hr concierge, video entryphone, lift, satellite TV, garden, laundry services, baby-sitting, cots, highchairs. Credit cards: None.*

SW3   Nell Gwynn House   65%   from £240

Tel 071-584 8317   Fax 071-823 7133

Sloane Avenue London SW3 3AX   Map 32 B/C3

In the heart of fashionable Chelsea, with its shopping and numerous quality restaurants stands the Nell Gwynn, an imposing building built in the 1930's. Of its 210 letting apartments, the vast majority are studio rooms with bathroom and tiny kitchen although there are a small number of one-bedded rooms with separate lounge. As all apartments are individually owned, the standard of furnishings and decor can vary considerably, a fact reflected in the rates charged. There's 24hr porterage and a doorman. Residents have full use of the leisure club in the basement, though at a charge of £30 per week. *Apartments 210. Nearest tube: Sloane Square and South Kensington. Parking: own garage, street (meters). Maid Service: Monday-Friday. Telephone charge: 6p (approx) per unit. Amenities: 24hr concierge, lift, leisure club. Credit cards: None.*

W1   No.1 Carlos Place   72%   from £1000

Tel 071-753 0744   Fax 071-753 0731

1 Carlos Place Mayfair London W1Y 5AE   Map 33 B3

Across from the Connaught, this characteristic Mayfair house offers apartments with up to 4 bedrooms, all newly refurbished, air-conditioned and double-glazed. Two and three bedroom apartments, some on split levels, offer large and comfortable accommodation with separate lounge and dining-room, and enough seating to entertain. One bedroom apartments are smaller and tend to be more jammed with furniture. All have comfortable bedrooms with sufficient cupboard space, radio alarm clock and portable television in master bedrooms. Marble bathrooms have Molton Brown toiletries and fluffy towels. A lot of attention has been put into the refurbishment of the kitchens which are well laid out with breakfast table and chairs, dishwasher, washing machine, tumble dryer, ceramic hob and microwave. The top floor penthouse has a hi-fi system and its own private patio with plants. In addition to a small sauna, the residents have free access to the local health club. *Apartments 11. Nearest tube: Marble Arch. Parking: NCP. Maid Service: daily. Telephone charge: 15p per unit.*

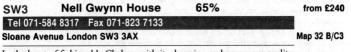

R E S E R V A T I O N S

0 8 0 0   2 4 3   1 6 3

Amenities: 24hr reception/porterage, video entryphone, lift, secretarial services, video, satellite TV, sauna, baby-sitting, cots, highchairs. Credit cards: All.

SW7   One Thirty   70%   from £415
Tel 071-370 6221   Fax 071-370 4293

130 Queen's Gate London SW7 5LE   Map 34 E1

Totally refurbished, this row of Victorian terraced houses offers excellent accommodation in well-furnished apartments, some with large sitting/dining room areas, each with a sofa bed for additional guests. There are four penthouses, several flats have balconies, all have double-glazing, independently controlled heating including ceiling fans, and well-equipped kitchens with microwave. *Apartments 54. Nearest tube: South Kensington. Parking: difficult (meters). Maid Service: daily (except Sunday). Telephone Charge: 25p per unit. Amenities: 24 hour porterage, lift, baby-sitting, cots, highchairs, satellite TV. Credit cards: All.*

Peerman Corporate Apartments   POA
Tel 071-584 7735   Fax 071-584 4594

Let on a one to ten year lease, the apartments, with several locations in central London, are decorated, furnished and equipped to the highest standards, an example being Kingston House South at Ellismore Gardens SW7 graded at 82%. Superbly and luxuriously fitted out with quiet good taste, all ancillary services (telephone, fax, fully equipped bar etc.) are charged *at cost*. The rooms are bright and airy, and most flats have a terrace overlooking the large rear courtyard. Bathrobes and notepaper can have company logos if required. *Maid Service: daily. Telephone Charge: standard BT rates. Amenities: 24hr security, lift, business facilities, cable TV, baby-sitting, cots, highchairs. Credit cards: None.*

SW1   Richmond Court   65%   from £375
Tel 071-245 1911   Fax 071-235 8018

200 Sloane Street London SW1   Map 35 B3

A 30s apartment block above the shops at the Harvey Nichols end of Sloane Street in the fashionable Knightsbridge area. Refurbishment of the common parts was just beginning in the summer of 1992 and will bring them up to the standard of the mostly one-bedroom apartments. Those on the lower floors are the more spacious. Reception/dining rooms have good free-standing furniture and smart comfortable sofas, bedrooms are generally furnished with white melamine units giving a bright fresh feel. Partly tiled bathrooms are mostly of good size and kitchens are fully equipped with oven, fridge, cooking utensils and 'oatmeal' pottery tableware. Smart, helpful porters can provide a shopping service if required and bed linen is changed weekly, towels daily. Minimum stay: 3 months. *Apartments 69. Nearest tube: Knightsbridge. Parking: none. Maid Service: Monday-Friday. Telephone charge: 11p per unit. Amenities: entryphone, lift. Credit cards: None.*

W2   Royal Court Apartments   61%   from £65
Tel 071-402 5077   Fax 071-724 0286   nightly

51 Gloucester Terrace London W2 3DH   Map 36 B2

Pretty hanging baskets and window boxes on the street indicate well-run apartments here, the best at this block of Victorian town houses being the smart Executive ones which boast superior furniture, quality fabrics, and thoughtful touches such as lighted wardrobes. All apartments, ranging from studios to three bedroom suites, have small kitchenettes with microwave. Some apartments are without carpets for guests who have allergies to certain materials. Woods of Windsor toiletries and tea/coffee trays await guests' arrival and there is also a small leisure centre and conference room, plus two foyer lounges. *Apartments 95. Nearest tube: Lancaster Gate. Parking: street (meters). Maid Service: daily. Telephone charge: 20p per unit. Amenities:24hr reception/security, lifts, laundry service, business facilities, satellite TV, conference room, sauna, spa bath, mini-gym. Credit cards: Access, Amex, Visa.*

SW1 St James Court Apartments 70% from £1140
Tel 071-834 6655   Fax 071-630 7587
Buckingham Gate London SW1 6AF — Map 37 B3

The apartments occupy a separate building to the rear of the similarly named hotel, which overlooks a plant filled courtyard, complete with ornate fountain. The long Edwardian building is divided into three separate houses, Falconers, Kings and Minsters. Falconers has recently been refurbished and offers high levels of luxury (including Italian marble-tiled bathrooms) to its patrons but at a price! They range from one bedroom to the palatial presidential suite. Minsters and Kings are more modest in furnishings (with an Indian influence) but still comfortable – though some do show signs of wear. Apartments range from single room studios to three bedroom suites with lounge, kitchen and bathroom. Guests have use of all hotel facilities. *Apartments 89. Nearest tube: St James. Parking: nearby car park (charge), on street (meters). Maid Service: twice daily. Telephone charge: 22p per unit. Amenities: 24hr reception, lift, garden, leisure club, laundry service, baby-sitting, cots. Credit cards: All.*

SW5 Serviced Apartments 70% from £700
Tel 071-244 8677   Fax 071-244 7331
26/27 Collingham Gardens London SW5 0HN — Map 38 C2

A fine example of Edwardian architecture, the apartments have been elegantly refurbished in traditional style. Opposite a typical Kensington square, the flats are light and airy, nicely furnished and newly redecorated. Each has a separate lounge (most with sofa beds), fully equipped kitchen and decent bathroom. A very good information pack is supplied and the staff are very pleased to shop or help guests in every way. *Apartments 23. Nearest tube: Earls Court. Parking: by arrangement. Maid Service: daily. Telephone Charge: 15p per unit. Amenities: 24hr receptionist, lift, business facilities, satellite TV, baby-sitting, cots, highchairs. Credit cards: All.*

NW3 Swiss Cottage Hotel and Apartments 60% from £540
Tel 071-722 2281   Fax 071-483 4588
4 Adamson Road London NW3 3HP — Map 39 A3

The self-contained apartments are housed in two Victorian buildings a short walk from the hotel (20 Adamson Road and 38 Fellows Road), situated in a leafy residential area behind the bustle of Finchley Road. English breakfast is included in the tariff, the only drawback being that it is only served in the hotel and last orders are at 9.30am. The apartments (mostly studio or one bedroomed) are modest but decently furnished, though the kitchens are on the small side and quite basic. However, they do have large fridge/freezers. The hotel provides a message waiting service and wake-up calls. *Apartments 17. Nearest tube: Swiss Cottage. Parking: on street. Maid service: twice weekly. Telephone charge: 25p per unit. Amenities:*

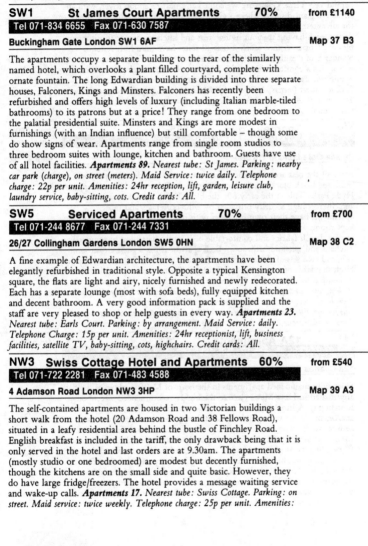

RESERVATIONS

0800 243 163

entryphone, garden, business facilities in hotel, baby-sitting, cots, highchairs.
Credit cards: All.

W1   10 Lees Place   63%
Tel 071-491 7055   Fax 071-629 288611

from £115
nightly

London W1Y 3RX

Map 40 B3

Just off Grosvenor Square and close to the American Embassy and Oxford
Street, the apartments are actually situated in a quiet pedestrian street
behind Lees Place. Guests are welcomed at a neat reception foyer, with an
attractive plant display, where a giant television controls cable TV input
for all suites. The one and two bedroomed apartments are quite modern in
design, each having spacious living areas and kitchens, decent furniture and
pleasant fabrics. A nice touch is that all suites have mini hi-fi systems.
Standards of cleanliness are high, and reception staff helpful, but the reality
is that this a comfortable Mayfair address rather than a glamorous one.
Minimum stay two weeks. *Apartments 11 Nearest tube: Marble Arch.*
Parking: street (meters) NCP nearby. Maid Service: daily. Telephone charge:
18p per unit. Amenities: 24hr concierge, lift, laundry service, baby-sitting, cots.
Credit cards: Access, Amex, Visa.

W8   Thorney Court   82%
Tel 071-581 5324   Fax 071-584 1659

from £800
low season

Palace Gate London W8 5NJ

Map 41 B2

Some of the best apartments in London are to be found at this purpose-
built, red-brick block overlooking Kensington Palace Gardens and opposite
Hyde Park. Built in the early 80s, the block has its own decorative gardens
and discreet high security provided by 24hr porterage, and most
apartments have their own balconies with spectacular views. Immaculately
kept rooms are huge, offering tip-top quality throughout – plenty of
seating, lavish fabrics and comfortable beds, with marvellously equipped
kitchens and splendid bathrooms. Each apartment has a guest cloakroom,
safe, and two sets of china, crystal and cutlery (the best for entertaining!).
High standards of service are typified by milk and newspaper delivery and
wake-up calls. *Apartments 60. Nearest tube: High Street Kensington.*
Parking:own underground. Maid Service: optional (daily at hourly charge).
Telephone charge: 12p per unit. Amenities: 24hr concierge/porterage,
entryphone, lifts, business facilities, cable TV, laundry service, baby-sitting, cots.
Credit cards: None

W1   12A Apartments   76%
Tel 071-493 6940   Fax 071-495 1887

from £400

12a Charles Street London W1X 7HB

Map 42 B3

Splendidly maintained apartments in the heart of Mayfair (three of the flats
are situated in Hays Mews close to the highly recommended Greenhouse
Restaurant). A listed building with a 300 year old staircase, most of the
apartments (some with polished wood floors) are on several levels, with
bedrooms, drawing room and dining room/kitchens on different floors.
Each is attractively furnished and pleasantly decorated with well-chosen
fabrics. Standards of housekeeping are high and kitchens have a dishwasher
and washing machine. No minimum length of stay. *Apartments 10.*
Nearest tube: Green Park. Parking: street (meters) NCP nearby. Maid Service:
Monday-Friday. Telephone charge: 15p per unit. Amenities: entryphone, lift,
business facilities, conference room, satellite TV, baby-sitting, cots, highchairs,
baby gates. Credit cards: Amex only.

RESERVATIONS

0800 243 163

W1   20 Hertford Street   60%   from £500
Tel 071-499 8881   Fax 071-727 0151

London W1Y 7DA   **Map 43 B3**

Ask for the best (refurbished) apartments at this Mayfair town house.
Many of the building's original architectural features have been retained,
including a sweeping staircase that ascends from the tiled entrance foyer.
The suites range from studio rooms to three bedroomed suites, all with
kitchenettes and ensuite bathrooms, and in addition to each having an
entryphone, there's a live-in housekeeper, and a janitor who can arrange
daily delivery of milk and newspapers; as well as shopping. There is no
minimum length of stay. *Apartments 10. Nearest tube: Hyde Park
Corner/Green Park. Parking: nearby NCP. Maid Service: daily. Telephone
charge: 24p per unit. Amenities: entryphone, lift, business facilities, laundry
service, baby-sitting, cots. Credit cards: Access, Amex, Visa.*

NW1   25 Dorset Square   75%   from £170
Tel 071-262 7505   Fax 071-723 0194   nightly

London NW1 6QN   **Map 44 A3**

A fine Georgian building opposite private gardens (residents have access),
the site of the original Lord's cricket ground, created by Thomas Lord in
1787. The cricketing theme extends throughout the house – fine prints, oil
paintings and old pictures alongside antiques, sumptuous fabrics, and
quality furniture – which has the atmosphere of a traditional London
townhouse. Drawing rooms have retained open fireplaces, one even has a
grand piano, and all have remote control TV and video recorder.
Comfortable bedrooms with stylish marble bathrooms, and modern
functional kitchens (some with dishwasher) are standard. Room service of
breakfast, plus teas, coffees and drinks (the building is licensed) throughout
the day. Each apartment (seven one-bedroom, five two-bedroom) has a fax
point and two telephones, one incorporating a clock/radio. *Apartments 12.
Nearest tube: Marylebone. Parking: street (meters) NCP nearby. Maid Service:
daily. Telephone charge: 20p per unit. Amenities: 24hr reception/concierge, lift,
garden, laundry service, baby-sitting. Credit cards: All.*

W1   23 Greengarden House   73%   from £110+VAT
Tel 071-935 9191   Fax 071-935 8858   nightly

St Christopher's Place London W1M 5HD   **Map 45 A3**

Situated in a smart pedestrian street between Oxford and Wigmore Streets,
the apartments are perhaps on the small side, but splendidly furnished in a
warm and individual style, some with period pieces, others more modern.
Sofa coverings and fabrics are of particularly high quality, and the
compact kitchens expensively fitted out with good equipment, including microwave
and wash/dryer. Excellent housekeeping is evident throughout these
apartments, which are well run, typified by the attractive window boxes
outside each. *Apartments 24. Nearest tube: Bond Street. Parking: difficult.
Maid Service: Monday-Friday. Telephone charge: 18p per unit. Amenities:
entryphone, lift, boardroom and business services, laundry service, cable TV,
baby-sitting, cots. Credit cards: All.*

THE
**APARTMENT
SERVICE**

RESERVATIONS

0800   243   163

W2 208 Sussex Gardens 66% from £500

Tel 071-723 4848 Fax 071-402 8885

London W2 2UD Map 46 B3

Two features of this refurbished building are a quite extraordinary penthouse apartment with its own private lift, and a recently opened basement swimming pool complex with sauna and spa bath. Opposite the entrance is a garden, though Hyde Park is only a stroll away. The apartments range from studios to those with three bedrooms and three bathrooms, all being decently furnished with new carpets, good furniture, practical kitchens and tiled bathrooms. *Apartments 36. Nearest tube: Lancaster Gate/Paddington. parking: own spaces. Maid Service: daily. Telephone charge: 20p per unit. Amenities: 24hr reception & security, lifts, business facilities, laundry service, cable TV, baby-sitting, cots, highchairs. Credit cards: All.*

W2 Westminster Suites 62% £80+VAT

Tel 071-286 5294 Fax 071-229 3917 nightly

13 Leinster Square London W2 4PR Map 47 B2

Adjoining the Westminster Hotel (guests can use the hotel's facilities and have them charged to their account), the suites are situated in a quiet residential street opposite a garden square to which there is key access. A short walk from Hyde Park and the bustling atmosphere of Queensway and Westbourne Grove, the apartments have their own entrance, yet some can also be reached via the hotel. They are pleasantly furnished (one of the basement ones has its own patio/garden) with good kitchens that include a washing machine and microwave, comfortable lounges (remote control TV and video), and functional bathrooms. Complimentary 'welcome pack' of basic groceries on arrival. *Apartment 8. Nearest tube: Bayswater or Queensway. Parking: street (meters). Maid Service: twice weekly. Telephone charge: 20p per unit. Amenities: video entryphone, lift, business facilities, garden, baby-sitting, cots, highchairs. Credit cards: All.*

THE APARTMENT SERVICE

RESERVATIONS

0800 243 163

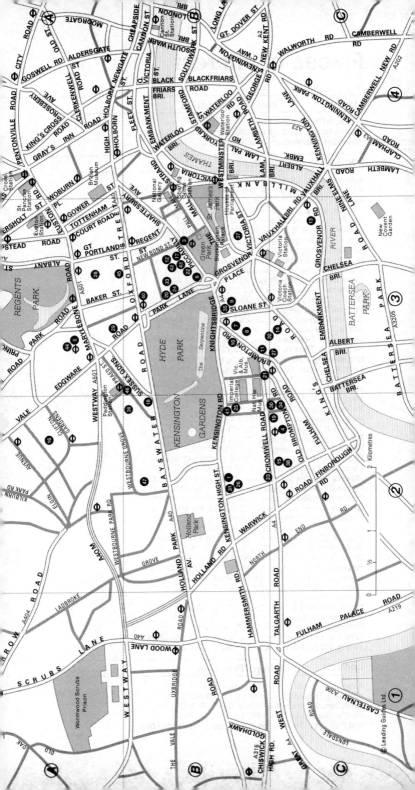

Places of interest

London Tourist Information

Transport Tel 071-222 1234.
Tourist Board Tel 071-730 3488.
Riverboat Information Tel 071-730 4812.

London Theatres

Adelphi Strand WC2 Tel 071-836 7611.
Albery St. Martin's Lane WC2 Tel 071-867 1115.
Aldwych Aldwych WC2 Tel 071-836 6404.
Ambassadors West Street, Cambridge Circus WC2 Tel 071-836 6111.
Apollo Shaftesbury Avenue W1 Tel 071-437 2663.
Apollo Victoria Wilton Road SW1 Tel 071-630 6262.
Arts 6-7 Gt Newport Street WC2 Tel 071-836 2132.
Astoria Charing Cross Road WC2 Tel 071-434 0403.
Bloomsbury Gordon Street WC1 Tel 071-387 9629.
Comedy Panton Street, Haymarket SW1 Tel 071-867 1045.
Drury Lane Theatre Royal WC2 Tel 071-836 8108.
Duchess Catherine Street WC2 Tel 071-836 8243.
Duke of York's St. Martin's Lane WC2 Tel 071-836 5122.
Fortune Russell Street WC2 Tel 071-836 2238.
Garrick Charing Cross Road WC2 Tel 071-379 6107.
Globe Shaftesbury Avenue W1 Tel 071-437 3667.
Greenwich Theatre Crooms Hill SE10 Tel 081-858 7755.
Haymarket Theatre Royal SW1 Tel 071-930 9832.
Her Majesty's Haymarket SW1 Tel 071-839 2244.
Lyric King Steeet, Hammersmith W6 Tel 081-741 2311.
Lyric Shaftesbury Avenue W1 Tel 071-437 3686.
Mayfair Stratton Street W1 Tel 071-629 3036.
Mermaid Puddle Dock Blackfriars EC4 Tel 071-410 0000.
National Upper Ground South Bank SE1 Tel 071-928 2252.
New London Parker Street WC2 Tel 071-405 0072.
Old Vic Waterloo Road SE1 Tel 071-928 7616.
Palace Shaftesbury Avenue W1 Tel 071-434 0909.
Palladium Argyll Street W1 Tel 071-437 7373.
Phoenix Charing Cross Road WC2 Tel 071-867 1044.
Piccadilly Denman Street W1 Tel 071-867 1118.
Players Theatre Villiers Street WC2 Tel 071-839 1134.
Prince Edward Old Compton Street W1 Tel 071-734 8951.
Prince of Wales Coventry Street W1 Tel 071-839 5972.
Queens Shaftesbury Avenue W1 Tel 071-494 5040.
Regents Park (Open Air) Regent's Park NW1 Tel 071-486 2431.
Royal Court Sloane Square SW1 Tel 071-730 1745.
Sadlers Wells Rosebery Avenue EC1 Tel 071-278 8916.
St. Martins West Street WC2 Tel 071-836 1443.
Savoy Strand WC2 Tel 071-836 8888.
Shaftesbury Shaftesbury Avenue WC2 Tel 071-379 5399.
Shaw Euston Road NW1 Tel 071-388 1394.
Strand Aldwych WC2 Tel 071-240 0300.
Vaudeville Strand WC2 Tel 071-836 9987.
Victoria Palace Victoria Street SW1 Tel 071-834 1317.
Westminster Palace Street SW1 Tel 071-834 0283.
Whitehall Whitehall SW1 Tel 071-867 1119.
Wyndham's Charing Cross Road WC2 Tel 071-836 3028.
Young Vic 66 The Cut Waterloo SE1 Tel 071-928 6363.

London Fringe Theatres

Almeida Almeida Street N1 Tel 071-359 4404.
Hackney Empire Mare Street E8 Tel 081-985 2424.
Hampstead Avenue Road NW3 Tel 071-722 9301.
King's Head Upper Street N1 Tel 071-226 1916.
Old Bull Arts Centre High Street, Barnet Tel 081-449 0048.

Riverside Studios Crisp Road W6 Tel 081-748 3354.

London   Concert Halls

Royal Opera House Covent Garden WC2 Tel 071-240 1066/240 1911.
English National Opera – The London Coliseum St Martin's Lane WC2
  Tel 071-836 3161.
Barbican Centre Silk Street EC2 Tel 071-638 4141.
Purcell Room South Bank SE1 Tel 071-928 3002.
Queen Elizabeth Hall South Bank SE1 Tel 071-928 8800.
Royal Albert Hall Kensington Gore SW7 Tel 071-589 8212.
Royal Festival Hall South Bank SE1 Tel 071-928 8800.
St. John's Smith Square Smith Square SW1 Tel 071-222 1061.
Wigmore Hall Wigmore Street W1 Tel 071-935 2141.

London   London Night Life

Hippodrome Charing Cross Road WC2 Tel 071-437 4311.
Limelight Shaftesbury Avenue WC2 Tel 071-434 0572.
Madame Jo-Jo's Brewer Street W1 Tel 071-734 2473.
Ronnie Scott's Frith Street W1 Tel 071-439 0747.
Stringfellows Upper St. Martin's Lane WC2 Tel 071-240 5534.
Stork Club Swallow Street W1 Tel 071-734 3686.
Xenon Piccadilly W1 Tel 071-734 9344.

London   Historic Houses, Castles and Gardens

Wellington Museum Apsley House, Hyde Park Corner W1 Tel 071-499
  5676.
Banqueting House Whitehall SW1 Tel 071-930 4179.
Chelsea Physic Garden Royal Hospital Road SW3 Tel 071-352 5646.
Chiswick House Burlington Lane W4 Tel 081-995 0508.
Ham House (NT) Ham, Richmond Tel 081-940 1950.
Hampton Court Palace East Molesey Tel 081-977 8441.
Hogarth's House Chiswick Tel 081-994 6757.
Keats House Wentworth Place, Keats Grove, Hampstead Tel 071-435 2062.
Kensington Palace W8 Tel 071-937 9561.
Kenwood House Hampstead Tel 081-348 1286.
Marble Hill House Richmond Road, Twickenham Tel 081-892 5115.
Osterley Park (NT) Isleworth, Middlesex TW7 4RB Tel 081-560 3918.
The Queen's House Greenwich SE10 Tel 081-858 4422.
Royal Botanic Gardens (Kew Gardens) Kew Tel 081-940 3321.
Syon House and Park Gardens Brentford Tel 081-560 0881/3.
Tower of London Tower Hill EC3 Tel 071-709 0765.

London   Museums and Art Galleries

Barbican Art Gallery Level 8, Barbican Centre EC2 Tel 071-638 4141 Ext
  306.
Bethnal Green Museum of Childhood Cambridge Heath Road E2 Tel 081-
  980 3204.
Boxing Museum Thomas à Becket Pub, Old Kent Road SE1 Tel 071-703
  2644.
British Museum & British Library Great Russell Street WC1 Tel 071-636
  1555.
Buckingham Palace The Queen's Gallery, Buckingham Palace Road SW1
  Tel 071-799 2331.
Cabinet War Rooms Clive Steps, King Charles Street SW1 Tel 071-930
  6961.
Cutty Sark Clipper Ship King William Walk, Greenwich SE10 Tel 081-858
  3445.
The Design Museum at Butlers Wharf Shad Thames SE1 Tel 071-403
  6933.
Anthony d'Offay Gallery 9/21 & 23 Dering Street, off New Bond Street W1
  Tel 071- 499 4100.
Dickens House Museum Doughty Street WC1 Tel 071-405 2127.
Dulwich Picture Gallery College Road SE21 Tel 081-693 5254.
Florence Nightingale Museum Lambeth Palace Road SE1 Tel 071-620
  0374.
Freud Museum 20 Maresfield Gardens, Hampstead NW3.

Geffrye Museum Kingsland Road E2 Tel 071-739 8368.
Guinness World of Records The Trocadero, Coventry Street W1 Tel 071-439 7331.
Hayward Gallery South Bank Centre Belvedere Rd SE1 Tel 071-928 3144 *Recorded information 071-261 0127.*
HMS Belfast Morgan's Lane, Tooley Street SE1 Tel 071-407 6434
Horniman Museum London Road, Forest Hill SE23 Tel 081-699 1872/2339/4911.
ICA Carlton House Terrace, The Mall SW1 Tel 071-930 0493 *Recorded Information on 071-930 6393.*
Imperial War Museum Lambeth Road SE1 Tel 071-735 8922.
Keats House (Wentworth Place) Keats Grove, Hampstead NW3 Tel 071-435 2062.
Kenwood House (EH) Hampstead Lane NW3 Tel 081-348 1286/1287.
Leighton House Museum Holland Park W11 Tel 071-602 3316.
London Dungeon Tooley Street SE1 Tel 071-403 0606.
London Planetarium Baker Street NW1 Tel 071-486 1121.
London Transport Museum Covent Garden WC2 Tel 071-379 6344.
Madame Tussaud's Waxworks Museum Baker Street W1 Tel 071-935 6861.
Mall Galleries Carlton House Terrace, The Mall SW1 Tel 071-930 6844.
Museum of Garden History (The Tradescant Trust) St Mary-at-Lambeth, Lambeth Palace Road SE1 Tel 071-261 1891.
Museum of London London Wall EC2 Tel 071-600 3699.
Museum of Mankind Burlington Gardens W1 Tel 071-636 1555.
Museum of the Moving Image (MOMI) South Bank, Waterloo SE1 Tel 071-401 2636.
National Army Museum Royal Hospital Road SW3 Tel 071-730 0717.
The National Gallery Trafalgar Square WC2 Tel 071-839 3321 *Recorded information on 071-839 3526.*
National Maritime Museum Romney Road, Greenwich SE10 Tel 081-858 4422.
National Portrait Gallery St. Martin's Place, Trafalgar Square WC2 Tel 071-306 0055.
Natural History Museum Cromwell Road, South Kensington SW7 Tel 071-938 9123.
Operating Theatre Museum and Herb Garret St. Thomas Street SE1 Tel 071-955 4791.
R.A.F. Museum Hendon NW9 Tel 081-205 2266.
Royal Academy of Arts Piccadilly W1 Tel 071-439 7438.
Science Museum Exhibition Road, South Kensington SW7 Tel 071-938 8000.
Serpentine Gallery Kensington Gardens W2 Tel 071-402 6075.
Sir John Soane's Museum Lincoln's Inn Fields WC2 Tel 071-430 0175.
Tate Gallery Millbank SW1 Tel 071- 821 1313 *Recorded information on 071-821 7128.*
Thames Barrier Visitors' Centre Unity Way, Woolwich SE18 Tel 081-854 1373.
Tower Bridge SE1 Tel 071-403 3761.
Tower of London Tower Hill EC3 Tel 071-709 0765.
Victoria and Albert Museum Cromwell Road, South Kensington SW7 Tel 071-938 8500.
Wallace Collection Hertford House, Manchester Square W1 Tel 071-935 0687.
Whitechapel Art Gallery Whitechapel High Street E1 Tel 071-377 0107.

London   Exhibition Halls

Wembley Arena, Conference and Exhibition Centre Tel 081-900 1234.
Olympia Kensington W14 Tel 071-603 3344.
Earls Court Warwick Road SW5 Tel 071-385 1200.
Business Design Centre Upper Street N1 Tel 071-359 3535.

London   Cathedrals

St. George's R.C. Cathedral Lambeth Road SE1 Tel 071-928 5256.
St. Paul's Cathedral EC4 Tel 071-248 4619.
Southwark Cathedral Borough High Street SE1 Tel 071-407 2939.

Westminster Abbey Broad Sanctuary SW1 Tel 071-222 5152.
Westminster R.C. Cathedral Ashley Place SW1 Tel 071-834 7452.

London   Swimming Pools and Sports Centres

Chelsea Sports Centre Manor Street, Chelsea Tel 071-352 6985.
Crystal Palace Sports Centre Ledrington Road, Norwood Tel 081-778 0131.
Dolphin Sports Centre Pimlico. Tel 071-798 8686.
Finsbury Leisure Complex 1-11 Ironmongers Row, Finsbury Tel 071-253 4011.
Ken Barrington Centre Fosters Oval, Kennington SE11 Tel 071-582 9495.
Kensington Sports Centre Tel 071- 727 9747.
Marshall Street Leisure Centre Tel 071-798 2007.
Porchester Baths Queensway Tel 071-229 9950.
Queen Mother Sports Centre Vauxhall Bridge Road Tel 071-798 2125.
Richmond Baths Old Deer Park, Richmond Tel 081-940 8461.
Seymour Leisure Centre Bryanston Place, Marylebone Tel 071-298 1421.
White City Pool Bloemfontein Road, White City Tel 081-734 3401.

London   Cricket & Tennis Venues

Lord's St. John's Wood NW8 Tel 071-289 1300
Lord's Gestetner Tour Tel 071-266 3825.
The Oval Kennington SE11 Tel 071-582 6660.
Queen's Club W14 Tel 071-385 3421.
Wimbledon (All England Lawn Tennis & Croquet Club) SW19 Tel 081-946 2244.

London   Football and Rugby Grounds

Arsenal Highbury N5 Tel 071-226 0304.
Charlton Athletic Selhurst Park SE25 Tel 081-771 6321.
Chelsea Stamford Bridge, Fulham SW5 Tel 071-385 5545.
Crystal Palace Selhurst Park SE25 Tel 081-653 4462.
Millwall The Den, New Cross SE14 Tel 071-639 3143.
Queens Park Rangers South Africa Road W12 Tel 081-743 0262.
Rugby Football Union Twickenham General Enquiries Tel 081-892 8161.
Tottenham Hotspur High Road, Tottenham N17 Tel 081-808 8080.
Wembley Stadium Tel 081-900 1234.
West Ham United Upton Park E13 Tel 081-472 2740.
Wimbledon Wimbledon SW19 Tel 081-946 6311.

London   Ice Rinks

Alexandra Palace Wood Green N22 Tel 081-365 2121.
Broadgate Arena Broadgate EC2 Tel 071-588 6565.
Lee Valley Leyton E10 Tel 081-533 3156.
Queens Bayswater W2 Tel 071-229 0172.
Streatham Streatham High Road SW16 Tel 081-769 7771.

London   Dry Ski Slopes

Alexandra Palace Ski Slope Tel 081-888 2284.
Beckton Alps Alpine Way E6 Tel 081-511 0351.
Crystal Palace National Sports Centre Tel 081-778 0131.
Hillingdon Sports Centre Uxbridge Tel 0895 55181.
Woolwich Ski Slope Repository Road SE18 Tel 081-317 1726.

London   Zoos and Wildlife Parks

London Zoo Regent's Park Tel 071-722 3333.
Brent Lodge Park Animal Centre Uxbridge Road Tel 081-579 2424.
Battersea Park Children's Zoo SW11 Tel 081-7530.

London   Other attractions

Battersea Dog's Home Battersea Park Road SW8 Tel 071-622 3626.
Pirate Ships Tobacco Dock E1 Tel 071-702 9681.
Highgate Cemetery Swain's Lane N6 Tel 081-340 1834.

Quick Reference Lists: London

Hotels under £80 for 2

Apollo Hotel **W8**
Aster House **SW7**
Atlas Hotel **W8**
Bardon Lodge **SE3**
Charles Bernard Hotel **NW3**
Clive Hotel **NW3**
Collin House **SW1**
Colonnade Hotel **W9**
Columbia Hotel **W2**
Concord Hotel **SW5**
Craven Gardens Hotel **W2**
Eden Plaza Hotel **SW7**
Elizabeth Hotel **SW1**

Forte Posthouse **NW3**
George Hotel **WC1**
Kensington Court Hotel **SW5**
Kensington Manor **SW7**
Hotel Lexham **W8**
Merryfield House **W1**
Hotel 167 **SW5**
Parkwood Hotel **W2**
President Hotel **WC1**
Prince Hotel **SW7**
La Réserve **SW10**
Terstan Hotel **SW5**
Yardley Court **SE9**

Restaurants under £40 for 2

Adam's Café **W12**
Bangkok **SW7**
Bedlington Café **W4**
Belgo **NW1**
Bitter Lemons Taverna **SW6**
Bloom's **E1**
Bloom's **NW11**
Bon Ton Roulet **SE24**
The Brackenbury **W6**
Buzkash **SW15**
Café Delancey **NW1**
Café Delancey **WC1**
Café du Marché **EC1**
California Pizza Company **W1**
Caravan Serai **W1**
Chi Mai **W3**
Chiang Mai **W1**
Chicago Pizza Pie Factory **W1**
Chicago Rib Shack **SW7**
Chuen Cheng Ku **W1**
Ciao **SW6**
Costa's Grill **W8**
Daphne **NW1**
Dell'Ugo **W1**
Depot **SW14**
Dragon Inn **W1**
The Eagle **EC1**
Eastern Eye **SE22**
Efes Kebab House **W1**
Est **W1**
Fanari **NW1**
Faulkners **E8**
Gavin's **SW15**
Geale's **W8**
Glaister's **SW10**
Good Friends **E14**
Gopal's of Soho **W1**
Grahame's Seafare **W1**
Great Nepalese **NW1**
Greek Valley **NW8**

Green Cottage **NW3**
Harveys Café **SW10**
Hellas **NW1**
Hong Kong **WC2**
Istanbul Iskembecisi **N16**
Jade Garden **W1**
Joe Allen **WC2**
Kalamaras **W2**
Kam's **W2**
Khyber Pass **SW7**
Lal Qila **W1**
Laurent **NW2**
Lemonia **NW1**
Lena's **SW11**
Lido **W1**
Little Akropolis **W1**
Lok Ho Fook **W1**
Majlis **SW7**
Malabar **W8**
Mandarin Kitchen **W2**
Mandeer **W1**
Memories of India **SW7**
New Fook Lam Moon **W1**
New Kam Tong **W2**
New World **W1**
Nontas **NW1**
Noor Jahan **SW5**
Nusa Dua **W1**
Oh'Boy **SW7**
Oliver's **W14**
Osteria Antica Bologna **SW11**
La Paesana **W8**
Peking Garden **W14**
Le Petit Prince **NW5**
Pizzeria Castello **SE1**
Poons **WC2**
Quality Chop House **EC1**
Ragam **W1**
Rajput **W12**
Rani **N3**

Rasa Sayang **W2**
Rasa Sayang **W1**
Ravi Shankar **NW1**
La Reash **W1**
Romantica Taverna **W2**
The Rotisserie **W12**
Sabras **NW10**
Sala Thai **W5**
Satay Hut **N1**
Sema **SE22**
Silver Lake **SE5**
Singapore **W4**
Sonargaon **N1**

Soulard **N1**
Sumos **W6**
Supan **W9**
Tandoori Lane **SW6**
Thailand Restaurant **SE14**
Tien Phat **SW6**
Tiger under the Table **NW11**
Topkapi **W1**
Topsy Tasty **W4**
Tuk Tuk Restaurant **N1**
Vijay **NW6**
Wine & Mousaka **W5**
Young's Rendezvous **W5**

Town House Hotels

Alexander Hotel **SW7**
Dorset Square Hotel **NW1**
Green Park Hotel **W1**

Pelham Hotel **SW7**
Pembridge Court Hotel **W2**
Portobello Hotel **W11**

Private House Hotels

Abbey Court **W2**
The Beaufort **SW3**
The Draycott **SW3**
Egerton House **SW3**

The Fenja **SW3**
Knightsbridge Green Hotel **SW1**
Number Sixteen **SW7**
22 Jermyn Street **SW1**

Hotels with Sporting Facilities

Tennis Courts

Cadogan Hotel **SW1**
Churchill Hotel **W1**
The Halcyon **W11**

Hyatt Carlton Tower **SW1**
SAS Portman Hotel **W1**
Scandic Crown Nelson Dock **SE16**

Indoor Swimming

The Berkeley **SW1**
Hotel Conrad **SW10**
The Dorchester **W1**
Grosvenor House **W1**
Holiday Inn Kings Cross/Bloomsbury **WC1**
Holiday Inn Marble Arch **W1**
London International **E14**
London Metropole **W2**
London Wilshire **NW1**

May Fair Inter-Continental **W1**
Le Meridien **W1**
Regent's Park Marriott Hotel **NW3**
Rembrandt Hotel **SW7**
St Giles Hotel **WC1**
Scandic Crown Nelson Dock **SE16**
Scandic Crown Victoria **SW1**
Swallow International Hotel **SW5**

Leisure Centres

Hotel Conrad **SW10**
The Dorchester **W1**
Grosvenor House **W1**
Holiday Inn Kings Cross/Bloomsbury **WC1**
London International **E14**
London Metropole **W2**
London Wilshire **NW1**

Le Meridien **W1**
Regent's Park Marriott Hotel **NW3**
Rembrandt Hotel **SW7**
St Giles Hotel **WC1**
Scandic Crown Nelson Dock **SE16**
Scandic Crown Victoria **SW1**
Swallow International Hotel **SW5**

Hotels with Wheelchair Facilities

Compiled in association with the Holiday Care Service 0293 774535

Berners Park Plaza **W1**
Bonnington Hotel **WC1**
Copthorne Tara **W8**
Cumberland Hotel **W1**
Forte Crest Regent's Park **W1**
Hyde Park Hotel **W1**

Inn on the Park Hotel **W1**
Inter-Continental Hotel **W1**
May Fair Inter-Continental Hotel **W1**
Ramada Hotel **W1**
The Westbury **W1**
White House **NW1**

Restaurants with a non-smoking area

Au Jardin des Gourmets **W1**
Bedlington Café **W4**
Bombay Brasserie **SW7**
Brown's Hotel **W1**
Bubb's **EC1**
Buzkash **SW15**
Café Fish **SW1**
California Pizza Company **W1**
Carraro's **SW8**
Caterino's **SW16**
Chicago Rib Shack **SW7**
Chicago Rib Shack II **WC2**
Chicago Pizza Pie Factory. **W1**
Churchill Hotel **W1**
Ciao **SW6**
Clarke's **W8**
The Connaught **W1**
Eastern Eye **SE22**
Faulkners **E8**
La Fin de la Chasse **N16**
Frederick's **N1**
Gavin's **SW15**
Gilbert's **SW7**
Gopal's of Soho **W1**
Grafton Français **SW4**
Inter-Continental Hotel **W1**

The Lanesborough, The Conservatory **SW1**
Lemonia **NW1**
Le Meridien, Terrace Garden Restnt **W1**
Mijanou **SW1**
Ming **W1**
Museum Street Café **WC1**
Newtons **SW4**
Pinocchio's **NW1**
Qinggis **NW3**
Rani **N3**
Rasa Sayang **W1**
La Reash **W1**
Royal Garden Hotel **W8**
Rue St Jacques **W1**
Sabras **NW10**
Sala Thai **W5**
San Martino **SW3**
La Sémillante **W1**
Sheraton Park Tower **SW1**
Sydney Street **SW3**
Tate Gallery Restaurant **SW1**
Thistells **SE22**
Twenty Trinity Gardens **SW9**
Villandry Dining Room **W1**

Romantic Restaurants

L'Aventure **NW8**
Blakes Hotel **SW7**
Blue Elephant **SW6**
Le Caprice **SW1**
Chez Moi **W11**
La Croisette **SW10**
The Dorchester: Terrace Restaurant **W1**
Ebury Court **SW1**
Le Gavroche **W1**
Gay Hussar **W1**
Gualtiero Marchesi at the Halkin **SW1**
The Halcyon **W11**
Hilaire **SW7**
L'Hippocampe **W1**
Hyatt Carlton Tower, Chelsea Room **SW1**

Inn on the Park Hotel, Four Seasons **W1**
Inter-Continental Hotel, Le Soufflé **W1**
The Lanesborough, The Dining Room **SW1**
Launceston Place **W8**
London Hilton on Park Lane **W1**
Mirabelle **W1**
Odette's **NW1**
Odin's **W1**
Pinocchio's **NW1**
The Ritz **W1**
Rue St Jacques **W1**
San Lorenzo **SW3**
The Savoy, River Restaurant **WC2**
White Tower **W1**

Open Air Eating

L'Accento Italiano **W2**
Al Basha **W8**
Al Hamra **W1**

Anna's Place **N1**
Au Bon Accueil **SW3**
L'Aventure **NW8**

Blueprint Café **SE1**
La Brasserie **SW3**
Buzkash **SW15**
Café Delancey **NW1**
Chapter 11 **SW10**
Christian's **W4**
Ciao **SW6**
Cibo **W14**
Dan's **SW3**
Depot **SW14**
La Fin de la Chasse **N16**
Frederick's **N1**
Fuji **W1**
The Halcyon **W11**
Lou Pescadou **SW5**

Luigi's **SE19**
Memories of India **SW7**
Mijanou **SW1**
Mirabelle **W1**
Nanking **W6**
Newtons **SW4**
Odette's **NW1**
Pollyanna's **SW11**
Le Pont de la Tour **SE1**
River Café **W6**
San Martino **SW3**
Sandrini **SW3**
1789 **E3**
Soho Soho **W1**
Vin Santo **SW10**

Early Evening Eating

Ajimura **WC2**
Al Basha **W8**
Al Bustan **SW1**
Al Hamra **W1**
Alastair Little **W1**
Arirang Korean Restaurant **W1**
Arisugawa **W1**
Arts Theatre Café **WC2**
Asuka **NW1**
The Athenaeum **W1**
Bacco **SW7**
Bahn Thai **W1**
Bedlington Café **W4**
Belgo **NW1**
Bentley's **W1**
Bhatti **WC2**
Bibendum Oyster Bar **SW3**
Bistrot 190 **SW7**
Bitter Lemons Taverna **SW6**
Bloom's **E1**
Bloom's **NW11**
Brasserie du Marché aux Puces **W10**
La Brasserie **SW3**
Buzkash **SW15**
Café Delancey **NW1**
Café Delancey **WC1**
Café Pelican **WC2**
Café du Marche **EC1**
Café Fish **SW1**
California Pizza Company **W1**
Le Caprice **SW1**
Caravan Serai **W1**
Caterino's **SW16**
Chapter 11 **SW10**
Chi Mai **W3**
Chiang Mai **W1**
Chicago Rib Shack II **WC2**
Chicago Pizza Pie Factory **W1**
Chicago Rib Shack **SW7**
Christopher's **WC2**
Chuen Cheng Ku **W1**
Churchill Hotel **W1**
Ciao **SW6**
Claridge's, The Causerie **W1**
Costa's Grill **W8**
Daphne **NW1**
Defune **W1**
Dell'Ugo **W1**

Depot **SW14**
The Dorchester **W1**
Dorset Square Hotel **NW1**
Dragon's Nest **W1**
Dragon Inn **W1**
Dukes Hotel **SW1**
Eastern Eye **SE22**
Efes Kebab House **W1**
L'Escargot **W1**
Est **W1**
Fanari **NW1**
Faulkners **E8**
Four Seasons **W2**
Frederick's **N1**
Fuji **W1**
Fung Shing **WC2**
Gavin's **SW15**
Gay Hussar **W1**
Geale's **W8**
Giovanni's **WC2**
Gonbei **WC1**
Good Earth **SW3**
Good Friends **E14**
Good Earth **NW7**
Gopal's of Soho **W1**
The Goring **SW1**
Grahame's Seafare **W1**
Great Nepalese **NW1**
Greek Valley **NW8**
Green's Restaurant & Oyster Bar **SW1**
Green Cottage **NW3**
Grill St Quentin **SW3**
Halepi **W2**
Hellas **NW1**
Hilton International Regent's Park, Kashi Noki **NW8**
Hilton International Kensington, Hiroko **W11**
Holiday Inn Mayfair **W1**
Hong Kong **WC2**
L'Hotel **SW3**
Hsing **W2**
Ikkyu **W1**
Inn on the Park: Lanes Restaurant **W1**
Isohama **SW1**
Istanbul Iskembecisi **N16**
The Ivy **WC2**
Jade Garden **W1**

Joe Allen **WC2**
Kam's **W2**
Kaya **W1**
Khan's of Kensington **SW7**
Khyber Pass **SW7**
Koto **NW1**
Lal Qila **W1**
The Langham **W1**
Laurent **NW2**
Lemonia **NW1**
Lido **W1**
Lindsay House **W1**
Little Akropolis **W1**
Lok Ho Fook **W1**
Luigi's **SE19**
Majlis **SW7**
Malabar **W8**
Mandarin Kitchen **W2**
Mandeer **W1**
Manzi's **WC2**
Manzi's **E14**
Maroush **W2**
Masako **W1**
Memories of India **SW7**
Le Meridien: Terrace Garden Restnt **W1**
Ming **W1**
Mr Ke **NW3**
Mitsukoshi **SW1**
Miyama **EC4**
Momo **W5**
Mon Plaisir **WC2**
Nakamura **W1**
New Fook Lam Moon **W1**
New Kam Tong **W2**
New World **W1**
Ninjin **W1**
Nontas **NW1**
Noor Jahan **SW5**
Now and Zen **WC2**
Nusa Dua **W1**
Oliver's **W14**
Orso **WC2**
Osteria Antica Bologna **SW11**
La Paesana **W8**
Panda **W1**
Pearl of Knightsbridge **SW1**
Peking Garden **W14**
Phoenicia **W8**
Pizzeria Castello **SE1**

Le Pont de la Tour **SE1**
Poons **WC1**
Poons **WC2**
Poons **W2**
Pun **SW7**
Qinggis **NW3**
Ragam **W1**
Rajput **W12**
Rani **N3**
Rasa Sayang **W1**
Rasa Sayang **W2**
Ravi Shankar **EC1**
Ravi Shankar **NW1**
La Reash **W1**
Red Fort **W1**
Romantica Taverna **W2**
Royal China **W2**
RSJ **SE1**
Rules **WC2**
Sabras **NW10**
St Moritz **W1**
Sala Thai **W5**
Satay Hut **N1**
The Savoy: Grill Room **WC2**
Sema **SE22**
Shampers **W1**
Sheekey's Restaurant **WC2**
Shogun **W1**
Silver Lake **SE5**
Simpson's-in-the-Strand **WC2**
Singapore **W4**
Singapore Garden **NW6**
Soho Soho **W1**
Sonargaon **N1**
The Square **SW1**
Sri Siam **W1**
Stephen Bull Bistro **EC1**
Sumos **W6**
Tandoori Lane **SW6**
Thailand Restaurant **SE14**
Tiger Lee **SW5**
Tiger under the Table **NW11**
Topkapi **W1**
Trattoria Lucca **NW1**
Tuk Tuk Restaurant **N1**
Vijay **NW6**
Wine & Mousaka **W5**
Yumi **W1**
Zen **SW3**
ZeNW3 **NW3**

Late Night Eating

L'Accento Italiano **W2**
Ajimura **WC2**
Al Basha **W8**
Al Bustan **SW1**
Al Hamra **W1**
Alastair Little **W1**
Alba **EC1**
L'Altro **W11**
Arirang Korean Restaurant **W1**
Asuka **NW1**
Au Bon Accueil **SW3**
Au Jardin des Gourmets **W1**
L'Aventure **NW8**

Bacco **SW7**
Bahn Thai **W1**
Balzac Restaurant **W12**
Bangkok **SW7**
Belgo **NW1**
Benihana **NW3**
Bertorelli **WC2**
Bhatti **WC2**
Bibendum **SW3**
Bistrot 190 **SW7**
Bitter Lemons Taverna **SW6**
Blakes Hotel **SW7**
Bloom's **NW11**

Blue Elephant **SW6**
Blueprint Café **SE1**
Bombay Brasserie **SW7**
Bon Ton Roulet **SE24**
Boulestin **WC2**
Boyd's **W8**
Le Braconnier **SW14**
Brasserie du Marché aux Puces **W10**
La Brasserie **SW3**
Brasserie Faubourg **SW8**
Buzkash **SW15**
Café Delancey **NW1**
Café Delancey **WC1**
Café Fish **SW1**
Café Pelican **WC2**
Café Royal Grill Room **W1**
California Pizza Company **W1**
Camden Brasserie **NW1**
Canal Brasserie **W10**
The Capital **SW3**
Le Caprice **SW1**
Caravan Serai **W1**
Carraro's **SW8**
Casa Cominetti **SE6**
Casale Franco **N1**
Caterino's **SW16**
Chapter 11 **SW10**
Cheng-Du **NW1**
Chez Liline **N4**
Chez Moi **W11**
Chi Mai **W3**
Chiang Mai **W1**
Chicago Rib Shack **SW7**
Chicago Pizza Pie Factory **W1**
Chicago Rib Shack II **WC2**
China Jazz **NW1**
Chinon **W14**
Christopher's **WC2**
Chuen Cheng Ku **W1**
Churchill Hotel **W1**
Chutney Mary **SW10**
Ciao **SW6**
Cibo **W14**
Claridge's **W1**
La Croisette **SW10**
Daphne **NW1**
Depot **SW14**
Don Pepe **NW8**
The Dorchester **W1**
La Dordogne **W4**
Dragon Inn **W1**
Dragon's Nest **W1**
Eastern Eye **SE22**
Ebury Court **SW1**
Efes Kebab House **W1**
Eleven Park Walk **SW10**
English Garden **SW3**
English House **SW3**
Enoteca **SW15**
L'Escargot **W1**
L'Escargot Doré **W8**
Est **W1**
L'Estaminet **WC2**
L'Etoile **W1**

La Famiglia **SW10**
Fanari **NW1**
Florians **N8**
Four Seasons **W2**
Foxtrot Oscar **SW3**
Frederick's **N1**
Fung Shing **WC2**
La Gaulette **W1**
Gavin's **SW15**
Le Gavroche **W1**
Gavver's **SW1**
Gay Hussar **W1**
Geale's **W8**
Giovanni's **WC2**
Glaister's **SW10**
Good Earth **NW7**
Good Earth **SW3**
Good Friends **E14**
Gopal's of Soho **W1**
Grafton Français **SW4**
Great Nepalese **NW1**
Greek Valley **NW8**
Green Cottage **NW3**
The Green Room **SW11**
Greenhouse **W1**
Green's Restaurant & Oyster Bar
    SW1
Grill St Quentin **SW3**
The Halcyon **W11**
Halepi **W2**
Halkin Hotel **SW1**
Harveys Café **SW10**
Harveys **SW17**
Hellas **NW1**
Hilaire **SW7**
L'Hippocampe **W1**
Hong Kong **WC2**
L'Hotel **SW3**
Hsing **W2**
Ikkyu **W1**
L'Incontro **SW1**
Inn on the Park Hotel **W1**
Inter-Continental Hotel **W1**
Istanbul Iskembecisi **N16**
The Ivy **WC2**
Jade Garden **W1**
Joe Allen **WC2**
Joe's Café **SW3**
Kalamaras **W2**
Kam's **W2**
Kaya **W1**
Kensington Place **W8**
Khan's of Kensington **SW7**
Khyber Pass **SW7**
Kundan **SW1**
Lal Qila **W1**
Langan's Brasserie **W1**
Langan's Bistro **W1**
Launceston Place **W8**
Laurent **NW2**
Leith's **W11**
Lemonia **NW1**
Lena's **SW11**
Lido **W1**

Lilly's **W11**
Lindsay House **W1**
Lok Ho Fook **W1**
London Hilton on Park Lane **W1**
Lou Pescadou **SW5**
Luigi's **SE19**
Majlis **SW7**
Malabar **W8**
Mandarin Kitchen **W2**
Manzi's **E14**
Manzi's **WC2**
Maroush **W2**
May Fair Inter-Continental **W1**
Memories of India **SW7**
Le Meridien, Terrace Garden Restaurant
 W1
Mijanou **SW1**
Mimmo d'Ischia **SW1**
Ming **W1**
Mirabelle **W1**
Mon Plaisir **WC2**
Monkeys **SW3**
Motcomb's **SW1**
Mr Kai **W1**
Mr Ke **NW3**
Mulligans of Mayfair **W1**
Nakano **SW1**
Nanking **W6**
Neal Street Restaurant **WC2**
Neshiko **N1**
New Fook Lam Moon **W1**
New Kam Tong **W2**
New World **W1**
Newtons **SW4**
Nico Central **W1**
Nikita's **SW10**
Nontas **NW1**
Noor Jahan **SW5**
Now and Zen **WC2**
Nusa Dua Restoran Indonesia **W1**
Odette's **NW1**
Odin's Restaurant **W1**
Ognisko Polskie **SW7**
Oh'Boy **SW17**
Oliver's **W14**
Olivo **SW1**
192 **W11**
Orso **WC2**
Osteria Antica Bologna **SW11**
Le P'tit Normand **SW18**
La Paesana **W8**
Panda **W1**
Pearl of Knightsbridge **SW1**
Peking Garden **W14**
La Perla **W1**
Peter's **NW6**
Le Petit Prince **NW5**
Phoenicia **W8**
Pinocchio's **NW1**
Pizzeria Castello **SE1**
Poissonnerie de l'Avenue **SW3**
Pollyanna's **SW11**
Pomegranates **SW1**
Le Pont de la Tour **SE1**
Poons **WC2**
Poons **WC1**

Poons **W2**
La Preferita **SW11**
Pun **SW7**
Qinggis **NW3**
Le Quai St Pierre **W8**
Quality Chop House **EC1**
Quincy's **NW2**
Ragam **W1**
Rajput **W12**
Rasa Sayang **W1**
Rasa Sayang **W2**
Ravi Shankar **NW1**
Ravi Shankar **EC1**
La Reash **W1**
Red Fort **W1**
The Ritz **W1**
Riva **SW13**
Romantica Taverna **W2**
The Rotisserie **W12**
Royal Garden Hotel **W8**
Royal China **W2**
RSJ **SE1**
Rue St Jacques **W1**
Rules **WC2**
St Moritz **W1**
St Quentin **SW3**
Sala Thai **W5**
Salloos **SW1**
Sambuca **SW3**
San Frediano **SW3**
San Lorenzo **SW3**
San Martino **SW3**
Sandrini **SW3**
Santini **SW1**
I Sardi **SW10**
The Savoy, River Restaurant **WC2**
Sema **SE22**
Shampers **W1**
Shanghai **W8**
Sheekey's Restaurant **WC2**
Sheraton Park Tower **SW1**
Shogun **W1**
Signor Sassi **SW1**
Silver Lake **SE5**
Simply Nico **SW1**
Singapore **W4**
Singapore Garden **NW6**
Singapore Garden Mayfair **W1**
Snows on the Green **W6**
Soho Soho **W1**
Sonargaon **N1**
Sonny's **SW13**
The Square **SW1**
Sri Siam **W1**
Sumos **W6**
Supan **W9**
Le Suquet **SW3**
Sydney Street **SW3**
The Tageen **WC2**
Tandoori Lane **SW6**
La Tante Claire **SW3**
Thierry's **SW3**
Tiger under the Table **NW11**
Tiger Lee **SW5**
Topkapi **W1**
Topsy Tasty **W4**
Tui **SW7**

Tuk Tuk Restaurant **N1**
Turner's **SW3**
Veronica's **W2**
Vijay **NW6**
Vin Santo **SW10**
Wakaba **NW3**
Walton's **SW3**

Wine & Mousaka **W5**
Wodka **W8**
Young's Rendezvous **W5**
Zen **SW3**
Zen Central **W1**
ZeNW3 **NW3**
Ziani **SW3**

Sunday Eating

(L) Lunch only   **(D)** Dinner only

Al Basha **W8**
Al Bustan **SW1**
Al Hamra **W1**
L'Altro **W11 (L)**
The Athenaeum **W1**
L'Aventure **NW8**
Bacco **SW7 (D)**
Bahn Thai **W1**
Basil Street Hotel **SW3**
Bedlington Café **W4 (D)**
Belgo **NW1**
Belvedere **W8**
Benihana **NW3**
The Berkeley **SW1**
Bhatti **WC2**
Bibendum Oyster Bar **SW3**
Bibendum **SW3**
Bistrot 190 **SW7**
Blakes Hotel **SW7**
Bloom's **E1**
Bloom's **NW11**
Blue Elephant **SW6**
Blueprint Café **SE1 (L)**
Bombay Brasserie **SW7**
Bon Ton Roulet **SE24 (L)**
Boyd's **W8**
The Brackenbury **W6 (L)**
Le Braconnier **SW14 (L)**
La Brasserie **SW3**
Brasserie du Marché aux Puces **W10 (L)**
Brown's Hotel **W1**
Buchan's **SW11**
Buzkash **SW15 (D)**
Café Delancey **NW1**
Café Delancey **WC1**
Café Pelican **WC2**
Camden Brasserie **NW1**
The Capital **SW3**
Le Caprice **SW1**
Caravan Serai **W1**
Carraro's **SW8 (L)**
Casale Franco **N1**
Cheng-Du **NW1**
Chez Liline **N4**
Chi Mai **W3 (D)**
Chiang Mai **W1 (D)**
Chicago Rib Shack **SW7**
Chicago Rib Shack II **WC2**
Chicago Pizza Pie Factory **W1**

China Jazz **NW1**
Christian's **W4 (L)**
Chuen Cheng Ku **W1**
Churchill Hotel **W1**
Chutney Mary **SW10**
Ciao **SW6**
Cibo **W14 (L)**
Claridge's **W1**
The Connaught **W1**
La Croisette **SW10**
Daphne's **SW3 (L)**
Depot **SW14**
Don Pepe **NW8 (L)**
The Dorchester **W1**
La Dordogne **W4 (D)**
Dorset Square Hotel **NW1 (D)**
Dragon Inn **W1**
Dragon's Nest **W1**
Dukes Hotel **SW1**
Eastern Eye **SE22**
Ebury Court **SW1**
Efes Kebab House II **W1**
Eleven Park Walk **SW10 (L)**
English House **SW3**
English Garden **SW3**
La Famiglia **SW10**
Florians **N8**
Four Seasons **W2**
Foxtrot Oscar **SW3 (L)**
Fuji **W1 (D)**
Fung Shing **WC2**
La Gaulette **W1 (L)**
Gavin's **SW15**
Glaister's **SW10**
Good Earth **SW3**
Good Earth **NW7**
Good Friends **E14**
Gopal's of Soho **W1**
The Goring **SW1**
Grafton Français **SW4 (L)**
Great Nepalese **NW1**
Green's Restaurant & Oyster Bar **SW1 (L)**
Greenhouse **W1 (L)**
Green Cottage **NW3**
The Green Room **SW11**
The Halcyon **W11**
Halepi **W2**
Harveys **SW17 (L)**
Harveys Café **SW10 (L)**
Hilton International Kensington, Hiroko
   W11

Hilton International Regent's Park, Kashi Noki **NW8**
Holiday Inn Mayfair **W1**
Hong Kong **WC2**
Hyatt Carlton Tower **SW1**
Ikkyu **W1 (D)**
L'Incontro **SW1 (D)**
Inn on the Park Hotel **W1**
Inter-Continental Hotel **W1**
Istanbul Iskembecisi **N16**
The Ivy **WC2**
Jade Garden **W1**
Joe Allen **WC2**
Joe's Café **SW3 (L)**
Kaya **W1 (D)**
Ken Lo's Memories of China **SW10**
Kensington Place **W8**
Khan's of Kensington **SW7**
Khyber Pass **SW7**
Lal Qila **W1**
The Lanesborough **SW1**
Launceston Place **W8 (L)**
Leith's **W11 (D)**
Lemonia **NW1 (L)**
Lena's **SW11 (D)**
Lido **W1**
Lindsay House **W1**
Lok Ho Fook **W1**
London Hilton on Park Lane **W1**
Lou Pescadou **SW5**
Majlis **SW7**
Malabar **W8**
Mandarin Kitchen **W2**
Manzi's **WC2 (D)**
Maroush **W2**
May Fair Inter-Continental **W1**
Memories of India **SW7**
Le Meridien: Terrace Garden Restnt **W1**
Le Midi **SW6 (L)**
Momo **W5**
Mr Kai **W1**
Mr Ke **NW3**
Mulligans of Mayfair **W1 (L)**
Nakamura **W1 (D)**
Nakano **SW1 (D)**
Nanking **W6**
New Fook Lam Moon **W1**
New Kam Tong **W2**
New World **W1**
Newtons **SW4**
Noor Jahan **SW5**
Now and Zen **WC2**
Odette's **NW1 (L)**
Ognisko Polskie **SW7**
Oliver's **W14**
Olivo **SW1 (D)**
192 **W11**
Orso **WC2**
Osteria Antica Bologna **SW11**
Le P'tit Normand **SW18**
Pearl of Knightsbridge **SW1**
Peking Garden **W14**
Peter's **NW6 (L)**
Le Petit Prince **NW5 (D)**
Phoenicia **W8**

Pollyanna's **SW11 (L)**
Le Pont de la Tour **SE1**
Poons **WC1**
Poons **W2**
Poons **WC2**
La Preferita **SW11**
Pun **SW7**
Qinggis **NW3**
Quality Chop House **EC1**
Ragam **W1**
Rajput **W12**
Rani **N3**
Rasa Sayang **W1**
Rasa Sayang **W2**
Ravi Shankar **EC1 (D)**
Ravi Shankar **NW1**
La Reash **W1**
Red Fort **W1**
The Ritz **W1**
Riva **SW13**
River Café **W6 (L)**
Romantica Taverna **W2**
Royal China **W2**
Rules **WC2**
Sabras **NW10 (D)**
St Quentin **SW3**
San Martino **SW3**
Sandrini **SW3**
Santini **SW1 (D)**
I Sardi **SW10**
Satay Hut **N1**
The Savoy **WC2**
Sema **SE22**
Shanghai **W8**
Sheraton Belgravia **SW1 (D)**
Sheraton Park Tower **SW1**
Shogun **W1 (D)**
Silver Lake **SE5 (D)**
Simpson's-in-the-Strand **WC2 (L)**
Singapore **W4**
Singapore Garden **NW6**
Snows on the Green **W6 (L)**
Sonargaon **N1**
Sonny's **SW13 (L)**
Spread Eagle Restaurant **SE10 (L)**
Sri Siam **W1 (D)**
Le Suquet **SW3**
Tandoori Lane **SW6**
Thierry's **SW3**
Thistells **SE22 (L)**
Tiger under the Table **NW11**
Tiger Lee **SW5 (D)**
Topkapi **W1**
Tui **SW7**
Turner's **SW3**
Twenty Trinity Gardens **SW9 (L)**
Vijay **NW6**
Walton's **SW3**
Wilson's **W14 (L)**
Wodka **W8**
Young's Rendezvous **W5**
Zen **SW3**
Zen Central **W1**
ZeNW3 **NW3**
Ziani **SW3**

National Cuisines

Belgian

Belgo **NW1**

British

Bentley's **W1**
Buchan's **SW11**
The Capital **SW3**
The Dorchester, Grill Room **W1**
Dukes Hotel **SW1**
Ebury Court **SW1**
English Garden **SW3**
English House **SW3**
The Goring **SW1**
Greenhouse **W1**
Green's Restaurant & Oyster Bar **SW1**
Langan's Brasserie **W1**
Launceston Place **W8**

Leith's **W11**
Lilly's **W11**
Lindsay House **W1**
Monkeys **SW3**
Motcomb's **SW1**
Oliver's **W14**
Quality Chop House **EC1**
The Ritz **W1**
Rules **WC2**
The Savoy, Grill Room **WC2**
Simpson's-in-the-Strand **WC2**
Walton's **SW3**
Wilton's **SW1**

Chinese

Cheng-Du **NW1**
Chi Mai **W3**
China Jazz **NW1**
Chuen Cheng Ku **W1**
The Dorchester, Oriental Room **W1**
Dragon Inn **W1**
Dragon's Nest **W1**
Four Seasons **W2**
Fung Shing **WC2**
Good Earth **SW3**
Good Earth **NW7**
Good Friends **E14**
Green Cottage **NW3**
Hong Kong **WC2**
Hsing **W2**
Jade Garden **W1**
Kam's **W2**
Ken Lo's Memories of China **SW1**
Ken Lo's Memories of China **SW10**
Lido **W1**
Lok Ho Fook **W1**
Mandarin Kitchen **W2**
Ming **W1**
Mr Kai **W1**

Mr Ke **NW3**
Nanking **W6**
New Fook Lam Moon **W1**
New Kam Tong **W2**
New World **W1**
Now and Zen **WC2**
Panda **W1**
Pearl of Knightsbridge **SW1**
Peking Garden **W14**
Poons **WC2**
Poons **WC1**
Poons **W2**
Pun **SW7**
Qinggis **NW3**
Royal China **W2**
Shanghai **W8**
Silver Lake **SE5**
Singapore **W4**
Tiger Lee **SW5**
Young's Rendezvous **W5**
Zen **SW3**
Zen Central **W1**
ZeNW3 **NW3**

French

L'Arlequin **SW8**
Au Bon Accueil **SW3**
Au Jardin des Gourmets **W1**
L'Aventure **NW8**
Balzac Restaurant **W12**
The Berkeley **SW1**
Boulestin **WC2**
Le Braconnier **SW14**
La Brasserie **SW3**
Brasserie Faubourg **SW8**
Bubb's **EC1**

Café Pelican **WC2**
Chez Moi **W11**
Claridge's, The Causerie **W1**
The Connaught **W1**
La Croisette **SW10**
The Dorchester, Terrace Restaurant **W1**
La Dordogne **W4**
L'Escargot Doré **W8**
L'Estaminet **WC2**
L'Etoile **W1**
La Fin de la Chasse **N16**

Le Gavroche **W1**
Gavver's **SW1**
Grafton Français **SW4**
Grill St Quentin **SW3**
L'Hippocampe **W1**
Hyatt Carlton Tower **SW1**
Inn on the Park Hotel **W1**
Inter-Continental Hotel **W1**
May Fair Inter-Continental **W1**
Le Meridien **W1**
Le Mesurier **EC1**
Le Midi **SW6**
Mijanou **SW1**
Mirabelle **W1**
Mon Plaisir **WC2**
Le Muscadet **W1**
Nico at Ninety **W1**
Nico Central **W1**

Le P'tit Normand **SW18**
Peter's **NW6**
Poissonnerie de l'Avenue **SW3**
Pollyanna's **SW11**
Le Poulbot **EC2**
Le Quai St Pierre **W8**
RSJ **SE1**
Rue St Jacques **W1**
St Quentin **SW3**
The Savoy, River Restaurant **WC2**
1789 **E3**
Simply Nico **SW1**
Soulard Restaurant **N1**
Spread Eagle Restaurant **SE10**
Le Suquet **SW3**
La Tante Claire **SW3**
Thistells **SE22**

Greek

Bitter Lemons Taverna **SW6**
Costa's Grill **W8**
Daphne **NW1**
Fanari **NW1**
Greek Valley **NW8**
Halepi **W2**
Hellas **NW1**

Kalamaras **W2**
Lemonia **NW1**
Little Akropolis **W1**
Nontas **NW1**
Romantica Taverna **W2**
Wine & Mousaka **W5**

Hungarian

Gay Hussar **W1**

Indian

Bhatti **WC2**
Bombay Brasserie **SW7**
Chutney Mary **SW10**
Eastern Eye **SE22**
Gopal's of Soho **W1**
Great Nepalese **NW1**
Khan's of Kensington **SW7**
Khyber Pass **SW7**
Kundan **SW1**
Lal Qila **W1**
Majlis **SW7**
Malabar **W8**
Mandeer **W1**

Memories of India **SW7**
Noor Jahan **SW5**
Ragam **W1**
Rajput **W12**
Rani **N3**
Ravi Shankar **NW1**
Ravi Shankar **EC1**
Red Fort **W1**
Sabras **NW10**
Salloos **SW1**
Sonargaon **N1**
Tandoori Lane **SW6**
Vijay **NW6**

Italian

L'Accento Italiano **W2**
Al San Vincenzo **W2**
Alba **EC1**
L'Altro **W11**
Arts Theatre Café **WC2**
Bacco **SW7**
Carraro's **SW8**
Casa Cominetti **SE6**
Casale Franco **N1**
Caterino's **SW16**
Ciao **SW6**
Cibo **W14**

Eleven Park Walk **SW10**
Enoteca **SW15**
La Famiglia **SW10**
Florians **N8**
Giovanni's **WC2**
Gualtiero Marchesi at the Halkin Hotel
SW1
L'Incontro **SW1**
Luigi's **SE19**
Mimmo d'Ischia **SW1**
Museum Street Café **WC1**
Neal Street Restaurant **WC2**

Olivo **SW1**
Orso **WC2**
Osteria Antica Bologna **SW11**
La Paesana **W8**
Pinocchio's **NW1**
Pizzeria Castello **SE1**
La Preferita **SW11**
Riva **SW13**
River Café **W6**
Sambuca **SW3**

San Frediano **SW3**
San Lorenzo **SW3**
San Martino **SW3**
Sandrini **SW3**
Santini **SW1**
I Sardi **SW10**
Signor Sassi **SW1**
Trattoria Lucca **NW1**
Vin Santo **SW10**
Ziani **SW3**

Japanese

Ajimura **WC2**
Arisugawa **W1**
Asuka **NW1**
Benihana **NW3**
Defune **W1**
Fuji **W1**
Gonbei **WC1**
Hilton International Kensington, Hiroko **W11**
Hilton International Regent's Park, Kashi
Noki **NW8**
Ikeda **W1**
Ikkyu **W1**
Isohama **SW1**
Koto **NW1**
Masako **W1**

Mitsukoshi **SW1**
Miyama **EC4**
Miyama **W1**
Momo **W5**
Nakamura **W1**
Nakano **SW1**
Neshiko **N1**
Ninjin **W1**
Saga **W1**
Shogun **W1**
Sumos **W6**
Suntory **SW1**
Tatsuso **EC1**
Wakaba **NW3**
Yumi **W1**

Korean

Arirang Korean Restaurant **W1**

Kaya **W1**

Lebanese

Al Basha **W8**
Al Bustan **SW1**
Al Hamra **W1**

Maroush **W2**
Phoenicia **W8**

North African

Adam's Café **W12**
Laurent **NW2**

Le Petit Prince **NW5**
La Reash **W1**

Polish

Ognisko Polskie **SW7**

Wodka **W8**

Russian

Nikita's **SW10**

South-East Asian

Nusa Dua **W1**
Rasa Sayang **W1**

Singapore Garden **NW6**
Tiger under the Table **NW11**

Spanish

Don Pepe **NW8**

Swedish

Anna's Place **N1**

Thai

Bahn Thai **W1**
Bangkok **SW7**
Bedlington Café **W4**
Blue Elephant **SW6**
Chiang Mai **W1**
Lena's **SW11**
Oh'Boy **SW17**
Sala Thai **W5**

Satay Hut **N1**
Sema **SE22**
Sri Siam **W1**
Supan **W9**
Thailand Restaurant **SE14**
Tui **SW7**
Tuk Tuk Restaurant **N1**

Turkish

Efes Kebab House **W1**
Istanbul Iskembecisi **N16**

Topkapi **W1**

Vietnamese

Tien Phat **SW6**

Seafood

L'Altro **W11**
Bentley's **W1**
Bibendum Oyster Bar **SW3**
Café Fish **SW1**
Chez Liline **N4**
La Croisette **SW10**
Faulkners **E8**
La Gaulette **W1**
Geale's **W8**
Grahame's Seafare **W1**

Green's Restaurant & Oyster Bar **SW1**
L'Hippocampe **W1**
Lou Pescadou **SW5**
Manzi's **E14**
Manzi's **WC2**
Poissonnerie de l'Avenue **SW3**
Le Quai St Pierre **W8**
Le Suquet **SW3**
Tiger Lee **SW5**
Wilton's **SW1**

Outstanding Desserts

Alastair Little **W1**
L'Arlequin **SW8**
Blakes **SW7**
Boyd's **W8**
The Capital **SW3**
Chinon **W14**
The Dorchester, Terrace Restaurant **W1**
Le Gavroche **W1**
Gualtiero Marchesi at the Halkin Hotel
   SW1
Harveys **SW17**
Inn on the Park Hotel, Four Seasons **W1**

Inter-Continental Hotel, Le Soufflé **W1**
Leith's **W11**
Mijanou **SW1**
Mirabelle **W1**
Nico at Ninety **W1**
Nico Central **W1**
Pollyanna's **SW11**
Pomegranates **SW1**
Rue St Jacques **W1**
Les Saveurs **W1**
The Savoy, Grill Room **WC2**
La Tante Claire **SW3**

Restaurants offering a good cheeseboard

Al San Vincenzo **W2**
The Argyll **SW3**
L'Arlequin **SW8**
The Athenaeum **W1**
Au Jardin des Gourmets **W1**
Basil Street Hotel **SW3**
The Berkeley **SW1**
Bibendum **SW3**
Billboard Café **NW6**
Boulestin **WC2**
The Brackenbury **W6**
Le Braconnier **SW14**
Brasserie du Marché aux Puces **W10**
Brasserie Faubourg **SW8**
Bubb's **EC1**
Buchan's **SW11**
Café du Marché **EC1**
Camden Brasserie **NW1**
The Capital **SW3**
Christian's **W4**
Claridge's, The Causerie **W1**
Claridge's **W1**
Clarke's **W8**
The Connaught **W1**
Corney & Barrow **EC2**
Crowthers **SW14**
Dan's **SW3**
The Dorchester, Terrace Restaurant & Grill
    Room **W1**
Ebury Court **SW1**
Eleven Park Walk **SW10**
English Garden **SW3**
L'Escargot **W1**
L'Estaminet **WC2**
La Fin de la Chasse **N16**
Foxtrot Oscar **SW3**
Frederick's **N1**
Le Gavroche **W1**
Gilbert's **SW7**
The Goring **SW1**
Grafton Français **SW4**
Greenhouse **W1**
Green's Restaurant & Oyster Bar **SW1**
Gualtiero Marchesi at the Halkin Hotel
    SW1
The Halcyon **W11**
Harveys **SW17**
Harveys Café **SW10**
Hilaire **SW7**
L'Hippocampe **W1**
L'Hotel **SW3**
Hyatt Carlton Tower **SW1**
Inter-Continental Hotel **W1**
The Lanesborough **W1**

Langan's Brasserie **W1**
The Langham **W1**
Launceston Place **W8**
Leith's **W11**
Lilly's **W11**
London Hilton on Park Lane **W1**
Luc's Restaurant & Brasserie **EC3**
May Fair Inter-Continental **W1**
Le Meridien **W1**
Mijanou **SW1**
Mirabelle **W1**
Mon Plaisir **WC2**
Monkeys **SW3**
Mulligans of Mayfair **W1**
Museum Street Café **WC1**
Neal Street Restaurant **WC2**
Nico at Ninety **W1**
Nico Central **W1**
Odette's **NW1**
Odin's Restaurant **W1**
Pied à Terre **W1**
Poissonnerie de l'Avenue **SW3**
Pomegranates **SW1**
Le Pont de la Tour **SE1**
Quincy's **NW2**
The Ritz **W1**
Riva **SW13**
River Café **W6**
Royal Garden Hotel **W8**
RSJ **SE1**
St Moritz **W1**
St Quentin **SW3**
San Frediano **SW3**
San Lorenzo **SW3**
Les Saveurs **W1**
The Savoy, Grill Room **WC2**
La Sémillante **W1**
Shampers **W1**
Sheraton Belgravia **SW1**
Simply Nico **SW1**
Simpson's-in-the-Strand **WC2**
Sonny's **SW13**
Stephen Bull Bistro **EC1**
Stephen Bull **W1**
La Tante Claire **SW3**
Tate Gallery Restaurant **SW1**
Thierry's **SW3**
Thistells **SE22**
Twenty Trinity Gardens **SW9**
Veronica's **W2**
Villandry Dining Room **W1**
Walton's **SW3**
Wilton's **SW1**

Restaurants with a good list of California wines

Alastair Little **W1**
The Argyll **SW3**
Bibendum **SW3**
Bombay Brasserie **SW7**
Boulestin **WC2**
Boyd's **W8**
California Pizza Company **W1**
Le Caprice **SW1**
Chapter 11 **SW10**
Christopher's **WC2**
Churchill Hotel **W1**
Claridge's **W1**
Clarke's **W8**
Crowthers **SW14**
The Dorchester **W1**
Dorset Square Hotel **NW1**
Dukes Hotel **SW1**
L'Escargot **W1**
Le Gavroche **W1**
Gilbert's **SW7**
The Goring **SW1**
Harveys **SW17**
Hilaire **SW7**
L'Incontro **SW1**
Inn on the Park Hotel **W1**
Inter-Continental Hotel **W1**

The Ivy **WC2**
Joe Allen **WC2**
Kensington Place **W8**
The Langham **W1**
Leith's **W11**
London Hilton on Park Lane **W1**
May Fair Inter-Continental **W1**
Le Meridien, Oak Room & Terrace Garden
   Restnt **W1**
Mijanou **SW1**
Nico at Ninety **W1**
Odette's **NW1**
Pomegranates **SW1**
Le Pont de la Tour **SE1**
The Ritz **W1**
Royal Garden Hotel **W8**
Rue St Jacques **W1**
The Savoy **WC2**
La Sémillante **W1**
Shampers **W1**
Simply Nico **SW1**
Stephen Bull Bistro **EC1**
Stephen Bull **W1**
Walton's **SW3**
Wodka **W8**

Outstanding Wine Lists

L'Arlequin **SW8**
Au Jardin des Gourmets **W1**
Bibendum **SW3**
Boulestin **WC2**
The Capital **SW3**
The Dorchester **W1**
Le Gavroche **W1**
The Goring **SW1**
Harveys **SW17**
Hilaire **SW7**
Hyatt Carlton Tower **SW1**
Inn on the Park **W1**
Inter-Continental Hotel **W1**

The Langham **W1**
Leith's **W11**
Le Meridien, Oak Room **W1**
Mijanou **SW1**
Mirabelle **W1**
Nico at Ninety **W1**
Pollyanna's **SW11**
Le Pont de la Tour **SE1**
The Ritz **W1**
RSJ **SE1**
Rue St Jacques **W1**
La Tante Claire **SW3**

Restaurants offering a good range of wines by the glass

Alastair Little **W1**
Au Jardin des Gourmets **W1**
Bibendum **SW3**
Blueprint Café **SE1**
Boyd's **W8**
The Brackenbury **W6**
Brasserie Lott **SW3**
Canal Brasserie **W10**
Ciao **SW6**
Claridge's **W1**
Clarke's **W8**

Corney & Barrow **EC2**
Crowthers **SW14**
Dell'Ugo **W1**
Depot **SW14**
Dorset Square Hotel **NW1**
English Garden **SW3**
L'Escargot **W1**
Green's Restaurant & Oyster Bar **SW1**
Gualtiero Marchesi at the Halkin Hotel
   SW1
The Halcyon **W11**

Hilaire **SW7**
L'Hotel **SW3**
Kensington Place **W8**
The Langham **W1**
Le Meridien, Terrace Garden **W1**
Mijanou **SW1**
Odette's **NW1**

192 **W11**
Le Pont de la Tour **SE1**
Spread Eagle Restaurant **SE10**
Stephen Bull Bistro **EC1**
Sydney Street **SW3**
Whittington's **EC4**
Wilton's **SW1**

primetime ™

"Primetime gives me control.
A last minute call, just before
a meeting gets me quickly up
to date. Alerts me to any
problems. That means I'm in
for no nasty surprises.

With Primetime I'm better
prepared to do business."

primetime™

"My customers know they can always leave a message".

"I wouldn't be competitive without one".

"My cellphone has paid for itself - many times over".

Allowing your business to be more efficient and more effective, Cellnet Primetime enables you to maximise the use of time - adding value to the working day, significantly enhancing the service you're able to offer your customers, and helping you keep in touch with colleagues and suppliers.

A truly comprehensive range of relevant services - many of them exclusive to Cellnet - make the mobile phone a real productivity tool.

cellnet

The nearest phone.

For further details call Cellnet on
0800 424 323

England

Abberley   Elms Hotel   71%   £97

Tel 0299 896666   Fax 0299 896804   **H**

Stockton Road Abberley Nr Worcester Hereford & Worcester WR6 6AT   **Map 10 B4**

A Queen Anne mansion built in 1710 by a pupil of Sir Christopher Wren,
the Elms caters for both private and business people (meeting rooms for up
to 60). Its elegant lines are enhanced by ten attractive acres of formal
gardens and parkland. The foyer, with slate floor and carved wooden
fireplace, makes a splendid impression on entry, and both here and in the
lounges and library fine antiques are found among good-quality
reproduction pieces. Bedrooms are traditional in the main house, lighter
and brighter in the converted coach house; some of the latter have
balconies, and all have well-equipped bathrooms en suite. There are four
studio suites. No dogs. Queens Moat Houses. **Rooms 25.** *Garden, tennis,*
putting, croquet, helipad. Access, Amex, Visa, ⓘ *Diners Club International*

Abbot's Salford   Salford Hall   66%   £95

Tel 0386 871300   Fax 0386 871301   **H**

Abbot's Salford Evesham Hereford & Worcester WR11 5UT   **Map 4 C1**

Dating from the late 15th century, this imposing Grade One listed mansion
is a comfortable, characterful establishment, with a half-timbered,
whitewashed wing and a fine walled garden. The central courtyard has
been glassed in to form a pleasant conservatory, giving striking views of its
quaintly gabled roofs. The lounge, once the Abbot's kitchen, displays
original meat hooks suspended from oak beams. Bedrooms, split between
the main house and the gate house, are mainly furnished with reproduction
pieces; many have exposed timberwork and mullioned windows.
Conferences for up to 50. No dogs. **Rooms 33.** *Garden, croquet, sauna,*
solarium, snooker, tennis. Access, Amex, Visa, ⓘ *Diners Club International*

Abingdon   Abingdon Lodge   61%   £80

Tel 0235 553456   Fax 0235 554117   **H**

Marcham Road Abingdon Oxfordshire OX14 1TZ   **Map 5 D2**

Clean-lined, modern low-rise hotel at the junction of the A34 and A415.
Day rooms include a distinctive octagonal bar. Several conference rooms
cater for up to 180 delegates. Children up to 14 stay free in parents' room.
Ample car parking. **Rooms 63.** *Access, Amex, Visa,* ⓘ *Diners Club International*

Abingdon   Upper Reaches   62%   £101

Tel 0235 522311   Fax 0235 555182   **H**

Thames Street Abingdon Oxfordshire OX14 3TA   **Map 5 D2**

Former corn mill standing on a virtual island between the Thames and the
Abbey Stream. Some bedrooms enjoy river views. Forte Heritage.
Rooms 25. *Terrace, fishing. Access, Amex, Visa,* ⓘ *Diners Club International*

Acle   Forte Travelodge   £40

Tel 0493 751970   **L**

A47 Acle bypass Acle Nr Norwich Norfolk NR13 3BE   **Map 6 D1**

At the junction of the A47 and the Acle bypass, to the east of Acle on the
main road between Norwich and Great Yarmouth. **Rooms 40.** *Access,*
Amex, Visa.

Alcester   Arrow Mill   £72

Tel 0789 762419   Fax 0789 765170   **I**

Arrow Alcester Warwickshire B49 5NL   **Map 4 C1**

The Arrow Mill was listed in the Domesday Book, when it was a working
flour mill valued at three shillings and sixpence! The stream-driven mill
wheel still turns in the restaurant, and day rooms feature heavy beams and

flagstones. Bedrooms of individual character use light, attractive fabrics and pine furniture. There's parking space for 200 cars, and a helipad. Dogs in kennels only. **Rooms 18.** *Garden, fishing. Access, Amex, Visa,*

Alcester   Places of Interest

Coughton Galleries   Coughton Court Tel 0789 762642.
Ragley Hall   Tel 0789 762090.

Aldeburgh	Brudenell Hotel	60%	£91
Tel 0728 452071 Fax 0728 454082			**H**
The Parade Aldeburgh Suffolk IP15 5BU			Map 6 D3

It's difficult to escape the North Sea at this esplanade hotel, where public rooms and many of the bedrooms look out on the briny. The elegant Music Room can accommodate up to 50 people for meetings and conferences. Forte Heritage. **Rooms 47.** *Access, Amex, Visa,*

Aldeburgh	Uplands	60%	£59
Tel 0728 452420			**H**
Victoria Road Aldeburgh Suffolk IP15 5DX			Map 6 D3

A Regency house, just opposite the parish church and a stone's throw from the seafront, which maintains the best aspects of a snug guest house. Public areas include a rear conservatory which opens to the landscaped gardens where a wing of chalets comprises fully half the accommodation. Remaining bedrooms in the house retain some period features and have a more characterful charm. No dogs. **Rooms 20.** *Garden. Access, Amex, Visa,*

Aldeburgh	Wentworth Hotel	67%	£84
Tel 0728 452312			**H**
Wentworth Road Aldeburgh Suffolk IP15 5BD			Map 6 D3

The Pritt family run this well-maintained seaside hotel with a country atmosphere. Log fires in the cocktail bar and lounge add to the warm welcome; downstairs there's a tastefully furnished lounge and a cosy bar that opens on to a sheltered garden terrace. Six larger bedrooms are described as "superior", and all but three rooms have neat carpeted bathrooms. **Rooms 31.** *Garden. Closed 2 weeks from 27 Dec. Access, Amex, Visa,*

Aldeburgh   Places of Interest

Tourist Information   Tel 0728 453637.
Snape Maltings Concert Hall   Snape Tel 0728 452935.
Sizewell Visitor Centre   Nr Leiston Tel 0728 642139.

Alderley Edge	Alderley Edge Hotel	75%	£117
Tel 0625 583033 Fax 0625 586343			**HR**
Macclesfield Road Alderley Edge Cheshire SK9 7BJ			Map 10 B2

Establishing itself as one of the North West's leading hotels, the Alderley Edge concentrates on good hotel-keeping rather than mere show. A conservatory, housing a lounge and restaurant, softens an otherwise stern Victorian exterior. Within, the sumptuous day rooms are complemented by the professionalism and sheer enthusiasm of the carefully hand-picked staff. The largest bedrooms (a few of which have four-poster beds) are effectively cottage suites and have armchairs, coffee table, a basket of fruit, tantalus of sherries and spa baths. In the smaller back bedrooms guests are rewarded with views over the hotel's own garden bird sanctuary. Children under 14 stay free in parents' room. **Rooms 32.** *Garden, dinner dances (monthly). Access, Amex, Visa,*

Restaurant   £80

Ignore the pretentious menu-speak and there is some genuinely good
cooking to be enjoyed here on a 3-course table d'hote (identical at both
lunch and dinner, but priced differently) and à la carte. Roasted
sweetbreads with mirabelle plums and Madeira sauce, Tay salmon with a
mild mustard and dill sauce, and Hebridean beef with bordelaise sauce and
black pudding choucroute typify Brian Joy's modern French style. Good
patisserie (from patissier Norbert Bataillard) is supplemented by the likes of
hot sticky toffee pudding for afters and there are some well-kept English
and French cheeses. **Seats 80.** Parties 20. Private Room. L 12-2 D 7-9.30.
Set L £15.50 Set D £20.50.

Aldridge   Fairlawns   62%   £78
Tel 0922 55122   Fax 0922 743210   **H**

Little Aston Road Aldridge Walsall West Midlands WS9 0NU   Map 10 C4

Accessible from junctions 5, 10 and 12 of the M6, a purpose-built hotel in
a rural setting, catering for up to 70 conference delegates. Six of the
bedrooms are suites and those in the original building are small, but
pleasantly decorated. **Rooms 35.** Garden. Access, Amex, Visa, Diners Club International

All Stretton   Stretton Hall Hotel   59%   £49
Tel 0694 723224   **H**

All Stretton Nr Church Stretton Shropshire SY6 6HG   Map 10 A4

On the A49 between Ludlow and Shrewsbury, this Victorian hotel is clean
and comfortable. Beyond the main hallway, with its oak dado panelling, is
a similarly panelled bar with Victorian polished wood fireplace. Bedrooms
vary in size and furniture, from basic fitted units to 50s' freestanding pieces
and almost-antiques. Favourite choice is the panelled four-poster room.
Bathrooms, three with shower and W/C only, are utilitarian. **Rooms 14.**
Garden. Access, Amex, Visa, Diners Club International

Allendale   Bishop Field   59%   £76
Tel 0434 683248   Fax 0434 683830   **H**

Whitfield Road Allendale Nr Hexham Northumberland NE47 9EJ   Map 15 B4

A mile out of Allendale on the Whitfield road, this former farmhouse was
converted in 1985 by Kathy and Keith Fairless and is now run by them
with their young daughter Bridget, who is also the chef. There's a cheerful,
relaxed atmosphere in the lounges, one of which has a cocktail bar; the
other is non-smoking. Bedrooms are comfortable and rather pretty, light
colour schemes contrasting well with dark-stained furniture. Cheaper B&B
accommodation (no credit card payments, children or pets) is offered for
couples in two rooms across the courtyard from the hotel. **Rooms 11.**
Garden, game fishing, shooting. Closed 2 wks Xmas. Access, Visa, Diners Club International

Alnwick   White Swan   58%   £75
Tel 0665 602109   Fax 0665 510400   **H**

Bondgate Within, Alnwick Northumberland NE66 1TD   Map 14 B3

The hotel's staircase, revolving doors and some carved oak panelling all
came from the SS Olympic (sister ship to the ill-fated Titanic) and fit quite
happily into this town-centre coaching inn. Children under 14 stay free in
parents' room. **Rooms 43.** Access, Amex, Visa.

Alnwick   Places of Interest

Tourist Information   Tel 0665 510665.
Morpeth Chantry Bagpipe Museum   The Chantry, Bridge Street, Morpeth
   Tel 0670 519466.
   Historic Houses, Castles and Gardens
Alnwick Castle   Tel 0665 510777.
Cragside House & Country Park (NT)   Rothbury Tel 0669 20333.

Howick Hall Garden   Howick Tel 0665 77285.
Wallington House, Walled Garden and Grounds (NT)
Cambo, Morpeth Tel 0670 74 283.

Alsager	Manor House	65%	£85

Tel 0270 884000   Fax 0270 882483   **H**

Audley Road Alsager Cheshire ST7 2QQ   **Map 10 B3**

A modern hotel set in its own grounds three miles from junction 16 of the
M6. The heart of the place is a 17th-century farm, and old beams preserve
a traditional feel in the restaurant, bars and several meeting rooms.
Bedrooms are divided between the original part and a new wing; in the
latter are two rooms adapted for disabled guests and two Executive rooms
with jacuzzis. Children up to 14 stay free in parents' room. Conference
facilities for 250. *Rooms 57. Garden, croquet, indoor swimming pool, snooker.
Access, Amex, Visa,* (1) *Diners Club International*

Alsager   Places of Interest

Little Moreton Hall (NT)   Tel 0260 272018 *4 miles.*

Alston	Lovelady Shield	68%	£76

Tel 0434 381203   Fax 0434 381515   **H**

Nenthead Road Alston Cumbria CA9 3LF   **Map 13 D4**

Two miles east of Alston in a remote and beautiful setting, this 1830s'
house is approached by a long drive and private bridge. Valley and
moorland views are enjoyed by all the bedrooms, which are well stocked
with reading material. Neat bathrooms have impulse showers. A country
house atmosphere is engendered by the welcoming Lyons family and their
attentive staff. No smoking restaurant. *Rooms 12. Garden, croquet, tennis.
Closed Jan-mid Feb. Access, Amex, Visa,* (1) *Diners Club International*

Alton	Forte Travelodge		£40

Tel 0420 62659   **L**

A31 Four Marks Winchester Road Alton Hampshire GU34 5HZ   **Map 4 D3**

On the A31 northbound, 5 miles south of Alton. Close to Winchester.
Rooms 31. Access, Amex, Visa.

Alton	Grange Hotel	61%	£61

Tel 0420 86565   Fax 0420 541346   **H**

17 London Road Holybourne Alton Hampshire GU34 4EG   **Map 5 D3**

The two-acre garden, overlooked by the lounge and sun terrace, is quite a
feature at the Levenes' friendly hotel. Croquet and putting are available,
and the owners are involved in the mid-Hants Balloon Club which meets
regularly at the hotel. Individually appointed bedrooms include two
honeymoon suites and the penthouse suite with a sunken bath. Small
conferences can be arranged for up to 40 delegates. Children's play area.
Rooms 34. Garden, croquet, putting. Closed Xmas. Access, Amex, Visa,
(1) *Diners Club International*

Alton	The Swan	58%	£91

Tel 0420 83777   Fax 0420 87975   **H**

High Street Alton Hampshire GU34 1AT   **Map 5 D3**

White-painted former coaching inn offering neat, practical accommodation
alongside unfussy but comfortable public areas. Friendly staff. Banqueting
and conference facilities for 120. Forte. *Rooms 36. Garden. Access, Amex,
Visa,* (1) *Diners Club International*

Alton   Places of Interest

Oates Memorial Library and the Gilbert White Museum
The Wakes, Selborne Tel 0420 50275.
Historic Houses, Castles and Gardens
Jane Austen's House   Chawton Tel 0420 83262.
Jenkyn Place Garden   Bentley Tel 0420 23118.

Altrincham   Bowdon Hotel   65%   £76

Tel 061-928 7121   Fax 061-927 7560   **H**

Langham Road Bowdon Altrincham Greater Manchester WA14 2HT   Map 10 B2

Victorian hotel with sympathetic extensions, on the B5161 and convenient
for the motorway network. Neat, practical accommodation, several
conference rooms and banqueting suites, a pub called *Silks* and an ample
car park. Children up to 14 stay free in parents' room. *Rooms 82. Access,
Amex, Visa,*  Diners Club International

Altrincham   Cresta Court   61%   £72

Tel 061-927 7272   Fax 061-926 9194   **H**

Church Street Altrincham Greater Manchester WA14 4DP   Map 10 B2

Handy for the motorway network, Manchester airport and the North-
West generally, the privately owned Cresta is geared up for conferences
and functions with the largest room (all of which are air-conditioned)
having a capacity of up to 400. Well-kept bedrooms offer all the usual
modern comforts. Children up to 12 stay free in parents' room.
Rooms 139. Coffee shop (9.30am-11pm). Access, Amex, Visa, Diners Club International

Altrincham   Francs   £35

Tel 061-941 3954   **R**

2 Goose Green Altrincham Greater Manchester   Map 10 B2

Sister restaurant to Francs in Chester. A French bistro offering grills, crepes,
fish, casseroles and a daily-changing *plat du jour* – all with a breath of
French air. A 2-course *Bon Marché* menu is served from 5-7.30pm for just
£5! Sunday lunch (£7.50) is always busy, with children under 10 fed free.
All desserts are now home-made. Outdoor eating on a terrace in good
weather. *Seats 80. Parties 40. L 12-3 D 5-11 (Sun 12-7.30). Closed Bank
Holidays. Access, Amex, Visa,* Diners Club International

Altrincham   George & Dragon   60%   £50

Tel 061-928 9933   Fax 061-929 8060   **H**

Manchester Road Altrincham Greater Manchester WA14 4PH   Map 10 B2

Smartly kept accommodation, Victorian-inspired bar-lounge. Children up
to 10 stay free in parents' room. No dogs. County Inns. *Rooms 47. Garden.
Access, Amex, Visa,* Diners Club International

Altrincham   Places of Interest

Dunham Massey Hall and Garden (NT)   Tel 061 941 1025.
Ice Rink   Devonshire Road Tel 061 926 8316.

Alveley   Mill Hotel   66%   £73

Tel 0746 780437   Fax 0746 780850   **H**

Birdsgreen Alveley Nr Bridgnorth Shropshire WV15 6HL   Map 10 B4

Just off the A442, midway between Kidderminster and Bridgnorth. Ten
acres of landscaped gardens surround The Mill, a 17th-century building
sympathetically restored and extended to include a variety of conference
facilities catering for up to 200. The mill workings can still be seen in the
rustic Mill Bar, and the lounge bar is large and well furnished. Bedrooms
are in a modern extension. No dogs. *Rooms 21. Garden, games room. Access,
Amex, Visa,* Diners Club International

Alveston   Alveston House   65%   £80

Tel 0454 415050   Fax 0454 415425   **H**

Alveston Nr Bristol Avon BS12 2LJ   Map 4 B2

Popular commercial hotel on A38 north of Bristol, with a predominance of single bedrooms. Much geared to the business and conference trade (up to 100 delegates). Ample parking. *Rooms 30. Garden, business centre. Access, Amex, Visa,*

Alveston   Forte Posthouse   62%   £64

Tel 0454 412521   Fax 0454 413920   **H**

Thornbury Road Alveston Nr Bristol Avon BS12 2LL   Map 4 B2

11 miles north of Bristol, close to M4/M5 intersection, an extended Tudor inn with a good conference trade (facilities for up to 100). *Rooms 74. Outdoor swimming pool, pitch & putt, children's play area. Access, Amex, Visa,*

Amberley   Amberley Inn   57%   £75

Tel 0453 872565   Fax 0453 872738   **H**

Amberley Nr Stroud Gloucestershire GL5 5AF   Map 4 B2

High on Minchinhampton Common, this sturdy, stone-built inn has been operated by the Price family for 25 years. Locals share the camaraderie of the lounge and Amberley Bars, while residents can relax and enjoy unrivalled views of Woodchester Valley from their own lounge. Bedrooms share this aspect or overlook the garden; all have colour TV, radios and a beverage tray with fresh milk. Four particularly pleasant rooms are in the Garden House. *Rooms 14. Garden. Access, Amex, Visa,* ◑ *Diners Club International*

Amberley   Amberley Castle   81%   £130

Tel 0798 831992   Fax 0798 831998   **HR**

Amberley Nr Arundel West Sussex BN18 9ND   Map 5 E4

A country hotel set within a 900-year-old castle promising serenity and tranquillity behind the stone battlements surrounding the magnificent building. Joy and Martin Cummings successfully combine modernity and antiquity in this unique setting, using carefully chosen antiques where appropriate. Bedrooms are named after local Sussex castles and have considerable charm; each has thoughtful extras like flowers, plants and video recorders (with a video library in each room). The day rooms are grand and peppered with suits of armour and historic weaponry as befits the grand castle setting. Magnificent bathrooms all have jacuzzi baths. Newly restored private dining and meeting rooms (for up to 45 delegates) include the richly panelled King Charles I room. Two new bedrooms have recently been completed, with views of the Castle gardens and ruined battlements. *Rooms 13. Garden, croquet. Access, Amex, Visa,* ◑ *Diners Club International*

Queen's Room Restaurant   £100

A baronial dining room that dates back to the 13th century and boasts a historic 17th-century hunting mural, reflected in the crystal animals which add charm to the quality table settings. Chef Nigel Boschetti offers two set menus and an à la carte with a varied choice of modern, French-inspired dishes: seafood bisque with armagnac, pan-fried loin of lamb with onion marmalade and tarragon sauce, fillet of beef with Stilton soufflé and port sauce are typical dishes. *Seats 36. Parties 10. Private Room. L 12-2.30 D 6-10. Set L from £18.50 Set D from £25.50.*

Ambleside   Kirkstone Foot   65%

Tel 053 94 32232   Fax 053 94 31110

£100*

H

Kirkstone Pass Road Ambleside Cumbria LA22 9EH

Map 13 D5

The original 17th-century manor house tends to look lost amid extensions and improvements, but there's a homely feel within, especially in the lounge and bar areas which look out on fine gardens and over Ambleside's rooftops. Bedrooms mainly have floral fabrics, colour co-ordinated schemes and smart modern furniture; approached by a maze of stairs and corridors, they come in a mish-mash of sizes, among which front-facing rooms are decidedly superior. No dogs. *Half-board terms only. **Rooms 16.** Garden. Closed Jan. Access, Amex, Visa,* ⓓ Diners Club International

Ambleside   Nanny Brow   62%

Tel 053 94 32036   Fax 053 94 32450

£110

H

Clappersgate Ambleside Cumbria LA22 9NF

Map 13 D5

An interesting Edwardian building, built in Tudor style, on a hillside above the Coniston road, Nanny Brow has fine, stepped gardens and views over the Brathay valley. Lounge and bar retain a cosy feel with open log fires and an adjacent snooker room for rainy days. Chintz decor predominates in the main-house bedrooms, which are generally preferable to those in the garden wing where added space and good views scarcely compensate for lack of character. *Rooms 19. Garden, croquet, spa bath, solarium, fishing, tennis. Closed 3 weeks Jan. Access, Amex, Visa.*

Ambleside   Rothay Manor   71%

Tel 053 94 33605   Fax 053 94 33607

£100

HR

Rothay Bridge Ambleside Cumbria LA22 0EH

Map 13 D5

A balconied Regency frontage is echoed by an elegant, restful interior of cool decor, deep-cushioned seating and garden views which are shared by the best, front-facing bedrooms. Of the three garden suites two are well suited to family use (children up to 10 stay free in parents' room) and the third is equipped for disabled guests. A convenient location on the Coniston road is handy for the bustle of Ambleside yet well protected from it in secluded grounds. The Nixons have been here since 1976 and personal touches are evident throughout; service is very friendly and attentive. Guests have free use of a nearby leisure club and permits may be obtained for trout fishing. Traditional afternoon tea is served every day between 3.30 and 5.30pm. No dogs. *Rooms 18. Garden, croquet. Closed early Jan-mid Feb. Access, Amex, Visa,* ⓓ Diners Club International

Restaurant

£66

Five-course nightly menus make the most of local produce, with wine suggestions appended to each course. Dishes typically run from mousseline of salmon with hollandaise sauce through cream of tomato and chervil soup to baked fillets of red mullet, braised wood pigeon and beef stroganoff, with Normandy apple flan or rum and blackcurrant cheesecake to finish. Lunch is a buffet Mon-Sat, with favourite roasts on Sunday (booking advisable). The setting of polished mahogany tables and soft candle-light accompanies an unfailingly traditional style of cooking and service. Prices are fair on a good all-round wine list; admirable half-bottle policy of opening a full bottle and charging three-fifths of the full price. No smoking. **Seats 60.** *Parties 30. Private Room. L 12.30-2 (buffet only Mon-Sat) (Sun 12.30-1.30) D 8-9. Set L £13 (Sun) Set D £21/£24.*

Ambleside   Wateredge Hotel   63%

Tel &   Fax 053 94 32332

£118

HR

Waterhead Bay Ambleside Cumbria LA22 0EP

Map 13 D5

A lakeside hotel of inherent charm, originally a row of 17th-century cottages, with added attractions of water-edge garden, jetty and rowing boat – hence no children under seven. Modern extensions have added

garden rooms with private balcony or patio and two spacious ground-floor
suites. A cosy bar, bright airy lounge and Windermere views provide the
unifying theme; the Cowap family and cheerful staff provide the welcome.
*Rooms 23. Garden, boating, coarse fishing. Closed Dec & Jan. Access, Amex,
Visa.*

Restaurant   £63

Nightly six-course dinners are taken at leisure in adjoining candle-lit
rooms. Cooking is careful and the choice sensibly limited, with typical
dishes like carrot and orange soup, trout with almonds and strawberry
shortbread. All bread, pastries and preserves are home-made. Friendly
service is again a plus, as is a non-smoking policy. Lighter lunches. *Seats 50.
Parties 12. L 12-2 D 7-8.30.*

Amesbury   Forte Travelodge   £40

Tel 0980 624966   **L**

A303 Amesbury Wiltshire SP4 7AS   Map 4 C3

At the junction of the A345 and the A303 eastbound, 8 miles north of
Salisbury on the major route for the West Country. *Rooms 32. Access,
Amex, Visa.*

Ampfield   Potters Heron Hotel   60%   £87

Tel 0703 266611   Fax 0703 251359   **H**

Ampfield Nr Romsey Hampshire SO51 9ZF   Map 5 D3

White-painted thatched building on the A31 with conference facilities for
up to 140. Lansbury. *Rooms 54. Keep-fit equipment, sauna, pool table. Access,
Amex, Visa,* (I) *Diners Club International*

Andover   White Hart Inn   £86

Tel 0264 352266   Fax 0264 323767   **I**

Bridge Street Andover Hampshire SP10 1BH   Map 4 C3

Former coaching inn in the centre of town. Period character evident in day
rooms; very acceptable accommodation. Conferences and banqueting for
up to 65. Forte. *Rooms 20. Access, Amex, Visa,* (I) *Diners Club International*

Andover   Places of Interest

Cricklade Theatre   Tel 0264 65698.
Hawk Conservancy Park   Weyhill Tel 0264 772252.
Thruxton Motor Racing Circuit   Tel 0264 772696.

Ansty   Ansty Hall   71%   £117

Tel 0203 612222   Fax 0203 602155   **H**

Ansty Nr Coventry Warwickshire CV7 9HZ   Map 11 D4

When it opened in 1988 there were just 13 bedrooms, most of them dating
back to the hall's founding in the late 17th century. The other rooms are in
a two-year-old conversion and both types overlook the lawns that provide
such a peaceful setting (yet it's only two minutes from junction 2 of the
M6). Smart reproduction furniture is used throughout, and the day rooms
have a quiet, traditional elegance. Small banquets and conferences (up to
80/70). *Rooms 31. Garden. Closed 5 days Xmas. Access, Amex, Visa,*
(I) *Diners Club International*

Appleby-in-Westmorland
Appleby Manor Hotel   66%   NEW   £92

Tel 076 83 51571   Fax 076 83 52888   **H R**

Roman Road Appleby-in-Westmorland Cumbria CA16 6JD   Map 13 D5

A relaxing and friendly family-owned hotel overlooking Appleby Castle
and the Eden valley. Most of the original (1870s) architectural features
remain, including the main fireplace and old hooks that used to carry rods

to hang tapestries and pictures. Bright and cheerful bedrooms, whether in the main house, modern wing or coach house annexe, provide everything you need, from powerful hairdryers to in-house video films. *Rooms 30. Garden, croquet, indoor swimming pool, spa bath, sauna, steam room, sunbed, mini-gym, snooker. Closed 3 days Xmas. Access, Amex, Visa,* 🄳 *Diners Club International*

Oak Room Restaurant

£40

A panelled room with a hand-painted tiled fireplace. No-nonsense food is served in decent portions with plenty of well-cooked vegetables. Dishes such as pot-roasted quail, Gressingham duck, and baked fillet of fresh cod will satisfy, and there's a commendable attitude to wine pricing – apart from four value-for-money fine wines, there's a fixed £4.50 mark-up on the purchase price of every bottle, and only £6 on champagnes (£23.50 for Moët!). *Seats 70. Parties 30. L 12-1.45 D 7-9. Closed 3 days Xmas. Set L & D £16.*

Appleby-in-Westmorland   Tufton Arms   66%

£80

Tel 076 83 51593   Fax 076 83 52761

H

Market Square Appleby-in-Westmorland Cumbria CA16 6XA

Map 13 D5

An unusual and rather evocative conversion of a once run-down Victorian pub, now restored with authentic pieces, period prints and atmospheric appeal. Clubby townspeople's bar and more restful conservatory dining. More Victorian features amd carefully updated bathrooms in the original bedrooms; a more modest modern wing is fitted out with the businessman in mind. *Rooms 19. Fishing. Access, Amex, Visa,* 🄳 *Diners Club International*

Applethwaite   Underscar Manor   74%

£100

Tel 076 87 75000   Fax 076 87 74904

HR

Applethwaite Keswick Cumbria CA12 4PH

Map 13 C5

One mile from the Keswick roundabout, the Italianate house, built in the Victorian era, commands spectacular views over Derwentwater. Set in 40 acres of gardens and woodland, like so many places in the Lake District, this can be described as the perfect spot. Much of the original architecture has been retained – ornate fireplaces and mouldings, bay windows and plasterwork ceilings, supplemented by many antiques, fine fabrics and carpets, elegant furniture, and lovely flower arrangements. Luxurious bedrooms have been carefully refurbished to a high standard, as have the bathrooms, and service under the direction of Pauline and Derek Harrison (who also own *Moss Nook* restaurant near Manchester Airport – see entry) is discreet and caring. Half-board terms only at weekends (£150). *Rooms 11. Garden. Access, Amex, Visa.*

Restaurant

£65

Two elegant rooms (both non-smoking), one domed conservatory-style, are the setting for Robert Thornton's sound cooking. Particular attention is paid to the artistic presentation of dishes, although this is in itself no fault when the ingredients and flavours succeed. Typical examples from the fixed-price-only menus might be an appetiser of fish kebab in a white wine sauce, a cheese soufflé with smoked salmon and a red pepper sauce, followed by maize-fed breast of chicken with crisp asparagus, wild mushrooms and a fine filo pastry parcel of leeks, finally ending with a tuile of tropical fruits and seasonal berries served with honey ice cream. Commendable and unobtrusive service. *Seats 60. Parties 40. Private Room. L 12-1.30 D 7-8.30. Set L £16.50 Set D £25.*

Arundel   Norfolk Arms   60%

£60

Tel 0903 882101   Fax 0903 884275

H

22 High Street Arundel West Sussex BN18 9AD

Map 5 E4

A Georgian coaching inn without the benefit of modernisation in the public rooms. By contrast, the bedrooms are bright, with pale floral patterns, and families of yellow ducks try to enliven the modern bathrooms. Newer rooms are in a detached wing to the rear. Functions and conferences for up to 100. **Rooms 34.** *Access, Amex, Visa,* **(I)** *Diners Club International*

Arundel   Places of Interest

Arundel Castle   Tel 0903 883136.
Denmans Garden   Fontwell Tel 0243 542808.
Arundel Wildfowl and Wetlands Trust   Tel 0903 883355.
Fontwell Park Racecourse   0243 543335.

Ascot   Berystede Hotel   67%   £122

Tel 0344 23311   Fax 0344 872301   **H**

Bagshot Road Sunninghill Ascot Berkshire SL5 9JH   Map 5 E2

Just to the south of Ascot, this Forte Grand hotel is based on a large Victorian house standing in its own 6 acres of wooded grounds. As popular with racegoers as business people, the public rooms and the best of the bedrooms are in the original house and share its period feel. The majority of the bedrooms, however, are in a modern extension. Recently refurbished conference and banqueting facilities for 120, supported by a newly opened business centre. **Rooms 91.** *Garden, outdoor swimming pool, croquet, putting, games room, dinner dance (Saturdays). Access, Amex, Visa,* **(I)** *Diners Club International*

Ascot   Hyn's   £50

Tel 0344 872583   **R**

4 Brockenhurst Road Ascot Berkshire   Map 5 E2

Peking, Szechuan and Cantonese all have their place on the menu (neatly and clearly printed, and no numbers!). Most of the dishes will be familiar to habitués of this most varied of cuisines, but slightly out of the ordinary are chicken liver with chili and garlic salt, Szechuan beef soup and steamed Dover sole with ginger and spring onions. 12.5% service charge is added to your bill. **Seats 90.** *Parties 10. L 12-2.30 D 6-11. Closed 25 & 26 Dec. Set meals from £19.50. Access, Amex, Visa,* **(I)** *Diners Club International*

Ascot   Royal Berkshire   76%   £168

Tel 0344 23322   Fax 0344 27100   **H R**

London Road Sunninghill Ascot Berkshire SL5 0PP   Map 5 E2

Previous occupants of this Queen Anne mansion, conveniently located between Ascot race course and the Polo Club, have included the Churchill family and a certain Colonel Horlicks (of malted drink fame) who developed the 15 acres of superb gardens and woodlands. Now operated by Hilton International, the public areas retain an air of elegance with restful colour schemes and quality furnishings. Bedrooms in the original house are spacious and stylish with freestanding furniture and plenty of extras; those in the extensions are a little simpler. The largest of the numerous conference rooms can accommodate up to 70 delegates theatre-style. **Rooms 81.** *Garden, croquet, indoor swimming pool, sauna, whirlpool bath, tennis, squash, putting, helipad. Access, Amex, Visa,* **(I)** *Diners Club International*

State Room Restaurant   £90

An elegant dining room overlooking manicured lawns makes an appropriate setting for Andy Richardson's refined and inventive cooking. Both à la carte and fixed-price menus are sensibly limited in extent enabling Andy to concentrate his considerable skills on such dishes as pan-fried foie gras with plum and raisin chutney and warm brioche loaf, breast of chicken with morel cream and stewed peppers, loin of venison with peppered noodles and mulled pear, and ginger and praline mousse with a candied orange marmalade. Plain dishes are available on request. **Seats 35.** *Parties 75. Private Room. L 12.30-2 D 7.30-9.30. Set L £19.95 Set D £28.*

Ascot   Places of Interest

Racecourse   Tel 0344 22211.
Ascot Park Polo Club   Wood Hall Tel 0344 20399.

Ashbourne   Ashbourne Oaks Lodge   66%   £78

Tel 0335 46666   Fax 0335 46549   **H**

Derby Road Ashbourne Derbyshire DE6 1XH   Map 10 C3

By the A52 just outside town, a new redbrick hotel lent some old-world
style by rustic-designed public areas. Bedrooms are neat and light but not
over-large. Banqueting/conference facilities for 190/250. There's an all-day
brasserie with a children's menu. No dogs. *Rooms 51. Garden. Access,
Amex, Visa,* (1) Diners Club International

Ashbourne   Callow Hall   69%   £85

Tel 0335 43403   Fax 0335 43624   **H**

Mappleton Road Ashbourne Derbyshire DE6 2AA   Map 10 C3

Five minutes' drive from the centre of Ashbourne, the Spencers' family
home is an ideal retreat. Approached by a tree-lined drive through 44 acres
of woodland, it enjoys a mile of private fishing on the nearby Bentley
Brook. Quality antiques and family memorabilia are the main features of
the recently extended drawing room and homely little bar. Bedrooms with
tasteful design and elegant furnishings of the highest standard provide
plenty of extras – from books and magazines to fresh fruit and mineral
water. Sumptuous tiled bathrooms boast bathrobes and locally made
toiletries. Private meetings for up to 30, banquets maximum 45. Under-10s
stay free in parents' room. No dogs. *Rooms 12. Garden, game fishing. Closed
2 weeks Jan/Feb. Access, Amex, Visa,* (1) Diners Club International

---

Ashford   Ashford International   71%   £107

Tel 0233 611444   Fax 0233 627708   **H**

Simone Weil Avenue Ashford Kent TN24 8UX   Map 7 C5

At the heart of this hotel, by junction 9 of the M20, is a long, glass-roofed
boulevard containing the spacious lobby. Various shops are down one side
– an art gallery, golf shop and Avis car hire among others – and a lively
bar, restaurant with smart cocktail bar plus a brasserie with tables spilling
out on to the tiled concourse, down the other. A fountain and a large, four-
face hanging clock complete the rather pleasing Continental air. Spacious
bedrooms are well laid out with a couple of easy chairs, breakfast tables
and good desk space, but are unremarkably decorated with muted colour
schemes and floral fabrics. 24hr room service. Queens Moat Houses.
*Rooms 200. Indoor swimming pool, sauna, solarium, whirlpool bath, beautician,
gymnasium, brasserie (7am-11pm). Access, Amex, Visa,* (1) Diners Club International

---

Ashford   Eastwell Manor   82%   £113

Tel 0233 635751   Fax 0233 635530   **HR**

Eastwell Park Boughton Aluph Ashford Kent TN25 4HR   Map 7 C5

It is difficult to believe that this splendid Jacobean-style mansion set in 62
acres of grounds was actually built in the 1920s. An open courtyard leads
through to public rooms that are every bit as impressive as the grand
exterior. Real fires burn in the large fireplaces of the stone-flagged entrance
hall and the mellow, oak panelled day rooms, some of which boast ceilings
with fine, detailed plasterwork and leather button-back armchairs. Spacious
bedrooms vary considerably but are traditionally furnished (usually
including an antique or two) and luxuriously appointed with large floral
print fabrics and many extras like magazines, fruit and mineral water. The
large bathrooms have bidets, bathrobes and quality toiletries. Queens Moat
Houses. *Rooms 23. Garden, croquet, tennis, snooker. Access, Amex, Visa,*
(1) Diners Club International

Restaurant   £102

A coffered ceiling, stone-mullioned windows and armed dining chairs all
contribute to a baronial feel here. Chef Mark Clayton is skilfully
producing varied and imaginative dishes for the two menus; one a short
table d'hote, the other rather longer with a minimum price of £32.50 for
the first two courses and the sweets priced à la carte. Grilled brill with
snow peas and olives, caramelised breast of duck with garlic polenta and
braised shallots, and fillet of beef topped with a cep mousse give the style.
No children under seven. **Seats 80.** Parties 65. Private Room. L 12.30-2
D 7-9.30 (Sat to 9.45). Set L £12.75/16.50 Set D £24.50.

♛

🏆

Ashford   Forte Posthouse   66%   £65

Tel 0233 625790   Fax 0233 643176   **H**

Canterbury Road Ashford Kent TN24 8QQ   Map 7 C5

Half a mile out of Ashford on the A28 to Canterbury. A modern hotel
based around a 17th-century barn, now the restaurant. Conferences for up
to 120 delegates. **Rooms 60.** Garden. Access, Amex, Visa, Diners Club International

---

Ashford   Holiday Inn Garden Court   65%   £70

Tel 0233 713333   Fax 0233 712082   **H**

Maidstone Road Hothfield Ashford Kent TN26 1AR   Map 7 C5

A no-frills Holiday Inn offering only limited services and public areas, but
good, spacious bedrooms with big beds and lightwood furniture. Good
value, with greatly reduced rates at weekends. **Rooms 104.** Keep-fit
equipment. Access, Amex, Visa, Diners Club International

Ashford   Travel Inn   £42

Tel 0223 712571   Fax 0223 713945   **L**

Maidstone Road (A20) Hothfield Ashford Kent TN26 1AP   Map 7 C5

30 minutes drive from both Dover and Folkestone Ferry Ports. **Rooms 40.**
Access, Amex, Visa, Diners Club International

Ashford   Places of Interest

Tourist Information Tel 0233 629165.
Godinton Park Tel 0233 620773.

Ashford-in-the-Water   Riverside Hotel   65%   £90

Tel 0629 814275   Fax 0629 812873   **H**

Fennel Street Ashford-in-the-Water Derbyshire DE4 1QF   Map 10 C2

The river in question is the Wye, which meanders past the Taylors'
Georgian hotel set in mature gardens near the centre of the village. There is
a certain old-fashioned charm to both the peaceful lounges (one of which
has wood panelling and garden views) and the bedrooms, which have
either four-poster or half-tester beds and soft furnishings hand-made by Sue
Taylor. Essentially a non-smoking hotel, although puffers may resort to the
bar or conservatory. A cottage on the bank of the river (some 200 yards
from the hotel) is let on a self-catering basis. **Rooms 15.** Garden,
croquet. Access, Amex, Visa.

Ashford-in-the-Water   Places of Interest

Buxton Tourist Information   Tel 0298 25106.
Buxton Opera House   Water Street Tel 0298 71382.
Buxton Museum and Art Gallery   Terrace Road Tel 0298 24658.

Ashington   Mill House Inn   £74
Tel 0903 892426   Fax 0903 892855   I

Mill Lane Ashington West Sussex RH20 3BZ   Map 5 E3

Comfortable, friendly and homely, this 300-year-old cottagey inn is clearly
signposted on the northbound carriage of the A24 (it's less easy to find
from the London side). Low ceilings and uneven floors characterise day
rooms and bedrooms, the latter quite well equipped but simply decorated
and generally on the small side. There are two four-poster rooms. *Rooms
10. Garden. Access, Amex, Visa,* (①) *Diners Club International*

Ashington   The Willows   £55
Tel 0903 892575   R

London Road Ashington West Sussex RH20 3JR   Map 7 A6

Set back from the A24, this 15th-century farmhouse retains an inglenook
fireplace and old black beams. Carl Illes's three-course, fixed-price menu
offers a good choice of dishes with traditional silver service of vegetables –
no tiny side plates here. Dishes range from the simple (cream of leek and
potato soup) to the more adventurous (squid with lemon grass, fresh
coriander and winter salad leaves tossed in chili and lime dressing), and
portions are invariably generous. Chocaholics should be well satisfied by
Willows truffle torte, baked white chocolate cheesecake or chocolate and
rum mousse. Vegetarians should notify their requirements in advance.
*Seats 26. Parties 30. L 12.30-2 D 7-10. Closed L Sat, D Sun, all Mon. Set L
£15.25 Set D £17.45. Access, Amex, Visa.*

Aspley Guise   Moore Place   70%   £75
Tel 0908 282000   Fax 0908 281888   H

The Square Aspley Guise Nr Woburn Bedfordshire MK17 8DW   Map 5 E1

Junction 13 of the M1 is just one-and-a-half miles away, but this finely
restored Georgian country house, built in 1786, stands in a peaceful village
square. Day rooms echo the image of a squire's residence in a rural idyll
and are decorated in handsome period style with some original features
remaining. Extra room has been gained by the addition of a
sympathetically designed bedroom courtyard block, joined to the original
house by a spacious glassed-in area containing the reception and lounge
seating. Airy bedrooms all have lightwood furnishings. *Rooms 54. Garden,
games room. Access, Amex, Visa,* (①) *Diners Club International*

Aston Clinton   Bell Inn   78%   £176
Tel 0296 630252   Fax 0296 631250   HR

London Road Aston Clinton Buckinghamshire HP22 5HP   Map 5 E2

Family owners generate a unique blend of homely charm and serious
professionalism in their 17th-century coaching inn on the A41. An
appealing mix of log-burning fire, fresh flowers and pine panelling sets the
scene in the public rooms, where the mark of time and history is firmly
stamped. The flagstoned smoking room with its brass ornaments and
sporting pictures, and the elegant dining room are particularly notable.
Bedrooms in the main house and those around a cobbled courtyard with a
fountain are individually decorated with co-ordinated fabrics and antique
pieces; some open directly on to the garden. Useful extras range from
fluffy towelling robes and toiletries to a mini-bar. Enjoyable breakfasts.
Large conference (up to 250) and banqueting (up to 300) facilities.
Rooms 21. Garden, croquet. Access, Amex, Visa

Restaurant ★ ↑ £95

New chef David Cavalier is building on the Bell's well-earned reputation for fine food, fostered over many years by owner, and food enthusiast, Michael Harris. Various menus include dishes both fashionable – red mullet with olives and basil, tortellini langoustine – and familiar – terrine of foie gras, tarte tatin – plus more recherché offerings such as 'tete de porc' Joël Robuchon and pigeon 'en vessie' (cooked inside a pig's bladder, but don't be put off, it's a splendid dish), all prepared with equal skill and flair. Sauces, like that with a nage of shellfish and savoy cabbage, are a triumph of balance and controlled complexity. One menu is based around a traditional Aylesbury duck expertly carved at the table. To finish try the 'Miniatures', a plated selection of mini-desserts, or a sampling from the newly introduced, and most impressive trolley of cheeses from around the British Isles. An extensive wine list, especially strong on burgandies, spans the world. *Seats 120. Private Room. L 12.30-2 D 7.30-9.45 (Sun to 8.45). Set meals from £17.35.*

Aston Clinton   Places of Interest

Zoological Museum, British Museum (Natural History)   Akeman Street, Tring Tel 044 282 4181 *3 miles.*

Axbridge   Oak House £55

Tel 0934 732444   Fax 0934 733112

I

The Square Axbridge Somerset BS26 2AP   Map 4 A3

In the centre of a medieval town 1½ miles from Cheddar, the Oak House has a long tradition of hospitality. Inside, there's a cosy, welcoming feel, particularly in the bar-lounge with its stone walls, beams and open fire, and in the bedrooms, some of which are in an annexe 50 yards from the main building. *Rooms 11. Access, Amex, Visa,*

Axbridge   Places of Interest

Tourist Information   Tel 0934 744071.
Cheddar Showcaves Museum and Exhibition   Tel 0934 742343.
MillfieldSchoolPoloClub   GunthorpeFarm,ChapelAllertonTel045842291.

Aylesbury   Forte Crest   69% £87

Tel 0296 393388   Fax 0296 392211

H

Aston Clinton Road Aylesbury Buckinghamshire HP22 5AA   Map 5 D2

A purpose-built modern hotel constructed around a central courtyard, alongside the A41 three miles east of the town centre. Public areas are open plan and very smart. The tile-floored foyer leads to spacious lounges, furnished in contemporary fashion and making good use of attractive, colourful fabrics. Bedrooms are of a fair size and decorated in restful shades, with solid furniture and fully tiled bathrooms. Banqueting facilities for 80, conferences up to 100. *Rooms 94. Indoor swimming pool, gymnasium, sauna. Access, Amex, Visa,*

Aylesbury   Hartwell House   86% £168

Tel 0296 747444   Fax 0296 747450

HR

Oxford Road Aylesbury Buckinghamshire HP17 8NL   Map 5 D2

80 acres of parkland surround this magnificent country house, once the home in exile of Louis XVIII of France. Dating back to the 16th century, it's notable for having two facades, one Jacobean and the other Georgian. Beautifully restored to its former glory by Historic House Hotels, it's the epitome of luxury. Day rooms have many notable features like rococo ceilings, choice antiques, oil paintings and chandeliers. Wonderful plump-cushioned seating spreads through the grandly proportioned reception rooms. Bedrooms show high standards of luxury and comfort; sumptuously appointed in impressive fashion, they employ antiques, rich fabrics and a host of pampering extras, plus huge beds. Bright, neatly fitted bathrooms. Motivated staff provide high levels of service. 100 yards from

the main house is the newly-built Hartwell Spa, modelled on an orangery inspired by Sir John Soane and incorporating fine leisure facilities – the grand 50-foot swimming pool is surrounded by an arched arcade and overlooked by a gallery where you will find the Spa Bar and Buttery. The new Hartwell function rooms are situated in a restored 18th-century coach house and can accommodate up to 100 delegates; the rooms are named after distinguished architects who have contributed to the evolution of Hartwell House – James Gibbs, James Wyatt, Henry Keene and Eric Throssell. There are also interesting rooms in the main house for private board meetings or dining. In addition to the new leisure and meeting facilities Hartwell Court houses 16 new bedrooms and suites. No children under 8. Dogs are not allowed in the grounds, but good kennels are nearby. *Rooms 48. Garden, indoor swimming pool, spa bath, steam room, sauna, gymnasium, beauty salon, solarium, Spa Café (7.30am-11pm, Sun 9am-10.30pm), fishing, croquet. Access, Amex, Visa,* 🔵 Diners Club International

Restaurant   £100

2- or 3-course, fixed-price luncheons offer particularly good value and choice, and might include a salmon and saffron paté with anchovy dressing or cream of leek and potato soup, followed by a choice of three meat and a fish dish and classic puddings. The long wine list has obviously been chosen with care and includes a good choice of half bottles and house wines at reasonable prices, plus a selection of rare Vouvrays and Australian liqueur muscat dessert wines. *Seats 70. Parties 8. Private Room. L 12.30-2 D 7.30-9.45. Set L £16.50 Set D £40.*

Aylesbury   Places of Interest

Tourist Information   Tel 0296 382308.
Limelight Theatre   Queen's Park Centre, Queen's Park. Tel 0296 431272.
Buckinghamshire County Museum   Tel 0296 88849.
Weedon Park Showground   Tel 0296 83734.
  Historic Houses, Castles and Gardens
Claydon House   Nr Winslow Tel 0296 730349.
Waddesdon Manor (NT)   Waddesdon Tel 0296 651211/651282.

Bagshot   Pennyhill Park   75%   £134
Tel 0276 71774   Fax 0276 73217   **H**

London Road Bagshot Surrey GU19 5ET   Map 5 E3

A driveway leads from the A30 to this well-equipped hotel and country club, where professional tuition is available in a number of sporting activities. Notable architectural features of the 19th-century house include the baronial-style foyer-lounge with stained-glass windows, exposed stone walls and slate floor, and the lounge, on two levels, with a beamed gallery upstairs and panelling downstairs. Bedrooms in the main building are spacious and charming, and those around the redeveloped courtyard vary from cosy and intimate to elegant mini-suites; all are named after flowers or shrubs, except for the luxurious Hayward suite. Children up to ten stay free in parents' room. *Rooms 76. Garden, outdoor swimming pool, sauna, solarium, tennis, 9-hole golf course, riding, stabling, fishing, clay-pigeon shooting. Access, Amex, Visa,* 🔵 Diners Club International

Bainbridge   Rose & Crown Inn   £68
Tel 0969 50225   Fax 0969 50735   **I**

Bainbridge Wensleydale North Yorkshire DL8 3EE   Map 15 B6

Overlooking the green in an attractive Wensleydale village, the Rose & Crown has a history going back to the 15th century. The famous Forest Horn, once used to guide lost travellers and still blown on winter evenings, hangs in the panelled hall. Elsewhere, old-world character is most notable in the low-beamed bar. Floral fabrics give the bedrooms a cottagey look; several rooms have four-poster beds. *Rooms 12. Garden. Access, Visa.*

Bakewell   Hassop Hall   74%   £93

Tel 0629 640488   Fax 0629 640577   **H**

Hassop Nr Bakewell Derbyshire DE4 1NS   Map 10 C2

The ancient seat of the Eyre family stands among trees and parkland at the heart of the Peak District National Park. Privately owned and run, it provides space, comfort and more than a little style: beyond the marbled hallway with its antiques and oil paintings is a chandeliered lounge in Regency style, a drawing room, a room for non-smokers and a relaxing oak-panelled bar. The large, luxurious bedrooms are individually decorated and furnished, with embroidered bed linen and splendidly appointed bathrooms. No dogs. *Rooms 13. Garden, tennis, croquet, helipad. Closed 3 days Xmas. Access, Amex, Visa,*

Bakewell   Places of Interest

Tourist Information   Tel 0629 813227.
Chatsworth House   Tel 0246 582204.
Haddon Hall   Tel 0629 812855.

Baldock   Forte Travelodge   £40

Tel 0462 835329   **L**

A1 Great North Road Hinxworth Nr Baldock Hertfordshire SG7 5EX   Map 5 E1

Southbound on the A1 in Hertfordshire, north of Baldock. Conveniently located for Bedford and Stevenage. *Rooms 40. Access, Amex, Visa.*

Bamburgh   Lord Crewe Arms   58%   £62

Tel 066 84 243   **H**

Front Street Bamburgh Northumberland NE69 7BL   Map 14 B2

Virtually in the shadow of Bamburgh Castle, the Lord Crewe has been owned and run by the Holland family for well over 20 years. This is splendid walking country so the choice of bars and lounges (one reserved for non-smokers) is most welcome for casual callers; one of the two restaurants is open all day in summer. Well-kept bedrooms offer modest comfort; they mostly have laminate-topped fitted furniture and TVs, but there are no radios or phones. Five rooms do not have en-suite facilities. No children under five. *Rooms 25. Closed Nov-Mar. Access, Visa.*

Bamburgh   Places of Interest

Bamburgh Castle   Tel 066 84 208.
Grace Darling Museum   Tel 0665 720037.
Bamburgh Beach

Banbury   Moat House   62%   £79

Tel 0295 259361   Fax 0295 270954   **H**

27-29 Oxford Road Banbury Oxfordshire OX16 9AH   Map 5 D1

A handsome Georgian house offering modern comforts. Star of the accommodation is the Blenheim Suite with a four-poster bed and whirlpool bath. Functions (up to 80) and conferences (to 100) are a speciality. *Rooms 48. Closed 26-31 Dec. Access, Amex, Visa,*

Banbury   Whately Hall   65%   £100

Tel 0295 263451   Fax 0295 271736   **H**

Banbury Cross Banbury Oxfordshire OX16 0AN   Map 5 D1

Dating from 1632, Whately Hall stands in gardens opposite Banbury Cross of nursery rhyme fame. Fine panelling, mullion windows and antiques give character to the day rooms. Bedrooms, some in a modern wing, all have well-lit, tiled bathrooms. Forte Heritage. *Rooms 74. Garden, croquet, coffee shop (9am-5pm). Access, Amex, Visa,*

Banbury   Places of Interest

Banbury Museum   Tel 0295 259855.
Open Air Pool   Tel 0295 62742.
Broughton Castle   Tel 0295 262624.
Farnborough Hall   Tel 0295 89202.
Upton House (NT)   Edgehill Tel 0295 87266.

Barford   Glebe Hotel   68%   £100

Tel 0926 624218 Fax 0926 624625	H

Church Street Barford Warwickshire CV35 8BS   Map 10 C4

The rectory to the Church of St Peter was converted for hotel use in 1948.
Today, though less than a mile from the M40/A46 junction, it claims to be
Warwickshire's best-kept secret. Extensions over the last five years have
added a spacious conservatory restaurant, the Glades leisure club and
conference facilities for up to 140. Bedrooms, individually decorated in soft
pastel shades, feature four-poster or crown canopy beds, and the bathrooms
are finished in gold plate with Italian marble floors. Children up to 12 stay
free in parents' room. *Rooms 36. Garden, croquet, indoor swimming pool,
keep-fit equipment, spa bath, sauna, steam room. Access, Amex, Visa,* **()** Diners Club International

Barnard Castle   Jersey Farm Hotel   59%   £52

Tel 0833 38223 Fax 0833 31988	H

Darlington Road Barnard Castle Co Durham DL12 8TA   Map 15 B5

A working farm surrounds this informal and friendly little hotel, which
current owners the Watsons started as a bed and breakfast place in 1965.
Public areas are homely and unfussy and the bedrooms, in the old
farmhouse and in extensions, are modest but comfortable, with
freestanding furniture and carpeted bathrooms. Superior rooms are larger,
with more extras, and there are six suites. A new conference centre can
cater for banquets up to 200 and conferences up to 150. *Rooms 22. Garden.
Access, Visa.*

Barnard Castle   Places of Interest

Historic Houses, Castles and Gardens
Barnard Castle   Tel 0833 38212.
Bowes Museum Gardens   Tel 0833 690606.
Raby Castle   Staindrop Tel 0833 38212.

Barnby Moor   Ye Olde Bell   60%   £90

Tel 0777 705121 Fax 0777 860424	H

Barnby Moor Nr Retford Nottinghamshire DN22 8QS   Map 11 D2

On the edge of Sherwood Forest, just a mile from the A1, Ye Olde Bell has
been offering hospitality to travellers for hundreds of years. Old oak
panelling, open fireplaces and diamond-pane leaded lights retain the
character of the public rooms while bedrooms offer modern amenities like
direct-dial phones and hairdryers. Conferences for up to 250 delegates.
Principal Hotels. *Rooms 55. Garden. Access, Amex, Visa,* **()** Diners Club International

Barnham Broom   Barnham Broom Hotel   62%   £80

Tel 060 545 393 Fax 060 545 8224	H

Honingham Road Barnham Broom Nr Norwich Norfolk NR9 3DD   Map 6 C1

A large modern complex comprising hotel, golf and country club and
conference centre (up to 200 delegates). All the bedrooms have writing
desks and other extras include radios in the bathrooms. *Rooms 52. Two
championship golf courses, indoor swimming pool, sauna, steam room, solarium,
spa bath, tennis, squash, snooker, hairdressing, beauty salon, coffee shop
(9.30am-11.30pm). Access, Amex, Visa,* **()** Diners Club International

Barnsley	Ardsley Moat House	65%	£90

H

Tel 0226 289401   Fax 0226 205374

Doncaster Road Ardsley Barnsley South Yorkshire S71 5EH   Map 10 C2

Mellow stone, late 18th-century mansion with modern extensions, housing
a good variety of conference and function rooms holding 14 to 300. 30
bedrooms will be designated non-smoking for 1993. *Rooms 73. Garden,
dinner dance (Fri). Access, Amex, Visa,* Diners Club International

Barnsley	Armstrong's		£50

R

Tel 0226 240113

6 Shambles Street Barnsley South Yorkshire S70 2SQ   Map 10 C2

A bright, informal café-bar opposite the town hall, serving an interesting
selection of dishes with a variety of influences: broad bean and ham soup;
red mullet fillets with ginger, coriander, olive oil and chili; roast duck
with apple purée and sherry vinegar sauce; noisettes of spring lamb
wrapped in bacon and sage with white wine; lemon curd with a compote
of citrus fruits. Lunch sees a choice of additional lighter dishes: perhaps
salmon and cod fishcakes with cream dill sauce or chicken and almond
risotto. *Seats 60. Parties 60. Private Room. L 12-2 D 7-10. Closed L Sat, all
Sun & Mon, Bank Holidays. Set D £12.95. Access, Visa.*

Barnsley	Forte Travelodge		£40

L

Tel 0226 298799

A633/635 Stairfoot Roundabout Barnsley South Yorkshire   Map 10 C2

At the roundabout of A633 and A635, close to the centre of Barnsley.
Both Sheffield and Wakefield are in easy reach. *Rooms 32. Access, Amex,
Visa.*

Barnsley	Restaurant Peano		£55

R

Tel 0226 244990

102 Dodworth Road Barnsley South Yorkshire S70 6HL   Map 10 C2

Robust, earthy cooking with no gimmicks is the signature of chef/patron
Michael Peano at his sturdy Victorian house close to junction 37 of the
M1. Creamy mussel soup and home-made gnocchi with ricotta cheese and
spinach on tomato sauce both produce good, honest flavours; the choice of
main dishes might include something as unsual as *waterzooi*, a traditional
Belgian casserole of chicken and seafood; brill, lemon sole, and monkfish
might appear among the choice of four main course dishes on a separate
daily fresh fish menu. Desserts are always interesting – mixed rhubarb
offerings, panna cotta, raspberry soufflé. Tracey Peano deftly supervises the
service; meticulous attention to detail includes a board of English
farmhouse cheeses and a short, carefully chosen wine list with a strong
Italian representation. *Seats 45. Parties 50. Private Room. L 12-2 D 7-9.30.
Closed L Mon, all Sun, 2 weeks Sep. Set L £11 Set D £9. Access, Amex,
Visa.*

Barnsley   Places of Interest

Cannon Hall   Cawthorne Tel 0226 790270.
Wentworth Castle   Stainborough Tel 0226 285426.
Oakwell Football Ground   Tel 0226 295353.

Barnstaple   Imperial Hotel   60%   £81

Tel 0271 45861   Fax 0271 24448   **H**

Taw Vale Parade Barnstaple Devon EX32 8NB   Map 3 D2

A solid Edwardian building overlooking the river Taw. Meeting rooms for up to 80 people. Forte. *Rooms 56. Access, Amex, Visa,* ⦿ *Diners Club International*

Barnstaple   Lynwood House   £61

Tel 0271 43695   Fax 0271 79340   **RR**

Bishop's Tawton Road Barnstaple Devon EX32 9DZ   Map 3 D2

An elegant and spacious restaurant with rooms. Ruth Roberts and her son Matthew cook in classical style. Seafood is the main speciality, with dishes like mussels in wine, garlic and parsley, chunky fish soup, poached skate wing, fresh scallops, pot of seafood and goujonettes of turbot. A couple of meat options might include grilled sirloin steak or pheasant sautéed with bacon, mushrooms, onions and red wine; also salads and a choice of vegetarian dishes. Chocaholics should leave room for the rich chocolate cup filled with white chocolate and Poire William liqueur on a dark chocolate sauce; alcoholics should be equally pleased with the vodka sorbet. Light 2- and 3-course business lunches are served Monday to Friday; there is also a long menu of lighter dishes. No smoking. *Seats 40.* Parties 80. Private Room. *L 12-2 D 7-10. Closed Sun. Access, Visa.*

Rooms   £68

Overnight guests are accommodated in five Executive bedrooms, all with armchairs and plenty of creature comforts. Separate breakfast room. No dogs. *Rooms 5.*

Barnstaple   Places of Interest

Tourist Information   Tel 0271 47177.
Arlington Court (NT)   Tel 0271 850296.
Marwood Hill   Marwood Tel 0271 42528.
Museum of North Devon incorporating **Royal Devon Yeomanry Museum**
  Tel 0271 46747.
Exmoor Bird Gardens   South Stowford Tel 05983 352/412.

Barton Mills   Forte Travelodge   £40

Tel 0638 717675   **L**

A11 Barton Mills Mildenhall Suffolk IP28 6AE   Map 6 B2

On the A11, at the 5 ways roundabout, 8 miles north-east of Newmarket. Close to Bury St Edmunds. *Rooms 32. Access, Amex, Visa.*

Barton Stacey   Forte Travelodge   £40

Tel 0264 72260   **L**

A303 Barton Stacey Nr Andover Hampshire SO21 3NP   Map 5 D3

On the A303 westbound – approximately 4 miles east of Andover. Close to Basingstoke with Newbury and Southampton within easy reach. *Rooms 20. Access, Amex, Visa.*

Barton-under-Needwood — Forte Travelodge — £40

L

Tel 0283 716784

A38 Barton-under-Needwood Burton-on-Trent Staffordshire DE13 3EH — Map 10 C3

On the A38 southbound, 3 miles to the south of Burton-on-Trent. *Rooms 40. Access, Amex, Visa.*

Barton-under-Needwood — Forte Travelodge — £40

L

Tel 0283 716343

A38 Barton-under-Needwood Burton-on-Trent Staffordshire DE13 8EG — Map 10 C3

On the A38 northbound, 4 miles south of Burton-on-Trent. *Rooms 20. Access, Amex, Visa.*

Basildon — Campanile Hotel — £36

L

Tel 0268 530810   Fax 0268 286710

Southend Arterial Road Pipps Hill Basildon Essex SS14 3AE — Map 7 B4

Take M25 junction 29, then Basildon exit from A127. *Rooms 98. Access, Amex, Visa,* Diners Club International

Basildon — Forte Crest — 59% — £97

H

Tel 0268 533955   Fax 0268 530119

Cranes Farm Road Basildon Essex SS14 3DG — Map 7 B4

Modern exterior, bright and pleasant accommodation, plus lake views from the conservatory-style bar. Banqueting facilities for up to 250, conferences to 300. *Rooms 110. Access, Amex, Visa,* Diners Club International

Basildon — Travel Inn — £42

L

Tel 0268 522227   Fax 0268 530092

Felmores East Mayne Basildon Essex SS13 1BW — Map 7 B4

Just off the M25 (J29), Southend 20 minutes drive. *Rooms 42. Access, Amex, Visa,* Diners Club International

Basildon — Places of Interest

Towngate Theatre   Pagel Mead Tel 0268 531343.

Basingstoke — Audleys Wood — 75% — £123

HR

Tel 0256 817555   Fax 0256 817500

Alton Road Basingstoke Hampshire RG25 2JT — Map 5 D3

Alongside the A339 Alton road, close to junction 6 of the M3. Built in the late 1880s and set in seven wooded acres, the house had a varied history before being transformed into a hotel of some luxury (it opened in 1989). A splendid carved oak fireplace graces the panelled lounge, which also features a minstrel's gallery. Similar panelling and a handsome fireplace are to be found in the bar. The majority of the bedrooms are in extensions: roomy and tastefully appointed, with marble-tiled bathrooms. Main-house bedrooms are even larger and more luxurious. Friendly staff. Mount Charlotte Thistle. *Rooms 71. Garden, croquet, pétanque, putting, golf practice net, bicycles. Access, Amex, Visa,* Diners Club International

Restaurant — £66

Situated in what was the original palm house and conservatory, the striking restaurant has an unusual vaulted wood ceiling. Terence Greenhouse, once Executive Head Chef on the *QE2*, is at the helm, and his menus continue to develop. Lunch is a 2- or 3-course fixed-price affair, although a two-course business lunch is also served, but from a trolley. Both table d'hote and à la carte menus are offered at dinner, with daily specials (perhaps supreme of maize-fed chicken with mushroom and roast walnut stuffing and a saffron sauce) and a small selection of interesting

vegetarian dishes in addition to grander dishes. Good cheeses, both French
and English, served with walnut bread, chilled grapes and celery. *Seats 74.
Parties 40. Private Room. L 12-1.45 (Sun to 2.15) D 7-9.45 (Fri & Sat to
10.15, Sun to 9.15). Closed L Sat, Bank Holidays. Set L £13.50 &
£14.95/£17.95 Set D from £20.*

Basingstoke   Forte Posthouse   64%   £63
Tel 0256 468181   Fax 0256 840081   **H**

Grove Road Basingstoke Hampshire RG21 3EE   Map 5 D3

Leave the M3 at junction 6 and follow signs for Alton on the A339.
Conference and banqueting facilities for up to 180 delegates. Children's
playroom and playground. *Rooms 84. Snooker. Access, Amex, Visa,*
Diners Club International

Basingstoke   Forte Travelodge   £40
Tel 0256 843566   **L**

Winchester Road Basingstoke Hampshire RG22 6HN   Map 5 D3

Next to the Stag & Hounds Harvester restaurant, close to Basingstoke
town centre. Less than 2 miles from junction 7 on the M3, off the A30
southbound, at the Brighton Hill roundabout, within easy access of
Reading and Newbury. *Rooms 32. Access, Amex, Visa.*

Basingstoke   Hee's   £40
Tel 0256 464410   **R**

23 Westminster House Basingstoke Hampshire RG21 1CS   Map 5 D3

Decent MSG-free Szechuan and Peking cooking on the edge of
Basingstoke's huge central shopping centre. Cheerful staff provide attentive
service. *Seats 80. Parties 85. L 12-2 D 6-11. Closed L Sun, 4 days Xmas. Set
meals from £12. Access, Amex, Visa,* Diners Club International

Basingstoke   Hilton Lodge   66%   £116
Tel 0256 460460   Fax 0256 840441   **H**

Old Common Road Black Dam Basingstoke Hampshire RG21 3PR   Map 5 D3

Bright, open-plan public areas, neat accommodation and numerous meeting
rooms (conferences for up to 160) at a modern hotel near junction 6 of the
M3. *Rooms 144. Indoor swimming pool, keep-fit equipment, sauna, assault
course. Access, Amex, Visa,* Diners Club International

Basingstoke   Hilton National   65%   £121
Tel 0256 20212   Fax 0256 842835   **H**

**Aldermaston Roundabout Ringway North Basingstoke Hampshire
RG24 9NV**   Map 5 D3

Modern hotel with bedrooms ranging from small singles to roomy, well-
appointed suites. Regular dinner dances. *Rooms 134. Indoor swimming pool,
keep-fit equipment, sauna. Access, Amex, Visa,* Diners Club International

Basingstoke   Travel Inn   £42

Tel 0256 811477   Fax 0256 819329   **L**

Worting Road Basingstoke Hampshire RG22 6PG   Map 5 D3

Situated in the centre of a leisure park, 40 minutes drive from Winchester Cathedral. **Rooms 49.** *Access, Amex, Visa,* 🅾 *Diners Club International*

Basingstoke   Places of Interest

Tourist Information   Tel 0256 817618.
The Vyne (NT)   Sherborne St. John Tel 0256 881337.
Basingstoke Ice Rink   Tel 0256 840219.

Baslow   Cavendish Hotel   70%   £106

Tel 0246 582311   Fax 0246 582312   **H**

Baslow Derbyshire DE4 1SP   Map 10 C2

The former *Peacock*, an inn for over 200 years, is set on the Chatsworth Estate, just off the A619, overlooking the rivers Derwent and Wye. Ten miles of fly-fishing are available to guests. Antique furniture, quality fabrics and a unique collection of Victorian fine art contribute an elegant and refined feel, the tile-floored foyer leading to sumptuous lounges and an airy conservatory. Recently remodelled bedrooms have, by their very nature, more limited space, though useful appointments include refrigerated bars and cosseting bathrobes. Breakfast is served all morning in the relaxed atmosphere of the Garden Room (open 11am-11pm). No dogs. **Rooms 24.** *Garden, putting, fishing. Access, Amex, Visa,* 🅾 *Diners Club International*

Baslow   Fischer's Baslow Hall   ★   £80

Tel 0246 583259   **RR**

Calver Road Baslow Derbyshire DE4 1RR   Map 10 C2

Approached by a curving, tree-lined drive, Baslow Hall is an impressive house dating from 1907, although it looks considerably older. A Chinese-inspired lounge and three separate dining rooms form an appealing and elegant restaurant, wherein one can enjoy Max Fischer's consistently rewarding cooking. Though not averse to using fashionable ingredients, he sticks to what what he knows best, producing precisely cooked, strong-flavoured dishes based on traditional methods. Fresh scallops in ravioli are served with sweet and sour aubergine, pan-fried calf's kidneys are accompanied by watercress and parsley mousses, while main-course dishes stick to more classic combinations: salmon in sorrel sauce, Dover sole fillets in chive sauce, calf's liver in cassis, fillet of beef with wild mushrooms and rack of lamb provençale. Menus are hand-written in English and descriptions kept to a minimum: "seafood minestrone" is as good, if not better, than many bombastically-described "nage" creations offered in grander establishments. The choice of desserts is often small, but might range from chocolate marquise to fresh strawberry millefeuille or caramel soufflé and ice cream, thus pleasing most tastes. Sunday lunch, when a choice of roasts is offered along with some five starters and desserts, is always popular. Simpler dishes are served from 10am in *Café Max* (a new venture), a room off the entrance hall. *Seats 35. Parties 40. Private Room. L 12-2 (Sun to 2.30) D 7-9.30 (Sat to 10). Closed L Mon, D Sun (except residents), 25 & 26 Dec. Set L £18.50 Set D £31.50. Access, Amex, Visa.*

Rooms   £95

Six appealing bedrooms (three large, three small) show great style and taste with choice antique pine furniture. En-suite bathrooms are neatly up-to-date, although one has an original enamel bath and shower.

Bassenthwaite   Armathwaite Hall   65%   £100

Tel 076 87 76551   Fax 076 87 76220   **H**

Bassenthwaite Lake Nr Keswick Cumbria CA12 4RE   Map 13 C5

The setting of this historic stately home is quiet and secluded, with woodland, parks and lake foreshore. Inside, the baronial feel is nurtured by oak panelling and ceilings, hunting trophies, oil paintings and pewterware. Best bedrooms in the main house have fine views and plenty of space, while rooms in the coach house/stable block are also spacious. A further bedroom wing is on line for 1993. An equestrian centre is nearby and offers carriage driving tuition among its facilities. Families are well catered for, with accommodation free for under-14s when sharing parents' room. A choice of conference rooms caters for up to 120. *Rooms 42. Garden, tennis, croquet, indoor swimming pool, gymnasium, sauna, solarium, riding, games room, spa bath, beauty salon, hairdressing, 9-hole pitch & putt, coarse and game fishing, mountain bikes, coffee shop (10am-10pm). Access, Amex, Visa,* Diners Club International

Bassenthwaite Lake   Pheasant Inn   65%   £88

Tel 076 87 76234   Fax 076 87 76002   **H**

Bassenthwaite Lake Nr Cockermouth Cumbria CA13 9YE   Map 13 C5

An archetypal Victorian roadside inn (although mercifully by-passed these days by the A66), which retains its abundant period appeal: open fires, beams hung with brasses, old prints and antique firearms. Well-kept gardens are an added summer attraction and are overlooked by tastefully furnished bedrooms in varying styles. Adequate, simply fitted bathrooms are the only obvious nod to modernity. No phones, TVs or dogs in bedrooms; no piped music or fruit machines in the public rooms – just the pervading lakeland peace and quiet. *Rooms 20. Closed 25 Dec. No credit cards.*

Bath   Apsley House   67%   £80

Tel 0225 336966   Fax 0225 425462   **H**

141 Newbridge Hill Bath Avon BA1 3PT   Map 4 B3

A mile west of the city centre on the A431, Apsley House is a handsome William IV mansion standing in well-kept gardens which augment the hotel's abundant peace and quiet. Seven en-suite bedrooms in the main house (adults only) are well-proportioned and roomy, with reproduction furniture and individual colour schemes. Three doubles and two singles with shared bathrooms in the adjacent coach house are more specifically reserved for families at much reduced rates. *Rooms 12. Garden. Access, Amex, Visa,* Diners Club International

Bath   Bath Spa Hotel   87%   £171

Tel 0225 444424   Fax 0225 444006   **HR**

Sydney Road Bath Avon BA2 6JF   Map 4 B3

The jewel in Forte's hotel crown is a converted 1830s' mansion standing in landscaped gardens with panoramic views over the city. Behind the elegant porticoed frontage is a good deal of style and luxury, from the entrance lobby with its elaborate plasterwork ceiling and fine carpets to the murals in the neo-classical Colonnade. Bedrooms, including seven suites, are beautifully decorated and furnished, with magnificent bathrooms. Guests enjoy very high standards of service and have free membership of the health and leisure spa. Extensive business facilities and theatre-style conferences for up to 120 delegates. Forte Grand. *Rooms 100. Garden, croquet, tennis, gymnasium, indoor swimming pool, spa bath, sauna, solarium, beauty salon, valeting, coffee shop (7am-6pm). Access, Amex, Visa,* Diners Club International

Restaurant   £85

Alec Howard's cooking finds a splendid setting in what was originally the ballroom. Fixed-price menus offer a choice of lighter or grander dishes,   ♕

each with the stamp of seasonal freshness and careful preparation: watercress soup with lime, marinated red mullet and vegetables with olive oil, grilled Dover sole, glazed Gressingham duck with apple and cider confit, pot-roast rump of veal with spinach and shiitake mushrooms. An alternative luncheon menu, served in the Colonnade, tempts with simpler offerings like baked goat's cheese and tomato tart, noodles with pesto and salami or rump steak with chips. Desserts are not to be missed, whether a homespun favourite like spotted dick or something more intriguing such as "crysalis" of apple with vanilla mousse and green apple sorbet. Sunday lunches offer a good choice that might start with chicken liver parfait with fig relish and toasted brioche followed by spinach- and pepper-filled saddle of lamb with a thyme jus, ending with bread-and-butter pudding with clotted cream. The wine list has a little of everything, with kind prices among the bin ends. Commendable wines by the glass. **Seats 100.** *Parties 150. Private Room. L 12-2.30 D 7-10 (Sat to 10.30). Set L £18.50 (Sun) Set D £32 & £42.*

Bath	Bath Hotel	66%	£100

Tel 0225 338855   Fax 0225 28941   **H**

Widcombe Basin Bath Avon BA2 4JP   **Map 4 B3**

Mainly business hotel by the Widcombe Basin: ramped entrances, spacious reception and airy day rooms. Limited but practical accommodation for families. **Rooms 93.** *Access, Amex, Visa,* Diners Club International

---

Bath	Circus Restaurant	£74

Tel 0225 330208   **R**

34 Brock Street Bath Avon BA1 2LN   **Map 4 B3**

Quality without fuss and formality remains the aim of this popular restaurant near the Royal Crescent. Two or three-course lunches with dishes like feuilleté of asparagus and mushrooms with a citrus butter sauce or brochette of chicken and smoked bacon are almost café style, while extended evening hours and menus encourage more leisurely dining over, perhaps, foie gras terrine, panaché of seafood *en papillote* and steamed lemon pudding with cream. **Seats 50.** *Parties 40. Private Room. L 11.30-2.30 D 6.30-10 (Sat to 11.30). Closed Sun & Mon, 25 & 26 Dec, 1 Jan, Easter Monday. Set L £8.75/£9.50. Access, Visa.*

Bath	Combe Grove Manor	71%	£126

Tel 0225 834644   Fax 0225 834961   **H**

Brassknocker Hill Monkton Combe Nr Bath Avon BA2 7HS   **Map 4 B3**

An elegant country mansion standing in 68 acres of landscaped woods and gardens, Combe Grove enjoys spectacular views across the Limpley Stoke valley, yet is just two miles from the city centre. Fine antiques and elegant fabrics are eye-catching features of sympathetically restored day rooms with bold floral patterns and hand-painted bathroom tiles lending some splendour to the manor house bedrooms. Housing the remaining rooms in no less spacious comfort, the newer Garden Lodge is adjacent to impressive leisure facilities where a crèche operates at weekends and public holidays. An all-day coffee shop derives character from its location in the manor vaults. No dogs. **Rooms 41.** *Garden, golf driving range, mini-golf, tennis, indoor & outdoor swimming pools, gymnasium, squash, spa bath, sauna, solarium, beautician. Access, Amex, Visa,* Diners Club International

Bath　　　Fountain House

£120

PH

Tel 0225 338622　Fax 0225 445855

9 Fountain Buildings Lansdown Road Bath Avon BA1 5DV

Map 4 B3

A Palladian mansion run since 1986 as an all-suite hotel catering for
families, tourists and business people. Each suite has a sitting room and a
fully-equipped kitchen, with individual front doors and entry phones to
ensure privacy. Room rates include continental breakfast (only), which
arrives each morning with the paper. Facilities offered include secretarial
services and lock-up garages. *Rooms 14. Access, Amex, Visa,*

Bath　　　Francis Hotel　　70%

£116

H

Tel 0225 324257　Fax 0225 319715

Queen Square Bath Avon BA1 2HH

Map 4 B3

A firmly traditional style of hotel, occupying a row of Bath-stone,
Georgian houses facing the gardens of Queen Square. Its interior is
complementary: the elegance of oil paintings, open fires and deep-
cushioned sofas in the lounge; the clubby atmosphere and red velvet decor
of the bar. Best, character bedrooms are also front-facing, with period
furniture, elegant fabrics and roomy bathrooms. Of a more functional
nature are those in a modern wing to the rear. No leisure facilties.
Conferences and banqueting facilities for up to 80. Children free in parents'
room up to the age of 14. Forte. *Rooms 94. Access, Amex, Visa,*

Bath　　　Garlands

£60

R

Tel 0225 442283

7 Edgar Buildings George Street Bath Avon BA1 2EE

Map 4 B3

Tom Bridgeman, chef, and Jo Bridgeman, front of house, own and run a
relaxed little restaurant that appeals to both tourists and a regular local
trade. French and English-inspired cuisine includes daily fish specials
(perhaps fillet of brill rolled with mousseline of crab and served with a
chive beurre blanc), and enjoyably different dishes like mosaic of guinea
fowl, pigeon and sweetbreads on an orange and Sauternes sauce or deep-
fried Cornish crab and sweet pepper pancake with watercress purée. Fixed-
price only lunches (2- or 3-course) and à la carte dinners. Diverse wine list
with interesting tasting notes. *Seats 28. Parties 14. L 12-2.15 D 7-10.30.
Closed L Mon, 25 & 26 Dec. Set L £11.75/£13.95. Access, Amex, Visa,*

Bath　　　Hilton National　　67%

£116

H

Tel 0225 463411　Fax 0225 464393

Walcot Street Bath Avon BA1 5BJ

Map 4 B3

Closest to shopping and sights, but limited forecourt parking. Spacious
public areas, business centre and leisure club; imposing new facade and
improved bedrooms. *Rooms 150. Indoor swimming pool, keep-fit equipment,
spa bath, sauna, solarium. Access, Amex, Visa,*

Bath　　　Lansdown Grove　　66%

£105

H

Tel 0225 315891　Fax 0225 448092

Lansdown Road Bath Avon BA1 5EH

Map 4 B3

High on a hill overlooking the city, the Lansdown offers an easy walk
down to the sights and shops, but a steep climb back. The grandly
proportioned drawing room has plenty of deep sofas to relax in while
admiring the view, and cheerful staff are always on hand for refreshments
or a drink from the popular bar. Bedrooms, predominantly with limed oak
furniture, are a bit of a sprawl; the best, with south-facing balconies, are in
the original main building. Children up to 16 stay free in parents' room.
Rooms 45. Garden. Access, Amex, Visa,

Bath   Newbridge House   63%   £95

Tel 0225 446676   Fax 0225 447541

35 Kelston Road Bath Avon BA1 3QH   Map 4 B3

A very private Georgian house in a spectacular location above the new
Bath Marina. Balconied, south-facing day rooms, including the Lord
Kirkwood boardroom (seating 12) overlook award-winning gardens, a
view shared by the best, period-style Victorian bedrooms. The smaller size
of rear twins and singles, with WC/shower only, is reflected in their price.
No bar, either, but the new Garden Room restaurant is in its infancy.
Children, pets and smokers are not welcomed. *Rooms 10. Garden. Access,
Amex, Visa,*

Bath   Priory Hotel   81%   £161

HR

Tel 0225 331922   Fax 0225 448276

Weston Road Bath Avon BA1 2XT   Map 4 B3

It's less than a mile from the city centre, but the setting is quiet and
beautiful, with two acres of fine gardens. Built in 1835 of Bath stone, the
house has an inviting, lived-in feel, due in no small measure to manager
Thomas Conboy and his loyal team. Fine antiques and portraits adorn the
lounges and orangery, which overlook the gardens, terrace and croquet
lawn. Bedrooms throughout meet the criterion of luxury, equally for their
individual decor of co-ordinated fabrics and period furniture, as for their
spacious bathrooms and immaculate standards of housekeeping. Most have
garden views. No dogs. *Rooms 21. Garden, outdoor swimming pool, croquet.
Access, Amex, Visa,*

Restaurant   £75

Three individually styled and interconnecting dining rooms provide the
luxury of a choice of settings to match your mood – the first room has
polished tables and antique-style chairs, the others are brighter with
bamboo-style chairs; muted pastel shades are used throughout. Long-
serving chef Michael Collom has sound instincts and a sure touch and
produces a standard menu that is executed correctly: bacon and mushroom
salad, noisettes of beef, escalope of salmon with orange and chive sauce. A
meringue-like raspberry soufflé with raspberry sorbet in pastry boats is a
fine example of Collom's dessert skills. Good selection of well-kept cheeses.
Vegetarian main courses always available. The wine list, though not
improved recently, does offer regular bin ends. *Parties 55. Private Room.
L 12-2 D 7-9. Set L £22 Set D £29.*

Bath   Queensberry Hotel   75%   £99

HR

Tel 0225 447928   Fax 0225 446065

Russel Street Bath Avon BA1 2QT   Map 4 B3

Stephen and Penny Ross, formerly of Homewood Park, now run a
luxurious and intimate little hotel in an 18th-century John Wood terrace.
Contemporary design and fine period furniture complement the stylish
Georgian interior with taste, and the thoughtfully created bedrooms offer
every luxury, as do the splendid bathrooms. Afternoon tea is served in the
drawing room. No dogs. *Rooms 22. Garden. Closed 2 wks Xmas/New Year.
Access, Amex, Visa,*

The Olive Tree Restaurant   £45

Downstairs is Bath's coolest, crispest restaurant, with white-tiled floor,
black wooden chairs amd rag-washed walls; bright watercolours and black-
and-white prints lend an air of the Mediterranean, which is reflected in
Stephen Ross's colourful, forcefully flavoured dishes. Provençal fish soup
with rouille and garlic croutons; seared salmon fillet with sun-dried
tomatoes, prawn and anchovy mayonnaise; baked aubergine with yellow
pepper sauce; calf's liver with bacon and braised onions illustrate the point.
Lemon tart and hot chocolate soufflé among some rather more mainstream

desserts. There's a three-course set lunch in addition to the short carte. Thursday is fish night. **Seats 44. Parties 40. Private Room. L 12-2 D 7-10.30. Set L £12.50.**

Bath   Royal Crescent Hotel   83%   £162
Tel 0225 319090   Fax 0225 339401   **HR**

16 Royal Crescent Bath Avon BA1 2LS   **Map 4 B3**

Comprising the two central houses of John Wood's 18th-century architectural masterpiece, with the garden Pavillion and Dower House behind and a unique sense of history and wealth of treasures within, this is a hotel of outstanding elegance. Every bedroom imparts a little of this character with handsome period furniture, original oils and supremely comfortable beds, many of them four-posters. Across the enclosed garden behind the crescent, the Dower House bedrooms have one of the best settings of any town hotel in this country; they are intimate and romantic in complete contrast to the grand suites of the main house that some might find intimidating. No bathroom wants for attendant luxury: Beau Nash and Jane Austen suites even have their own spa pools. Private dining and conference facilities are kept discreetly separate in the Royal Crescent Mews. No dogs. **Rooms 42.** Garden, croquet, plunge pool, valeting. Access, Amex, Visa, ○ *Diners Club International*

Dower House Restaurant   ★   £95

Be it neo-classicism, post-modernism or whatever, new chef Stephen Blake has brought his style from Le Talbooth to the Crescent. A starter of two nearly translucent ravioli of lobster set across succulent sautéed scallops in a butter sauce infused with basil and tomato is simple enough, but carefully balanced and well executed. Canon of lamb scores not only for quality and flavour but also for its presentation with vegetable vermicelli and Meaux mustard sauce. Nougat glacé with a tuile basket of summer fruits and a raspberry coulis is an excellent example of a classic dish executed in an uncomplicated manner wtih a fine consideration of the balance between sweet and sour. Good, dainty amuse-gueule to start, but the cheeseboard is apparently unloved. Sadly, the atmosphere is altogether *too* serious and solemn and the fine sommelier deserves better than the fairly ordinary wine list. **Seats 65.** Parties 40. Private Room. L 12.30-2 D 7-9.30. Set L from £18.50 Set D from £25.

Bath   Places of Interest

Tourist Information   Tel 0225 462831.
Theatre Royal   Sawclose Tel 0225 448815.
  Historic Houses, Castles and Gardens
Claverton Manor   Tel 0225 460503 *American Museum in Britain.*
Crowe Hall Gardens   Widcombe Hill Tel 0225 310322.
Dyrham Park   near Junction 18 of M4 Tel 027582 2501.
Priston Mill   Nr Bath Tel 0225 23894.
Sally Lunn's House   Tel 0225 61634.
Bath Racecourse   Tel 0451 20517.
  Museums and Art Galleries
Museum of Costume Assembly Rooms   Tel 0225 461111 Ext 2785.
Roman Baths Museum   Tel 0225 461111 Ext 2785.
Number One Royal Crescent (Bath Preservation Trust)   Tel 0225 428126.
Victoria Art Gallery   Tel 0225 461111 Ext 2772.

Battle   Netherfield Place   78%   £90
Tel 042 46 4455   Fax 042 46 4024   **HR**

Battle East Sussex TN33 9PP   **Map 7 C6**

Owners Helen and Michael Collier supervise the running of their Georgian-style country retreat, and Michael now does the cooking. Thirty acres of parkland make a very peaceful setting, and the extensive gardens provide most of the flowers that are a feature in the bright, spacious drawing room. Bedrooms are mostly of a very good size, and have sitting

areas. All are beautifully furnished and there are two comfortable chairs
and a writing desk in each. Carpeted bathrooms have good-quality
toiletries, bathrobes and thick towels. Children stay free in parents' room.
Rooms 14. Garden, croquet, putting, tennis. Closed 2 weeks Xmas/New Year.
Access, Amex, Visa,

Restaurant   £70

The redwood panelled dining room has garden views and is rather more
restrained than the menu descriptions. Dishes are 'escorted with',
'surrounded by a moat of' or 'married in' rather than just 'with' their sauces,
but the results are enjoyable and the ingredients first-rate. Local venison,
lamb from the Sussex downs and wild salmon are accompanied by
vegetables or salads that mostly come from their own extensive kitchen
garden. There's a seasonally-changing à la carte and daily-changing table
d'hote menu at night and the two fixed-price 'Executive' lunch menus
include a half bottle of house wine per person. Some classic claret vintages
considerably cheaper than elsewhere, and great burgundy growers on a
splendid wine list. *Seats 50. Private Room. L 12-2 D 7-9.30 (Sun to 9). Set L
£14.50 & £15.95 Set D £22.50.*

Battle   Places of Interest

Tourist Information   Tel 04246 3721.
Battle Abbey   Tel 04246 3792.
    Museums and Art Galleries
Battle Museum Langton House.
Buckleys Shop Museum   Tel 04246 4269.
The Almonry   Tel 04246 2727.

Bawtry   The Crown   64%   £81

Tel 0302 710341   Fax 0302 711798   H

High Street Bawtry South Yorkshire DN10 6JW   Map 11 D2

A sturdy old coaching inn, over 300 years old, encompassing
conference/function rooms for 15 to 170. Most bedrooms are in a modern
wing: 50% non-smoking, one four-poster room, another equipped for
disabled guests. Forte Heritage. *Rooms 57. Garden, croquet, news kiosk.*
Access, Amex, Visa,

Beaconsfield   Bellhouse Hotel   67%   £140

Tel 0753 887211   Fax 0753 888231   H

Oxford Road Beaconsfield Buckinghamshire HP9 2XE   Map 5 E2

De Vere hotel on the A40, close to junction 2 of the M40. Impressive new
frontage; six separate conference suites accommodating 10 to 450 delegates.
Popular leisure club includes beauty therapy. *Rooms 136. Indoor swimming
pool, spa baths, sauna, solarium, beauty salon, gymnasium, squash, snooker.*
Access, Amex, Visa,

Beaconsfield   Places of Interest

Bekonscot Model Village   Tel 0494 672919.
Chiltern Open Air Museum Newland Park   Tel 02407 71117 *5 miles.*
Milton's Cottage   Tel 02407 2313.

Beanacre   Beechfield House   72%   £110

Tel 0225 703700   Fax 0225 790118   H

Beanacre Nr Melksham Wiltshire SN12 7PU   Map 4 B2

Now under new management, this Bath-stone mansion of Victorian origin
stands in seven acres of gardens and orchards, ringed by plantations of
poplar and pine; bedrooms derive their names from many of the rare trees
that dot the estate. The hotel is less inspiring than the grounds, though,
with two modern wings housing bedrooms. A covered walkway connects
to converted coach houses bordering the outdoor swimming pool. Interiors

contain a wealth of period and antique furniture, and are graced by ornate moulded ceilings, fabric canopies and festoon blinds. Carpeted bathrooms vary in size, but are enlivened throughout by good overhead lighting and brass fittings. **Rooms 20.** *Garden, outdoor swimming pool, tennis, croquet. Access, Amex, Visa,*

Bearsted   Soufflé   £70   R

Tel 0622 37065

The Green Bearsted Maidstone Kent ME14 4DN   Map 7 C5

A pretty, cottagey restaurant with wood beams and crisp white napery, standing on one side of the village green. There's a choice of fixed-price menus on weekdays and a more involved one on Saturdays, all written up on a blackboard. Andy Blyth's cooking is confident and attractively presented, with generous portions. Notably, good saucing enhances dishes like *feuilleté aux moules, filet de dorade beurre blanc* and *rognons d'agneau sauce moutarde.* **Seats 44.** *Parties 44. L 12-1.45 D 7-9.30. Closed L Sat & Mon, all Sun, Xmas/New Year, 2 weeks Jan. Set L £18.90 Set D £28.90. Access, Amex, Visa,*

Bearsted   Tudor Park   67%   £109   H

Tel 0622 34334   Fax 0622 735360

Ashford Road Bearsted Nr Maidstone Kent ME14 4NQ   Map 7 C5

Near junction 8 of the M20 and just two miles from Leeds Castle. Extensive leisure facilities that include a spectacular 18-hole golf course and swimming pool are the main attraction at this modern hotel. The public rooms are interestingly laid out and include an intimate piano bar, the garden restaurant overlooking the golf course and a plum-coloured cocktail bar. Bedrooms are of a good size and feature large, comfortable beds. Families are well catered for with babysitting and baby listening available. Banqueting/conference facilities for 216/275. **Rooms 120.** *Indoor swimming pool, spa bath, sauna, solarium, gymnasium, snooker, squash, tennis, car hire, coffee shop (10am-10pm), beautician, children's play area, golf, helipad. Access, Amex, Visa,*

Beaulieu   Montagu Arms   68%   £96   ⊖H

Tel 0590 612324   Fax 0590 612188

Beaulieu New Forest Hampshire SO42 7ZL   Map 4 C4

Situated in the centre of a charming village, the 13th-century Montagu Arms is near the Abbey and the motor museum. The comfortable, relaxed feel is greatly enhanced by the welcoming log fires that warm the foyer and lounge in cooler months. There's also a library bar and conservatory. Individually furnished bedrooms (some with four-posters or brass bedsteads) have modern bathrooms. Children sharing parents' rooms are charged at £15 per night including breakfast. **Rooms 24.** *Garden. Access, Amex, Visa,*

Beaulieu   Places of Interest

Tourist Information   Tel 0590 612345 ext 278.
Beaulieu Abbey and **National Motor Museum**   Tel 0590 612345.

Bebington   Forte Travelodge   £40   L

Tel 051-327 2489

A41 Bebington New Chester Road Eastham Wirral Merseyside L62 9AQ   Map 10 A2

On the A41 northbound, off junction 5 of the M53. **Rooms 31.** *Access, Amex, Visa.*

Beccles   Waveney House   59%   £60

Tel 0502 712270   Fax 0502 712660

Puddingmoor Beccles Suffolk NR34 9PL   Map 6 D2

Boating people appreciate the riverside position of 16th-century Waveney
House, and there's a certain amount of nautical chat in the bar and
residents' lounge. Even bedrooms have a shipboard feel with creaking
floorboards, uneven walls and beams beneath which to duck. *Rooms 13.
Garden, fishing, mooring. Access, Amex, Visa,*

Beccles   Places of Interest

Marina Theatre   Lowestoft Tel 0502 573318.
Somerleyton Hall   Nr Lowestoft Tel 0502 730224/730308.
Kessingland Beach *4 miles south of Lowestoft.*
Lowestoft Beach.
Pleasurewood Hill American Theme Park   Corton Tel 0493 441611.

Beckingham   Black Swan   £50

Tel 0636 626474   R

Hillside Beckingham Lincolnshire LN5 0RF   Map 11 E3

A converted village pub with a country atmosphere: exposed beams, open
fires and complementary pink decor. Chef-proprietor Anton Indans offers a
short carte and good-value, fixed-price menu covering a range from
creamed leek and chicken soufflé, mixed seafood casserole and pheasant and
herb sausage to Dover sole, marinated fillet of beef, roast loin of lamb and
baked pheasant breast. Dishes are often involved – pigeon breast salad with
bacon croutons, Anna-style potatoes and caraway sauce or lavender- and
honey-marinated fillet of beef topped with a Stilton mousse and served
with spinach and a port sauce – but invariably successful. Chocoholics are
admirably catered for by the dessert offerings. Sunday lunch offers more
interesting diversions than traditional roast meats. Short, but excellent
value wine list with straightforward descriptions. No smoking. *Seats 30.
Parties 14. Private Room. L Sun 12-2, otherwise by arrangement D 7-10.
Closed D Sun, all Mon. Set L £12.50 Set D £13.50. Access, Visa,*

Bedford   Moat House   65%   £85

Tel 0234 355131   Fax 0234 340447   H

2 St Mary's Street Bedford Bedfordshire MK42 0AR   Map 6 A3

Modern tower block in a prime riverside position in the town centre.
Banqueting and conference facilities for 300+. Monthly dinner dance.
Rooms 100. Keep-fit equipment, sauna. Access, Amex, Visa, ◑ Diners Club

Bedford   Woodlands Manor   70%   £97

Tel 0234 363281   Fax 0234 272390   H

Green Lane Clapham Bedford Bedfordshire MK41 6EP   Map 6 A3

Thoughtful service is one of the pleasures of a stay at this honey-coloured
turn-of-the-century manor house in its own grounds off the A6 north of
Bedford. Best of the bedrooms, housed in a sympathetic extension, are
spacious and stylishly furnished, with sofas and breakfast tables. These, and
other refurbished bedrooms, have impressive bathrooms with Italian
marble tiling. The hotel has been run unpretentiously by Richard Lee and
Duncan Gear for the last 16 years. No children under seven. No dogs.
Rooms 25. Garden, croquet, helipad. Access, Amex, Visa.

Bedford   Places of Interest

Tourist Information   Tel 0234 215226.
Bowen West Community Theatre   Tel 0234 2193331.
The Swiss Garden   Old Warden, Biggleswade Tel 0234 228330.
Wrest Park House and Gardens   Silsoe, Nr Ampthill Tel 0525 60718.
Stagsden Bird Gardens   Tel 02302 2745.
   Museums and Art Galleries
Bromham Mill   Bromham Tel 0234 228330.
Cecil Higgins Art Gallery and Museum   Tel 0234 211222.
Bedford Museum   Tel 0234 53323.
The Shuttleworth Collection (Aviation History)   Old Warden, Biggleswade
   Tel 076 727 288.

Belford   Blue Bell Hotel   63%   £76

Tel 0668 213543   Fax 0668 213787   **H**

Market Square Belford Northumberland NE70 7NE   Map 14 B2

A creeper-clad, family-run hotel in the centre of the village. Much period
charm has been retained, with two bedrooms in the old coach house
opposite; one is particularly suited to disabled guests, the other has bunk
beds for families with up to three children; both are en suite. Children up
to 14 stay free in their parents' room in the main building, where all
rooms are decorated with smart, matching fabrics in a traditional style. A
public bar is across a courtyard, leaving the cocktail bar free for residents.
Nearby, Cheviot House is under the same ownership and offers guest house
accommodation. *Rooms 17. Garden. Access, Amex, Visa,* **(1)** Diners Club International

Belton   Belton Woods Hotel   72%   £115

Tel 0476 593200   Fax 0476 74547   **H**

Belton Nr Grantham Lincolnshire NG32 2LN   Map 11 E3

Just off the A607, north of Grantham, a modern complex standing in 475
acres of grounds, with outstanding sports facilities that are matched by
equally impressive accommodation. A spacious, high-ceilinged lounge
leading off the main foyer is filled with parlour plants and hanging baskets,
and overlooks one of three golf courses (two 18-hole and one 9-hole). The
cocktail bar on the first floor is more club-like, with easy chairs and rich
decor. Spacious bedrooms have good seating and working areas; plain
painted walls lighten up the use of contemporary fabrics. Ambassador
rooms feature extras like a mini-bar and settee. Excellent facilities for
children include a children's playground and swimming pool, cots and
baby-sitting. *Rooms 96. Garden, indoor swimming pool, spa bath, sauna, steam
room, solarium, beauty salon, hairdressing, gymnasium, games room, snooker, golf
courses (9 & 18 hole), golf driving range, fishing, tennis, coffee shop (7am–
10.30pm). Access, Amex, Visa,* **(1)** Diners Club International

Belton   Places of Interest

Tourist Information   Tel 0476 66444.
   Historic Houses, Castles and Gardens
Belton House (NT)   Tel 0476 66116.
Fulbeck Hall   Tel 0400 72205.
Woolsthorpe Manor (NT)   Tel 0476 860338 *Birthplace of Sir Isaac Newton.*
Belvoir Castle   Tel 0476 870262.

Berwick-upon-Tweed   Funnywayt'mekalivin   NEW   £45

Tel 0289 308827   **R**

41 Bridge Street Berwick-upon-Tweed Northumberland TD15 1ES   Map 14 B2

Elizabeth Middlemiss has moved premises to just down the street and over
the road, gaining a drinks licence, more room and a more relaxed
atmosphere. Dinner is a set menu served at a set time and starts

with a complimentary glass of white port or pineau de Charentes; this could be followed by carrot and Lord Lambourne soup with good crusty bread, scallops with a coriander and lentil sauce, then stuffed shoulder of Borders lamb with gooseberry and mint sauce accompanied by dauphinoise potatoes and brussels sprouts. To finish, bramble and cassis syllabub with warm butter shortbread and Teviotdale cheese. The wine list is simple and sensibly priced. Vegetarians should notify in advance. Lunch (and dinner Sun-Tues) by arrangement for parties of eight or more. *Seats 32. Parties 17. Private Room. D only at 8. Closed Sun-Tues, 25 & 26 Dec, 1 Jan. Set D £17.50. Access, Visa.*

| Berwick-upon-Tweed | Kings Arms | 59% | £70 |

Tel 0289 307454   Fax 0289 308867   H

Hide Hill Berwick-upon-Tweed Northumberland TD15 1EJ   Map 14 B2

Dating from the 18th century, this town-centre hotel offers agreeable overnight accommodation that includes seven rooms with four-posters. Solid oakwood furnishings give a reassuringly traditional feel, and there's plenty of room to relax in the chandelier-hung lounge and the cocktail bar. The Royal Suite is a popular venue for banquets and conferences for up to 150/200. *Rooms 36. Coffee shop (9.30-6). Access, Amex, Visa,* Diners Club International

Berwick-upon-Tweed   Places of Interest

Tourist Information   Tel 0289 330733.
Lindisfarne Castle   Holy Island Tel 0289 89244 *Causeway flooded at high tide.*
Berwick Borough Museum & Art Gallery (EH)   Tel 0289 330933.
Manderston Duns   Tel 0361 83450 *15 miles.*
Paxton House   Tel 0289 86291.

| Beverley | Beverley Arms | 62% | £101 |

Tel 0482 869241   Fax 0482 870907   H

North Bar Within Beverley Humberside HU17 8DD   Map 11 E1

300-year-old coaching inn that retains a certain period interest. Bedrooms are mostly in a modern block. Conference facilities for up to 80. Forte. *Rooms 57. Courtyard/patio, news kiosk, coffee shop (9.30am-6.30pm). Access, Amex, Visa,* Diners Club International

Beverley   Places of Interest

Art Gallery and Museum   Tel 0482 882255.
Beverley Minster   Tel 0482 868540.
Racecourse   Tel 0482 867488.

| Bibury | The Swan | 69% | £120 |

Tel 0285 740204   Fax 0285 740473   H

Bibury Gloucestershire GL7 5NW   Map 4 C2

A romantic, ivy-covered hotel in a picture-postcard setting with its pretty riverside garden and private fishing. Day rooms consist of chintzy parlour and writing room and a smart, oak-panelled bar. Bedrooms have recently been restyled with an evocative Victorian feel; yet the new bathrooms are splendidly modern, some featuring bright marble tiling and jacuzzi baths, others fine patterned reproduction stoneware; most have separate de luxe showers. Private, state-of-the-art boardroom for ten. Modern all-day brasserie and coffee shop. *Rooms 18. Garden, croquet, fishing. Access, Visa.*

Bideford   Yeoldon House   60%   £75

Tel 0237 474400   Fax 0237 476618   **H**

Durrant Lane Northam Nr Bideford Devon EX39 2RL   Map 2 C2

Solid Victorian building in grounds reaching down to the river Torridge.
Homely day rooms and bedrooms, most with fine views. *Rooms 10. Garden.
Access, Amex, Visa,* ◑ *Diners Club International*

Bideford   Places of Interest

Rosemoor Garden, The Royal Horticultural Society   Nr Great Torrington
   Tel 0805 24067.

Bigbury-on-Sea   Burgh Island Hotel   66%   £148*

Tel 0548 810514   Fax 0548 810243   **H**

Burgh Island Bigbury-on-Sea Devon TQ7 4AU   Map 3 D3

A 26-acre private island with a unique Art Deco hotel restored by current
owners Beatrice and Tony Porter to its 1930 splendour. That splendour
includes the Palm Court with its Peacock Dome, a glass sun lounge, jet-
black glass and pink mirrors on the staircase, and a magnificent ballroom.
Period furniture abounds in day rooms and in the bedrooms, all of which
are suites. A lift serves all three floors. Banqueting/conference facilities for
100 delegates. You should telephone for the best time to arrive, which
depends largely on the tide (a giant sea tractor makes the short trip from
the mainland and is available free to residents for coming and going
thereafter). *Half-board terms only. No dogs. *Rooms 14. Garden, sauna,
solarium, tennis, keep-fit equipment, games room, snooker, sea fishing. Access,
Amex, Visa.*

Bilbrough   Bilbrough Manor   75%   £105

Tel 0937 834002   Fax 0937 834724   **H R**

Bilbrough York North Yorkshire YO2 3PH   Map 11 D1

An attractive manor house among fine Georgian gardens in a quiet village
off the A64, six miles from York. Though the present house "only" dates
from 1901, there's been an abode here for some 700 years, and it's probably
best known as the family home of Thomas Fairfax, Cromwell's right-hand
man. The Manor was restored by Colin and Sue Bell who continue to run
it in professional fashion. Day rooms include a foyer-bar and a splendid
lounge with lightwood panelling and comfortable sofas. Prettily decorated
bedrooms are light and airy with carefully matched colour schemes and
soft furnishings, but rather plain modern furniture. Compact, carpeted
bathrooms. *Rooms 12. Garden, croquet. Closed 25-29 Dec. Access, Amex,
Visa,* ◑ *Diners Club International*

Restaurant   £65

Chef Andrew Pressley maintains the house tradition of quality cooking.
The carte is now written in English and dishes are individually priced; hot
pot of Dublin Bay prawns and queen scallops in a shellfish sauce and puff
pastry case tops the starters, while a choice of lobster, wild salmon, fillet
steak au poivre, maize-fed chicken with artichoke, duck breast and calf's
liver might follow. A choice of vegetarian dishes is always offered, as is a
2- to 4-course *menu gourmet. Seats 70. Parties 40. Private Room. L 12-2
D 7-9.30 (Sun to 9). Set L £10.50 (Sunday £14.50) Set D £20.*

♔

♨

Billingshurst   Forte Travelodge

Tel 0403 782711

A29 Five Oaks Billingshurst West Sussex RH14 9AE

£40

L

Map 5 E3

On the A29 northbound, 8 miles south-west of Horsham. *Rooms 26.*
Access, Amex, Visa.

Bingley   Bankfield Hotel   61%

Tel 0274 567123   Fax 0274 551331

Bradford Road Bingley West Yorkshire BD16 1TV

£105

H

Map 10 C1

A castellated Gothic frontage that "wouldn't look out of place on a
Hollywood film set". Inside, handsome Victorian day rooms and mainly
modern, decent-sized bedrooms. Conference facilities for up to 250. Jarvis
Hotels. *Rooms 103. Garden, dinner dance (weekly). Access, Amex, Visa,*

Birdlip   Kingshead House

Tel 0452 862299

Birdlip Nr Gloucester Gloucestershire GL4 8JH

£55

RR

Map 4 B2

Judy and Warren Knock run a relaxed country restaurant with the help of
local girls. Judy adapts French and English recipes (some dating from the
18th century): cream of swede and ginger soup; breasts of pheasant and
pigeon with a wild mushroom sauce; fillet of lemon sole baked in a spiced
cream; raspberry fool with hazelnut shortbread. Set meal prices indicate
minimum charges. Traditional Sunday lunches. Lots of half bottles on a
concise and informative wine list with friendly prices. *Seats 32. Parties 34.*
L 12.30-2.15 (Sun to 2) D 7.30-10. Closed L Sat, D Sun, all Mon, 25 & 26
Dec, 1 Jan. Set L £14 (Sun £15) Set D £22.50. Access, Amex, Visa,

Room

£50

The one and only en-suite double bedroom is a delightful place to stop
over for a night. Birdlip lies on the lovely Cotswold Way and is
equidistant (8 miles) from Gloucester and Cheltenham.

Birkenhead   Bowler Hat Hotel   65%

Tel 051-652 4931   Fax 051-653 8127

2 Talbot Road Oxton Birkenhead Merseyside L43 2HH

£70

H

Map 10 A2

One mile off the M63, junction 3, a large Victorian house with the
majority of rooms in a redbrick extension to the rear. Meeting rooms for
up to 80. Children up to 12 stay free in parents' room. *Rooms 29. Garden,*
croquet. Access, Amex, Visa,

Birkenhead   Places of Interest

Tourist Information   Woodside Visitors Centre Tel 051 647 6780.
Birkenhead Park   Tel 051 647 2366.
Williamson Art Gallery and Museum   Tel 051 652 4177.
Lady Lever Art Gallery   Port Sunlight Village Tel 051 645 3623.
Oval Sports Centre Bebington   Tel 051 645 0551.

Birmingham   Birmingham Metropole   72%

Tel 021-780 4242   Fax 021-780 3923

National Exhibition Centre Birmingham West Midlands B40 1PP

£160

H

Map 10 C4

A new wing has brought the complement of rooms to over 800 at this
huge modern hotel at the heart of the National Exhibition Centre. Decor is
light and up-to-date, and the matching fabrics are contemporary in style;
all rooms have smart, solid furniture and modern tiled bathrooms with
good mirrors and showers. The Metropole caters largely for conference
delegates and business folk and there is a large allocation of single rooms in

the adjoining building (once the Warwick), while the main hotel offers
largely twin rooms and a number of suites. Twenty-six pairs of rooms
interconnect, making them ideal for family use. Public areas include a
striking foyer and a bar-lounge with mirrored columns and contemporary
seating and decor. 700 car parking spaces are available free to residents. The
magnificent conference and banqueting facilities cater for up to 2000
delegates. *Rooms 806. Squash. Closed Xmas/New Year. Access, Amex, Visa,*
🌐 *Diners Club International*

Birmingham	Campanile Hotel	£36
Tel 021-622 4925 Fax 021-622 4195		**L**
Irving Street Lee Bank Birmingham West Midlands B1 1DH		Map 10 C4

City-centre site, off Bristol street, near Queensway. *Rooms 50. Access,
Amex, Visa,* 🌐 *Diners Club International*

Birmingham	Chung Ying	£37
Tel 021-622 5669		**R**
16 Wrottesley Street Birmingham West Midlands B5 6RT		Map 10 C4

The Chinese flock to this well-established, traditionally appointed
restaurant for its long Cantonese menu. The choice extends to well over
300 dishes, from crispy fried chicken wings through assorted beef and pork
to sizzling dishes and casseroles (braised brisket with spices, duck's web
with mixed vegetables, eel with roast belly pork, lamb with dried bean
curd). Seafood covers a very wide range, too, and there are more than 40
items on the dim sum list. *Seats 220. Private Room. Meals 12-12. Closed 25
Dec. Access, Amex, Visa,* 🌐 *Diners Club International*

Birmingham	Chung Ying Garden	£37
Tel 021-666 6622		**R**
17 Thorp Street Birmingham West Midlands B5 4AT		Map 10 C4

Sister and near neighbour of the original Chung Ying, this has more
modern decor, with pillars, plants and murals. The menu is no less
extensive and the chef's specialities include deep-fried chicken stuffed with
banana, paper-wrapped fillet of beef, fried fish cake with mangetout and
steamed pork pie with salted egg. Dim sum features on the menu, with a
greater choice at lunchtime. *Seats 300. Parties 240. Private Room. Meals 12-
12 (Sun to 11). Closed 25 Dec. Access, Amex, Visa,* 🌐 *Diners Club International*

Birmingham	Copthorne Hotel	70%	£123
Tel 021-200 2727 Fax 021-200 1197			**H**
Paradise Circus Birmingham West Midlands B3 3HJ			Map 10 C4

On a busy traffic island known as Paradise Circus, the Copthorne's black
glass exterior towers above the city's inner ring road. Inside, all is sleek and
contemporary; the marble-floored foyer leads to a raised bar-lounge done
out in midnight blue. Grey and plum are the main colours for the
bedrooms, whose bathrooms are provided with large mirrors and plenty of
shelf space. *Rooms 212. Indoor swimming pool, sauna, solarium, spa bath, steam
room, gymnasium, coffee shop (7am-9pm), news kiosk. Access, Amex, Visa,*
🌐 *Diners Club International*

Birmingham	Forte Crest	68%	£97
Tel 021-643 8171 Fax 021-631 2528			**H**
Smallbrook Queensway Birmingham West Midlands B5 4EW			Map 10 C4

By the inner ring road, a concrete tower hotel with adjacent multi-storey
car park. A small reception area shares space with a business support centre
which co-ordinates conferences for up to 630. Most of the bedrooms and
all the day rooms have recently been refurbished. Formerly the Albany.
*Rooms 254. Indoor swimming pool, keep-fit equipment, sauna, solarium, squash.
Access, Amex, Visa,* 🌐 *Diners Club International*

Birmingham	Forte Posthouse	60%	£67

Tel 021-357 7444   Fax 021-357 7503   **H**

Chapel Lane Great Barr Birmingham West Midlands B43 7BG   Map 10 C4

Practical, modern hotel on the A34, near junction 7 of the M6. Conference and banqueting facilities for 150. *Rooms 192. Garden, indoor & outdoor swimming pool, spa bath, sauna, children's playroom and playground. Access, Amex, Visa,* (D) *Diners Club International*

Birmingham	Granada Lodge	£43

Tel 021-550 3261   Fax 021-501 2880   **L**

M5 junction 3/4 Frankley Birmingham West Midlands B32 4AR   Map 10 C4

Rooms 60. Access, Amex, Visa, (D) *Diners Club International*

Birmingham	Henry's	£42

Tel 021-200 1136   **R**

27 St Paul's Square Birmingham West Midlands B17 9QH   Map 10 C4

A short drive from the city centre, a purpose-built restaurant on split levels, serviced by friendly staff. As at its sister restaurant, the Cantonese menu is extensive and dishes competently cooked. Stuffed crab claws and skewered satays among predictable starters cede to sizzling grilled salmon, sliced fillet steak and loin of lamb with black bean, spring onion and ginger or spicy yellow bean sauce. *Seats 140. Private Room. L 12-2 D 6-11 (Fri & Sat to 11.30). Closed Sun, Bank Holidays, 1 week Aug. Set meals from £13. Access, Amex, Visa,* (D) *Diners Club International*

Birmingham	Henry Wong	£42

Tel 021-427 9799   **R**

283 High Street Harborne Birmingham West Midlands B3 1RB   Map 10 C4

Sister restaurant to *Henry's*, a bright airy restaurant at the top end of Harborne, two miles from the city centre. Similarly extensive Cantonese menus produce capably cooked rather than inspired results. Paper-wrapped prawns, wun tun soup, char siu Cantonese pork and yau choi green vegetables with oyster sauce attest to their authenticity. Helpful, friendly service is above average. *Seats 120. Parties 70. Private Room. L 12-1.45 D 6-11 (Fri & Sat to 11.30). Closed Sun, Bank Holidays, 1 week Aug. Set meals from £13. Access, Amex, Visa,* (D) *Diners Club International*

Birmingham	Holiday Inn	70%	£124

Tel 021-631 2000   Fax 021-643 9018   **H**

Holliday Street Birmingham West Midlands B1 1HH   Map 10 C4

Located above an NCP car park in the city centre, this modern high-rise hotel with its numerous conference and meeting rooms (holding up to 160), smart public areas and choice of two bars, is a popular venue for the business community. The bedrooms all have individually controllable air-conditioning and ample work space; Executive rooms boast king-size beds and fax machines. Bathrooms are well lit, with large mirrors and decent showers. *Rooms 288. Indoor swimming pool, spa bath, sauna, solarium, keep-fit equipment, kiosk. Access, Amex, Visa,* (D) *Diners Club International*

Birmingham	Hyatt Regency	77%	£170

Tel 021-643 1234   Fax 021-616 2323   **HR**

2 Bridge Street Birmingham West Midlands B1 2JZ   Map 10 C4

Next to the new International Convention Centre stands a striking 25-storey feature on Birmingham's skyline. The impressive glass-roofed atrium is cool and stylish and features columns, plants, trees and even a fountain. A marble-floored reception boasts its own elegant lounge, while the bar, *Aston's*, is compact and subtly lit. The luxuriously appointed bedrooms are spacious and air-conditioned, featuring quality modern furniture and fashionably uncluttered decor. Equally splendid, marble-floored bathrooms. Floor-to-ceiling windows afford fine views over the Second City. Guests have the use of the well-equipped *Club Active* leisure centre in the basement. Young, smart and willing staff. Conference facilities for up to 240, banqueting to 170. **Rooms 319.** *Indoor swimming pool, gymnasium, sauna, solarium, steam room, spa bath, business centre, café (6.30am–midnight).* *Access, Amex, Visa,*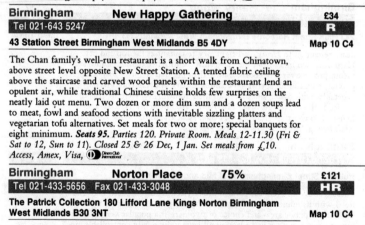

Number 282   £45

The stylish brasserie is the Hyatt's main restaurant and specialises in fresh seafood dishes ranging from smoked haddock tart or clam chowder to daily specials such as parrot fish or blue fin tuna. Quietly elegant, yet informal, surroundings with robust and interesting cooking. **Seats 70.** *Parties 20. Private Room. L 12–3 D 6.30–12. Set L from £13. Closed L Sat, all Sun.*

Birmingham	Midland Hotel	67%	£99
Tel 021-643 2601 Fax 021-643 5075			**H**
New Street Birmingham West Midlands B2 4JT			Map 10 C4

Family-owned for 200 years, the Midland undergoes continuous improvement, greatly enhancing a fine old Victorian building. Bedrooms are now especially good with soft decor, pretty co-ordinated fabrics and matching furniture – a cut above the competition. The smart bathrooms are neatly tiled and brightly lit. Spacious day rooms reflect another hotel age, with moulded ceilings and period furniture. Three bars cater for most ages and tastes and include a smoky public bar with a pub feel. **Rooms 111.** *Games room, coffee shop (10.30am–6pm). Access, Amex, Visa,*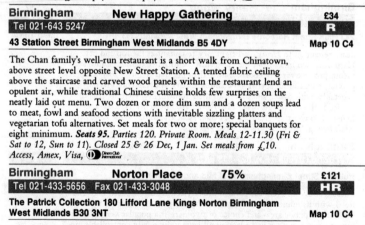

Birmingham	New Happy Gathering	£34
Tel 021-643 5247		**R**
43 Station Street Birmingham West Midlands B5 4DY		Map 10 C4

The Chan family's well-run restaurant is a short walk from Chinatown, above street level opposite New Street Station. A tented fabric ceiling above the staircase and carved wood panels within the restaurant lend an opulent air, while traditional Chinese cuisine holds few surprises on the neatly laid out menu. Two dozen or more dim sum and a dozen soups lead to meat, fowl and seafood sections with inevitable sizzling platters and vegetarian tofu alternatives. Set meals for two or more; special banquets for eight minimum. **Seats 95.** *Parties 120. Private Room. Meals 12–11.30 (Fri & Sat to 12, Sun to 11). Closed 25 & 26 Dec, 1 Jan. Set meals from £10. Access, Amex, Visa,*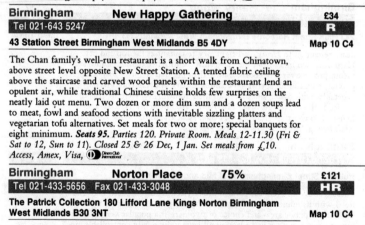

Birmingham	Norton Place	75%	£121
Tel 021-433-5656 Fax 021-433-3048			**HR**
The Patrick Collection 180 Lifford Lane Kings Norton Birmingham West Midlands B30 3NT			Map 10 C4

A highly individual, modern building in the unlikely setting of the grounds of the Patrick Car Collection. Landscaped grounds surround the single-storeyed design. No expense has been spared in creating the bedrooms, which are impressive, yet not large, and beautifully decorated with individual furnishings, stained-glass windows and original paintings. The eye-catching decor and co-ordinated fabrics are complemented by classically styled furniture and a host of extras. Marble-tiled bathrooms with gold fittings are equally luxurious. Day rooms include a conservatory and a plant-filled bar-lounge furnished in summery style. Staff are young and keen. A swimming pool and fitness centre have been added this year. Conference and banqueting facilities for up to 140. **Rooms 10.** *Garden, keep-fit equipment, indoor swimming pool, croquet. Access, Amex, Visa,*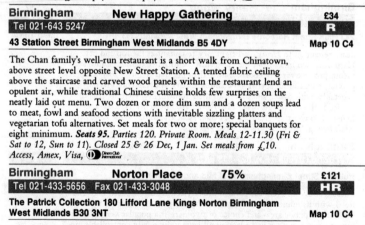

Lombard Room £75

Anthony John Morgan cooks in a modern style and the staff serve in a helpful and efficient manner. Dishes are generally adventurous (white onion and thyme broth topped with a cheese soufflé or pot-roasted, honey-glazed Gressingham duck served with pickled nectarines and a ginger and Sauternes sauce) and the wine list should match most tastes. *Seats 50. Parties 50. Private Room. L 12-2.30 D 7-10 (Sun to 9). Set L £12.95 Set D £16.50.*

Birmingham Novotel 61% £100

Tel 021-643 2000 Fax 021-643 9796 **H**

70 Broad Street Birmingham West Midlands B1 2HT Map 10 C4

Close to the Convention Centre, a very modern Novotel with comfortable bedrooms and both leisure and business centres. Underground car park. No dogs. *Rooms 148. Gymnasium, sauna. Access, Amex, Visa,* 🅓 *Diners Club International*

Birmingham Plough & Harrow 65% £101

Tel 021-454 4111 Fax 021-454 1868 **H**

135 Hagley Road Edgbaston Birmingham West Midlands B16 8LS Map 10 C4

With only 44 rooms, the Plough and Harrow, perhaps understandably, seems not to be on Forte's priority list: porterage is no longer provided; only the most rudimentary room service is available; gone are the bathrobes and 'luxury' toiletries – resulting in a drop of 8% from last year's grading. A few of the staff still belong to the old school and do their best to maintain standards, but these days it's a real struggle. Loyal visitors still appreciate the Victorian heritage and the traditional touches. The restaurant, featured in these pages last year, is expensive and also on the wane. A sad state of affairs at what was our 1981 Hotel of the Year. Forte Heritage. *Rooms 44. Access, Amex, Visa,* 🅓 *Diners Club International*

Birmingham Purple Rooms £35

Tel 021-702 2193 **R**

1076 Stratford Road Hall Green Birmingham West Midlands B28 8AD Map 10 C4

Set at the city end of a shopping parade on a dual carriageway leading through the suburbs towards Shirley. Silver service, the usual hot plates, a floating candle atop the pink-clothed tables, plus fairly-priced Indian and Bangladeshi food. *Seats 70. Parties 30. Private Room. L 12-2 D 5-12 (Fri & Sat to 1). Closed L Mon-Thu, 25 Dec. Set L from £5.95 Set D from £6.95. Access, Amex, Visa.*

Birmingham Rajdoot £40

Tel 021-643 8805 **R**

12 Albert Street Birmingham West Midlands B4 7UD Map 10 C4

Rajdoot opened in Chelsea in 1966 and was the first to use the tandoor in Europe. In the comfortable, quietly opulent Birmingham branch (as in the other outlets in Manchester and Dublin) the clay oven turns out not only good lamb, chicken and prawn dishes (also fish tikka), but mackerel, lamb's kidneys and vegetable shashlik. Among the curries is lamb narial – an interesting preparation including coconut milk and lemon. Ultimately, Mr Sarda's interior decor and style take precedence over the substance of the food (lobster masala and bhuna still appear on the menu). *Seats 74. Parties 40. L 12-2.15 D 6.30-11.30. Closed L Sun, Bank Holidays. Set L from £8 Set D from £13.50. Access, Amex, Visa,* 🅓 *Diners Club International*

Birmingham Royal Angus Thistle 65% £102

Tel 021-236 4211 Fax 021-233 2195 **H**

St Chads Queensway Birmingham West Midlands B4 6HY Map 10 C4

Modern city-centre hotel alongside the inner ring road, with easy parking. Summery day rooms, good-size bedrooms, up-to-date accessories. *Rooms 133. Access, Amex, Visa,* 🅓 *Diners Club International*

Birmingham Sloans £80

`Tel 021-455 6697  Fax 021-454 4335` **R**

**27 Chad Square Hawthorne Road Edgbaston Birmingham
West Midlands B15 3TQ** Map 10 C4

Set in a small suburban shopping precinct, this smart, pale green, split-level
restaurant is run in exemplary fashion by owner John Narbett. Serving
staff are attentive and genuinely friendly while in the kitchen, sound
technique and the avoidance of shortcuts ensures reliably good results on
the plate. Ballotine of chicken with foie gras, wild mushrooms and
pistachios, and savoury ravioli of guinea fowl are handled as surely as the
simpler dishes from the menu like salmon fish cakes with parsley sauce and
pot-roasted Norfolk duckling with apple and bilberry sauce. Both fixed-
price *menus du jour* (with a good choice at both lunch and dinner) and à la
carte menus are offered. Mostly French wines on a decent list, with a good
regional and country selection under £20. *Seats 60. Parties 80. L 12-2
D 7-10. Closed L Sat, all Sun, Bank Holidays, 1 week from 25 Dec. Set L
£14.50/£16.50 Set D £23. Access, Amex, Visa,*

Birmingham Strathallan Thistle 63% £102

`Tel 021-455 9777  Fax 021-454 9432` **H**

225 Hagley Road Edgbaston Birmingham West Midlands B16 9RY Map 10 C4

Circular modern building on the busy A465, very convenient for
Edgbaston cricket ground. Flexible conference facilities. Easy, mainly
covered parking. *Rooms 167. Access, Amex, Visa,*

Birmingham Swallow Hotel 77% £120

`Tel 021-452 1144  Fax 021-456 3442` **HR**

12 Hagley Road Five Ways Birmingham West Midlands B16 8SJ Map 10 C4

An imposing Edwardian building, strikingly transformed into a quality
luxury hotel. The foyer features sparkling Italian marble floors, rich
mahogany woodwork and crystal chandeliers; there is a refined drawing
room elegantly decorated with oil paintings, a quiet, dignified library and a
handsome bar with colourful floral displays throughout. The air-
conditioned bedrooms are stylish, well-proportioned and comfortable.
Beautiful fabrics are complemented by fine inlaid furniture and bathrooms
are impressive, with marble tiling and a host of extras. An interestingly
designed leisure club is based around an Egyptian theme. Attentive,
professional staff. *Rooms 98. Terrace, indoor swimming pool, sauna, solarium,
whirlpool bath, gymnasium, hairdressing, beauty therapy. Access, Amex, Visa,*

Sir Edward Elgar Restaurant ↑ £96

Striking trompe-l'oeil hand-painted murals enhance the Edwardian setting
of a fine restaurant in which the kitchen's classical compositions are a
development of the Elgar theme. There's a suitably light touch to both, as
Idris Caldora's food interprets the texture and counterpoints of the master's
music. Noteworthy dishes include a tartlet of onion and smoked bacon
with dandelion salad, pan-fried scallops with artichokes and herb noodles,
and veal fillet with tomato and basil confit glazed with Gruyère. Hot peach
soufflé, fruit sorbets with meringue or French and English cheeses to
follow. Singing pianist Mon-Sat. *Seats 50. Parties 12. Private Room.
L 12.30-2.30 D 7.30-10.30. Closed L Sat. Set L £15.50 Set D £23.50.*

Langtry's £60

British cookery to traditional recipes produces daily lunchtime dishes of
Midlands faggots with mushy peas and West Country chicken, bacon and
parsley pie. Omelette Arnold Bennett, guinea fowl with bubble and squeak
and steamed apple sponge extend the English offerings à la carte. *Seats 50.
Parties 50. Private Room. L 11.30-3 D 6-10. Closed Sun, Bank Holidays.*

Birmingham Airport — Forte Posthouse — 61% — £67

Tel 021-782 8141   Fax 021-782 2476

Coventry Road Birmingham Airport Birmingham
West Midlands B26 3QW — Map 10 C4

30s hotel with a modernised interior, standing on the A45. Conference and
banqueting facilities for up to 150. *Rooms 136. Croquet, children's playroom.*
Access, Amex, Visa, 🌐 *Diners Club International*

Birmingham Airport — Novotel — 65% — £88

Tel 021-782 7000   Fax 021-782 0445

Birmingham International Airport Birmingham West Midlands B26 3QL — Map 10 C4

In a prime site opposite the airport's main terminals, this Novotel has
sound-proofed bedrooms and stylish day rooms. Conference and
banqueting facilities for around 35. *Rooms 195. Access, Amex, Visa,*
🌐 *Diners Club International*

Birmingham   Places of Interest

Convention and Visitor Bureau City Arcade Tel 021 643 2514.
Convention and Visitor Bureau National Exhibition Centre
   Tel 021 780 4321.
Information Desk Birmingham Airport Tel 021 767 7145/6.
Birmingham Cathedral Tel 021 236 4333.
County Cricket Ground Edgbaston Tel 021 446 4422.
Aston Villa Football Ground Villa Park Tel 021 327 6604.
Ackers Park Trust Dry Ski Slope Small Heath Tel 021 771 4448.
Drayton Manor Park Nr Tamworth Tel 0827 287979.
Birmingham Nature Centre Tel 021 472 7775.
Dudley Zoo Tel 0384 252401.
   Theatres and Concert Halls
Alexandra Theatre Station Street Tel 021 643 3180.
Birmingham Hippodrome (Royal Ballet) Hurst Street Tel 021 622 7286.
Birmingham Repertory Theatre Broad Street Tel 021 236 4755.
Crescent Theatre Cumberland Street Tel 021 643 5858.
Midlands Arts Centre Cannon Hill Park Tel 021 440 4221.
City of Birmingham Symphony Orchestra Symphony Hall, International
   Convention Centre Tel 021 7828282.
   Historic Houses, Castles and Gardens
Aston Hall Tel 021 327 0062.
Birmingham Botanical Gardens and Glasshouses Edgbaston
   Tel 021 454 1860.
Castle Bromwich Hall Gardens Tel 021 749 4100.
University of Birmingham Botanic Garden Tel 021 414 5613.
   Museums and Art Galleries
Birmingham Museum and Art Gallery Tel 021 235 2834.
Black Country Museum Tipton Road, Dudley Tel 021 557 9643.
Museum of Science and Industry Tel 021 236 1022.
The Patrick Collection (Autoworld) Tel 021 459 9111.

Bishop's Tawton — Halmpstone Manor — 67% — £100

Tel 0271 830321   Fax 0271 830826

Bishop's Tawton Barnstaple Devon EX32 0EA — Map 3 D2

A working farm as well as a small country hotel, with lovely views of a
valley, rolling hills and a pretty garden. The welcome is friendly and
informal, and guests can relax with tea cakes in the comfort of a
traditionally furnished lounge. Bedrooms are decorated and appointed to a
high standard: lovely fabrics, antiques, either four-posters or brass and
coronet beds, tiled bathrooms (two with shower/WC only). Breakfasts are
good, and nothing is too much trouble for the owners and staff. No
children under 12. *Rooms 5. Garden. Access, Amex, Visa,* 🌐 *Diners Club International*

Restaurant   £65

Prime meat, game and fish, carefully cooked and appropriately sauced by
Jane Stanbury, are used for the dishes served in the panelled dining rooms.
Pheasant sausage with wild rice or smoked salmon rolls filled with prawns
and seafood sauce might precede fillet of Devonshire beef or lightly curried
schnitzel of veal with pineapple. Rich sweets from the trolley. *Seats 24.
Parties 20. L by arrangement D 7-9.30. Set D £27.50.*

Blackburn   Moat House   58%   £83

Tel 0254 264441   Fax 0254 682435   **H**

Preston New Road Blackburn Lancashire BB2 7BE   Map 10 B1

A modern Queens Moat Houses franchise with a distinctive gabled roof
and extensive conference facilities (for up to 350 theatre-style). *Rooms 98.*
Access, Amex, Visa, ⓘ *Diners Club International*

Blackburn   Places of Interest

Tourist Information   Tel 0254 53277.
Empire Theatre   Tel 0254 698859.
Gawthorpe Hall (NT)   Padiham Tel 0282 78511.
Blackburn Cathedral   Tel 0254 51491.
Blackburn Rovers Football Ground   Ewood Park Tel 0254 55432.
Blackburn Arena   Tel 0254 668686 *Ice Rink.*
Pendle Ski Club   Sabden Tel 0200 23939.
Ski Rossendale   Rawtenstall Tel 0706 228844.
   Museums and Art Galleries
Pendle Heritage Centre   ·Nelson, Nr Barrowford Tel 0282 695366.
Blackburn Museum and Art Gallery   Museum Street Tel 0254 667130.
**Towneley Hall Art Gallery and Museums and Museums of Local Crafts
   and Industries**   Burnley Tel 0282 24213.
Museum of Childhood   Church Street, Ribchester Tel 0254 878520.

Blackpool   Imperial Hotel   64%   £109

Tel 0253 23971   Fax 0253 751784   **H**

North Promenade Blackpool Lancashire FY1 2HB   Map 10 A1

A degree of Victorian grandeur survives at this Forte Grand hotel
overlooking the sea on the North Promenade. Generally good-sized
bedrooms offer all the usual modern conveniences. Conferences/banqueting
for 500/450. *Rooms 183. Indoor swimming pool, sauna, steam room, solarium,
spa bath, keep-fit equipment. Access, Amex, Visa,* ⓘ *Diners Club International*

Blackpool   Pembroke Hotel   67%   £122

Tel 0253 23434   Fax 0253 27864   **H**

North Promenade Blackpool Lancashire FY1 5JQ   Map 10 A1

A modern conference hotel with facilities for up to 900 delegates (theatre-
style) and up to 600 for banqueting. In the main holiday season families are
well catered for, with a playroom, baby-sitting and a supervised crèche
(9am-9pm) as well as a separate children's menu. A large swimming pool
and Springs night club are among the leisure amenities. Metropole Hotels.
Rooms 274. Indoor swimming pool, sauna, solarium. Access, Amex, Visa,
ⓘ *Diners Club International*

Blackpool   September Brasserie   £62

Tel 0253 23282   **R**

15-17 Queen Street Blackpool Lancashire FY1 1PU   Map 10 A1

Unusually sited above a hairdresser's shop, alongside Blackpool's fish
parlours, Michael Golowicz's restaurant is an unexpected find. Blue and
peach rag-rolled walls, a stencilled frieze and limed wood create a stylish
atmosphere in which to enjoy his cooking, which provides five dishes at
each course. The style ranges from cromesquis of calf's sweetbreads with
field mushrooms and wasabi mayonnaise or wild rabbit terrine with

cranberry chutney and fresh laverbread to rack of lamb with olive and mustard crust and civet of kangaroo on green lentils – self-styled "creative, eclectic cooking" indeed! The aim is to use ingredients free of chemicals, additives and colourings wherever possible, a policy admirably demonstrated by the choice of six organic dessert wines served by the glass. *Seats 34. L 12-2.30 D 7-9.30. Closed Sun & Mon, 25 & 26 Dec, Good Friday. Access, Amex, Visa,*

Blackpool   Places of Interest

Tourist Information   Clifton Street Tel 0253 21623.
Tourist Information   Coronation Street Tel 0253 21891.
Chingle Hall   Goosnargh Tel 0772 861082.
Stanley Park Cricket Ground   Tel 0253 33347.
Blackpool Icedrome   Tel 0253 41707.
Blackpool Zoo   Tel 0253 65027.
   Theatres and Concert Halls
South Pier Theatre   The Promenade Tel 0253 43096.
Winter Gardens and Opera House   Church Street Tel 0253 27786.

Blackwater Long's	£59
Tel 0872 561111	**R**
Blackwater Truro Cornwall TR4 8HH	Map 2 B3

Ann Long thinks, eats and sleeps cooking, and visitors to her elegant creeper-clad house will quickly recognise the hard work and skill inherent in her modern British cooking. Typically, a smooth piccalilli soup should get the taste buds revving, followed by Stilton cheesecake, best end of lamb in puff pastry with apple and laverbread purée or green-pepper-pasted chicken and pigeon breasts with celery and Marsala sauce to move into overdrive. Sunday lunch starts with "a light mixed beginning", then soup and a choice of three modern main courses and sweets to finish. A short, well-annotated wine list. No children under 8. *Seats 35. Parties 8. Private Room. L (Sun only) 12.30-1.45 D 7.30-9.30. Closed D Sun-Tue, all Bank Holidays, 3/4 weeks Jan/Feb. Set L (Sun) £11.25. Access, Visa.*

Blakeney Blakeney Hotel 64%	£108
Tel 0263 740797 Fax 0263 740795	**H**
The Quay Blakeney Nr Holt Norfolk NR25 7NE	Map 6 C1

A family-owned hotel, run in traditional style, on the quayside overlooking the National Trust harbour. Public rooms include a first-floor sun lounge which enjoys to the full the fine views across the salt marshes towards Blakeney Point. Many front-facing bedrooms share the view; there are several mini-suites, a four-poster room and a ground-floor room suitable for wheelchairs. Some rooms in an annexe have private patios. The Mayflower ballroom holds 200 for meetings or banquets. *Rooms 60. Garden, indoor swimming pool, keep-fit equipment, spa bath, sauna, snooker. Access, Amex, Visa,*

Blakeney Manor Hotel 58%	£68
Tel 0263 740376 Fax 0263 741116	**H**
Blakeney Nr Holt Norfolk NR25 7ND	Map 6 C1

Privately-owned 17th-century former farmhouse on the north coast of Norfolk, right next to salt marshes and a harbour inlet – ideal for yachtsmen and bird-watchers. A flagstoned entrance hall leads into day rooms that include a spacious lounge. Spotless bedrooms with candlewick bedspreads and simple, white laminate units are arranged in single-storeyed outhouses around neat courtyards. Charming walled garden seating area. No children under 10. *Rooms 36. Garden, bowling green. No credit cards.*

Blakeney   Places of Interest

Holkham Hall   Tel 0328 710227.
Walsingham Abbey   Walsingham Tel 0328 820259.

Blanchland   Lord Crewe Arms   63%   £94

Tel 0434 675251   Fax 0434 675337   **H**

Blanchland Nr Consett Co Durham DH8 9SP   Map 15 B4

Situated in one of the most unspoilt villages in England, with a sense of
history imparted by beams, flagstones and thick walls – some parts of the
building date back to the 13th century. The atmospheric, stone-vaulted
crypt is now a public bar. Eight bedrooms in the main house are decorated
in solid traditional style while others are in a more contemporary mode.
Children up to 14 stay free in parents' room. *Rooms 18. Garden. Access,
Amex, Visa,*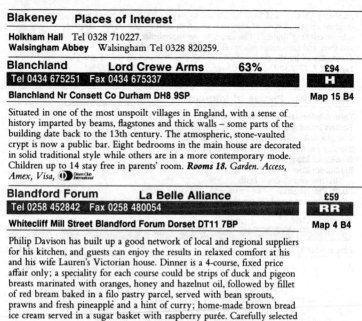

Blandford Forum   La Belle Alliance   £59

Tel 0258 452842   Fax 0258 480054   **RR**

Whitecliff Mill Street Blandford Forum Dorset DT11 7BP   Map 4 B4

Philip Davison has built up a good network of local and regional suppliers
for his kitchen, and guests can enjoy the results in relaxed comfort at his
and his wife Lauren's Victorian house. Dinner is a 4-course, fixed price
affair only; a speciality for each course could be strips of duck and pigeon
breasts marinated with oranges, honey and hazelnut oil, followed by fillet
of red bream baked in a filo pastry parcel, served with bean sprouts,
prawns and fresh pineapple and a hint of curry; home-made brown bread
ice cream served in a sugar basket with raspberry purée. Carefully selected
wine list at fair prices. No smoking in dining room. *Seats 30. Parties 40.
Private Room. L by arrangement only D 7-9.30 (Sat to 10). Closed Sun (open
Bank Holiday weekends), Mon, all Jan. Set D from £22. Access, Amex, Visa,*
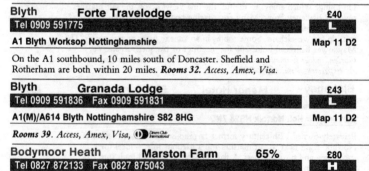

Rooms   £62

Six pretty bedrooms are all individually decorated and have the usual
home comforts.

Blandford Forum   Places of Interest

Tourist Information   Tel 0258 454770.
Milton Abbey   Milton Abbas Tel 0258 880484.

Blyth   Forte Travelodge   £40

Tel 0909 591775   **L**

A1 Blyth Worksop Nottinghamshire   Map 11 D2

On the A1 southbound, 10 miles south of Doncaster. Sheffield and
Rotherham are both within 20 miles. *Rooms 32. Access, Amex, Visa.*

Blyth   Granada Lodge   £43

Tel 0909 591836   Fax 0909 591831   **L**

A1(M)/A614 Blyth Nottinghamshire S82 8HG   Map 11 D2

Rooms 39. Access, Amex, Visa,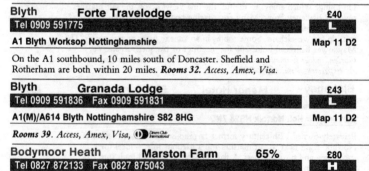

Bodymoor Heath   Marston Farm   65%   £80

Tel 0827 872133   Fax 0827 875043   **H**

Dog Lane Bodymoor Heath Nr Sutton Coldfield Warwickshire B76 9JD   Map 10 C4

Ten minutes drive from Birmingham Airport and the NEC, Marston
Farm is just off junction 9 of the M42: follow signs to Kingsbury and
Bodymoor Heath. A 17th-century farmhouse forms the main body of the
hotel, deriving both character and intimacy from oak beams and inglenook

fireplaces. A recent conversion of the barn has added 20 uniform bedrooms and a boardroom with conference accommodation for up to 45 and banqueting space for 95. *Rooms 38. Garden, tennis, fishing. Access, Amex, Visa,*

Bognor Regis   Royal Norfolk   60%   £76
Tel 0243 826222   Fax 0243 826325   H
The Esplanade Bognor Regis West Sussex PO21 2LH   Map 5 E4

The hotel dates from the 1830s and has entertained such notables as Queen Alexandra and Napoleon III. Bedrooms, in various styles, are generally bright and pleasant. Forte Heritage. *Rooms 51. Garden, outdoor swimming pool, tennis. Access, Amex, Visa,*

Bollington   Mauro's   £60
Tel 0625 573898   R
88 Palmerston Street Bollington Nr Macclesfield Cheshire SK10 5PW   Map 10 C2

The Mauro family run an authentic north Italian restaurant with a feast of flavours in the *antipasti alla caprese,* served from a trolley. Home-made noodles and ravioli are served several ways and market-fresh fish heads a list of daily specials. Lighter dishes on a good-value, 3-course lunch menu. Exclusively Italian wines, as one might expect. *Seats 50. L 12.15-2 (Sat to 1.30) D 7-10 (Sat to 10.30). Closed Sun & Mon, 25 & 26 Dec, 3 weeks Aug/Sep. Set L £8.20. Access, Amex, Visa.*

Bolton   Egerton House   63%   £85
Tel 0204 307171   Fax 0204 593030   H
off Blackburn Road Egerton Bolton Lancashire BL7 9PL   Map 10 B2

Rank-owned Victorian house set among trees and lawns just off the A466. Bright, comfortable lounge and bar, bedrooms graded either standard or superior. Guests have free use of the leisure facilities at the Last Drop Village Hotel, two minutes drive away. A self-contained function suite includes the Barn, catering for up to 150 delegates. Children up to the age of five stay free in parents' room. Ample parking. *Rooms 32. Garden. Closed 27 Dec. Access, Amex, Visa,*

Bolton   Forte Posthouse   58%   £63
Tel 0204 651511   Fax 0204 61064   H
Beaumont Road Bolton Greater Manchester BL3 4TA   Map 10 B2

70s' hotel on the outskirts of Bolton, near junction 5 of the M61. Two-level bedroom block. Conference/banqueting facilities for 120/90. *Rooms 96. Garden. Access, Amex, Visa,*

Bolton   Last Drop Village Hotel   68%   £85
Tel 0204 591131   Fax 0204 304122   H
Hospital Road Bromley Cross Bolton Lancashire BL7 9PZ   Map 10 B2

A collection of 18th-century moorland farm buildings has been skilfully turned into a village with cottages, gardens, craft shops, a pub, a tea shop and, at its heart, a comfortable and well-equipped hotel. Day rooms retain some original features, while bedrooms are mainly bright and modern. Top of the range is the Lancaster Suite with traditional decor, a four-poster and a panelled lounge. Children up to 15 stay free in parents' room. There are extensive conference facilities (in a choice of rooms) for up to 220 delegates. *Rooms 83. Indoor swimming pool, gymnasium, sauna, spa bath, squash, beautician, hairdressing, snooker, coffee shop (10am-5.30pm). Access, Amex, Visa,*

Bolton   Pack Horse Hotel   62%   £74

Tel 0204 27261   Fax 0204 364352   **H**

Nelson Square Bradshawgate Bolton Greater Manchester BLI 1DP   **Map 10 B2**

Redbrick building in the town centre, with up-to-date accommodation,
cheerful bars and a thriving conference business (six rooms handling up to
275 delegates). Children up to 14 stay free in parents' room. De Vere.
Rooms 73. Access, Amex, Visa, (I) *Diners Club International*

Bolton   Places of Interest

Tourist Information   Tel 0204 364333.
Little Theatre   Hanover Street Tel 0204 24469.
Octagon Theatre   Howell Croft, South Bolton Tel 0204 20661.

Bolton Abbey   Devonshire Arms   73%   £110

Tel 0756 710441   Fax 0756 710564   **H**

Bolton Abbey Nr Skipton North Yorkshire BD23 6AJ   **Map 15 B6**

On the A59, by the edge of the Abbey estate, a much-extended 18th-
century coaching inn owned by the Duke of Devonshire. Set in 12 acres of
grounds amid an area of outstanding natural beauty, it is furnished and
appointed with much thought. Well-proportioned day rooms feature
choice antiques and oil paintings from the Devonshire family home of
Chatsworth in Derbyshire. The best bedrooms, in the main house, are
individually themed and again show carefully chosen furnishings and
fabrics. Numerous little extras like a decanter of sherry, magazines and
flowers are a welcoming touch. The majority of bedrooms in more recent
wings are more uniform in size and style, though they are equally inviting
and comfortable. Bathrooms are a little cramped. Switched-on management
lead a young team. Good breakfast served in the conservatory, snack food
in the bar. Children stay free in parents' room. *Rooms 40. Garden, croquet,
putting, fishing, helipad. Access, Amex, Visa,* (I) *Diners Club International*

Bonchurch   Winterbourne Hotel   64%   £94

Tel 0983 852535   Fax 0983 853056   **H**

Bonchurch Isle of Wight PO38 1RQ   **Map 5 D4**

An enchanting garden complete with waterfalls and sea views is the
outstanding feature of the hotel where Charles Dickens wrote most of
David Copperfield; bedrooms are named after characters in the novel. A
charming lounge with French windows opening on to the terrace and
garden is the principal day room. Bedrooms range from tiny singles with
basic fitted furniture to spacious and airy rooms, particularly five in the
converted coach house. *Rooms 19. Garden, outdoor swimming pool. Closed
mid Nov-early Mar. Access, Amex, Visa,* (I) *Diners Club International*

Boreham Street   White Friars Hotel   57%   £60

Tel 0323 832355   Fax 0323 833882   **H**

Boreham Street Nr Herstmonceux East Sussex BN27 4SE   **Map 7 B6**

Built in 1721, and converted to a hotel in the 1930s. Day rooms and some
bedrooms have old-fashioned charm; nine more up-to-date rooms are in a
separate cottage block. Informal restaurant in the cellars. Characterful,
beamed conference room for up to 30 delegates. *Rooms 21. Garden. Access,
Amex, Visa,* (I) *Diners Club International*

Boroughbridge   The Crown   63%   £50

Tel 0423 322328   Fax 0423 324512   **H**

Horsefair Boroughbridge North Yorkshire YO5 9LB   **Map 15 C6**

Taking advantage of an enforced closure due to flooding, the Crown has
completely refurbished and remodelled the ground floor to create a
comfortable oak dado-panelled reception/lounge, smart bar and a number

of function rooms where, once or twice a month, public dinner dances are held – often with cabaret. Banqueting/conference facilities for 140/200 guests. Redecorated bedrooms have all the usual amenities (except for the TVs not being remote-control). Smart, carpeted bathrooms all have showers over tubs. Children stay free in parents' room. *Rooms 42. Access, Amex, Visa,* (D) *Diners Club International*

Borrowdale   Borrowdale Hotel   60%

	£82*
Tel 076 87 77224 Fax 076 87 77338	**H**
Borrowdale Keswick-on-Derwentwater Cumbria	Map 13 C5

A stone's throw from Derwentwater, three miles from Kewsick on the B5284, stands a solid, greystone hotel whose style of hospitality resists change. Early bed for children, dress code for dinner and * half-board terms only. Lovely enclosed garden overlooked by a restyled bar and patio: chintzy lounges, lake views and restrained service. *Rooms 34. Garden. Access, Visa.*

Borrowdale   Stakis Lodore Swiss Hotel   71%

	£160*
Tel 076 87 77285 Fax 076 87 77343	**H**
Borrowdale Keswick Cumbria CA12 5UX	Map 13 C5

Holiday hotel set in 40 acres by Derwentwater; good family facilities and convenient for Keswick ferry (3 miles) and town (3 miles). Picture windows afford splendid views from day rooms and the best, front-facing bedrooms. Several splendid family rooms; resident nanny in summer. Conference/banqueting facilities for 80/70. * Half-board terms only. No dogs. Stakis Hotels. *Rooms 70. Garden, tennis, indoor & outdoor swimming pools, gymnasium, squash, sauna, solarium, beauty salon, hairdressing, games room, nursery, crèche, lock-up garage. Access, Amex, Visa,* (D) *Diners Club International*

Bosham   Millstream Hotel   63%

	£89
Tel 0243 573234 Fax 0243 573459	**H**
Bosham Lane Bosham West Sussex PO18 8HL	Map 5 D4

Part small manor house, part malthouse, the peaceful Millstream is an attractive small hotel just a short walk from the heart of a picturesque sailing village. A rattan-furnished bar and sunny lounge are agreeable places for a drink or a chat. Bedrooms, mostly furnished with reproduction antiques, include mini-safes and bathroom scales among their accessories. *Rooms 29. Garden. Access, Amex, Visa,* (D) *Diners Club International*

Boston   New England Hotel   56%

	£76
Tel 0205 365255 Fax 0205 310597	**H**
49 Wide Bargate Boston Lincolnshire PE21 6SH	Map 11 F3

Former coaching inn in the town centre with decent-sized bedrooms; bathrooms are simple and compact. On the ground floor a small cocktail bar acts as a buffer between the public bar-lounge and the restaurant. Forte Heritage. *Rooms 25. Access, Amex, Visa,* (D) *Diners Club International*

Boston   Places of Interest

Tourist Information   Tel 0205 356656.

Botley   Cobbett's

	£60
Tel 0489 782068	**R**
15 The Square Botley Southampton Hampshire SO3 2EA	Map 5 D4

You can hear the chimes of the neighbouring church clock in this charming 16th-century cottage with beamed ceilings and timbered walls. Charles and Lucie Skipwith will soon have been in charge for 20 years, and for the last seven Peter Hayes has been producing robust French regional dishes. Crisp millefeuille of snails and flageolet beans and medallions of wild venison with crunchy diced celeriac with a red wine

game sauce are examples of well-balanced and subtle kitchencraft. Finish on
a high note with the *assiette de desserts* – all the desserts in miniature. The
cheeses, mainly French, are also hard to decline. **Seats 40.** Private Room.
L 12-2 D 7.30-10 (Sat from 7). Closed L Mon & Sat, D Sun, Bank Holidays,
2 weeks summer, 2 weeks winter. Set L £15. Access, Amex, Visa.

| Boughton Monchelsea | Tanyard Hotel | 63% | £75 |

Tel 0622 744705 — **H**

Wierton Hill Boughton Monchelsea Nr Maidstone Kent ME17 4JT — **Map 7 C5**

Jan Davies, owner for 10 years, aims for a house party atmosphere.
Beautiful views over the Kentish Weald, a secluded location and 14th-
century architecture make the Tanyard a house of great charm and
character. A huge stone inglenook fireplace dominates the homely lounge,
complemented by beams and period-style furniture. Bedrooms have
uneven floors, beamed ceilings and walls and exposed stonework. No
children under six, no dogs. **Rooms 6.** Garden, croquet. Closed Dec-Jan.
Access, Amex, Visa, Diners Club International

| Bournemouth | Carlton Hotel | 78% | £150 |

Tel 0202 552011   Fax 0202 299573 — **H**

East Overcliff Bournemouth Dorset BH1 3DN — **Map 4 C4**

Easily Bournemouth's best, the privately-owned hotel has a luxurious and
opulent feel about it. Welcoming staff greet guests with a smile and the
smart foyer sets the tone for the public areas; a walnut and mahogany-
panelled library houses volumes of leather-bound books, cabinets filled
with antiques and objets d'art, a bracket clock, and comfortable armchairs;
a cocktail bar with leather chairs contains framed pencil sketches of the
famous and antique mirrors; there's also a bright lounge which leads on to
a sunny conservatory. Most of the suites and bedrooms have views of the
coastline and have been refurbished to a high standard, and there's a
continuous restyling programme in operation for the rest. Bathrooms are
designed to pamper. Conference/banqueting for 140/120. No dogs. No
children under 12. **Rooms 70.** Garden, outdoor swimming pool, sauna,
solarium, whirlpool bath, gymnasium, beauty salon, hairdressing, snooker. Access,
Amex, Visa, Diners Club International

| Bournemouth | Elysée Restaurant | | £50 |

Tel 0202 789299 — **R**

160 Commercial Road Bournemouth Dorset BH2 5LX — **Map 4 C4**

Through an archway off Commercial Road, awnings and window boxes
front a French restaurant with a simple decor of black and white tiles and
brick columns. Chef-manager Noel Malnoe, who hails from Brittany,
produces a good variety of well-constructed dishes, from chicken mousse
with a red pepper sauce and garlicky snails in puff pastry to salmon steak
with spinach sauce, beef fillet with wild mushrooms and venison with red
cabbage and cranberry sauce. Sensibly short, all-French wine list. **Seats 30.**
Parties 8. L 12-2.30 D 7-11 (Sat to 11.30). Closed Mon. Set L £6.90 Set D
£9.90/£19.95. Access, Amex, Visa, Diners Club International

| Bournemouth | Forte Posthouse | 59% | £64 |

Tel 0202 553262   Fax 0202 557698 — **H**

The Lansdowne Bournemouth Dorset BH1 2PR — **Map 4 C4**

Circular hotel on three floors above a spiral car park. Practical modern
bedrooms and roomy open-plan public areas. Conferences for up to 100.
Rooms 98. Access, Amex, Visa, Diners Club International

Bournemouth Henry's £20

| Tel 0202 297887 | R |

6 Lansdowne Road Bournemouth Dorset BH1 1SD Map 4 C4

Interesting, reasonably-priced vegetarian, vegan and gluten-free dishes
prepared daily by a dedicated crew; mushroom and potato burgers; spicy
aubergine and bean casserole; mushroom flan. A little less snacky and a
touch more expensive at night. *Seats 50. Parties 50. Private Room. L 9-2.30
D 5.30-11. Closed Sun in winter, Bank Holidays. No credit cards.*

Bournemouth Langtry Manor 62% £79

| Tel 0202 553887   Fax 0202 290115 | H |

26 Derby Road East Cliff Bournemouth Dorset BH1 3QB Map 4 C4

The house was built by Edward VII, then Prince of Wales, for Lillie
Langtry. Their story is commemorated throughout the hotel and there's a
glass case filled with memorabilia on the first floor. Public rooms have a
period flavour; best of these is the dining hall with its minstrel's gallery.
Bedrooms vary considerably in size and opulence; some smaller rooms
have been put together to make suites, others have four-poster beds; most
can best be described as romantic. *Rooms 27. Garden. Access, Amex, Visa,*
(Diners Club International)

Bournemouth Norfolk Royale 70% £132

| Tel 0202 551521   Fax 0202 299729 | H |

Richmond Hill Bournemouth Dorset BH2 6EN Map 4 C4

Centrally located on Richmond Hill, behind a grand facade with listed
cast-ironwork, the Norfolk Royale successfully recreates the Edwardian
atmosphere of Bournemouth's heyday while moving with the times. A
chandeliered foyer leads into a glass and steel atrium housing a leisure
centre and the Orangery coffee shop, full of ferns, trellis work and cane
furniture. Spacious bedrooms have comfortable beds and reflect a range of
Edwardian designs, with composite fitments from hairdryers to mini-bars.
They range from singles to one-bedroom suites and studio suites with
whirlpool baths. The four function/conference suites (120 banqueting, 80
theatre-style) all carry Duke of Norfolk family names. No dogs. *Rooms 95.
Sauna, steam room. Access, Amex, Visa,* (Diners Club International)

Bournemouth Ocean Palace £45

| Tel 0202 559130 | R |

8 Priory Road Bournemouth Dorset BH2 5DG Map 4 C4

A short walk from the conference centre and sea front, this modern,
purpose-built restaurant has a conservatory-style frontage, simple decor and
plain walls hung with contemporary Chinese artwork. Hing Wong's
excellent cooking skills cover Peking and Szechuan styles, with special
vegetarian and good set-price seafood menus. Interesting choices from
nearly two hundred dishes include a variety of oyster, duck and sizzling
dishes. *Seats 140. Parties 150. Private Room. L 12-2.30 D 6-11.30. Closed 3
days Xmas. Set L from £5.80 Set D from £13. Access, Amex, Visa,* (Diners Club International)

Bournemouth Palace Court 71% £108

| Tel 0202 557681   Fax 0202 554918 | H |

Westover Road Bournemouth Dorset BH1 2BZ Map 4 C4

Now complete, extensive refurbishment has returned this between-the-
wars, high-rise hotel to its former splendour. Spacious public areas have
been strikingly re-modelled and refurbished in 1930s style; the front
lounge with leather armchairs in pale yellow and pale pink and the split-
level lounge/bar on the first floor in darker, more sophisticated tones.
Conservatory-style windows have taken advantage of views across the
Solent to the Isle of Wight. A further café/lounge has rattan furniture and
ceiling fans slowly swishing overhead. Bedroom decor varies but all rooms

have freestanding furniture, many with walnut veneer pieces, and smartly-tiled bathrooms. Eight de-luxe rooms live up to their name with mirrored bedheads (containing cassette players as well as radios) and bathrooms with spa baths, private mini-saunas and exercise bicycles; only the less-than-luxurious toiletries spoil the effect. Rooms at the front have balconies with outdoor seating. 24hr room service can provide hot meals even in the middle of the night. Banqueting/conference facilities for 250/200. Ample garage parking. No children under 6. *Rooms 108. Indoor swimming pool, spa baths, sauna, solarium, snooker. Access, Amex, Visa,*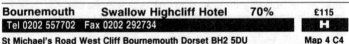

Bournemouth   Royal Bath Hotel   73%   £140

Tel 0202 555555   Fax 0202 554158   **HR**

Bath Road Bournemouth Dorset BH1 2EW   **Map 4 C4**

A heated kidney-shaped swimming pool is the central feature of the splendid Leisure Pavilion, an up-to-date attraction of the Victorian Royal Bath (now over 150 years old). The hotel stands in a three-acre garden, with clifftop views out to sea. Space and elegance are keynotes, both in the bars and lounges, and in the good-sized bedrooms, many of which face the sea. Rooms have very smart built-in furniture in mahogany or cream finish and modern bathrooms with brass fittings plus good toiletries. Supervised crèche daily in high season. No dogs. De Vere Hotels. *Rooms 131. Garden, indoor swimming pool, sauna, solarium, spa bath, steam room, gymnasium, beauty salon, hairdressing, putting, croquet, snooker, coffee shop (10.30am-8.15pm), children's playground, garage. Access, Amex, Visa,*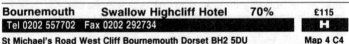

Oscar's Restaurant

Dining in the grand style from a long and mainly classical French menu. *Seats 40. L 12.30-2.15 D 6.30-10.15. Closed Sun, 25 Dec. Set L from £14.50 Set D from £25.*

Bournemouth   Swallow Highcliff Hotel   70%   £115

Tel 0202 557702   Fax 0202 292734   **H**

St Michael's Road West Cliff Bournemouth Dorset BH2 5DU   **Map 4 C4**

An imposing Victorian hotel with splendid clifftop location giving many of the rooms fine marine views. A funicular lift carries guests from hotel to promenade. Good-sized bedrooms in the main house have dark period-style furniture, those in the converted coastguard cottages smart lightwood furniture. Numerous public rooms include a terrace bar, lounge for non-smokers and Magnums night club. Magnificent conference facilities can cope with up to 500 delegates. *Rooms 157. Garden, outdoor swimming pool, sauna, solarium, tennis, putting, games room, snooker, crèche (daily in summer 10am-6pm), children's play area, baby-listening, night club. Access, Amex, Visa,*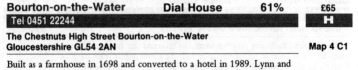

Bournemouth   Places of Interest

Tourist Information   Westover Road Tel 0202 789789.
Pavilion Theatre   Westover Road Tel 0202 297297.
Pier Theatre   Bournemouth Pier Tel 0202 20250.

Bourton-on-the-Water   Dial House   61%   £65

Tel 0451 22244   **H**

The Chestnuts High Street Bourton-on-the-Water Gloucestershire GL54 2AN   **Map 4 C1**

Built as a farmhouse in 1698 and converted to a hotel in 1989. Lynn and Peter Boxall have carefully enhanced the interior with family antiques and four-posters; understated decor adds to the charm of buildings and contents. Downstairs is the lounge with inglenooks, leather sofas and plentiful reading matter, upstairs bedrooms that include some with half-testers or four-posters. No children under eight. *Rooms 10. Garden, croquet. Access, Visa.*

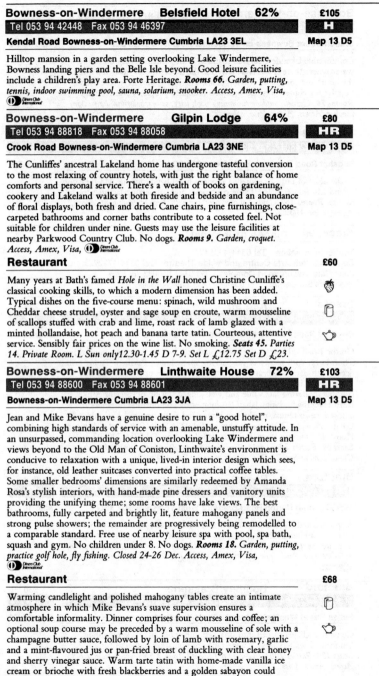

Bowness-on-Windermere   Belsfield Hotel   62%   £105

Tel 053 94 42448   Fax 053 94 46397   **H**

Kendal Road Bowness-on-Windermere Cumbria LA23 3EL   **Map 13 D5**

Hilltop mansion in a garden setting overlooking Lake Windermere,
Bowness landing piers and the Belle Isle beyond. Good leisure facilities
include a children's play area. Forte Heritage. *Rooms 66. Garden, putting,
tennis, indoor swimming pool, sauna, solarium, snooker. Access, Amex, Visa,*

Bowness-on-Windermere   Gilpin Lodge   64%   £80

Tel 053 94 88818   Fax 053 94 88058   **HR**

Crook Road Bowness-on-Windermere Cumbria LA23 3NE   **Map 13 D5**

The Cunliffes' ancestral Lakeland home has undergone tasteful conversion
to the most relaxing of country hotels, with just the right balance of home
comforts and personal service. There's a wealth of books on gardening,
cookery and Lakeland walks at both fireside and bedside and an abundance
of floral displays, both fresh and dried. Cane chairs, pine furnishings, close-
carpeted bathrooms and corner baths contribute to a cosseted feel. Not
suitable for children under nine. Guests may use the leisure facilities at
nearby Parkwood Country Club. No dogs. *Rooms 9. Garden, croquet.
Access, Amex, Visa,*

Restaurant   £60

Many years at Bath's famed *Hole in the Wall* honed Christine Cunliffe's
classical cooking skills, to which a modern dimension has been added.
Typical dishes on the five-course menu: spinach, wild mushroom and
Cheddar cheese strudel, oyster and sage soup en croute, warm mousseline
of scallops stuffed with crab and lime, roast rack of lamb glazed with a
minted hollandaise, hot peach and banana tarte tatin. Courteous, attentive
service. Sensibly fair prices on the wine list. No smoking. *Seats 45. Parties
14. Private Room. L Sun only12.30-1.45 D 7-9. Set L £12.75 Set D £23.*

Bowness-on-Windermere   Linthwaite House   72%   £103

Tel 053 94 88600   Fax 053 94 88601   **HR**

Bowness-on-Windermere Cumbria LA23 3JA   **Map 13 D5**

Jean and Mike Bevans have a genuine desire to run a "good hotel",
combining high standards of service with an amenable, unstuffy attitude. In
an unsurpassed, commanding location overlooking Lake Windermere and
views beyond to the Old Man of Coniston, Linthwaite's environment is
conducive to relaxation with a unique, lived-in interior design which sees,
for instance, old leather suitcases converted into practical coffee tables.
Some smaller bedrooms' dimensions are similarly redeemed by Amanda
Rosa's stylish interiors, with hand-made pine dressers and vanitory units
providing the unifying theme; some rooms have lake views. The best
bathrooms, fully carpeted and brightly lit, feature mahogany panels and
strong pulse showers; the remainder are progressively being remodelled to
a comparable standard. Free use of nearby leisure spa with pool, spa bath,
squash and gym. No children under 8. No dogs. *Rooms 18. Garden, putting,
practice golf hole, fly fishing. Closed 24-26 Dec. Access, Amex, Visa,*

Restaurant   £68

Warming candlelight and polished mahogany tables create an intimate
atmosphere in which Mike Bevans's suave supervision ensures a
comfortable informality. Dinner comprises four courses and coffee; an
optional soup course may be preceded by a warm mousseline of sole with a
champagne butter sauce, followed by loin of lamb with rosemary, garlic
and a mint-flavoured jus or pan-fried breast of duckling with clear honey
and sherry vinegar sauce. Warm tarte tatin with home-made vanilla ice
cream or brioche with fresh blackberries and a golden sabayon could
complete a fine meal. Lighter lunches also offered. No smoking. *Seats 30.
Parties 35. Private Room. L Sun only 12-2 D 7.15-9.
Set L £12.50 Set D £25.*

Bowness-on-Windermere   Old England Hotel   65%   £115

Tel 053 94 42444   Fax 053 94 43432

Church Street Bowness-on-Windermere Cumbria LA23 3DF   Map 13 D5

Comfortable lakeside Georgian mansion with gardens giving on to the
water where there is a private jetty for the hotel's motor boat (for hire by
the hour) and for guests' rowing boats. The best rooms have lake views.
Popular for conferences and banquets (120/225 people). Forte Heritage.
*Rooms 79. Garden, outdoor swimming pool, jetty, sauna, solarium, hair salon,
snooker. Access, Amex, Visa,*

Bracknell   Hilton National   69%   £129

Tel 0344 424801   Fax 0344 487454

Bagshot Road Bracknell Berkshire RG12 3QJ   Map 5 E2

In the heart of busy Bracknell, a modern hotel handy for the M3 (junction
3) and M4 (junction 10). Large conference and banqueting facilities for up
to 300. *Rooms 167. Sauna, plunge pool, spa bath, keep-fit equipment. Access,
Amex, Visa,*

Bracknell   Places of Interest

Tourist Information   Tel 0344 423149.
South Hill Park Arts Centre and Wilde Theatre   Tel 0344 472272.
John Nike Leisuresport Complex   Tel 0344 860033 *Ice Rink.*
Bracknell Ski Centre   Tel 0344 427435 *Dry Ski Slope.*

Bradford   Aagrah   £25

Tel 0274 668818   R

Bradford Road Pudsey Nr Bradford West Yorkshire   Map 10 C1

On the Bradford lane of the Leeds-Bradford dual carriageway approaching
Thornbury, with plenty of car parking space. Indian-Pakistani Tudor grill
decor with dark oak beams, batik tablecloths, brass ornaments and tidy
waiting staff in dark-blue ethnic outfits. The successful Aagrah formula
continues, offering fair value and well-judged spicing of specialities like
lamb Hyderbady. Noor Jahan (an interesting combination of tandoori
chicken, lamb bhuna, mushroom bhuna and pilau rice) and Kashmir
kebabs. *Also at:* 27 Westgate, Shipley Tel 0274 594660 & Unit 4, Unicorn
House, Devonshire Place, Keighley Road Skipton Tel 0756 790807.
*Seats 64. Parties 20. D 6-11.30 (Fri & Sat 6-12) (Meals Sun 12-11.30).
Closed L Mon-Sat, 25 Dec. Access, Amex, Visa,*

Bradford   Bharat   £30

Tel 0274 521200   R

496-502 Great Horton Road Bradford West Yorkshire BD7 4EG   Map 10 C1

A spacious Indian restaurant under a first-floor social club. Tandoori dishes,
curries of all heats. Chef's special is whole leg of lamb (kurchi) for 4 people
or more. *Seats 48. Parties 10. L 12-1.45 D 6-11.45. Closed L Sun, all Mon,
25 & 26 Dec. Set L from £5.99 Set D from £12.25. Access, Amex, Visa,*

Bradford   Bombay Brasserie   £30

Tel 0274 737564   R

Simes Street Westgate Bradford West Yorkshire   Map 10 C1

Converted chapel turned into smart, Bombay old city-style restaurant.
Uniformed waiters serve a wide range of upmarket Indian dishes.
*Seats 130. Parties 200. L 12-2 D 6-12. Set L from £5.95 Set D from £6.95.
Access, Amex, Visa.*

Bradford K2 £20

Tel 0274 723704 **R**

116 Lumb Lane Bradford West Yorkshire BD8 7RS Map 10 C1

Clear, rich spicing comes from a father-and-son team who both cook a
distinctive style of bhunas and balti reductions. Fine roti, outstanding balti
milli julli with fresh dhaniya leaf and fresh vegetables. *Seats 66. Parties 36.
Private Room. Meals 8am-midnight.* Diners Club International

Bradford Nawaab £30

Tel 0274 720371 **R**

32 Manor Row Bradford West Yorkshire Map 10 C1

Set in a former banking house, atop Manor Row, with pink walls, gilded
plasterwork and an interior fountain, the Nawab has an extensive Pakistani
menu of some eighty-five main courses made from variations around eight
basic curries and tandoori specialities. Both a dish of balti-cooked diced
chicken and lamb with coriander leaf and chicken in well-spiced masala
reduction are served in their own cooking pans. Lightly crisped tandoori
nan and well-flavoured pilao rice accompany. *Seats 120. Parties 140. Private
Room. L 12-2 D 6-12.30 (Fri & Sat to 1.30, Sun 12-12). Closed L Sat.*
Access, Amex, Visa, Diners Club International

Bradford Restaurant 19 ★ £80

Tel 0274 492559 **RR**

19 North Park Road, Heaton Bradford
West Yorkshire BD9 4NT Map 10 C1

A large Victorian house, once a wool merchant's home, situated in a
residential suburb of the city overlooking Lister Park and the Cartwright
Hall Museum. Tables are well spaced and immaculately set in the high-
ceilinged room. Stephen Smith's hand-written menus offer a choice of
three- or four-course fixed-price options, with the top of the range
covering sautéed monkfish with couscous and a sweet pepper sauce; roast
loin of spring lamb with a pea and mint mousse, apple and sage jelly; roast
breast of quail with mushroom and pine kernel ravioli on a bed of
asparagus; roast saddle of rabbit with ham- and tarragon-stuffed leg and a
mustard sauce. The lower-priced menu offers three courses with no choice
(perhaps a warm salad of artichoke hearts, bacon, smoked chicken and
poached quail's eggs, followed by escalopes of salmon with tagliatelle and
then lemon tart) but excellent value. Desserts are always tempting: prunes
soaked in Armagnac with frangipan and vanilla custard, rhubarb and
ginger crème brulée with rhubarb sorbet or hot plum and almond tart
with honey ice cream. Partner Robert Barbour runs front of house with a
flair that suitably matches the eye-catching presentation of Stephen's dishes.
*Seats 36. Parties 12. L by arrangement D 7-10. Closed Sun & Mon, 1 week
Xmas, 1 week May, 1 week Aug/Sep. Set D £16.50 & £26/£28.* Access,
Amex, Visa, Diners Club International

Rooms £85

Four comfortable rooms, named after works of art by Russell Flint, are
all decorated with antiques and have smart en-suite bathrooms.

Bradford Novotel 60% £70

Tel 0274 683683 Fax 0274 651342 **H**

Merrydale Road Bradford West Yorkshire BD4 6SA Map 10 C1

A faceless modern exterior houses comfortable and smart accommodation.
Conference/banqueting facilities for 300/250. *Rooms 132. Garden, outdoor
swimming pool, coffee shop (6am-12am).* Access, Amex, Visa, Diners Club International

Bradford — PLS Gujrati Pure Vegetarian — £20

Tel 0274 720398   Fax 0274 724296

R

260 Great Horton Road Bradford West Yorkshire BD7 1PX

Map 10 C1

Subash Patel and family run the only genuinely authentic Gujerati
vegetarian restaurant in the region, offering Indian country cooking with a
simple menu of five thalis but without even a gesture to Western form or
style. Unusual fresh Indian vegetables, kalora, juwar, karela, sour tamarind
achar, fresh puris, lime pickle, creamy shrikhand or mango khas, all
wonderfully contrasting flavours. Unlicenced. *Seats 28. Parties 40. Private
Room. D only 5-11 (Sat to 11.30). Closed Mon. Access, Amex, Visa,*

Bradford — Stakis Norfolk Gardens — 65% — £106

Tel 0274 734734   Fax 0274 306146

H

Hall Ings Bradford West Yorkshire BD1 5SH

Map 10 C1

In the city centre, yet only a few minutes from the M62, the Norfolk
Gardens is a major conference venue with facilities for up to 700 delegates.
If you feel lucky, there's a Stakis casino next door. *Rooms 120. Coffee shop
(24 hrs). Access, Amex, Visa,*

Bradford — Victoria Hotel — 61% — £77

Tel 0274 728706   Fax 0274 736358

H

Bridge Street Bradford West Yorkshire BD1 1JX

Map 10 C1

Situated next to the main railway station, with public rooms on a grand
scale. Clean and comfortable bedrooms. *Rooms 59. Access, Amex, Visa,*

Bradford   Places of Interest

Tourist Information   Tel 0274 753678.
Alhambra Theatre   Morely Street Tel 0274 752000.
Bradford Cathedral   Tel 0274 725958.
Mecca Leisure Ice Rink   Tel 0274 729091.
   Museums and Art Galleries
Colour Museum   Tel 0274 390955.
Cartwright Hall Art Gallery   Tel 0274 493313.
National Museum of Photography, Film and Television   Tel 0274 727488.
Also houses Britain's only IMAX cinema.

Bradford-on-Avon — Woolley Grange — 75% — £89

Tel 022 16 4705   Fax 022 16 4059

HR

Woolley Green Bradford-on-Avon Wiltshire BA15 1TX

Map 4 B3

A splendid Jacobean building set in lovely grounds, Woolley Grange is a
friendly, relaxed and civilised country house hotel catering well for
families, especially those including small children. Owners Nigel and
Heather Chapman take excellent care of their guests, a policy which results
in many repeat bookings. A variety of specially commissioned paintings
and floral displays is found thoughout, reinforcing the homely, traditional
atmosphere. The panelled drawing room has a log fire, period furniture
and comfortable seating, and there's also a small sitting room and a
delightful conservatory with a flagstone floor and rattan furniture. The
bedrooms are individually decorated in country style, with period beds,
stripped pine, polished floors, flowers and pictures; many of the rooms
have gas coal fires and all have nice little touches like home-made biscuits,
fruit and mineral water. Bathrooms (some with shower/WC only) have
Victorian fittings. There is a separate children's barn with attendant nanny.
Egon Ronay's *...and Baby Comes Too* Guide Family Hotel of the Year
1992. *Rooms 20. Garden, outdoor swimming pool, tennis, croquet, snooker.
Access, Amex, Visa,*

Restaurant   £85

Twin dining rooms are light and inviting with humorous paintings
adorning the soft-coloured walls. New chef Colin White's fixed-price
menus offer a good choice, perhaps covering turbot ceviche, Cumbrian air-
dried ham and melon, grilled scallops with leeks and ham, roast free-range
chicken with lemon risotto and sherry vinegar sauce, and salmis of pigeon
with red wine sauce and liver paté crouton. Many of the vegetables come
from the hotel's own walled garden. Rhubarb and custard parfait, warm
cherry tart with clotted cream or dark and white chocolate terrine with
raspberry sauce might round off your meal. Honest, welcoming and
friendly, with food to match. There are some reasonably priced wines on
the decent, all-round wine list. Simpler food is offered on a Terrace menu.
*Seats 52. Parties 30. Private Room. L 12-2.30 (Sat & Sun to 3) D 7-10. Set L
(£16 Sun) £24.50 Set D £26.*

Bradford-on-Avon   Places of Interest

Tourist Information   Tel 02216 5797.
Iford Manor Gardens   Tel 02216 3146/2840/2364.

Braithwaite   Ivy House   66%   £62*

`Tel 076 87 78338`   **H**

Braithwaite Nr Keswick Cumbria CA12 5SY   Map 13 C5

Nick and Wendy Shill run a hotel of warmth and character in a small
17th-century house at the foot of the Lakeland fells. Guests are made
welcome in the beamed lounge, where they can enjoy a drink. Fine old
furniture and objets d'art are found in the neat bedrooms, which include a
honeymoon suite with four-poster. *Half-board terms only. No dogs.
Rooms 12. Closed 2 weeks Dec/Jan. Access, Amex, Visa,  *Diners Club International*

Bramhall   Moat House   63%   £85

`Tel 061-439 8116   Fax 061-440 8071`   **H**

Bramhall Lane South Bramhall Cheshire SK7 2EB   Map 10 B2

Built in 1972 and since expanded and refurbished four years ago, a well-
kept hotel that appeals to both leisure and business visitors. Conference and
banqueting facilities for up to 150. *Rooms 65. Sauna, gymnasium. Access,
Amex, Visa,* Diners Club International

Bramhope   Forte Crest   66%   £98

`Tel 0532 842911   Fax 0532 843451`   **H**

Bramhope Nr Leeds West Yorkshire LS16 9JJ   Map 10 C1

16 acres of grounds. Swimming pool. Keep-fit amenities. Conference
facilities for up to 150. *Rooms 126. Garden, indoor swimming pool, sauna,
solarium, gymnasium, weekend games room, coffee shop (10am-10.30pm). Access,
Amex, Visa,* Diners Club International

Bramhope   Parkway Hotel   63%   £119

`Tel 0532 672551   Fax 0532 674410`   **H**

Otley Road Bramhope Nr Leeds West Yorkshire LS16 8AG   Map 10 C1

Mock-Tudor hotel in a rural location adjoining Golden Acre Park
gardens. Smart, up-to-date accommodation with good leisure facilities
(including a health and fitness assessment centre and running track) and
two acres of gardens. Conference/banqueting amenties for up to 250/300.
*Rooms 103. Garden, indoor swimming pool, steam room, spa bath, sauna,
solarium, beauty salon, keep-fit equipment, snooker, tennis, dinner dance (Sat).
Access, Amex, Visa,* Diners Club International

Bramley Bramley Grange 66% £85

Tel 0483 893434 Fax 0483 893835 **H**

281 Horsham Road Bramley Nr Guildford Surrey GU5 0BL Map 5 E3

Seven acres of gardens and woodland make a pleasant country setting for the conferences (for up to 150) and management meetings that are the majority of the business at this splendid Victorian/mock-Tudor building. Public areas, bedrooms and bathrooms are all bright and modern, having been recently refurbished. Twenty bedrooms are in a new wing, all with views over the gardens. No dogs. *Rooms 45. Garden, croquet. Access, Amex, Visa.*

Brampton Farlam Hall 75% £150*

Tel 069 77 46234 Fax 069 77 46683 **HR**

Hallbankgate Brampton Cumbria CA8 2NG Map 13 D4

The hotel stands on the A684 two miles from Brampton – not in Farlam village. Set in lovely grounds complete with stream and ornamental lake, the original 17th-century farmhouse was enlarged to form a manor house in Victorian times. The Quinion and Stevenson families' latter-day conversion to charming country house hotel features Victorian-design wallpapers and authentically re-upholstered original pieces. Plants and fresh flowers, books and board games enhance the lived-in feel. Individually decorated bedrooms are a model of taste; most have space for a sitting area, and bathrooms are modern and well equipped; the finest is a Victorian recreation in dark mahogany. Splendid breakfasts and the charm and courtesy of the resident hosts contribute greatly to a memorable stay. No children under five. *Half-board terms only. *Rooms 13. Garden, croquet. Closed 25-30 Dec, Feb. Access, Visa.*

Restaurant £60

Guests are requested to arrive at 7.30 to order in the bar or front lounge. This air of formality extends to dinner. Barry Quinion's nightly fixed-price only menu offers a small choice of three dishes at each course, making full use of local produce in dishes typified by Parma-style West Cumberland ham (served with melon), poached salmon with a langoustine and dry sherry sauce or individual pigeon, port and wild mushroom pie. Short, but diverse wine list. *Seats 40. Parties 30. Private Room. D only at 8. Set D from £25.*

Brampton Tarn End £50

Tel 069 77 2340 **RR**

Talkin Tarn Brampton Nr Carlisle Cumbria CA8 1LS Map 13 D4

There are grand views of Talkin Tarn from the tiny lounge and dining room of this old red sandstone inn-cum-restaurant, two miles south-east of Brampton on the B6413. The firmly French à la carte menu changes quarterly but has weekly seasonal and vegetarian supplements; lamb's kidneys with juniper berries and gin, ragout of seafood, noisettes of lamb with Drambuie and oranges or tenderloin of pork with sugar-glazed apple indicate the style. Light lunches are served in the bar. *Seats 30. Parties 15. Private Room. D only 7.30-8.45 (light lunches 12-2). Closed Feb, D Sun in winter (except residents). Access, Amex, Visa,*

Rooms £62

TVs and teamakers provide essential comforts in six otherwise fairly basic bedrooms; bathrooms are tiled and neatly kept. No dogs.

Brandon   Brandon Hall   65%   £101

Tel 0203 542571   Fax 0203 544909   **H**

Brandon Nr Coventry Warwickshire CV8 3FW   Map 11 D4

An elegant mansion with a country house air, set in 17 acres of grounds. Most of the accommodation (40 rooms) is in a modern extension. Banqueting/conference facilities for up to 120. Forte Heritage. *Rooms 60. Garden, pitch & putt, squash, games room. Access, Amex, Visa,* 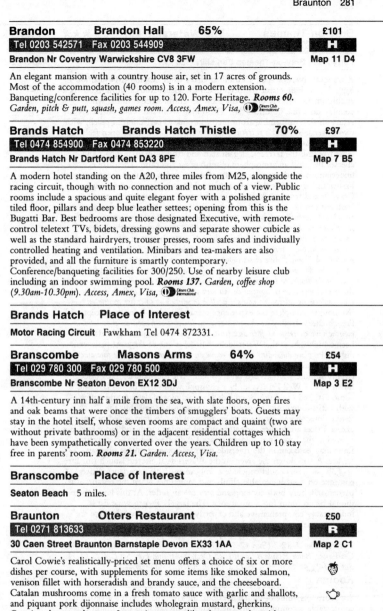 Diners Club International

Brands Hatch   Brands Hatch Thistle   70%   £97

Tel 0474 854900   Fax 0474 853220   **H**

Brands Hatch Nr Dartford Kent DA3 8PE   Map 7 B5

A modern hotel standing on the A20, three miles from M25, alongside the racing circuit, though with no connection and not much of a view. Public rooms include a spacious and quite elegant foyer with a polished granite tiled floor, pillars and deep blue leather settees; opening from this is the Bugatti Bar. Best bedrooms are those designated Executive, with remote-control teletext TVs, bidets, dressing gowns and separate shower cubicle as well as the standard hairdryers, trouser presses, room safes and individually controlled heating and ventilation. Minibars and tea-makers are also provided, and all the furniture is smartly contemporary. Conference/banqueting facilities for 300/250. Use of nearby leisure club including an indoor swimming pool. *Rooms 137. Garden, coffee shop (9.30am-10.30pm). Access, Amex, Visa,* Diners Club International

Brands Hatch   Place of Interest

Motor Racing Circuit   Fawkham Tel 0474 872331.

Branscombe   Masons Arms   64%   £54

Tel 029 780 300   Fax 029 780 500   **H**

Branscombe Nr Seaton Devon EX12 3DJ   Map 3 E2

A 14th-century inn half a mile from the sea, with slate floors, open fires and oak beams that were once the timbers of smugglers' boats. Guests may stay in the hotel itself, whose seven rooms are compact and quaint (two are without private bathrooms) or in the adjacent residential cottages which have been sympathetically converted over the years. Children up to 10 stay free in parents' room. *Rooms 21. Garden. Access, Visa.*

Branscombe   Place of Interest

Seaton Beach   5 miles.

Braunton   Otters Restaurant   £50

Tel 0271 813633   **R**

30 Caen Street Braunton Barnstaple Devon EX33 1AA   Map 2 C1

Carol Cowie's realistically-priced set menu offers a choice of six or more dishes per course, with supplements for some items like smoked salmon, venison fillet with horseradish and brandy sauce, and the cheeseboard. Catalan mushrooms come in a fresh tomato sauce with garlic and shallots, and piquant pork dijonnaise includes wholegrain mustard, gherkins, Gruyère cheese and cream. Interesting sweets like plum pancake with a Cointreau sabayon sauce, home-made passion fruit ice cream with a blackcurrant coulis, and pineapple baked Alaska; on Wednesday nights there is a special Starters and Sweets menu (priced à la carte) in addition to the regular menu. Local demand keeps prawn cocktail and fillet steak on the menu too, but these, too, are executed with style. Smoking is not allowed before 9.30pm. *Seats 40. Parties 45. D only 7-9.30. Closed Sun (& Mon in winter except Xmas), Bank Holidays, 2 weeks Nov, 2 weeks Mar. Set D £16.95. Access, Amex, Visa.*

Bray-on-Thames   The Waterside Inn   ★★★   £160

Tel 0628 20691   Fax 0628 784710   **RR**

Ferry Road Bray-on-Thames Berkshire SL6 2AT   Map 5 E2

A tranquil riverside spot, 45 minutes' drive from London (M4 junction
8/9). A new lease of life has been given to Michel Roux's world-renowned
establishment – surely one of the most delightful settings in the whole
country on a fine summer's day. The dining room has been completely
refurbished, transforming from pretty in pink to perfection in peach, with
two fewer tables and a mirrored back wall creating a more open feel; the
six bedrooms are also a recent addition. The charming setting (check for a
table fronting the terrace), elegant staff and trolleys of Armagnacs and
cheeses all instill an atmosphere of seriousness and calm. The carte is
underpinned by the superb quality of stocks and wines used for sauces, and
luxurious ingredients (lobster, truffle, wild mushrooms) in many dishes.
Crayfish and trout are kept live in a fish tank and prepared to order, so
freshness can be guaranteed in dishes like *truite au bleu, beurre de nage et
peluches de cerfeuil* and *langoustines et fruits de mer (écrevisses) aux tagliatelles,
sauce nantua*. A menu exceptionnel (£54.50) matches everything that it
promises in dishes extracted from the à la carte (but in smaller portions); a
recent example offered five courses that included *noix de Saint-Jacques
marinées à l'huile d'olive et ses moules au safran* or *ballotine de foie gras au
vert-tendre de poireaux, vinaigrette de truffes* to commence, followed by both
quenelle de brochet à la lyonnaise and *cornette de sorbet colonel*; for main course
there was a choice of *agneau de lait aux petits primeurs à la fleur de thym,
sauce paloise* or *aileron de poussin poelé à la minute et sa cuisse confite en
chausson*; to complete the experience one could select from the exceptional
French cheese trolley or choose between *ivoirine et frisson au chocolat à la
menthe vive* or *crepe soufflée aux fruits de la passion*. Desserts have always
been a highlight at the Waterside as Michel is one of *the* great patissiers;
dishes like *glace amandine dans sa coque en couverture et tartelette fine aux
mirabelles* and airborne *soufflé chaud aux framboises* are well worth the
twenty minute wait advised on the menu. The four-course, fixed-price
lunch served Wed-Fri (typically vichyssoise with sorrel or smoked fish,
salmon-stuffed monkfish or cote de boeuf, choice of desserts and coffee
with petits fours) may be considered a bargain by some, but the
temptations offered by the carte might well lead to unexpected pecuniary
excess. Prices are higher for Saturday and Sunday lunch and more choice is
offered at the latter (no children under 12). Coffee and first-class petits
fours may be taken in the riverside summer-house or on the open-air
terrace. A trip down the river on the Waterside II electric launch (for hire
at £35 per hour) could conclude a truly memorable experience. Prices
continue on their inexorable climb, and sometimes when the restaurant is
particularly busy both cooking and service can suffer. At this level, there
should be no room for complacency. The largely French wine list is
indisputably comprehensive and expertly compiled, and while there are
some reasonably priced bottles, most are expensive – even for a restaurant
of this class; the house bubbly will set you back £42. **Seats 80. Parties 85.
Private Room.** L 12-2 (Sun 12-3) D 7-10. Closed all Mon, L Tue, D Sun mid
Oct-Easter, Bank Holidays (open L 25 Dec), Xmas-mid Feb. Set L £27 (£34
Sat, £34/£42 Sun) + L & D £54.50. Access, Visa, ⓓ Diners Club International

Rooms   £105

Six bedrooms, some of which overlook the river, have been converted into
comfortable accommodation. The baking at breakfast, as one might expect,
is well worth jumping out of bed for. No children under 12.

Brentwood   Forte Posthouse   61%   £61

Tel 0277 260260   Fax 0277 264264   **H**

Brook Street Brentwood Essex CM14 5NF   Map 7 B4

Accommodation at this comfortable hotel by the M25/A12 includes 30 new rooms and 37 of Executive standard. Conference/banqueting facilities for 120. *Rooms 150. Garden, indoor swimming pool, sauna, solarium, gymnasium, coffee shop (10am-10.30pm). Access, Amex, Visa,* ① *Diners Club International*

Brentwood   Forte Travelodge   £40

Tel 0277 810819   **L**

A127 East Horndon Nr Brentwood Essex CM13 3LL   Map 7 B4

Located 5 minutes off junction 29 of the M25 on the A127 southbound, in the grounds of Halfway House. *Rooms 22. Access, Amex, Visa.*

Brentwood   Moat House   67%   £113

Tel 0277 225252   Fax 0277 262809   **H**

London Road Brentwood Essex CM14 4NR   Map 7 B4

Originally a Tudor hunting lodge (there's a splendidly preserved game larder in the formal gardens), and mentioned by Pepys in his diaries, the hotel has since been considerably extended but very much in keeping with the original house. The lounge is a good example; a modern addition, it has been built in Tudor style with some fine, genuinely old, linenfold panelling and reproduction plaster ceiling. Three bedrooms in the main house have antique carved beds and a period feel, while other rooms are more modern, ranged motel-style around the garden. There are now also nine service apartments. Banqueting/conference facilities for 85/60. *Rooms 33. Garden. Access, Amex, Visa,* ① *Diners Club International*

Brentwood   Places of Interest

Southend-on-Sea Tourist Information   Tel 0702 355122.
Southend-on-Sea Central Museum   Tel 0702 330214.
Prittlewell Priory Museum   Priory Park, Southend-on-Sea Tel 0702 342878.
South Church Park Cricket Ground   Southend-on-Sea Tel 0702 610111.

Bridlington   Expanse Hotel   60%   £70

Tel 0262 675347   Fax 0262 604928   **H**

North Marine Drive Bridlington Humberside YO15 2LS   Map 15 D6

Purpose-built in 1937, the Expanse is a traditional seaside hotel that has been owned by the Seymour family since 1948. Many of its guests are regulars, while others come for business meetings and conferences (for up to 50). Public and lounge bars are agreeable places to relax, and quite a few of the bedrooms enjoy sea views; some have balconies. No dogs. *Rooms 48. Access, Amex, Visa,* ① *Diners Club International*

Bridlington   Places of Interest

Burton Agnes Hall   Near Bridlington Tel 026289 324.
Bridlington North and South Beaches.

Bridport   Riverside Restaurant   £36

Tel 0308 22011   **R**

West Bay Bridport Dorset DT6 4EZ   Map 4 A4

The menu at this friendly, relaxed restaurant is 95% fish and shellfish, simply prepared as ordered to bring out all the freshness and flavour. At a typical session you might find oysters, stuffed clams, brill, red mullet, skate, sole, gurnard and monkfish, with turbot and lobster heading the luxury stakes. West Bay scallops in wine and garlic shouldn't be missed, and apple pie with clotted cream makes a splendid end. They also serve breakfasts, snacks and teas in the café section. Hours may be extended in high season. *Seats 80. Parties 100. L 11.30-3 (Sat & Sun to 4) D 6.30-8.30. Closed D Sun, all Mon (except Bank Holidays & high season), early Dec-early Mar.* Access, Visa, ◑ Diners Club International

Bridport   Places of Interest

Mapperton House   Tel 0308 862645.
Parnham House & Gardens   Tel 0308 862204.

Brighouse	Forte Crest	68%	£98
Tel 0484 400400 Fax 0484 400068			**H**

Coalpit Lane Clifton Village Brighouse West Yorkshire HD6 4HW   Map 10 C1

Close to junction 25 of the M62, the hotel sports a refreshingly different Italianate decor. Two-thirds of the bedrooms are designated non-smoking and there are eight new Lady Executive rooms. Good leisure facilities; seven meeting/banqueting rooms accommodating 20-200. **Rooms 94.** *Garden, croquet, indoor swimming pool, sauna, solarium, spa pool, beauty salon, coffee shop (8am-11pm).* Access, Amex, Visa, ◑ Diners Club International

Brightling	Jack Fuller's	NEW	£36
Tel 042 482 212			**R**

Brightling Nr Robertsbridge East Sussex TN32 5HD   Map 7 B6

One mile from Brightling on the Robertsbridge road, a former pub has now been totally transformed into a country restaurant by Roger and Shirl Berman. Oak beams, exposed stone walls and a huge inglenook fireplace give character and red check tablecloths lend an air of informality. That the menu lists no starters (although the likes of melon and smoked salmon are available on request) is explicable in the light of the massive main courses. Pies, puddings, stews and casseroles are the mainstay with side dishes such as buttery bubble and squelch or cheesy spinach and brown rice – hardly haute cuisine but satisfying and filling. For real trenchermen the calorific afters include no less than eight hot puds of the spotted dick and bread pudding variety. The menu's priced a little higher at night, but still represents tremendous value for money. Suitable for families. *Seats 72. Parties 75. L 12-2.30 D 7-10. Closed D Sun, all Mon, 25 Dec.* Access, Visa, ◑ Diners Club International

Brighton	Bedford Hotel	66%	£117
Tel 0273 29744 Fax 0273 775877			**H**

King's Road Brighton East Sussex BN1 2JF   Map 7 B6

On the lower five floors of a tall apartment block on the seafront, a modern establishment with spacious public areas. *Oliver's Bar* in Dickens style is the focal point of the day rooms. Bedrooms are large, with quality modern furniture and compact bathrooms, all with showers. Guests may use the leisure facilities of the *Metropole Hotel*, just 100 yards away. Car park for 50 cars. Seven conference suites provide versatile facilities for up to 450 delegates. **Rooms 129.** Access, Amex, Visa, ◑ Diners Club International

Brighton	Black Chapati		£43
Tel 0273 699011			**R**

12 Circus Parade New England Road Brighton East Sussex BN1 4GW   Map 7 B6

The decor is plain and minimalist, the only colour other than black being provided by a few abstract prints. Stephen Funnell's Indian-inspired food is equally free of clichés, and Brighton is certainly the richer for it. Courgette flowers are stuffed with spiced mushrooms and served on a red pepper sauce; the monkfish pakora is fried in gram flour batter and served with tomato chutney. Hyderabadi chicken is cooked with roasted fennel, Madras-style lamb curry with onions, chilis and coconut milk. The chef's favourite drink, Breton cider, is an excellent accompaniment. Dinner is a fixed-price affair; Sunday lunch is a buffet. *Seats 30. L by arrangement (Sun 1-3) D 7-10.30. Closed L Tue, D Sun, all Mon & Bank Holidays. Set L £7.95 Set D £16.50.* Access, Visa, ◑ Diners Club International

Brighton   Brighton Metropole   70%   £149

Tel 0273 775432   Fax 0273 207764   **H**

King's Road Brighton East Sussex BN1 2FU   **Map 7 B6**

Geared to the business executive, the Metropole boasts massive and diverse
conference facilities (for up to 1800 delegates) and vast exhibition space.
The broad, deep foyer leads to an elegant drawing room with crystal
chandeliers, finely detailed plasterwork and settees and armchairs round
marble-topped tables. There is a second peaceful lounge and a dark,
atmospheric cocktail bar. Good-size bedrooms, furnished in smart
lightwood, include 14 suites with sea-facing balconies. Some rooms are
large enough for settees as well as the standard two chairs and table.
Children up to 12 stay free in parents' room. *Rooms 328. Indoor swimming
pool, sauna, solarium, spa bath, gymnasium, beauty salon, hairdressing, night
club. Access, Amex, Visa,*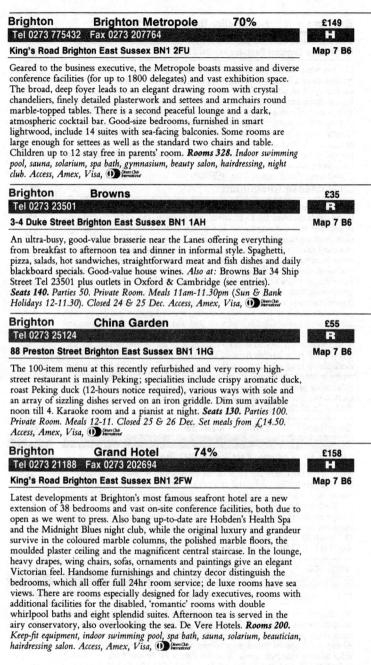

Brighton   Browns   £35

Tel 0273 23501   **R**

3-4 Duke Street Brighton East Sussex BN1 1AH   **Map 7 B6**

An ultra-busy, good-value brasserie near the Lanes offering everything
from breakfast to afternoon tea and dinner in informal style. Spaghetti,
pizza, salads, hot sandwiches, straightforward meat and fish dishes and daily
blackboard specials. Good-value house wines. *Also at:* Browns Bar 34 Ship
Street Tel 23501 plus outlets in Oxford & Cambridge (see entries).
*Seats 140. Parties 50. Private Room. Meals 11am-11.30pm (Sun & Bank
Holidays 12-11.30). Closed 24 & 25 Dec. Access, Amex, Visa,*

Brighton   China Garden   £55

Tel 0273 25124   **R**

88 Preston Street Brighton East Sussex BN1 1HG   **Map 7 B6**

The 100-item menu at this recently refurbished and very roomy high-
street restaurant is mainly Peking; specialities include crispy aromatic duck,
roast Peking duck (12-hours notice required), various ways with sole and
an array of sizzling dishes served on an iron griddle. Dim sum available
noon till 4. Karaoke room and a pianist at night. *Seats 130. Parties 100.
Private Room. Meals 12-11. Closed 25 & 26 Dec. Set meals from £14.50.
Access, Amex, Visa,*

Brighton   Grand Hotel   74%   £158

Tel 0273 21188   Fax 0273 202694   **H**

King's Road Brighton East Sussex BN1 2FW   **Map 7 B6**

Latest developments at Brighton's most famous seafront hotel are a new
extension of 38 bedrooms and vast on-site conference facilities, both due to
open as we went to press. Also bang up-to-date are Hobden's Health Spa
and the Midnight Blues night club, while the original luxury and grandeur
survive in the coloured marble columns, the polished marble floors, the
moulded plaster ceiling and the magnificent central staircase. In the lounge,
heavy drapes, wing chairs, sofas, ornaments and paintings give an elegant
Victorian feel. Handsome furnishings and chintzy decor distinguish the
bedrooms, which all offer full 24hr room service; de luxe rooms have sea
views. There are rooms especially designed for lady executives, rooms with
additional facilities for the disabled, 'romantic' rooms with double
whirlpool baths and eight splendid suites. Afternoon tea is served in the
airy conservatory, also overlooking the sea. De Vere Hotels. *Rooms 200.
Keep-fit equipment, indoor swimming pool, spa bath, sauna, solarium, beautician,
hairdressing salon. Access, Amex, Visa,*

Brighton   Hospitality Inn   79%   £155

Tel 0273 206700   Fax 0273 820692

HR

Kings Road Brighton East Sussex BN1 2GS   Map 7 B6

Ultra-modern seafront hotel with many striking features, notably the
massive atrium foyer, a vast glass-topped space in the heart of the hotel
overhung on all sides by four storeys of rooms and decorated with lush
foliage. Bedrooms all offer views of the Terrace and stylish accommodation
with a mix of darkwood modern furniture, muted fabric colours, double-
glazing and air-conditioning; bathrooms are spacious and well equipped.
Conference/banqueting facilities for 300/200 and good leisure facilities for
delegates. Children are accommodated free of charge if they share their
parents' room. Private underground parking. **Rooms 204.** *Indoor swimming
pool, sauna, solarium, gymnasium, beauty salon, hairdressing, gift shop
(7am-11pm). Access, Amex, Visa,* Diners Club International.

La Noblesse Restaurant   £80

Executive chef Richard Lyth oversees the hotel's kitchens, while Colin
Flood heads the team for La Noblesse, where there is an old-fashioned sense
of presence in the dining room. The style is evolved nouvelle – smoked
salmon-wrapped scampi in tarragon sauce, herb-topped brill with a
rosemary sauce, poached pears in a brandy snap basket. A 2- or 3-course
menu du marché is offered at lunchtime Monday-Friday; *menus noblesse* and
gourmand, along with the à la carte, are on offer for dinner only (Mon-Sat)
and changed every two weeks. The *noblesse* might include parsnip and
potato soup with scallops followed by poached guinea fowl breast with a
thyme sauce and an iced nougat with raspberry sauce to finish, while the
gourmand extends to five courses including smoked pigeon and bacon salad,
salmon with lentils, fillet of beef with port and oyster mushroom sauce and
French cheeses. A Sunday menu (£15.75 including a glass of Bucks Fizz) is
served from noon to 9.30 in the Promenade Brasserie overlooking the sea,
where fixed-price lunches (from £11.50) and a hot and cold buffet are also
available 10.15am-10.30pm. Snacks are served in Barts bar and the Atrium,
where morning coffee and afternoon tea are also available (3-6pm).
Reasonably priced wines on a shortish list. **Seats 50.** *L 12-2.15 D 7-10.15.
La Noblesse closed L Sat, all Sun, some Bank Holidays.
Set L £13.50 Set D £21.95.*

Brighton   Langan's Bistro   £62

Tel 0273 606933

R

1 Paston Place Brighton East Sussex BN2 1HA   Map 7 B6

Away from the centre and close to the marina, this is one of Brighton's
best restaurants. Chic, colourful and relaxed, it offers a short menu (half a
dozen choices for each course) of simply prepared, easy-to-enjoy dishes such
as mixed terrines, bacon and quail's egg salad, baby guinea fowl with herbs,
halibut meunière and a pastry tulip filled with sorbets. Also a fixed-price
luncheon menu (two choices per course). **Seats 42.** *Parties 10. L 12.30-2.30
D 7.30-10.30. Closed L Sat, D Sun, all Mon, 26 Dec, 2 weeks Jan, 2 weeks
Aug. Set L £13.50. Access, Amex, Visa,* Diners Club International.

Brighton   La Marinade   £45

Tel 0273 600992

R

77 St George's Road Kemp Town Brighton East Sussex BN2 5QT   Map 7 B6

Popular, unpretentious and thoroughly reliable little restaurant serving
straightforward bistro food. Coarse paté, garlicky snails in mushroom cups;
lamb chops provençale and guinea fowl normande are typical choices.
Always a fish special. Fixed-price menus only, with a particularly good-
value Sunday roast/fish lunch. **Seats 36.** *Parties 28. Private Room. L 12.15-2
D 7.15-10. Closed L Sat, D Sun, all Mon. Set L £13.50 (£12.95 Sun) Set D
£15.95. Access, Amex, Visa.*

Brighton   Old Ship Hotel   65%   £105

H

King's Road Brighton East Sussex BN1 1NR   Map 7 B6

There's a long tradition of hospitality at this privately-owned seafront
hotel, which caters admirably for private and business visitors. Children are
well looked after, and two (up to the age of 16) can stay free in their
parents' room; a supervised crèche operates from 4-11pm on Fridays and
Saturdays. The panelled Tettersell's Bar is a popular place for a drink, and
guests are invited to look at the extensive wine cellar. Many of the double-
glazed bedrooms have sea views. Regular dinner dance on Saturday nights.
Rooms 152. Access, Amex, Visa, **(I)** Diners Club International

Brighton   Topps Hotel   69%   £79

HR

17 Regency Square Brighton East Sussex BN1 2FG   Map 7 B6

Two Regency properties overlooking a square near the seafront make a
fine setting for a very friendly, agreeable hotel that tries to provide a real
home from home. There's a simple lounge/reception where drinks are
served and, upstairs, well-appointed bedrooms with fabric-lined walls and
antiqued pine furniture offer a touch of luxury. All have armchairs or
sofas, flowers, drinks trays and excellent bathrooms; five have seating areas,
and the star of the show is a double room with four-poster and balcony.
No dogs. *Rooms 14. Access, Amex, Visa,* **(I)** Diners Club International

Bottoms Restaurant   £48

Unpretentious English cooking in a pretty basement setting. Pauline
Collins prepares a fixed-price dinner menu typified by a thick, nourishing
vegetable soup, grilled prawns wrapped in bacon, lamb's kidneys in a
mustard sauce and veal chop topped with mushroom, garlic and
breadcrumbs. Steak and kidney pie is always available in winter. *Seats 24,
Parties 10. D only 7-9.30. Closed Sun & Wed, Jan. Set D £18.95.*

Brighton   Places of Interest

Tourist Information   Tel 0273 23755.
Sallis Benney Theatre   Grand Parade Tel 0273 604141.
Theatre Royal   Tel 0273 28488.
Brighton Concert Centre   Tel 0273 203131.
The Dome Complex   Tel 0273 674357.
Royal Pavilion   Tel 0273 603005.
Brighton Museum and Art Gallery   Church Street Tel 0273 603005.
Brighton Cricket Ground   Eaton Road, Hove Tel 0273 732161.
Brighton Football Ground   Tel 0273 739535.
Brighton Racecourse   Tel 0273 682912/603580.
Brighton Ice Rink   Tel 0273 24677.
Euroski Dry Ski Slope   Tel 0273 688258.

Brighton (Hove)   Sackville Hotel   61%   £70

Tel 0273 736292   Fax 0273 205759   **H**

189 Kingsway Hove Brighton East Sussex BN3 4GU   Map 7 B6

A hotel since 1930, the independently-owned Sackville occupies a seafront position, and some of the bedrooms have balconies to make the most of the view. *Rooms 45. Access, Amex, Visa,* 🔵 *Diners Club International*

Brighton (Hove)   Whitehaven Hotel   56%   £70

Tel 0273 778355   Fax 0273 731177   **H**

Wilbury Road Brighton East Sussex BN3 3JP   Map 7 B6

Standards of cleanliness and repair are high at this small, modestly comfortable hotel in a quiet street a short stroll from the sea-front. Unrestricted street parking is another plus. No children under 8. No dogs. *Rooms 17. Garden, solarium. Access, Amex, Visa,* 🔵 *Diners Club International*

Brimfield   Poppies Restaurant   £67

Tel 058 472 230   **RR**

The Roebuck Hotel Brimfield Nr Ludlow Shropshire SY8 4NE   Map 10 B4

The bright, cheery restaurant with parquet floor and cane-back chairs is an extension of Brimfield's village local – Egon Ronay's Guides 1992 Pub of the Year. A self-taught cook, Carole Evans displays a fine command of compositions, colours and textures; smoked venison with pickled damsons and crab ravioli and lemon grass sauce being typically inventive starters. Pork tenderloin, threaded with lovage, has a grain mustard sauce; with John Dory it might be one of rhubarb and coriander. A long dessert menu includes hot chocolate soufflé with white chocolate ice cream, and there is a memorable British cheese list. A lighter blackboard menu operates in the bar. Service shines. *Seats 36. Parties 40. Private Room. L 12-2 D 7-10. Closed Sun & Mon, Xmas, 2 weeks Feb, 1 week Oct. Access, Visa.*

Rooms   £60

Three lovely cottage bedrooms, two doubles with wc/shower only and a twin with full bathroom, contain limed-oak furniture and pretty floral fabrics. Fine country breakfasts include Herefordshire apple juice, local honey and home-made sausages.

Brimfield   Places of Interest

Burford House Gardens   Tel 0584 810777.

Bristol   Aztec Hotel   74%   £100

Tel 0454 301090   Fax 0454 201593   **H**

Aztec West Business Park Almondsbury Bristol Avon BS12 4TS   Map 4 B2

A smart, professionally run purpose-built, modern hotel in the Shire Group, owned by brewers Daniel Thwaites. It provides a good balance of facilities between mid-week conferences and weekend family breaks. All bedrooms are of Executive standard with coffee tables, writing desk and fax point; children under 14 are accommodated free in their parents' rooms. Syndicate rooms convert to family use at weekends with wall-mounted let-down beds. Day rooms are more than adequate, with lounges on two levels in the central 'lodge' and a smart snooker room. The hotel also has a fine leisure club and its own Black Sheep pub. Conference facilities for up to 200, banqueting up to 250. Light meals and snacks are served in Danby's Bar; more formal dining in Quarter Jacks restaurant. Regional specialities at breakfast include Somerset venison sausages and Alderley trout served with scrambled eggs. In a modern business park near junction 16 of the M5 (south of the M4/M5 interchange). *Rooms 88. Garden, indoor swimming pool, gymnasium, squash, sauna, solarium, steam room, children's playground. Access, Amex, Visa,* 🔵 *Diners Club International*

Bristol   **Berkeley Square Hotel**   **69%**   £104

Tel 0272 254000   Fax 0272 252970   **H**

15 Berkeley Square Bristol Avon BS8 1HB   **Map 4 B2**

Only a minute's walk from Park Street and Queen's Road shopping areas,
the elegant Georgian Berkeley overlooks a quiet tree-lined square. There's
meter parking here, which the porter will tend on guests' behalf till 10am.
Well-equipped bedrooms vary from practical singles to spacious suites,
their names drawn from eminent Bristolians. Small lounge and restaurant
at street level, with a state-of-the-art basement bar and café (7.30am-10pm).
Rooms 43. Closed Xmas. Access, Amex, Visa,

Bristol   **Blue Goose**   £45

Tel 0272 420940   **R**

344 Gloucester Road Bristol Avon   **Map 4 B2**

Interesting and unusal super-bistro dishes: profiteroles with avocado mousse
and roasted hazelnuts, poached chicken in Thai curry sauce, home-made
beetroot fettuccine, hot date and ginger pudding. *Seats 80. Parties 80.
Private Room. D only 6.30-11.45. Closed Sun. Set D £12.50. Access, Visa.*

Bristol   **Bristol Marriott**   £129

Tel 0272 294281   Fax 0272 225838   **H**

Lower Castle Street Bristol Avon BS1 3AD   **Map 4 B2**

Town-centre tower with recently extended conference and banqueting
suites (that now incorporate the adjacent former cinema). Dependable
accommodation; major refurbishment has taken place since transforming
from its previous incarnation as a Holiday Inn; this occurred after our press
date, therefore too late for grading. *Rooms 284. Indoor swimming pool,
sauna, whirlpool bath, keep-fit equipment, coffee shop (11am-11pm). Access,
Amex, Visa,*

Bristol   **Forte Crest**   **67%**   £97

Tel 0272 564242   Fax 0272 569735   **H**

Filton Road Hambrook Bristol Avon BS16 1QX   **Map 4 B2**

City fringe hotel in 16 acres with its own lake. Health and fitness club;
large conference trade, with facilities for up to 500 delegates. Close to the
M32 (J1, take A4174) and M4 (from J19). *Rooms 197. Indoor swimming
pool, gymnasium, spa bath, sauna, solarium. Access, Amex, Visa,*

Bristol   **Grand Hotel**   **64%**   £96

Tel 0272 291645   Fax 0272 227619   **H**

Broad Street Bristol Avon BS1 2EL   **Map 4 B2**

Late Victorian Italianate building, now showing its age, suffering from
inaccessibility and poor parking. Services are not as grand as they once
were. No leisure facilities, but conference facilities (though hardly state-of-
the-art) and banqueting for up to 500. Mount Charlotte Thistle.
Rooms 178. Access, Amex, Visa,

Bristol   **Harveys Restaurant**   ↑   £80

Tel 0272 277665   Fax 0272 253378   **R**

12 Denmark Street Bristol Avon BS1 5DQ   **Map 4 B2**

Arguably Bristol's most celebrated restaurant, evocatively housed in the
centuries-old wine vaults, Harveys is enjoying a welcome revival since the
arrival of chef Ramon Farthing. His cooking here, altogether lighter and
more textured than before, is thoroughly modern and refreshingly unfussy:
his decision to halve the length of the menu alone inspires confidence.
Particularly to be applauded is the two-course luncheon: both warm salad
of herring with new potatoes and veal medallions with morel sauce tempt

and please the palate. A la carte, the choice is typified by crab and parsley mousse accompanied by strips of vegetables flavoured with ginger and a light tomato vinaigrette, or breast of woodpigeon sliced on an apple and parsnip rösti with roasted goose liver. To finish, perhaps hot passion fruit soufflé with a strawberry sorbet. The classic wine list includes exceptional clarets and ports of the finest pedigree. *Seats 120. Parties 60. Private Room. L 12-2.30 D 7-11. Closed L Sat, all Sun. Set L £14.95. Access, Amex, Visa,* ⓓ Diners Club International

Bristol   Hilton Hotel   72%   £132
Tel 0272 260041   Fax 0272 230089   H
Redcliffe Way Bristol Avon BS1 6NJ   Map 4 B2

On the inner circuit road overlooking St Mary Redcliffe Church which, being floodlit at night, provides a useful landmark. All the bedrooms have now been refurbished with whitewood furniture and floral fabrics. Bathrooms have also been improved with a smarter marble finish and better lighting. The top Plaza floor has its own reception desk and many further extras in the rooms: flowers, fruit, mineral water, teletext TV and bathrobes. Public areas are open-plan in style and there are extensive conference facilities for up to 400 delegates. A buffet breakfast is served in a historic room built originally as a kiln for the Phoenix glassworks in 1785. *Rooms 201. Indoor swimming pool, sauna, steam room, solarium, whirlpool bath, keep-fit equipment. Access, Amex, Visa,* ⓓ Diners Club International

Bristol   Howard's   £50
Tel 0272 262921   R
1a Avon Crescent Bristol Avon BS1 6XQ   Map 4 B2

Cross the old Hotwells swing bridge (following signs to the *SS Great Britain*): Howard's – in a Georgian building – faces the Cumberland Basin with dining on two floors. Menus retain diverse influences from Thai chicken in filo pastry and venison and pheasant casserole to traditional puddings and crème brulée. Home-smoked fish, good bread, large portions and country wines. Fixed-price lunches and dinners are now offered. *Seats 60. Parties 40. Private Room. L 12-2 D 7-11, Sat 7-11.30. Closed L Sat, all Sun, 25 & 26 Dec. Set L £13 Set D £15. Access, Visa.*

Bristol   Hunt's   £60
Tel 0272 265580   R
26 Broad Street Bristol Avon BS1 2HG   Map 4 B2

The former partners at *Markwick's*, Andy and Anne Hunt, operate in small, intimate surroundings a stone's throw away by St John's Gate (parking is tricky). Strong on fish, daily menus might feature Cornish scallops, followed by monkfish with brandy and crab or turbot and salmon with Pernod and anise. Alternatives include house charcuterie, hot goat's cheese with herb vinaigrette, Provence-style braised pheasant or venison medallions with sweet gherkins and sour cream; perhaps cranberry and kirsch soufflé to follow, or iced nougat with honeyed sauce anglaise. Now open for patisserie and coffee from 8.30am, with a bargain business lunch offering house wine as an aperitif. *Seats 40. Parties 6. L 12-2 D 7-10. Closed L Sat, all Sun & Mon, Bank Holidays, 2 weeks Aug. Set L £10.95. Access, Visa.*

Bristol   Jameson's Restaurant   £50
Tel 0272 276565   R
30 Upper Maudlin Street Bristol Avon BS2 8DJ   Map 4 B2

Opposite the Royal Infirmary, a well-patronised, lively and informal bistro with an extensive menu that includes imaginative vegetarian selections. Listed on a blackboard are the day's fresh fish dishes featuring for example, sardines, sea bream, monkfish and a Mediterranean fish soup benefiting from good stock and a strong aïoli. Otherwise, the style of the menu follows the lines of lamb mignonettes on mint hollandaise, creamy dauphinoise potatoes and crisp, unsauced vegetables. Accomplished cooking and an evolving wine list with good Australian bottles. Service is friendly and the music at times equally lively. **Seats 70.** *Parties 35. Private Room. L 12-2 D 7.30-11.30. Closed all Sun in summer, D Sun in winter. Set L £10.50 Set D £14.95/£17.90. Access, Visa.*

Bristol	**Lettonie**	**£80**
Tel 0272 686456		**R**
9 Druid Hill Stoke Bishop Bristol Avon BS9 1EW		Map 4 B2

Martin and Sian Blunos's highly personalised outfit consistently evidences culinary skills rarely found in any of our major cities' suburbs. French menus devoted to style produce a good choice – perhaps crab raviolis with crab and ginger cream sauce, lightly scrambled duck egg with Sevruga caviar and blinis (for a supplementary charge) or clear rabbit and celery soup served with potted rabbit and toasted brioche to start, followed by roast Gressingham duck with leg confit and a sherry sauce or pig's trotter with morel mushrooms and a Madeira sauce. Braised oxtail (served off the bone) with snail raviolis and a rich sherry sauce shows that Martin's cooking style is just off the mainstream – but certainly for the better. Goat's cheese raviolis with a lemon butter sauce are an interesting alternative to the good selection of cheeses, while desserts can be as rich as the main courses: chocolate marquise with kumquats and a Grand Marnier syrup or caramel ice cream with warm bitter chocolate sauce; apple glazed with an almond sabayon on a Calvados parfait, or rhubarb and ginger mousse with a crisp almond biscuit are lighter alternatives. Prices have rocketed in the last year or so, reflecting the rightful acclaim of the cooking (if not the setting); nevertheless, at £30 for the fixed-price, three-course dinner one might expect to have either service or coffee (or both) included. **Seats 24.** *Parties 16. L 12.30-1.30 D 7-9.30. Closed Sun & Mon, Bank Holidays, 2 weeks Xmas, 4 days Easter. Set L £15.95 Set D £29.95. Access, Amex, Visa.*

Bristol	**Markwick's**	**£70**
Tel 0272 262658		**R**
43 Corn Street Bristol Avon BS1 1HT		Map 4 B2

An established success in a refined, bistroesque basement (once a bank vault). Stephen Markwick has developed his *Bistro 21* style here with cooking that is notable more for positive flavours than polished perfection. A la carte, his fish soup with aïoli and grilled goat's cheese with brioche and tapénade are firm favourites. Market fish (delivered daily from Cornwall), lamb noisettes with ratatouille, and guinea fowl with apple and calvados equally typify the style. Daily fixed-price menus might add a ragout of scallops and mussels, calf's kidneys with lime and lime, and hazelnut soufflé pancakes. Carefully chosen wines offer much of value, and service under Judy Markwick flows smoothly enough at all but the busiest times. **Seats 50.** *Parties 16. Private Room. L 12-2 D 7-10. Closed Sat & Sun, Bank Holidays, 10 days Xmas, 10 days Easter, 2 weeks Aug. Set L £13.75 Set D £21.50. Access, Visa.*

Bristol	**Michael's Restaurant**	**£60**
Tel 0272 276190		**R**
129 Hotwell Road Bristol Avon BS8 4RU		Map 4 B2

Long-established and popular west-of-centre venue where notable Victorian decor and informal atmosphere contribute to the sense of occasion. Excellent lunchtime value; more ambitious dinners with eclectic menu and variable results. **Seats 36.** *Private Room. L 12.30-2 D 7-11. Closed L Sat, all Sun & Mon, Bank Holidays. Set L from £12.50 Set D from £22.50. Access, Amex, Visa,*

Bristol   Moat House   72%   £100

Tel 0272 255010   Fax 0272 255040   **H**

Victoria Street Bristol Avon BS1 6HY   Map 4 B2

A strikingly modern, redbrick building standing on the site of the Old
City Wall, on the corner of Victoria Street and Temple Way, in the milieu
of Bristol's rapidly expanding, high-tech business quarter. Catering mainly
for the executive and conference market (for up to 200 delegates), the
modern bedrooms mix well-lit desk space, multipoint telephone and fax
line with uninspiring decor and plastic marble-look units in the bathrooms.
40 bedrooms are designated non-smoking and two are specially fitted for
the disabled; four air-conditioned, spacious suites have spa baths and
bathrobes provided. An open-plan foyer/lounge is noisy but reception and
porterage are effectively run. Free underground parking with direct lift
access to bedroom floors poses a security problem. *Rooms 132. Keep-fit
equipment, solarium, news kiosk. Access, Amex, Visa,*

Bristol   Redwood Lodge   64%   £85

Tel 0275 393901   Fax 0275 392104   **H**

Beggar Bush Lane Failand Bristol Avon BS8 3TG   Map 4 B2

Barely ten minutes from the city centre (via Clifton Bridge), off the A370,
Redwood bristles with conference facilities (for up to 175 delegates), and
boasts Bristol's largest leisure club. Individual residents may lose out on
quiet corners, bedroom space and room service, which is sporadic at best.
Weekenders with families fare better, as there's plenty to do: an all-day
coffee shop, 175-seat cinema, trampolining, and regular crèche facilities are
available (10am-1pm). Country Club Hotels. *Rooms 112. Garden, keep-fit
equipment, sauna, solarium, beauty salon, squash, badminton, tennis, snooker,
indoor, outdoor & children's swimming pools, cinema, coffee shop (9.30am-
10.30pm), children's playroom & playground. Access, Amex, Visa,*

Bristol   Rodney Hotel   64%   £87

Tel 0272 735422   Fax 0272 741082   **HR**

4 Rodney Place Clifton Down Road Bristol Avon BS8 4HY   Map 4 B2

A stone's throw from Brunel's famed suspension bridge, the Rodney
comprises a 1980s mansion conversion of one of Clifton's earliest Georgian
terraces. At ground level, lounge, bar and restaurant are small and intimate,
with mainly female staff to contribute a friendly welcome. Among the
50% of single bedrooms choose a "Superior" for extra space and a larger
bed. The rooms take their names from the ships of Admiral Rodney's fleet
at Saints in 1782. Children up to 12 stay free in parents' room. *Rooms 31.
Access, Amex, Visa,*

Marguerite Restaurant   £50

Run as a concession by Patrick and Sue Glennie-Smith, the restaurant is
open for dinner only, Monday to Saturday. Prices are very reasonable on a
menu that draws its inspiration from across the world: fish soup with aïoli,
roast chicken breast with tarragon, smoked pork loin with Boston beans,
Thai salad of rare sirloin with a coriander dressing, baked apple with
vanilla custard. *Seats 42. Parties 8. D only 6.30-10.30. Closed Sun. Set D
from £13.95.*

Bristol   Stakis Bristol Hotel   64%   £106

Tel 0454 201144   Fax 0454 612022   **H**

Woodlands Way Patchway Bristol Avon BS12 4JF   Map 4 B2

Single-storey modern hotel six miles from Bristol centre, at J16 of the M5,
one mile from J20 of the M4. Standard and club bedrooms; conference
(for up to 80) and leisure facilities. Formerly the Stakis Leisure Lodge.
Children up to the age of 14 stay free in parents' room. 24hr room-service
snacks. *Rooms 111. Garden, indoor swimming pool, spa bath, sauna, solarium.
Access, Amex, Visa,*

Bristol Swallow Royal Hotel 77% NEW £110
Tel 0272 255100   Fax 0272 251515 **HR**

College Green Bristol Avon BS1 5TE Map 4 B2

Swallow's multi-million pound development, faced in Bath stone, newly
dominates approaches to College Green and Bristol Cathedral. Equally
impressive, on arrival, is the Spanish marble hall flanked by country house
elegance in the Drawing room and Club Bar, and a basement Leisure Club
of Roman bath design. Secure covered parking is a bonus. Generous space
and stylish individual decor establish bedrooms high in the comfort
category; marble bathrooms are well-lit. Staff are smart, attentive and
motivated; company policy, it appears, is responsible for some lapses in
service (no evening turn-down for instance) which such investment
deserves. Banqueting and conference facilities for up to 250. *Rooms 242.*
Indoor swimming pool, sauna, solarium, spa bath, beauty salon, hairdressing,
keep-fit equipment. Access, Amex, Visa,

Palm Court Restaurant £65

The grand Palm Court extends through three floors lined in Bath stone
with curved balustrades and topped by stained glass skylights. Menus
follow the grand format while the service is formal yet unfussy. A fixed-
price "Concept of the Kitchen" may run through glazed asparagus with
salmon tartare, poached oyster, rosemary-infused lamb and summer
pudding, supplemented by seasonal à la carte. *Seats 60. Parties 8. D only*
7-10. Closed Sun & Mon. Set D £21

Terrace Restaurant £50

A stylish, relaxed setting overlooking Cathedral Square. Moderately priced
table d'hote and lighter meals from cod and mash to goat's cheese ravioli.
Seats 150. Parties 20. Private Room. L 12.30-2.30 D 6.30-10.30. Set L £14
Set D £18.

Bristol Unicorn Hotel 62% £75
Tel 0272 230333   Fax 0272 230300 **H**

Princes Street Bristol Avon BS1 4QF Map 4 B2

Quayside budget hotel with generally small bedrooms (single rooms are
minute). Separate conference facilities for 360. Bright café; gloomy
waterfront pub. Rank Hotels. *Rooms 245. Coffee shop (7am-2.30pm &*
6-10.15pm, all day at weekends). Access, Amex, Visa,

Bristol Places of Interest

Tourist Information Tel 0272 260767.
Algars Manor Iron Acton Tel 045422 372.
Bristol Cathedral Tel 0272 264879.
Phoenix County Cricket Ground Tel 0272 245216.
Mecca Leisure Centre - Ice Rink Tel 0272 260343.
Bristol Zoo Tel 0272 738951.
   Theatres and Concert Halls
Bristol Hippodrome St. Augustine's Parade Tel 0272 265524.
Bristol New Vic and Bristol Old Vic Theatre Royal Tel 0272 277466.
   Museums and Art Galleries
Arnolfini Gallery Tel 0272 299191.
Bristol Industrial Museum Tel 0272 251470.
Bristol Museum and Art Gallery Tel 0272 223571.
Maritime Heritage Centre and SS Great Britain Tel 0272 260680.

Brixham   Quayside Hotel   59%   £76

Tel 0803 855751   Fax 0803 882733   **H**

King Street Brixham Devon TQ5 9TJ   Map 3 D3

The charming if maze-like feel given by narrow hallways and variously
sized rooms betrays the hotel's origins as six fisherman's cottages. The
former inhabitants would have approved of the little nautically-themed bar
sharing downstairs space with a simple, 70s-furnished lounge. Upstairs, two
bedrooms have four-poster beds while the best of the rest share a view
over the picturesque inner harbour. Mainly very small bathrooms. The
Prince William conference room, with its own entrance and a splendid
view, can accommodate 16 boardroom-style, 30 theatre-style. *Rooms 29.*
Access, Amex, Visa, **①** *Diners Club International*

Broadway   Broadway Hotel   60%   £86

Tel 0386 852401   Fax 0386 853879   **H**

The Green Broadway Hereford & Worcester WR12 7AA   Map 4 C1

Once a 15th-century inn and monastic guest house, now a hotel of charm
and comfort. Behind the mellow stone walls the day rooms include a small
galleried lounge with a high timbered ceiling and leaded light windows.
Bedrooms, by contrast, are generally simple and modern, although the
Abbots Room features a four-poster; the Garden room, predictably but
usefully, has direct access to the garden. All are well kept, with impeccably
tiled bathrooms also benefiting from good housekeeping. No dogs.
Rooms 20. Garden. Access, Amex, Visa, **①** *Diners Club International*

Broadway   Collin House   65%   £96

Tel 0386 858354   **HR**

Collin Lane Broadway Hereford & Worcester WR12 7PB   Map 4 C1

A Cotswold-stone house about a mile north-west of Broadway signposted
off the A44 Evesham road (turn right at Collin Lane). Judith and John
Mills and their friendly staff offer a warm welcome and plenty of advice
on what to see and do in the neighbourhood (a book of handwritten notes
is placed in each bedroom). Rooms are spacious and have a cottagey feel
with country furnishings and pretty floral fabrics. In the winter months
blazing log fires bring cheer to the lounge and bar. *Rooms 7. Garden,*
croquet, outdoor swimming pool. Closed 24-29 Dec. Access, Visa.

Restaurant   £60

In the oak-beamed restaurant great store is set by fresh local ingredients.
Duck is something of a speciality; recent offerings included crisply roasted
breast with spiced red cabbage and glazed apple, and casseroled with herb
dumplings. Other choices could include pan-fried oated herring with grain
mustard sauce; sauté of lamb's kidneys with a cardamom and orange sauce;
oxtail casserole and a flan of spinach and Double Gloucester with a tomato
and rosemary sauce. Bar and garden lunches are an alternative to the fixed-
price menu, and there's a traditional Sunday lunch (children welcome). The
price of the three-course dinner is shown against the main course. Some
good prices on the concise wine list. *Seats 24. Parties 32. L 12-1.30*
D 7-9. Set L £14.50 Set D from £18.

Broadway   Dormy House   69%   £110

Tel 0386 852711   Fax 0386 858636   **HR**

Willersey Hill Broadway Hereford & Worcester WR12 7LF   Map 4 C1

Just off the A44, on an escarpment above Broadway and with views over
the local golf course and the Vale of Evesham, Dormy House is an
extended 17th-century farmhouse. Beams, exposed stonework and tiled
floors set the tone in the main house, whose two homely lounges have fine
bay windows. Converted outbuildings house cottagey, comfortable

bedrooms, many also with timbered ceilings; two rooms have four-posters.
Delegates at the purpose-built conference centre (catering for up to 200)
seem to appreciate the rustic, Cotswold-stone bar where less formal lunch
and dinner menus are available (as well as afternoon tea). Families
welcome; baby-sitting by arrangement; children's supper menu. *Rooms 49.*
Garden, table tennis. Access, Amex, Visa, (D)🔷

Restaurant   £88

A conservatory overlooks the garden and surrounding countryside, giving
a brighter alternative to the more formal, dimly-lit dining room, where
John Sanderson produces à la carte, table d'hote, vegetarian and gourmet
menus that all display a modern leaning in both presentation and content.
Trio of salmon (smoked, tartare and gravad lax), Cornish crabmeat with
diced gherkin and sweet red pepper coulis, medallion of beef fillet with
stir-fried vegetables and a sauce of soy, honey and sherry, gratin of red
fruits with a red berry and Cointreau sorbet in a brandy snap basket are all
typical of the style. Good French cheeses from Pierre Androuet served with
walnut and raisin bread. Rather too many notes accompany the wines on
an unexceptional list. *Seats 80. Parties 40. Private Room. L 12.30-2 (Sun to
2.30) D 7.30-9.30 (Fri & Sat from 7, Sun to 9). Closed L Sat, 3 days Xmas.
Set L £14 Set D £25.50.*

Broadway	Hunters Lodge	£47
Tel 0386 853247		**R**
High Street Broadway Hereford & Worcester WR12 7DT		Map 4 C1

Kurt and Dottie Friedli have played host at their mellow 19th-century
home for fifteen years now promising no rules, no frowns and no
minimum charge. Kurt's weekly table d'hote lunch might offer cheese
soufflé fritters and salmon hollandaise; from the seasonal carte go perhaps
for prawns and vegetable strudel with yoghurt dressing and devilled best
end of lamb with herb crumbs. But do leave room for the tempting
desserts, deftly displayed on the sideboard. *Seats 50. Parties 40. Private
Room. L 12.30-2 D 7.30-10. Closed D Sun, all Mon, 2 weeks Feb, 2 weeks
Aug. Set L £12.85 Set D £12.50. Access, Amex, Visa,* (D)🔷

Broadway	Lygon Arms	78%	£172
Tel 0386 852255	Fax 0386 858611		**HR**
High Street Broadway Hereford & Worcester WR12 7DU			Map 4 C1

World-renowned, naming Oliver Cromwell and Charles I among its
historic clientele since 1532. Quietly dominating the high street, the
frontage is deceptive, as extensions over the years have taken it back some
distance to the rear. The magnificent Country Club leisure complex is the
latest building addition and has a grand, galleried swimming pool. A very
'English' hotel, with beautiful old-world charm in its polished stone floors,
low-beamed ceilings, wood panelling, magnificent open fireplaces and
bedrooms furnished with antiques. The unique combination of modern
hotel and characterful inn is exemplified by the contrast between the
creaking, uneven floors in the main house and marble floors of the
bathrooms. Staff manage to be helpful and friendly at the same time as
being discreet and professional. Conference facilities for up to 80. A gem of
a hotel under the ownership of the Savoy Group. *Rooms 66. Garden, tennis,
snooker, valeting, helipad, indoor swimming pool, spa bath, beauty salon, fitness
studio, roof garden, sauna, solarium, steam room, tennis, snooker, lock-up garage,
wine bar, shop, clay-pigeon shooting. Access, Amex, Visa,* (D)🔷

The Great Hall Restaurant   £80

An open fire, flickering candlelight and elegant table settings suitably
enhance the historic ambience of the high-ceilinged Great Hall. Chef Clive
Howe offers a mixture of traditional and more modern styles on both the
three-course tables d'hote and à la carte menus. Smoked duck and beetroot
broth and roast rack of lamb with a risotto of cracked wheat sit happily
beside baked Cheshire cheese and apple tart and almond blancmange with

rhubarb compote. Daily-changing menus ebb and flow with the seasons
providing the likes of leek and potato soup with Caerphilly croutons,
Cornish crab with beetroot and sour cream, gratinated salmon with
Evesham asparagus and chervil sauce, and swede and chive purée among
the vegetables. There's always a separate four-course vegetarian menu
(£29.50) and a variety of British and Irish farmhouse cheeses (served with
walnut bread); a daily traditional pudding, perhaps apricot Bakewell
pudding, and mother's favourite "Wait'n'See" are among the desserts. A
helpful wine list with a good selection of half bottles. *Seats 120. Parties 10.
Private Room. L 12.30-2 D 7.30-9.15. Set L £18.25 Set D £27.75.*

Brockenhurst	Balmer Lawn Hotel	65%	£90
Tel 0590 23116 Fax 0590 23864			**H**
Lyndhurst Road Brockenhurst Hampshire SO42 7ZL			Map 4 C4

A much-extended former hunting lodge in the heart of the New Forest,
with plenty of leisure facilities both inside and out. Children stay free in
parents' bedrooms. *Rooms 58. Garden, indoor & outdoor swimming pools,
keep-fit equipment, spa bath, sauna, solarium, squash, tennis. Access, Amex,
Visa,* **Diners Club International**

Brockenhurst	Careys Manor	67%	£99
Tel 0590 23551 Fax 0590 22799			**H**
Brockenhurst Hampshire SO42 7QH			Map 4 C4

A mellow brick manor house set in landscaped grounds eight miles from
junction 1 of the M27. In the splendidly airy lounge a variety of deep-
cushioned seating offers relaxation, while more active moments can be
passed on the hotel's mountain bikes or in the supervised gym. Most of the
accommodation is in the garden wing and includes the spacious
Knightwood rooms with balconies or patios overlooking the walled
garden. There are six four-posters. Regular dances on Saturday nights in
winter. *Rooms 80. Indoor swimming pool, spa bath, sauna, solarium, steam
room, beauty therapy, putting, croquet. Access, Amex, Visa,* **Diners Club International**

Brockenhurst	Le Poussin	★	£75
Tel 0590 23063			**R**
The Courtyard 49-55 Brookley Road Brockenhurst Hampshire SO42 7RB			Map 4 C4

Reached via an arched passage from the main street, a small flagstone-
floored lounge leads on to the dining room with pastel drapes and 'poultry
prints'. First-rate ingredients, including some of the dozen or so varieties of
wild mushroom to be found in the nearby New Forest, are used to great
effect on the short, fixed-price menu (choose two or three courses) that
might begin with rabbit mousse-stuffed morels with a marc de
Gewurztraminer sauce, and their own home-cured bresaola before a nage
of seafood with fennel, and whole sea-bass with sweet pepper sauce; main
dishes might be fillet of beef with pleurottes, and lamb cutlets with
ratatouille. A couple of puds might include passion fruit soufflé, and on
occasion, the Grand Dessert 'Le Poussin' – a selection of five different small
desserts together on one plate. Luncheon is nothing short of a real bargain.
Notice is required for vegetarian dishes. No smoking. Quite a good choice
of wines under £20. *Seats 24. Parties 25. L 12-2 D 7-10.30. Closed D Sun,
all Mon, 2 weeks Jan. Set L £10/£13/£16 (Sun £12.50/£15) Set D
£20/£25. Access, Visa.*

Brome	Oaksmere	67%	£70
Tel 0379 870326 Fax 0379 870051			**H**
Brome Eye Suffolk IP23 8AJ			Map 6 C2

Ancient topiary surrounds this part-Tudor, part-Victorian hotel. Old
rough-hewn beams, time-worn tiled floor and rustic furniture feature in
the atmospheric bar and the rebuilt Victorian conservatory makes a most

appealing lounge. Bedrooms in the Tudor part have exposed timbers and oak furniture while those in the Victorian half are furnished with antiques. Most have been individually redecorated in some style using fine fabrics; smart bathrooms include wood-panelled baths and brass fittings. *Rooms 11. Garden. Access, Amex, Visa,* ●

Bromley   Bromley Court   66%   £85
Tel 081-464 5011   Fax 081-460 0899   **H**
Bromley Hill Bromley Kent BR1 4JD   Map 7 B5

A large modern accommodation and conference block (catering for up to 170) adjoins the original 1820s building at a popular hotel alongside the A21. The foyer serves as an airy lounge, and there's a choice of attractive bars (one opens on to a patio overlooking the gardens), plus a conservatory and coffee shop. Bedrooms of varying sizes are smartly furnished in light wood or rattan, and bathrooms with tubs also have shower risers. Dinner dance Saturday night in the Garden Restaurant. Smart banqueting facilities for up to 250. Families are well catered for with babysitting, baby listening and children's play area during family Sunday lunch; children up to the age of 8 free in parents' room. *Rooms 119. Garden, putting, driving net. Access, Amex, Visa,* ●

Bromsgrove   Country Court   69%   £112
Tel 021-447 7888   Fax 021-447 7273   **H**
Birmingham Road Bromsgrove Hereford & Worcester B61 0JB   Map 10 C4

Modern hotel built around a charming garden courtyard, complete with fountains and ponds, and offering large, well-designed bedrooms which include (with the businessman in mind) a spacious well-lit work desk with second telephone, a comfortable sofa, glass-topped coffee table and mini-bar. Good bathrooms with marble vanity units have generous towelling. Large brass chandeliers illuminate the impressive lobby, where the bold floral pattern of the settees is repeated in the luxurious carpeting and a ghostly white grand player-piano tinkles away in the smart sunken bar. *Rooms 141. Garden, indoor swimming pool, sauna, solarium, whirlpool bath, steam room, kiosk. Access, Amex, Visa,* ●

Bromsgrove   Grafton Manor   70%   £105
Tel 0527 579007   Fax 0527 575221   **HR**
Grafton Lane Bromsgrove Hereford & Worcester B61 7HA   Map 10 C4

Water gardens, a lake and a formal herb garden are all part of the six acres of well-tended grounds surrounding this Elizabethan manor house. Personally run by the Morris family, the whole place feels warm and lived-in. The sole day-room is the Great Parlour with ornate ceiling, open fireplace, comfortable sofas and, in one corner, the hotel's bar. Bedrooms vary in size, but not in standard; all are restored and decorated in traditional style and, in winter, some have their own open fires. No dogs. *Rooms 9. Garden, croquet. Access, Amex, Visa,* ●

Restaurant   £75

Simon Morris's English style of cooking is quite distinctive, not only in the judicious use of some of the 100 fresh herbs to be found in the garden here, but also in his fresh, unblinkered approach that allows roast fillet of pork larded with lovage to be served with a chive and vanilla sauce and morel mushrooms; or Cornish mussel pudding to come with a vermouth sauce. Other typical dishes from the fixed-price dinner might be wood pigeon terrine with savoy cabbage and quince jelly, fennel-stuffed chicken with carrot and coriander sauce, and, from amongst the puds, a lavender custard terrine with poached strawberries and white peaches. Vegetarians rate their own separate menu. *Seats 45. Parties 14. L 12.30-1.45 D 7.30-9 (Sat to 9.30, Sun at 7.30 only). Closed L Sat. Set L from £20.50 Set D from £28.50.*

Bromsgrove   Perry Hall   56%   £93

Tel 0527 579976   Fax 0527 575998   **H**

Kidderminster Road Bromsgrove Hereford & Worcester B61 7JN   Map 10 C4

Just 2½ miles from the M42, creeper-covered Perry Hall was once the
home of the poet AE Housman (who wrote *The Shropshire Lad*). Bedrooms
provide all the usual modern amenities. Conference facilities for up to 120
delegates. Jarvis Hotels. *Rooms 58. Garden. Access, Amex, Visa,* ⓘ 🍷

Bromsgrove   Places of Interest

Forge Mill Museum and Bordesley Abbey   Tel 0527 62509.
Avoncroft Museum of Buildings   Stoke Heath Tel 0527 31363/31886.

Broughton   Broughton Park   64%   £89

Tel 0772 864087   Fax 0772 861728   **HR**

418 Garstang Road Broughton Nr Preston Lancashire PR3 5JB   Map 10 A1

An extended Victorian mansion close to junction 1 of the M55, geared
towards the business and conference trade (maximum capacity 220). The
main bar-lounge and coffee shop are open-plan on split levels, with access
to two restaurants. Two tiers of accommodation are also offered, Executive
bedrooms being particularly well equipped. Comprehensive leisure
facilities. Under-16s stay free in parents' room. No dogs. *Rooms 98. Garden,
indoor swimming pool, sauna, solarium, spa bath, male & female gymnasia,
hairdressing, beauty salon, snooker, coffee shop (10am-10pm). Access, Amex,
Visa,* ⓘ 🍷

Courtyard Restaurant   £74

Traditional and seasonal choices on a British carte and tables d'hote. Catch
of the day, roast of the day. *Seats 80. Parties 30. L 12-2 D 7-10 (Sun to
9.30). Closed L Sat. Set L £13.25 Set D £17.95.*

Broxted   Whitehall   72%   £105

Tel 0279 850603   Fax 0279 850385   **HR**

Church End Broxted Essex CM6 2BZ   Map 6 B3

Leave the M11 at junction 8 and take the A120 westwards following signs
to Broxted; look out for the village church and this gabled, 15th-century
Elizabethan manor house is next door. Attention to detail is the keynote
here, from the comfortable lounge with a log fire and views of the garden,
to the spectacular timbered dining room. Bedrooms are all of a good size
and are bright and cheerful with modern fabrics, table lamps and Oriental
rugs. Staff are friendly and housekeeping throughout is faultless. The
beamed Barn House, a most characterful function room, can accommodate
up to 120 people. *Rooms 25. Garden, outdoor swimming pool, tennis. Access,
Amex, Visa,* ⓘ 🍷

Restaurant   £80

Full of crooked timbers, the 600-year-old vaulted dining room is
splendidly atmospheric in contrast with young Liverpudlian Paul Flavell's
cooking which is modern in style (ravioli of wild mushrooms, cod with
chervil and soya sauce) with light, delicate saucing and artistic, yet unfussy,
presentation. For the same price one can choose between a six-course *menu
surprise* or the more conventional three-course, multi-choice menu. An
excellent wine list at keen prices with New World wines listed by grape
variety. *Seats 60. Parties 20. Private Room. L 12.30-1.30 D 7.30-9.30 (Sun
to 8.30). Closed L Sat, 26-30 Dec. Set L from £19 Set D £31.50.*

Buckland   Buckland Manor   79%   £145

Tel 0386 852626   Fax 0386 853557   **HR**

Buckland Nr Broadway Hereford & Worcester WR12 7LY   Map 4 C1

Set in 10 acres of beautiful grounds, the magnificent Cotswold-stone manor
house dates in part from the 13th century. Its immaculately maintained
interior holds real character and not a little luxury, with antique furniture

used throughout. Panelling, portraits and pot plants adorn the access to every bedroom; these vary from smallish to palatial and all are enhanced by deep-pile carpets, fine soft furnishings and really comfortable beds. Remodelled bathrooms, some with separate walk-in showers, offer high-class toiletries, bathrobes and thick towels. Excellent housekeeping and friendly, willing staff. No children under 12. No dogs. **Rooms 11.** *Garden, croquet, putting, outdoor swimming pool, tennis. Access, Amex, Visa,*

Restaurant

Seasonal à la carte dinners and a fixed-price Sunday lunch show quality purchasing, but no great inspiration. Mainly cold desserts. English regional cheeses. An imposing wine list of wines from around the globe, with a good house selection and France extensively represented. **Seats 38.** Parties 38. L 12.30-1.45 D 7.30-8.45. Set L £25.

£110

| **Buckler's Hard** | **Master Builder's House** | £80 |
| Tel & Fax 0590 616253 | | |

Buckler's Hard Nr Beaulieu Hampshire SO42 7XB — Map 5 D4

An 18th-century hotel in a village famed for shipbuilding. Heavy beams and rustic furnishings make the welcoming bars popular with yachtsmen and tourists alike, and residents have their own homely lounge with easy chairs, period furniture and a large inglenook fireplace. Creaky floorboards and old-world charm make the six bedrooms in the main house appealing; rooms in a purpose-built block are plainer but well equipped. **Rooms 23.** *Garden. Access, Amex, Visa,*

| **Bucklow Hill** | **The Swan** | 62% | £75 H |
| Tel 0565 830295 Fax 0565 830614 | | | |

Bucklow Hill Knutsford Cheshire WA16 6RD — Map 10 B2

A mix of old and new coaching inn, with modern bedrooms and the odd beam for character. 10 minutes from Manchester Airport and close by the M6 (J19) and M56 (J7). Executive rooms have king-size beds and whirlpool baths; recently refurbished family rooms are around a courtyard. Friday to Sunday nights at lower rates. De Vere. **Rooms 70.** *Garden. Access, Amex, Visa,*

| **Bunbury** | **Wild Boar** | 67% | £75 H |
| Tel 0829 260309 Fax 0829 261081 | | | |

Whitchurch Road Bunbury Nr Tarporley Cheshire CW6 9NW — Map 10 B2

On the A49 Whitchurch to Warrington road, in the shadow of Beeston Castle, the Wild Boar is a handsome 17th-century hunting lodge with impressive, black and white timbered exterior. A lofty foyer-lounge and decent-sized bedrooms are in a modern, sympathetically designed building that adjoins the original. The Penthouse Suite function room has a tented ceiling and its own bar and the less impressive Gallery Room caters for smaller meetings. Rank Hotels. **Rooms 37.** *Access, Amex, Visa,*

Bunbury Places of Interest

Beeston Castle Nr Bunbury Tel 0829 260464.
Peckforton Castle Tel 0829 260930.
Cholmondeley Castle Gardens Malpas Tel 0829 720383.
Cheshire Polo Club Mill Pool House, Park Road, Oulton Tel 0829 760650.
Oulton Park Motor Racing Circuit Little Budworth Tel 0829 760301.

| **Burford** | **Bay Tree** | 67% | £97 H |
| Tel 099 382 2791 Fax 099 382 3008 | | | |

Sheep Street Burford Oxfordshire OX8 4LW — Map 4 C2

Situated just off the main street, the Bay Tree has its origins in the 16th century. Oak beams, flagstones and good solid furnishings give the day rooms a homely, traditional feel and bedrooms are in keeping (some have

four-posters). Ten rooms are in a cottage, while others overlook an
attractive terraced garden. *Rooms 23. Garden, croquet. Access, Amex, Visa,*

Burford   Places of Interest

Royal Air Force Polo Association   RAF Brize Norton,
   Carterton Tel 0993 842551 Ext 547.
Brize Norton Ski Slope   Carterton Tel 0993 824924.
Cotswold Wildlife Park   Tel 099 382 3006.

Burley   Burley Manor   61%   £78
Tel 0425 403522   Fax 0425 403227   H

Burley Nr Ringwood Hampshire BH24 4BS   Map 4 C4

A fine Victorian manor house surrounded by 54 acres of parkland in the
heart of the New Forest. Families and dogs are encouraged. Period decor
includes stone fireplaces, a creaky staircase with carved balustrade and
unusual commode side-tables. Bedrooms are simply decorated and have
smart, tiled bathrooms; converted stable-block rooms are the largest and
have the best views, plus steps leading directly down onto the lawns.
Riding stables in the grounds offer rides in the New Forest for both
novices and experts. *Rooms 30. Garden, outdoor swimming pool, hairdressing,
putting, croquet, coarse fishing. Access, Amex, Visa,*

Burnham   Burnham Beeches Moat House   68%   £95
Tel 0628 603333   Fax 0628 603994   H

Burnham Buckinghamshire SL1 8DP   Map 5 E2

An elegant Georgian building with period public areas and smart modern
bedrooms. Banqueting facilities for 150, conferences up to 180. *Rooms 75.
Garden, keep-fit equipment, spa bath, sauna, solarium, tennis. Access, Amex,
Visa,*

Burnham   Grovefield Hotel   63%   £76
Tel 0628 603131   Fax 0628 668078   H

Taplow Common Road Burnham Buckinghamshire SL1 8LP   Map 5 E2

Built in 1904 for a member of the Fuller brewing family, the house stands
in seven well-kept acres. The setting is one of its main assets, and the fine
new Huntswood function suite (banqueting up to 120, conferences for 50)
and some of the well-appointed bedrooms open on to the grounds. The
John Fuller room is suitable for smaller meetings and private dinners. The
cocktail bar and lounge provide ample space for guests to relax. *Rooms 38.
Garden, croquet, putting, bowling. Closed Xmas/New Year. Access, Amex, Visa,*

Burnham-on-Crouch   Contented Sole   £60
Tel 0621 782139   R

80 High Street Burnham-on-Crouch Essex CM0 8AA   Map 7 C4

Father and son Ray and Simon Walton share the honours at their cottagey
high street restaurant. Ray's French menu offers plenty of fish dishes –
tagliatelle of scallops, seafood pancakes and monkfish Thermidor – balanced
by chicken livers sautéed with bacon, roasts of chicken and duck and
variously sauced steaks for meat-lovers. Simon supervises front of house and
leads diners through to apple fritters for dessert, or perhaps a savoury of
soft roes on toast. No credit cards. *Seats 60. Parties 60. Private Room.
L 12-2 D 7-9.30. Closed Sun & Mon, Bank Holidays (open Good Friday),
2 weeks Jul, 4 weeks Xmas. Set L £10. No credit cards.*

Burnley   Forte Travelodge

	£40
Tel 0282 416039	**L**

Cavalry Barracks Barracks Road Burnley Lancashire BB11 4AS   **Map 10 B1**

At the junction between A671 and A679 on the outskirts of Burnley, close to junction 10 of the M65. *Rooms 32. Access, Amex, Visa.*

Burton-on-Trent   Dovecliffe Hall   68%

	£84
Tel 0283 31818	**H**

Dovecliffe Road Stretton Nr Burton-on-Trent Staffordshire DE13 0DJ   **Map 10 C3**

A Georgian-style period house set in its own attractive gardens and seven acres of pasture by the River Dart. Though unexceptional, the bedrooms are pleasant, with mineral water, sweets, pot-pourri and quality toiletries among thoughtful extras. The restaurant appears to be the mainstay of the hotel these days, with the letting bedrooms a useful adjunct for diners. No dogs. *Rooms 7. Garden. Access, Visa.*

Burton-on-Trent   Riverside Inn

	£68
Tel 0283 511234 Fax 0283 511441	**I**

Riverside Drive Branston Burton-on-Trent Staffordshire DE14 3EP   **Map 10 C3**

The hotel stands on the banks of the river Trent, where it has fishing rights. Day rooms make good use of beams, linenfold panelling, copperware and greenery, and the bar has a little thatched roof. Modestly furnished bedrooms are not large but are very well kept, with pretty floral fabrics and the immaculate bathrooms (all with showers over tubs) boast quality toiletries. Friendly staff enhance the inn's appeal. Conference facilities for up to 150 delegates. *Rooms 22. Garden, fishing.*
Access, Amex, Visa.

Burton-on-Trent   Places of Interest

Tourist Information   Tel 0283 45454.
Bass Museum, Visitor Centre and Shire Horse Stables   Tel 0283 511000.
Heritage Brewery Museum   Tel 0283 69226.
Swadlincote   Tel 0283 217200.

Burtonwood   Forte Travelodge

	£40
Tel 0925 710376	**L**

M62 Burtonwood Warrington Cheshire WA5 3AX   **Map 10 B2**

On the westbound carriageway of the M62 at the Welcome Break Service Area between junctions 7 and 9. *Rooms 40. Access, Amex, Visa.*

Bury   Normandie Hotel   64%

	£83
Tel 061-764 3869 Fax 061-764 4866	**HR**

Elbut Lane Birtle Nr Bury Greater Manchester BL9 6UT   **Map 10 B1**

A narrow lane off the B6222 leads to the Normandie, standing in the shadow of the Pennines. Run by enthusiastic mother and son team, Gill and Max Moussa, it provides comfortable, up-to-date accommodation. Luxury rooms are the best, with rural views, attractive fabrics and plenty of work space. Bathrooms are fully tiled and have splendid showers. Standard rooms are more modest. Day rooms include a homely lounge and a small bar. Staff are genuine, helpful and friendly. *Rooms 24. Garden. Closed 1 wk Easter, 2 wks Xmas. Access, Amex, Visa,*

Restaurant

£65

Burgundian chef Pascal Pommier is now ably assisted by Edward Denny (formerly at the *Box Tree* in Ilkley) and cooking in a fashionably modern, down-to-earth, rustic style offering both a seasonal carte and a *menu du jour*.

Simpler dishes on the daily fixed-price dinner might include Jerusalem
artichoke mousse with leeks and carrots or ravioli of salmon with herb-
scented sauce, followed by braised, stuffed Chinese leaves with spicy
vegetable stock, a fresh fish dish and warm Bakewell tart or iced ginger
meringue with an orange sauce. A la carte is more involved, but with a
similar mix of French and English influences: Dublin Bay prawn
consommé, fricassee of snails with mushrooms and asparagus in a pastry
tart, rack of lamb with haricot beans, calf's liver with bacon and mustard
sauce. Desserts are a high point – try the *assiette de friandises aux parfums de
noix* (a trio of nut desserts) or a hot vanilla and Grand Marnier *soufflé
Rothschild* with candied fruits. Lunch is a 2- or 3-course, fixed-price affair
with a choice of three dishes per course: perhaps hot vegetable tartlet,
home-made soup or chicken liver paté to start, followed by beef casserole,
escalope of salmon with pepper-scented oil or mushroom and spinach
pancakes; blackcurrant bavarois, crème brulée or *tarte fine aux pommes* to
finish. A helpful wine list with a good selection of half bottles;
predominantly French, but with Australia also well represented. *Seats 50.
Parties 20. L 12-2 D 7-9.30 (Sat to 10). Closed L Sat & Mon, all Sun, Bank
Holidays. Set L £12.50/£15 Set D £18.95.*

Bury   Places of Interest

Rochdale Art Gallery   Tel 0706 342154.

Bury St Edmunds	Angel Hotel	69%	£120
Tel 0284 753926 Fax 0284 750092			**H**
Angel Hill Bury St Edmunds Suffolk IP33 1LT			**Map 6 C2**

In continuous use as a hotel since 1452, the vine-clad Angel is to this day in
private hands, priding itself on a high level of customer care and service.
The lounge exudes quiet comfort, with deep-cushioned sofas facing the log
fire; below, the 11th-century vaults make a striking setting for one of the
two restaurants. Pride of place among the individually furnished and
decorated bedrooms goes to the Charles Dickens room, where four-poster
and antique furniture are sympathetically added to by today's expected
accoutrements. Bathrooms, indeed, are entirely modern with good over-
tub showers and plentiful toiletries; most also have bidets. Banqueting
facilities for 150, conferences for 150. Secure covered garage. *Rooms 40.
Access, Amex, Visa,* **(I)** Diners Club International

Bury St Edmunds	Butterfly Hotel	62%	£67
Tel 0284 760884 Fax 0284 755476			**H**
Symonds Road Bury St Edmunds Suffolk IP32 7BW			**Map 6 C2**

Take the Bury East exit from the A45 to the Butterfly, a modern low-riser
with modest accommodation. Delegate and private dining rooms for up to
40. Under-12s free in parents' room. No dogs. *Rooms 66. Access, Amex,
Visa,* **(I)** Diners Club International

Bury St Edmunds	Suffolk Hotel	59%	£86
Tel 0284 753995 Fax 0284 753097			**H**
38 Buttermarket Bury St Edmunds Suffolk IP33 1DL			**Map 6 C2**

Handsome town-centre inn, formerly the Greyhound, with all-day Suffolk
pantry and Viking bar. Charter Room conference/dining venue for 35.
Under-16s free in parents' room. Forte Heritage. *Rooms 33. Coffee shop
(8am-4pm, 6 days) Access, Amex, Visa,* **(I)** Diners Club International

Bury St Edmunds   Places of Interest

Tourist Information   Tel 0284 764667.
Ickworth House and Gardens (NT)   Tel 0284 735270.

Calbourne	Swainston Manor	66%	£76

Tel 0983 521121   Fax 0983 521406   **H**

Calbourne Isle of Wight PO30 4HX   Map 5 D4

Set in 32 acres of parkland, the manor is Georgian in appearance although
much older in parts. Classical columns grace the spacious entrance hall and
brown plush bar and there is an elegantly proportioned drawing room.
Bedrooms are of a good size and feature mahogany furniture and plenty of
little extras. The Woodward family have been welcoming guests for nearly
20 years. *Rooms 17. Garden, indoor swimming pool, fishing. Access, Amex,
Visa,* *Diners Club International*

Calstock	Danescombe Valley Hotel	72%	£175*

Tel 0822 832414   **HR**

Lower Kelly Calstock Cornwall PL18 9RY   Map 2 C3

A romantic haven of tranquillity in a "hidden valley" near a sleepy Cornish
village. Danescombe Valley Hotel was originally built for Lord Ashburton,
who chose a beautiful site overlooking the tidal river Tamar. It lies in a
lane parallel to the river, half a mile west of the village. The lounge is
particularly attractive, with deep-cushioned settees, lots of books and
magazines, fine artwork and fresh flowers; the intimate, slate-floored bar
has Lloyd Loom chairs, an open fire in winter and a terrace. Three
bedrooms have French doors opening on to a shared verandah running
around two sides of the house; all rooms have views over the river and
boast a mixture of antiques and fine traditional furniture, sofas and
excellent bathrooms. Breakfasts are "long, light and lazy affairs to provide a
gentle start to the day". *Half-board terms only. Note unusual closing
times. No children under 12. No dogs. *Rooms 5. Garden, mooring. Closed
Wed & Thurs, also Nov-Easter (open Xmas) Access, Amex, Visa,* Diners Club International

Restaurant   £66

Dinner is always a highlight of a stay at Danescombe. Anna Smith cooks
balanced four-course, fixed-price dinners (no choice, but discussion
welcome) that are largely Italian-inspired; fresh, abundant local ingredients
are treated simply, but carefully, to enhance flavours. Typical dishes might
include grilled asparagus or baked goat's cheese with mixed leaf salad to
start, followed by roast duck breast with balsamic vinegar sauce, smoked
haddock with parsley pesto or Tamar salmon roasted with spices; fine
West Country unpasteurised farmhouse cheeses next, then perhaps caramel
rice pudding with soft fruit, warm chocolate and hazelnut tart with crème
fraiche ice cream or rhubarb and lemon tart. A carefully compiled wine
list with exceptionally kind prices and a leaning towards good Italian
wines; bottles are listed by grape variety. Booking is essential. No smoking
in the dining room. 3% surcharge for credit card payments. *Seats 10.
Parties 10. D only at 7.30 for 8. Set D £27.50.*

Calstock   Places of Interest

Cotehele House (NT)   Tel 0579 50434.

Camberley	Frimley Hall	68%	£111

Tel 0276 28321   Fax 0276 691253   **H**

Portsmouth Road Camberley Surrey GU15 2BG   Map 5 E3

A short distance from J3 of the M3, a turn-of-the-century Victorian manor
house surrounded by splendid grounds that are floodlit at night.
Magnificent stained-glass windows overlook an impressive carved wooden

staircase – Victorian style that is carried through to the traditionally
furnished bedrooms in the main house, two of which have four-poster
beds. However, most of the bedrooms are located in a modern extension
and are smaller, but equally appealing; 16 are designated non-smoking.
Families are well catered for, particularly at weekends when rates are
reduced. Conference and meeting rooms have Victorian character as well
and cater for up to 60 delegates. Forte Heritage. *Rooms 67. Garden. Access,
Amex, Visa,* ⓓ

Camberley	Tithas	£30
Tel 0276 65803		**R**
31 High Street Camberley Surrey GU15 3RE		**Map 5 E3**

Mildly spicy, north Indian/Bengali cooking in modest surroundings. Meat
and vegetarian set meals (thali) offer particularly good value. *Seats 65.
Parties 15. Private Room. L 12-2.30 D 6.30-12. Closed 25 & 26 Dec.
Set meals from £9.95. No credit cards.*

Cambridge	Arundel House	60%	£57
Tel 0223 67701 Fax 0223 67721			**H**
53 Chesterton Road Cambridge Cambridgeshire CB4 3AN			**Map 6 B3**

A footbridge opposite the hotel, formed from a row of Victorian houses,
leads across the river Cam to Jesus Green near the city centre. A gas
fireplace and brass chandeliers keep the reception-lounge area in period
with the building, yet the general decor varies little from red plush dralon.
Public rooms are clean and in good repair, but otherwise unexceptional. 22
bedrooms are in a coach-house annexe and single rooms have shower and
WC only. *Rooms 88. Garden. Closed 25 & 26 Dec. Access, Amex, Visa,*
ⓓ

Cambridge	Browns	£30
Tel 0223 461655		**R**
23 Trumpington Street Cambridge Cambridgeshire CB2 1QA		**Map 6 B3**

Opposite the Fitzwilliam Museum, this is one of a small chain of Browns
(the others are in Brighton and Oxford). The all-day menu spans hot
sandwiches, spaghetti, salads, savoury pies, burgers, ribs, steaks, daily fish
specials and puddings. Separate children's menu. *Seats 240. Parties 40.
Private Room. Meals 11am-11.30pm (Sun & Bank Holidays 12-11.30pm).
Access, Amex, Visa,* ⓓ

Cambridge	Cambridge Lodge	58%	£80
Tel 0223 352833 Fax 0223 355166			**H**
Huntingdon Road Cambridge Cambridgeshire CB3 0DQ			**Map 6 B3**

A mock-Tudor building standing in a secluded garden on the outskirts of
the city. Three of the bedrooms have shower/washbasin only; top of the
range is the bridal suite. Children stay free in parents' room up to ten years
of age. The Garden Room is used for small meetings or conferences.
Rooms 11. Closed Xmas/New Year. Access, Amex, Visa, ⓓ

Cambridge	Cambridgeshire Moat House	63%	£78
Tel 0954 780555 Fax 0954 780010			**H**
Bar Hill Cambridge Cambridgeshire CB3 8EU			**Map 6 B3**

The grounds of this well-designed modern hotel on the A604 include a
golf course (available to guests at a 50% reduction on green fees). There's
also a leisure centre and numerous conference suites, the largest with a
capacity of 180, theatre-style. Several bedrooms are suitable for family use,
and baby-listening and baby-sitting can be organised. Children have their
own paddling pool. *Rooms 100. Garden, indoor swimming pool, spa bath,
solarium, steam room, keep-fit equipment, squash, tennis, pool table, dinner dance
(Sat). Closed 25 & 26 Dec. Access, Amex, Visa,* ⓓ

Cambridge — Charlie Chan — £44

Tel 0223 61763 — R

14 Regent Street Cambridge Cambridgeshire CB1 2DB — **Map 6 B3**

The simply appointed ground floor dining room and the much plusher Blue Lagoon upstairs offer the same selection of Chinese dishes. There are set meals for two or more, and the lengthy à la carte runs the gamut from bang-bang chicken and barbecued spare ribs to crispy duck, Szechuan-style prawns, steamed Dover sole and sizzling beef with green peppers and black bean sauce. Reliable but not remarkable cooking, good serving staff. The Blue Lagoon provides a night-club ambience, with musical entertainment at weekends. ***Seats 120.*** *Parties 100. Private Room. L 12-2.15 D 6-11.15. Closed 25 & 26 Dec. Set meals from £10. Access, Amex, Visa.*

Cambridge — Forte Posthouse — 67% — £67

Tel 0223 237000 Fax 0223 233426 — H

Lakeview Bridge Road Cambridge Cambridgeshire CB4 4PH — **Map 6 B3**

Well geared to the needs of private guests, families and business people, this smart modern hotel stands at the junction of the A45 and B1049. ***Rooms 118.*** *Garden, indoor swimming pool, keep-fit equipment, spa bath, sauna, solarium. Access, Amex, Visa,* Diners Club International

Cambridge — Garden House — 69% — £130

Tel 0223 63421 Fax 0223 316605 — H

Granta Place Mill Lane Cambridge Cambridgeshire CB2 1RT — **Map 6 B3**

A modern hotel near the city centre, yet enjoying ample parking and riverside frontage, the hotel also owns the adjacent boatyard which hires out most of the punts to be seen on the river Cam. The smart cocktail bar and lounge take full advantage of the setting, with the conservatory extensions and patio beyond. Standardised bedrooms offer good levels of comfort but some (those over the kitchen and particularly those near the roof-mounted hotel plant) can be noisy. Friendly staff, many of whom are long-serving, provide good service which extends to the polishing of shoes left outside rooms at night. Meeting rooms for up to 200. Queens Moat Houses. ***Rooms 118.*** *Garden, punting. Access, Amex, Visa,* Diners Club International

Cambridge — Gonville Hotel — 60% — £79

Tel 0223 66611 Fax 0223 315470 — H

Gonville Place Cambridge Cambridgeshire CB1 1LY — **Map 6 B3**

A central location, views over Parker's Piece (a large green) and its own parking are the main attractions. An extension in the early 70s enlarged the original Victorian house, providing good-sized additional bedrooms. New management took over in 1992 with plans to refurbish the hotel. ***Rooms 62.*** *Closed 5 days Xmas. Access, Amex, Visa,* Diners Club International

Cambridge — Holiday Inn — 68% — £119

Tel 0223 464466 Fax 0223 464440 — H

Downing Street Cambridge Cambridgeshire CB2 3DT — **Map 6 B3**

A recently built hotel with neo-classical facade, right in the heart of the city. An escalator leads up from the marble-floored lobby to the first-floor reception desk and atrium-style, open-plan public areas. Air-conditioned bedrooms are the standard Holiday Inn product, combining comfort with practicality. Executive rooms get various extras plus the beds turned down in the evening. Limited amount of free parking. Conference facilities for up to 150. ***Rooms 199.*** *Courtyard garden, indoor swimming pool. Access, Amex, Visa,* Diners Club International

Cambridge   Midsummer House   ★   £100

Tel 0223 69299   **R**

Midsummer Common Cambridge Cambridgeshire CB4 3AE   Map 6 B3

On Midsummer Common, next to a footbridge over the river Cam, this old house offers a number of dining rooms, two on the first floor (one with terrace overlooking river) and another on the ground floor. The latter is a dark blue room that gives onto a pretty double conservatory extending into the verdant, walled garden. A couple of tables under huge parasols are the perfect setting for alfresco summer dining. Chef-patron Hans Schweizer offers a good-length, fixed-price menu plus a daily-changing six-course chef's choice menu that might include terrine of salmon and turbot on a light pimento cream, pink-roasted Barbary duck with rhubarb and Gewürztraminer or fillet of beef masked with a Pommard and shallot sauce. Fine desserts such as caramelised apples in filo pastry with home-made fudge sauce. Excellent wines from first-rate growers. *Seats 65. Parties 100. Private Room. L 12.15-1.30 D 7.15-9.30. Closed L Sat, D Sun & Mon, 26 Dec, 1 Jan. Set L £16.95 Set D £28. Access, Amex, Visa,* ⓘ

Cambridge   University Arms   65%   £110

Tel 0223 351241   **H**

Regent Street Cambridge Cambridgeshire CB2 1AD   Map 6 B3

Recent refurbishment has revived the Edwardian splendour of the public rooms at this city-centre De Vere hotel. Conference facilities include a ballroom which can accommodate 300 delegates theatre-style. *Rooms 117. Access, Amex, Visa,* ⓘ

Cambridge   Places of Interest

Tourist Information   Tel 0223 322640.
Cambridge and Newmarket Polo Club   Botolph Lane Tel 0223 314010.
Linton Zoo   Linton Tel 0223 891308.
   Theatres and Concert Halls
ADC Theatre   Park Street Tel 0223 355246.
Arts Theatre   St. Edward's Passage Tel 0223 355246.
Corn Exchange   Parsons Court, Wheeler Street Tel 0223 358977.
The Junction   Clifton Road Tel 0223 412600.
   Historic Houses, Castles and Gardens
Anglesey Abbey (NT)   Tel 0223 811200.
University Botanic Garden   Tel 0223 336265.
Wimpole Hall (NT)   Tel 0223 207257.
   Museums and Art Galleries
Cambridge and County Folk Museum   Tel 0223 355159.
Fitzwilliam Museum   Tel 0223 332900.
Kettles Yard   Tel 0223 352124.
The Scott Polar Research Institute   Tel 0223 336540.
Imperial War Museum   Duxford Airfield. Tel 0223 833963 or 835000
   (*information line*).

Campsea Ashe   Old Rectory   £50

Tel 0728 746524   **RR**

Campsea Ashe Nr Woodbridge Suffolk IP13 0PU   Map 6 D3

Enter this large 17th-century house and you step into Stewart Bassett's home. The welcome is genuine, the service informal and the food generally excellent. There is no choice of menu, so mention preferences when booking. Items on recent menus have included spicy fish with marinated mushroom, samphire and a wild rice and sunflower seed salad; poached fillet of halibut stuffed with spinach; braised leg of lamb with rosemary, lemon zest and cream; roast marinated fillet of venison; plus good cheeses. Desserts run from filo pastry tarts filled with strawberries and topped with a hot meringue to sticky toffee pudding. Home-baked breads, home-made jams. Carefully chosen and personal wine list, decently priced, with helpful introductions. No smoking. **Seats 30. Parties 40. Private Room. D only 7.30-9. Closed Sun, Xmas/New Year, 2 weeks Feb, 1 week Nov. Set D £18. Access, Amex, Visa, **

Rooms £50

Six bedrooms are bright, homely and comfortable, with lovely drawings, prints and antiques. The elegant drawing room opens on to a terrace and the gardens.

Cannock	Travel Inn		£42
Tel 0543 572721	Fax 0543 466130		L
Watling Street Cannock Staffordshire WS11 1SJ			Map 10 C3

40 minutes drive from Birmingham International Airport and Alton Towers Theme Park. **Rooms 38. Access, Amex, Visa,**

Canterbury	Canterbury Hotel	58%	£58
Tel 0227 450551	Fax 0227 450873		H
71 New Dover Road Canterbury Kent CT1 3DZ			Map 7 C5

Next door to the Ebury Hotel, ten minutes walk up the New Dover Road, a small privately-owned hotel offering modest accommodation in pine-furnished rooms. **Rooms 27. Access, Amex, Visa,**

Canterbury	Chaucer Hotel	61%	£90
Tel 0227 464427	Fax 0227 450397		H
63 Ivy Lane Canterbury Kent CT1 1TT			Map 7 C5

A large, traditional bar also serves as the lounge in a comfortable Forte Heritage hotel created from an extended Georgian house. Close to the city centre. Conference/banqueting facilities for 120. **Rooms 42. Access, Amex, Visa,**

Canterbury	County Hotel	68%	£97
Tel 0227 766266	Fax 0227 451512		HR
High Street Canterbury Kent CT1 2RX			Map 7 C5

A civilised, privately-owned town-centre hotel steeped in history, dating back to 1588. Original timbers and Tudor panels are used to good effect in ground-floor day rooms, and there's a particularly appealing residents' lounge on the first floor housing the best, heavily-carved antique pieces. Decent-sized bedrooms are disparate in style – Tudor, Georgian and Colonial – many with sitting areas and all now sporting smartly tiled bathrooms. The pedestrianisation of the High Street has greatly improved the general peace and quiet at night. Drivers should obtain directions to the rear (via Stour Street), where covered garaging is available at a supplementary charge. Conference suites accommodate private functions for 15 to 160 guests. No dogs. **Rooms 73. Garage, coffee shop (10.30am-11pm). Access, Amex, Visa,**

Sully's Restaurant £60

Elaborate modern lighting and mirror-panelled walls are in marked contrast to the timbered foyer and Tudor bar. Today's menus are similarly in a modern mode: asparagus feuilleté with chive cream and a ballotine of trout with vanilla-scented lobster sauce indicate the style, but the execution is lacking in finesse. Dover sole and sirloin steak still dot the à la carte; raspberry shortbread with spiced berry coulis and apple tart with cinnamon ice cream attempt to enliven the sweet selection. **Seats 50. Parties 120. Private Room. L 12.30-2.30 D 7-10.Set L £12/£14.50 Set D £14.50-£18.50.**

Canterbury   Ebury Hotel   58%   £60

Tel 0227 768433   Fax 0227 459187   **H**

65 New Dover Road Canterbury Kent CT1 3DX   Map 7 C5

Two Victorian houses, standing just back from the road, with a large
garden and a small indoor swimming pool. Simply appointed bedrooms;
four self-catering flats. Family owned and run. *Rooms 15. Garden, indoor
swimming pool. Closed 24 Dec-14 Jan. Access, Amex, Visa.*

Canterbury   Falstaff Hotel   £80

Tel 0227 462138   Fax 0227 463525   **I**

8 St Dunstan's Street Canterbury Kent CT2 8AF   Map 7 C5

A centuries-old coaching inn whose day rooms get character from original
beams, leaded windows and polished oak tables. Bedrooms are neat and
pretty and the majority use solid modern furniture that suits the feel of the
place perfectly. Children under 16 are accommodated free – with a full
traditional English breakfast – when sharing with an adult. Within easy
walking distance of the city centre, near the Westgate Tower. No dogs.
Lansbury Hotels. *Rooms 25. Access, Amex, Visa,* **(D)** Diners Club International

Canterbury   Howfield Manor   68%   £75

Tel 0227 738294   Fax 0227 731535   **H**

Chartham Hatch Canterbury Kent CT4 7HQ   Map 7 C5

An attractive old manor house on the A28 to the west of Canterbury, with
interesting architectural features. Evidence of its long history can be seen in
features like the huge inglenook fireplace in the lounge and priest hole in
the bar. New-wing bedrooms are spacious and have good solid oak
furniture, but those in the original house are more characterful with some
exposed beams; all offer numerous little comforts and have smart, well-
kept bathrooms. Conference/banqueting for 80. No children under 5. No
dogs. *Rooms 13. Garden, croquet. Access, Amex, Visa.*

Canterbury   River Kwai   £40

Tel 0227 462090   **R**

49 Castle Street Canterbury Kent CT1 2PY   Map 7 C5

Thai restaurant with the usual range of spicy salads, fiery curries and a
range of one-dish rice or noodle dishes. *Pud Thai* – fried rice noodles with
shrimps, crab meat, bean sprouts, ground peanuts, egg and chopped salted
turnips – is a speciality. Reduced, but good value fixed-price menu at
lunchtime. *Seats 70. Parties 30. Private Room. L 12-2.30 D 6-11. Closed
L Mon, 25 & 26 Dec. Set L £6.50 Set D £12.50.
Access, Amex, Visa,* **(D)** Diners Club International

Canterbury   Slatters Hotel   57%   £74

Tel 0227 463271   Fax 0227 764117   **H**

St Margarets Street Canterbury Kent CT1 2DR   Map 7 C5

Close to the city centre and cathedral, a Queens Moat Houses hotel with
facilities for families (extra beds, baby-sitting, children up to 16 free in
parents' rooms) and business people (meeting rooms for up to 100). Small
car park to the rear. *Rooms 31. Access, Amex, Visa,* **(D)** Diners Club International

Canterbury   Places of Interest

Tourist Information   Tel 0227 766567.
Marlowe Theatre   St. Peter's Street Tel 0227 67246.
Canterbury Cathedral   Tel 0227 762862.
St. Lawrence Cricket Ground   Tel 0227 456886.
Lydden Hill Motor Racing Circuit   Tel 0304 830557.
Model Village   Westcliff, Ramsgate Tel 0843 592543 *15 miles.*
  Historic Houses, Castles and Gardens

Quex House   Birchington Tel 0843 42168.
Goodnestone Park Gardens   Nr Wingham Tel 0304 840218.
Chilham Castle   Nr Canterbury Tel 0227 730319.
Zoos and Wildlife Parks
Howletts Zoo Park   Bekesbourne Tel 0227 721286.
Blean Bird Park   Honey Hill Tel 0227 471666.
Wingham Bird Park   Little Rusham Bird Farm, Wingham
Tel 0227 720836.

Carcroft   Forte Travelodge   £40

`Tel 0302 330841`   **L**

A1 Great North Road Carcroft Nr Doncaster South Yorkshire   Map 11 D2

On the A1 northbound, 6 miles north of Doncaster. Leeds, Sheffield and
York are all within easy reach. *Rooms 40. Access, Amex, Visa.*

Carlisle   Granada Lodge   £43

`Tel 069 74 73131   Fax 069 74 73669`   **L**

M6 junction 41/42 Southwaite Carlisle Cumbria CA4 0NT   Map 13 D4

Rooms 39. Access, Amex, Visa,

Carlisle   Swallow Hilltop   58%   £80

`Tel 0228 29255   Fax 0228 25238`   **H**

London Road Carlisle Cumbria CA1 2PQ   Map 13 D4

Leave the M6 at junction 42 and take the A6 to find a practical, if
unexceptional, modern hotel with conference rooms for up to 500 and
many leisure facilities. *Rooms 92. Garden, indoor swimming pool, spa bath,
sauna, keep-fit equipment, putting, golf practice net. Access, Amex, Visa,*

Carlisle   Places of Interest

Tourist Information   Tel 0228 512444.
Carlisle Castle   Tel 0228 31777.
Carlisle Cathedral   Tel 0228 48151.
Carlisle Racecourse   Tel 0228 22504.
Carlisle Ski Club   Tel 022 31607.

Carlyon Bay   Carlyon Bay Hotel   68%   £132

`Tel 0726 812304   Fax 0726 814938`   **H**

Sea Road Carlyon Nr St Austell Cornwall PL25 3RD   Map 2 B3

Set in 250 acres of sub-tropical gardens and grounds, the hotel enjoys
superb views over the bay. It was built in 1930, and, while still admirably
fulfilling its role of family holiday hotel, it also offers extensive
conference/function facilities (for up to 200/250 delegates). Large-
windowed lounges, furnished in traditional style, make the most of the
splendid setting, as do most of the light, attractive bedrooms. *Rooms 73.
Garden, croquet, 18-hole golf course, 9-hole approach golf course, tennis, helipad,
indoor & outdoor swimming pools, spa bath, sauna, solarium, snooker, children's
playground, dinner dance (monthly). Access, Amex, Visa,*

Carlyon Bay   Porth Avallen Hotel   61%   £71

`Tel 0726 812802   Fax 0726 817097`   **H**

Sea Road Carlyon Bay St Austell Cornwall PL25 3SG   Map 2 B3

New owners have recently taken over at this well-situated hotel where the
major attraction of panoramic views over the bay and coastline contributes
greatly to a restful air. Approached by a private coastal road, the hotel
stands in extensive gardens. Public rooms are comfortable and uncluttered
and include a sun lounge that looks out to sea. Pleasant bedrooms of
varying sizes and decor are light and airy; many may have fine views and all
but four have en-suite facilities. Nine are suitable for family use. No dogs.
Rooms 24. Garden. Access, Amex, Visa,

Cartmel   Aynsome Manor   60%   £101*
Tel 053 95 36653   Fax 053 95 36016   H
Cartmel Nr Grange-over-Sands Cumbria LA11 6HH   Map 13 D6

1992 marked a decade here for the Varley family, who run a warm,
welcoming house of 16th-century origins. Open fires, magazines and a
porcelain doll collection create a homely atmosphere. Accommodation,
divided between main house and converted stables, has an equally
traditional feel. Adequate, modest bathrooms. *Half-board terms only.
Rooms 13. Garden. Closed 2-28 Jan. Access, Amex, Visa.

Cartmel   Uplands   £65
Tel 053 95 36248   RR
Haggs Lane Cartmel Cumbria LA11 6HD   Map 13 D6

The menu still declares itself to be 'in the Miller Howe manner', and
indeed chef Tom Peter and his wife Diana both once worked at John
Tovey's fine hotel. Tom's small-choice menus offer plenty of interesting
combinations, as shown by a tureen of fennel and almond soup with warm
wholemeal bread and a starter of fresh Morecambe Bay shrimps in lightly
curried mayonnaise served in a Galia melon. Lunch offers little choice
(alternatives only at each of the first two courses, plus a few desserts), but is
always interesting: perhaps mushroom and apple soup followed by sea bass
with fennel and Pernod sauce or a breast of chicken stuffed with a cheese
and herb paté. The varied assortment of vegetables that accompany main
courses is always a strong point. Fixed-price-only menus offer three courses
at lunch and four at dinner. *Seats 28. Parties 12. L 12.30 for 1 D 7.30 for 8.
Closed Mon, Jan & Feb. Set L £13.50 Set D £24. Access, Amex, Visa.*

Rooms   £76

The house is smartly Edwardian in style and the five en-suite (three with
shower) bedrooms are tastefully decorated and furnished. All have TVs.
No children under eight.

Cartmel   Places of Interest

HolkerHallandLakelandMotorMuseum Cark-in-CartmelTel0539558328.
Cartmel Racecourse   Tel 05395 36340.

Castle Cary   Bond's   63%   £52
Tel 0963 50464   HR
Ansford Hill Castle Cary Somerset BA7 7JP   Map 4 B3

Formerly the Half Moon coaching inn, Bond's is a listed Georgian house
just off the A371. Creeper-clad without and cosily cosseting within, its
emphasis on informal good living is epitomised by glowing log fires in bar
and lounge, and period bedrooms, each with its own appeal,
which lack nothing in comfort. True personal service from Kevin and
Yvonne Bond sets the seal on guests' well-being. Good breakfasts. No
children under 8. No dogs. *Rooms 7. Garden. Closed 1 week Xmas. Access,
Visa.*

Restaurant   £55

Yvonne's weekly-changing menu and nightly table d'hote contain few
surprises but plenty of choice; her cooking is substantial and nourishing,
the dishes attractive. Quail and chicken livers on brioche with hollandaise,
an intermediate course of hake fillet stuffed with apricots and parsley, and
braised veal with cider and Marsala sauce are all typical choices. Plenty of
puddings (perhaps almond sponge with plum compote) and a good cheese
selection extend the options to four or five courses. No smoking. *Seats 20.
Parties 10. D only 7-9.30. Set D £12.75 & £18.50/£22.*

Castle Combe   Castle Inn   £45

Tel & Fax 0249 782461   I

Castle Combe Nr Chippenham Wiltshire SN14 7HN   Map 4 B2

Castle Combe has often won awards for being the prettiest village in England; at its heart is the 12th-century Castle Inn. Exposed stone walls mix with fitted carpets in the two main bars, and the vaulted former wine cellars have become a games room with skittles, pool and other traditional pub games. Cottagey bedrooms have carpeted bathrooms. Children under 10 stay free in parents' room. *Rooms 9. Garden. L 12-1.45 D 7.30-9.30. Access, Amex, Visa.*

Castle Combe   Manor House   76%   £135

Tel 0249 782206   Fax 0249 782159   **HR**

Castle Combe Nr Chippenham Wiltshire SN14 7HR   Map 4 B2

A manor house at Castle Combe existed here before the Norman Conquest, and parts of a later 16th-century house remain today. Recently exposed stone walls, beams, fireplaces and kilns, embellished with oak panelling and antique furniture create true period appeal. 26 acres of garden and parkland are viewed from these splendid rooms where log fires burn the year round. Main-house bedrooms are no less superb: antiques plus four-poster and tester beds are handsome features, mini-bars and whirlpool baths the up-to-date accoutrements. Remaining bedrooms, some of them smaller, are housed in neighbouring cottages. Three characterful rooms of varying size are offered for board meetings and private dining: maximum 100. Dogs £10 per night. *Rooms 36. Garden, croquet, outdoor swimming pool, fishing, tennis, helipad. Access, Amex, Visa,*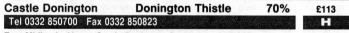

Restaurant   £60

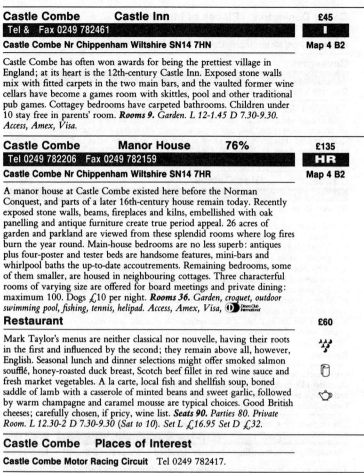

Mark Taylor's menus are neither classical nor nouvelle, having their roots in the first and influenced by the second; they remain above all, however, English. Seasonal lunch and dinner selections might offer smoked salmon soufflé, honey-roasted duck breast, Scotch beef fillet in red wine sauce and fresh market vegetables. A la carte, local fish and shellfish soup, boned saddle of lamb with a casserole of minted beans and sweet garlic, followed by warm champagne and caramel mousse are typical choices. Good British cheeses; carefully chosen, if pricy, wine list. *Seats 90. Parties 80. Private Room. L 12.30-2 D 7.30-9.30 (Sat to 10). Set L £16.95 Set D £32.*

Castle Combe   Places of Interest

Castle Combe Motor Racing Circuit   Tel 0249 782417.

Castle Donington   Donington Thistle   70%   £113

Tel 0332 850700   Fax 0332 850823   **H**

East Midlands Airport Castle Donington Derbyshire DE7 2SH   Map 11 D3

Located within the perimeter of the East Midlands Airport, this modern low-rise Mount Charlotte Thistle hotel is also close to Donington motor racing circuit and the M1, with Alton Towers just a few minutes' drive away. A stone-tiled floor features in the spacious foyer and pine furniture in the bar. Bedrooms are decorated in restful shades with floral fabrics and lightwood units. Executive bedrooms, and the four suites, have mini-bars and various extras in the bathrooms like towelling robes and more luxurious toiletries. 24hr room service can rustle up a hot meal in the middle of the night. Conference/banqueting facilities for 200/180. *Rooms 110. Indoor swimming pool, sauna, solarium, spa bath, keep-fit equipment, airport courtesy bus. Access, Amex, Visa,*

Castle Donington   Places of Interest

The Donington Motor Museum   Donington Park Tel 0332 810048.
Donington Park Motor Racing Circuit   Tel 0332 810048.

Cavendish   Alfonso's

£60

Tel 0787 280372

R

Cavendish Nr Sudbury Suffolk CO10 8BB

Map 6 C3

Alfonso and Veronica Barricella have been providing authentic Italian food
in an English village for 20 years. Among the favourites in their repertoire
are lasagne, minestrone, *pollo alla cacciatora*, *vitello alla milanese* and (a house
creation) fillet steak served on a crouton with paté, artichoke, olive and
brandy sauce. *Seats 30. Parties 30. L 12-2.30 D 7-9.30 (Sat to 10). Closed
L Mon-Fri, D Sun. Set L £12.50. Access, Amex, Visa,* ⓓ *Diners Club International*

Cawston   Grey Gables

£48

Tel 0603 871259

RR

Norwich Road Cawston Norwich Norfolk NR10 4EY

Map 6 C1

A small Georgian house with a Victorian facade, just behind the Ratcatcher
pub about a mile south of Cawston, provides a homely setting for Rosalind
Snaith's wholesome cooking. The short, fixed-price menu of three, four or
five courses makes good use of seasonal produce in dishes such as country
paté with date chutney, trout with almonds, pheasant cooked with celery,
apple wine and cream, or roast leg of lamb with plum jelly. There's a
quirky, wide-ranging wine list (anything on the expensive side is marked
POA) or – a curious and not very useful feature – you can bring your
own, subject to a corkage equating to the mark-up of an equivalent bottle
on the list but not less than £5; nevertheless, bottles are quite decently
priced. No children under 5. *Seats 30. Parties 22. Private Room. D only
7-8.30. Closed 24-26 Dec. Set D £17-£21. Access, Visa.*

Rooms

£50

Six peaceful bedrooms offer traditional furnishings together with hotel
amenities like direct-dial telephone, TV, radio, and en-suite, carpeted
bathrooms. Bedroom number 1 is the best and carries a small supplement.
Garden, lawn tennis.

Chaddesley Corbett   Brockencote Hall   75%

£90

Tel 0562 777876   Fax 0562 777872

H

Chaddesley Corbett Nr Kidderminster Hereford & Worcester DY10 4PY

Map 10 B4

There's a strong French influence at Brockencote, from owners Josephe
Petitjean and his wife Alison to what appears to be the majority of staff,
making it easy to imagine being over the Channel, rather than in the heart
of England. The classically-styled white-painted house stands in 70 acres of
open parkland with mature grounds, a lake and interesting trees. Its
interior has a relaxed atmosphere and nicely proportioned day rooms such
as a splendid, naturally light bar with soft pine and ceiling-high maple
panelling. All eight immaculate bedrooms have country views, with
understated decor and co-ordinated fabrics. Modern en-suite facilities with
bath and shower. The staff are keen, motivated and polite. *Rooms 8.
Garden. Closed 2 weeks Xmas/New Year. Access, Amex, Visa,* ⓓ *Diners Club International*

Chadlington   The Manor   76%

£110

Tel 0608 76711

HR

Chadlington Oxfordshire OX7 3LX

Map 4 C1

The Grants' mellow stone house, set in extensive grounds in a pretty
Cotswold village, has a wonderfully relaxing atmosphere and the owners
and staff couldn't be more helpful and attentive. Beyond the panelled
entrance lounge is a second lounge with an open fire where drinks are

served in the absence of any bar. Splendid bedrooms are the high point: individually designed and tastefully furnished with antiques and period pieces, they're full of little indulgences like fresh fruit and mineral water, plus plentiful bath foam in the gold-tapped bathrooms. *Rooms 7. Garden. Access, Visa,* ⊙ *Diners Club International*

Restaurant   £60

Chris Grant's dinner reflects what's best in the daily market; space is limited and non-residents should book. Soup, perhaps celery and lovage, is followed by an intermediate course such as brioche with Madeira and mushrooms or smoked trout salad; for main course baked salmon with hollandaise or duck breast with orange, honey and ginger. Home-made sweets continue to be a strong point, with cheeses and biscuits following. David Grant's superb wine list features some excellent half bottles and some vintage first-growth clarets at almost giveaway prices; several English wines and ports, too, also at fair prices. *Seats 25. Parties 10. Private Room. D only 7-9. Set D £25.50.*

Chagford	Gidleigh Park	82%	£292*
Tel 0647 432367	Fax 0647 432574		**HR**
Chagford Devon TQ13 8HH			Map 3 D2

The quintessential country house hotel, Gidleigh nestles in a sheltered fold of the Teign valley with splendid views of Nattadon and Meldon hills. Paul and Kay Henderson's years of dedication and unstinting hard work won for them our Hotel of the Year award in 1990; their constant improvements have produced a dozen extremely comfortable bedrooms in the main house, two exquisite suites, and a separate three-room cottage standing in woodland across the river. Quality antiques, deep enormous sofas and pleasing floral arrangements are features of the panelled lounge and luxurious bar (where fine wines are served by the glass from the Cruvinet machine): discreet good taste is evident at every turn and service from the delightful staff is exceptional. Corned beef hash with poached egg, Irish potato bread and black pudding with boudin blanc and a herb mustard sauce are among Shaun Hill's interesting breakfast offerings. The tiny hamlet of Gidleigh, settled by King Harold's mother, Gydda, dates from the eleventh century, but to find the hotel don't go there, following instead the road signed from Chagford village. *Half-board terms only. Rooms 15. Garden, croquet, bowls, game fishing, tennis. Access, Visa.*

Restaurant   ★★   £112

Shaun Hill's cooking perfectly complements the style, decor and location of the hotel. His choice of suppliers confirms that he has a healthy attitude towards our environment and his dishes reflect the superb raw materials that he seeks out – from Brixham crab served as a salad with herb mayonnaise to Dart river salmon, grilled and served with basil and tomato. The fixed-price menus are, refreshingly, written in straightforward, unpretentious English, giving little indication of the involved nature of the dishes; lunch (steeply priced, even for the captive resident market) might see a choice of only two dishes to start (crab salad or saffron risotto) and for the main course (the aforementioned salmon or ragout of spring lamb and vegetables), but extends to cheeses and good desserts afterwards. Forty pence per meal is added to each account (unless requested not) and donated to a local charity – Farms for City Children. Dinner, also only at fixed prices, sees a choice of four or seven courses, the latter with a £7 supplement for residents; the good choice might range from salad of lettuces with grilled Dover sole and herb dressing, grilled red mullet with ginger, garlic and tomato or ragout of rabbit with pasta and a pecorino and olive oil sauce to start, to roast corn-fed pigeon with gnocchi and sage, steamed sea bass with dill and crème fraiche or grilled Scottish fillet steak with Meaux mustard sauce. Lemon tart with caramelised banana, Kirsch mousse and rum baba with cherries, and white chocolate and pistachio terrine with raspberry sauce typify the desserts. The seven-course speciality menu has to be ordered by an entire table and offers no choice to start, but might cover home-cured bresaola with poached leeks in mustard dressing, sautéed scallops with lentil and coriander sauce, saffron risotto, noisettes of spring lamb with artichoke heart and pea purée; then sorbet, cheeses and a choice of desserts. Prices quoted include service – hurrah! The wine list (read Paul Henderson's interesting notes on his buying and pricing policy) is exceptional, with depth everywhere you look and Italy unusually well represented. *Seats 40. Private Room. L 12.30-2 D 7-9. Set L £33/£43 Set D £43 & £50.*

Chagford	Great Tree Hotel	61%	£75
Tel 0647 432491			**H**
Sandy Park Chagford Devon TQ13 8JS			Map 3 D2

The Eaton-Grays' relaxed hotel, a former hunting lodge, stands in 18 acres of gardens and woodland, commanding splendid views of Dartmoor and the surrounding countryside. There's an old, rather Colonial character to the entrance hall with its ornate fireplace and a carved wooden staircase leading down to a raftered bar and lounge. Most of the bedrooms are at ground level with south-facing French windows. The Great Tree ambience is epitomised by complimentary sherry on arrival. *Rooms 12. Garden.* Access, Amex, Visa,

---

Chagford	Mill End	63%	£83
Tel 0647 432282 Fax 0647 433106			**H**
Sandy Park Chagford Devon TQ13 8JN			Map 3 D2

The old flour mill, whose wheel still turns in the courtyard, has been a hotel for about 60 years. It stands in the beautiful valley of the river Teign, on whose banks the hotel has fishing rights. Shooting is another popular pastime, while for quiet relaxation the chintzy sitting rooms have the appeal of a well-loved private house. Bedrooms are furnished with a mixture of traditional, antique and modern pieces. Children sharing their parents' room are accommodated free; good facilities for young families. The hotel is on the A382 (don't turn off towards Chagford). *Rooms 17. Garden, fishing, shooting. Closed 10 days mid-Dec. Access, Amex, Visa,*

Chagford   Places of Interest

Okehampton Tourist Information   Tel 0837 53020.
Museum of Dartmoor Life   Tel 0837 522951.

Chapel Amble	Maltsters Arms		£50
Tel 0208 812473			**R**
Chapel Amble Wadebridge Cornwall PL27 6EU			Map 2 B3

Well worth the short detour, just off the A39 outside Wadebridge, to find an unprepossessing village pub where chef/proprietor Jeff Pollard specialises in seafood, plus fine home-made items like Cornish fish soup, chicken jambalaya and treacle tart. A full à la carte is offered at both sessions in addition to bar snacks at lunchtime and a good-value set dinner menu. This latter might include a choice of four dishes per course and offer four Loch Fyne oysters to start followed by whole sea bream flamed in pernod and then light lemon tart to finish. Mussels, oysters, crevettes, langoustines and lobster (from their own tank) make an appearance on a shellfish platter, and there's also usually a selection of chargrilled chicken, beef and pasta dishes. Desserts include treacle tart, bread-and-butter pudding, French apple tart with Calvados, plus an unusual selection of tip-top cheeses from the South-West. Outdoor eating in the garden in good weather. *Seats 100. Parties 55. Private Room. L 12-2.30 (to 3 in summer) D 7-9.30 (from 6.30 in summer). Set D £13.95. Access, Visa.*

Chapeltown — Greenhead House £65

Tel 0742 469004 — **R**

84 Burncross Road Chapeltown Nr Sheffield South Yorkshire S30 4SF — Map 10 C2

Neil and Anne Allen's pretty little restaurant north of Sheffield offers a monthly-changing menu that might range from bouchée of salmon and asparagus or galantine of quail with pistachios and truffle to roulade of turkey with morels and fillet of sea bass with a fresh tomato sauce. Your choice of main course determines the overall meal price. Robust cooking, carefully executed. **Seats 30.** *Parties 34. Private Room. D only 7.15-9. Closed Sun & Mon, Bank Holidays, 2 weeks Apr, 2 weeks Aug. Set D from £25. Access, Amex, Visa.*

Charingworth — Charingworth Manor 79% £110

Tel 038 678 555   Fax 038 678 353 — **HR**

Charingworth Nr Chipping Camden Gloucestershire GL55 6NS — Map 4 C1

An idyllic setting, especially on a balmy summer's day, the immaculately kept gardens (part of 54 acres) overlook the hotel's estates, with superb views far beyond. The present building dates back to the 14th century and beams showing the original medieval decoration can still be clearly seen. Both the sitting room and dining room (a low-ceilinged series of eating areas) have mullion windows and oak beams; the former also has hand-stencilled walls, rugs on the polished wood floor and a stone fireplace plus an unnecessary preponderance of hotel group literature. There's no formal bar – drinks are served direct from the cellar. Individually decorated bedrooms and suites have good furnishings and thoughtful touches such as fresh fruit, home-made biscuits and glasses of Madeira awaiting guests on arrival. Courtyard and Cottage bedrooms, created from the original stables and farm buildings, are smaller, but benefit from splendid marble bathrooms and a separate shower. Willing staff ensure an enjoyable stay here, and the romantic setting will suit honeymooning couples. A purpose-built Leisure Spa was added last year. **Rooms 24.** *Garden. Access, Amex, Visa,* Diners Club International

Restaurant £80

A series of low-ceilinged, beamed rooms with pink and green decor makes an intimate setting. Chef Tony Robson-Burrell offers a variety of menus that range from straightforward lunches to a seven-course Epicurean feast. His style is firmly in a fashionable manner based around good classical skills: from a pasta pillow of brill and girolles on a delicate mussel sauce to fillet of Scottish beef with a carpaccio of peppers and a trio of traditional British puddings (bread-and-butter, lemon meringue and jam roly poly). The wine list is quite comprehensive (with a few bargains) and is peppered with quotes from imbibing poets. **Seats 50.** *Parties 12. Private Room. L 12.30-2 D 7.30-9.30 (Sat to 10). Set L £15.50 Set D £31/£36.*

Charlbury — Bell Hotel £75

Tel 0608 810278   Fax 0608 811447 — **I**

Church Street Charlbury Oxfordshire OX7 3PP — Map 4 C1

Once a coaching inn, the Bell stands in the centre of town on the banks of the Evenlode. Day rooms, including a flagstoned bar, have a comfortable, traditional appeal, and bedrooms offer adequate accommodation. Small functions are catered for (up to 55 people) and fishing, gliding and hot-air ballooning are among the activities which the hotel can organise. Children up to 16 stay free in parents' room. **Rooms 14.** *Garden. Access, Amex, Visa,* Diners Club International

| Charlbury | The Bull at Charlbury | NEW | £40 |

Tel 0608 811536   **IR**

Sheep Street Charlbury Oxfordshire   Map 4 C1

Environmentally condemned some three years ago, it is perhaps fitting that
the Bull, on Sheep Street, should have reopened with so serious a bias
towards quality dining. The entire ground floor puts food first in
interlinked rooms full of Cotswold stone and beautifully restored
inglenooks. Integral, rather than after thought, the half-dozen bedrooms
(two with full bathrooms and four with WC/shower only) nestle under
the steeply sloping eaves of Charlbury's oldest inn. *Rooms 6. Access, Visa.*

Restaurant   £50

Returning to his Cotswold roots, chef Nick Gill brings an unparalleled
pedigree to the iced crudités, home-made soup, simple entrées (rib-eye beef,
corn-fed chicken, whole trout) and home-made pastries which constitute
his all-embracing dinner at a refreshingly realistic price. Early indications
are of widespread acceptance of his latest concept. Mid-week lunches are by
prior arrangement; otherwise, lighter bar food is available. *Seats 60.*
Parties 10. L 12-2 D 7-9.30. Closed D Sun. Set meals from £14.

| Charlecote | Charlecote Pheasant | 62% | £85 |

Tel 0789 470333   Fax 0789 470222   **H**

Charlecote Nr Warwick Warwickshire CV35 9EN   Map 4 C1

Public rooms are in old beamed farmhouse buildings, bedrooms (including
seven new Executive rooms) in a modern block. Conference and
banqueting facilities up to 120. Queens Moat Houses. *Rooms 67. Garden,*
keep-fit equipment, outdoor swimming pool, steam room, solarium. Access, Amex,
Visa, Diners Club International

| Chartham | Thruxted Oast | | £68 |

Tel 0227 730080   **PH**

Mystole Chartham Nr Canterbury Kent CT4 7BX   Map 7 C5

Built as an oast-house in 1791, it performed its hop-drying functions until
1986, when owners Tim and Hilary Derouet converted it to hotel use. It
has just three bedrooms, with beams, conical roofs, pine furniture and
patchwork quilts. Beams are also a feature in the lounge, which houses an
artwork collection (there's a picture-framing business on the premises). The
large farmhouse kitchen serves as the breakfast room; eggs come from their
own hens. No children under eight. No dogs. Check directions as it's
slightly off the beaten track; four miles from Canterbury. *Rooms 3.*
Garden, croquet. Access, Amex, Visa, Diners Club International

| Chedington | Chedington Court | 71% | £130* |

Tel 0935 891265   Fax 0935 891442   **HR**

Chedington Nr Beaminster Dorset DT8 3HY   Map 4 A4

Winding lanes lead you to a secluded Jacobean-style manor set on high
ground surrounded by 10 acres of terraced grounds and views down to a
lake and across the surrounding countryside; the interior is equally
handsome and pleasing to the eye, although there is little of the atmosphere
of other fine country house hotels. Peace and quiet are offered in
abundance, but hotel conveniences are limited. A fine carved oak dresser
dominates the entrance hall and, in the lounge, leaded windows, a log fire
and comfortable velour sofas give a sense of timeless peace. Bedrooms are
furnished in a very homely fashion, with solid pieces, ornaments, books
and mineral water among the thoughtful extras; larger rooms have
armchairs and tables. Bathrooms have separate shower cubicles and good
toiletries. Good breakfasts. *Half-board terms; notify by 10am if dinner
not required. The hotel's own golf course and 15-acre practice ground are
nearby.

Rooms 10. Garden, croquet, snooker, 9-hole golf. Closed Jan & Feb. Access, Amex, Visa.

Restaurant £68

Five-course dinner menus change daily, making good use of fresh ingredients: a choice of two starters might be pot-roasted, boned quail with shallots and port or layered vegetable terrine with herb mayonnaise, followed by both no-choice meat and fish courses (a vegetarian option is always offered). Sweets are served from a trolley and there's an exceptional selection of British farmhouse cheeses. A splendid range of wines, half bottles in particular, on a comprehensive and carefully compiled list that spans the world. Prices are **Seats 26. Parties 20. Private Room. D only 7-9. Set D £26.50.**

Chedington   Hazel Barton   75%   NEW   £95
Tel 0935 891613   Fax 0935 891370   H
Chedington Nr Beaminster Dorset DT8 3HY   Map 4 A4

A delightful country house, though not a particularly pretty building (mid 19th-century), with sweeping views across beautifully maintained gardens. It's splendidly and comfortably furnished, crammed with genuine antiques, fine paintings, quality furniture and tasteful fabrics. Open fires add warmth and an abundance of fresh flowers and plants indicate personal and homely touches. The four individually decorated bedrooms offer comfort and luxury in abundance and the classy bathrooms have quality fittings, good lighting and powerful showers; bathrobes and Floris toiletries are provided. Breakfasts (no other meals are served) are exceptional, with home-made jams, a selection of breads and toast, fine coffee and a choice of several teas. The house is charmingly run with great style by Beryl Schiller, previously at *Bishopstrow House* (qv). A wood-panelled boardroom holds up to 12. No dogs. **Rooms 4. Garden, croquet, snooker. Access, Amex, Visa.**

Cheltenham   Hotel de la Bere   64%   £96
Tel 0242 237771   Fax 0242 236016   H
Southam Cheltenham Gloucestershire GL52 3NH   Map 4 B1

3 miles out of town on the Winchcombe road, convenient for the racecourse. Lots of historic interest in a much-extended Tudor mansion, including a cellar bar. Conference and leisure facilities show the modern side. **Rooms 57. Garden, outdoor swimming pool, sauna, solarium, squash, tennis, badminton, snooker. Access, Amex, Visa.**

Cheltenham   Le Champignon Sauvage   ★↑   £70
Tel 0242 573449   R
24-26 Suffolk Road Cheltenham Gloucestershire GL50 2AQ   Map 4 B1

David Everitt-Matthias is surely the rising star among the younger generation chefs who inhabit England's heartland (Oakes, Redmond and Patrick MacDonald to name just three). As with the restaurant's decor, toned down in colour and refined with modern and impressionist prints (the mushroom pictures are now relegated to the tiny lounge area), so have David's abundant skills come to the fore, backed up with ever greater confidence to produce dishes of individuality and invention. Spiced pigeon breast with gateau of garlic and aubergine and a chocolate-infused jus appears simply as "amuse bouche" (compare with MacDonald's black pudding and onion mash!). Chicken and spinach galette on split pea purée with a green pea ravioli makes its distinguished debut as a finely-crafted signature starter. More forcefully flavoured, without losing sight of either texture or balance, is his fillet of lamb topped with tapénade, and served on a rösti with morels, braised fennel and a translucent tarragon jus. A millefeuille of summer fruits, Pavlova-style, and bitter chocolate tart with white chocolate ice cream exhibit commensurate skills in patisserie. The three-course set price lunch of this quality represents superb value: at dinner the *menu surprise* adds a further four memorable dishes. Easy-to-use wine list with helpful notes; splendid choice under £20. **Seats 30.** *Parties 24. L 12.30-1.30 D 7.30-9.30. Closed L Sat, all Sun, Bank Holidays, 1 week Xmas, 2 weeks Jun. Set L from £17 Set D £23.95/£26.95 & £45. Access, Amex, Visa.*

Cheltenham	Cheltenham Park	69%	£106

Tel 0242 222021   Fax 0242 226935   **H**

Cirencester Road Charlton Kings Cheltenham
Gloucestershire GL53 8EA   **Map 4 B1**

The style of the original building is Georgian but most of the accommodation is in modular rooms in a long wing just a couple of years old. Rooms in the main house, where the public areas are located, are more individual, but contemporary fabrics and lightwood units are standard throughout. Work on the leisure centre had not been completed when we went to press. **Rooms 154.** Garden. Access, Amex, Visa, (**D**) Diners Club International

Cheltenham	Epicurean	★	£70

Tel 0242 518898   Fax 0242 511526   **R**

Cleveland House Evesham Road Cheltenham
Gloucestershire GL52 2AH   **Map 4 B1**

Housed in a small, independently-owned Regency hotel (On the Park – see entry below) just north of town. Its rather theatrical decor provides a splendid stage for Patrick MacDonald's impressive cooking. His philosophy of keeping things simple, allowing individual flavours full rein, is fully justified in dishes like roast foie gras with shallots, tartlet of leeks, chicken and scallops with Sauternes, and stuffed pig's trotters. Patrick has reverted to the original Epicurean menu with a £45 nine-course tasting menu and either a £25 or £35 route on a limited-choice, twin-track menu that comes together at the dessert stage with the likes of Calvados soufflé, lemon tart, and treacle pudding with custard. Home-made petits fours accompany the excellent coffee. Wines are generally pricy, though the new list includes some decent bottles under £20. **Seats 32.** *Parties 16. L 12.30-2.30 D 7-10.15 (Fri & Sat 6-10.45). Closed D Sun, all Mon. Set L £15.50 (£14 Sun) Set D £25-£45. Access, Amex, Visa,* (**D**) Diners Club International

Cheltenham	Golden Valley Thistle	69%	£108

Tel 0242 232691   Fax 0242 221846   **H**

Gloucester Road Cheltenham Gloucestershire GL51 0TS   **Map 4 B1**

On the outskirts of Cheltenham, one mile from junction 11 of the M5 (next to GCHQ) and two miles from the town centre. The bright, modern Garden Lounge has wicker furniture and its own patio. Extensive conference facilities and a good new leisure club. **Rooms 124.** *Garden, indoor swimming pool, spa bath, sauna, solarium, beautician, tennis. Access, Amex, Visa,* (**D**) Diners Club International

Cheltenham	Greenway	80%	£120

Tel 0242 862352   Fax 0242 362780   **HR**

Shurdington Cheltenham Gloucestershire GL51 5UG   **Map 4 B1**

Ever since Tony Elliott bought this Elizabethan building in the early 80s, the Guide has always considered the hotel a stylish, warm and friendly country house, situated in the very heart of the Cotswolds and surrounded by beautifully maintained formal gardens and parkland. All rooms, be they bedrooms or public rooms, have lovely views of the countryside, and the converted Georgian brick-built stables do not look out of place with the main house. In summer you can stroll into the gardens from the elegant, comfortable and spacious drawing room, bar or conservatory dining room, and in winter you can settle down in front of cosy log fires; in other words, just relax. From the moment of your welcome in the splendid entrance hall with its antiques and paintings, the hotel's team of friendly and attentive staff will look after you. Bedrooms, most with a separate shower in the en-suite bathrooms, are charmingly decorated and furnished, offering bathrobes, good toiletries and cosseting extras, and whether you stay in the main house or the cleverly restored coach house, you can be assured of excellent housekeeping throughout, and good breakfast the next morning. No children under seven. No dogs. **Rooms 19.** *Garden, croquet. Closed 2 weeks Xmas. Access, Amex, Visa,*

Restaurant £65

The conservatory dining room is a splendid place to enjoy lunch with delightful views or a relaxed dinner by candle-light. Dishes are light and attractive: home-smoked scallops with a salad of Brussels sprout leaves and bacon strips, poached artichoke filled with white crab meat, salmon steak with braised fennel on a saffron sauce, roast breast of pigeon with wild mushrooms, rack of lamb with rosemary-flavoured gravy. Good safe wine list with plenty of bottles under £20. **Seats 50.** *Parties 18. Private Room. L 12-2 D 7-9.30 (Sun to 8). Closed L Sat, Bank Holidays.* Set L £13 Set D £28.

Cheltenham   On The Park   68%   £64

Tel 0242 518898   Fax 0242 511526

Evesham Road Cheltenham Gloucestershire GL52 2AH   Map 4 B1

Overlooking a small park in the Pittville area of Cheltenham, a Regency house has been restored and refurbished to create an intimate town-house hotel. Antique-furnished bedrooms have all been individually decorated and have good en-suite bathrooms. The starred *Epicurean* restaurant in the same building is separately owned and run but does offer a special three-course dinner at £17.50 exclusively to hotel guests. No dogs. **Rooms 8.** *Access, Amex, Visa,*

Cheltenham   Queen's Hotel   69%   £119

Tel 0242 514724   Fax 0242 224145

The Promenade Cheltenham Gloucestershire GL50 1NN   Map 4 B1

Built early in Queen Victoria's reign, and named in her honour, this imposing white colonnaded hotel overlooks the Imperial Gardens. The lofty foyer/lounge creates an air of elegance echoed in the magnificent stairwell and Napier Bar. Bedrooms (the best of which are on the first floor) include six suites and several Executive rooms. All are neatly maintained and have desk space, armchairs and the usual extras. Extensive conference and banquet trade, catering for up to 200. Forte. **Rooms 77.** *Access, Amex, Visa,*

Cheltenham   Redmond's   ★   £75

Tel 0242 672017

Cleeve Hill Cheltenham Gloucestershire GL52 3PR   Map 4 B1

Enjoying quite spectacular views over the valley towards the Malverns, the setting is superb and the food similarly so. The three-or-four course menus are always imaginative, but without unnecessary gimmicks, giving a choice of just four or so dishes per course. Spices and herbs are cleverly used to enhance the natural flavours of the freshest ingredients possible, accompanied by well-executed sauces like vanilla and orange with breast of maize-fed chicken or shellfish served with pan-fried scallops and salmon. Redmond's invention is typified in dishes of lemon, onion and chicken soup and sliced Cornish crab sausage in a very mild curry and coriander consommé. Fine cheeses, hot lime soufflé with ginger ice cream or prune and Armagnac parfait with caramel sauce to finish. A small, carefully selected, beautifully scripted list of interesting, good-value wines is arranged by style and grape variety; ask for advice. **Seats 36.** *Parties 18. Private Room. L 12.30-2 D 7.15-10. Closed L Sat, D Sun, all Mon, 1 week Jan.* Set D £28.60. *Access, Visa.*

see over

Rooms   £75

Five simply furnished and decorated bedrooms offer comfortable, unfussy
overnight accommodation. Each has its own en-suite facilities.

Cheltenham   Staithes   £65

| Tel 0242 260666 | R |

12 Suffolk Road Cheltenham Gloucestershire GL50 2AQ   Map 4 B1

Family-run restaurant with serious cooking and lots of good ideas.
Millefeuille of sautéed duck livers, pine kernels and spinach with red
pepper sauce; smoked haddock and Dublin Bay prawns wrapped in pasta
and served on a bed of leeks; fillet steak on a croute of wild mushroom
terrine with Madeira sauce. Orange bread-and-butter pudding is served
with a warm Grand Marnier custard sauce. English and Continental
cheeses, plus a straightforward wine list. A seven-course menu surprise
(£37.50) is also available (booking needed). No smoking. Lunch is by
prior arrangement only. *Seats 28. Parties 30. D 7-9.45. Closed Sun & Mon.*
Access, Amex, Visa.

Cheltenham   Travel Inn   £42

| Tel 0242 233847   Fax 0242 244887 | L |

Tewkesbury Road Uckington Cheltenham Gloucestershire GL51 9SL   Map 4 B1

Situated conveniently close to the Cotswolds, 10 minutes drive from
Cheltenham race course. *Rooms 40. Access, Amex, Visa,*

Cheltenham   Places of Interest

Tourist Information   Tel 0242 522878.
Sudeley Castle   Winchcombe Tel 0242 602308.
Chedworth Roman Villa (NT)   Yanworth, Nr Cheltenham Tel 024289 256.
Cheltenham Art Gallery and Museum   Tel 0242 237431.
Pittville Pump Room Museum   Gallery of Fashion Pittville Tel 0242 512740.
Cheltenham Racecourse   Tel 0242 513014.
  Theatres and Concert Halls
Everyman Theatre   Tel 0242 512515.
Pittville Pump Room   Tel 0242 523690.
Playhouse Theatre   Tel 0242 522852.
Shaftesbury Hall Theatre   Tel 0242 22795.

Chelwood   Chelwood House   63%   £75

| Tel 0761 490730   Fax ext 504 | HR |

Chelwood Bristol Avon BS18 4NH   Map 4 B3

A former Dower House, dating from the reign of Charles II, with lovely,
unspoilt views across rolling countryside towards Bath, some 10 miles
away. Owners Jill and Rudi Birk, who clearly love the place, have created
a warm and welcoming atmosphere in their six years here. The lounge,
boasting fine listed panelling, opens to an attractive staircase leading to
individually styled bedrooms which some may find over-fussy. The
French, Chinese and Victorian themed rooms all have four-posters, and
some humour is shown in naming the smallest one Lilliput. Home-made
fruit compote is a feature of good, traditional breakfasts. No children under
10. No dogs. *Rooms 8. Garden, croquet. Access, Amex, Visa,*

Restaurant   £50

The conservatory-style "restaurant in a garden", with plants, fountain and
gazebo, is decorated with murals. Traditional goulash and coq au vin are
the staples of a value-for-money table d'hote dinner: à la carte, Rudi's
repertoire draws on many specialities from his native Bavaria. Set Sunday
lunch and light lunches at bargain prices through the week. *Seats 24.*
Parties 8. L 12-1.15 D 7-9 (Sun to 8, residents only). Closed 2 weeks
Xmas/New Year. Set L £13.50 Set D £12.50.

Chenies   Bedford Arms Thistle   64%   £108

Tel 0923 283301   Fax 0923 284825   **H**

Chenies Nr Rickmansworth Buckinghamshire WD3 6EQ   Map 5 E2

Redbrick hotel on the edge of the village. Banqueting facilities for 65, conferences up to 30. Two bars. *Rooms 10. Access, Amex, Visa,* ⓓ🇩🇮🇳🇪🇷🇸

Chenies   Places of Interest

Moor Park Mansion   Rickmansworth Tel 0923 776611.

Chessington   Travel Inn   £42

Tel 0372 744060   Fax 0372 720889   **L**

Leatherhead Road Chessington Surrey KT9 2NE   Map 5 E3

Adjacent to Chessington World of Adventure, 10 minutes drive from Hampton Court and both Sandown and Epsom race courses. *Rooms 42. Access, Amex, Visa,* ⓓ

Chester   Abbots Well   62%   £90

Tel 0244 332121   Fax 0244 335287   **H**

Whitchurch Road Christleton Chester Cheshire CH3 5QL   Map 10 A2

One mile from the M53, a low-rise hotel on the A41, east of Chester. Conference/banqueting facilities for 230/180. Dinner dances every Saturday from September to April. Jarvis. *Rooms 127. Garden, indoor swimming pool, gymnasium, spa bath, sauna, solarium, snooker. Access, Amex, Visa,* ⓓ

Chester   Blossoms Hotel   63%   £101

Tel 0244 323186   Fax 0244 346433   **H**

St John Street Chester Cheshire CH1 1HL   Map 10 A2

A characterful mix of 18th-century charm and modern refurbishment Just off one of Chester's main shopping streets. Banqueting facilities for up to 50, conferences for 100. Forte. *Rooms 64. Access, Amex, Visa,*

Chester   Chester Grosvenor   84%   £190

Tel 0244 324024   Fax 0244 313246   **HR**

Eastgate Street Chester Cheshire CH1 1LT   Map 10 A2

Our 1993 Hotel of the Year, this is a splendid example of how good city-centre hotels can be. Always in the forefront of Cheshire life, no expense has been spared in the recent restoration of the distinctive Bath stone and mock-Tudor half-timbered frontage, and the reconstruction of the interior, which includes an imposing marble-floored lobby (use the lifts and you'll miss the magnificent central staircase and glittering chandelier), a Bernard Grenot-designed half-panelled library and smart Parisian brasserie (where breakfast is served) with a polished wood floor and high-backed leather banquette seating. Styles throughout the smart air-conditioned bedrooms (with large beds) are highly individual in mahogany, yew or pickled pine; antiques abound and the quality of fabrics is kept to the highest standards. Lots of attention to detail in evidence – comfortable seating, wardrobes with internal lighting, turn-down service, telephone extension in the marble bathrooms that have smart Amtico floor tiles, large towels and bathrobes, powerful showers and Floris toiletries. Corridor call bells and coded keys assist privacy, and garage security (direct access from the Newgate St car park) has also been enhanced. Service sets a benchmark under the supervision of the two Jonathans (managing director Slater and general manager Ritchie) on behalf of the Duke of Westminster's Grosvenor Estates. Stylish banqueting/conference facilities for 220/250. Children up to the age of 12 stay free in parents' room. *Rooms 78. Sauna, solarium, gymnasium, brasserie (7am-11pm), valeting, flower shop. Access, Amex, Visa,*

Arkle Restaurant ★ £110

Sophisticated dining with service to match makes for a first-class act in this stylish and elegant room. Polished mahogany tables boast sparkling silver and fine wine glasses, and the generous amuse-gueule, offered in the library, followed by the chef's appetiser are almost meals in themselves. Assorted breads, baked daily on the premises, cannot be bettered, and despite hard times, the best Echiré butter is still served. For lunch there's a *menu du marché* and *petite carte* – in the evening a more elaborate *à la carte*, or six-course *menu gourmand* painstakingly explained by the restaurant manager. Executive chef Paul Reed and chef Simon Radley execute dishes in a modern style, though many are firmly rooted in classical techniques: a wonderful mousseline of Bresse pigeon with artichokes, surrounded by other cuts of the bird, or roast sea scallops with foie gras, truffle and sweet Sauternes to start followed by *frivolité d'abats* (a collection of roast sweetbreads, trotter, foie gras and tongues), two daily fish dishes (sea bass or turbot perhaps) or duck roasted with cloves, accompanied by an apple charlotte and port juices. Fine cheeses, French from Pierre Androuët, British from Aldridge, are expertly defined and precede desserts which are difficult to resist – a selection of chocolate miniature helpings or a Swiss-sponge charlotte with seasonal berries. A good (if expensive) wine list with many French classics; Germany and the New World are also well represented. *Seats 45. Parties 45. Private Room. L 12-2.30 D 7-10.30. Closed L Mon, all Sun, Bank Holidays. SetL £18/£22.50 Set D £37.*

Chester   Chester International   69%   £150
Tel 0244 322330 Fax 0244 316118	**H**
Trinity Street Chester Cheshire CH1 2BD	Map 10 A2

Centrally located, large modern hotel with good conference and leisure facilities (for around 400). Unexceptional bedrooms and bathrooms. Dinner dances on Fridays and Saturdays. Queens Moat Houses. **Rooms 152.** *Sauna, solarium, spa bath, gymnasium. Closed 3 days Xmas. Access, Amex, Visa,* Diners Club International

Chester   Chester Resort Hotel   62%   £75
Tel 0244 851551 Fax 0244 851089	**H**
Backford Cross Chester Cheshire CH1 6PE	Map 10 A2

North of the city at the A41/A5117 junction, this is a popular conference hotel, with facilities for 200+. Children up to 14 stay free in parents' room. Work on a leisure centre is due to start at the end of 1992. **Rooms 113.** *Access, Amex, Visa,* Diners Club International

Chester   Crabwall Manor   76%   £140
Tel 0244 851666 Fax 0244 851400	**HR**
Parkgate Road Mollington Chester Cheshire CH1 6NE	Map 10 A2

Crabwall Manor, which dates from 1850, stands three miles north of Chester on the A540 Hoylake road. Public areas are in soft, light colours and, in the hall, the base of a grandiose stone spiral staircase creates an intimate seating space by an open fire. The bedrooms offer individual decor, with bold use of colour and fabrics; they boast armchairs, sofas, small dining tables and all manner of thoughtful extras such as fruit, mineral water and sherry. Well-equipped bathrooms have shower cubicles and robes. Service is of a particularly high standard. No dogs. **Rooms 48.** *Garden, croquet, snooker, helipad. Access, Amex, Visa,* Diners Club International

Restaurant   £75

Mike Truelove's imaginative, well thought-out menus (both à la carte and fixed-price with a good choice) provide modern interpretations of classical French and English dishes: mousseline of sole and salmon with confit of tomato and basil sauce, scallops marinated in lime and ginger, best end of lamb with hot leek terrine and soy vinaigrette, roast sweetbreads with leeks, pine kernels and a port sauce. Desserts might include iced praline soufflé or a chocolate tart with sablé pastry on an orange syrup. A selection of English farmhouse cheeses is complemented by a choice of ports dating back to 1945. Any restaurant, given the money, can stock an impressive range of fine claret and Burgundy, but the skill lies in backing this up with good wines from elsewhere that most diners can afford. Here Beaujolais, Loire and Alsace perform this valuable service, helped by a peppering of French provincial wines. Australia and California are good, too, and there are stacks and stacks of half bottles. Winner of our 1993 Cellar of the Year North of England regional award. *Seats 120. Parties 20. Private Room. L 12.30-2 D 7-9.45 (Sat to 10, Sun to 9). Set L £14.50 Set D £25.50.*

Chester   Forte Posthouse   62%   £67

Tel 0244 680111   Fax 0244 674100

H

Wrexham Road Chester Cheshire CH4 9DL   Map 10 A2

Modern redbrick hotel on the A483, two miles south of the city centre. Amenities include a health and fitness club, ample car parking and five conference rooms (100+ capacity). *Rooms 107. Gymnasium, indoor swimming pool, spa bath, sauna, solarium. Access, Amex, Visa,*

Chester   Franc's   £35

Tel 0244 317952   Fax 0244 340690

R

14 Cuppin Street Chester Cheshire CH1 2BN   Map 10 A2

Cheerful, bustling brasserie with old timber beams, ceiling fans and French rock music. The eating choice is wide, with anything from a quick snack to a grande bouffe on offer, and classics like boudin (blanc or noir), terrine de campagne, moules marinière and coq au vin to the fore. Good-value Sunday lunch 'bouffe'. Short list of wines, unhelpfully listing no vintages. *Seats 110. Parties 60. Private Room. L 12-3 D 6-11 (plats du jour 12-7). Closed 1-3 Jan, 25 & 26 Dec. Set L £7.50 Set D £9.85. Access, Amex, Visa.*

Chester   Mollington Banastre   67%   £95

Tel 0244 851471   Fax 0244 851165

H

Parkgate Road Chester Cheshire CH1 6NN   Map 10 A2

Comfortable accommodation, plus good leisure and conference facilities (for up to 250 delegates) in an extended Victorian mansion surrounded by gardens. *Rooms 66. Garden, croquet, putting, indoor swimming pool, gymnasium, squash, sauna, solarium, whirlpool bath, beautician, hairdressing, coffee shop (7.30am -10pm). Access, Amex, Visa,*

Chester   Rowton Hall   64%   £88

Tel 0244 335262   Fax 0244 335464

H

Whitchurch Road Chester Cheshire CH3 6AD   Map 10 A2

Standing three miles out of Chester on the A41, on the site of a battle during the Civil War. There's a spacious reception area and a lounge bar looking out on to the smart indoor pool. Rooms in the old house are stylish and individual, those in the adjoining wing more functional. Good leisure amenities and conference facilities for up to 200. *Rooms 42. Garden, croquet, indoor swimming pool, sauna, solarium, spa bath, gymnasium, squash, coffee bar (9am-11pm). Closed 25 & 26 Dec. Access, Amex, Visa,*

Chester   Places of Interest

Chester Visitor Centre Tel 0244 351609.
Town Hall   Tel 0244 313126.
Gateway Theatre   Hamilton Place Tel 0244 340392.
The Boat Museum   Ellesmere Port Tel 051 355 5017 *Britain's premier canal museum.*
Grosvenor Museum   Grosvenor Street Tel 0244 321616.
Chester Cathedral   Tel 0244 324756.
Chester Racecourse   Tel 0244 323170.
Chester Zoo   Upton-by-Chester Tel 0244 380280.

Chester-le-Street   Lumley Castle   69%   £105

Tel 091-389 1111   Fax 091-387 1437   **H**

Chester-le-Street Durham DH3 4NX   **Map 15 B4**

A magnificent 13th-century castle which has been turned into a highly
individual hotel. The interior oozes character and furnishings have been
carefully chosen to harmonise. Comfortable armchairs, period furniture, oil
paintings and ornaments make the lounge elegant, and there's a stylish
library with 3000 books. Main bedrooms are spacious and appealing, with
top-quality fabrics and beautiful decor combined with good antique
furniture; feature Castle rooms have some added attraction like a raised
sleeping area or a Queen Anne four-poster. Most rooms are in the
courtyard and are smaller but equally stylish. No dogs. *Rooms 65. Garden,
sauna, snooker, helipad. Closed 25 & 26 Dec, 1 Jan. Access, Amex, Visa,*
(D) *Diners Club International*

Chester-le-Street   Places of Interest

The North of England Open Air Museum   Beamish, Nr Chester-le-Street
   Tel 0207 231811.
Lambton Park Showground   Tel 091 388 5459.

Chesterfield   Chesterfield Hotel   59%   £69

Tel 0246 271141   Fax 0246 220719   **H**

Malkin Street Chesterfield Derbyshire S41 7UA   **Map 10 C2**

Central former Victorian railway hotel, just off the by-pass. Purpose-built
Peak Leisure Centre and conference suite for up to 230 delegates. Children
under 16 stay free in parents' room. No dogs. *Rooms 73. Indoor swimming
pool, gymnasium, spa bath, sauna, steam room, solarium, beauty salon, snooker.
Access, Amex, Visa,* **(D)** *Diners Club International*

Chesterfield   Forte Travelodge   £40

Tel 0246 455411   **L**

A61 Brimington Road North Wittington Moor Chesterfield Derbyshire   **Map 10 C2**

On the A61 Chesterfield inner ring road on the northern outskirts of the
town. *Rooms 20. Access, Amex, Visa.*

Chesterfield   Places of Interest

Tourist Information   Tel 0246 207777.
Bolsover Castle   Tel 0246 823349.
Hardwick Hall (NT)   Tel 0246 850430.
   Theatres and Concert Halls
Chesterfield Arts Centre   Tel 0246 208061.
Pomegranate Theatre   Tel 0246 232901.
The Winding Wheel   Tel 0246 209552.

Chichester   Comme Ça   £55

Tel 0243 788724   **R**

67 Broyle Road Chichester West Sussex   **Map 5 E4**

Close enough to the Festival Theatre (3 minutes walk) to offer a
straightforward pre- and post-theatre menu, this former pub is now a
French restaurant with a bar. Chef-patron Michel Navet cooks in a sound,
classically-based style, offering a good choice of dishes to please most palates
– from chicken liver paté and deep-fried Camembert with gooseberry and
brandy sauce to Dover sole and entrecote with green pepper sauce. Popular
family Sunday lunches and bar lunches. *Seats 42. Parties 40. L 12-2 D 7-10
(6-10.30 on theatre nights). Closed D Sun, all Mon, Bank Holidays. Set L
£14.50. Access, Visa,* **(D)** *Diners Club International*

Chichester   Dolphin & Anchor   63%   £96

Tel 0243 785121   Fax 0243 533408   H

West Street Chichester West Sussex PO19 1QE   Map 5 E4

Built in the 17th century, the Dolphin and the Anchor were rivals until
united in 1910. Best bedrooms (which attract a supplementary charge) are
at the front, with cathedral views. Forte Heritage. Conference and
banqueting ballroom (once the Liberal Assembly Rooms) caters for up to
180. **Rooms 49.** *Access, Amex, Visa,* (1) *Diners Club International*

Chichester   Thompson's   £65

Tel 0243 528832   R

30a Southgate Chichester West Sussex PO19 1DR   Map 5 E4

First-floor, spacious and smart room with a good choice of classical dishes
interpreted in a modern style. Dinner is the main attraction with the likes
of spinach and duck liver parfait or smoked salmon in herb pancakes with
a chive cream sauce, followed by scallop and mussel millefeuille, roast
turbot with Madeira sauce, Sussex jugged hare or tournedos with shredded
pastrami. Lunch prices are kinder and dishes simpler (black pudding and
bacon rosette with watercress, salmon kedgeree, bangers and mash with
onion gravy and spotted dick with vanilla sauce). Short, carefully chosen
wine list; interesting choice of coffees. **Seats 40.** *L 12.30-2 D 7.30-11.*
Closed L Mon, all Sun, Bank Holidays ex Good Friday.
Access, Visa, (1) *Diners Club International*

Chichester   Places of Interest

Tourist Information   Tel 0243 775888.
Chichester Festival Theatre   Oaklands Park Tel 0243 781312.
West Dean Gardens   Tel 0243 63301.
Chichester Cathedral   Tel 0243 782595.
The Roman Palace   Fishbourne Tel 0243 785859.
Weald and Downland Open Air Museum   Singleton Tel 024 363 348.
Chichester Harbour   Area of outstanding natural beauty.

Chiddingfold   Crown Inn   £57

Tel 042 868 2255   I

The Green Chiddingfold Nr Godalming Surrey GU8 4TX   Map 5 E3

Established as a hostelry in 1285, the mellow half-timbered Crown is one
of the oldest recorded inns in England. Linenfold panelling, stained glass in
mullioned windows, creaking stairs and passages leading to atmospheric
bedrooms with sloping floors, bowed walls, beams and solid furniture
show its age. Annexe rooms are contrastingly light and modern. **Rooms 8.**
Access, Amex, Visa, (1) *Diners Club International*

Chilgrove   White Horse Inn   £60

Tel 0243 59219   Fax 0243 59301   R

High Street Chilgrove Nr Chichester West Sussex PO18 9HX   Map 5 E3

The wine cellar alone is worth the trip, but the setting of this old, cottagey
inn amid glorious Sussex countryside is another major attraction. Wine
expert Barry Phillips has been here for more than 20 years and chef-
partner Neil Rusbridger cooks in a confident style harmonious with the
oenological attractions. Fine, fresh ingredients feature in appealing dishes
like terrine of smoked lamb fillets and courgettes served on a chilled
tomato coulis, steamed breasts of pigeon served on a celeriac purée and
daily special fish and vegetarian dishes – perhaps wild mushroom and
aubergine strudel. Offal is interestingly treated – try the trio of calf's
sweetbreads (with bacon), kidneys (with apple and calvados) and brains
(with black butter and capers) if it's on the menu. Desserts include a variety
of home-made ice creams. Outdoor eating for 12 on a patio in good
weather. Fixed-price menus only, with 10% service automatically added.
One of the country's finest wine lists includes a splendid selection available

by the glass. *Seats 70. Parties 70. Private Room. L 12-1.45 D 7-9.30 (Sat to 10). Closed D Sun, all Mon, Xmas, Feb, last week Oct. Set L £16.50 Set D £22 (£23.50 Sat). Access, Visa,* Diners Club International

Chinnor   Sir Charles Napier Inn   £70

| Tel 0494 483011 | R |

Sprigg's Alley Nr Chinnor Oxfordshire OX9 4BX   **Map 5 D2**

Though this fine country restaurant in an old village inn is only ten minutes drive from the M40 (at exit 6), prospective diners should check directions when booking. On arrival you'll find a merry jumble of furniture and similarly informal atmosphere and service. Seasonal produce, much of it from the Griffiths' own vegetable garden features prominently on the hand-written menus and is handled with care and respect by Sardinian chef, Batiste Tolu. Local asparagus with hollandaise, Oxfordshire boar with apple sauce, Cornish lobster with chive and some exemplary English desserts uniformly live up to expectations. The wine list is a quaffer's paradise, with a fascinating selection at near bargain prices, and some wonderful dessert wines. Winner of our 1993 Midlands/Heart of England Regional Cellar of the Year award. *Seats 80. Parties 85. Private Room. L 12-2 (Sat & Sun 12.30-3) D 7.30-10 (Sat to 10.30). Closed D Sun, all Mon, Bank Holidays. Set L £13.50 Set D £15. Access, Visa.*

Chippenham   Granada Lodge   £43

| Tel 0666 837097   Fax 0666 837112 | L |

M4 junction 17/18 Leigh Delamere Chippenham Wiltshire SN4 6LB   **Map 4 B2**

Rooms 35. Access, Amex, Visa, Diners Club International

Chipping Camden   Cotswold House   69%   £90

| Tel 0386 840330   Fax 0386 840310 | H |

The Square Chipping Camden Gloucestershire GL55 6AN   **Map 4 C1**

Robert and Gill Greenstock's civilised 17th-century hotel overlooks the town square. Under a crystal chandelier, a fine spiralling staircase leads up from the stone-floored entrance hall to appealing accommodation with individually themed bedrooms. These include a Garden Room with views over the garden, the quaintly named Aunt Lizzie's room and a colonial room resplendent with four-poster bed and pineapple-based decor. Public areas have an understated elegance, with well-chosen antique furniture and complementary, strong-patterned fabrics. The small drawing room is particularly fine. The tiled-floored *Greenstock's* is an informal, all-day café/bar that leads out on to a willow-shaded courtyard. Cheerful and friendly staff try hard to give personal attention to their customers. No children under eight. No dogs. *Rooms 15. Garden, croquet, café/bar (9.30am-10.30pm) Closed 25 & 26 Dec. Access, Amex, Visa,* Diners Club International

Chipping Campden   Noel Arms   61%   £78

| Tel 0386 840317   Fax 0386 841136 | H |

High Street Chipping Campden Gloucestershire GL55 6AT   **Map 4 C1**

Bedrooms at the town's oldest hostelry are divided more or less evenly between those in a rustic style with antique furniture in the main part to a modern look in a new wing. Among the day rooms are a foyer decked with weaponry, a conservatory adjoining the restaurant and stone-walled bar and a new conference facility. *Rooms 26. Access, Amex, Visa.*

Chipping Campden   Seymour House   66%   £91

| Tel 0386 840429   Fax 0386 840369 | **H** |

High Street Chipping Campden Gloucestershire GL55 6AH   Map 4 C1

A listed 18th-century high street hotel built of mellow Cotswold stone
whose first-class bedrooms are the strong point, employing quality Italian
furniture to offset the original stonework and exposed beams. A 90-year-
old vine features in the restaurant and a 500-year-old yew tree in the small
garden at the rear; the latter is overlooked by a charming patio. A garden
cottage holds further bedrooms. Children up to 14 stay free in parents'
room. *Rooms 15. Garden. Access, Amex, Visa.*

Chipping Campden   Places of Interest

Tourist Information   Tel 0386 840101.
Hidcote Manor Garden (NT)   Hidcote Bartrim Tel 0386 438333.
Kiftsgate Court Garden   Tel 0386 438777.

Chipping Norton   Crown & Cushion   £75

| Tel 0608 642533   Fax 0608 642926 | **I** |

High Street Chipping Norton Oxfordshire OX7 5AD   Map 4 C1

Accommodation at this privately owned former coaching inn (dating in
parts from 1497) ranges from budget rooms in the annexe up to suites
with separate lounge, writing bureau, sofa and traditional cast-iron bath.
There are also some rooms with four-poster/half-tester beds. Public areas
include a cosy lounge, beamed bar, numerous conference rooms (for up to
200) and a leisure club. *Rooms 40. Gymnasium, indoor swimming pool, sauna,
solarium, squash, snooker. Access, Amex, Visa,* 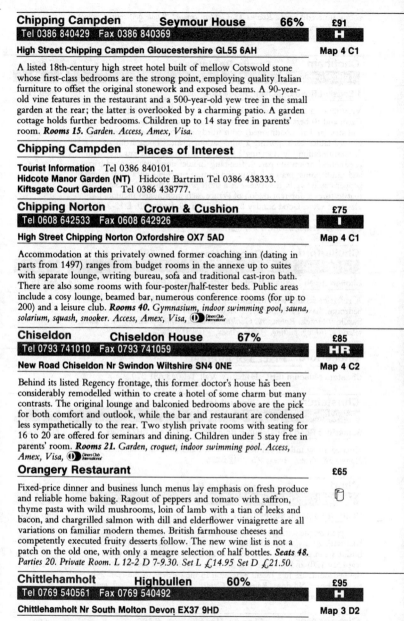 *Diners Club International*

Chiseldon   Chiseldon House   67%   £85

| Tel 0793 741010   Fax 0793 741059 | **HR** |

New Road Chiseldon Nr Swindon Wiltshire SN4 0NE   Map 4 C2

Behind its listed Regency frontage, this former doctor's house has been
considerably remodelled within to create a hotel of some charm but many
contrasts. The original lounge and balconied bedrooms above are the pick
for both comfort and outlook, while the bar and restaurant are condensed
less sympathetically to the rear. Two stylish private rooms with seating for
16 to 20 are offered for seminars and dining. Children under 5 stay free in
parents' room. *Rooms 21. Garden, croquet, indoor swimming pool. Access,
Amex, Visa,* *Diners Club International*

Orangery Restaurant   £65

Fixed-price dinner and business lunch menus lay emphasis on fresh produce
and reliable home baking. Ragout of peppers and tomato with saffron,
thyme pasta with wild mushrooms, loin of lamb with a tian of leeks and
bacon, and chargrilled salmon with dill and elderflower vinaigrette are all
variations on familiar modern themes. British farmhouse cheeses and
competently executed fruity desserts follow. The new wine list is not a
patch on the old one, with only a meagre selection of half bottles. *Seats 48.
Parties 20. Private Room. L 12-2 D 7-9.30. Set L £14.95 Set D £21.50.*

Chittlehamholt   Highbullen   60%   £95

| Tel 0769 540561   Fax 0769 540492 | **H** |

Chittlehamholt Nr South Molton Devon EX37 9HD   Map 3 D2

A splendid Victorian mansion standing in parkland on high ground
between the Mole and Taw valleys. Bedrooms in comfortably traditional
style are in the main house, an adjoining property in a country-style garden
and a group of nearby cottages. Sports and leisure facilities are excellent,
while for less active moments the drawing room, conservatory and library
are ideal spots. There's always plenty to do, but there are also restrictions –
no children under eight, no dogs, no smoking in the restaurant or breakfast

room, no credit cards. **Rooms 35.** *Garden, croquet, 9-hole golf course, indoor putting, indoor & outdoor swimming pools, indoor & outdoor tennis, squash, spa bath, sauna, solarium, hair salon, snooker, sports shop, helipad. No credit cards.*

Chobham   Quails Restaurant   £55
Tel 0276 858491   **R**

1 Bagshot Road Chobham Surrey GU24 8BP   **Map 7A5**

Very much a family affair with Chris and Debbie Wale in the kitchen and Carol and Robert Wale looking after front of house. The interior is light and airy (and air-conditioned) with sturdy country chairs around crisply-clothed tables, each sporting a mini-parlour plant. Choose from an interesting, monthly-changing à la carte menu – red deer sausages with caramelised onion filo parcel; free-range poulet noir with smoked bacon and mushrooms; prawn, halibut and salmon brochette on a tomato and red pepper coulis typify the style – or a short *prix fixe* menu (not Sat & Sun) that features a different region of France each month, and includes two glasses of wine. Good Sunday lunches. **Seats 40.** *Parties 40. L 12-2 D 7-10. Closed L Sat, D Sun, all Mon, 26 Dec, 1 Jan. Set meals £14.95 Sun L £12.95. Access, Amex, Visa,*

Chollerford   George Hotel   59%   £98
Tel 0434 681611   Fax 0434 681727   **H**

Chollerford Nr Hexham Northumberland NE46 4EW   **Map 15 B4**

A riverside setting with delightful gardens and good leisure facilities. Most bedrooms have garden or river views and have been recently refurbished. Swallow Hotels. **Rooms 50.** *Garden, indoor swimming pool, spa bath, sauna, solarium, fishing, putting. Access, Amex, Visa,*

Chollerford   Places of Interest

Chesters Museum (EH)   Hadrian's Wall Tel 043 681 379.

Christchurch   Travel Inn   £42
Tel 0202 485376   Fax 0202 474939   **L**

Somerford Road Christchurch Bournemouth Dorset BH23 3QG   **Map 4 C4**

Situated a few miles from both Mudeford and Boscombe beaches. **Rooms 38.** *Access, Amex, Visa,*

Churt   Frensham Pond Hotel   62%   £88
Tel 025 125 5161   Fax 025 125 2631   **H**

Churt Nr Farnham Surrey GU10 2BQ   **Map 5 E3**

In a picturesque setting overlooking the pond (actually the size of a small lake with a busy weekend sailing club), the hotel caters well for both business and private visitors. Features include four conference suites (capacity 120) and a leisure club with its own bar and restaurant. Most of the bedrooms are in a recent extension in the gardens to the rear. 24hr room service. No dogs. **Rooms 53.** *Garden, indoor swimming pool, sauna, solarium, squash, keep-fit equipment. Access, Amex, Visa,*

Cirencester   Fleece Hotel   64%   £92
Tel 0285 658507   Fax 0285 651017   **H**

Market Square Cirencester Gloucestershire GL7 4NZ   **Map 4 C2**

Timber-fronted Tudor coaching inn in town centre. Generally modest bedrooms. Resort Hotels. **Rooms 25.** *Coffee shop. Access, Amex, Visa,*

Cirencester   Stratton House   62%

£73

Tel 0285 651761   Fax 0285 640024

H

Gloucester Road Cirencester Gloucestershire GL7 2LE

Map 4 C2

1992 saw 16 more bedrooms and extended conference facilities (up to 120 delegates) at this former wool-merchant's house. Impressive original features include the flagstoned hall, an elegant drawing room overlooking the walled garden and the Jacobean bar with its huge inglenook. Bedrooms are either traditional or modern. Children up to 12 stay free in parents' room. **Rooms 41.** Garden, croquet. Access, Amex, Visa, **D** Diners Club International

Cirencester   Tatyan's

£45

Tel 0285 653529

R

27 Castle Street Cirencester Gloucestershire GL7 1QD

Map 4 C2

Szechuan, Hunan and Peking regional cooking provide the specialities on a wide-ranging evening menu; lunches are more limited, but good value nonetheless. Friendly and helpful service. **Seats 64.** Parties 20. L 12-2 D 6.30-10.30 (Sat to 11). Closed L Sun, 5 days Xmas. Set L from £8.50 Set D from £11.50. Access, Amex, Visa, **D** Diners Club International

Clanfield   The Plough at Clanfield

£80

Tel 036 781 222   Fax 036 781 596

IR

Bourton Road Clanfield Oxfordshire OX8 2RB

Map 4 C2

Occupying a central position in pretty Clanfield village the Plough is a 16th-century Cotswold stone manor house that's more of an inn than a hotel. The lack of a residents' lounge restricts guests to either their bedrooms – all of which are of a good size and comfortably equipped (four have whirlpool baths) – or the bar, which is no real penalty if original character in the form of old beams and a stone fireplace is to your liking. No dogs. **Rooms 6.** Garden. Access, Amex, Visa, **D** Diners Club International

Restaurant

£60

Stephen Parker uses select produce to cook dishes both modern and traditional, showing English and French influences. Mousseline of smoked haddock wrapped in smoked salmon on a chive butter fondue, paupiette of oyster and sole glazed with champagne and dill, and local pheasant braised with thyme, cranberries and chestnuts are typical choices. Puddings are a speciality. Lighter lunches (snacks and sandwiches) are also available. **Seats 45.** Parties 28. Private Room. L 12-2 D 7-10 (Sun to 9.30). Set L £14.50 Set D £22.95.

Clawton   Court Barn   61%

£70

Tel 040 927 219

H

Clawton Holsworthy Devon EX22 6PS

Map 2 C2

Five acres of garden surround a delightful manor house three miles south of Holsworthy (follow the A388). Day rooms like the lounge and tiny bar are easy places to relax. The bedrooms are simple but individual in feel with a number of thoughtful extras. Three rooms are suitable for family use, and children up to 14 stay free in parents' room. Cots, high chairs and baby-listening are available. **Rooms 8.** Garden, pitch & putt, putting, badminton. Closed 1 wk Jan. Access, Amex, Visa, **D** Diners Club International

Claygate   Les Alouettes

£90

Tel 0372 464882

R

7 High Street Claygate Esher Surrey KT10 0JW

Map 5 E3

In the lovely setting of a gabled house, Michel Perraud produces fine food on a sophisticated French menu. Highly accomplished and accurately cooked are typical dishes of *petit feuilleté de champignons et d'asperges sauce mousseline*, an *osso buco de lotte braisé façon grand-mère*, and intriguing *canette de Gressingham rotie crispy au citrus*. A daily fixed-price menu of limited

choice supplements the carte with the best of the day's market shopping.
To finish, a fine *crepe soufflé Suzette sauce orange* and cheeses from Philippe
Olivier are no less assiduously presented. Highly priced, predominantly
French wines. *Seats 60. Parties 65. L 12.15-2 D 7-9.30 (Sat to 10). Closed
L Sat, all Sun, Bank Holidays, 2 weeks Aug. Set meals £22.50.*
Access, Amex, Visa.

Clayton-le-Woods   Pines Hotel   67%   £65

Tel 0772 38551   Fax ext 302   **H**

Preston Road Clayton-le-Woods Nr Chorley Lancashire PR6 7ED   Map 10 B1

Mature wooded grounds provide an attractive setting for this much-
extended Victorian house on the A6. Best value among the
accommodation is offered in the generously-sized superior rooms decorated
with stylish modern fabrics. Conference facilities for up to 100. No dogs.
Rooms 39. Garden. Closed 25 & 26 Dec. Access, Amex, Visa.

Clearwell   Clearwell Castle   69%   £80

Tel 0594 832320   Fax 0594 835523   **H**

Clearwell Nr Coleford Gloucestershire GL16 8LG   Map 4 B2

Clearwell's first occupation dates from Roman times; the present 18th-
century castle, built in classic neo-Gothic style, was restored in 1929. As a
hotel much splendour remains, though guests' footsteps may echo in its
enormous halls. The bar is smaller and clubby. Stately bedrooms with four-
posters and half-testers possess modern amenities of teletext and dial-out
telephones. *Rooms 16. Garden, croquet, game fishing, clay-pigeon shooting.*
Access, Amex, Visa, 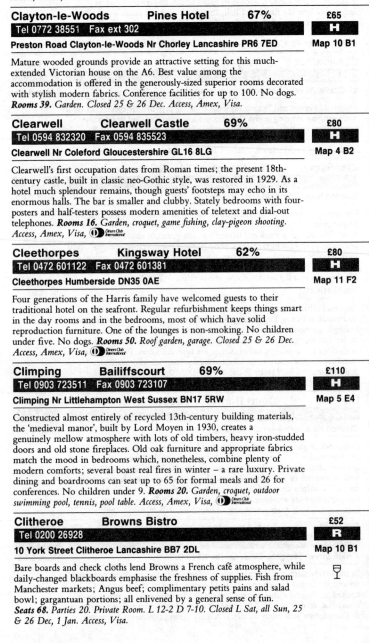

Cleethorpes   Kingsway Hotel   62%   £80

Tel 0472 601122   Fax 0472 601381   **H**

Cleethorpes Humberside DN35 0AE   Map 11 F2

Four generations of the Harris family have welcomed guests to their
traditional hotel on the seafront. Regular refurbishment keeps things smart
in the day rooms and in the bedrooms, most of which have solid
reproduction furniture. One of the lounges is non-smoking. No children
under five. No dogs. *Rooms 50. Roof garden, garage. Closed 25 & 26 Dec.*
Access, Amex, Visa,

Climping   Bailiffscourt   69%   £110

Tel 0903 723511   Fax 0903 723107   **H**

Climping Nr Littlehampton West Sussex BN17 5RW   Map 5 E4

Constructed almost entirely of recycled 13th-century building materials,
the 'medieval manor', built by Lord Moyen in 1930, creates a
genuinely mellow atmosphere with lots of old timbers, heavy iron-studded
doors and old stone fireplaces. Old oak furniture and appropriate fabrics
match the mood in bedrooms which, nonetheless, combine plenty of
modern comforts; several boast real fires in winter – a rare luxury. Private
dining and boardrooms can seat up to 65 for formal meals and 26 for
conferences. No children under 9. *Rooms 20. Garden, croquet, outdoor*
swimming pool, tennis, pool table. Access, Amex, Visa,

Clitheroe   Browns Bistro   £52

Tel 0200 26928   **R**

10 York Street Clitheroe Lancashire BB7 2DL   Map 10 B1

Bare boards and check cloths lend Browns a French café atmosphere, while
daily-changed blackboards emphasise the freshness of supplies. Fish from
Manchester markets; Angus beef; complimentary petits pains and salad
bowl; gargantuan portions; all enlivened by a general sense of fun.
Seats 68. Parties 20. Private Room. L 12-2 D 7-10. Closed L Sat, all Sun, 25
& 26 Dec, 1 Jan. Access, Visa.

Clitheroe   Places of Interest

Browsholme Hall   Tel 025486 330.

Clun   Old Post Office

£60

RR

Tel 0588 640687

9 The Square Clun Shropshire SY7 8JA

Map 10 A4

Richard Arbuthnot, chef-patron at Clun's attractively converted Post
Office, cooks in robust style, offering a short, interesting choice of dishes
that could include baked onion tart with mushrooms or lamb's sweetbread
with rosemary and whisky sauce to start, followed by breast of guinea fowl
with its sausage, Madeira sauce and polenta or vegetable strudel with
thyme sauce. For dessert, perhaps lemon tart, spiced brown bread ice
cream, Scotch woodcock or chocolate slab with mango coulis. The terrace,
which overlooks Clun, is a nice spot for a drink before your meal.
Seats 30. Parties 30. Private Room. L 12.30-1.30 (by appointment)
D 7.30-9.30 (Sun to 8.30). Closed Mon, Tue & mid Jan-mid Mar.
Access, Visa.

Rooms

£42

Two homely, well-kept bedrooms share a spotless bathroom. No dogs.

Coatham Mundeville   Hall Garth   68%

£80

H

Tel 0325 300400   Fax 0325 310083

Coatham Mundeville Nr Darlington Co Durham DL1 3LU

Map 15 B5

A solid stone hotel standing in lovely gardens just minutes from the
A1/A167 intersection. Accommodation ranges from rooms in the old
house furnished in period style (some with four-poster beds) to modern
rooms in a separate block. Lounges offer a choice of decor and style, but
consistent comfort. The Stables bar has a pubby atmosphere and offers
snacks and real ales. Conference/banqueting facilities for 300/250 in the
Brafferton Suite. *Rooms 42. Garden, outdoor swimming pool, sauna, solarium,*
keep-fit equipment, tennis, 3-hole pitch & putt, croquet. Closed 24-26 Dec.
Access, Amex, Visa, Diners Club International

Cobham   Hilton National   65%

£129

H

Tel 0932 864471   Fax 0932 868017

Seven Hills Road South Cobham Surrey KT11 1EW

Map 5 E3

Neville Chamberlain's original house has been swallowed into new wings.
The hotel, situated just off the A3 (Cobham exit), has recently seen major
refurbishment. Plenty of work space in the bedrooms. *Rooms 152. Garden,*
indoor swimming pool, tennis, squash, sauna, solarium, spa bath, steam room,
keep-fit equipment. Access, Amex, Visa, Diners Club International

Cobham   Woodlands Park   69%

£137

H

Tel 0372 843933   Fax 0372 842704

Woodlands Lane Stoke d'Abernon Cobham Surrey KT11 3QB

Map 5 E3

The carefully restored former home of the match-making Bryant family is
a magnificent example of late-Victorian country house style. Particularly
striking is the grand hall with its galleried landing, panelled walls and
stained-glass ceiling. This fine room is the only residents' lounge and
conference delegates sometimes spill over from the bar. Bedrooms range
from handsome suites with original built-in furniture in the main house to
smaller but equally comfortable rooms in the wing. All offer an array of
extras, including, on our latest visit, fresh carnations. The buffet breakfast
provides decent quality and variety. Select Hotels. *Rooms 58. Tennis,*
putting, croquet. Access, Amex, Visa, Diners Club International

Cobham   Places of Interest

Painshill Park and Gardens   Tel 0932 868113.

Cockermouth	Quince & Medlar	£30
Tel 0900 823579		**R**
13 Castlegate Cockermouth Cumbria CA13 9EU		Map 13 C5

Next to Cockermouth Castle, a candle-lit vegetarian restaurant run on
informal lines. Some typical dishes: celery and Stilton soup, roast parsnip
and cashew nut ring, asparagus, broccoli and toasted almond pancake. Fine
summer pudding, bread-and-butter pudding with apricot sauce, rennet-free
cheeses served with home-made oatcakes and some organic wines. Light
classical music. No smoking. *Seats 26. Parties 14. D only 7-9.30. Closed
Mon, Bank Holidays, 24-26 Dec, 3 weeks Feb, 1 week Oct. Access, Visa.*

Cockermouth   Places of Interest

Wordsworth House (NT)   Tel 0900 824805.

Coggeshall	White Hart	69%	£82
Tel 0376 561654 Fax 0376 561789			**HR**
Market End Coggeshall Essex CO6 1NH			Map 6 C3

A centuries-old inn that still retains all its character with flagstone floors,
low beams, inglenook fireplace and no fewer than two resident ghosts.
Careful renovation and refurbishment in recent years has added style and
comfort to the atmospheric surroundings. Individually decorated
bedrooms, 12 in a new extension, offer little extras like fresh fruit and
mineral water. Room service is limited to continental breakfast. *Rooms 18.
Garden. Access, Amex, Visa,* ①

Restaurant   £60

A long, low and narrow dining room with sturdy beams and cheerful staff.
An Italian menu ranges from risotto milanese and spaghetti carbonara to
escalope of veal cooked in Marsala wine. *Seats 70. L 12-2 D 7-10.
Closed D Sun.*

Coggeshall   Places of Interest

Braintree Tourist Information   Tel 0376 550066
Paycocke's   Tel 0376 561305.

Colchester	Butterfly Hotel	61% NEW	£67
Tel 0206 230900 Fax 0206 231095			**H**
Old Ipswich Road Ardleigh Colchester Essex CO7 7QY			Map 6 E3

Colchester's newest hotel is part of a small chain offering practical
accommodation (there is separate work space in all the bedrooms) and
conference facilities for up to 80 delegates. No dogs. Located on the
A12/A120 near the Business Parks. *Rooms 50.
Access, Amex, Visa,* ①

Colchester   Places of Interest

Tourist Information   Tel 0206 712920.
Colchester Arts Centre   St. Marys-at-the-Walls, Church Street
    Tel 0206 577301.
Mercury Theatre   Balkerne Gate Tel 0206 577301.
Colchester Museums   Tel 0206 712931.
Castle Park Cricket Ground   Tel 0206 574028.
Colchester Garrison Polo Club   East Mersea Tel 0206 383049.
Colchester Zoo   Stanway Tel 0206 331292.
Clacton Beach *13 miles SE Colchester.*
    Historic Houses, Castles and Gardens
Beth Chatto Gardens   Elmstead Market Tel 0206 822007.

Layer Marney Tower   Tiptree Tel 0206 330784.
St. Osyth   Priory St. Osyth Tel 0225 820492.

Colerne	**Lucknam Park**	**83%**	**£151**

Tel 0225 742777   Fax 0225 743536   **HR**

Colerne Wiltshire SN14 8AZ   **Map 4 B2**

Approached by a straight mile of beech-lined drive, Lucknam is a gracious
Georgian house in a tranquil setting six miles from Bath on the southern
edge of the Cotswolds. The house has a particularly English feel and is
luxuriously fitted with sound taste. Day rooms are spacious and extremely
elegant with soft colours, choice antiques and oil paintings plus deep-
cushioned sofas. Sumptuously comfortable bedrooms are appointed to the
highest standards with handsome furnishings and fittings suiting a house
of this stature. Each is individually decorated in quintessential English style
and most of the marble-tiled bathrooms boast double sinks. Housekeeping
is immaculate. In addition to the leisure spa (conceived in the style of a
Roman villa and set in the old walled garden) there are two floodlit tennis
courts. Impeccably dressed young staff do their jobs very well. *Rooms 42.*
Garden, croquet, tennis, helipad, indoor swimming pool, spa bath, sauna, steam
room, keep-fit equipment, beauty salon, hairdressing, snooker. Access, Amex,
Visa, Diners Club International

Restaurant   **£90**

Discreet, polished service and a truly elegant dining room certainly set
expectations high and chef Michael Womersley's cooking strives hard to
match the surroundings. His menus are fixed-price, offering an interesting
selection of dishes with a strong English bias and a heavy reliance on fresh
local ingredients – from charlotte of asparagus with pan-fried morels and a
wild mushroom sauce or grilled salmis of wood pigeon with baked
aubergines to a galette of Cornish crab and scallops on a bed of onions
braised in cream, and roast Gressingham duck filled with a confit of its legs
with figs, sultanas and almonds. Vegetarians may be tempted by grilled
avocado and buttered spinach with soft-boiled quail's eggs and a
coconut sabayon; similarly, those with a sweet tooth may appreciate a hazel
nut 'box' served with a mocca sauce and cherries marinated in Armagnac
or hot blackcurrant soufflé 'kir royale'. Lunch is a two- or three-course
affair offering equally involved dishes. Solid wine list, long in champagnes,
clarets and burgundies, though little under £20. No children under 12.
Seats 75. Parties 75. Private Room. L 12.30-2 D 7.30-9.30 (Sat to 10). Set L
£17.50/£19.50 Set D £37.50.

Colsterworth	**Forte Travelodge**	**£40**

Tel 0476 861181   **L**

A1 southbound Colsterworth Nr Grantham Lincolnshire NG33 5JJ   **Map 11 E3**

Located at the roundabout of the junction of the A1 with A151, 8 miles
south of Grantham. *Rooms 32. Access, Amex, Visa.*

Coniston	**Sun Hotel**	**63%**	**£70**

Tel 053 94 41248   **H**

Coniston Cumbria LA21 8HQ   **Map 13 C5**

The Old Man of Coniston creates a spectacular backdrop to this handsome
Victorian house in a hillside setting overlooking the village. Views from a
stylish, book-filled lounge are conducive to relaxation, while the adjacent
16th-century inn will appeal to the more convivial. Generally spacious
bedrooms incorporate seating areas and are carpeted through to bright, airy
bathrooms. No dogs. *Rooms 11. Garden. Closed Xmas, Jan. Access, Visa.*

Coniston   Places of Interest

Ravenglass Tourist Information   Tel 0229 717278.
Muncaster Castle and Gardens   Tel 0229 717614 *28 miles.*
The Owl Centre   Muncaster Castle Tel 0229 717393 *28 miles.*
Beatrix Potter Gallery (NT)   Main Street, Hawkshead Tel 09666 355.
Brantwood House and Garden   (Home of John Ruskin) Coniston
   Tel 05394 41396.

Constantine Bay	Treglos Hotel	65%	£134*
Tel 0841 520727 Fax 0841 521163			**H**
Constantine Bay St Merryn Padstow Cornwall PL28 8JH			Map 2 B3

A friendly, well-run hotel just five minutes from the sea, overlooking
Constantine Bay and Trevose Golf Course. It's a popular place, so balcony
rooms are booked well in advance. All the public rooms except the bar
have sea views; the three comfortable and traditional lounges are bright
and airy. Bedrooms have simple white laminate units, large windows and
compact bathrooms. There are four flats in the grounds. *Half-board terms
only. Rooms 44. Garden, indoor swimming pool, spa bath, croquet, games room,
snooker, lock-up garages. Closed early Nov-early Mar. Access, Visa.*

Constantine Bay   Places of Interest

Constantine Bay, Harlyn Bay and Treyarnon Bay Beaches.

Cooden	Cooden Resort Hotel	60%	£75
Tel 042 43 2281 Fax 042 43 6142			**H**
Cooden Sea Road Bexhill-on-Sea East Sussex TN39 4TT			Map 7 B6

Right on the beach, with views across Pevensey Bay, this 30s' hotel caters
well for both leisure and business guests. There are facilities for up to 200
conference delegates, a health and leisure club, a modern lounge, a cocktail
bar and a tavern serving real ale. One of the bedrooms has been adapted
for disabled guests; 12 are suitable for family use. *Rooms 41. Garden,
keep-fit equipment, indoor & outdoor swimming pools, spa bath, sauna, solarium,
beautician, hairdressing, squash. Access, Amex, Visa,*  *Diners Club International*

Cooden   Places of Interest

Bexhill Beach.

Copdock	Ipswich Moat House	64%	£84
Tel 0473 86444 Fax 0473 86801			**H**
London Road Copdock Nr Ipswich Suffolk IP8 3JD			Map 6 C3

Friendly modern hotel set in four acres of grounds just off the A12, three
miles south of Ipswich. Besides practical, up-to-date accommodation the
hotel offers extensive conference facilities (up to 500 delegates) and a well-
equipped health and fitness club. *Rooms 74. Indoor swimming pool, keep-fit
facilities, spa bath, sauna, solarium. Access, Amex, Visa,*  *Diners Club International*

Corfe Castle	Mortons House Hotel	62%	£90
Tel 0929 480988 Fax 0929 480820			**H**
45 East Street Corfe Castle Dorset BH20 5EE			Map 4 C4

An Elizabethan manor house, almost in the shadow of the castle, enlarged
in 1666 and again more recently with a sympathetic extension housing the
best of the bedrooms. Day rooms include a fine oak-panelled drawing
room (warmed by an open log fire in winter), an entrance hall with old
stone fireplace and a pleasant little bar. Bedrooms are furnished with either
antique or reproduction pieces. Children up to the age of 5 free in parents'
room. Conference facilities for up to 65 delegates. *Rooms 17. Garden.
Access, Amex, Visa.*

Corfe Castle   Places of Interest

Corfe Castle (NT) Nr Wareham Tel 0929 480921.

Cornhill-on-Tweed   Tillmouth Park   60%   £86

Tel 0890 2255   **H**

Cornhill-on-Tweed Northumberland TD12 4UU   Map 14 B2

Built in 1882 and in its current role for 35 years, this is first and foremost a fishing hotel, offering a complete package of accommodation, fishing, boat and gillie. Perched high above the Tweed they own five miles of fishing rights on the river. Photographs in the cosy public rooms are very much in a fishing theme, so too the conversation. There's a cosy little cocktail bar, a galleried lounge and two other sitting rooms. Bedrooms, one with two single four-posters, are quaintly old-fashioned. *Rooms 13. Garden, coarse & game fishing. Access, Amex, Visa,*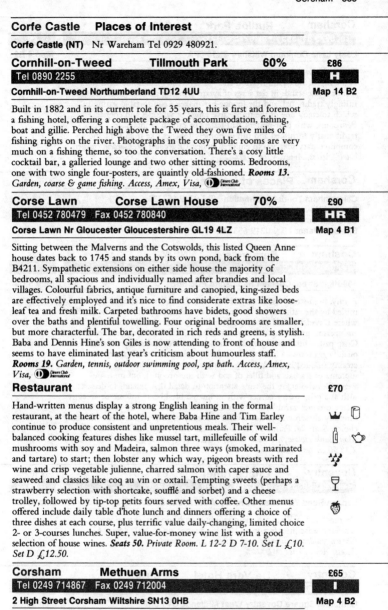

Corse Lawn   Corse Lawn House   70%   £90

Tel 0452 780479 Fax 0452 780840   **HR**

Corse Lawn Nr Gloucester Gloucestershire GL19 4LZ   Map 4 B1

Sitting between the Malverns and the Cotswolds, this listed Queen Anne house dates back to 1745 and stands by its own pond, back from the B4211. Sympathetic extensions on either side house the majority of bedrooms, all spacious and individually named after brandies and local villages. Colourful fabrics, antique furniture and canopied, king-sized beds are effectively employed and it's nice to find considerate extras like loose-leaf tea and fresh milk. Carpeted bathrooms have bidets, good showers over the baths and plentiful towelling. Four original bedrooms are smaller, but more characterful. The bar, decorated in rich reds and greens, is stylish. Baba and Dennis Hine's son Giles is now attending to front of house and seems to have eliminated last year's criticism about humourless staff. *Rooms 19. Garden, tennis, outdoor swimming pool, spa bath. Access, Amex, Visa,*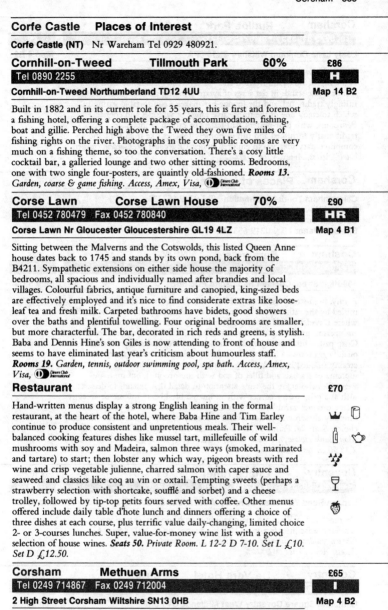

Restaurant   £70

Hand-written menus display a strong English leaning in the formal restaurant, at the heart of the hotel, where Baba Hine and Tim Earley continue to produce consistent and unpretentious meals. Their well-balanced cooking features dishes like mussel tart, millefeuille of wild mushrooms with soy and Madeira, salmon three ways (smoked, marinated and tartare) to start; then lobster any which way, pigeon breasts with red wine and crisp vegetable julienne, charred salmon with caper sauce and seaweed and classics like coq au vin or oxtail. Tempting sweets (perhaps a strawberry selection with shortcake, soufflé and sorbet) and a cheese trolley, followed by tip-top petits fours served with coffee. Other menus offered include daily table d'hote lunch and dinners offering a choice of three dishes at each course, plus terrific value daily-changing, limited choice 2- or 3-courses lunches. Super, value-for-money wine list with a good selection of house wines. *Seats 50. Private Room. L 12-2 D 7-10. Set L £10. Set D £12.50.*

Corsham   Methuen Arms   £65

Tel 0249 714867 Fax 0249 712004   **I**

2 High Street Corsham Wiltshire SN13 0HB   Map 4 B2

Exposed oak beams and 500-year-old rubble-stone walls in the 100-foot Long Bar attest to the antiquity of this old town-centre inn and add to its special character. Main-building bedrooms include two of family size: twelve further rooms, some with showers only, are in a loft conversion and an adjoining cottage. Private meetings for 20; banqueting accommodates 120. Well maintained and enthusiastically run by the Long family. No dogs. *Rooms 25. Garden, skittle alley. Closed 26 Dec, 1 Jan. Access, Visa.*

Corsham   Rudloe Park   64%

£80

H

Tel 0225 810555 Fax 0225 811412

Leafy Lane Corsham Wiltshire SN13 0PA

Map 4 B2

The Park's wooded drive leads off the A4 between Chippenham and Bath, at the top of Box Hill. Marion and Ian Overend's handsome Bath-stone manor house stands in ten acres of award-winning gardens. Decor within is fittingly traditional, and the lounge-bar makes a comfortable setting in which to enjoy one of the impressive range of whiskies and cognacs. Bedrooms, with four-posters, half-testers or crown canopies, are traditionally furnished and full of homely touches like fresh fruit and complimentary sherry. No children under 10. *Rooms 11. Garden, croquet, bowls. Access, Amex, Visa,*

Corsham   Places of Interest

Chippenham Tourist Information   Tel 0249 657733.
Bowood House and Gardens   Calne Tel 0249 812102.
Corsham Court   Tel 0249 712214.
Sheldon Manor   Tel 0249 653120.

Cosham   Barnard's   NEW

£45

R

Tel 0705 370226

109 High Street Cosham Hampshire PO6 3BB

Map 5 D4

A tiny, high-street restaurant hidden behind heavy red curtains. Don't be misled by the rather sparse decoration for the real appeal lies in the kitchen, where David Barnard cooks single-handedly with obvious confidence and enthusiasm, producing a menu that requires varied skills and disciplines. Crisp pastry filled with Jerusalem artichoke purée and softly poached quail's eggs shows a light touch as does omelette Arnold Bennett with its creamy smoked haddock filling. Fish is a favourite medium (as in a supreme of sea bass and fillet of cod with mushrooms), but meat and vegetables also enjoy the same attention to detail that extends to desserts such as a crisp pastry cornet with an intense blackberry mousse or an eggy crème caramel garnished with freshly poached pear. Keenly priced and carefully chosen wines. Good-value weekday fixed-price lunches with small choice. *Seats 24. Parties 24. L 12-2 D 7.30-9.30. Closed L Sat, all Sun & Mon, Bank Holidays, 1 week Xmas, 2 weeks Aug. Set L £12.95 Set D £18.50. Access, Visa.*

Coventry   Chace Hotel   61%

£102

H

Tel 0203 303398 Fax 0203 301816

London Road Willenhall Coventry West Midlands CV3 4EQ

Map 10 C4

On the A423, a Victorian main building with modern extensions. Conference facilities for up to 100, banqueting up to 120. *Rooms 67. Garden, outdoor swimming pool, children's playground. Access, Amex, Visa,*

Coventry   De Vere Hotel   69%

£176

H

Tel 0203 633733 Fax 0203 225299

Cathedral Square Coventry West Midlands CV1 5RP

Map 10 C4

A large modern hotel, which enjoys direct access to the Cathedral square through a conservatory. Attractive public areas include a spacious foyer (staff are welcoming and helpful) and the popular Daimler bar-lounge decorated with pictures of one of Coventry's most famous cars. Generously sized bedrooms with cathedral views are smart and well equipped, with plenty of working space and colourfully tiled bathrooms. Conference and banqueting facilities for around 270. *Rooms 190. Access, Amex, Visa,*

Coventry   Forte Crest   66%   £70
Tel 0203 613261   Fax 0203 614318   H
Hinckley Road Coventry West Midlands CV2 2HP   Map 10 C4

Purpose-built business centre and a fully equipped leisure club go with the modern amenities in the bedrooms. *Rooms 147. Gymnasium, spa bath, sauna, solarium, beautician, games room, snooker, croquet, coffee shop (7am-11pm). Access, Amex, Visa,*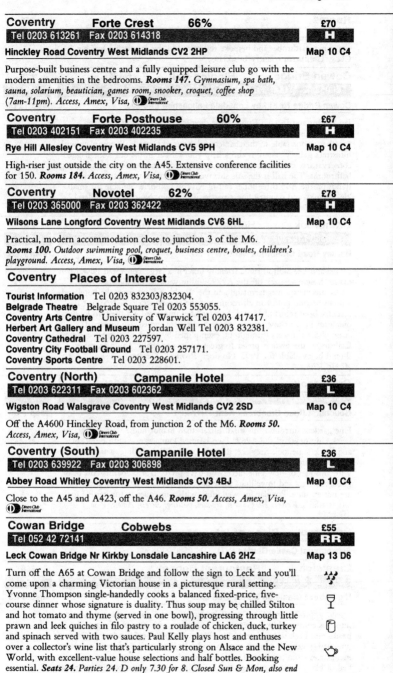

Coventry   Forte Posthouse   60%   £67
Tel 0203 402151   Fax 0203 402235   H
Rye Hill Allesley Coventry West Midlands CV5 9PH   Map 10 C4

High-riser just outside the city on the A45. Extensive conference facilities for 150. *Rooms 184. Access, Amex, Visa,*

Coventry   Novotel   62%   £78
Tel 0203 365000   Fax 0203 362422   H
Wilsons Lane Longford Coventry West Midlands CV6 6HL   Map 10 C4

Practical, modern accommodation close to junction 3 of the M6. *Rooms 100. Outdoor swimming pool, croquet, business centre, boules, children's playground. Access, Amex, Visa,*

Coventry   Places of Interest

Tourist Information   Tel 0203 832303/832304.
Belgrade Theatre   Belgrade Square Tel 0203 553055.
Coventry Arts Centre   University of Warwick Tel 0203 417417.
Herbert Art Gallery and Museum   Jordan Well Tel 0203 832381.
Coventry Cathedral   Tel 0203 227597.
Coventry City Football Ground   Tel 0203 257171.
Coventry Sports Centre   Tel 0203 228601.

Coventry (North)   Campanile Hotel   £36
Tel 0203 622311   Fax 0203 602362   L
Wigston Road Walsgrave Coventry West Midlands CV2 2SD   Map 10 C4

Off the A4600 Hinckley Road, from junction 2 of the M6. *Rooms 50. Access, Amex, Visa,*

Coventry (South)   Campanile Hotel   £36
Tel 0203 639922   Fax 0203 306898   L
Abbey Road Whitley Coventry West Midlands CV3 4BJ   Map 10 C4

Close to the A45 and A423, off the A46. *Rooms 50. Access, Amex, Visa,*

Cowan Bridge   Cobwebs   £55
Tel 052 42 72141   RR
Leck Cowan Bridge Nr Kirkby Lonsdale Lancashire LA6 2HZ   Map 13 D6

Turn off the A65 at Cowan Bridge and follow the sign to Leck and you'll come upon a charming Victorian house in a picturesque rural setting. Yvonne Thompson single-handedly cooks a balanced fixed-price, five-course dinner whose signature is duality. Thus soup may be chilled Stilton and hot tomato and thyme (served in one bowl), progressing through little prawn and leek quiches in filo pastry to a roulade of chicken, duck, turkey and spinach served with two sauces. Paul Kelly plays host and enthuses over a collector's wine list that's particularly strong on Alsace and the New World, with excellent-value house selections and half bottles. Booking essential. *Seats 24. Parties 24. D only 7.30 for 8. Closed Sun & Mon, also end Dec-mid Mar. Set D £21. Access, Visa.*

Rooms   £56

Five bedrooms in individual colour schemes are Victorian-style and
charming. Bathrobes and bespoke toiletries add the pampering touches.
Classy Cumbrian country breakfasts.

Cowan Bridge   Hipping Hall   64%   £75

`Tel 052 42 71187   Fax 052 42 72452`   **H**

Cowan Bridge Nr Kirkby Lonsdale Lancashire LA6 2JJ   Map 13 D6

Ian Bryant and Jocelyn Ruffle pride themselves on creating a relaxed
country-house atmosphere; guests meet for drinks round the fire and dine
together at one table in the characterful, beamed Great Hall, complete with
minstrel's gallery. There is also a help-yourself bar in the old stone-flagged
conservatory. Bedrooms are bright, pretty and comfortable, with gleaming
bathrooms. The hall is the sole survivor of a 15th-century hamlet and
stands on the A65 three miles east of Kirkby Lonsdale. Suitable for small
'think-tanks' and country house parties in a group. No children under 12.
Rooms 7. Garden. Closed Dec-Feb. Access, Visa.

Cranbrook   Hartley Mount   62%   £70

`Tel 0580 712230   Fax 0580 712588`   **H**

Hartley Road Cranbrook Kent TN17 3QX   Map 7 C5

Lionel and Lee Skilton run a friendly hotel in a large, converted Edwardian
manor house, set back off the A229, within walking distance of town.
There are views over farmland and the Weald of Kent from the hotel and
a non-smoking policy in all rooms but the conservatory. Bedrooms have
recently been refurbished and their facilities improved. Of the two lounges,
one leads into a conservatory where breakfast is served. An informal
atmosphere pervades throughout, exemplified by a lack of formal reception
facilities, as the owners prefer to greet guests personally. Lawn tennis
should be available for 1993. No dogs. *Rooms 7. Garden, croquet.
Access, Visa.*

Cranbrook   Kennel Holt Hotel   66%   £95

`Tel 0580 712032   Fax 0580 712931`   **H**

Goudhurst Road Cranbrook Kent TN17 2PT   Map 7 C5

Fine gardens surround this small Elizabethan manor house with distinctive
brick chimneys, off the A262. Two beamed lounges, one with floral sofas
and brick inglenook fireplace, the other, with oak panelling, acting as the
bar. Bedrooms, mostly with plain woodchip walls, are variously furnished
with antiques or new pine pieces and have pretty fabrics. Bathrooms boast
good toiletries and towelling; three have shower and WC only and two
are not en suite. Popular for weddings, with a marquee in the garden for
larger affairs. *Rooms 10. Garden, croquet, putting. Access, Amex, Visa,*

Cranbrook   Place of Interest

Sissinghurst Castle Garden (NT)   Tel 0580 712850.

Cranleigh   Restaurant Bonnet   £66

`Tel 0483 273889`   **R**

High Street Cranleigh Surrey GU6 8AE   Map 5 E3

Friendly, professional French staff put guests at ease the moment they step
into this comfortably unpretentious restaurant with its mix of exposed
beams and back-to-back pews. Jean-Pierre Bonnet's open kitchen prepares
interesting dishes in honest, unfussy style. Typical choices on the fixed-price
menus run from feuilleté of mushrooms or honey-basted quail served on a
bed of blanched sour cabbage to fillet of lamb with sauce soubise and roast
garlic. To finish, perhaps nougat glacé with a red fruit coulis. The dinner
price includes an aperitif with amuse-gueule, half a bottle of house wine
and coffee with petits fours; lunches offer particularly good value. Parking

is behind the restaurant in the municipal car park by the leisure centre. Sister restaurant to *La Barbe* in Reigate and *La Bonne Auberge* in South Godstone. **Seats 50. Parties 35.** L 12-2 D 7-10. Closed L Sat, D Sun, all Mon, Bank Holidays. Set L £14.75 Set D £29.75. Access, Amex, Visa.

Crathorne	Crathorne Hall	72%	£105
Tel 0642 700398 Fax 0642 700814			**H**
Crathorne Nr Yarm Cleveland TS15 0AR			Map 15 C5

At the end of a long driveway, among 15 acres of beautiful countryside between the Yorkshire Dales and the North Yorkshire Moors, the imposing hall was one of the last major houses built in the Edwardian era. Now fully restored to its former glory by Richard Branson's Voyager Hotels. Great care has been taken with refurbishment to retain the house's inherent character. The sumptuous drawing room is a good example of this work, with large oil paintings of the Kings George hanging either side of a fine fireplace and abundant comfortable seating. Similar style and taste is shown in the bedrooms and bathrooms, where choice furnishings and rich fabrics contribute to the elegant decor and luxurious feel. Improvements are continuing with further rooms planned. Themed weekends are popular, involving fishing, murder/mystery events, birdwatching and wine appreciation. Conference/banqueting facilities for 160/120. **Rooms 37.** *Garden.* Access, Amex, Visa, (I) Diners Club International

Crawley	George Hotel	64%	£96
Tel 0293 524215 Fax 0293 548565			**H**
High Street Crawley West Sussex RH10 1BS			Map 7 B5

An old gallows sign announces this town-centre coaching inn in the Forte Hertitage group. Some parts are beamed and atmospheric, others modern. **Rooms 86.** Access, Amex, Visa, (I) Diners Club International

Crawley   Places of Interest

Leonardslee Gardens   Lower Beeding Tel 0403 891212.
Gatwick Zoo   Charlwood Tel 0293 862312.

Crewe	Forte Travelodge	£40
Tel 0270 883157		**L**
M6/A500 Alsager Road Barthomley Nr Crewe Cheshire CW2 5PT		Map 10 B3

At junction 16 of the M6 and A500 between Nantwich and Stoke-on-Trent, off the junction roundabout signposted to Alsager. **Rooms 42.** Access, Amex, Visa.

Crick	Forte Posthouse Northampton/Rugby	64%	£67
Tel 0788 822101 Fax 0788 823955			**H**
Crick Northamptonshire NN6 7XR			Map 11 D4

Low-rise modern hotel near junction 18 on the M1, 7 miles from Rugby. 14 meeting rooms, conference facilities for 185. **Rooms 88.** *Garden, indoor swimming pool, gymnasium, sauna, solarium, coffee shop (7am-10.30pm, till 7pm weekends).* Access, Amex, Visa, (I) Diners Club International

Crook	Wild Boar Hotel	60%	£110
Tel 0539 445225 Fax 0539 442498			**H**
Crook Nr Windermere Cumbria LA23 3NF			Map 13 D5

Abundant character still pervades the coaching inn where, reputedly, Westmorland's last wild boar was killed (in King John's time), though today's building is predominantly Victorian. Public rooms are a mass of blackened beams, log fires and ancient oak furniture, the oldest dating from 1635. Much of this character is reflected in a few main-house bedrooms with four-posters; more modern wings include two suites with spa baths; bathrooms are generally on the small side. Free golf at Keswick golf club (Mon-Fri). **Rooms 36.** *Garden.* Access, Amex, Visa, (I) Diners Club International

Crooklands   Crooklands Hotel   60%   £84

Tel 053 95 67432   Fax 053 95 67525   **H**

Crooklands Nr Kendal Cumbria LA7 7NW   Map 13 D6

Minutes from the M6 (junction 36) on the A65; a collection of farm buildings adjoining an original ale house contain the public rooms. Best accommodation, with neat, well equipped bathrooms, is in the recently-built 16-bedroom extension. *Rooms 30. Garden, snooker, coffee shop (7.30am-10pm). Access, Amex, Visa,* ① *Diners Club International*

Crosby-on-Eden   Crosby Lodge   66%   £85

Tel 0228 573618   Fax 0228 573428   **HR**

High Crosby Crosby-on-Eden Nr Carlisle Cumbria CA6 4QZ   Map 13 D4

Follow the B6264 up the Eden valley from Carlisle; Patricia and Michael Sedgwick's Georgian country house with Victorian embellishments overlooks mature parkland and the river. The elegant entrance hall contains Oriental carpets, antiques and a welcoming open fire and sets the tone; a carved staircase leads up to spacious, well-proportioned bedrooms with luxury fabrics used throughout; one room features a half-tester. By comparison, the converted stable block offers accommodation on an altogether more modest scale. *Rooms 11. Garden. Closed 24 Dec-end Jan. Access, Amex, Visa.*

Restaurant   £65

Michael Sedgwick has spent twenty years here indulging his house guests with traditional cooking (local shrimps on garlic toast, stuffed mussels, smoked salmon with horseradish, broccoli and courgette soup, duckling with orange sauce, rump of beef with Guinness and raisins, saltimbocca), but has not overlooked modern influences – try his Solway salmon marinated in red wine with herbs and walnut oil, if it's on the menu. Seafood and seasonal game are specialities, and everything is home-made – from amuse-gueule to petits fours. No smoking. Helpful notes against each wine on the select list. *Seats 50. Parties 20. Private Room. L 12.15-1.30 D 7.30-9 (Sun to 8). Set L £14.50 Set D £23.*

Croydon   Croydon Park   69%   £130

Tel 081-680 9200   Fax 081-760 0426   **H**

7 Altyre Road Croydon Surrey CR9 5AA   Map 7 B5

A roomy hotel opposite the Law Courts, with plenty of covered parking. The foyer is spacious but offers only limited seating, while the gas-lit Whistlers Bar is a more intimate spot. Bedrooms have queen-size beds and uniform decor, air-conditioning and compact bathrooms. There's a leisure centre, and conference/banqueting facilities for up to 300. Air-conditioned bedrooms offer the usual up-to-date accessories. Two floors are designated no smoking. Children up to 18 are accommodated free in parents' room. Formerly a Holiday Inn. *Rooms 214. Garden, gymnasium, indoor swimming pool, spa bath, sauna, solarium, squash. Access, Amex, Visa,* ① *Diners Club International*

Croydon   Forte Posthouse   61%   £67

Tel 081-688 5185   Fax 081-681 6438   **H**

Purley Way Croydon Surrey CR9 4LT   Map 7 B5

Convenient location, aside the A23, with flexible conference facilities for 40 to 170 delegates. Refurbished bedrooms are an improvement, with 50% now designated non-smoking. *Rooms 83. 24hr coffee shop. Access, Amex, Visa,* ① *Diners Club International*

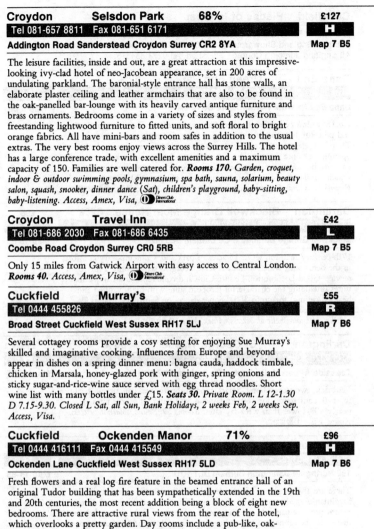

Croydon   Selsdon Park   68%   £127   H

Tel 081-657 8811   Fax 081-651 6171

Addington Road Sanderstead Croydon Surrey CR2 8YA   Map 7 B5

The leisure facilities, inside and out, are a great attraction at this impressive-looking ivy-clad hotel of neo-Jacobean appearance, set in 200 acres of undulating parkland. The baronial-style entrance hall has stone walls, an elaborate plaster ceiling and leather armchairs that are also to be found in the oak-panelled bar-lounge with its heavily carved antique furniture and brass ornaments. Bedrooms come in a variety of sizes and styles from freestanding lightwood furniture to fitted units, and soft floral to bright orange fabrics. All have mini-bars and room safes in addition to the usual extras. The very best rooms enjoy views across the Surrey Hills. The hotel has a large conference trade, with excellent amenities and a maximum capacity of 150. Families are well catered for. *Rooms 170. Garden, croquet, indoor & outdoor swimming pools, gymnasium, spa bath, sauna, solarium, beauty salon, squash, snooker, dinner dance (Sat), children's playground, baby-sitting, baby-listening. Access, Amex, Visa,* Diners Club International

Croydon   Travel Inn   £42   L

Tel 081-686 2030   Fax 081-686 6435

Coombe Road Croydon Surrey CR0 5RB   Map 7 B5

Only 15 miles from Gatwick Airport with easy access to Central London. *Rooms 40. Access, Amex, Visa,* Diners Club International

Cuckfield   Murray's   £55   R

Tel 0444 455826

Broad Street Cuckfield West Sussex RH17 5LJ   Map 7 B6

Several cottagey rooms provide a cosy setting for enjoying Sue Murray's skilled and imaginative cooking. Influences from Europe and beyond appear in dishes on a spring dinner menu: bagna cauda, haddock timbale, chicken in Marsala, honey-glazed pork with ginger, spring onions and sticky sugar-and-rice-wine sauce served with egg thread noodles. Short wine list with many bottles under £15. *Seats 30. Private Room. L 12-1.30 D 7.15-9.30. Closed L Sat, all Sun, Bank Holidays, 2 weeks Feb, 2 weeks Sep. Access, Visa.*

Cuckfield   Ockenden Manor   71%   £96   H

Tel 0444 416111   Fax 0444 415549

Ockenden Lane Cuckfield West Sussex RH17 5LD   Map 7 B6

Fresh flowers and a real log fire feature in the beamed entrance hall of an original Tudor building that has been sympathetically extended in the 19th and 20th centuries, the most recent addition being a block of eight new bedrooms. There are attractive rural views from the rear of the hotel, which overlooks a pretty garden. Day rooms include a pub-like, oak-panelled bar and a sunny sitting room. Bedrooms, three of which have four-poster beds, come in a variety of styles and include both reproduction and original antiques and many extras. *Rooms 22. Garden. Access, Amex, Visa,* Diners Club International

Cuckfield   Places of Interest

Wakehurst Place Garden (NT)   Tel 0444 892701 *7 miles.*
South of England Showground   Tel 0444 892700 *5 miles.*
All England Jumping Course   Hickstead Tel 0273 834315.

Dane End   Green End Park   62%   £86

`Tel 0920 438344   Fax 0920 438523`   **H**

Dane End Nr Ware Hertfordshire SG12 0NY   Map 6 B3

An 18th-century house set in eight acres of gardens. The setting is rustic
and peaceful, but it's just a short drive from the major road network.
There's an elegant style to day rooms that include an impressive bar
opening out onto a patio. The best of the ten bedrooms look out over the
gardens, but are generally poor relations to the impressive public rooms
which are designed to cater for conferences of up to 120 delegates.
Rooms 10. Garden, tennis, croquet, putting. Access, Amex, Visa,

Darlington   Blackwell Grange Moat House   62%   £96

`Tel 0325 380888   Fax 0325 380899`   **H**

Blackwell Grange Darlington Co Durham DL3 8QH   Map 15 B5

17th-century mansion set in 15 acres of parkland. Contemporary comforts
in the bedrooms, which include several Georgian state rooms. 24hr room
service. Good Locomotion Leisure Club and conference and banqueting
suites (including the characterful Jacobean suite with high, vaulted and
beamed ceiling) for up to 300. Dinner dances on Saturdays. *Rooms 99.*
Garden, indoor swimming pool, croquet, spa bath, sauna, solarium, gymnasium,
putting, pétanque, helipad. Access, Amex, Visa,

Darlington   St George Thistle   56%   £79

`Tel 0325 332631   Fax 0325 333851`   **H**

Teesside Airport Nr Darlington Co Durham DL2 1RH   Map 15 B5

Redbrick, two-storey hotel. Smart, modern bedrooms. Banqueting facilities
for 120, conferences for 160. Friday and Saturday night tariff rates are
nearly 40% lower than weekday rates. *Rooms 59. Sauna, solarium. Access,*
Amex, Visa,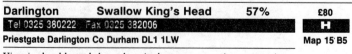

Darlington   Sardis   £50

`Tel 0325 461222`   **R**

196 Northgate Darlington Durham DL1 1QU   Map 15 B5

There are always plenty of reliable Italian dishes on the menu at this
Sardinian-owned town-centre restaurant. Three-course lunch and dinner
menus promise pasta al ragu and pork valdostana at fixed prices. A la carte,
there may be cannelloni at lunchtime, fusilli with pecorino cheese and
vitello all'Emiliano on the dinner menu. Look no further than the house
wine and Italian page for some surprising choices. *Seats 50. Parties 30.*
Private Room. L 12-2 D 7-10. Closed Sun, Bank Holidays. Set L £8.95 Set D
£16. Access, Visa.

Darlington   Swallow King's Head   57%   £80

`Tel 0325 380222   Fax 0325 382006`   **H**

Priestgate Darlington Co Durham DL1 1LW   Map 15 B5

Victorian hotel located above shops in the town centre. A new extension
housing 26 Executive category rooms opened in the Spring of 1992.
Meeting rooms for up to 200 people. *Rooms 85.*
Access, Amex, Visa,

Darlington	Victor's Restaurant	£50

Tel 0325 480818   R

84 Victoria Road Darlington Durham DL1 5JW   Map 15 B5

The set menu offers a choice of around five starters and five main dishes, separated by a soup or sorbet. Five-spice turkey with watercress, stuffed vine leaves, fillets of trout in filo pastry with minted cream and venison chop with yoghurt and redcurrant jelly show the range. For afters, tyrophiles should explore the impressive list of locally produced cheeses. *Seats 30. Parties 30. L 12-2 D 7-10.30. Closed Sun & Mon, 1 week Xmas. Set L £7.50 Set D £18. Access, Amex, Visa,* **D** *Diners Club International*

Darlington	White Horse	61%	£64

Tel 0325 382121   Fax 0325 355953   H

Harrowgate Hill Darlington Durham DL1 3LD   Map 15 B5

Former mock-Tudor pub with decent-size bedrooms in modern redbrick block. Children stay free in parents' room. *Rooms 40. Access, Amex, Visa,* **D** *Diners Club International*

Darlington   Places of Interest

Tourist Information   Tel 0325 382698.
Darlington Arts Centre   Vane Terrace Tel 0325 483168.
Darlington Civic Theatre   Parkgate Tel 0325 486555.
Darlington Railway Centre and Museum   North Road Station
    Tel 0325 460532.
Catterick Indoor Ski Slope   Tel 0748 833788.

Dartmouth	Carved Angel	★★	£90

Tel 0803 832465   R

2 South Embankment Dartmouth Devon TQ6 9BH   Map 3 D3

In a delightful quayside setting overlooking the harbour, this inviting restaurant, our 1993 Restaurant of the Year, has been home to Joyce Molyneux's talents since 1975. To describe her as England's doyenne of Mediterranean cooking is no overstatement: she calmly cooks in the open-plan kitchen, in full view of a crowded restaurant. Dishes are served in deep earthenware platters and the flavours contained are similarly outsize, reflecting the extent of her knowledge and understanding of English palates, transcending the cooking's putative origins. French provincial may be her base, but influences from far and wide may be detected. Decisions are difficult when ordering: Dartmouth crab with guacamole and herb mayonnaise or a puff of sweetbreads and mushrooms with Marsala? The marvellous brill with fennel, lemon and virgin oil or a duck plate – breast with spiced apple, leg stuffed with green olives, neck sausage with turnips? Elderflower fritters with strawberry sauce or a plate of five different chocolate puddings? Her consistent endeavours in preparation produce so much to please, from squid and monkfish amuse gueule, through a selection of wonderful breads and on to sweet fudge petits fours. Attention to detail extends to vegetables such as fine Jersey royal potatoes, skinned baby broad beans and spinach leaf parcels. A goat's cheese and hazelnut soufflé, sorbet or selection of British cheeses is offered in addition to the 2- or 3-course fixed-price menus at dinner. Joyce Molyneux doesn't follow safe traditions, but shows clear insights into taste interactions in a modern manner. Desserts certainly don't get overlooked, with typically fine orange and chocolate mousse roulade on a sharp orange cream, rhubarb in a honey cinnamon custard or pistachio and almond loaf with apricot sauce. Confident and friendly service from smartly dressed, charming girls. An improved New World selection on an excellent all-round list that inlcudes good house wines and a red and white of the month. *Seats 35. Parties 45. Private Room. L 12.30-2 D 7.30-9. Closed D Sun, all Mon, Bank Holidays except Good Friday, 6 weeks Jan/Feb, 1st week Oct. Set L £22.50 Set D £42. No credit cards.*

Dartmouth   Royal Castle Hotel   £74

Tel 0803 833033   Fax 0803 835445

I

11 The Quay Dartmouth Devon TQ6 9PS

Map 3 D3

Two Tudor merchants' houses became a hostelry in the early 1700s and the castellated facade (a Regency addition) explains the name. Antique furniture, Tudor fireplaces, oak beams fashioned from ships' timbers and a 300-year-old cooking range are among many reminders of the past, and in some of the bedrooms four-poster and brass beds are in use. River-view rooms are the most sought after. *Rooms 25. Garage parking.*
Access, Amex, Visa,  *Diners Club International*

Dartmouth   Stoke Lodge   60%   £67

Tel 0803 770523

H

Stoke Fleming Dartmouth Devon TQ6 0RA

Map 3 D3

Family-run, and with family holidays very much in mind, the hotel overlooks the village and the sea. The sun terrace is a popular spot when the weather's kind, and inside are homely, unpretentious lounges and neat bedrooms. *Rooms 24. Garden, indoor & outdoor swimming pools, tennis, putting, keep-fit equipment, giant chess. Access, Visa,* *Diners Club International*

Dartmouth   Places of Interest

Tourist Information   Tel 0803 834224.
Coleton Fishacre Garden (NT)   Coleton Tel 0804 25466.

Dedham   Dedham Vale Hotel   67%   £87

Tel 0206 322273   Fax 0206 322752

H

Stratford Road Dedham Nr Colchester Essex CO7 6HW

Map 6 C3

Part of the Talbooth group, this is a neat Edwardian house set in three acres of terraced gardens within half a mile of the A12. The charming lounge is comfortable and tastefully furnished, and the atmosphere throughout is pleasantly relaxing. Individually furnished bedrooms have enormous bath towels. No dogs. *Rooms 6. Garden. Access, Amex, Visa,* *Diners Club International*

Dedham   Fountain House & Dedham Hall   £50

Tel 0206 323027

R

Brook Street Dedham Nr Colchester Essex CO7 6AD

Map 6 C3

A lovely location for Wendy Anne Sarton's straightforward cooking which is complemented by a long wine list that includes a fine selection of half bottles. The menu changes weekly and is a fixed-price affair with simple dishes like avocado with smoked mackerel mousse or courgette and vignotte soup to start, fillet of salmon with spinach in puff pastry, devilled lamb's kidneys, and a selection of sweets or a cheeseboard.
Rooms 12. Seats 37. Parties 50. Private Room. L 12.15-3 Sun only D 7.30-10. Closed D Sun, all Mon, Bank Holidays. Set L £14.50 Set D £16.50. Access, Visa.

Dedham   Maison Talbooth   78%   £138

Tel 0206 322367   Fax 0206 322752

H

Stratford Road Dedham Nr Colchester Essex CO7 6HN

Map 6 C3

In the north-east corner of Essex, where the river Stour forms the boundary with Suffolk, Maison Talbooth stands in an area of great beauty immortalised in the paintings of John Constable. The outstanding hotel-keeping of Gerald Milsom has now reached its 40th year of progress from Talbooth's origins as a simple tea room to today's tranquil hotel and riverside restaurant (see entry below). All is calm and restful in the sunny lounge with its deep-cushioned armchairs, profusion of fresh flowers and views down Dedham Vale. The bedrooms, suites almost, strike a happy

balance between the shameless luxury of fine co-ordinated fabrics and
crown canopied beds and the quiet homeliness of abundant magazines,
fresh fruit and a drinks tray. Bathrooms are superb, some with vast sunken
tubs, all containing quality bath sheets and bespoke toiletries. **Rooms 10.**
Garden, croquet, giant chess. Access, Amex, Visa, (I)

Dedham	Le Talbooth	★	£95
Tel 0206 323150			**R**

Gunhill Dedham Nr Colchester Essex CO7 6HP — Map 6 C3

A short walk from the hotel (though transport is provided for residents),
Le Talbooth is set in a sprawling, timbered Tudor house close to a bridge
where tolls were once collected from coachmen and bargees. Looking out
to the riverside patio and gardens, it's predominantly pink and blue with
blackened oak beams, Windsor chairs and oak tables – one of England's
gorgeous summer restaurants. For so traditional a setting, Lee Timmins's
cooking is refreshingly modern (albeit with a touch of caution), with much
juxtaposition of colours, textures and flavours, and transposition of sauces
from carte to table d'hote. Nuggets of monkfish are sautéed with Oriental
vegetables in soya sauce and sesame oil; salmon poached with vegetable
tagliatelle and parsley and tomato cream; a stew of wild rabbit in Madeira
cream sauce is encased in puff pastry. A good-value lunch might feature
fish ragout (monkfish, codling, red mullet) with lemon and thyme butter
sauce, followed by sautéed lamb's kidneys with rösti and a bacon and onion
jus; wonderful raspberry cheesecake "and its coulis" to finish. Desserts on
the carte might also include a classic English trio of lemon meringue,
sherry trifle and treacle sponge; excellent English farmhouse cheeses are
also offered. Sunday lunches offer a good choice, including a traditional
roast. Outstanding wine list with helpful notes that include a breakdown of
recent claret vintages and background on growers and shippers. **Seats 70.**
*Parties 70. Private Room. L 12-2 D 7-9.30. Set L £20.35 (Sun £21.95) inc
service. Access, Amex, Visa,* (I)

Dedham   Places of Interest

Castle House   (Home of painter Sir Alfred Munnings) Tel 0206 322127.

Derby	Forte Posthouse	61%	£64
Tel 0332 514933 Fax 0332 518668			**H**

Pastures Hill Littleover Derby Derbyshire DE3 7BA — Map 10 C3

Neat, unfussy businessman's accommodation three miles west of the city
centre on the A5250. Extensive grounds include a children's play area.
Conference and banqueting for up to 60. **Rooms 62.** *Access, Amex, Visa,*
(I)

Derby	International Hotel	62%	£60
Tel 0332 369321 Fax 0332 294430			**H**

Burton Road Derby Derbyshire DE3 6AD — Map 10 C3

On the A5250 south-west of the city centre, the privately owned
International concentrates very much on conference and exhibition
business. Of the numerous meeting rooms, the largest comfortably seats up
to 50 theatre-style. Bedrooms offer many extras and the suites boast spa
baths. Greatly reduced rates at weekends. **Rooms 62.** *Dinner dance (weekly).
Access, Amex, Visa,* (I)

Derby   Places of Interest

Tourist Information   Tel 0332 255802.
Derby Playhouse   Eagle Centre Tel 0332 363275.
Guildhall Theatre   Market Place Tel 0332 255447.
Derby Cathedral   Tel 0332 41201.
Elvaston Castle Museum   Tel 0332 571342.
Royal Crown Derby Museum   Tel 0332 47051.

Derby Cricket Ground   Tel 0332 383211.
Derby County Football Ground   Tel 0332 40105.
Wingfield Park Showground   Belper Tel 0602 324653.
   Historic Houses, Castles and Gardens
Calke Abbey and Park (NT)   Tel 0332 863822.
Kedleston Hall   Tel 0332 842191.
Melbourne Hall and Gardens   Melbourne Tel 0332 862502.
Sudbury Hall (NT)   Tel 0283 585305.

Desborough   Forte Travelodge   £40

Tel 0536 762034   **L**

A6 Harborough Road Desborough Northamptonshire   Map 11 D4

On the A6 southbound, 4 miles south-east of Market Harborough and 5
miles north of West Kettering. Close to the A14 – the new A1/M1 link
road. *Rooms 32. Access, Amex, Visa.*

Dinnington   Dinnington Hall   65%   £55

Tel &   Fax 0909 569661   **H**

Falcon Way Dinnington Nr Sheffield South Yorkshire S31 7NY   Map 11 D2

Dinnington Hall is a Georgian manor house standing in three acres of
gardens amid a council development in a mining village. Once derelict, it
is now comfortable and homely, with a parquet-floored lounge where
chintzy chairs are arranged around a log fire, and a pubby bar. Bedrooms
range from singles to an Executive suite with its own cocktail bar and a
sunken bath. One room has a four-poster. Call hotel for exact directions.
Rooms 10. Garden. Access, Amex, Visa, **①** *Diners Club International*

Dinnington   Places of Interest

Clumber Park (NT)   Nr Worksop Tel 0909 476592.
Hodsock Priory   Blyth Tel 0909 591204.
Roche Abbey   Maltby Tel 0709 812739.

Diss   Weavers   £45

Tel 0379 642411   **R**

Market Hill Diss Norfolk IP22 3JZ   Map 6 C2

Built in the 15th century as a chapel for the weavers' guild, this
characterful town-centre restaurant is oak-timbered inside with original
paintings on the walls. Lunch offers a good value wine-bar-like menu (no
starters apart from soup) ranging from lasagne to pigeon breast in a sloe
gin and juniper sauce; dinner is more conventional, and a little more
expensive, with a good choice of starters like asparagus hollandaise and
melon and mango with peach shnapps followed by main dishes such as
guinea fowl with marsala and prune sauce and sage dumplings, lamb with
garlic and rosemary, and baked Cromer crab. Chef-patron William Bavin's
cooking is robust and hearty and portions are generous. No smoking
before 2pm at lunchtime or 9.30pm in the evening. Extensive wine list
with a few bargains to be had. *Seats 80. Parties 45. Private Room. L 12-2
D 7-9.30. Closed L Sat, D Mon, all Sun, Bank Holidays, Xmas, 1 week end
Aug. Access, Visa,* **①** *Diners Club International*

Diss   Places of Interest

Bressingham Live Steam Museum and Gardens
   Tel 0379 88 386/0379 88 382.
Banham Zoo   Banham Tel 095 387 476.

Doncaster   Campanile Hotel   £36

Tel 0302 370770   Fax 0302 370813   **L**

Doncaster Leisure Park Bawtry Doncaster South Yorkshire DN4 7PD   Map 11 D2

Close to the race course, off the A638. Closest motorway junction is
junction 3 of the M18, off junction 2 of the A1(M). *Rooms 50. Access,
Amex, Visa,* **①** *Diners Club International*

Doncaster	Danum Swallow Hotel	64%	£86

Tel 0302 342261   Fax 0302 329034   **H**

High Street Doncaster South Yorkshire DN1 1DN   Map 11 D2

An Edwardian building in the centre of town; inside it's been thoroughly modernised (except for the Crystal Suite which can accommodate up to 350 delegates in period style) with comfortable, spacious public areas and bedrooms which boast irons and ironing boards in addition to the usual amenities. *Rooms 66. Hairdressing, coffee shop (9am-5pm). Access, Amex, Visa,* 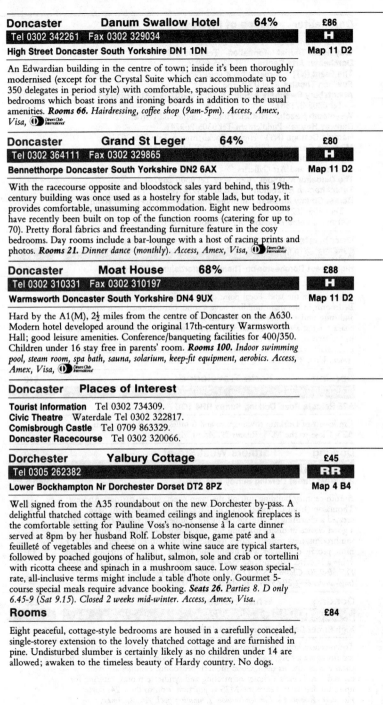 Diners Club International

Doncaster	Grand St Leger	64%	£80

Tel 0302 364111   Fax 0302 329865   **H**

Bennetthorpe Doncaster South Yorkshire DN2 6AX   Map 11 D2

With the racecourse opposite and bloodstock sales yard behind, this 19th-century building was once used as a hostelry for stable lads, but today, it provides comfortable, unassuming accommodation. Eight new bedrooms have recently been built on top of the function rooms (catering for up to 70). Pretty floral fabrics and freestanding furniture feature in the cosy bedrooms. Day rooms include a bar-lounge with a host of racing prints and photos. *Rooms 21. Dinner dance (monthly). Access, Amex, Visa,* Diners Club International

Doncaster	Moat House	68%	£88

Tel 0302 310331   Fax 0302 310197   **H**

Warmsworth Doncaster South Yorkshire DN4 9UX   Map 11 D2

Hard by the A1(M), 2½ miles from the centre of Doncaster on the A630. Modern hotel developed around the original 17th-century Warmsworth Hall; good leisure amenities. Conference/banqueting facilities for 400/350. Children under 16 stay free in parents' room. *Rooms 100. Indoor swimming pool, steam room, spa bath, sauna, solarium, keep-fit equipment, aerobics. Access, Amex, Visa,* Diners Club International

Doncaster   Places of Interest

Tourist Information   Tel 0302 734309.
Civic Theatre   Waterdale Tel 0302 322817.
Comisbrough Castle   Tel 0709 863329.
Doncaster Racecourse   Tel 0302 320066.

Dorchester	Yalbury Cottage		£45

Tel 0305 262382   **RR**

Lower Bockhampton Nr Dorchester Dorset DT2 8PZ   Map 4 B4

Well signed from the A35 roundabout on the new Dorchester by-pass. A delightful thatched cottage with beamed ceilings and inglenook fireplaces is the comfortable setting for Pauline Voss's no-nonsense à la carte dinner served at 8pm by her husband Rolf. Lobster bisque, game paté and a feuilleté of vegetables and cheese on a white wine sauce are typical starters, followed by poached goujons of halibut, salmon, sole and crab or tortellini with ricotta cheese and spinach in a mushroom sauce. Low season special-rate, all-inclusive terms might include a table d'hote only. Gourmet 5-course special meals require advance booking. *Seats 26. Parties 8. D only 6.45-9 (Sat 9.15). Closed 2 weeks mid-winter. Access, Amex, Visa.*

Rooms   £84

Eight peaceful, cottage-style bedrooms are housed in a carefully concealed, single-storey extension to the lovely thatched cottage and are furnished in pine. Undisturbed slumber is certainly likely as no children under 14 are allowed; awaken to the timeless beauty of Hardy country. No dogs.

Dorchester   Places of Interest

Tourist Information   Tel 0305 267992.
Weymouth Tourist Information   Tel 0305 772444.
Dorchester Arts Centre   Tel 0305 66926.
The Giant (NT)   Cerne Abbas *8 miles North.*
Pavillion Theatre   Tel 0305 783225.
Abbotsbury Swannery & Sub-Tropical Gardens   Abbotsbury
   Tel 0305 871387.
Weymouth Beach.   Historic Houses, Castles and Gardens
Danway House   Puddletown Tel 0305 269741.
Hardy's Cottage (NT)   Higher Bockhampton Tel 0305 262366.
Minterne Gardens   Minterne Magna Tel 0300 341370.
Wolfeton House   Tel 0305 263500.
   Museums and Art Galleries
The Dinosaur Museum   Icen Way Tel 0305 269741.
Tutankhamun Exhibition   Tel 0305 269741.
Dorset County Museum   Includes Thomas Hardy memorial room
   Tel 0305 262735.
Warmwell Leisure Resort Dry Ski Slope   Tel 0305 852911.

Dorchester-on-Thames   George Hotel   £85

| Tel 0865 340404 | **I** |

High Street Dorchester-on-Thames Oxfordshire OX9 8HH   Map 5 D2

With a history spanning more than 500 years, the George is one of the
oldest inns in the land. Focal point of the public area is a fine beamed bar.
Bedrooms in the main building have a solid, old-fashioned feel, some cosy
and snug under oak beams, two with four-posters. Other rooms have less
character but are still very adequate. Small meetings and seminars are held
in the two rooms of a self-contained annexe; the beamed Stable room is
particularly characterful. *Rooms 18. Garden. Closed 1 week Xmas. Access,
Amex, Visa,* ![Diners Club International]

Dorking   Forte Travelodge   £40

| Tel 0306 740361 | **L** |

A25 Reigate Road Dorking Surrey RH4 1QB   Map 5 E3

½ mile east of Dorking town centre and 6 miles west of Reigate on the
A25. Close to the M25. *Rooms 29. Access, Amex, Visa.*

Dorking   Partners West Street   £80

| Tel 0306 882826 | **R** |

2-4 West Street Dorking Surrey RH4 1BL   Map 5 E3

A 16th-century building, just off the main street, where partners Andrew
Thomason (front of house) and Tim McEntire (in the kitchen) have
created a charmingly intimate restaurant. Dinner is a fixed-price affair with
a good choice of dishes spanning the sophisticated – ravioli of shiitake
mushrooms, new season's lamb's tongue with sweetbreads – and the rather
more prosaic calf's liver with bubble and squeak. Lunchtime brings a good-
value à la carte. No smoking. *Seats 45. Parties 30. Private Room. L 12.30-2
D 7.30-9.30. Closed L Sat, D Sun, all Mon, Bank Holidays. Set D £17.60
(mid-week) & £29.65. Access, Amex, Visa,* ![Diners Club International]

Dorking   White Horse   62%   £96

| Tel 0306 881138   Fax 0306 887241 | **H** |

High Street Dorking Surrey RH14 1BE   Map 5 E3

Town-centre hotel developed from an old coaching inn. Oak beams and
log fires give a cosy, traditional feel to the day rooms, while in summer the
patio comes into its own. Good modern bedrooms. Families are well
catered for. There's a choice of meeting and syndicate rooms, catering for
up to 60 delegates. Leave the M25 at junction 9 on to the A24. Forte
Heritage. *Rooms 68. Garden, outdoor swimming pool. Access, Amex,
Visa,* ![Diners Club International]

Dorking   Places of Interest

Polesden Lacey (NT) Nr Dorking Tel 0372 58203 or 52048.
Thorndike Theatre Leatherhead Tel 0372 376211.

Dorrington   Country Friends   £65
Tel 074 373 707   RR
Dorrington Nr Shrewsbury Shropshire SY5 7JD   Map 10 A4

A half-timbered house turned into a comfortable restaurant with rooms.
Chef-patron Charles Whittaker heads the team in the kitchen, producing
such dishes as salmon quenelles with ginger and lemon grass sauce,
courgette soufflé with tomato sauce, calf's liver with citrus fruit, or venison
with blackcurrant and beetroot sauce. Puddings like banoffi pie, praline and
armagnac ice cream, and hot white chocolate soufflé with chocolate sauce.
Simple, no-choice fixed-price menu. Snacks in the bar at lunchtime. No
smoking in restaurant while others are eating. *Seats 45. Parties 60. L 12-2
D 7-9. Closed Sun & Mon, Bank Holidays, last week Jul, first week Oct. Set
meals £15.90. Access, Amex, Visa,* ⓓ

Rooms   £42

Good-quality coach-house bedrooms are attractive with antiques, if sparing
with extras. Two are not en suite. None have phones or TVs. Room price
includes breakfast of Bucks Fizz and scrambled eggs with smoked salmon.
Rooms 3.

Dovedale   Izaak Walton Hotel   59%   £90
Tel 033 529 555   Fax 033 529 539   H
Dovedale Nr Ashbourne Derbyshire DE6 2AY   Map 10 C3

A splendidly located hilltop hotel on the Duke of Rutland's estates; its
17th-century farmhouse building affords rolling views of Thorpe Cloud
and Dovedale in the Peak District Park. Leather chesterfield sofas and open
fires add comfort and warmth to the public rooms; bedrooms are more
noteworthy for the vistas without than the space within. Conference suite
for 60. Under-15s stay free in parents' room. *Rooms 34. Dinner dance (Sat),
helipad. Access, Amex, Visa,* ⓓ

Dovedale   Peveril of the Peak   60%   £96
Tel 033 529 333   Fax 033 529 507   H
Thorpe Dovedale Nr Ashbourne Derbyshire DE6 2AW   Map 10 C3

At the foot of the 900ft Thorpe Cloud mountain in the heart of the Peak
District, the Peveril of the Peak has been attracting ramblers and country
lovers for over 100 years. Probably the original Thorpe Rectory, its origins
are obscure, but much local Derbyshire stone is evident in the public
rooms. Bedrooms are traditional. The Dovedale Centre caters for meetings
of up to 45. Forte Heritage. *Rooms 47. Garden, tennis. Access, Amex, Visa,*
ⓓ

Dover   Forte Posthouse   63%   £64
Tel 0304 821222   Fax 0304 825576   H
Singledge Lane Whitfield Dover Kent CT16 3LF   Map 7 D5

Modern low-riser alongside the A2, 3 miles from the ferry terminal.
Banqueting/conference facilities for 20/40. *Rooms 67. Garden. Access,
Amex, Visa,* ⓓ

Dover   Moat House   66%   £100

Tel 0304 203270   Fax 0304 213230   **H**

Townwall Street Dover Kent CT16 1SZ   Map 7 D5

Formerly a Holiday Inn, now a Queens Moat Houses business hotel
situated on the seafront. Large beds and spacious bedrooms.
Banqueting/conference facilities for 120/150. Greatly reduced rates at
weekends. **Rooms 79.** *Indoor swimming pool. Access, Amex, Visa,*

Dover   Travel Inn   £42

Tel 0304 213339   Fax 0304 214504   **L**

Folkestone Road Dover Kent CT15 7AB   Map 7 D5

Less than 10 minutes drive from the cross-Channel Ferry Port. **Rooms 30.**
Access, Amex, Visa,

Dover   White Cliffs Hotel   58%   £72

Tel 0304 203633   Fax 0304 216320   **H**

Seafront Dover Kent CT17 9BP   Map 7 D5

Traditional hotel on Dover seafront, within a few minutes of the cross-
channel ferry and hovercraft terminals. Terraced sun lounge, adequate
accommodation and secure garaging. **Rooms 56.** *Access, Amex, Visa,*

Dover   Places of Interest

Tourist Information   Tel 0304 205108.
Dover Castle   Tel 0304 201628.

Driffield   Bell Hotel   £75

Tel 0377 46661   Fax 0377 43228   **I**

Market Place Driffield Humberside YO25 7AP   Map 15 D6

Period charm and modern amenities combine in a coaching inn that's more
than 250 years old. Conference (up to 300) and function (up to 200)
facilities are in the restored Old Town Hall, and further conversion houses
a leisure complex. Day rooms include the 18th-century wood-panelled Oak
Room, the flagstoned Old Corn Exchange buffet/bar and a residents'
lounge. Bedrooms boast antique furniture and up-to-date comforts. No
children under 12. No dogs. **Rooms 14.** *Garden, indoor swimming pool, spa
bath, steam room, sauna, solarium, squash. Closed 25-27 Dec. Access, Amex,
Visa,*

Driffield   Places of Interest

Burton Agnes Hall   Tel 026 289 324.
Sledmere House and Gardens   Sledmere Tel 0377 86208.

Droitwich   Forte Travelodge   £40

Tel 0527 86545   **L**

A38 Rashwood Hill Droitwich Hereford & Worcester WR9 8DA   Map 10 B4

½ mile west of junction 5 on the M5 and 2 miles north of Droitwich.
Rooms 32. *Access, Amex, Visa.*

Droitwich Spa   Chateau Impney   70%   £140

Tel 0905 774411   Fax 0905 772971   **H**

Droitwich Spa Hereford & Worcester WR9 0BB   Map 4 B1

Chateau Impney was built in the French style around 1875, but while the
well-tended gardens and surrounding parkland buttress an impressive
grandeur, all other associations with things pastoral and aristocratic no
longer apply. Proximity to junction 5 of the M5 has pushed the premises

here almost exclusively towards conferences and functions (for up to 300 delegates). A few fine features survive, noticeably a magnificent carved wood staircase and high ceilings supported by marble columns. Main-house bedrooms, though spacious, are bland and have incongruously compact bathrooms while the Impney Court building offers newer but smaller accommodation. Nine apartments are also in a separate block. Children and dogs are not really welcomed. Impney Hotels. *Rooms 114. Garden, sauna, solarium, gymnasium, tennis, games room, helipad. Closed Xmas. Access, Amex, Visa,* **(ID)** *Diners Club International*

Droitwich Spa   Raven Hotel   66%   £140

Tel 0905 772224   Fax 0905 772371   **H**

St Andrews Street Droitwich Spa Hereford & Worcester WR9 8DU   Map 4 B1

Specialising in conferences and banqueting (for up to 150/250), the Raven also takes very good care of private guests, putting a premium on courtesy and professionalism. It's a handsome timber-framed building, parts of it going back to the 16th century. Overnight accommodation is more up-to-date than the exterior might suggest. Opposite the *Worcestershire Brine Baths* hotel, currently undergoing refurbishment and also owned by Impney Hotels. *Rooms 72. Garden. Access, Amex, Visa,* **(ID)**

Droitwich Spa   Places of Interest

Norbury Theatre   Friar Street Tel 0905 770154.
Hanbury Hall (NT)   Tel 052 784 214.
Droitwich Heritage Centre   Tel 0905 774312.

Dronfield   Brothers at the Chantry   NEW   £45

Tel 0246 413014   **R**

Church Street Dronfield Derbyshire S18 6QB   Map 10 C2

Culinary brothers chef Wayne and patissier Jamie Bosworth, two young men with formidable pedigrees, are showing plenty of promise here, though the new venture is still in its infancy. A la carte dinners show plenty of invention: the cooking isn't over-complicated and flavours are clear and precise in dishes like sauté of scallops with pesto or beef tournedos topped with Stilton. Lighter lunches on weekdays in the conservatory; plus a traditional Sunday lunch. A rather stylish Georgian bed and breakfast guest house, the Chantry is run by retired super-troupers Roy and Jackie Toaduff – they're brothers, too. *Seats 40. Parties 70. Private Room. L 12-2.30 D 7-9. Closed D Sun, all Mon. Access, Amex, Visa.*

Dudley   Forte Travelodge   £40

Tel 0384 481579   **L**

A461 Dudley Road Dudley West Midlands DY5 1LQ   Map 10 B4

Situated on the A461 at Brierley Hill 3 miles west of Dudley towards Stourbridge, very close to Merry Hill centre. Birmingham 10 miles. No adjacent restaurant facilities. *Rooms 32. Access, Amex, Visa.*

Dulverton   Ashwick House   68%   £78

Tel 0398 23868   **HR**

Dulverton Somerset TA22 9QD   Map 3 D2

Richard Sherwood runs the quietest of houses in deep country on the fringe of Exmoor – take the Tarr Steps road to the moor from Dulverton. Constructed of Wellington brick in 1901, the house's William Morris interior still boasts original wallpapers; although the present reconstruction dates only from 1980, an evocative Edwardian atmosphere has carefully been retained. Thus, beside your turned-down bed you'll find a goodnight sweet and an Edward Bear hot-water bottle. Bedrooms are spacious, with lovely parkland views and rather dated, chintzy decor. Sweeping lawns lead down to water gardens, thus no children under 8. No dogs. *Rooms 6. Garden. No credit cards.*   *see over*

Restaurant

£58

Richard's capable one-man show extends to the kitchen and dinner, when a named, hand-written scroll menu is presented to each diner. Choice is limited to the first and fourth courses: local asparagus with orange butter sauce or tomato and red pepper soup preceding an avocado terrine, then maybe noisettes of lamb with a port wine sauce before a choice between elderflower and geranium leaf sorbet, chocolate truffle slice and a selection of local cheeses. Far from grand, the food mirrors the intimacy of the surroundings, as residents readily become acquainted. Non-residents should book early. *Seats 30. Parties 40. Private Room. L (Sun only) 12.30-1.45 D 7.15-8.30. Set L £12.50 Set D £18.95.*

Dulverton   Carnarvon Arms   60%

£60

H

Tel 0398 23302   Fax 0398 24022

Dulverton Somerset TA22 9AE

Map 3 D2

Purpose-built for the 4th Earl of Carnarvon in 1874, the Carnarvon Arms is very much geared to walkers, horse-riders (stabling if you bring your own, hunters and ponies available at a nearby establishment) and particularly fishermen, with seven miles of trout and salmon fishing on the rivers Exe and Barle. The lounges are large, old-fashioned and relaxing, with open fires, splendid views and flower displays. Bedrooms are modest but comfortable enough; children up to 15 stay free in parents' room between October and May. *Rooms 25. Garden, croquet, outdoor swimming pool, tennis, fishing, stabling, clay-pigeon shooting, snooker. Access, Visa,*

Dunbridge   Mill Arms Inn   NEW

£55

R

Tel 0794 40401

Dunbridge Nr Romsey Hampshire

Map 4 C3

Shaun Green cooks fresh produce, much of it local, in a refreshing and unpretentious manner at a busy conservatory restaurant attached to this whitewashed village free house near the railway station. A few modern influences appear on the straightforward menu and portions are often generous. Memorable fresh mussels, daily fresh fish, a choice of steaks and monthly, fixed-price limited choice menus, plus friendly, attentive service. *Seats 60. Parties 60. L 12-2 (Sun to 2.30) D 7-10 (Fri & Sat to 10.30). Access, Amex, Visa,*

Dunkirk   Petty France Hotel   65%

£84

H

Tel 045 423 361   Fax 045 423 768

Dunkirk Badminton Avon GL9 1AF

Map 4 B2

Eye-catching gardens alongside the A46 (4 miles north of M4 junction 18) provide both the setting for Petty France's well-proportioned Georgian house and the floral displays which adorn hall and lounge. Accommodation is divided between the main house and a converted stable block; a traditional feel with period furniture and floral fabrics in the former gives way to cottagey curtains and lightwood fittings in the stable rooms. Here the less mobile may find upstairs bathrooms inconvenient. *Rooms 20. Garden, croquet. Access, Amex, Visa,*

Dunchurch   Dun Cow

£55

I

Tel 0788 810233   Fax 0788 521243

The Green Dunchurch Nr Rugby Warwickshire CV22 6NJ

Map 11 D4

New owners are installed at this characterful hotel dating back to the 17th century. It has kept the feel of the period with fine panelling, beams, old prints and large, lived-in pieces of furniture. Real ale is on tap to complete the scene. Traditional is also the basic style of the bedrooms, half of which are across the road. Two rooms have four-posters. *Rooms 21. Garden. Access, Amex, Visa,*

Dunchurch	Forte Travelodge	£40
Tel 0788 521528		**L**

A45 London Road Thurlaston Dunchurch Nr Rugby
West Midlands CV23 9LG   **Map 5 D1**

Off the M45, on the A45 westbound, 3 miles south of Rugby town centre;
8 miles east of Coventry. *Rooms 40. Access, Amex, Visa.*

Dunstable	Forte Travelodge	£40
Tel 0525 211177		**L**

A5 Watling Street Hockliffe Dunstable Bedfordshire LU7 9LZ   **Map 5 E1**

On the A5, 3 miles north of Dunstable. Close to Milton Keynes and Luton.
Rooms 28. Access, Amex, Visa.

Dunstable	Old Palace Lodge	66%	£100
Tel 0582 662201 Fax 0582 696422			**H**

Church Street Dunstable Bedfordshire LU5 4RT   **Map 5 E1**

Creeper climbs thickly over a hotel developed from a building believed to
date back to the Lodge of the Royal Palace of Dunstable, around 1100. In
the absence of a lounge, the comfortably furnished bar is the focal point of
the day rooms. Bedrooms have good darkwood furniture, breakfast or
coffee tables and armchairs or sofas. Some rooms are designated non-
smoking. *Rooms 49. Access, Amex, Visa,* **①** Diners Club International

Dunstable	Places of Interest

Tourist Information   Tel 0582 471012.
Whipsnade Wildlife Park   Tel 0582 872171.

Dunster	Luttrell Arms	64%	£106
Tel 0643 821555 Fax 0643 821567			**H**

High Street Dunster Nr Minehead Somerset TA24 8SG   **Map 3 E1**

A creeper-clad hotel of great historical interest, built in the 15th century
as a guest house for the monks of Cleeve Abbey. Impressive architectural
features include a superb Gothic hall (now the lounge) with hammer-beam
roof and gargantuan fireplace, and a timbered Tudor bar in the former
kitchen. Bedrooms offer solid 20th-century comforts and functional
modern bathrooms. Forte Heritage. *Rooms 27. Garden, garage. Access,
Amex, Visa,* **①** Diners Club International

Dunster	Places of Interest

Dunster Castle and Gardens (NT)   Nr Minehead Tel 0643 821314.

Durham	Royal County Hotel	67%	£98
Tel 091-386 6821 Fax 091-386 0704			**H**

Old Elvet Durham Co Durham DH1 3JN   **Map 15 B4**

Attractively decorated rooms in a large business-orientated hotel close to
the cathedral and castle. Fine leisure facilities attract weekend guests.
Swallow Hotels. *Rooms 150. Indoor swimming pool, spa bath, sauna, solarium,
gymnasium, beauty and hair salons, coffee shop (7am-9.30pm). Access, Amex,
Visa,* **①** Diners Club International

Durham	Places of Interest

Tourist Information   Tel 091-384 3720.
Auckland Castle   Bishop Auckland Tel 0388 601627.
Spectrum Leisure Centre Dry Ski Slope   Willington Tel 0388 747000.
Botanic Garden University of Durham   Tel 091-374 2671.
Durham Castle   Tel 091-374 3863.
Durham Light Infantry Museum and Durham Arts Centre   Tel 091-384 2214.

354 England

Durham Cathedral Tel 091-386 4266.
Durham Ice Rink Tel 091-386 4065.
Durham County Cricket Club Houghton-le-Spring Tel 091-512 0178.

Easington	Grinkle Park	70%	£80

Tel 0287 640515   Fax 0287 641278

H

Easington Loftus Nr Saltburn-by-Sea Cleveland TS13 4UB   Map 15 C5

Sweeping lawns and mature pines and rhododendrons surround a
formidable mansion set in parkland just off the A174. The atmosphere
inside is refined and quietly elegant. The delightful Camellia Room, with
picture windows, festoon blinds and wicker seating, has camellias actually
growing up through the floor, and in the foyer-bar the roaring winter fire
is reflected in the darkwood panelling. Bedrooms are named after local
flora, birds and places; they're stylishly decorated, with light, restful colour
schemes. *Rooms 20. Garden, game fishing, tennis, snooker. Access, Amex,
Visa,* (I) *Diners Club International*

East Boldon	Forsters	£62

Tel 091-519 0929

R

2 St Bedes Station Road East Boldon Tyne & Wear NE36 0LE   Map 15 C4

Sophisticated-looking exterior with Venetian blinds in the windows of the
double shop frontage. Just seven tables are closely packed. Barry Forster
offers a short dinner carte that might range from pea, pear and watercress
soup, sauté of Thai-flavoured prawns or Swiss cheese and ham soufflé,
through crispy breast of duck with grilled black pudding and olive oil
mash or roast loin of venison with walnuts, bacon lardons and mushrooms,
to a warmed steam sponge with butterscotch sauce and vanilla ice cream or
white chocolate truffle laced with Grand Marnier. Fresh fish appears on a
list of daily specials that might include roast sardines, moules marinière or
sea bass roasted Chinese style. Sunday lunch (£14.50) is a 3-course, fixed-
price affair. Barry's wife Sue runs a small, well-trained front-of-house team
with a rare blend of professionalism and warmth. Not much thought has
gone into the wine list, with house champagne almost the dearest bottle!
*Seats 28. Parties 28. L Sun only 12-2 D 7-10.30. Closed D Sun, all Mon.
Set L £14.50. Access, Amex, Visa,* (I) *Diners Club International*

East Boldon   Places of Interest

South Shields Tourist Information Tel 091-454 6612.
Old Customs House Tel 091-454 0269.
Souter Lighthouse (NT) Whitburn Tel 091-529 3161.

East Buckland	Lower Pitt	£50

Tel &   Fax 0598 760243

RR

East Buckland Barnstaple Devon EX32 0TD   Map 3 D2

Run by Suzanne and Jerome Lyons since 1978, Lower Pitt is an old stone
farmhouse with a bright conservatory dining room extension, in a quiet
setting two miles off the A361 North Devon link road. A typically
tempting dinner menu might include courgette roulade filled with cheese
and herb paté followed by loin of local pork with apples and shallots in a
cider and cream sauce, good English cheeses and sticky toffee and date
pudding with butterscotch sauce. *Seats 32. Parties 18. Private Room. D only
7-8.30. Closed Sun & Mon (except residents), 25 & 26 Dec. Access, Visa.*

Rooms
£100*

Three double rooms, one with bath, two with shower, are available for
diners. No phones or TVs. No children under 11. No dogs. *Half board
terms only.

East Dereham	**King's Head**		**£46**
Tel 0362 693842 Fax 0362 693776			**I**
Norwich Street East Dereham Norfolk NR19 1AD			Map 6 C1

A modest, but immaculately kept 17th-century coaching inn near the town centre. A cosy red-carpeted bar looks out past the patio to a bowling green beyond. Spotless bedrooms offer tea-making kits, remote-control TVs and neat bathrooms. **Rooms 15.** *Garden, tennis, patio, bowling. Access, Amex, Visa,*

East Dereham	**Phoenix Hotel**	**59%**	**£76**
Tel 0362 692276			**H**
Church Street East Dereham Norfolk NR19 1DL			Map 6 C1

Bright redbrick 60s' hotel in the centre of town. Neat, practical bedrooms and function/conference suite accommodating up to 160. Forte Heritage. **Rooms 23.** *Access, Amex, Visa,*

East Grinstead	**Gravetye Manor**	**84%**	**£164**
Tel 0342 810567 Fax 0342 810080			**HR**
Vowels Lane East Grinstead West Sussex RH19 4LJ			Map 7 B5

The civilised hospitality and gracious charm of Peter Herbert and staff (for whom nothing is too much trouble) continue to provide an object lesson in how a country house hotel should be run. The care and attention to every last detail both within the splendidly transformed Elizabethan manor house and in the grounds is perfectly illustrated in the recent construction of the new wing (just four immaculate bedrooms were added) and in the time and expense involved in restoring to its former glory the William Robinson English garden ravaged by the storms of recent winters past. Flower displays grace the already gracious day rooms, which include a really delightful sitting room with oak panelling and an ornate moulded ceiling, and the newly refurbished entrance hall – much brighter than in the past – with carefully selected chair patterns. Supplementing the already delightful bedrooms (several of which have almost doubled in size and hugely benefited from the refurbishment), the spacious new rooms, beautifully designed and each with its own personal style, are named after trees; the comfortable beds, antique furniture and sumptuous fabrics are models of good taste; books, magazines, post cards, bedside radios and TVs concealed behind tapestry screens are among a long list of thoughtful extras. The new bathrooms, too, with his and her washbasins, bidet and power shower over the bath provide every conceivable need, and are havens of comfort. No children under 7. No dogs. **Rooms 18.** *Garden, croquet, fishing. No credit cards.*

Restaurant ★↑ £105

Long known for its consistency and for the eminent chefs who have worked here in the past, the elegant restaurant continues, under Stephen Morey, to achieve admirable results. The menus are a delightful balance of the modern and the traditional, light and robust dishes, natural and complex flavours, and attention to detail, both in presentation and accuracy of cooking. Fish has always featured prominently (incidentally the salmon is smoked in their own smokehouse) and a quenelle of pike with freshwater crayfish and a glazed tarragon cream sauce was faultless. So, too, a steamed fillet of turbot with fennel and dill. A fricassée of guinea fowl served in a deep dish with lardons, mushrooms, olives and herbs can almost be described as old-fashioned dish, contrasting with the modern interpretation of cooking noisettes of lamb – topped with chicken and tarragon mousseline and served with a light lamb jus. Desserts include a peach tatin (well worth the twenty minute wait), a delicious gratin of the hotel's own berries, and a creamy rice pudding. Cheeses are expectional. A splendid all-round wine list with gems everywhere you look and an especially commendable half bottle selection. Winner of the 1993 Home Counties Regional Cellar of the Year and also 1993 California Cellar of the Year awards. Service is two stars plus – the staff are immaculate in every sense. The addition of 17½% value added tax can be a shock when the bill is presented; all menu prices exclude vat – an eccentric practice, but *do* include service. **Seats 42. Parties 18. Private Room.** L 12.30-2 D 7.30-9.30 (*Sun to 9*). Closed D 25 Dec. Set L £19 (+vat) Set D £22 (+vat).

East Grinstead   Woodbury House   67%   £75

Tel 0342 313657   Fax 0342 314801

Lewes Road East Grinstead West Sussex RH19 3UD   Map 7 B5

Half a mile south of the town, on the main A22, stands this small and attractively decorated owner-managed hotel. Late-Victorian in construction, it now boasts a chintzy lounge and conservatory dining room with a lovely summer patio, a private boardroom for meetings or dinners (max 20), and gracious bedrooms, each individual in style and decor and most with garden and countryside views. Friendly personal service from proprietors Jane and Michael Medforth. Children under 7 stay free in parents' room. **Rooms 14.** *Garden, coffee shop (9.30am-10pm).* Access, Amex, Visa, Diners Club

East Grinstead   Places of Interest

Hammerwood Park   Tel 0342 850594 or 088 385 2366.
Lingfield Park Racecourse   Tel 0342 834800.

East Horsley   Thatchers Resort Hotel   63%   £95

Tel 048 65 4291   Fax 048 65 4222

Epsom Road East Horsley Surrey KT24 6TB   Map 5 E3

Mock-Tudor building in three acres of grounds. Modern decor in the bedrooms; two four-poster rooms; several family rooms (children up to 14 stay free in parents' room). Plans for 1992/3 include more bedrooms, an additional conference room (holding up to 120) and a health and leisure club. **Rooms 59.** *Garden, outdoor swimming pool, baby-sitting, baby-listening, helipad.* Access, Amex, Visa, Diners Club

East Stoke   Kemps Country House Hotel   56%   £78

Tel 0929 462563   Fax 0929 405287

East Stoke Nr Wareham Dorset BH20 6AL   Map 4 B4

A quiet country hotel converted from a Victorian rectory. Best accommodation is provided by six spacious pine-furnished rooms in a separate block. Some have whirlpool baths, and one boasts a modern four-poster. Children up to seven stay free in parents' room. Banqueting/conference facilities for 120/80. No dogs. **Rooms 15.** *Garden.* Access, Amex, Visa, Diners Club

East Stoke   Places of Interest

Athelhampton House and Gardens   Athelhampton Tel 0305 848363.
Clouds Hill (NT)   Near Wool Tel 0305 267992 *Cottage home of T E Lawrence.*
The Tank Museum Bovington Camp   Nr Wool Tel 0929 403329 or 403463.

Eastbourne   Cavendish Hotel   68%   £124

Tel 0323 410222   Fax 0323 410941

Grand Parade Eastbourne East Sussex BN21 4DH   Map 7 B6

Well maintained and imposing seafront hotel with an unsympathetic balconied modern corner extension. Large banqueting facilities (for up to 350) plus conferences for up to 150. Guests have complimentary use of the nearby David Lloyd sports and leisure club. Families are made welcome with helpful amenities provided; children up to the age of 7 are accommodated free in parents' room. The middle range of De Vere's range of hotels in Eastbourne. **Rooms 112.** *Games room.* Access, Amex, Visa, Diners Club

Eastbourne   Grand Hotel   75%   £150

| Tel 0323 412345   Fax 0323 412233 |
HR

King Edward's Parade Eastbourne East Sussex BN21 4EQ   **Map 7 B6**

Sound management and smart, committed staff try hard to keep up the
grand image and reputation for good service at a whitewashed, seafront
establishment that dates back to Victorian times. Marble pillars, crystal
chandeliers, vast corridors and high-domed day rooms evoke a more
leisurely, bygone age of spacious and gracious hotels. Some of the sea-facing
bedrooms have balconies and are huge, with bright furniture and up-to-
date fabrics, but not all are as smart or as generous in size. 24hr room
service, comprehensive leisure and exercise facilities, themed weekend
breaks and children's hostesses keep the Grand apace with its more modern
competitors. Families well catered for. De Vere. **Rooms 164.** *Garden, indoor
& outdoor swimming pools, spa bath, sauna, solarium, beauty & hairdressing
salons, keep-fit equipment, snooker. Access, Amex, Visa,* ①

Mirabelle Restaurant   ↑   £67

Chef Keith Mitchell produces imaginative menus executed with flair and
served by polished and professional staff in elegant surroundings. Fixed-
price lunch (2- or 3-course) and dinner (4-course, priced by choice of main
course) menus offer a small choice of dishes like crab bisque, a ragout of
sole and mussels with carrots and coriander, a daily roast served from a
silver trolley, smoked haddock, salmon and crab cakes with a tomato and
chive compote, or English lamb chump chop topped with a leek and onion
soubise and a rosemary jus. In addition, an à la carte offers classic dishes
with modern touches – try sautéed slices of milk-fed calf's liver served with
a balsamic vinegar, spring onion and ginger wine sauce or a trio of English
lamb medallions with basil, tarragon and lovage mousselines and a tomato
jus. Cheeses are accompanied by home-made bread and there's a choice of
classic desserts such as glazed lime chiboust with citrus fruits and ginger, or
a grand chocolate temptation. Longish list of wines inlcudes half a dozen
English wines and a choice of 16 brandies by the glass. **Seats 50. Parties 50.**
*Private Room. L 12.30-2.30 D 7-10.30. Closed Sun & Mon, Bank Holidays,
2 weeks Jan, 2 weeks Aug. Set L from £13 Set D from £19.50.*

Eastbourne   Queen's Hotel   67%   £93

| Tel 0323 22822   Fax 0323 31056 |
H

Marine Parade Eastbourne East Sussex BN21 3DY   **Map 7 B6**

Large white Victorian-built hotel overlooking the pier and sea. Equally
popular for conferences (up to 300 delegates) and leisure visits. Good free
parking. De Vere. **Rooms 108.** *Games room (summer). Access, Amex,
Visa,* ①

Eastbourne   Wish Tower Hotel   66%   £90

| Tel 0323 22676   Fax 0323 21474 |
H

King Edward's Parade Eastbourne East Sussex BN21 4EB   **Map 7 B6**

The hotel stands on the seafront overlooking the Wish Tower, a martello
tower that is now a Napoleonic and World War II museum. Bedrooms are
in attractively up-to-date style, with modern comforts like double-glazing,
and many enjoy sea views. Children up to 14 stay free in parents' room.
Conference facilities for up to 60. Principal Hotels. **Rooms 65.** *Access,
Amex, Visa,* ①

Eastbourne   Places of Interest

Tourist Information   Tel 0323 411400.
Michelham Priory   Upper Dicker, Nr Hailsham Tel 0323 844224.
Towner Art Gallery and Local History Museum   Tel 0323 411688.
Tower No 73   (The Wish Tower) Tel 0323 410440.
Eastbourne and Bexhill Beaches.
Devonshire Park Centre (Tennis)   Tel 0323 415400.

Theatres and Concert Halls
Congress Theatre Devonshire Park Tel 0323 410000.
Devonshire Park Theatre Tel 0323 410000.
Royal Hippodrome Theatre Tel 0323 410000.

Eastleigh Forte Crest Southampton 66% £87
Tel 0703 619700 Fax 0703 643945 H
Leigh Road Passfield Avenue Eastleigh Hampshire SO5 5PG Map 5 D3

Modern low-rise hotel just off A34. Features include a business centre and a new leisure centre. Children's playground. *Rooms 120. Indoor swimming pool, spa bath, steam room, beauty salon. Access, Amex, Visa,* ◐ Diners Club International

---

Eastleigh Forte Travelodge £40
Tel 0703 616813 L
Twyford Road Eastleigh Nr Southampton Hampshire Map 5 D3

On the Twyford Road, off the A335. 5 miles north of Southampton and 6 miles south of Winchester. *Rooms 32. Access, Amex, Visa.*

Easton Clarke's £50
Tel 0603 880241 R
Dereham Road Easton Norwich Norfolk NR9 5AH Map 6 C1

Adrian and Rachael Clarke, who made a name for themselves at the *Fox & Goose*, Fressingfield, run a cheerful little restaurant on the A47, six miles out of Norwich. A la carte and set menus provide plenty of good eating, from seafood pancake or lamb's sweetbreads with a cream and French mustard sauce to grilled brill with lemon and parsley butter, breast of duck with blackcurrant sauce and veal escalopes cooked in a cognac, cream, mushroom and tarragon sauce. *Seats 50. Parties 50. Private Room. L 12-2 D 7-9.30. Closed D Sun, all Mon, 1 Jan. Set meals from £13.50. Access, Amex, Visa,* ◐ Diners Club International

---

Easton Grey Whatley Manor 73% £109
Tel 0666 822888 Fax 0666 826120 H
Easton Grey Malmesbury Wiltshire SN16 0RB Map 4 B2

Fine gardens, a terrace looking down the Avon valley and various leisure facilities in the grounds are among the many attractions of this delightful ivy-clad Cotswold manor house. A flagstone-floored foyer, library bar and a spacious pine-panelled drawing room are stylish without being intimidating, with log fires, antiques and scatter rugs contributing to the country house charm. Private dining areas accommodate 80 (conferences for 65), discreetly separate from the day rooms. Manor House, Tudor and Terrace wings accommodate a dozen of the best bedrooms, while in the more secluded Court House (where tea-makers replace room service) ten are conveniently located on the ground floor. *Rooms 29. Garden, croquet, outdoor swimming pool, sauna, solarium, spa bath, games room, fishing, helipad. Access, Amex, Visa,* ◐ Diners Club International

---

Eccleshall St George Hotel £55
Tel 0785 850300 Fax 0785 851452 I
Castle Street Eccleshall Staffordshire ST21 6DF Map 10 B3

Behind the white-painted frontage of this 17th-century coaching inn is a mixture of modern and old that includes a well-equipped business centre and an inglenook fireplace in the bar – the focal point of the inn, with old beams and copper-topped tables. Bedrooms are kept in immaculate order and have plenty of character, some with fireplaces and exposed timbers. Small conferences are held in the first-floor Old Library room with bare brick walls and beams. *Rooms 10. Access, Amex, Visa,* ◐ Diners Club International

Edenbridge　　Honours Mill Restaurant　　£60

Tel 0732 866757　　**R**

87 High Street Edenbridge Kent TN8 5AU　　Map 5 F3

A converted mill is the charming setting for some careful French cooking from the kitchen of Martin Radmall. Well-balanced fixed-price menus are inclusive of coffee, petits fours and service; on weekday evenings an additional £25 menu is offered with simpler dishes and a smaller choice plus a half bottle of wine. Casserole of mussels with fennel, Roquefort soufflé, noisette of lamb with cepes wrapped in leeks and roast duck with Chinese spices demonstrate the range. Desserts might include both tarte aux poires and summer pudding. The New World misses out on the otherwise decent wine list. *Seats 38. Parties 40. L 12.15-2 D 7.15-10. Closed L Sat, D Sun, all Mon, 1 week Xmas. Set L £14.50 (Sun £22.50) Set D £25/£31.75. Access, Visa,*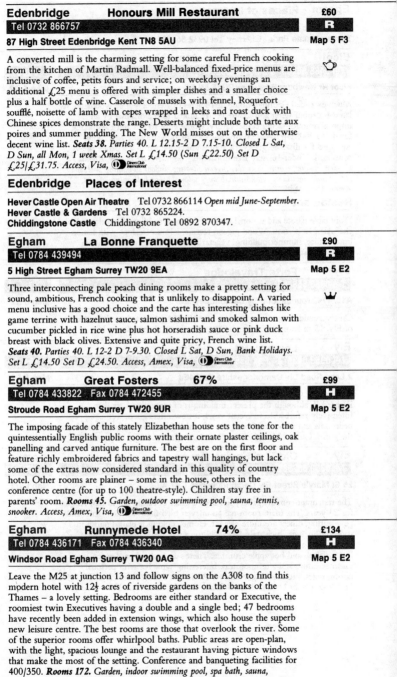

Edenbridge　　Places of Interest

Hever Castle Open Air Theatre　Tel 0732 866114 *Open mid June-September.*
Hever Castle & Gardens　Tel 0732 865224.
Chiddingstone Castle　Chiddingstone Tel 0892 870347.

Egham　　La Bonne Franquette　　£90

Tel 0784 439494　　**R**

5 High Street Egham Surrey TW20 9EA　　Map 5 E2

Three interconnecting pale peach dining rooms make a pretty setting for sound, ambitious, French cooking that is unlikely to disappoint. A varied menu inclusive has a good choice and the carte has interesting dishes like game terrine with hazelnut sauce, salmon sashimi and smoked salmon with cucumber pickled in rice wine plus hot horseradish sauce or pink duck breast with black olives. Extensive and quite pricy, French wine list. *Seats 40. Parties 40. L 12-2 D 7-9.30. Closed L Sat, D Sun, Bank Holidays. Set L £14.50 Set D £24.50. Access, Amex, Visa,*

Egham　　Great Fosters　　67%　　£99

Tel 0784 433822　Fax 0784 472455　　**H**

Stroude Road Egham Surrey TW20 9UR　　Map 5 E2

The imposing facade of this stately Elizabethan house sets the tone for the quintessentially English public rooms with their ornate plaster ceilings, oak panelling and carved antique furniture. The best are on the first floor and feature richly embroidered fabrics and tapestry wall hangings, but lack some of the extras now considered standard in this quality of country hotel. Other rooms are plainer – some in the house, others in the conference centre (for up to 100 theatre-style). Children stay free in parents' room. *Rooms 45. Garden, outdoor swimming pool, sauna, tennis, snooker. Access, Amex, Visa,*

Egham　　Runnymede Hotel　　74%　　£134

Tel 0784 436171　Fax 0784 436340　　**H**

Windsor Road Egham Surrey TW20 0AG　　Map 5 E2

Leave the M25 at junction 13 and follow signs on the A308 to find this modern hotel with 12½ acres of riverside gardens on the banks of the Thames – a lovely setting. Bedrooms are either standard or Executive, the roomiest twin Executives having a double and a single bed; 47 bedrooms have recently been added in extension wings, which also house the superb new leisure centre. The best rooms are those that overlook the river. Some of the superior rooms offer whirlpool baths. Public areas are open-plan, with the light, spacious lounge and the restaurant having picture windows that make the most of the setting. Conference and banqueting facilities for 400/350. *Rooms 172. Garden, indoor swimming pool, spa bath, sauna, solarium, beauty and hair salon, tennis, coarse fishing, croquet, putting, helipad. Access, Amex, Visa,*

Egham   Places of Interest

Guards Polo Club   Windsor Great Park, Englefield Green Tel 0784 434212.
Thorpe Theme Park   Chertsey Tel 0932 569393.

Elcot   Elcot Park   67%   £105

Tel 0488 58100   Fax 0488 58288   **HR**

Elcot Nr Newbury Berkshire RG16 8NJ   Map 5 D2

Much-extended Georgian house in 16 acres of Kennet Valley woodland, its
latest bedroom wing and leisure centre linked to the original by an
impressive south-facing conservatory. Conference rooms and banqueting
for up to 200. Up-to-date bedrooms include non-smoking and rooms
equipped for disabled guests. 18 rooms are contained in a separate mews
courtyard. Under-16s stay free in parents' room. Resort Hotels. *Rooms 75.*
Garden, croquet, tennis, laser clay-pigeon shooting, indoor swimming pool, spa
bath, sauna, solarium, gymnasium, beauty salon, hot-air ballooning. Access,
Amex, Visa, 💳 *Diners Club International*

Restaurant

Daily table d'hote and seasonal carte in the modern idiom from dependable
chef Alex Robertson. Wood pigeon terrine, salmon escalope with lemon
butter sauce, summer pudding, vegetarian choices, regional farmhouse
cheeses and speciality teas.

Ely   Forte Travelodge   £40

Tel 0353 668499   **L**

A10/A142 roundabout Ely Cambridgeshire   Map 6 B2

On the roundabout at the junction of A10/A142. Situated on the outskirts
of Ely, 15 miles north of Cambridge. *Rooms 39. Access, Amex, Visa.*

Ely   Lamb Hotel   62%   £75

Tel 0353 663574   Fax 0353 666350   **H**

2 Lynn Road Ely Cambridgeshire CB7 4EJ   Map 6 B2

Close to the Cathedral, the Lamb can trace its history back to the reign of
Richard II, although the present building is of somewhat later date.
Intensively refurbished in recent years, it now offers good, well-equipped
bedrooms and a choice of bars, one of which (the Fenman) is popular with
the locals. Queens Moat Houses. *Rooms 32. Access, Amex, Visa,* 💳 *Diners Club International*

Ely   Old Fire Engine House   £50

Tel 0353 662582   **R**

25 St Mary's Street Ely Cambridgeshire CB7 4ER   Map 6 B2

The restaurant-cum-art gallery has been a pillar of eating out in East Anglia
for 24 years. The main room has an uneven tiled floor, kitchen tables and
pew seating, others are more elegant. Home cooking is plain English in
style and includes such stalwarts as Stilton soup, steak and kidney pie,
jugged hare and duck with orange sauce. The style continues with sweets
like syllabub and hot apple crumble. There's an orchard garden for
summer eating and afternoon teas. Interesting wine list with personal
tasting notes. No smoking. *Seats 60. Parties 40. Private Room. L 12.30-2*
D 7.30-9. Closed D Sun, Bank Holidays, 2 weeks Xmas/New Year. Access,
Visa.

Ely   Places of Interest

Tourist Information   Tel 0353 662062.
Ely Cathedral   Tel 0353 667735.
  Museums and Art Galleries
Ely Museum   Tel 0353 666655.
The Stained Glass Museum   North Triforium, Ely Cathedral Tel 0223
  327367.
Oliver Cromwell's House   Tel 0353 662062.

Emsworth	36 On The Quay	↑	£74

Tel 0243 375592   **R**

The Quay South Street Emsworth Hampshire PO10 7EG   Map 5 D4

A pretty pale yellow restaurant in a cottagey old building right down by
the quay. Everything is of the best quality here, from stylish silver-plated
cutlery to elegant china. With new chef Frank Eckermann has come a new
menu format with a frequently-changing menu gastronomique (unusually
offering a small choice in most courses) that is proving even more popular
than the seasonally based à la carte. A lot of attention is given to
presentation, with vegetables often served as a garnish with the main dish,
thus pleasing the eye in advance of the palate. Lobster and scallop
mousseline garnished with real caviar on a champagne and chive sauce,
rack of new season's lamb with cream of tarragon sauce, and a millefeuille
of wild salmon and turbot are typical dishes; desserts might be a délice of
apricots or aspic of red summer fruits and oranges. *Seats 45. Parties 12.
Private Room. L 12-2 D 7-10. Closed L Sat, all Sun, Bank Holidays, 1 week
Jan, 2 weeks Sep. Set D from £27.50. Access, Amex, Visa,* Diners Club International

Epping	Forte Posthouse	63%	£63

Tel 0992 573137   Fax 0992 560402   **H**

High Road Bell Common Epping Essex CM16 4DG   Map 7 B4

16th-century heritage still shows in the public rooms; bedrooms are in a
modern wing. Banqueting for 85, conferences facilities for 100. *Rooms 79.
Access, Amex, Visa,* Diners Club International

Erpingham	Ark		£45

Tel 0263 761535   **RR**

The Street Erpingham Norfolk NR11 7QB   Map 6 C1

An old flint cottage set deep in rural Norfolk four miles north of
Aylesham off the A140. Sheila Kidd is self-taught and her traditional and
modern British cooking (Dover sole with parsley and anchovy butter) has
French (Provencal beef daube), Italian (fennel risotto) and Greek (sautéed
squid with lemon and garlic) influences. Fresh local ingredients are used
whenever possible, and many of the vegetables and herbs come from her
garden. Vegetarian dishes available. Several good bottles under £20 on the
wine list. No smoking. *Seats 28. L (Sun only) 12.30-2 D 7-9.30 (Sat to 10).
Closed D Sun & Mon, all Tue in winter, part of Oct. Sun L £11.
No credit cards.*

Rooms   £85

Three bedrooms, two with en-suite facilities, are available for overnight
stays, but only to non-smokers.

Esher	Good Earth		£50

Tel 0372 462489   **R**

14-18 High Street Esher Surrey KT10 9RT   Map 5 E3

Reliable cooking in comfortable surroundings, with speedy, attentive
service. The China-wide menu sticks mainly to familiar items, with the
occasional slightly less usual dish such as salmon steak (steamed or pan-
fried), Szechuan-style veal or a vegetarian combination called faked yellow

fish comprising mashed split peas, Chinese mushrooms and spring onions.
*See also outlets under London section. Seats 95. Parties 80. L 12-2.30
D 6-11.15 (Sun 12.30-10.30). Closed 24-27 Dec. Set D from £16.00. Access,
Amex, Visa,* ○ *Diners Club International*

Esher   Places of Interest

Chessington World of Adventures   Tel 0372 727227.
Claremont Landscape Garden (NT)   Tel 0372 69421.
Kempton Park Racecourse   Tel 0932 782292.
Sandown Park Racecourse   Tel 0372 463072.
Ham Polo Club   20 Queens Road Tel 081 398 3263.
Sandown Ski School   Tel 0372 65588.

Eton   Antico

Tel 0753 863977

42 High Street Eton Berkshire SL4 6BD

£55

R

Map 5 E2

Long-established Italian ristorante with traditional menu in characterful
18th-century building in the High Street. Booking advisable. *Seats 65.
L 12.30-2.30 D 7-10.30. Closed L Sat, all Sun, Bank Holidays. Access, Amex,
Visa,* ○ *Diners Club International*

Eton   Christopher Hotel

Tel 0753 852359   Fax 0753 830914

110 High Street Eton Berkshire SL4 6AN

£80

I

Map 5 E2

Former coaching inn on the High Street. Best bedrooms are in the main
house, others in courtyard chalets that are being redecorated. There are two
bars and a patio. Children up to the age of 12 are free in their parents'
room. Dogs in courtyard rooms only. *Rooms 34. Access, Amex, Visa,*
○ *Diners Club International*

Evershot   Summer Lodge   72%

Tel 0935 83424   Fax 0935 83005

Evershot Dorchester Dorset DT2 0JR

£130

HR

Map 4 B4

Nigel and Margaret Corbett's peaceful Georgian home, with its picturesque
sheltered garden, is a haven for outdoor types. There are miles of walks
through Hardy country; grass and hard tennis courts and a heated outdoor
swimming pool; guests can even hunt with the Cattistock. Fresh garden
flowers embellish the lounge, bar and reading room, bedecked with
pictures and ornaments to create a home from home. Spacious bedrooms
with rattan furniture, armchair and settee have a similarly sunny feel, and
the bathrooms are spotless. Arrive in time for home-baked afternoon tea
and don't leave without sampling the super country breakfast. Private
meetings by arrangement (max 25). No children under eight. *Rooms 17.
Outdoor swimming pool, tennis, croquet. Closed 2 weeks Jan. Access, Visa.*

Restaurant

£78

Dinner is a candle-lit affair overseen by an effusive Nigel Corbett, whose
manner contrasts with that of the demure waitresses. A single soup
(excellent creamy carrot and orange served from a tureen) separates a
decent choice of starters and main courses from the fixed-price menu. Pan-
fried monkfish with tomato and ginger coulis and chargrilled fillet of lamb
(accompanied on a recent visit by a too-sharp mint béarnaise tartlet) are
typical choices. High marks for the lovely bread rolls, the fine board of
local English cheeses and some delicious desserts, including a faultless hot
caramel soufflé accompanied by a side plate of brandy and honey ice
cream. The wine list is splendidly easy to use and has a good selection of
half bottles. *Seats 50. Private Room. L 12.30-1.30 D 7.30-9. Set L from
£17.50 Set D £32.50.*

Eversley · New Mill Restaurant · £75
Tel 0734 732277   Fax 0734 328780 · R
New Mill Road Eversley Hampshire RG27 0RA · Map 5 D2

A converted riverside mill house complete with ducks, waterwheel and an idyllic setting. The Blackwater river runs gently by the restaurant, which boasts an open fire place, wood-panelled ceilings and exposed beams. Robert Allen's cooking is in a modern style that reflects the disciplines he learned at *The Dorchester* and *Hintlesham Hall*: basil and sweet pepper gateau with fresh scallops, glazed goat's cheese on a bed of spinach with smoked bacon and pine kernels, tender rib-eye steak with shallot and red wine sauce, and medallions of monkfish filled with salmon on a bed of leeks. A trio of well-constructed patés (comprising a rich chicken liver version, a rabbit and pigeon roulade and a fish terrine wrapped in leek with pistachios) is served with redcurrant jelly and is typical of the attention to detail shown in the cooking. Hot apples with honey and cinnamon in a puff pastry shell and English custard, sticky toffee pudding and warm eau de vie-soaked fruits glazed with Amaretto sabayon are popular desserts. Good trolley of British cheeses served with home-made walnut bread. The less formal, beamed *Grill Room* offers equally admirable food at more down-to-earth prices, including a good roast at Sunday lunchtimes. Serious wine list, carefully chosen, with helpful notes. **Seats 80.** *Parties 110. Private Room. L 12-2 D 7-10 (Grill Room: Sun 12.30-8). Restaurant closed L Sat, all Sun & Mon. Grill Room closed L Sat, 26 & 27 Dec, 1 Jan. Set L £19.50 Set D £25.50. Access, Amex, Visa,* Diners Club International

Evesham · Evesham Hotel · 62% · £90
Tel 0386 765566   Fax 0386 765443 · H
Cooper's Lane Evesham Hereford & Worcester WR11 6DA · Map 4 C1

The first and enduring impression of the Jenkinson family's modernised Tudor mansion set in 2½ acres (dominated by a large old cedar of Lebanon) is of fun, friendliness and a truly relaxed atmosphere. That feeling starts in the foyer, continues in the chintzy bar and is still strong in the bedrooms which are provided with all sorts of extras, from games and cards to teddy bears and rubber ducks. The whole caboodle is mildly eccentric and very friendly towards families. **Rooms 40.** *Garden, indoor swimming pool, croquet. Closed 25 & 26 Dec. Access, Amex, Visa,* Diners Club International

Evesham · Riverside Hotel · 68% · £72
Tel 0386 446200   Fax 0386 40021 · HR
The Parks Offenham Road Evesham Hereford & Worcester WR11 5JP · Map 4 C1

Check directions when booking, as this white pebbledash house is awkward to find. It is run by the amiable Willmotts and stands in three acres by the river Avon. On entering, a colourful fresco of river life greets guests, while downstairs an attractive lounge is decorated in corals and greens with plenty of comfortable seating. Bedrooms, with river views, are pretty and appealing, soft colours and co-ordinated fabrics being well employed. Staff are smartly attired, keen and obviously enjoy their jobs. No dogs. **Rooms 7.** *Garden. Access, Visa.*

Restaurant · £55

Fine views over the river Avon from the dining room, where Rosemary Willmott offers fixed-price, hand-written, daily-changing menus with a good choice of dishes that might encompass hot chicken livers with bacon, garlic and cream, fresh salmon and tarragon fishcakes, brill with fresh asparagus, prawn and cheese sauce, and herb-crumbed rack of local lamb with garlic-tossed courgettes. Straightforward fare, interestingly cooked and presented. Lunch snacks in the bar (except Sundays). The list of liqueurs, Highland and Island malt whiskies, Armagnacs and eaux-de vie is exceptional. **Seats 40.** *Parties 48. L 12-2 (Sun to 1.30) D 7.30-9. Closed D Sun, all Mon. Set L £14.50 (£15.95 Sun) Set D £17.95.*

Evesham   Places of Interest

Tourist Information   Tel 0386 446944.
Snowshill Manor (NT)   Broadway Tel 0386 852410.

Exeter	**Buckerell Lodge**	66%	£74

Tel 0392 52451   Fax 0392 412114

H

157 Topsham Road Exeter Devon EX2 4SQ

Map 3 D2

A much-extended Regency house set in peaceful grounds a mile from the town centre. Bedrooms include Executive, Lady Executive and one with a spa bath. Children up to 12 stay free in parents' room. Meeting rooms and a purpose-built conference centre (for up to 60 delegates). *Rooms 54. Garden. Access, Amex, Visa,* ⓘ *Diners Club International*

Exeter	**Forte Crest**	69%	£91

Tel 0392 412812   Fax 0392 413549

H

Southern Hay East Exeter Devon EX1 1QF

Map 3 D2

1989-built hotel with cathedral views from some of the bedrooms. Conference facilities for up to 180 delegates. *Rooms 110. Indoor swimming pool, gymnasium, sauna, spa bath, solarium. Access, Amex, Visa,* ⓘ *Diners Club International*

Exeter	**Rougemont Hotel**	63%	£79

Tel 0392 54982   Fax 0392 420928

H

Queen Street Exeter Devon EX4 3SP

Map 3 D2

Modernised Victorian hotel in the city centre. Its popular conference facilities include five suites for up to 300. Mount Charlotte Thistle. *Rooms 90. Access, Amex, Visa,* ⓘ *Diners Club International*

Exeter	**Royal Clarence**	71%	£95

Tel 0392 58464   Fax 0392 439423

H

Cathedral Yard Exeter Devon EX1 1HD

Map 3 D2

Overlooking Exeter Cathedral, spectacularly floodlit at night, the Royal Clarence claims to be the first inn in Britain to receive the title "hotel". Behind its Georgian facade the building contains several architectural styles and retains an atmosphere steeped in the past. Every one of the bedrooms is in Tudor, Georgian or Victorian style. A wealth of oak panelling, moulded friezes and covings, gilt-framed mirrors and period furniture contrive to unify the theme. By comparison, bathrooms are thoroughly modern, though smallish. The stately Georgian-style Clarence Room accommodates conferences and banquets for up to 150. No dogs. Queens Moat Houses. *Rooms 56. Access, Amex, Visa,* ⓘ *Diners Club International*

Exeter	**White Hart**	61%	£78

Tel 0392 79897   Fax 0392 50159

H

South Street Exeter Devon EX1 1EE

Map 3 D2

Owned by Davy's Wine Bars, an ancient inn at the heart of town, dating from the 15th century and originally a resting place for monks. Built around an attractive cobbled courtyard, off which are various bars where exposed beams timbers and bulging walls abound. The residents' lounge in the oldest part sports an uneven and unusual plasterwork ceiling. Most bedrooms are in a modern extension and have a purpose-built look with functional fitted units. Six rooms have shower and WC only. *Bottlescrue Bill's* Wine Bar is off the car park and the cobbled wine garden comes into its own during good weather. Banquets/conferences for 60/70. *Rooms 61. Access, Amex, Visa,* ⓘ *Diners Club International*

Exeter   Places of Interest

Tourist Information   Tel 0392 265297.
The Barnfield Theatre   Tel 0392 21951.
Northcott Theatre   Stocker Road Tel 0392 56181.
Exeter Maritime Museum   The Haven Tel 0392 58075.
Exeter Cathedral   Tel 0392 55573.
Exeter Racecourse   Tel 0392 832599.
Exeter Ski Club   Tel 0392 211322.
Westpoint Showground   Tel 0392 444777.
   Historic Houses, Castles and Gardens
Killerton (NT)   Tel 0392 881345.
University of Exeter Garden   Tel 0392 263263.
Bickleigh Castle   Tel 08845 363 *13 miles.*

Exmouth	Imperial Hotel	60%	£101
Tel & Fax 0395 274761			**H**
The Esplanade Exmouth Devon EX8 2SW			Map 3 E3

Popular whitewashed Forte Heritage holiday hotel on the esplanade.
Conference/banqueting facilities for 40. Children up to the age of 16 free
in parents' room. *Rooms 57. Garden, outdoor swimming pool, tennis. Access,
Amex, Visa,* (I) Diners Club International

Exmouth   Places of Interest

Budleigh Salterton Beach.

Eyton	Marsh Country Hotel	67%	£100
Tel 0568 613952			**HR**
Eyton Leominster Hereford & Worcester HR6 0AG			Map 4 A1

Just north of Leominster, a haven of peace and tranquillity standing in an
acre or so of award-winning gardens. Martin and Jacqueline Gilleland run
the house on informal and personable lines, greeting guests at their
delightful home. Dating from the 14th century, the old hall is now a
splendid lounge, sympathetically furnished and immensely relaxing.
Bedrooms, all named after birds, are smallish but stylish, with pretty fabrics
and pine furniture. The whole place has a wonderfully relaxed air and
housekeeping is immaculate. Characterful conference rooms for up to 30.
No dogs. *Rooms 5. Garden. Access, Visa.*

Restaurant   £70

Quality home cooking served in a pretty restaurant with garden views.
Fixed-price menus offer the likes of chicken and asparagus soup, smoked
mackerel puffs with fennel and cucumber, prawn mousse wrapped in
smoked salmon, breast of duck in port and orange sauce, and fillet of beef
with tomato and onion. Simple sweets like fresh pineapple with Kirsch ice
cream. No smoking. *Seats 24. Parties 24. L by arrangement D 7.30-9.30.
Set D £27.50.*

Fairford	Bull Hotel	60%	£50
Tel 0285 712535 Fax 0285 713782			**H**
Market Place Fairford Gloucestershire GL7 4AA			Map 4 C2

Fishing rights on the river Coln are an attraction at an ancient inn that was
once a monk's changing house (there's still a secret underground passage
connecting to the church). The bar boasts stone walls, low beams and log
fires, and there's a homely little lounge. Corridors and many bedrooms
feature sloping floors, oak beams and low ceilings. Now owned by Arkell's
Brewery. No dogs. *Rooms 20. Garden, coarse and game fishing. Access,
Amex, Visa,* (I) Diners Club International

Fairford — Hyperion House — 63% — £70

Tel 0285 712349   Fax 0285 713126

H

London Street Fairford Gloucestershire GL7 4AH

Map 4 C2

A comfortable, Cotswold-stone establishment on the A417 Cirencester to Burford road. The hotel takes its name from the 1933 Derby winner, and the bar and restaurant have a racing theme. Bedrooms, all doubles, twin or triples, include Executive rooms offering the most space. Children up to 12 stay free in parents' room. *Rooms 27. Garden. Access, Amex, Visa,*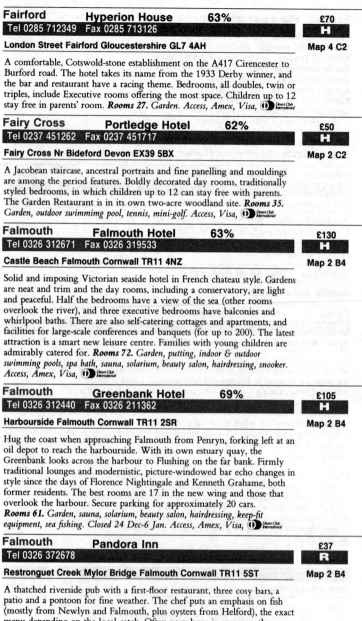

Fairy Cross — Portledge Hotel — 62% — £50

Tel 0237 451262   Fax 0237 451717

H

Fairy Cross Nr Bideford Devon EX39 5BX

Map 2 C2

A Jacobean staircase, ancestral portraits and fine panelling and mouldings are among the period features. Boldly decorated day rooms, traditionally styled bedrooms, in which children up to 12 can stay free with parents. The Garden Restaurant is in its own two-acre woodland site. *Rooms 35. Garden, outdoor swimmimg pool, tennis, mini-golf. Access, Visa,*

Falmouth — Falmouth Hotel — 63% — £130

Tel 0326 312671   Fax 0326 319533

H

Castle Beach Falmouth Cornwall TR11 4NZ

Map 2 B4

Solid and imposing Victorian seaside hotel in French chateau style. Gardens are neat and trim and the day rooms, including a conservatory, are light and peaceful. Half the bedrooms have a view of the sea (other rooms overlook the river), and three executive bedrooms have balconies and whirlpool baths. There are also self-catering cottages and apartments, and facilities for large-scale conferences and banquets (for up to 200). The latest attraction is a smart new leisure centre. Families with young children are admirably catered for. *Rooms 72. Garden, putting, indoor & outdoor swimming pools, spa bath, sauna, solarium, beauty salon, hairdressing, snooker. Access, Amex, Visa,*

Falmouth — Greenbank Hotel — 69% — £105

Tel 0326 312440   Fax 0326 211362

H

Harbourside Falmouth Cornwall TR11 2SR

Map 2 B4

Hug the coast when approaching Falmouth from Penryn, forking left at an oil depot to reach the harbourside. With its own estuary quay, the Greenbank looks across the harbour to Flushing on the far bank. Firmly traditional lounges and modernistic, picture-windowed bar echo changes in style since the days of Florence Nightingale and Kenneth Grahame, both former residents. The best rooms are 17 in the new wing and those that overlook the harbour. Secure parking for approximately 20 cars. *Rooms 61. Garden, sauna, solarium, beauty salon, hairdressing, keep-fit equipment, sea fishing. Closed 24 Dec-6 Jan. Access, Amex, Visa,*

Falmouth — Pandora Inn — £37

Tel 0326 372678

R

Restronguet Creek Mylor Bridge Falmouth Cornwall TR11 5ST

Map 2 B4

A thatched riverside pub with a first-floor restaurant, three cosy bars, a patio and a pontoon for fine weather. The chef puts an emphasis on fish (mostly from Newlyn and Falmouth, plus oysters from Helford), the exact menu depending on the local catch. Often very busy in summer, the restaurant is sometimes closed in winter. Ask for directions when booking. *Seats 40. Parties 60. Private Room. D only 7-10 (Sun to 9.30). Access, Visa.*

Falmouth   St Michael's Hotel   65%   £82

Tel 0326 312707   Fax 0326 211772   **H**

Gyllingvase Beach Seafront Falmouth Cornwall TR11 4NB   Map 2 B4

Within yards of the beach, St Michael's is a holiday resort hotel and
conference centre (for up to 150 delegates) with a self-contained leisure
complex. It's well set up for family holidays, including 15 family-size
bedrooms, baby-sitting and baby-listening, a children's menu, high chairs,
high teas and a children's activity organiser during school holidays.
*Rooms 73. Garden, indoor swimming pool, keep-fit equipment, spa bath, sauna,
water sports. Access, Amex, Visa,*

Falmouth   Seafood Bar   £45

Tel 0326 315129   **R**

Lower Quay Hill Falmouth Cornwall   Map 2 B4

Down a few steps in a steep passageway leading to the quay, this chaotic
dive serves the very freshest of fish; the range is from crab and watercress
soup and moules marinière to carpetbagger steak (an oyster in its 'pocket')
and medallions of monkfish with ginger, sherry and green peppercorns.
*Seats 24. Parties 12. D only 7-11. Closed Sun & Mon, also Tue & Wed in
winter, 10 days Xmas. Access, Visa.*

Falmouth   Places of Interest

Tourist Information   Tel 0326 312300.
Falmouth Arts Centre   Church Street Tel 0326 314566.
Princess Pavillion   Melville Road Tel 0326 311277.

Fareham   Red Lion   57%   £81

Tel 0329 822640   Fax 0329 823579   **H**

East Street Fareham Hampshire PO16 0BP   Map 5 D4

A Lansbury Group hotel equidistant from Portsmouth and Southampton.
Originally a coaching inn, it still has some period character. Conferences
facilities for up to 120. No dogs. *Rooms 44. Garden, sauna. Access, Amex,
Visa,*

Fareham   Solent Hotel   75%   £101

Tel 0489 880000   Fax 0489 880007   **H**

Solent Business Park Whiteley Fareham Hampshire PO15 7AJ   Map 5 D4

Adjacent to junction 9 of M27 (10 miles from both Portsmouth and
Southampton), a modern hotel that successfully balances the contrasting
needs for conference trade (for up to 200 delegates), leisure breaks and
single businessmen. The three functions are separated physically in the
building's design, but high standards of service do not exclude one at the
expense of another. All of the bedrooms are of executive standard, in
traditional style, with both working and relaxing space and comprehensive
comforts from bathrobes to mini-bars. Suites accommodate syndicate,
business and interview requirements in the week and have ample space for
families at weekends; children up to 15 are accommodated free in parents'
room. Baby sitting, baby listening, cots and a children's menu plus high
chairs in the restaurant are all available. Committed young staff and expert
management show good direction throughout. Shire Inns. *Rooms 90.
Indoor swimming pool, whirlpool bath, children's splash pool, sauna, steam room,
solarium, keep-fit equipment, squash, snooker. Access, Amex, Visa,*

Fareham   Places of Interest

Tourist Information   Tel 0329 221342.
Titchfield Abbey   Titchfield Tel 0329 43016.

Farnborough	Forte Crest	66%	£97

Tel 0252 545051   Fax 0252 377210   **H**

Lynchford Road Farnborough Hampshire GU14 6AZ   Map 5 E3

Handsome Edwardian building alongside A325. Day rooms have period
appeal, bedrooms are mainly modern. Banqueting and conference facilities
for 200. **Rooms 110.** *Indoor swimming pool, keep-fit equipment, spa bath,
solarium, beauty salon. Access, Amex, Visa,*

Farnham	Bishop's Table Hotel	62%	£81

Tel 0252 710222   Fax 0252 733494   **H**

27 West Street Farnham Surrey GU9 7DR   Map 5 E3

A small, Georgian town-centre hotel with individually decorated
bedrooms, most now including some antique furniture and French pine
beds. Kass and Mariam Verjee, a brother and sister team, run the place in
friendly style. Peaceful, secluded garden with a magnificent cedar tree to
the rear. Children up to 14 free in parents' room. **Rooms 18.** *Garden. Closed
1 week Xmas/New Year. Access, Amex, Visa,*

Farnham	Bush Hotel	62%	£101

Tel 0252 715237   Fax 0252 733530   **H**

The Borough Farnham Surrey GU9 7NN   Map 5 E3

17th-century buildings cluster around a cobbled courtyard at a well-kept
Forte hotel in the town centre. Most bedrooms are in a newer wing that
overlooks the garden. **Rooms 68.** *Garden, coffee shop (10am-6pm). Access,
Amex, Visa,*

Farnham	Krug's		£55

Tel 0252 723277   **R**

84 West Street Farnham Surrey GU9 7EN   Map 5 E3

A homely Austrian restaurant with a stag's head, log-burning stove and
Alpine folksy tablecloths setting the scene for Gerhard Krug's competent
and authentic national cooking. Dinner proceeds at a leisurely pace and
dishes such as game soup, knuckle of venison with rösti and noodles or
smoked pork bratwurst and dumplings on sauerkraut reflect the style. Fine
home-cooked desserts include pancakes filled with apricot purée and praline
or cinnamon-laced apfelstrüdel. The sign over the door reads "wine for
truth, beer for strength and water for germs"; the beer is draught
Warsteiner. **Seats 85.** *Parties 60. Private Room. L 12-2.30 D 7-11.30. Closed
L Sat, all Sun & Mon, Bank Holidays. Set L £8. Access, Visa.*

Farnham	Trevena House	59%	£59

Tel 0252 716908   Fax 0252 722583   **H**

Alton Road Farnham Surrey GU10 5ER   Map 5 E3

Look out for the sign and the tree-lined drive on the A31, a mile from
Farnham towards Winchester. The house has a Tudor/Gothic appearance,
and public areas are in a similar style with a huge stone fireplace in the
foyer/lounge and a nice ribbed ceiling in the comfortable, panelled bar.
Bedrooms offer modest comforts and the general atmosphere is relaxed
and friendly. **Rooms 20.** *Garden, croquet, tennis.
Access, Amex, Visa,*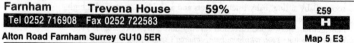

Farnham   Places of Interest

Farnham Tourist Information   Tel 0252 715109.
Aldershot Tourist Information   Tel 0252 20968.
Aldershot Military Museum   Tel 0252 314598.
Crosswater Farm and Gardens Churt   Tel 025125 2698.
Birdworld   Tel 0420 22140.
Aldershot Ice Rink   Tel 0252 336464.
Stainforth Ski Centre   Aldershot Tel 0252 25889.

Farnley Tyas	Golden Cock	£65
Tel 0484 666644		R
Farnley Tyas Nr Huddersfield West Yorkshire HD4 6UD		Map 10 C1

A long-established village inn with a brasserie and charcuterie alongside the
small restaurant where enthusiastic owners and a new lady chef, Karen
Browes, are sincere in their efforts to bring modern English cooking to the
Huddersfield area. Weekly-changing fixed-price menus offer the likes of
mushroom pithiviers, lamb's liver with sage and onion, and bread-and-
butter pudding. More adventurous ravioli of scallops and prawns on
chervil and saffron sauce, and a trio of beef, pork and lamb fillets round a
courgette soufflé typify the style of à la carte dishes. Ambitious desserts (the
undecided can try "a little of everything") or a plate of English and
Continental cheeses to follow. Fixed-price Sunday lunches offer a good
choice. *Seats 40. Parties 50. Private Room. L 12-2 D 7-10 (bookings preferred
for all meals). Closed D Sun, all Mon. Set meals £11.50. Access, Amex, Visa,*
Diners Club International

Faugh	String of Horses Inn	£65
Tel 022 870 297 Fax 022 870 675		I
Heads Hook Faugh Nr Carlisle Cumbria CA4 9EG		Map 13 D4

Coaching inn with an unbroken 300-year history, in a tiny hamlet off the
A69. The rustic bar and lounges sport a plethora of panelling, oak beams,
polished brass and similar trappings. Those in the bedrooms are rather
more surprising: Hollywood-style brass fittings, corner baths and
proprietor Eric Tasker's complimentary hangover kit. *Rooms 14. Garden,
outdoor swimming pool, keep-fit equipment, spa bath, sauna, solarium. Closed 25
& 26 Dec. Access, Amex, Visa,* **Diners Club International**

Faversham	Read's	£80
Tel 0795 535344 Fax 0795 591200		R
Painter's Forstal Faversham Kent ME13 0EE		Map 7 C5

Chef-patron David Pitchford produces daily 3-course, fixed-price menus
with up to seven choices per course at dinner; for budding bon viveurs he
admirably adds a special *menu des enfants* (£7.50). From lunchtime's crab
and salmon fishcakes in brioche crumbs with beurre blanc and local wood
pigeon roasted with rösti potatoes and black pudding, evening choices add
an extra layer of complexity which can veer towards the rich side; hot
soufflé of Parmesan and Montgomery Cheddar is served on glazed smoked
haddock in cream sauce, roast farmyard duckling breast with caramelised
oranges and Grand Marnier jus. Though puddings seem to be something of
a poor relation (chocoholics will, however, be well sated), commendable
British cheeses are served with oatmeal wafers. Several classics on the wine
lists (regular and old/unusual) at fair prices; some good bottles under £20.
*Seats 40. Parties 12. Private Room. L 12-2 D 7-10. Closed Sun & Mon, Bank
Holidays, 2 weeks Aug. Set L £13.50 Set D £27.50. Access, Amex, Visa,*
Diners Club International

Fawkham   Brandshatch Place   67%   £106

Tel 0474 872239   Fax 0474 879652   H

Ash Green Fawkham Kent DA3 8NQ   Map 7 B5

Built by the Duke of Norfolk in 1806 as a country cottage, the redbrick house is now quite imposing, set in 12 acres of gardens, and close to the Paddock entrance of Brands Hatch motor racing circuit. The bedrooms are refreshingly furnished in non-designer style, and have thoughtful extras like mineral water and sweets provided. Pale green public rooms are unexceptional apart from the clubby bar in Frederick's, a fine leisure centre with large swimming pool. Hidden Hotels. *Rooms 29. Garden, croquet, indoor swimming pool, gymnasium, spa bath, sauna, solarium, squash, snooker, dinner dance (monthly). Access, Amex, Visa,* **①** *Diners Club International*

Fawkham   Places of Interest

Orchard Theatre Home Gardens   Dartford Tel 0322 34333.
Hesketh Park Cricket Ground   Dartford Tel 0322 225152.

Felixstowe   Orwell Moat House   69%   £90

Tel 0394 285511   Fax 0394 670687   H

Hamilton Road Felixstowe Suffolk IP11 7DX   Map 6 D3

Comfortable public rooms retain many period features at this Victorian town-centre hotel; bedrooms offer all the usual modern comforts. Conference facilities for up to 200 delegates. Ample free parking. *Rooms 58. Access, Amex, Visa,* **①** *Diners Club International*

Felsted   Rumbles Cottage   £53

Tel 0371 820996   R

Braintree Road Felsted Essex CM6 3DJ   Map 7 B4

The whitewashed 16th-century cottage has low, beamed ceilings, four dining rooms and enthusiastic chef-proprietress Joy Hadley. Her eclectic English menu offers a choice of five dishes per course and might include Indonesian spiced vegetable soup, smoked chicken and tarragon mousseline or wine and honey-marinated trout served with lemon and lime fromage frais to start, followed by beef and horseradish pie, Far Eastern-spiced cod or juniper-stuffed duck with lentil and cider sauce. There is always an unusual vegetarian dish such as cashew nut curry or courgette and raisin couscous on the menu. Rhubarb and elderflower heart (served with a glass of elderflower wine), apricot and almond fool or, perhaps, toffee, banana and coconut "sludge" to finish. Guinea pig menus (£12.50) for tasting experimental dishes are offered to adventurous diners on Tuesday, Wednesday and Thursday. Joy has now opened a second restaurant at 4 St James Street, Castle Hedingham, Essex (Tel 0787 61490 open D Wed-Sat & L Sun). A 2% discount is given to diners not paying by credit card. *Seats 50. Parties 25. Private Room. L Sun only 12-2 D 7-9. Closed D Sun, all Mon, Bank Holidays. Access, Visa.*

Fenstanton   Forte Travelodge   £40

Tel 0954 30919   L

A604 Fenstanton Nr Cambridge Cambridgeshire   Map 6 B2

Located on the eastbound side of the A604, 4 miles south-east of Huntingdon and 10 miles north-west of Cambridge. *Rooms 40. Access, Amex, Visa.*

Ferndown   **Dormy Hotel**   71%   £115

Tel 0202 872121   Fax 0202 895388   **H**

New Road Ferndown Dorset BH22 8ES   Map 4 C4

Manager Derek Silk has kept standards high here since 1977. Guests will
find plenty to please them: public rooms include an all-day bar and coffee
shop with well-upholstered rattan furniture, and a further bar with oak-
panelled walls, red plush chesterfields and a real log fire. The leisure club's
facilities are extensive: there's a children's games room and club rooms
with snooker, pool, darts and table tennis; both the gym and pool and
wonderfully light and airy. Bedrooms offer good standards of modern
comfort. Well geared-up for conferences with some 10 meeting rooms, the
largest of which can accommodate up to 250 delegates in theatre style. De
Vere. *Rooms 128. Garden, indoor swimming pool, sauna, solarium, whirlpool
bath, gymnasium, beauty salon, tennis, squash, snooker, coffee shop
(10am-10pm). Access, Amex, Visa,*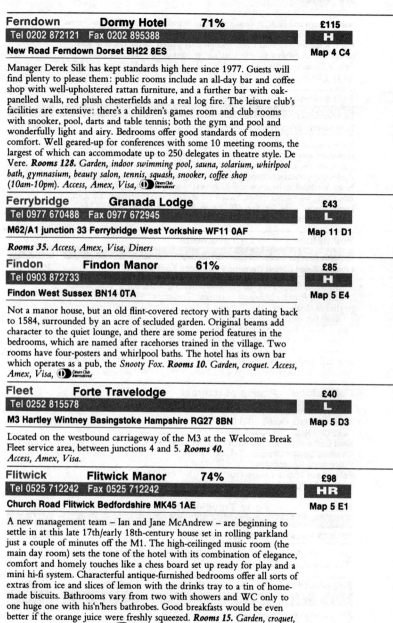

Ferrybridge   **Granada Lodge**   £43

Tel 0977 670488   Fax 0977 672945   **L**

M62/A1 junction 33 Ferrybridge West Yorkshire WF11 0AF   Map 11 D1

Rooms 35. Access, Amex, Visa, Diners

Findon   **Findon Manor**   61%   £85

Tel 0903 872733   **H**

Findon West Sussex BN14 0TA   Map 5 E4

Not a manor house, but an old flint-covered rectory with parts dating back
to 1584, surrounded by an acre of secluded garden. Original beams add
character to the quiet lounge, and there are some period features in the
bedrooms, which are named after racehorses trained in the village. Two
rooms have four-posters and whirlpool baths. The hotel has its own bar
which operates as a pub, the *Snooty Fox*. *Rooms 10. Garden, croquet. Access,
Amex, Visa,*

Fleet   **Forte Travelodge**   £40

Tel 0252 815578   **L**

M3 Hartley Wintney Basingstoke Hampshire RG27 8BN   Map 5 D3

Located on the westbound carriageway of the M3 at the Welcome Break
Fleet service area, between junctions 4 and 5. *Rooms 40.
Access, Amex, Visa.*

Flitwick   **Flitwick Manor**   74%   £98

Tel 0525 712242   Fax 0525 712242   **HR**

Church Road Flitwick Bedfordshire MK45 1AE   Map 5 E1

A new management team – Ian and Jane McAndrew – are beginning to
settle in at this late 17th/early 18th-century house set in rolling parkland
just a couple of minutes off the M1. The high-ceilinged music room (the
main day room) sets the tone of the hotel with its combination of elegance,
comfort and homely touches like a chess board set up ready for play and a
mini hi-fi system. Characterful antique-furnished bedrooms offer all sorts of
extras from ice and slices of lemon with the drinks tray to a tin of home-
made biscuits. Bathrooms vary from two with showers and WC only to
one huge one with his'n'hers bathrobes. Good breakfasts would be even
better if the orange juice were freshly squeezed. *Rooms 15. Garden, croquet,
putting. Access, Amex, Visa,*

Restaurant   £85

After several moves in recent years Ian McAndrew is cooking here and
returning to the sort of form that earned him a star for his first restaurant
in Canterbury. Carrot and celery ragout with sorrel under a filo pastry lid,
and a trio of lamb cutlet, crispy lamb salad and lamb and spinach sausage

with tomato and basil jus demonstrate his brand of restrained inventiveness. Attention to detail includes home-baked bread rolls and, on the service front, something to read being thoughtfully placed on the tables of lone diners. Lunch offers a shorter selection of light dishes. *Seats 60. Parties 65. Private Room. L 12.30-1.45 (Sun 12-2) D 7-9.30 (Sun 7.30-9). Set L £19.50 Set D £29.50.*

Folkestone Paul's £43

Tel 0303 59697 **R**

2a Bouverie Road West, Folkestone Kent CT20 2RX Map 7 C5

Pastel decorations abound in the Haggers' converted house in which the restaurant and bar areas have recently been extended. A pink menu announces the uncomplicated cooking on offer from Paul Hagger: home-made soups, pheasant cannelloni, monkfish poached in cream, chicken breast wrapped in bacon with hollandaise sauce, plus always a few interesting vegetarian dishes. Sweets are served from the trolley. Longish, keenly-priced wine list. *Seats 80. Parties 30. L 12-2.30 D 7.30-9.30 (Sat 7-10pm) Closed 25 & 26 Dec. Access, Visa.*

Folkestone La Tavernetta £45

Tel 0303 54955 **R**

Leaside Court Clifton Gardens Folkestone Kent CT20 2EY Map 7 C5

Chef-partner Felice Puricelli has been providing sound Italian cuisine since 1965 in his friendly basement restaurant. Traditionally-based dishes (tagliolini al salmone, pollo lorreine, bistecca boscaiola) are supplemented by fresh fish specialities (sea bass, lobster, turbot, sole purchased from local fishing boats) on an extensive and varied menu. *Al dente* fettuccine with seafood sauce or crispy whitebait might precede fillet steak in Madeira sauce or sautéed calf's liver with sage. Simple but good sweets. Small choice, fixed-price lunches. *Seats 55. Parties 35. L 12-2.30 D 6-10.30. Closed Sun, Bank Holidays. Set L from £9. Access, Amex, Visa,* **(D)** Diners Club International

Folkestone Places of Interest

Tourist Information Tel 0303 58594.
Metropole Arts Centre Tel 0303 55070.
Leas Cliff Hall Tel 0303 53191.
Kent Battle of Britain Museum Tel 0303 893140.
Cheriton Cricket Ground Tel 0303 53366.
Folkestone Racecourse Tel 0303 66407.
Folkestone Sports Centre Trust Tel 0303 850333.
Swingfield Butterfly Centre Swingfield Tel 0303 83244.

Fontwell Forte Travelodge £40

Tel 0243 543972 **L**

A27/A29 Fontwell West Sussex BN18 0SB Map 5 E4

On the A27, 5 miles north of Bognor Regis, close to Brighton and Worthing. *Rooms 32. Access, Amex, Visa.*

Fossebridge Fossebridge Inn 65% £60

Tel 0285 720721 Fax 0285 720793 **H**

Fossebridge Northleach Gloucestershire GL54 3JS Map 4 C2

An ivy-clad coaching inn standing alongside the A429 and lying on the banks of the river Coln where it crosses the Fosse Way. Views from the bedrooms at the rear of the house overlook lawns leading down to a lake teeming with trout. The 15th-century Bridge Bar has exposed beams, stone walls and a flagstone floor. Children up to 12 stay free in parents' room. *Rooms 9. Garden, croquet, coarse fishing, games room. Access, Amex, Visa,* **(D)** Diners Club International

Framlingham   The Crown   62%   £96

Tel 0728 723521   **H**

Market Hill Framlingham Suffolk IP13 9AN   Map 6 D3

A Forte Heritage hotel that stands out from the crowd with much 16th-century period charm. A flagstoned foyer/lounge and public bar have beamed ceilings and open fires, with a creaking staircase leading up to simple bedrooms furnished with freestanding oak units. The best bedroom has a panelled oak four-poster and floral print settee. *Rooms 14. Access, Amex, Visa,* **◑** *Diners Club International*

Framlingham   Places of Interest

Framlingham Castle   Tel 0728 723330.

Freshford   Homewood Park   79%   £120

Tel 0225 723731   Fax 0225 723820   **HR**

Hinton Charterhouse Freshford Bath Avon BA3 6BB   Map 4 B3

Just off the A36 Salisbury road, five miles from Bath city centre, adjacent to the ruins of 13th-century Hinton Abbey. Ten acres of woodland and informal gardens overlooking the Avon valley are the timelessly elegant setting of this extended 18th-century house. New owners have taken over since we awarded Homewood Park the title Hotel of the Year in 1987, but the award plaque remains in reception and doesn't look out of place alongside the watercolours by Peter Scott, framed collections of antique fans and Hermès scarves – all of which add to the atmosphere of well-being. Bedrooms and bathrooms are sumptuous, each individually decorated in the best of taste, with easy chairs, magazines and complimentary drinks. *Rooms 15. Garden, tennis, croquet. Access, Amex, Visa,* **◑** *Diners Club International*

Restaurant   £75

Two comfortable dining rooms overlooking the gardens are the delightful stage for fixed-price dinners enhanced daily by the best from the fish market. Pan-fried king scallops are served with a sauce of baby lentils, bacon and thyme and a terrine of duck and apricots is served with Cumberland sauce; you might find these among the seven or so starters. Main courses range from saddle of Somerset roe deer with port and ginger sauce to chestnut- and pine kernel-stuffed guinea fowl with Madeira sauce. Caramelised apples in brioche with rum and raisin custard or sharp lemon bavarois on an orange coulis keep the interest going right to the end of dinner. *Seats 60. Parties 70. Private Room. L 12-1.45 D 7-9.30. Set L £17.50 Set D £29.50.*

Freshwater   Farringford Hotel   57%   £86

Tel 0983 752500   **H**

Bedbury Lane Freshwater Isle of Wight PO40 9PE   Map 4 C4

Once the home of Alfred Lord Tennyson, this 18th-century Gothic-style house is now a peaceful holiday hotel whose neat gardens border National Trust downland. Day rooms include a French-windowed drawing room, a small bar and a library with Tennyson memorabilia. Bedrooms are modest and neat, and there are also a number of self-catering Cottage and Garden suites in the grounds. Children are welcome, and baby-sitting and baby-listening can be arranged. *Rooms 19. Outdoor swimming pool, 9-hole golf course, putting, bowling green, tennis, croquet, children's play area. Access, Amex, Visa,* **◑** *Diners Club International*

Fressingfield   Fox & Goose   £52

Tel 037 986 247   **R**

Fressingfield Nr Diss Suffolk IP21 5PB   Map 6 C2

In a lovely old black-and-white inn by the church, cook/patronne Ruth
Watson and chef Brendan Ansbro produce a menu whose inspiration is
worldwide. British traditionalists can stay at home with cold Butley oysters
and hot herb sausages, oak-smoked salmon, cod and chips, local game
pudding or the Sunday lunchtime roast sirloin of beef (order by midday
Saturday). Culinary explorers could go for Chinese-style duck with
pancakes, grilled calamari with polenta, beef carpaccio or Afghan rice
pudding. Many dishes are available as either starters or main courses.
Patron David Watson is responsible for the outstanding list of 400 +
wines. *Seats 50. Parties 25. Private Room. L 12-2 D 7-9.30. Closed Mon &
Tue, 2 weeks Xmas, 3 weeks Jul.* **(1)** *Diners Club International*

Frilford Heath   Dog House Hotel   £70

Tel 0865 390830   Fax 0865 390860   **I**

Frilford Heath Nr Abingdon Oxfordshire OX13 6QY   Map 5 D2

The 17th-century Dog House has rooms in contemporary cottage style and
11 new rooms. Furniture is good-quality pine (one room has a pine four-
poster), and accessories include remote-control teletext TV. Bathrooms
have smart modern tiling, large mirrors and good lighting. Children's play
area. *Rooms 19. Garden. Access, Amex, Visa,* **(1)** *Diners Club International*

Garforth   Hilton National   61%   £108

Tel 0532 866556   **H**

Wakefield Road Garforth Nr Leeds West Yorkshire LS25 1LH   Map 11 D1

Stylish public areas raise expectations for the bedrooms, which although
well kept, are small and fairly ordinary. Leisure centre. *Rooms 144. Garden,
indoor swimming pool, sauna, solarium, pool table, keep-fit equipment. Access,
Amex, Visa,* **(1)** *Diners Club International*

Gateshead   Forte Travelodge   £40

Tel 0748 823768   **L**

A194 Leam Lane Wardley Whitemare Pool Nr Gateshead
Tyne & Wear NE10 8YB   Map 15 B4

On the outskirts of Newcastle upon Tyne, 4 miles east of Gateshead town
centre and 8 miles west of Sunderland. *Rooms 41. Access, Amex, Visa.*

Gateshead   Springfield Hotel   63%   £95

Tel 091-477 4121   Fax 091-477 7213   **H**

Durham Road Low Fell Gateshead Tyne & Wear NE9 5BT   Map 15 B4

Jarvis business hotel by the A6127, 4 miles from A1(M) junction.
Conference/banqueting facilities for 120/100. Children up to 16 free in
parents' room. *Rooms 60. Access, Amex, Visa,* **(1)** *Diners Club International*

Gateshead   Swallow Hotel   60%   £82

Tel 091-477 1105   Fax 091-478 7214   **H**

High West Street Gateshead Tyne & Wear NE8 1PE   Map 15 B4

A leisure club, ample secure car parking and conference facilities for up to
350 are among the amenities at this modern hotel three miles from the
A1(M) and one mile from the city centre – check directions. *Rooms 103.
Indoor swimming pool, keep-fit equipment, spa bath, sauna, steam room,
solarium. Access, Amex, Visa,*  **(1)** *Diners Club International*

Gateshead   Places of Interest

Tourist Information   Tel 091-477 3478.
Caedmon Hall   Tel 091-477 3478.
Gibside Chapel and Grounds (NT)   Gibside Tel 0207 542255.
Bede Monastery Museum   Jarrow Tel 091-489 2106.
Wickham Thorns Farm Ski Slope   Dunston Tel 091-460 8746.
Gateshead International Sports Stadium   Tel 091-478 1687.

| Gatwick Airport | Chequers Thistle | 66% | £106 |

Tel 0293 786992   Fax 0293 820625   **H**

Brighton Road Horley Surrey RH16 8PH   **Map 7 B5**

Much extended from its coaching inn days, the Chequers stands by a
roundabout on the A23. Bedrooms have all the expected comforts, plus
24hr room service. Conference/banqueting facilities for 85/60. *Rooms 78.*
Outdoor swimming pool, coffee shop (10am-10pm) Access, Amex, Visa, (D) *Diners Club International*

| Gatwick Airport | Copthorne Effingham Park | 72% | £126 |

Tel 0342 714994   Fax 0342 716039   **H**

West Park Road Copthorne West Sussex RH10 3EU   **Map 7 B5**

Four sequoia trees originally imported from Oregon to commemorate
Wellington's victory at Waterloo line the driveway. There's lots more of
interest in the modernised stately home, including a large rotunda
conference centre (catering for up to 500 delegates) that still contains some
of the vintage racing cars for which it was originally built. Decent-sized
bedrooms have reproduction furniture including a breakfast table. Best
rooms have private balconies. *Rooms 122. Garden, 9-hole golf course, croquet,
indoor swimming pool, gymnasium, Turkish bath, sauna, spa bath, beautician,
hairdressing. Access, Amex, Visa,* (D) *Diners Club International*

| Gatwick Airport | Copthorne London Gatwick | 69% | £127 |

Tel 0342 714971   Fax 0342 717375   **H**

Copthorne Nr Crawley West Sussex RH10 3PG   **Map 7 B5**

Set in 100 acres of gardens and woodland, the Copthorne is centred round
a 16th-century farmhouse. Oak beams and log fires keep the period feel in
the White Swan pub, and many of the bedrooms are also in a traditional
style. There are rooms for disabled guests and non-smokers, and the newest
rooms, in the Connoisseur wing, boast corner jacuzzis. The hotel has
several bars and restaurants, conference/banqueting suites (for around 120)
and facilities for sport and leisure. Six minutes from the airport (not on the
flight path) and just two from the M23 (junction 10, then A24).
*Rooms 227. Garden, croquet, gymnasium, sauna, solarium, squash, beautician,
coffee shop (5.30am-3pm & 6pm-11pm). Access, Amex, Visa,* (D) *Diners Club International*

| Gatwick Airport | Europa Gatwick | 68% | £100 |

Tel 0293 886666   Fax 0293 886680   **H**

Balcombe Road Maidenbower Nr Crawley West Sussex RH10 4ZR   **Map 7 B5**

On the B2036 about 15 minutes from the airport, the Europa is a modern
low-rise hotel built in hacienda style, with whitewashed walls and
terracotta roofs. Inside, it's just as distinctive, and reception impresses first
with its tall rafters, terrazzo marble floor and dark mahogany furniture.
There are two restaurants (Chinese and Mediterranean), a lounge bar for
lighter meals, a cocktail bar, numerous syndicate rooms and a health and
leisure centre. Smart bedrooms with polished wood and autumnal colour
schemes range up to Executive rooms with sofa beds and work areas, and
Club rooms with whirlpool baths. Parking for 250 cars. *Rooms 211.
Garden, indoor swimming pool, gymnasium, spa bath, sauna, solarium,
beautician, hairdressing. Access, Amex, Visa,* (D) *Diners Club International*

Gatwick Airport   Forte Crest Gatwick   74%   £99

Tel 0293 567070   Fax 0293 567739   **H**

North Terminal Gatwick Airport West Sussex RH6 0PH   Map 7 B5

Formerly the *Gatwick Sterling*, Gatwick's most distinctive hotel has a
covered walkway from the north terminal leading directly into the eight
storey-high atrium, under which a bar and café take on an open-air feel.
Public areas are modernistic, even a bit austere, and the uniformly
furnished bedrooms are stark, though comfortable, with chrome fittings
and black and white decor; striped bedcovers provide a dash of colour. A
surprisingly easy-to-use, high-tech TV system displays messages, flight
information, a running total of the bill and even a check-out facility in
addition to regular viewing. It's worth the extra to stay on the Sterling
Club floor with its separate lounge, complimentary cocktail, continental
breakfast and various extras in the rooms. Staff are smart, friendly and
helpful. Prices have been reduced under the new ownership of Forte.
*Rooms 474. Indoor swimming pool, sauna, solarium, gymnasium, keep-fit
equipment, business centre, 24hr café, news kiosk, hairdressing, British Airways
ticket desk. Access, Amex, Visa,* Diners Club International

Gatwick Airport   Forte Posthouse Gatwick   63%   £64

Tel 0293 771621   Fax 0293 771054   **H**

Povey Cross Road Horley Surrey RH6 0BA   Map 7 B5

On the A23 a mile north of the airport. Good modern bedrooms, choice of
conference and meeting rooms (up to 150 delegates), large long-term car
park. *Rooms 216. Outdoor swimming pool, coffee shop (7am-10pm), airport
courtesy coach (from 6.15am). Access, Amex, Visa,* Diners Club International

Gatwick Airport   Gatwick Concorde Hotel   61%   £104

Tel 0293 533441   Fax 0293 535369   **H**

Church Road Lowfield Heath Crawley West Sussex RH11 0PQ   Map 7 B5

Queens Moat Houses hotel off the A23. Some of the bedrooms overlook
the runways. Courtesy coach from airport and station. *Rooms 116. Access,
Amex, Visa,* Diners Club International

Gatwick Airport   Gatwick Hilton International   72%   £150

Tel 0293 518080   Fax 0293 28980   **H**

Gatwick West Sussex RH11 0PD   Map 7 B5

A pedestrian walkway directly connects Gatwick's south terminal with this
large hotel's four-storey central atrium; a full-size replica of Jason, Amy
Johnson's biplane, hangs from the ceiling. Good-sized bedrooms have easy
chairs, breakfast tables, large beds and all the extras one would expect from
an international hotel; TVs even display flight information, very useful if
your plane is delayed. The Jockey Bar's horse-racing theme harks back to
the days when Gatwick racecourse was on this site. Conferences for up to
500. *Rooms 550. Indoor swimming pool, sauna, solarium, spa bath, steam room,
gymnasium, beauty salon, hairdressing, games room, kiosk, florist, business centre,
24hr coffee shop. Access, Amex, Visa,* Diners Club International

Gatwick Airport   Gatwick Penta Hotel   70%   £133

Tel 0293 820169   Fax 0293 820259   **H**

Povey Cross Road Horley Surrey RH6 0BE   Map 7 B5

Well-signposted, large modern hotel just off the A23. Spacious and stylish
public areas include the Brighton Belle bar (based on an old Pullman
carriage) with walls that are lined with railway memorabilia; leather sofas,
large brass table lamps and a marble-tiled floor make the foyer-lounge an
attractive area. The best bedrooms are spacious and well equipped, with
efficient sound-proofing, good air-conditioning and neutral decor, but
standard rooms have regular, darkwood furniture and are generally
unexciting. The extensive leisure centre includes three squash courts. Good,

self-contained conference facilities for up to 150 delegates. Courtesy coaches to the airport. **Rooms 260.** *Garden, coffee shop (10am-6pm), beautician, indoor swimming pool, sauna, solarium, spa bath, gymnasium, squash. Access, Amex, Visa,*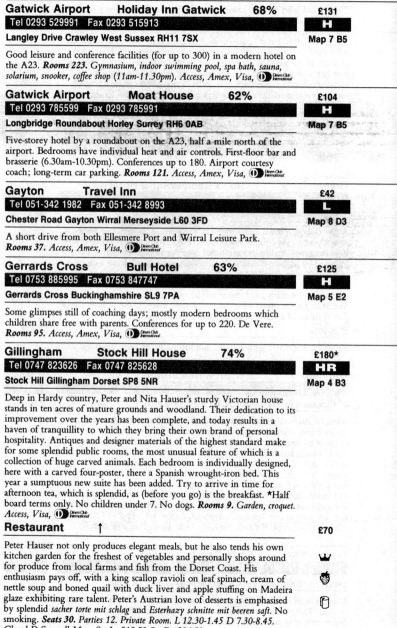

Gatwick Airport	Holiday Inn Gatwick	68%	£131
Tel 0293 529991 Fax 0293 515913			**H**
Langley Drive Crawley West Sussex RH11 7SX			Map 7 B5

Good leisure and conference facilities (for up to 300) in a modern hotel on the A23. **Rooms 223.** *Gymnasium, indoor swimming pool, spa bath, sauna, solarium, snooker, coffee shop (11am-11.30pm). Access, Amex, Visa,*

Gatwick Airport	Moat House	62%	£104
Tel 0293 785599 Fax 0293 785991			**H**
Longbridge Roundabout Horley Surrey RH6 0AB			Map 7 B5

Five-storey hotel by a roundabout on the A23, half a mile north of the airport. Bedrooms have individual heat and air controls. First-floor bar and brasserie (6.30am-10.30pm). Conferences up to 180. Airport courtesy coach; long-term car parking. **Rooms 121.** *Access, Amex, Visa,*

Gayton	Travel Inn		£42
Tel 051-342 1982 Fax 051-342 8993			**L**
Chester Road Gayton Wirral Merseyside L60 3FD			Map 8 D3

A short drive from both Ellesmere Port and Wirral Leisure Park. **Rooms 37.** *Access, Amex, Visa,*

Gerrards Cross	Bull Hotel	63%	£125
Tel 0753 885995 Fax 0753 847747			**H**
Gerrards Cross Buckinghamshire SL9 7PA			Map 5 E2

Some glimpses still of coaching days; mostly modern bedrooms which children share free with parents. Conferences for up to 220. De Vere. **Rooms 95.** *Access, Amex, Visa,*

Gillingham	Stock Hill House	74%	£180*
Tel 0747 823626 Fax 0747 825628			**H R**
Stock Hill Gillingham Dorset SP8 5NR			Map 4 B3

Deep in Hardy country, Peter and Nita Hauser's sturdy Victorian house stands in ten acres of mature grounds and woodland. Their dedication to its improvement over the years has been complete, and today results in a haven of tranquillity to which they bring their own brand of personal hospitality. Antiques and designer materials of the highest standard make for some splendid public rooms, the most unusual feature of which is a collection of huge carved animals. Each bedroom is individually designed, here with a carved four-poster, there a Spanish wrought-iron bed. This year a sumptuous new suite has been added. Try to arrive in time for afternoon tea, which is splendid, as (before you go) is the breakfast. *Half board terms only. No children under 7. No dogs. **Rooms 9.** *Garden, croquet. Access, Visa,*

Restaurant ↑   £70

Peter Hauser not only produces elegant meals, but he also tends his own kitchen garden for the freshest of vegetables and personally shops around for produce from local farms and fish from the Dorset Coast. His enthusiasm pays off, with a king scallop ravioli on leaf spinach, cream of nettle soup and boned quail with duck liver and apple stuffing on Madeira glaze exhibiting rare talent. Peter's Austrian love of desserts is emphasised by splendid *sacher torte mit schlag* and *Esterhazy schnitte mit beeren saft.* No smoking. **Seats 30.** *Parties 12. Private Room. L 12.30-1.45 D 7.30-8.45. Closed D Sun, all Mon. Set L £18.50 Set D £26.50.*

Gittisham — Combe House — 73% — £92

H

Tel 0404 42756   Fax 0404 46004

Gittisham Nr Honiton Devon EX14 0AD — Map 3 E2

Thérèse and John Boswell came here in 1970, and both are very much involved in the day-to-day running of their stately Elizabethan mansion. The 3000-acre estate is predictably peaceful, and there are views of the Blackmore Hills, but it's not remote, being less than two miles from the A30. Public rooms have carved panelling in the entrance hall, ancestral portraits in the panelled drawing room, a charming pink sitting room, a cosy bar with pictures of John's horse-racing activities (the hotel owns several racehorses trained nearby – visits to the stables can be arranged), and everywhere architectural features, antiques and personal touches by painter and sculptress Thérèse (and her mother). Bedrooms vary in size and price, larger rooms tending to have better views and more interesting furniture and pictures. Two rooms have four-poster beds. The hotel owns fishing rights on the River Otter, with a season running from April to the end of September. *Rooms 15. Garden, croquet, fishing. Access, Amex, Visa,*

Glastonbury — No. 3 Restaurant & Hotel — £75

RR

Tel 0458 832129

3 Magdelene Street Glastonbury Somerset BA6 9EW — Map 4 A3

A fine Georgian town house adjoining the ruins of Glastonbury Abbey. Ann Tynan serves a fixed-price menu with a good choice that might offer liver stroganoff, scallop purses, stuffed peach or smoked salmon to start, followed by an inter-course sorbet and then guinea fowl, lamb with orange and ginger sauce, flambéed fillet of beef, magret of duck or walnut and cashew en croute. Interesting ice creams (with Chinese ginger syrup or praline and Amaretto) and cheese served with celery and fruits alongside five or so desserts. *Seats 20. Parties 10. Private Room. D only 7.30-9. Closed Sun & Mon, 25 Dec-1 Feb. Set D £26. Access, Visa.*

Rooms — £86

Six stylish bedrooms with antiques and bathrooms en suite. No dogs.

Glemsford — Barrett's Restaurant — £65

R

Tel 0787 281573

31 Egremont Street Glemsford Nr Sudbury Suffolk CO10 7SA — Map 6 C3

Nicholas Barrett's restaurant is a welcome find in a small village off the beaten track. Country tranquillity and a loyal following, catered for front-of-house by wife Diane, has allowed the owner to perfect his flavour combinations and delicate saucing. The style of cooking is modern British with a slight French feel, as in chicken livers in a crispy pastry case with grapes, mushrooms and a Madeira jus, or baked fillet of sea bass with garlic and lardons of bacon. Hot rum and raisin soufflé with matching ice cream, and bitter chocolate parfait with white chocolate sorbet and confit of kumquats are strong temptations to move on to a third course. Excellent wines, strong in fine Bordeaux. *Seats 18. L (Sun only) 12-2 D 7-9.30. Closed D Sun, Bank Holidays. Set L £13.95. Access, Visa,*

Gloucester — Forte Crest — 66% — £87

H

Tel 0452 613311   Fax 0452 371036

Crest Way Barnwood Gloucester Gloucestershire GL4 7RX — Map 4 B1

Modern hotel on the A417, strong on conference (up to 100) and leisure facilities. Lady Crest rooms cater well for female executives. *Rooms 123. Indoor swimming pool, spa bath, sauna. Access, Amex, Visa,*

Gloucester   Hatherley Manor   65%   £74

Tel 0452 730217   Fax 0452 731032   **H**

Down Hatherley Lane Gloucester Gloucestershire GL2 9QA   **Map 4 B1**

Forty acres of parkland and pasture surround a refurbished 17th-century manor two miles north of Gloucester. Private guests and conference delegates (up to 200) are both well catered for, the former in comfortable bars and a lounge, the latter chiefly in the Hatherley Suite with its own entrance, bar and servery kitchen kept well away from the hotel proper. A few standard bedrooms are in the old part, but the majority are in the 'de luxe' category with satellite TV and good work space. A few are suitable for family use and there's a four-poster honeymoon suite. *Rooms 55. Garden, croquet. Access, Amex, Visa,* ⓘ *Diners Club International*

Gloucester   Hatton Court   75%   £90

Tel 0452 617412   Fax 0452 612945   **H**

Upton Hill Upton St Leonards Gloucester Gloucestershire GL4 8DE   **Map 4 B1**

Ignore the M5 and you can enjoy wonderful views over the Severn Valley from an extended 17th-century house set in 37 acres of greenery on a ridge alongside the B4073, three miles from Gloucester. Inside the ivy-clad building it's a refined, yet busy business catering for weekday conferences of up to 30 delegates. A glass of port or sherry greets guests on arrival in the stylishly furnished foyer. Eighteen bedrooms are in the main house with further smaller (and more uniform) ones in an adjoining wing, reached from outside the house. All have the same level of extras like bathrobes, sweets, fruit and mineral water. Bathrooms (some with whirlpool baths) are bright, neat and carpeted. Terrace lunches in summer. Plans are afoot for extended leisure facilities (sauna, workout area, solarium, jacuzzi) in 1993 – check when booking. *Rooms 45. Garden, outdoor swimming pool (May-Oct). Access, Amex, Visa,* ⓘ *Diners Club International*

Carringtons Restaurant   £75

The views vie with the cooking for pride of place in the elegant dining room. The cooking usually wins with good value "taste of modern French" and "taste of tradition" menus from new chef Mark Douglas. *Seats 80. Parties 16. Private Room. L 12-2 D 7.30-10 (Sun to 9.30). Set L £14 Set D £19.75.*

Gloucester   Travel Inn   £42

Tel 0452 523519   Fax 0452 300924   **L**

Tewkesbury Road Longford Gloucester Gloucestershire GL2 9BE   **Map 4 B1**

Not far from Gloucester Cathedral. The inn itself boasts a children's play area. *Rooms 40. Access, Amex, Visa,* ⓘ *Diners Club International*

Gloucester   Travel Inn   £42

Tel 0452 862521   Fax 0452 864926   **L**

Witcombe Nr Gloucester Gloucestershire GL3 4SS   **Map 4 B1**

Situated under the foothills of the Cotswolds. *Rooms 40. Access, Amex, Visa,* ⓘ *Diners Club International*

Gloucester   Places of Interest

Tourist Information   Tel 0452 421188.
Berkeley Castle   Berkeley Tel 0453 810332.
Westbury Court Garden (NT)   Westbury-on-Severn Tel 045276 461.
Gloucester Cathedral   Tel 0452 24167.
Gloucester Ski Centre   Tel 0452 414 300.
    Museums and Art Galleries
Nature in Art   (The International Centre for Wildlife Art) Tel 0452 731422.
City Museum and Art Gallery   Tel 0452 24131.

The Robert Opie Collection   Museum of Advertising and Packaging, Gloucester Docks Tel 0452 302309.
Zoos and Wildlife Parks
National Birds of Prey Centre   Tel 0531 820286.
Wildfowl and Wetlands Trust   Slimbridge Tel 045 389 0827.

Goathland	Mallyan Spout	61%	£65

Tel 0947 86206 — **H**

Goathland Whitby North Yorkshire YO22 5AN   Map 15 C5

In a remote village nine miles from Whitby the hotel takes its name from a waterfall just a short walk away. Stone-built and clad in ivy, it's a homely, welcoming place with family owners; the lounges and bars provide ample space for relaxation. Cottage-style bedrooms include six rooms in a converted coach house. The two best rooms have balconies and views of the valley and moors beyond. Two studio flats are also available for self-catering. *Rooms 24. Garden. Access, Amex, Visa,*

Godalming	Inn on the Lake		£75

Tel 0483 415575   Fax 0483 860445 — **I**

Ockford Road Godalming Surrey GU7 1RH   Map 5 E3

A charming inn run by Joy and Martin Cummings, set in 2 acres of lovely gardens with lawns leading down to the lake (and the main London-Portsmouth railway line beyond). Businessmen jaded by blander establishments will find stylish accommodation with thoughtful extras such as magazines, sewing kits, trouser presses and hairdryers in the best bedrooms; six rooms have spa baths and balconies. There's a convivial pubby bar with a bar snack menu and a welcoming log fire in winter. Function facilities for up to 150. *Rooms 20. Garden. Access, Amex, Visa,*

Godalming   Places of Interest

Vann House   Hambledon Tel 0428 683413.

Golant	Cormorant Hotel	62%	£76

Tel & Fax 0726 833426 — **H**

Golant Nr Fowey Cornwall PL23 1LL   Map 2 C3

The riverside setting in a small fishing village is a great attraction, and the bedrooms, day rooms and swimming pool all enjoy the views. Bedrooms are airy, warm and comfortable, and there's a honeymoon room. The swimming pool, set higher than the hotel, has a sliding roof for summer days. No children under 12. *Rooms 11. Garden, indoor swimming pool. Access, Amex, Visa.*

Goodwood	Goodwood Park	67%	£99

Tel 0243 775537   Fax 0243 533802 — **H**

Goodwood Nr Chichester West Sussex PO18 0QB   Map 5 E4

Within the 12,000 acre grounds of Goodwood House estate, a much modernised and extended old house plays host to hotel, golf and country club rolled into one. Residential conferences (max 100) and banqueting for up to 120 are the mainstay of mid-week business, while weekends are busy with guests who make full use of the extensive leisure facilities. All-day coffee shop. Children's play area. Under-16s stay free in parents' room. No dogs. Theatre breaks include tickets to the nearby Chichester Festival Theatre, and racing breaks at Glorious Goodwood are also popular. Families well catered for. Country Club Hotels. *Rooms 89. Garden, indoor swimming pool, sauna, solarium, spa bath, hair & beauty salons, snooker, tennis, squash, keep-fit equipment, 18-hole golf course, driving range. Access, Amex, Visa,*

Goodwood   Places of Interest

Goodwood House   Tel 0243 774107.
Goodwood Racecourse   Tel 0243 774107.

Gordano   Forte Travelodge   £40
Tel 0275 373709   **L**

Gordano service area M5 Gordano Nr Portbury Avon BS20 9XG   Map 4 A3

7 miles from Bristol city centre at junction 19 of the M5 motorway.
Rooms 40. Access, Amex, Visa.

Goring-on-Thames   The Leatherne Bottel   £60
Tel 0491 872667   **R**

Goring-on-Thames Berkshire RG8 0HS   Map 5 D2

You'll find signs to this delightfully situated riverside restaurant from the
B4009 north of Goring. It's a wonderfully friendly and informal
establishment (although prices charged are not commensurate with the
limp linen and basic tableware provided) and Keith Read is an enthusiastic
and unpretentious chef, relying on the freshness and quality of his
ingredients. His menus change monthly, making fine use of seasonal
produce, with game in winter, seafood the star in summer. Fresh herbs and
the chargrill are both favoured; typical dishes include home-made pasta
with wild mushroom and black olive pesto, maize-fed chicken breast with
pancetta and chilis, and ginger-marinated salmon. Portions are invariably
generous, particularly desserts like blueberry tart piled high with berries
and cassis then topped with whipped cream. Home-made bread (tomato
and black olive, spinach and walnut) is sold to take away, if ordered in
advance. Two handsome dining rooms, plus 20 tables set on an outdoor
terrace in good weather. Natasha, an Edwardian saloon launch, is available
for a riverborne aperitif. *Seats 45. Parties 20. Private Room. L 12.30-2 (Sat
& Sun to 2.30) D 7-9.30 (Sun 7.30-9). Closed 25 Dec. Access, Amex, Visa.*

Goudhurst   Star & Eagle Inn   £40
Tel 0580 211512   **I**

High Street Goudhurst Kent TN17 1AL   Map 7 B5

The bedrooms at this gabled 14th-century inn come in all shapes and sizes,
and one sports a restored four-poster bed. In the public areas period appeal
survives in exposed beams, open brick fireplaces and old settles. No dogs.
Whitbread Hotels. *Rooms 11. Garden. Access, Amex, Visa.*

Goudhurst   Places of Interest

Bedgebury National Pinetum   Tel 0580 211044.

Grantham   Forte Travelodge   £40
Tel 0476 77500   **L**

**A1 Grantham service area Gonerby Moor Grantham Lincolnshire NG32
2AB**   Map 11 E3

At the Welcome Break service area on the A1 – 4 miles north of
Grantham, 10 miles south of Newark-on-Trent. *Rooms 40. Access, Amex,
Visa.*

Grantham   Granada Lodge   £43
Tel 0476 860686   Fax 0476 861078   **L**
A1/A151 Colsterworth Grantham Lincolnshire NG33 5JR   Map 11 E3

Rooms 38. Access, Amex, Visa, Diners

Grasmere   Michael's Nook   79%   £152*
Tel 053 94 35496   Fax 053 94 35765   **HR**
Grasmere Nr Ambleside Cumbria LA22 9RP   Map 13 D5

An extended Victorian stone-built mansion in a hillside garden setting with
wonderful rhododendrons. Reg Gifford opened it as a hotel in 1969, and
his impressive collection of prints, rugs, furniture and porcelain fills the day
rooms. Two of the bedrooms are picture-windowed suites with private
patios offering comprehensive space and comfort. All are provided with a
host of luxuries, from fresh flowers and fruit to bath salts and robes. No
children between the ages of one and six. No dogs. Leisure facilities
available at the nearby Wordsworth Hotel. *Half-board terms only.
Rooms 14. Garden. Access, Amex, Visa, 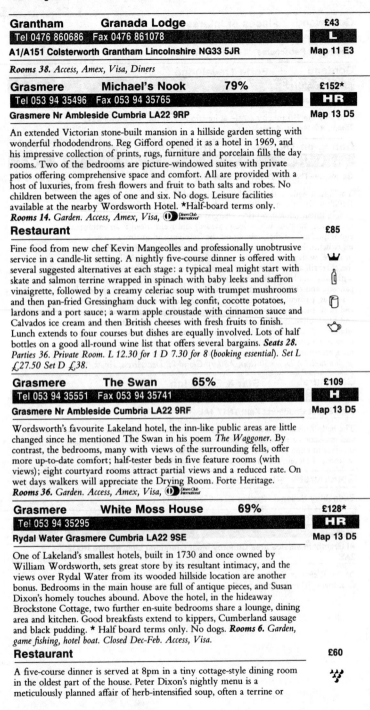 Diners Club International

Restaurant   £85

Fine food from new chef Kevin Mangeolles and professionally unobtrusive
service in a candle-lit setting. A nightly five-course dinner is offered with
several suggested alternatives at each stage: a typical meal might start with
skate and salmon terrine wrapped in spinach with baby leeks and saffron
vinaigrette, followed by a creamy celeriac soup with trumpet mushrooms
and then pan-fried Gressingham duck with leg confit, cocotte potatoes,
lardons and a port sauce; a warm apple croustade with cinnamon sauce and
Calvados ice cream and then British cheeses with fresh fruits to finish.
Lunch extends to four courses but dishes are equally involved. Lots of half
bottles on a good all-round wine list that offers several bargains. *Seats 28.
Parties 36. Private Room. L 12.30 for 1 D 7.30 for 8 (booking essential). Set L
£27.50 Set D £38.*

Grasmere   The Swan   65%   £109
Tel 053 94 35551   Fax 053 94 35741   **H**
Grasmere Nr Ambleside Cumbria LA22 9RF   Map 13 D5

Wordsworth's favourite Lakeland hotel, the inn-like public areas are little
changed since he mentioned The Swan in his poem *The Waggoner*. By
contrast, the bedrooms, many with views of the surrounding fells, offer
more up-to-date comfort; half-tester beds in five feature rooms (with
views); eight courtyard rooms attract partial views and a reduced rate. On
wet days walkers will appreciate the Drying Room. Forte Heritage.
Rooms 36. Garden. Access, Amex, Visa, Diners Club International

Grasmere   White Moss House   69%   £128*
Tel 053 94 35295   **HR**
Rydal Water Grasmere Cumbria LA22 9SE   Map 13 D5

One of Lakeland's smallest hotels, built in 1730 and once owned by
William Wordsworth, sets great store by its resultant intimacy, and the
views over Rydal Water from its wooded hillside location are another
bonus. Bedrooms in the main house are full of antique pieces, and Susan
Dixon's homely touches abound. Above the hotel, in the hideaway
Brockstone Cottage, two further en-suite bedrooms share a lounge, dining
area and kitchen. Good breakfasts extend to kippers, Cumberland sausage
and black pudding. * Half board terms only. No dogs. *Rooms 6. Garden,
game fishing, hotel boat. Closed Dec-Feb. Access, Visa.*

Restaurant   £60

A five-course dinner is served at 8pm in a tiny cottage-style dining room
in the oldest part of the house. Peter Dixon's nightly menu is a
meticulously planned affair of herb-intensified soup, often a terrine or

soufflé of fish, and main course of Lakeland lamb, or wild mallard, perhaps, balanced by imaginative vegetable accompaniments. There's choice only at the dessert stage (usually four classic puddings – from Mrs Beeton's chocolate pudding to poached pear with Poire William and Gewürztraminer sorbet), followed by first-rate British farmhouse cheeses with home-made oatmeal biscuits. Fair prices on a decent wine list that features familiar names, particularly from France; useful tasting notes. No smoking. **Seats 18.** *D only at 8. Closed Sun. Set D £25.*

Grasmere   Wordsworth Hotel   72%   £116
HR
Tel 053 94 35592   Fax 053 94 35765
Grasmere Nr Ambleside Cumbria LA22 9SW   Map 13 D5

Centrally located in Grasmere village, the Wordsworth's two acres of well-tended gardens and paddock nevertheless promise calm and tranquillity. The conservatory bar and adjacent lounge have bold floral fabrics, some cane seating and the best of the views. The more active will enjoy the well-equipped leisure centre or the Dove & Olive Branch pub. Individually decorated bedrooms vary widely in size and aspect; the best are two suites with whirlpool baths and an antique-furnished four-poster room. Many rooms are suitable for family use, and baby-sitting and baby-listening are available. **Rooms 37.** *Garden, indoor swimming pool, spa bath, sauna, solarium, keep-fit equipment, games room. Access, Amex, Visa,*

Prelude Restaurant   £74

There's a traditional feel to the dining room but many of the variations on Bernard Warne's menus have a modern ring. Jellied terrine of seasonal fowl and game, grilled monkfish and prawn sausage on a soft herb sauce, millefeuille of rabbit on a duet of sweet pepper sauces finished with strawberries, steak topped with Stilton mousse on toasted brioche, rosewater and passion fruit mousse with crystallised freesias. **Seats 60.** *Parties 100. Private Room. L 12.30-2 D 7-9 (Fri & Sat to 9.30). Set L £17.50 Set D £29.50.*

Grasmere   Places of Interest

Dove Cottage and Wordsworth Museum   Tel 09665 544/547.

Grayshott   Woods Place   £50
R
Tel 0428 605555
Headley Road Grayshott Nr Hindhead Surrey GU26 6LB   Map 5 E3

There is a rustic slant to Eric Norrgren's authentic Scandinavian cooking in the unlikely setting of a former butcher's shop in a small village just off the A3 near Hindhead. Homely cooking encompasses a range of hearty, relatively uncomplicated dishes: gravlax (try it with a glass of ice-cold akvavit), Camembert deep-fried with preserved cloudberries, fillet of beef marinated and served with a mustard and horseradish dip. Preserved duck with sweet and sour cabbage, Danish frigadeller (meat balls) and pike with a fresh tomato sauce might also feature on a menu that changes little from season to season. Note the 5% surcharge when paying by credit card. **Seats 30.** *Parties 30. D only 7-11. Closed Sun & Mon, 1 week Xmas. Access, Amex, Visa,*

Great Ayton   Ayton Hall   73%   £105
H
Tel 0642 723595   Fax 0642 722149
Low Green Great Ayton Nr Middlesbrough North Yorkshire TS9 6PW   Map 15 C5

Six acres of landscaped ground surround Ayton Hall, seven miles south of Middlesbrough on the A172. Inside the Grade II listed building a Moroccan-style reception area-cum-cocktail bar gives on to a spacious, drawing room with huge picture windows, antiques and a cool pastel decor; ornaments, magazines and attractive pictures provide a homely feel. The bedrooms are equipped with antique or pine furniture; they offer an

exceptional range of extras, both large and small. No dogs. *Rooms 11.*
Garden, tennis, croquet, archery, clay-pigeon shooting. Access, Amex,
Visa, ()

Great Baddow	Pontlands Park	70%	£99

Tel 0245 76444   Fax 0245 478393   **H**

West Hanningfield Road Great Baddow Nr Chelmsford Essex CM2 8HR   Map 7 B4

A friendly mid-Victorian hotel with an attractive health and leisure centre.
Bedrooms in the wing are huge, with high ceilings, separate sitting areas,
large beds, quality reproduction furniture and bright, stylish fabrics. Rooms
in the main house are similar but smaller; all bathrooms boast bidets, high-
class toiletries and good carpeting and decor. Public areas include a marble-
effect entrance hall, a comfortable bar, an elegant lounge and a nice little
garden room with lots of plants and Lloyd Loom chairs. Bright and airy
garden coffee shop. Dogs in kennels only. Children not allowed in health
centre during members' hours. 10% service charge is added to all
accommodation, food and bar final bills. *Rooms 17. Garden, indoor &*
outdoor swimming pools, sauna, spa bath, keep-fit equipment, beautician,
hairdressing, coffee shop (10am-10pm). Closed 1 week Jan. Access, Amex,
Visa, ()

Great Baddow   Places of Interest

Hyde Hall Garden   Rettendon Tel 0245 400256.
Chelmsford Cathedral   Tel 0245 263660.
New Writtle Road Cricket Ground   Tel 0245 252420.
Riverside Ice and Leisure Centre   Tel 0245 269417.
Great Leighs Showground   Tel 0245 361259.

Great Dunmow	Saracen's Head	58%	£91

Tel 0371 873901   Fax 0371 875743   **H**

High Street Great Dunmow Essex CM6 1AG   **Map 6 B3**

Forte hotel blending Tudor and Georgian architectural features with a
modern wing of bedrooms. Banqueting and conference facilities for around
50. Families with children well catered for, with babysitting and listening
available. *Rooms 24. Access, Amex, Visa,* ()

Great Dunmow	The Starr		£75

Tel 0371 874321   Fax 0371 876337   **RR**

Market Place Great Dunmow Essex CM6 1AX   **Map 6 B3**

The Starr is a small family-run restaurant, the dining area being in the old
stable block at the back of the main building. London markets and local
sources supply the raw materials for Mark Fisher's well-conceived dishes:
soft herring roes in puff pastry with poppy seed and spinach, parcel of
rabbit with leeks, Aylesbury duck with honey and figs, fillet of brill with
octopus pilaff, beignets soufflés with lemon curd. Lighter lunchtime options
are available Monday to Friday. A physically small list of good-value wines
is exceptionally well chosen, mostly French but Australia and New Zealand
also make a good showing. *Seats 50. Parties 12. L 12-1.30 D 7-9.30. Closed*
L Sat, D Sun, 1 week Jan. Set L £10 (Sun £20) Set D £19. Access, Amex,
Visa, ()

Rooms   £85

Eight bedrooms, with names like the Oak Room, the Brass Room and the
Poppy Room, are furnished mainly with antiques.

Great Dunmow   Places of Interest

Saling Hall Garden   Great Saling Tel 0371 850141.

Great Gonerby	Harry's Place	£80
Tel 0476 61780		**R**
17 High Street Great Gonerby Grantham Lincolnshire NG31 8JS		Map 11 E3

Harry Hallam cooks and his wife Caroline serves a meticulously planned meal to just ten diners at their tiny restaurant set in an elegant Georgian house. Each session sees a separate hand-written menu of two choices per course (plus optional French and English cheeses), on which Harry's elaborate creations are carefully described. Thus, "terrine of Scarborough lobster served with Sevruga caviar, lemon and dill mayonnaise and a salad of green leaves", followed perhaps by "filleted loin of lamb roasted with basil, tomatoes, olive oil and white wine, served with roasted sweet red peppers and aubergine" are sufficient to tempt the most discerning diner, and results live up to their promise. For pre-booked parties, a complementary wine may be proposed to accompany each course; the Chateau Guiraud 1983 1er cru Sauternes, for instance, particularly appeals with an apple and cognac soufflé. *Seats 10. Parties 10. Private Room. L 12-2 D 7-9.30. Closed Sun & Mon, Bank Holidays, 1 week Xmas. Access, Visa.*

Great Milton	Le Manoir aux Quat'Saisons	85%	£184
Tel 0844 278881 Fax 0844 278847			**HR**
Church Road Great Milton Oxfordshire OX9 7PD			Map 5 D2

Service and housekeeping are among the best in the country at this 15th-century manor house built by a French nobleman, set in 25 acres of grounds. A flagstoned inner foyer is a showpiece for the accolades bestowed upon Raymond Blanc for his cooking and leads into lounges that are models of restrained good taste, created by interior designer Michael Priest. Antique and immaculate reproduction furniture set a refined tone that is echoed throughout the whole house. All the luxury extras that one might expect from an 80%+ hotel are in the bedrooms, including a comfortable settee, decanter of Madeira, sugared almonds, sewing kit with silk thread and a bowl of 14 fresh fruits. Rooms in the new wing lead out on to patio gardens with wrought-iron furniture. The beautiful bathrooms feature jacuzzi or whirlpool baths, gold-plated fittings, huge fluffy towels and luxurious bathrobes. Cooked breakfasts are, of course, superb but not served in the bedrooms. One mile from junction 7 of the M40, 7 miles from Oxford and 40 miles from London. *Rooms 19. Garden, croquet, outdoor swimming pool, tennis. Access, Amex, Visa,*

Restaurant ★★★

£195

The dining rooms consist of two rooms and a conservatory. The latter is bright and airy, green and pink the dominating colours, with cane chairs. The other rooms are more formal with oak beams, smart purple fabrics and oil paintings on the plain-painted walls. Fresh flowers come from Albert Ring (credited on the menu as head gardener) who tends the manor house's extensive gardens. A *menu gourmand* comprises five courses of seasonal specialities that might include *assiette apéritive, mosaïque de volailles et petits légumes confits au vinaigre de miel, mousse d'asperges à l'infusion de cerfeuil, bouillon de poissons de roche, granité au vin rouge, médaillon de boeuf aux saveurs des sous-bois, les trois petits bonheurs du manoir*, finishing with exquisite *petits fours*. Faultless preparation and perfect execution is what one always *expects* from Raymond Blanc's brigade (led by head chef Clive Fretwell), but there are occasional hiccups. From the carte one might choose wild salmon and caviar *en gelée*, roasted langoustines, poached scallops and wild salmon in a coriander-scented jus, salad of duck and crayfish, fricassée of chanterelles and snails, or tomato consommé with red pepper mousse and ricotta cheese ravioli to commence; to follow, eight or so meat and four fish dishes might range from roast best end of suckling pig with marjoram-scented jus or braised veal sweetbreads with truffle

sabayon and fondue of watercress, to pan-fried fillets of red mullet, sea
bream, John Dory, scorpion fish and baby squid on olive and fennel purée
and a bouillabaisse jus, or crab gateau scented with caraway seeds and
poached fillets of sole with a Gewurztraminer and chive sauce. Superb
desserts are epitomised by *Le Café Crème* – concentrated espresso ice cream
served in a wafer-thin Valrhona bitter chocolate cup topped with a Kirsch
sabayon. A three-course, daily-changing *menu du jour* offers alternatives at
each course: perhaps salad of lamb on a bed of artichokes and green beans
or mousse of squab livers with a port and tomato sauce to start, followed
by rosemary-scented medallions of monkfish served with a meat jus or
boned leg of Bresse chicken filled with a mousse and accompanied by baby
leeks and a wild mushroom sauce; tip-top cheeses, chocolate soufflé with
prune ice cream or warmed raspberries with a vanilla and raspberry sauce
(*à la façon Maman Blanc*) to finish. Service is usually exemplary and there's
an air of unhurried professionalism throughout, leaving guests time to
savour their meal. The wine list, although uninspiringly presented, is long,
finely balanced and French orientated; country wines are the best value,
but there are also some superb top names, serious Italians and good half
bottles. *Seats 95. Parties 46. Private Room. L 12.15-2.15 D7.15-10.15. Set L
£29.50 Set D £59.50.*

Great Snoring	Old Rectory	61%	£80
Tel 0328 820597 Fax 0328 820048			**H**
Barsham Road Great Snoring Nr Fakenham Norfolk NR21 0HP			Map 6 C1

Behind the church on the Barsham road, the Old Rectory retains some
pleasing architectural features, including stone-mullioned windows
bordered by frieze tiles. Day rooms are peaceful and old-fashioned and
there are some fine period furnishings in the handsomely proportioned
bedrooms. The Sheltons, some newly built brick and flint cottages in the
grounds, offer a greater degree of privacy and seclusion, each having its
own living room and kitchen. No children under 12. No dogs. *Rooms 6.
Garden. Amex,* ⓘ Diners Club International

Great Yarmouth	Carlton Hotel	67%	£79
Tel 0493 855234 Fax 0493 852220			**H**
Marine Parade Great Yarmouth Norfolk NR30 3JE			Map 6 D1

With its fine seafront location and recent complete refurbishment, the
Carlton is the flagship of East Anglia's Waveney Inns Group. An
impressive interior now houses conference facilities from 5 to 150 and
banqueting for 120. Bonuses for individual guests include the all-day café-
bar and a hair salon. Bedrooms have bright colour schemes and smart tiled
bathrooms. *Rooms 90. Access, Amex, Visa,* ⓘ Diners Club International

Great Yarmouth   Seafood Restaurant   £55

`Tel 0493 856009`   **R**

85 North Quay Great Yarmouth Norfolk NR30 1JF   Map 6 D1

There's a tankful of live lobsters, and an excellent selection of seafood and
shellfish, much of it arriving daily from Lowestoft, that could include
Dover sole, cod, skate, turbot, monkfish and giant prawns. Fish can be
served grilled, poached, in batter or with a sauce. Steaks for meat-eaters,
surf'n'turf for a mixed palate. Good wines include some drier Germans.
*Seats 40. Parties 40. L 12-1.45 D 7-10.30. Closed L Sat, all Sun, Bank
Holidays, 3 weeks Xmas.* Access, Amex, Visa, 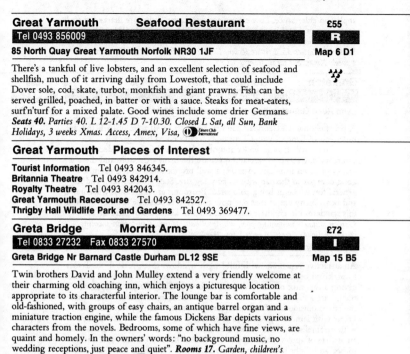 *Diners Club International*

Great Yarmouth   Places of Interest

Tourist Information   Tel 0493 846345.
Britannia Theatre   Tel 0493 842914.
Royalty Theatre   Tel 0493 842043.
Great Yarmouth Racecourse   Tel 0493 842527.
Thrigby Hall Wildlife Park and Gardens   Tel 0493 369477.

Greta Bridge   Morritt Arms   £72

`Tel 0833 27232   Fax 0833 27570`   **I**

Greta Bridge Nr Barnard Castle Durham DL12 9SE   Map 15 B5

Twin brothers David and John Mulley extend a very friendly welcome at
their charming old coaching inn, which enjoys a picturesque location
appropriate to its characterful interior. The lounge bar is comfortable and
old-fashioned, with groups of easy chairs, an antique barrel organ and a
miniature traction engine, while the famous Dickens Bar depicts various
characters from the novels. Bedrooms, some of which have fine views, are
quaint and homely. In the owners' words: "no background music, no
wedding receptions, just peace and quiet". *Rooms 17. Garden, children's
playground.* Access, Amex, Visa, *Diners Club International*

Grimsby   Forte Crest   64%   £87

`Tel 0472 350295   Fax 0472 241354`   **H**

Littlecoates Road Grimsby Humberside DN34 4LX   Map 11 F1

Friendly and peaceful late-60s hotel on the outskirts of town, overlooking a
golf course. Business-oriented in the week (catering for conferences of up to
250 delegates), popular with families at weekends. *Rooms 52.* Access, Amex,
Visa, *Diners Club International*

Grimsby   Places of Interest

Tourist Information   Tel 0472 240180.
Leisure Centre Ice Rink   Tel 0472 242000.
Animal Gardens Mablethorpe   Tel 05074 73346.

Grimsthorpe   Black Horse Inn   £52

`Tel 077 832 247   Fax 077 839 3990`   **IR**

Grimsthorpe Bourne Lincolnshire PE10 0LY   Map 11 E3

A mellow stone building which was once a farmhouse, the inn still retains
an old-world atmosphere. Exposed beams, stone walls and a log fire
characterise the traditional public bar and there's a homely, relaxing
lounge. Bedrooms are bright, cheerful and cottagey, with floral fabrics,
books, magazines and fresh flowers. Bathrooms are neat and simple. *Rooms
4. Garden.* Access, Amex, Visa.

Restaurant   £55

Traditional English cooking to match the surroundings. The 4-course
menu is fixed-price, (but many dishes carry a supplement) and offers the
likes of chicken liver paté, Mrs Beeton's beefsteak, kidney and mushroom
pie, Grimsby plaice with tartare sauce and Elizabethan pork with Bramley

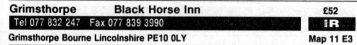

apple and cider sauce. Low-calorie and vegetarian dishes are marked as such
on the menu. Snackier items include speciality open sandwiches – York
ham, Cromer crab and Stilton cheese. No children under 12 in restaurant.
*Seats 40. Parties 35. Private Room. L 12-2 D 7-9.30 (Sat to 10). Closed Sun,
1 week Xmas. Set meals from £15.95.*

Grimston   Congham Hall   76%   £99

Tel 0485 600250   Fax 0485 601191   **HR**

Lynn Road Grimston King's Lynn Norfolk PE32 1AH   Map 6 B1

A privately-owned Georgian country house set in 40 acres of parkland, six
miles east of King's Lynn. Christine Forecast's noted herb garden
contributes baskets of lavender and other herbs and flowers to decorate the
summery day rooms. Peace and quiet are the main attractions and there is
plenty of room in which to relax; a well-proportioned sitting room is a
good contrast to the bar with its cosy log fire. Staff are charming and the
general feel is one of being pampered. Bedrooms are individually decorated
and boast many extras that one now comes to expect in a country hotel of
this standard. No children under 12. Dogs in kennels only. *Rooms 14.
Garden, outdoor swimming pool, whirlpool bath, tennis, clay-pigeon shooting,
cricket, helipad. Access, Amex, Visa,* (I) Diners Club International.

Orangery Restaurant   £85

An attractive restaurant with full-length windows that overlook the lawns
to parkland beyond. The glass roof in the centre of the room trails plants,
giving a fine mix of the formal and informal. Chef Murray Chapman's
menus are a suitable match to the venue – from light summer lunches on
the lawns outside to a fixed-price carte that runs from papillote of quail
breast with lemon, sage and red onion relish to pan-fried breast of duck
with caramelised garlic, a mousse of its own livers and a thyme sauce, and
an assiette of apples (baked apple tart, chilled Bavarian cream, and spiced
sorbet with light toffee sauce). *Seats 50. Parties 12. Private Room. L 12.30-2
D 7.30-9.30. Closed L Sat & Bank Holidays. Set L £13.50/£15.00 Set D
£30.*

Grindleford   Maynard Arms   £72

Tel 0433 630321   Fax 0433 630445   **I**

Main Road Grindleford Derbyshire S30 1HP   Map 10 C2

At the heart of the Peak National Park amid fine walking country stands
this imposing Victorian house. Splendid stained-glass windows feature
throughout the hotel, which has a welcoming and informal air. Bedrooms
of good size are decorated and furnished in various styles. Most offer fine
views over Hope Valley. Dark blue tiling in the bathrooms. Public areas
include a homely residents' lounge, two bars and a ballroom. *Rooms 13.
Garden. Access, Amex, Visa,* (I) Diners Club International.

Grizedale   Grizedale Lodge   61%   £64

Tel 053 94 36532   **HR**

Grizedale Nr Hawkshead Cumbria LA22 0QL   Map 13 D5

The Lambs' hidden hotel, small and homely, welcomes so many annual
returnees that you'll need to book well in advance. Comfortable rewards
are found in the roomy lounge, cheery bar and spick-and-span cottage-style
bedrooms; three rooms are in a newly-built extension. All have en-suite
facilities (four with showers only); one is a family room with a double
and two single beds; one has a four-poster. No dogs. *Rooms 9. Garden.
Closed Jan-mid Feb. Access, Visa.*

Restaurant in the Forest   £45

Margaret Lamb's home-style cooking befits the atmosphere of a former
hunting lodge. Choices on the short menu rely heavily on local produce
and are substantial in both flavours and volume. Roast ribs of beef, Penrith
lamb, local trout and duckling form the centrepieces, to which hearty

puddings add a fitting finale. *Seats 30. Parties 35. Private Room.*
L 12.15-1.45 D 7-8.30 (Sun at 7). Set D £16.95.

| Guildford | The Angel | 71% | £122 |

Tel 0483 64555   Fax 0483 33770

91 High Street Guildford Surrey GU1 3DP   Map 5 E3

Purchased privately from Forte hotels, the Angel has reopened as a "Posting
House and Livery" with much of the style that was formerly lacking. Nine
of the eleven bedrooms are full suites and all are furnished to the same high
standard with reproduction antique furniture and a variety of stylish fabrics
with bedhead drapes and quilted covers. Smart marble bathrooms boast
large soft towels and bathrobes. The only day room is a small galleried
lounge with ancient redbrick inglenook fireplace, old black timbers and
deep, comfortable settees and armchairs, where drinks are served to
residents and diners only. Beds are turned down in the evenings and
excellent breakfasts make a fine start to the day. *Rooms 11. Access, Amex,*
Visa, *Diners Club International*

| Guildford | Forte Crest | 68% | £97 |

Tel 0483 574444   Fax 0483 302960

Egerton Road Guildford Surrey GU2 5XZ   Map 5 E3

Darkwood panelling and a white marble fireplace lend a very civilised air
to the public areas at this smart modern hotel on the outskirts of town
(follow signs for the University). Very much geared-up to the
requirements of business travellers with ample free parking, secretarial
services and meeting rooms and they can even provide a personal pager for
use within the hotel, ensuring that you do not miss a vital call.
Comprehensive 24hr room service. *Rooms 111. Garden, indoor swimming*
pool, sauna, solarium, gymnasium, keep-fit equipment, coffee shop (7am-11pm).
Access, Amex, Visa, *Diners Club International*

| Guildford | Mandarin | £35 |

Tel 0483 572293

13 Epsom Road Guildford Surrey GU1 3JT   Map 5 E3

Modern, cool decor with black lacquered chairs and spotlit tables add up to
a quietly chic ambience in a friendly restaurant at the top of the town.
Cooking covers Peking, Szechuan and Cantonese styles with both
outstanding crispy aromatic duck and unusal deep-fried quail showing flair
in the kitchen, though other dishes like Mongolian hot pot lamb and
griddled dumplings are more ordinary. *Seats 55. Parties 55. L 12.30-2.30*
D 6-10.30 (Fri & Sat to 11). Closed L Sun, 25 & 26 Dec. Set D from
£14.50. Access, Amex, Visa, *Diners Club International*

Guildford   Places of Interest

Tourist Information   Tel 0483 444007.
Yvonne Arnaud Theatre   Millbrook Tel 0483 64571.
Guildford Cathedral   Tel 0483 65287.
Woodbridge Road Cricket Ground   Tel 0483 572181.
Combined Services Polo Committee   Pirbright Tel 0483 798449.
Stoke Park Showground   Tel 0483 414651.
   Historic Houses, Castles and Gardens
Clandon Park and Garden (NT)   Tel 0483 222482.
Coverwood Lakes   Ewhurst Tel 0306 731103.
Hatchlands Park House and Gardens (NT)   East Clandon Tel 0483
   222787.
Loseley House   Tel 0483 304440.
Wisley Garden   (The Royal Horticultural Society) Wisley Tel 0938
   224234.
   Museums and Art Galleries
British Red Cross Museum and Archives   Barnett Hill, Wonersh. Tel
   0483 898595.

Gallery 90   Ward Street Tel 0483 444741.
Guildford Museum   Tel 0483 444750.

Guiseley	Prachee	£30

Tel 0943 872531	**R**

Whitecross Guiseley Nr Bradford West Yorkshire   Map 10 C1

Tandoori restaurant opposite Harry Ramsden's fish and chip restaurant at Whitecross. *Seats 56. Parties 25. L 12-2 D 6-12. Access, Visa.*

Guist	Tollbridge	£65

Tel 036 284 359	**R**

Dereham Road Guist Norfolk NR20 5NU   Map 6 C1

A redbrick house with an open-air, floodlit terrace dining area overlooking the rushes on the banks of the river Wensum. The menu format has changed to a fixed-price affair from which one can choose either a two, three or four-course option. Starters like Cromer crab with sweet grapefruit and seafood dressing, and twice-baked cheese soufflé are followed by a salad course before main dishes such as honey-glazed Gressingham duck with cranberry sauce, and cassoulet. Puddings might include an alcoholic white chocolate sorbet (made with vodka and Noilly Prat) and strawberry tart. No smoking. Concise wine list with personal notes and fair prices. *Seats 50. Parties 60. L (Sun only) 12.30-1.30 D 7.30-9 (Sat from 7). Closed D Sun, all Mon, 3 weeks Jan. Set L £9.95 (3-course) Set D £21-50-27.50. Access, Visa.*

Gulworthy	Horn of Plenty	★	£85

Tel & Fax 0822 832528	**RR**

Gulworthy Tavistock Devon PL19 8JD   Map 2 C3

Diners will soak in glorious summer vistas of the Tamar Valley and all but touch the wallflowers and rhododendrons through the picture windows. To this idyllic and timeless setting hosts Elaine and Ian Gatehouse bring an immediacy of warmth and chef Peter Gorton his wealth of talent. A fixed-price dinner menu of limited but excellent choice continues along the same lines as those set by previous owner Sonia Stevenson, and always includes a fresh fish of the day. Terrine of rabbit with apricot chutney and roast rack of lamb with a red pepper sauce could be among the meaty options. A la carte, dishes become more involved, with the likes of Cornish lobster and vegetable salad with tempura asparagus, mushroom-stuffed quail with wild rice risotto, breast of duck with wild mushrooms wrapped in a cabbage leaf and served with a port wine sauce, and grilled turbot on tomatoes, sweet peppers and saffron with a white wine and basil sauce. Sweets are usually excellent and there's a good selection of local cheeses. *Seats 48. Parties 50. Private Room. L 12-2 D 7-9.30. Closed L Mon, 25 & 26 Dec. Set L £14.50/£17.50 Set D £24.50. Access, Amex, Visa.*

Rooms   £78

Standing separately, six of the seven en-suite bedrooms have their own balconies with superb views looking west, facing their own walled garden. Pine furnishings and natural wood beams abound. Room-service breakfasts are indecently good – indulge! *Rooms 7. Garden.*

Hackness	Hackness Grange	60%	£116

Tel 0723 882345 Fax 0723 882391	**H**

Hackness Nr Scarborough North Yorkshire YO13 0JW   Map 15 D6

An attractive 19th-century house standing in its own grounds among the wonderful North York Moors. However, inside is less exciting than the setting: the bar, which overlooks a large pond, has distinctly old-fashioned furnishings. Bedrooms, some of which are in a converted two-storey stable-block, are only modestly appointed with functional furniture. Dogs in kennels only. *Rooms 28. Garden, indoor swimming pool, tennis, putting, croquet. Access, Amex, Visa,*

Hadley Wood   West Lodge Park   66%   £104

Tel 081-440 8311   Fax 081-449 3698   **H**

Cockfosters Road Hadley Wood Nr Barnet Hertfordshire EN4 0PY   Map 7 B4

An extended 19th-century country house set in parkland that includes an
arboretum and a lake. Inside, there's an orderly, civilised feel in the lounge,
plentifully supplied with armchairs, in the brick-walled bar and in the four
conference rooms (catering for up to 80 delegates). Bedrooms are
individually decorated and furnished, and the majority have small entrance
lobbies. The hotel is on the A111 halfway between the M25 (exit 24) and
Cockfosters underground station. Free use of nearby leisure centre. No
dogs. *Rooms 50. Garden, croquet, putting, rowing, bar billiards, helipad. Access,
Amex, Visa,*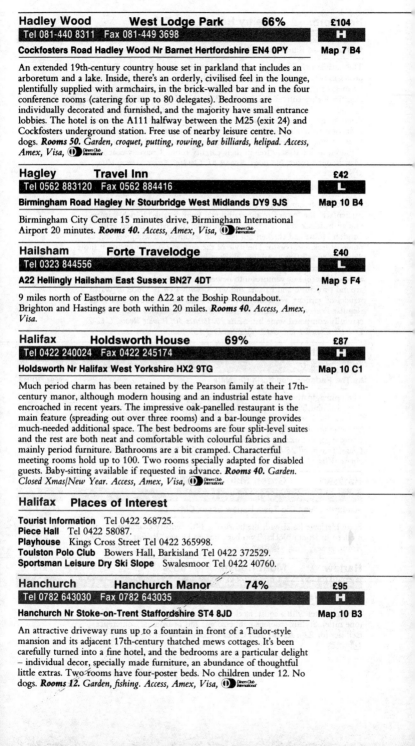

Hagley   Travel Inn   £42

Tel 0562 883120   Fax 0562 884416   **L**

Birmingham Road Hagley Nr Stourbridge West Midlands DY9 9JS   Map 10 B4

Birmingham City Centre 15 minutes drive, Birmingham International
Airport 20 minutes. *Rooms 40. Access, Amex, Visa,*

Hailsham   Forte Travelodge   £40

Tel 0323 844556   **L**

A22 Hellingly Hailsham East Sussex BN27 4DT   Map 5 F4

9 miles north of Eastbourne on the A22 at the Boship Roundabout.
Brighton and Hastings are both within 20 miles. *Rooms 40. Access, Amex,
Visa.*

Halifax   Holdsworth House   69%   £87

Tel 0422 240024   Fax 0422 245174   **H**

Holdsworth Nr Halifax West Yorkshire HX2 9TG   Map 10 C1

Much period charm has been retained by the Pearson family at their 17th-
century manor, although modern housing and an industrial estate have
encroached in recent years. The impressive oak-panelled restaurant is the
main feature (spreading out over three rooms) and a bar-lounge provides
much-needed additional space. The best bedrooms are four split-level suites
and the rest are both neat and comfortable with colourful fabrics and
mainly period furniture. Bathrooms are a bit cramped. Characterful
meeting rooms hold up to 100. Two rooms specially adapted for disabled
guests. Baby-sitting available if requested in advance. *Rooms 40. Garden.
Closed Xmas/New Year. Access, Amex, Visa,*

Halifax   Places of Interest

Tourist Information   Tel 0422 368725.
Piece Hall   Tel 0422 58087.
Playhouse   Kings Cross Street Tel 0422 365998.
Toulston Polo Club   Bowers Hall, Barkisland Tel 0422 372529.
Sportsman Leisure Dry Ski Slope   Swalesmoor Tel 0422 40760.

Hanchurch   Hanchurch Manor   74%   £95

Tel 0782 643030   Fax 0782 643035   **H**

Hanchurch Nr Stoke-on-Trent Staffordshire ST4 8JD   Map 10 B3

An attractive driveway runs up to a fountain in front of a Tudor-style
mansion and its adjacent 17th-century thatched mews cottages. It's been
carefully turned into a fine hotel, and the bedrooms are a particular delight
– individual decor, specially made furniture, an abundance of thoughtful
little extras. Two rooms have four-poster beds. No children under 12. No
dogs. *Rooms 12. Garden, fishing. Access, Amex, Visa,*

Handforth   Belfry Hotel   71%   £91

Tel 061-437 0511   Fax 061-499 0597   **HR**

Stanley Road Handforth Nr Wilmslow Cheshire SK9 3LD   Map 10 B2

The outside may be functional and uninspiring, but inside the Belfry is a
professionally run and exceptionally well-maintained hotel. It's mainly
business oriented, and the Beech family look to provide all the modern
facilities for executives. Reception is floored with pink marble, the lounge
has cream-coloured silk-effect walls and the bar is strikingly up to date in
shades of grey. The hotel's solid virtues are felt strongly in the spotless
bedrooms, where good room service obviates the need for tea-makers.
Dark mahogany furniture adds to the comfortable feel. Seven suites.
Children under 10 stay free in their parents' room. Courtesy coach to
Manchester airport. No dogs. *Rooms 81. Garden. Access, Amex, Visa,*

Restaurant   £60

Smooth, professional service and a menu that makes interesting reading,
particularly the "return to the traditional English table" which features
Finnan haddock and crab rissoles with watercress sauce, mixed grill
London House and chicken hot pot with scrumpy, russet apples and a
purée of leek and potato. The style of the carte sticks with tradition (hors
d'oeuvre served from a trolley, chicken liver paté with apple and raisin
chutney, bacon-wrapped king prawns, Dover sole, roast duck with orange
and port sauce) but ventures into newer territory with chicken wrapped
around prosciutto and banana and served with a curry sauce, or warm
strudel of garlicky vegetables and mushrooms on a peanut butter sauce.
Regular Friday night dinner dances. Lots of classics (some old) on a
carefully composed wine list. *Seats 90. Parties 30. Private Room. L 12-2
D 7-10. Closed 1 Jan. Set L £12 Set D £15.*

Handforth   Handforth Chinese Restaurant   £45

Tel 0625 531670   **R**

8a The Paddock Handforth Cheshire   Map 10 B2

The unimaginative name for this restaurant, plus its locality in a parade of
shops in suburban Manchester, does little justice to the good, honest
Chinese food on offer. Sound cooking and professional service are matched
by some notable Peking inspired dishes: aromatic crispy duck, grilled
dumplings, and sizzling beef. *Seats 85. Parties 10. L 12-2 D 5.30-11.30.
Closed L Sun, all 25 & 26 Dec. Set L from £5.50 Set D from £14. Access,
Amex, Visa.*

Harlow   Green Man   60%   £91

Tel 0279 442521   Fax 0279 626113   **H**

Mulberry Green Old Town Harlow Essex CM17 0ET   Map 7 B4

Forte Heritage hotel with the heart of a 14th-century coaching inn and
modern bedroom blocks. Two bars, but no lounge. *Rooms 55. Garden.
Access, Amex, Visa,*

Harlow   Moat House   68%   £72

Tel 0279 422441   Fax 0279 635094   **H**

Southern Way Harlow Essex CM18 7BA   Map 7 B4

Modern hotel with a squat, faceless exterior close to junction 7 of M11
(one mile). Stylish, spacious public rooms and bedrooms. Conference
facilities for 220. *Rooms 120. Closed 24 Dec-1 Jan. Access, Amex, Visa,*

Harlow   Places of Interest

The Playhouse   The High Tel 0279 431945.
Epping Forest District Museum   Tel 0992 716882.
Harlow Ski School   Tel 0279 444100.

Harome	Pheasant Hotel	68%	£70

Tel 0439 71241

H

Harome Nr Helmsley North Yorkshire YO6 5JG

Map 15 C6

The village smithy, the village shop and two cottages were transformed
into a comfortable and relaxed hotel by the pond and millstream. Day
rooms comprise a little oak-beamed bar, a restaurant and a lounge that
opens on to a flagstoned terrace. Bedrooms include three suites in
outbuildings. No children under 12. *Rooms 18. Garden. Closed Xmas/New
Year, Jan-Feb. No credit cards.*

Harpenden	Glen Eagle Hotel	63%	£100

Tel 0582 760271   Fax 0582 460819

H

1 Luton Road Harpenden Hertfordshire AL5 2PX

Map 5 E2

The Glen Eagle's rather functional redbrick, two-storey structure, given a
third floor by its dormered roof, isn't relieved by the sprawl of the tarmac
car-park out front. It takes a view over the rear terracing and gardens to
restore a favourable impression while the sight of the foyer's multi-hued
parquet flooring and galleried landing dispels earlier qualms. Bedrooms are
decently-sized with well-equipped marble-effect bathrooms. *Rooms 50.
Garden. Access, Amex, Visa,*

Harpenden	Moat House	68%	£109

Tel 0582 764111   Fax 0582 769858

H

Southdown Road Harpenden Hertfordshire AL5 1PE

Map 5 E2

Elegant redbrick Georgian house, just off A1081. Tastefully decorated day
rooms and well-equipped bedrooms. Family facilities. *Rooms 53. Access,
Amex, Visa,*

Harrogate	Café Fleur		£42

Tel 0423 503034

R

3 Royal Parade Harrogate North Yorkshire HG1 2SZ

Map 15 C6

Opposite the Crown Hotel, a reasonably priced French brasserie-style
restaurant with a lively and informal atmosphere. Simple fare runs from
grilled sardines and pasta with roast peppers to poached salmon with an
orange and basil sauce, calf's liver and ribeye steak. Steak sandwich is a
popular quick-snack speciality. Set menus include Petite Fleur, which is
very cheap (and even cheaper before 7.30). *Seats 56. Parties 12. D only
6-9.30. Closed 25 & 26 Dec, 1 Jan. Set D £6.95/£7.95 & £14.95. Access,
Visa.*

Harrogate	The Crown	67%	£98

Tel 0423 567755   Fax 0423 502284

H

Crown Place Harrogate North Yorkshire HG1 2RZ

Map 15 C6

Forte Heritage hotel originally built in 1740 as a coaching inn, but of the
grander variety. Free use of the Majestic's leisure facilities.
Conferences/banquets for up to 450/300. *Rooms 121. Access, Amex, Visa,*

Harrogate — Drum & Monkey — £45

Tel 0423 502650 — **R**

5 Montpellier Gardens Harrogate North Yorkshire HG1 2TF — Map 15 C6

Bustling fish restaurant on two floors with cramped tables. Simple dishes
fare best on a menu that ranges from oysters and mussels to Dover sole,
seafood pie and lobster salad. *Seats 48. Parties 8. L 12-2.30 D 7-10.15.
Closed Sun, Xmas/New Year. Access, Visa.*

Harrogate — Hospitality Inn — 61% — £93

Tel 0423 564601   Fax 0423 507508 — **H**

West Park Prospect Place Harrogate North Yorkshire HG1 1LB — Map 15 C6

A row of town-centre converted Georgian town houses. Children up to 14
free in parents' room. Conference and banqueting facilities for up to 120.
Mount Charlotte Thistle. *Rooms 71. Access, Amex, Visa,* 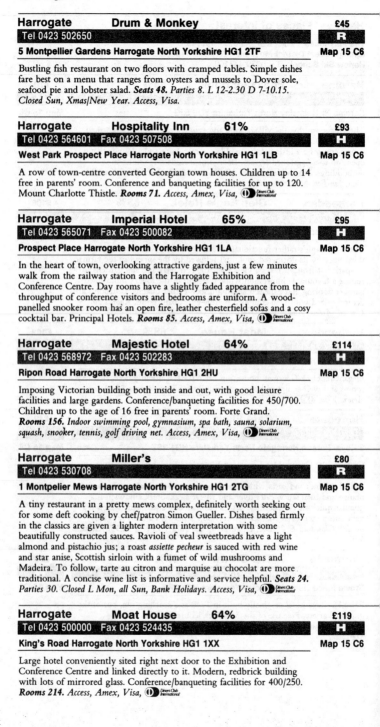 DinersClub International

Harrogate — Imperial Hotel — 65% — £95

Tel 0423 565071   Fax 0423 500082 — **H**

Prospect Place Harrogate North Yorkshire HG1 1LA — Map 15 C6

In the heart of town, overlooking attractive gardens, just a few minutes
walk from the railway station and the Harrogate Exhibition and
Conference Centre. Day rooms have a slightly faded appearance from the
throughput of conference visitors and bedrooms are uniform. A wood-
panelled snooker room has an open fire, leather chesterfield sofas and a cosy
cocktail bar. Principal Hotels. *Rooms 85. Access, Amex, Visa,* DinersClub International

Harrogate — Majestic Hotel — 64% — £114

Tel 0423 568972   Fax 0423 502283 — **H**

Ripon Road Harrogate North Yorkshire HG1 2HU — Map 15 C6

Imposing Victorian building both inside and out, with good leisure
facilities and large gardens. Conference/banqueting facilities for 450/700.
Children up to the age of 16 free in parents' room. Forte Grand.
*Rooms 156. Indoor swimming pool, gymnasium, spa bath, sauna, solarium,
squash, snooker, tennis, golf driving net. Access, Amex, Visa,* DinersClub International

Harrogate — Miller's — £80

Tel 0423 530708 — **R**

1 Montpelier Mews Harrogate North Yorkshire HG1 2TG — Map 15 C6

A tiny restaurant in a pretty mews complex, definitely worth seeking out
for some deft cooking by chef/patron Simon Gueller. Dishes based firmly
in the classics are given a lighter modern interpretation with some
beautifully constructed sauces. Ravioli of veal sweetbreads have a light
almond and pistachio jus; a roast *assiette pecheur* is sauced with red wine
and star anise, Scottish sirloin with a fumet of wild mushrooms and
Madeira. To follow, tarte au citron and marquise au chocolat are more
traditional. A concise wine list is informative and service helpful. *Seats 24.
Parties 30. Closed L Mon, all Sun, Bank Holidays. Access, Visa,* DinersClub International

Harrogate — Moat House — 64% — £119

Tel 0423 500000   Fax 0423 524435 — **H**

King's Road Harrogate North Yorkshire HG1 1XX — Map 15 C6

Large hotel conveniently sited right next door to the Exhibition and
Conference Centre and linked directly to it. Modern, redbrick building
with lots of mirrored glass. Conference/banqueting facilities for 400/250.
Rooms 214. Access, Amex, Visa, DinersClub International

Harrogate   Old Swan Hotel   69%

£122

HR

Tel 0423 500055   Fax 0423 501154

Swan Road Harrogate North Yorkshire HG1 2SR

Map 15 C6

Probably the town's best hotel, an imposing ivy-clad building set in attractive private gardens near the centre of town, not far from Harrogate's Exhibition and Conference Centre (5 minutes walk away). When Agatha Christie mysteriously vanished in 1926 it was here, at the Old Swan, that she was discovered some days later, making this a particularly fitting venue for the Super Sleuth weekends held from time to time for aspiring Misses Marple and Hercule Poirots. The atmosphere of Victorian times is evoked by some handsome architectural features (the Wedgwood room, where breakfast is served) and fine antiques (the grandfather clock in the main lobby). Committed staff and good housekeeping are major pluses, as is the ample parking. Conference facilities for up to 400. Children under 12 stay free in parents' room. *Rooms 135. Garden. Access, Amex, Visa,* ◑ *Diners Club International*

Library Restaurant

£70

Delightfully traditional, the elegant room offers cooking a cut above standards usually found in provincial hotels of this size. Despite some rather flowery menu prose, executive chef Trevor Whitehead produces appealing and modern dishes with aplomb: home-made tomato raviolis with mushrooms, rich beef consommé, toasted fillet of fresh sea bass, medallions of veal – all admirably executed. Desserts are displayed on a pyramid centrepiece; a summer pudding was faultless. Decent cheeses; the so-so wine list has helpful notes. *Seats 28. Parties 40. L 12.30-2 D 7-10. Set L from £9.95 Set D £18.*

Harrogate   Hotel St George   63%

£99

H

Tel 0423 561431   Fax 0423 530037

Ripon Road Harrogate North Yorkshire HG1 2SY

Map 15 C6

Edwardian-styled interiors and good-sized bedrooms behind an ivy-clad facade. Extensive conference facilities (for up to 300 delegates) and a modern leisure club. Swallow Hotels. *Rooms 93. Garden, indoor swimming pool, keep-fit equipment, spa bath, solarium, sauna, steam room. Access, Amex, Visa,* ◑ *Diners Club International*

Harrogate   Studley Hotel   66%

£78

H

Tel 0423 560425   Fax 0423 530967

28 Swan Road Harrogate North Yorkshire HG1 2SE

Map 15 C6

A well-run, homely hotel in a peaceful location by Valley Gardens. The attractive front is made up of a terrace of houses, and at the back there's a good car park. Lounge and bar offer easy relaxation, the former containing a gallery of local artists' work. There are two restaurants, one specialising in seafood. Good-quality built-in units furnish the bedrooms, whose well co-ordinated colour schemes extend to the excellent bathrooms. No children under eight. *Rooms 36. Garden. Access, Amex, Visa,* ◑ *Diners Club International*

Harrogate   Tannin Level

£35

R

Tel 0423 560595

5 Raglan Street Harrogate North Yorkshire HG1 1LE

Map 15 C6

Basement wine bar on a corner site with brick walls and flagstone floor, offering a choice of nearly 400 wines. The food, once playing second string to the vinous offerings, now features the likes of jambon persillé, venison with redcurrant glaze, Toulouse sausage with sauerkraut, duck confit, tortelloni with wild mushroom sauce, pear and almond tart and bread-and-butter pudding on blackboard menus. Simple, tasty fare. *Seats 75. Private Room. L 12-2 D 5.30-10 (Sat from 6.30). Closed Sun. Access, Visa.*

Harrogate   Places of Interest

Harrogate Tourist Information Tel 0423 525666.
Harrogate Conference and Exhibition Centre Tel 0423 500500.
Royal Pump Room Museum Tel 0423 503340.
Harrogate Theatre Tel 0423 502116.
Wetherby Racecourse Tel 0937 582035.
Harrogate Ski Centre Tel 0423 505457.
Great Yorkshire Showground Tel 0423 561536.

Hartlebury   Forte Travelodge   £40

Tel 0299 250553   **L**

**A449 Shorthill Nurseries Hartlebury Kidderminster
Hereford & Worcester DY11 6DR**   Map 10 B4

On the southbound carriageway of the A449, 4 miles south of
Kidderminster. *Rooms 32. Access, Amex, Visa.*

Hartlepool   Grand Hotel   59%   £60

Tel 0429 266345   Fax 0429 265217   **H**

Swainson Street Hartlepool Cleveland TS24 8AA   Map 15 C5

A balconied Victorian ballroom tops the function/conference facilities at
this handsome redbrick hotel close to the shopping centre. Children under
14 sharing parents' room are accommodated free. *Rooms 41. Access, Amex,
Visa,* ⓞ Diners Club International

Hartshead Moor   Forte Travelodge   £40

Tel 0274 851706   **L**

**Hartshead Moor service area Clifton Brighouse
West Yorkshire HD6 4RJ**   Map 10 C1

Located on the eastbound carriageway of the M62 at the Welcome Break
service area between junctions 25 and 26. *Rooms 40. Access, Amex, Visa.*

Harvington   The Mill   67%   £85

Tel &   Fax 0386 870688   **HR**

Anchor Lane Harvington Nr Evesham Hereford & Worcester WR11 5NR   Map 4 C1

Signposted off the A439, four miles from Evesham, the Mill is a stylishly
converted Georgian malting mill. Created by Simon and Jane Greenhalgh,
it is indeed a civilised and peaceful place, set in eight acres of wooded
parkland. Immaculate bedrooms have delightful views of the garden and
willow trees by the 600ft river Avon frontage and are attractively
appointed with up-to-date, carpeted bathrooms. Day rooms include a
lovely lounge that opens on to the lawns. Beautifully maintained and run
on friendly lines. No children under 10. No dogs, but kennelling nearby.
*Rooms 15. Garden, outdoor swimming pool, fishing, tennis, croquet. Closed
5 days Xmas. Access, Visa.*

Restaurant   £55

The pretty dining room is decorated in soft peach and grey and overlooks
the lawns and river. Jane Greenhalgh and her small team cook in an
admirably straightforward fashion. A 2- or 3-course table d'hote lunch is
served in the restaurant or snacks in the lounge by the fire or on the
terrace; Sunday lunch always features a children's menu and a traditional
roast. Dinner offers the widest choice – from Arbroath smokie tartlet or
pigeon breast salad to lettuce-wrapped salmon and sole and venison pie.
*Seats 40. Parties 40. L 12-1.45 D 7-8.45 (Sun to 8.30). Set L
£11.95/£13.95 (£10.95/£12.95 Sun)*

Harwich   Pier at Harwich

£50
RR

Tel 0255 241212   Fax 0255 322752

The Quay Harwich Essex CO12 3HH

Map 6 D3

Overlooking the harbour, the first-floor restaurant is just the place to enjoy good, fresh seafood which comes both plain (shallow-fried Dover sole, deep-fried cod and chips) and fancy (lobster thermidor, monkfish tail with provençale sauce). The choice is extensive – from crab terrine, oysters or coquilles St Jacques mornay to fish pie and a filo pastry gateau of cod, salmon and prawns. Other, more standard fare, like melon and grapefruit cocktail, rack of lamb and rib of beef should satisfy other tastes. The *Ha'penny Pier* on the ground floor is a second, family-orientated restaurant ,offering a children's menu and a mainly fish menu. A succinct wine list at sensible prices. *Seats 70. Parties 30. L 12-2 D 6-9.30 (Sun to 9). Set L £9 Set D £16. Access, Amex, Visa,*

Rooms

£68

Accommodation comprises six bedrooms of varying standards, all with a nautical theme. All have en-suite bathrooms.

Haslemere   Lythe Hill Hotel   67%

£102
H

Tel 0428 651251   Fax 0428 644131

Petworth Road Haslemere Surrey GU27 3BQ

Map 5 E3

Lythe Hill comprises a cluster of ancient farm buildings, including a splendid half-timbered farmhouse. Five bedrooms of character are in this part; the Henry VIII room has a four-poster dated 1614 and is popular with honeymooners. Other bedrooms are also attractive, individually appointed and all with Italian marble-tiled bathrooms. Banqueting/conference facilities for 130/60. The hotel stands on the B2131, one mile and a half from Haslemere. *Rooms 40. Garden, croquet, tennis, dinner dance (Saturdays in winter). Access, Amex, Visa,*

Haslemere   Morel's   ★

£90
R

Tel 0428 651462

23 Lower Street Haslemere Surrey GU27 2NY

Map 5 E3

Jean-Yves Morel's culinary prowess remains as remarkable as ever in his delightful little restaurant created from a row of terraced cottages complete with old beams. His à la carte menu is at a fixed price and full of novel dishes, including Camembert soufflé with Calvados sauce and fried apple or timbale of veal kidneys in sweet and sour sauce. Both these and more traditional dishes like *soupe de poissons* or *filet de porc aux pommes et Calvados* share Jean-Yves passion for skilled, careful preparation and attractive, yet unfussy presentation. The *assiette du chef* is a spectacular array of seven desserts in miniature. A superb 5-or-6-course gastronomic menu also shows off his talents. Several bottles under £20 on an exclusively French wine list. *Seats 50. Parties 12. L 12.30-2 D 7-10. Closed L Sat, all Sun & Mon, Bank Holidays except Good Friday, 2 weeks Feb, 2 weeks Sep. Set L £19.50 Set D £23.50 (both inc ½ bottle house wine). Access, Amex, Visa,*

Hastings   Cinque Ports Hotel   66%

£74
H

Tel 0424 439222   Fax 0424 437277

Summerfields Hastings East Sussex TN34 1ET

Map 7 C6

A hotel styled in the modern American low-rise fashion, with bright, spacious public areas furnished with good-quality period-style settees and armchairs. There are seven purpose-built conference rooms for up to 320 delegates. Children up to 12 stay free in parents' room. No dogs. *Rooms 40. Access, Amex, Visa,*

Hastings   Röser's   ★   £60

Tel 0424 712218   R

**64 Eversfield Place St Leonards on Sea Nr Hastings
East Sussex TN37 6DB**   Map 7 C6

A small, snug restaurant opposite the pier, with dark-panelled walls and booth seating. Seaside restaurants are not usually known for their quality, but this is certainly an exception. Gerald Röser takes his influences mainly from France and his native Germany, and many dishes show innovative touches; hare and marjoram terrine, aubergine soufflé with red pepper and fresh mint sauce, oak smoke-roasted salmon with a chive and mild horseradish sauce, wild boar chop with lentil sauce. There's a super list of classic wines (note the Chablis) and an improved new world selection. *Seats 40. Parties 35. Private Room. L 12-2 D 7-10. Closed L Sat, all Sun & Mon, Bank Holidays, 1 week Jan, 1 week Aug. Set L from £15.95. Access, Amex, Visa,* ⓪ *Diners Club International*

Hastings   Royal Victoria Hotel   70%   £75

Tel 0424 445544   Fax 0424 721995   H

The Marina St Leonards-on-Sea Nr Hastings East Sussex TN38 0BD   Map 7 C6

The seafront Royal Victoria retains the grand style of architecture that graced the age. A marble staircase sweeps up from the foyer and in the first-floor piano lounge-cum-bar there are pillars, arches and ornate plaster mouldings, plus sea views. All the bedrooms are designated as suites, with either a separate sitting room or a large sitting area. A recent change of ownership now finds it under the management of Resort Hotels. *Rooms 51. Access, Amex, Visa,* ⓪ *Diners Club International*

Hastings   Places of Interest

Tourist Information   Tel 0424 718888.
Stables Theatre   Tel 0424 423221.
Great Dixter House and Gardens   Northiam Tel 0797 253160.
Hastings Castle and 1066 Story   Tel 0424 717963.
Shipwreck Heritage Centre   Tel 0424 437452.
Museum and Art Gallery   Tel 0424 721202.

Hatch Beauchamp   Farthings Hotel   70%   £94

Tel 0823 480664   H

Hatch Beauchamp Nr Taunton Somerset TA3 6SG   Map 3 E2

Only four miles from the M5 (junction 25) and the A303, yet "miles from anywhere", the Coopers' quiet Georgian house stands in three acres of beautiful, secluded gardens. Accommodation comprises three doubles, two twins and one single bedroom with immaculately kept, cottagey decor and traditional period furniture; one room features a unique spiral mahogany staircase to its bathroom. Open fires warm the lamp-lit lounge and bar where the accent is on friendly, personal service. *Rooms 6. Garden. Access, Amex, Visa.*

Hatfield Heath   Down Hall   71%   £123

Tel 0279 731441   Fax 0279 730416   H

Hatfield Heath Nr Bishop's Stortford Hertfordshire CM22 7AS   Map 7 B4

Very much geared to conferences, Down Hall is a splendid Italianate mansion set in 100 acres of parkland. The handsome exterior is matched in the day rooms: the focal point is the main lounge with its Italian stone fireplace, huge crystal chandeliers and furniture ornate with ormolu, and the canopied bar boasts a green marble counter and matching tables. Bedrooms are divided between the main house and the sympathetically designed west wing (opened 1990); wing rooms have larger and more luxurious bathrooms, mini-bars and extra phones in the bathrooms and on the desks. *Rooms 103. Garden, croquet, putting, indoor swimming pool, spa bath, sauna, snooker. Access, Amex, Visa,* ⓪ *Diners Club International*

Hatherleigh   George Hotel   £60

Tel 0837 810454   Fax 0837 810901   **I**

Market Street Hatherleigh Nr Okehampton Devon EX20 3JN   Map 3 D2

Originally a sanctuary for monks, later brew house, tavern, coaching inn and law court. The cob-and-thatch building still has old-fashioned appeal. Bedrooms are comfortable and traditionally furnished. *Rooms 11. Garden, outdoor swimming pool, snooker. Access, Visa.*

Hathersage   Hathersage Inn   £68

Tel 0433 650259   Fax 0433 651199   **I**

Hathersage Derbyshire S30 1BB   Map 10 C2

The ivy-clad, stone-built inn stands by Hathersage's steep main street; pub to the front where the Cricketers bar is full of local memorabilia and quietly residential to the rear with a lounge bar and cosy dining room. Bedrooms are neatly kept, with plenty of extras from TV and radio/alarm to drinks tray and fresh fruit. Best bedrooms are in the Morley Lodge; boardroom conferences (max 12) in the Elcock Room. *Rooms 15. Access, Amex, Visa,*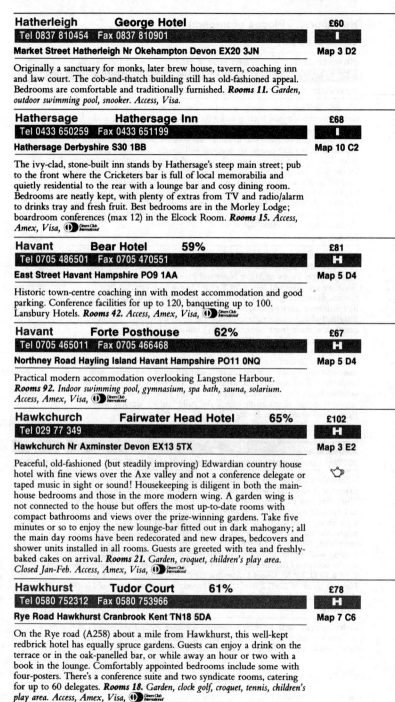

Havant   Bear Hotel   59%   £81

Tel 0705 486501   Fax 0705 470551   **H**

East Street Havant Hampshire PO9 1AA   Map 5 D4

Historic town-centre coaching inn with modest accommodation and good parking. Conference facilities for up to 120, banqueting up to 100. Lansbury Hotels. *Rooms 42. Access, Amex, Visa,*

Havant   Forte Posthouse   62%   £67

Tel 0705 465011   Fax 0705 466468   **H**

Northney Road Hayling Island Havant Hampshire PO11 0NQ   Map 5 D4

Practical modern accommodation overlooking Langstone Harbour. *Rooms 92. Indoor swimming pool, gymnasium, spa bath, sauna, solarium. Access, Amex, Visa,*

Hawkchurch   Fairwater Head Hotel   65%   £102

Tel 029 77 349   **H**

Hawkchurch Nr Axminster Devon EX13 5TX   Map 3 E2

Peaceful, old-fashioned (but steadily improving) Edwardian country house hotel with fine views over the Axe valley and not a conference delegate or taped music in sight or sound! Housekeeping is diligent in both the main-house bedrooms and those in the more modern wing. A garden wing is not connected to the house but offers the most up-to-date rooms with compact bathrooms and views over the prize-winning gardens. Take five minutes or so to enjoy the new lounge-bar fitted out in dark mahogany; all the main day rooms have been redecorated and new drapes, bedcovers and shower units installed in all rooms. Guests are greeted with tea and freshly-baked cakes on arrival. *Rooms 21. Garden, croquet, children's play area. Closed Jan-Feb. Access, Amex, Visa,*

Hawkhurst   Tudor Court   61%   £78

Tel 0580 752312   Fax 0580 753966   **H**

Rye Road Hawkhurst Cranbrook Kent TN18 5DA   Map 7 C6

On the Rye road (A258) about a mile from Hawkhurst, this well-kept redbrick hotel has equally spruce gardens. Guests can enjoy a drink on the terrace or in the oak-panelled bar, or while away an hour or two with a book in the lounge. Comfortably appointed bedrooms include some with four-posters. There's a conference suite and two syndicate rooms, catering for up to 60 delegates. *Rooms 18. Garden, clock golf, croquet, tennis, children's play area. Access, Amex, Visa,*

Hawkhurst   Places of Interest

Bodiam Castle (NT)

Hawkshead   Tarn Hows Hotel   71% NEW   £88

Tel 053 94 36696 Fax 053 94 36766	**HR**

Hawkshead Nr Ambleside Cumbria LA22 0PR   Map 13 C5

The lake at Tarn Hows is signposted off the B5286 between Ambleside
and Hawkshead, so the hotel is easily found. Set in 25 acres, the house has
interesting Gothic architecture and dates back to mid-Victorian times; it is
in a magnificent location and has fine valley views. Totally refurbished in
the last year, the day rooms are spacious and comfortable – the drawing
room has an old working gramophone – and the smart bedrooms (duvets
on the beds, satellite TV), including a ground-floor suite fully equipped for
disabled guests, are in a traditional and functional style. Decent bathrooms
have good showers over the tubs, but fans can be noisy. Small conferences
for up to 20 delegates. *Rooms 19. Garden, croquet, spa bath, sauna, solarium,
gymnasium, tennis, coarse fishing, outdoor play area, clay-pigeon shooting.
Access, Amex, Visa,*

Restaurant   ↑   £55

The Lake District has always had fine chefs scattered about (remember the
Johnson family at *Tullythwaite House*, Underbarrow and – still going
strong – John Tovey at *Miller Howe* and Francis Coulson at *Sharrow Bay*).
Well, we can now add to the list Kevin Cape who is cooking here.
Connaught-trained (previously a starred chef at the *Bell* in Aston Clinton),
he combines traditional English and classical French cooking on
imaginative and creative menus, using the finest ingredients. Sauces are
exemplary, made from meaty (or fishy) home-made stocks, and
presentation is artistically stylish. A four-course dinner is served, preceded
by an appetiser, then perhaps a melon soup followed by several choices in
each section. Braised lamb en gelée studded with vegetables and tarragon,
roast scallops in a white wine jus, fillet of red mullet on noodles with
perfectly cooked vegetables, a warm lobster vinaigrette and a galette of
potatoes typify the style. Finish with a summer pudding on a pool of
raspberry coulis. Home-made breads and rolls. Smooth service. *Seats 75.
Parties 20. Private Room. D only 7-9. Set D £21.95.*

Haworth   Weavers   £50

Tel 0535 643822	**RR**

15 West Lane Haworth Nr Bradford West Yorkshire BD22 8DU   Map 10 C1

Follow signs for the Bronte Parsonage (and use its car park) to find a
characterful restaurant formed out of a row of old weaver's cottages.
'Yorkshire Pud wi' rich onion gravy', calf's liver with bubble and squeak
and mustard sauce, Pennine beefsteak and onion pie, and roast filet of pork
with herbs, apple sauce, crackling and scrumpy cider gravy are typical of
dishes that are created with a light touch from mainly local produce. Afters
include the likes of 'Old school Pud' and 'Nannies meringue', the latter
coming with cream, brown bread ice-cream and apricot sauce. Cheerful
service completes the satisfying picture. *Seats 45. Parties 16. Private Room.
L 12-1.30 D 7-9.30. Closed L Mon-Sat (& Sun in summer), Mon, Bank
Holidays (open 25 Dec), 2 weeks Xmas, 2 weeks Jul. Set meals from £11.50.
Access, Amex, Visa,*

Rooms

Bedrooms, each with en-suite bathroom, combine antique pieces with
modern touches like TV, video, direct-dial phone and trouser press. All
have views over the Parsonage and village to the moors beyond.

Haworth   Places of Interest

Bronte Parsonage   Tel 0535 42323.

Haydock   Forte Posthouse   65%   £67

Tel 0942 717878   Fax 0942 718419   **H**

Lodge Lane Newton-le-Willows Haydock Merseyside WA12 0JG   **Map 10 B2**

Smart, modern and well-organised hotel. Half the bedrooms are of the
better Executive standard. Health club and children's play area and
playroom at weekends. Conference/banqueting facilities for 170/130.
Rooms 136. *Garden, indoor swimming pool, gymnasium, spa bath, sauna,
solarium. Access, Amex, Visa,* Diners Club International

Haydock   Forte Travelodge   £40

Tel 0942 272055   **L**

A580 Piele Road Haydock St Helens Merseyside WA11 9TL   **Map 10 B2**

On the A580 westbound, 2 miles west of junction 23 on the M6.
Rooms 40. *Access, Amex, Visa.*

Haydock   Haydock Thistle   67%   £107

Tel 0942 272000   Fax 0942 711092   **H**

Penny Lane Haydock St Helens Merseyside WA11 9SG   **Map 10 B2**

Neo-Georgian, low-rise lodge by junction 23 of the M6 with spacious
lounge and bedrooms. Leisure spa and conference facilities for up to 200
delegates. Good-value family accommodation Fri & Sat nights. **Rooms 139.**
*Indoor swimming pool, spa bath, sauna, solarium, gymnasium, snooker. Access,
Amex, Visa,* Diners Club International

Haydock   Places of Interest

Haydock Park Racecourse   Tel 0942 727345.

Hayes   Travel Inn   £42

Tel 081-573 7479   Fax 081-569 1204   **L**

362 Uxbridge Road Hayes Middlesex UB4 0HE   **Map 7 A4**

10 minutes drive from Heathrow Airport. **Rooms 40.** *Access, Amex, Visa,*
Diners Club International

Hayfield   Bridge End Restaurant   £65

Tel 0663 747321   **RR**

7 Church Street Hayfield Derbyshire SK12 5JE   **Map 10 C2**

French-inspired cooking in a modern English idiom at a village centre
guest house and restaurant with a bistro atmosphere. Goat's cheese tart; sea
bass ceviche; smoked duck salad; grilled turbot with leeks; roast marinated
venison; aubergine and lentil charlotte; fruity and boozy desserts. **Seats 48.**
Parties 40. Private Room. D only 7.30-10. Closed Sun & Mon.
Access, Visa, Diners Club International

Rooms   £36

Four en-suite bedrooms in attractive cottage style with pine furnishings and
bedsteads, have a secure separate entrance. 10% dinner discount for
residents.

Hayfield   Places of Interest

Lyme Park House and Gardens   Disley Tel 0663 762023.

Haytor   Bel Alp House   72%   £126

| Tel 0364 661217   Fax 0364 661292 | **H** |

Haytor Nr Bovey Tracey Devon TQ13 9XX   Map 3 D3

With its hillside location commanding splendid views over the rolling
Devonshire countryside, this fine Edwardian house and its gardens have
been much improved by the Curnocks over the last ten years. Peace and
quiet show in the antique-furnished day rooms, amply supplied with
armchairs, sofas and a host of pot plants. The atmosphere is more that of
being a house guest in a large family home than of staying in a hotel.
Light, airy bedrooms have plain walls, matching floral fabrics, more
armchairs and pot plants, and carpeted bathrooms (two with the original
Edwardian tubs on marble plinths) with quality toiletries. Housekeeping
and repair are immaculate throughout. *Rooms 9. Garden, croquet, snooker.
Closed Dec-Feb. Access, Visa.*

Heathrow Airport   Berkeley Arms Hotel   67%   £110

| Tel 081-897 2121   Fax 081-897 7014 | **H** |

Bath Road Cranford Middlesex TW5 9QF   Map 5 E2

On the A4 two miles from Heathrow. An agreeable Jarvis hotel set around
a delightful garden complete with fountain and pond. All bedrooms
recently refurbished. State-of-the-art conference facilities for up to 150.
Rooms 56. Access, Amex, Visa, **Diners Club International**

Heathrow Airport   Edwardian International   76%   £206

| Tel 081-759 6311   Fax 081-759 4559 | **H** |

Bath Road Hayes Middlesex UB3 5AW   Map 5 E2

Behind its glass and marble facade the Edwardian International offers
abundant style, comfort, service and modern amenities. Public areas include
a vast foyer (necessary when a jumbo jet-load of delayed passengers arrives)
with carpet-strewn pink marble floor, cocktail bar-cum-lounge with deep
sofas in a variety of rich fabrics and polo-themed bar sporting real saddles
in place of bar stools. Bedrooms, though not large, are visually appealing
with decoratively painted lightwood furniture and stylishly colourful
matching bedcovers and curtains. There are numerous luxurious suites
with marble-lined bathrooms, spa baths, separate impulse showers and twin
washbasins with gold fittings; some rooms have four-posters. Children up
to 14 stay free in parents' room. Residential conferences are an important
part of the business here with a fully-equipped business centre and a
theatre-style capacity of 500+. *Rooms 462. Indoor swimming pool, sauna,
solarium, gymnasium, spa bath, beauty & hair salon, news kiosk, coffee shop
(6am-11pm). Access, Amex, Visa,* **Diners Club International**

Heathrow Airport   Excelsior Hotel   71%   £118

| Tel 081-759 6611   Fax 081-759 3421 | **H** |

Bath Road West Drayton Middlesex UB7 0DU   Map 5 E2

A huge, modern hotel near the airport terminals with 248 Executive
rooms, 16 suites, 100 rooms non-smoking and five equipped for
wheelchair-bound guests. A spacious, marble-floored foyer sets the tone for
the day rooms, which include two bars, one in plush and mahogany. A
branch of the *Wheelers* fish restaurant group (also owned by Forte) has
recently opened. Children up to 14 free in parents' room.
Conference/banqueting facilities for 800. Forte Grand. *Rooms 839. Indoor
swimming pool, sauna, solarium, spa bath, beauty & hair salons, flower shop,
coffee shop (Noon-midnight). Access, Amex, Visa,* **Diners Club International**

Heathrow Airport   Forte Crest   68%   £99

Tel 081-759 2323   Fax 081-897 6130   **H**

Sipson Road West Drayton Middlesex UB7 0JU   **Map 5 E2**

Familiar landmark by the M4 turn-off to Heathrow, ten storeys high and
dating from the mid-70s. Carvery, Chinese and Italian restaurants.
Conference facilities for up to 200. *Rooms 572. Brasserie (10am-11pm),
keep-fit equipment, sauna. Access, Amex, Visa,*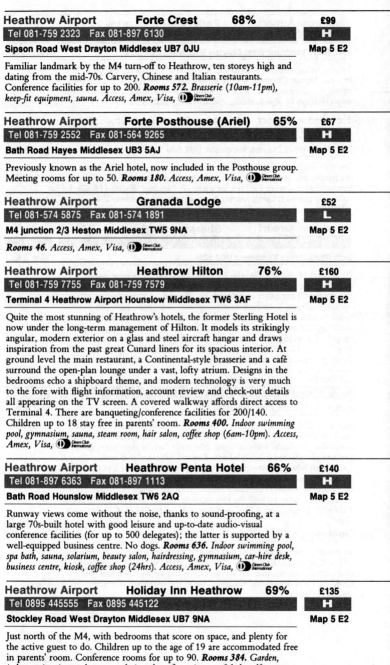

Heathrow Airport   Forte Posthouse (Ariel)   65%   £67

Tel 081-759 2552   Fax 081-564 9265   **H**

Bath Road Hayes Middlesex UB3 5AJ   **Map 5 E2**

Previously known as the Ariel hotel, now included in the Posthouse group.
Meeting rooms for up to 50. *Rooms 180. Access, Amex, Visa,*

Heathrow Airport   Granada Lodge   £52

Tel 081-574 5875   Fax 081-574 1891   **L**

M4 junction 2/3 Heston Middlesex TW5 9NA   **Map 5 E2**

Rooms 46. Access, Amex, Visa,

Heathrow Airport   Heathrow Hilton   76%   £160

Tel 081-759 7755   Fax 081-759 7579   **H**

Terminal 4 Heathrow Airport Hounslow Middlesex TW6 3AF   **Map 5 E2**

Quite the most stunning of Heathrow's hotels, the former Sterling Hotel is
now under the long-term management of Hilton. It models its strikingly
angular, modern exterior on a glass and steel aircraft hangar and draws
inspiration from the past great Cunard liners for its spacious interior. At
ground level the main restaurant, a Continental-style brasserie and a café
surround the open-plan lounge under a vast, lofty atrium. Designs in the
bedrooms echo a shipboard theme, and modern technology is very much
to the fore with flight information, account review and check-out details
all appearing on the TV screen. A covered walkway affords direct access to
Terminal 4. There are banqueting/conference facilities for 200/140.
Children up to 18 stay free in parents' room. *Rooms 400. Indoor swimming
pool, gymnasium, sauna, steam room, hair salon, coffee shop (6am-10pm). Access,
Amex, Visa,*

Heathrow Airport   Heathrow Penta Hotel   66%   £140

Tel 081-897 6363   Fax 081-897 1113   **H**

Bath Road Hounslow Middlesex TW6 2AQ   **Map 5 E2**

Runway views come without the noise, thanks to sound-proofing, at a
large 70s-built hotel with good leisure and up-to-date audio-visual
conference facilities (for up to 500 delegates); the latter is supported by a
well-equipped business centre. No dogs. *Rooms 636. Indoor swimming pool,
spa bath, sauna, solarium, beauty salon, hairdressing, gymnasium, car-hire desk,
business centre, kiosk, coffee shop (24hrs). Access, Amex, Visa,*

Heathrow Airport   Holiday Inn Heathrow   69%   £135

Tel 0895 445555   Fax 0895 445122   **H**

Stockley Road West Drayton Middlesex UB7 9NA   **Map 5 E2**

Just north of the M4, with bedrooms that score on space, and plenty for
the active guest to do. Children up to the age of 19 are accommodated free
in parents' room. Conference rooms for up to 90. *Rooms 384. Garden,
indoor swimming pool, sauna, solarium, keep-fit equipment, 9-hole golf course,
helipad, coffee shop (6.30am-10.30pm), news kiosk. Access, Amex, Visa,*

Heathrow Airport   Park Hotel   61%   £111

Tel 081-759 2400   Fax 081-759 5278   **H**

Bath Road Longford West Drayton Middlesex UB7 0EQ   Map 5 E2

Triple glazing and air-conditioning in all the bedrooms are big pluses at a low-rise Mount Charlotte hotel located between the A4 and the airport's runways. Conferences for up to 600. *Rooms 306. Car-hire desk, kiosk, coffee shop (10.30am-11.30pm). Access, Amex, Visa,* ⓓ *Diners Club International*

Heathrow Airport   Sheraton Heathrow Hotel   70%   £103

Tel 081-759 2424   Fax 081-759 2091   **H**

Bath Road West Drayton Middlesex UB7 0HJ   Map 5 E2

Decent-sized bedrooms are stylishly contemporary, with good showers in the bathrooms. Bright day rooms include a long-hours coffee shop and banqueting/conference facilities for up to 80. No dogs. *Rooms 415. Garden, coffee shop (6am-11.30pm), courtesy bus to airport. Access, Amex, Visa,* ⓓ *Diners Club International*

Heathrow Airport   Sheraton Skyline   73%   £157

Tel 081-759 2535   Fax 081-750 9150   **H**

Bath Road Hayes Middlesex UB3 5BP   Map 5 E2

Focal point of this hotel on the A4 is the Patio Caribe, a large indoor tropical garden complete with palm trees, swimming pool, bar and music. Diamond Lil's bar offers nightly cabaret. Good-sized bedrooms are right up-to-the-minute, with air-conditioning, automated mini-bars, computer links, sprinklers and smoke detector system (31 rooms are designated no-smoking). Greatly reduced weekend rates. Conference and banqueting facilities for up to 500. Children up to 16 stay free in parents' room. No dogs. *Rooms 352. Indoor swimming pool, solarium, hairdressing, boutique, florist, gift shop, coffee shop (6am-1am). Access, Amex, Visa,* ⓓ *Diners Club International*

Helford   Riverside   £70

Tel 0326 231443   Fax 0326 231443   **R R**

Helford Nr Helston Cornwall TR12 6JU   Map 2 B4

Edward and Susie Darrell's pretty cottage restaurant, overlooking a tidal creek on the Helford estuary, continues to please and impress. The cooking, essentially provincial without being inherently French, deservedly gives pride of place to the finest local fish: Cornish lobster glazed with champagne sabayon; monkfish roast with a cabbage, sultana and nutmeg farce. Meat dishes too, some good desserts like the white chocolate terrine on raspberry coulis; home-made biscuits with the trolley of cheeses. New World wines offer perhaps the best value on the decent wine list. *Seats 35. Parties 12. D only 7.30-9.30. Closed Nov-Feb. Set D £18 & £28. No credit cards.*

Rooms   £75

Bedrooms, three in the house and three in a separate cottage – are pretty and well equipped. Breakfast – Continental-style only, with home-made croissants and marmalade – is served on the terrace with fabulous views. Children are welcome, but no under-14s in the restaurant. No dogs. *Rooms 6. Garden.*

Helland Bridge   Tredethy Country Hotel   56%   £52

Tel 020 884 262   Fax 020 884 707   **H**

Helland Bridge Bodmin Cornwall PL30 4QS   Map 2 B3

Take the A389 from Bodmin, then the B3266 to Camelford to find this grey-stoned country house, standing on a bank of the Camel valley, in a tranquil setting of nine wooded acres. Best bedrooms are at the light and sunny front half, whereas rooms at the back only have views of the courtyard and another wing. There are also ten self-catering cottages in the grounds. *Rooms 11. Garden, outdoor swimming pool. Access, Amex, Visa,*

Helland Bridge   Places of Interest

Bodmin Tourist Information   Tel 0208 76616.
Tintagel Castle (EH)   Tel 0840 770328 *18 miles.*
Trebarwith Strand Beach *12 miles.*
Lanhydrock   Bodmin Tel 0208 73320.
Pencarrow House and Garden   Nr Bodmin Tel 020884 369.
Royal Cornwall Showground   Nr Wadebridge Tel 0208 812183.

Helmsley   Black Swan   69%   £111

Tel 0439 70466   Fax 0439 70174   **H**

Market Place Helmsley North Yorkshire YO6 5BJ   Map 15 C6

Standing by the market square, comprising an Elizabethan coaching inn, a Georgian house and a Tudor rectory. Day rooms, including several lounges, are all very traditional, with heavy timbers, low beamed ceilings and cottagey decor. Residents have their own bar as well as the public bar, both being small, cosy and welcoming. Bedrooms at the rear are modern and uniform in size, with good-quality Italian furniture; those at the front boast hand-built traditional oak furniture. All are individually decorated with well-co-ordinated chintzy fabrics and 12 are designated non-smoking; the restaurant is another smokeless zone. Forte Heritage. *Rooms 44. Garden, croquet. Access, Amex, Visa,*

Helmsley   Feversham Arms   65%   £70

Tel 0439 70766   Fax 0439 70346   **H**

1 High Street Helmsley North Yorkshire YO6 5AG   Map 15 C6

Rebuilt in 1855 by the Earl of Feversham, the inn has been lovingly cared for since 1967 by Gonzalo and Rowan de Aragues. They've moved with the times, and continual upgrading has not destroyed its period appeal. Bedrooms, all with little luxury touches like personalised toiletries, include some with four-posters. New garden furniture, sunbeds and period lighting around the pool and gardens are the latest improvements. *Rooms 18. Garden, outdoor swimming pool, tennis. Access, Amex, Visa,*

Helmsley   Places of Interest

Rievaulx Abbey   Helmsley Tel 04396 228.
Rievaulx Terrace and Temples.

Henley-on-Thames   Red Lion   62%   £108

Tel 0491 572161   Fax 0491 410039   **H**

Hart Street Henley-on-Thames Oxfordshire RG9 2AR   Map 5 D2

Wisteria creeps around the frontage of a 16th-century building overlooking the finishing post of the Henley Royal Regatta rowing course. Antique pine panelling is a feature in some of the day rooms, and in the bar flagstones and a log fire produce a rustic air. There are two banqueting/conference suites (for up to 75). Bedrooms generally combine period appeal with modern comfort. *Rooms 26. Access, Amex, Visa.*

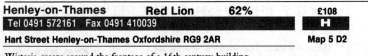

Henley-on-Thames   Places of Interest

Tourist Information   Tel 0491 578034.
Fawley Court   - Marian Fathers Historic House and Museum Tel 0491
574917.
Greys Court (NT)   Rotherfield Grey. Tel 04917 529.
Stonor Park   Tel 049 163 587.

Hereford	Moat House	63%	£78
Tel 0432 354301 Fax 0432 275114			**H**
Belmont Road Hereford Hereford & Worcester HR2 7BF			Map 4 A1

A mile and a half from the city centre on the Abergavenny road.
Accommodation divided between discreet motel-style units and a spacious
new extension. *Rooms 60. Garden. Access, Amex, Visa,* *Diners Club International*

Hereford	Travel Inn		£42
Tel 0432 274853 Fax 0432 343003			**L**
Holmer Road Holmer Nr Hereford Hereford & Worcester HR4 9RS			Map 4 A1

Hereford race course and leisure centre 5 minutes walk. *Rooms 40. Access,
Amex, Visa,* **Diners Club International**

Hereford   Places of Interest

Tourist Information   Tel 0432 268430.
New Hereford Theatre   Tel 0432 268785.
Hereford Cathedral   Tel 0432 359880.
  Historic Houses, Castles and Gardens
Dinmore Manor and Gardens   Leominster Tel 043271 240.
Moccas Court, House and Parkland   Moccas Tel 09817 381.
The Weir Garden (NT)   Swainshill Tel 098122 697.
Hereford Racecourse   Tel 0432 273560.
  Museums and Art Galleries
Hereford City Museum and Art Gallery   Tel 0432 268121 ext 207.
Cider Museum and King Offa Cider Brandy Distillery   Hereford Cider
  Museum Trust Tel 0432 354207.
Churchill Gardens Museum   Tel 0432 267409.
The Old House   Tel 0432 268121.

Herne Bay   L'Escargot   £55

Tel 0227 372876   R

22 High Street Herne Bay Kent CT6 5LH   Map 7 C5

Alain and Joyce Bessemoulin are charming hosts and their friendly,
informal restaurant has an uncomplicated appeal. Alain cooks in a
competent and unfussy fashion using good fresh ingredients in largely
classic dishes. Start with a home-made country-style paté; move on to a
breast of chicken with a light cream sauce of shallots and asparagus and
finish with a nice home-made dessert. *Seats 40. Parties 10. L 12-1.30
D 7-9.30 (Sun one sitting at 7). Closed Thu, 2 weeks Jan, 2 weeks Sep. Set L
£10.25 Set D £10.95. Access, Visa.*

Herne Bay   Places of Interest

Brambles English Wildlife Rare Breeds Centre   Wealdon Forest Park
  Tel 0227 7123.
Margate
Tourist Information   Tel 0843 220241.
Winter Gardens   Tel 0843 292795.
Bembon Brothers Theme Park   Tel 0843 227011.
Cliftonville Aquarium   Tel 0843 221951.

Hersham   The Dining Room   £60

Tel 0932 231686   R

10 Queens Road The Village Green Hersham Surrey KT22 5LS   Map 7 A5

A very English restaurant, from the Laura Ashley decor of the four
interconnecting dining rooms to the steak and kidney pie, toad-in-the-hole
and spotted dick that form the backbone of a menu that wanders freely
round the English counties: hot Gloucester cheese and ale pot with toast
soldiers; Norfolk turkey and leek pie with apricot stuffing; Aylesbury
duckling with rum-soaked apple; Somerset lamb steak with cider, fruit and
mint; Berkshire hog (pork chop with mushroom cream sauce). An
excursion to Scotland finds Cowdenbeath haggis with bashed neeps, while
Wales contributes Anglesey egg with smoked haddock and leek in a cream
sauce. *Seats 90. Parties 30. Private Room. L 12-2 (Sun to 2.30) D 7-10.30
(Sat from 6.30). Closed L Sat, D Sun, Bank Holidays, 1 week Xmas. Access,
Amex, Visa.*

Herstmonceux   Sundial Restaurant   £82

Tel 0323 832217   R

Gardner Street Herstmonceux East Sussex BN27 4LA   Map 7 B6

Established for 25 years, Laurette and Giuseppe Bertoli's pretty 17th-
century cottage has a garden and terraces for alfresco summer lunches
overlooking the Sussex countryside, and continues to be run with homely
pride. Diners are treated like guests at a dinner party, and for private
dining (up to 20) are offered their own room. Giuseppe's menu is varied
and extensive: bouillabaisse with rouille; fine goose and pork rillettes;
lobster with Créole rice; veal fillets with Grand Marnier sauce; and, for 2
or more, a five-course *menu gourmandise*. Best value wines on a fine list are
from the Rhone and Loire; house wines are sensibly priced, classic
burgundies and clarets on the high side. *Seats 50. Parties 50. Private Room.
L 12.30-2.30 D 7.30-9.30 (Sat to 10). Closed D Sun, all Mon, 2/3 weeks
Aug/Sep, Xmas-mid Jan. Set L £15.50 Set D £24.50. Access, Amex, Visa,*

Diners Club
International

Hertingfordbury   White Horse Hotel   63%   £101

Tel 0992 586791   Fax 0992 550809   **H**

Hertingfordbury Road Hertingfordbury Hertfordshire SG14 2LB   **Map 7 B4**

Once a coaching inn on the Cambridge-Reading run, now a mix of
Georgian facade, earlier interiors and modern bedroom blocks. Forte
Heritage. *Rooms 42. Garden. Access, Amex, Visa,*  *Diners Club International*

Hertingfordbury   Places of Interest

Hatfield House and Gardens   Hatfield Tel 0707 262823.

Hethersett   Park Farm   64%   £72

Tel 0603 810264   Fax 0603 812104   **H**

Hethersett Nr Norwich Norfolk NR9 3DL   **Map 6 C2**

Off the A11 London road, five miles south of Norwich, this family-run
hotel is approached down an avenue of lime trees. The small, Georgian
farmhouse has grown over the years into a substantial hotel with rooms in
converted farm buildings, surrounded by well-kept gardens to the rear of
the house. There's a bewildering range of room standards, with the best
including whirlpool baths and hi-fi systems. General decor is modern, but
without being stylish. Purpose-built leisure club includes a large pool.
*Rooms 38. Garden, croquet, indoor swimming pool, sauna, spa bath, steam room,
solarium, keep-fit equipment, games room, snooker, tennis, helipad, coffee shop
(12-2pm & 6-9pm). Closed 25-27 Dec. Access, Amex, Visa,* Diners Club International

Hexham   Beaumont Hotel   58%   £75

Tel &   Fax 0434 602331   **H**

Beaumont Street Hexham Northumberland NE46 3LT   **Map 15 B4**

Popular business hotel overlooking parkland next to the abbey. Function
facilities for up to 100 people. No dogs. *Rooms 23. Keep-fit equipment.
Closed 25 & 26 Dec. Access, Amex, Visa,* Diners Club International

Hexham   Places of Interest

Museum of Border History   Tel 0434 604011 *Not Weekends*
Hexham Racecourse   Tel 0434 603738.

High Wycombe   Forte Posthouse   65%   £67

Tel 0494 442100   Fax 0494 474031   **H**

Crest Road High Wycombe Buckinghamshire HP11 1TL   **Map 5 E2**

Low-riser by junction 4 of the M40, with conference and banqueting
facilities for around 100. *Rooms 106. Garden, children's playground, snooker.
Access, Amex, Visa,* Diners Club International

High Wycombe   Places of Interest

Tourist Information   Tel 0494 421892.
Wycombe Sports Centre Swimming Pool   Tel 0494 446324.
  Historic Houses, Castles and Gardens
Hughenden Manor (NT)   Tel 0494 532580 *Home of Benjamin Disraeli.*
West Wycombe Park (NT)   West Wycombe Tel 0494 24411.
Chenies Manor House and Garden   Little Chalfont Tel 0494 2888 *8
miles on A404.*

Hinckley   Hinckley Island Hotel   64%   £74

Tel 0455 631122   Fax 0455 634536   **H**

Watling Street Hinckley Leicestershire LE10 3JA   **Map 11 D4**

Adjacent to exit 1 of the M69, at the junction of the A5, this conference-
oriented hotel covers some 15 acres. A huge statue of Neptune greets
arrivals in the marble-floored, mirror-ceilinged foyer. Accommodation is

comfortable but the newer de luxe rooms are more spacious, stylishly up-to-date and smartly fitted out with marble-tiled bathrooms. Standard rooms are aptly named, with plain wallcoverings and dull fabrics. *Rooms 253. Indoor swimming pool, spa bath, sauna, solarium, beautician, hairdressing, gymnasium, snooker, fishing, news kiosk, coffee shop (7am-10pm) Access, Amex, Visa,* ⓓ *Diners Club International*

Hinckley Places of Interest

Nuneaton Tourist Information Tel 0203 384027.
Arbury Hall Tel 0203 382804 or 0676 40259 *8 miles.*
Twycross Zoo Morton-Juxta-Twycross, Atherstone Tel 0827 880250.

Hindhead Xian

	£55
Tel 0428 604222	**R**
9 London Road Hindhead Surrey	Map 7 A5

An unprepossessing redbrick facade, almost on top of the traffic lights at the Hindhead crossroads on the A3, conceals an unusually good Oriental restaurant. Oriental, because although the menu is mainly Chinese, it also includes such dishes as Vietnamese or Korean-style barbecued beef, Nabemono one-pot dishes, sukiyaki and Mongolian hot-pot. Sizzling fillet of beef in black pepper sauce was none the worse for not being authentically Chinese and the aromatic Heung So Crispy Duck is a dish to remember (and return for). *Seats 60. Parties 20. Private Room. L 12-2 D 7-10.30. Closed L Sat & Mon, all Sun, Bank Holidays. Set meals from £13. Access, Visa.*

Hintlesham Hintlesham Hall 82%

	£104
Tel 047 387 334 Fax 047 387 463	**HR**
Hintlesham Nr Ipswich Suffolk IP8 3NS	Map 6 C3

A well-managed and comfortable country house hotel with a symmetrical facade that dates back to Georgian times. Behind the stuccoed front is an Elizabethan house built in the 1570s with a heavily-timbered second floor and tall redbrick chimneys. Reception rooms are both grand and welcoming: the library features an interesting hand-painted floor and warming fire in the marble fireplace during winter. An old stable block has been transformed to accommodate bedrooms, one of which houses the workings of the estate clock. Extravagant toiletries are provided in all the bathrooms, which are mainly marble. A new 18-hole golf course is overlooked by the rooms to the rear of the house. *Rooms 33. Garden, tennis, riding, croquet, game fishing, snooker, golf. Access, Amex, Visa,* ⓓ *Diners Club International*

Restaurant £90

The two dining areas vary greatly: one a small parlour with pine panelling, the other a magnificent, high-ceilinged salon with ornate plasterwork. Well-planned, three-course fixed-price menus Sunday to Thursday evenings and weekday lunchtimes supplement the regular à la carte. Ravioli of red mullet with its own mousse, escalopes of foie gras on brioche with caramalised orange, duck and beetroot consommé, escalopes of veal on spinach noodles with oyster mushroom sauce and poached salmon with niçoise salad typify the style. A keenly-priced and adventurous wine list with a good choice of half bottles, and lots of personal notes. No smoking. *Seats 137. Parties 137. Private Room. L 12-1.45 D 7-9.30. Closed L Sat. Set L £18.50 Set D £19.50.*

Hinton Hinton Grange 62%

	£89
Tel 0275 822916 Fax 0275 823285	**HR**
Hinton Nr Dyrham Park Avon SN14 8HG	Map 4 B2

The Lindsay-Walkers' conversion of a derelict farmhouse and outbuilding has brought a touch of country living only minutes from Bath and the M4 (junction 18). The main building comprises a 15th-century stone-flagged bar and a lounge in simple Chinese style; a conservatory houses both bar and heated swimming pool. Bedrooms in the surrounding buildings are Victorian-style recreations, with period washstands and bathing alcoves. There are antique four-posters and open fires. A lake has a tiny island with one tree and a summer house from which one can fish for trout. The Palm Court conservatory pool-side bar area is kept at tropical heat all year round, even providing bananas for the restaurant in season. No children under 15. *Rooms 17. Garden, croquet, 9-hole pitch & putt, indoor swimming pool, sauna, solarium, keep-fit equipment, tennis, fishing. Access, Amex, Visa,* ⓘ *Diners Club International*

Ole Inglenook Restaurant   £50

Informal surroundings for sound cooking by new chef Miles Cooper, who has taken over from owner May Lindsay-Walker. The short à la carte is typified by a galantine of red mullet wrapped in smoked salmon with a cucumber and yoghurt dressing, a salad of smoked duck with orange and walnuts, and baked fillet of brill with a duo of capsicum sauces; simpler dishes are always available on request. Vegetarians are well catered for. *Seats 60. Parties 12. Private Room. L by arrangement D 7-9.30 (Sun to 9). Set D from £15.95.*

| Hockley Heath | Nuthurst Grange | 74% | £117 |

Tel 0564 783972   Fax 0564 783919

HR

Nuthurst Grange Lane Hockley Heath Warwickshire B94 5NL

Map 10 C4

The original redbrick house has been added to a number of times over the last 100 years, but the overall result is a surprisingly handsome building, helped by its setting in extensive landscaped grounds. David Randolph's restaurant takes pride of place on the ground floor along with a pair of plush chesterfield-furnished lounges (one for non-smokers) where drinks are also served; there is no bar. Pretty, individually-decorated bedrooms are spacious and comfortable with sofas and armchairs alongside the freestanding, darkwood furniture, and extras ranging from books, chocolates and fruit to more mundane fly-spray and shoe-cleaning kit. Poly-cotton duvets are standard but more traditional bedding is available on request. Bathrooms all have 'airspace' tubs, telephone extensions and bathrobes. No dogs. *Rooms 15. Garden, croquet, helipad. Closed 1 week Xmas. Access, Amex, Visa,* ⓘ *Diners Club International*

Restaurant   £60

Chef-proprietor David Randolph ensures that the restaurant remains very much the centrepiece of the hotel. Fine fresh produce is handled with great care and his dishes are notable for honest, distinctive flavours and attractive presentation: pig's trotter filled with chicken mousseline, tomato and mozzaralla tart with basil, fillet of beef with truffled mushroom sauce, spiced pancakes with green ginger wine sauce and a rum and raisin ice cream. No smoking (puffers can use the lounge if desperate). A concise wine list has a good house selection. *Seats 50. Parties 60. Private Room. L 12-2.30 D 7-9.30. Closed L Sat. Set L £13.50 Set D £17.50.*

| Holbeton | Alston Hall | 66% | £65 |

Tel 075 530 555   Fax 075 530 494

H

Alston Cross Holbeton Plymouth Devon PL8 1HN

Map 3 D3

Some four miles out of Plymouth, off the Knightsbridge road, the ivy-clad Edwardian manor house stands in the heart of a sheltered valley with views to the sea beyond. Day rooms surround the oak-panelled great hall with its stained glass windows and upper gallery. The best bedrooms, approached from here, are good sized and well-appointed, with firmly traditional appeal. Two private rooms accommodate dining for 40 and combine for conferences of 100. Under 14s stay free in their parents' room. *Rooms 20. Indoor & outdoor swimming pool, gymnasium, solarium, sauna, tennis, garden, croquet. Access, Amex, Visa,* ⓘ *Diners Club International*

Hollingbourne	Great Danes	63%	£78

Tel 0622 30022   Fax 0622 735290   **H**

Ashford Road Hollingbourne Kent ME17 1RE   Map 7 C5

With new owners (Jarvis) have come a brand-new conference centre
(catering for up to 600 – the largest in Kent), refurbished public areas and
an ongoing programme to update the bedrooms. Close to junction 8 of the
M20. *Rooms 126. Garden, indoor swimming pool, croquet, tennis, pitch & putt,
mini-golf, netball court, five-a-side football pitch, helipad, games room, grill
(7am-midnight). Access, Amex, Visa,*

Hope Cove	Cottage Hotel	56%	£80

Tel 0548 561555   **H**

Hope Cove Nr Kingsbridge Devon TQ7 3HJ   Map 3 D3

John and Janet Ireland are the resident proprietors of this popular family
holiday hotel extended, originally, from just one small cottage. It stands in
a fine clifftop position in gardens close to the beach. The main lounge is
largely 30s in style, and the cocktail bar was built from the timbers of a
wrecked ship. The sun terrace is the place to be in summer.
Accommodation includes de luxe rooms with extra accessories; just over
half the rooms have en-suite facilities and some have balconies. A few
singles at the back miss out on the sea views. Children up to 12 stay free in
parents' room. *Rooms 35. Garden, games room. Closed Jan. No credit cards.*

Hope Cove	Lantern Lodge	59%	£79

Tel 0548 561280   **H**

Grand View Road Hope Cove Nr Kingsbridge Devon TQ7 3HE   Map 3 D3

Splendid sea views (they stretch from Bolt Tail to The Great Mew Stone
outside Plymouth Sound) and a welcoming feel account for the popularity
of this pleasant clifftop hotel. It's easy to relax in the cosy little bar or in
the homely lounges with their antique pieces and choice of TV or books.
Individually furnished bedrooms (three with four-posters) are well kept,
with neat bath or shower rooms. No children under ten. No dogs.
*Rooms 14. Garden, indoor swimming pool, solarium, keep-fit equipment,
putting. Closed Dec-Feb. Access, Visa.*

Horley	Langshott Manor	71%	£114

Tel 0293 786680   Fax 0293 783905   **HR**

Langshott Horley Surrey RH6 9LN   Map 7 B5

The considerable charm of this small Elizabethan manor house comes
partly from its domestic scale (it has just five bedrooms) and partly from
the relaxed, informal style in which it is run by New Zealanders Patricia
and Geoffrey Noble. Family photos and fresh flowers in the oak-panelled
drawing room and atmospheric entrance hall enhance the homely
impression. The pretty, antique-filled bedrooms offer more home comforts:
books, magazines, mineral water, bathrobes and big soft towels. A courtesy
Jaguar car is available for the short trip to Gatwick airport (plus two
weeks' free parking), making this a popular spot from which to start a
honeymoon. A real gem of a hotel in a tranquil setting with over two
acres of grounds, only slightly tarnished by its proximity to modern
housing on two sides. *Rooms 5. Garden, croquet. Closed 3 days Xmas. Access,
Amex, Visa,*

Restaurant   £57

Diners sit together around a polished oval table set with silver candlesticks.
Two private rooms are also available for guests requiring privacy. The
fixed-price, four-course lunch and dinner menus usually have a small choice
of dinner-party dishes served in generous portions. Open to non-residents
by prior appointment only. *Seats 12. Parties 8. Private Room.
L by arrangement D 7.30-9.30. Set L £19.50 Set D £22.50.*

Horndon on the Hill   Hill House

£50

RR

Tel 0375 642463   Fax 0375 361611

High Road Horndon on the Hill Essex SS17 8LD

Map 7 B4

A wide range of starters and main courses on the fixed-price menu is full
of reliable choices; for starters Cornish cheese tart, chicken and basil sausage
or lamb sweetbreads baked in filo pastry. Main courses perhaps include
fillet of brill with sweet pepper sauce and pork loin with tomato, brandy
and black pepper cream; to finish apple charlotte with whisky anglaise or
English farmhouse cheeses. Predictable, but extremely sensibly-priced wine
list (champagne from £16). *Seats 30. Parties 32. L 12.30-2 D 7.30-9.45.
Closed L Sat, all Sun & Mon, Bank Holidays, 5 days Xmas. Set meals
£17.95. Access, Amex, Visa.*

Rooms

£54

Ten bright en-suite bedrooms, two with spa baths. (The owners' Bell Inn is
next door.)

Horsham   Travel Inn

£42

L

Tel 0403 50141   Fax 0403 270797

57 North Street Horsham West Sussex RH12 1RB

Map 5 E3

20 minutes drive from Gatwick Airport. *Rooms 40. Access, Amex, Visa,
Diners Club International*

Horton   French Partridge

£50

R

Tel 0604 870033

Horton Nr Northampton Northamptonshire NN7 2AP

Map 5 D1

The Partridges have been serving good food at their friendly restaurant
since 1963 and have many loyal customers. Bottle-green walls hung with
oil paintings, black leather banquettes and polished mahogany tables create
a sedate, traditional ambience. Dishes are mainly, but not exclusively,
French on the four-course, fixed-price menu: fish or carrot and lentil soup,
prawn roulade or rillettes of pork might be followed by breaded pork
cutlets with cheese sauce, mousse of pheasant in pastry or venison steak
with juniper and gin sauce, plus an interesting course inbetween (poached
egg and mushrooms in pastry case or warm sole and mussel mousse).
Typically, iced orange soufflé with Grand Marnier, choux buns and fresh
fruit pavlova might be among the puddings. Fair prices on a sound wine
list. Smoking discouraged. *Seats 40. Parties 10. D only 7.30-9. Closed Sun &
Mon, 2 weeks Xmas, 2 weeks Easter, 3 weeks Jul/Aug. Set D £21. No credit
cards.*

Horton-cum-Studley   Studley Priory   64%

£98

H

Tel 086 735 203   Fax 086 735 613

Horton-cum-Studley Nr Oxford Oxfordshire OX9 1AZ

Map 5 D2

A striking Elizabethan building set in 13 acres of wooded grounds.
Impressive day rooms include a splendid hall panelled in pitch pine, a lofty
drawing room and a Victorian bar. Six bedrooms are in the main house
(antiques, some wood panelling, one with a four-poster), while the
majority are in the Jacobean wing reached through a labyrnth of corridors.
These rooms are smaller and more modern. Small conferences are big
business here, so you'll sometimes be sharing the drawing room with the
delegates. *Rooms 19. Garden, tennis, clay-pigeon shooting. Access, Amex, Visa,
Diners Club International*

| Huddersfield | George Hotel | 62% | £80 |

Tel 0484 515444   Fax 0484 535056   **H**

St George's Square Huddersfield West Yorkshire HD1 1JA   **Map 10 C1**

In the main square opposite the railway station, a large Victorian building housing conferences (max. 200) and banqueting for 150. Refitted bedrooms are stylish with up-to-date facilities. Children under 12 stay free in parents' room. *Rooms 60. Access, Amex, Visa,* ⓘ *Diners Club International*

| Huddersfield | Pennine Hilton National | 66% | £100 |

Tel 0422 375431   Fax 0422 310067   **H**

Ainley Top Huddersfield West Yorkshire HD3 3RH   **Map 10 C1**

Attractive, contemporary style bedrooms with small, but bright, bathrooms. Children up to 16 stay free in parents' room. Leisure Centre, conference facilities for up to 450. *Rooms 118. Pool, sauna, steam room, gymnasium, coffee shop (7am-10pm), beautician. Access, Amex, Visa,* ⓘ *Diners Club International*

| Huddersfield | Places of Interest |

Tourist Information   Tel 0484 430808.
Holmfirth Postcard Museum   Holmfirth Tel 0484 682231.
Huddersfield Art Gallery   Tel 0484 513808.

| Hull | Campanile Hotel | | £36 |

Tel 0482 25530   Fax 0482 587538   **L**

**Beverley Road/Freetown Way Kingston-upon-Hull
Humberside HU2 9AN**   **Map 11 E1**

Within the city centre, near the station off the A63. *Rooms 50. Access, Amex, Visa,* ⓘ *Diners Club International*

| Hull | Ceruttis | | £60 |

Tel 0482 28501   Fax 0482 587597   **R**

10 Nelson Street Hull Humberside HU1 1XE   **Map 11 E1**

Approaching 20 years in its harbourside location, the Cerutti family's friendly restaurant deals almost exclusively in fish and seafood. Local favourites include crab bisque, lobster Orlando, Dover sole and cold seafood platter. Meat, if you must, is fillet steak. *Seats 40. Parties 40. Private Room. L 12-2 D 7-9.30. Closed L Sat, all Sun, Bank Holidays, 1 week Xmas. Access, Visa.*

| Hull | Forte Crest | 69% | £107 |

Tel 0482 225221   Fax 0482 213299   **H**

Castle Street Hull Humberside HU1 2BX   **Map 11 E1**

Alongside the impressive dock development, the best rooms in this purpose-built hotel have balconies and fine views over the marina. Conferences for up to 140, banqueting for 120. *Rooms 99. Indoor swimming pool, gymnasium, sauna, solarium, beauty salon. Access, Amex, Visa,* ⓘ *Diners Club International*

Hull   Forte Posthouse   62%   £67

Tel 0482 645212   Fax 0482 643332   **H**

Ferriby High Road Hull Humberside HU14 3LG   Map 11 E1

Comfortable modern hotel outside Hull, overlooking the remarkable
suspension bridge. Children's playroom and playground. **Rooms 97.**
Croquet. Access, Amex, Visa, Diners Club International

Hull   Places of Interest

Tourist Information   Tel 0482 223559.
Burton Constable Hall and Gardens   Tel 0964 562400.
Hull City Football Ground   Tel 0482 51119.
Humberside Ice Arena   Tel 0482 25252.
  Theatres and Concert Halls
New Theatre   Tel 0482 20244.
Spring Street Theatre   Tel 0482 20491.
Truck Theatre   Tel 0482 225800.
  Museums and Art Galleries
Ferens Art Gallery   Tel 0482 222750.
Town Docks Museum   Tel 0482 222737.
University of Hull Art Collection   Tel 0482 465192.
Wilberforce House and Georgian Houses   Tel 0482 222737.

Hungerford   Bear Hotel   63%   £90

Tel 0488 682512   Fax 0488 684357   **H**

Charnham Street Hungerford Berkshire RG17 0EL   Map 4 C2

On the A4 on the outskirts of town, one of England's most historic inns,
once owned by Henry VIII, provides modern comforts in evocative
surroundings. Guests have the use of free health facilities at the nearby
Elcot Park Hotel (3 miles away, under the same ownership of Resort
Hotels) and squash, gym, saunas, snooker and skittles at the Meadowview
Leisure Club (50 yards away). Children up to the age of 12 free in parents'
room. **Rooms 41.** *Garden. Access, Amex, Visa,* Diners Club International

Hunstrete   Hunstrete House   75%   £150

Tel 0761 490578   Fax 0761 490732   **HR**

Hunstrete Chelwood Nr Bath Avon BS18 4NS   Map 4 B3

Sadly, following our reports that standards had not slipped after the
departure of the Dupays family several years ago, our inspectors found
much wanting at this handsome Georgian-style country house hotel this
year. Breakfast without toast or freshly squeezed orange juice is
unacceptable at the prices charged; and both management and staff need
motivation. Ten miles from Bath and Bristol, set in 92 acres of lovely
parkland on the edge of the Mendip Hills, the gardens are beautifully
maintained, providing the kitchen with the bulk of its needs. Though
looking rather tired, the public rooms have an air of luxury and
refinement that pervades the whole establishment; the drawing room and
library are especially pleasing with fine period furniture and fabrics,
antiques and log-burning fires. Bedrooms, boasting fine views, are
individually designed, showing the same impeccable taste with quality
freestanding furniture and plenty of thoughtful extras such as sherry, fruit
and a flask of cool water; bathrooms offer thick towels, bathrobes and a
generous supply of Penhaligon toiletries. Clipper Hotels have a marvellous
property here and we hope that they will restore it to its previous high
standing as a tip-top country hotel at the head of its fleet. No children
under 9. No dogs. **Rooms 24.** *Garden, croquet, outdoor swimming pool, tennis.
Access, Visa.*

Restaurant   £85

The main dining room is a sympathetic extension to the house. The
separate Terrace room is allocated to non-smokers when not required as a
conference venue. Dishes of note are black pudding with shallot confit and   ♕

apple galette, and a ragout of fish with lobster ravioli on a cherry tomato
vinaigrette. Fruit and vegetable sauces are well executed and a light hand is
applied to pastry. There's a fine collection of English cheeses and classic
French wines include some exquisite burgundies. Willing staff, but
sometimes lacking direction. *Seats 50. Parties 50. Private Room.*
L 12.30-2.30 D 7.30-9.30. Set L £15 Set D £29.50.

Huntingdon   Old Bridge Hotel   68%   £92

Tel 0480 52681   Fax 0480 411017   **HR**

1 High Street Huntingdon Cambridgeshire PE18 6TQ   Map 6 B2

Gardens run down to the river Ouse from this recently refurbished,
creeper-clad Georgian hotel close to the town centre (on the inner ring
road). Pastel murals decorate the Terrace lounge (where informal meals are
served) and in winter a log fire warms the panelled bar. Well-equipped
bedrooms are individually and stylishly designed, the best being quite
spacious; huge towels and plenty of toiletries in the bathrooms. Afternoon
tea in the lounge is a civilised affair. The business conference room holds
up to 50. Poste Hotels. *Rooms 26. Garden, private jetty. Access, Amex, Visa,*

Restaurant   £70

The handsome dining room has limed oak panels and is home to some
enjoyable traditional cooking – Arbroath smokies, creamed Stilton with
candied pear, roast joint of the day served from a silver carving wagon,
Dover sole, spinach and garlic-stuffed corn-fed chicken breast on a sorrel
cream sauce. Bread-and-butter pudding, iced chocolate parfait on rum
custard with fresh berries, cheeses with walnut bread to follow. John
Hoskins compiles the splendid wine list (see also *George at Stamford*), that
has a good selection of half bottles, as well as some of the kindest prices
around. *Seats 38. Parties 39. Private Room. L 12-2 D 7-10.*
Set Sun L £14.95.

Huntingdon   Places of Interest

Island Hall   Godmanchester Tel 0480 459676.
The Cromwell Museum   Tel 0480 425830.
Huntingdon Racecourse   Tel 0480 453373.

Huntsham   Huntsham Court   68%   £99

Tel 039 86 365   Fax 039 86 456   **HR**

Huntsham Bampton Nr Tiverton Devon EX16 7NA   Map 3 D2

A rather gaunt Victorian Gothic pile run in friendly, very casual style by
owners Mogens and Andrea Bolwig. Eating is communal, there's an
honour system in the bar, and you just wander into the kitchen if you need
anything. There's great atmosphere in the day rooms (log fires, a panelled
great hall, splendid pieces of furniture) and in the roomy bedrooms, named
after composers, there are Victorian beds and baths and pre-war radios
with an authentic crackle – not a teasmaid in sight! The hotel is dedicated
to music, with the classical variety played *forte* in the evening. The day
starts with an excellent buffet breakfast. No dogs. Children are well catered
for and accommodated free of charge if they share their parents' room;
baby-sitting is available. No dogs, however "good" or "small". *Rooms 17.*
Garden, tennis, croquet, coarse fishing, shooting, bicycles, sauna, solarium,
snooker. Access, Amex, Visa,

Restaurant   £72

Five-course dinners (no choice, but variations possible in advance) are
enjoyed in leisurely fashion at a convivial candle-lit table. Duck from a
local farm, roasted crisp and escorted by a Périgord sauce, is a favourite
dish, so too fillet of brill sauce américaine, and for dessert, treacle tart.
Guests are welcome to browse around the wine cellars where they'll find
the New World and Spain particularly well represented; fair prices and
some bottles charged only for what you drink. *Seats 30. Parties 30. Private*
Room. D only 8-10.30. Set D £28.

Huntsham   Places of Interest

Tiverton Tourist Information   0884 255827.
Knightshayes Court (NT)   Nr Tiverton Tel 0884 254665.
Tiverton Castle   Tel 0884 253200.
The Tiverton Museum   Tel 0884 256295.

Hurley   Ye Olde Bell   65%   £105

Tel 0628 825881   Fax 0628 825939   **H**

High Street Hurley Nr Maidenhead Berkshire SL6 5LX   **Map 5 D2**

A black-and-white inn which was built in 1135 as a guest house for a
Benedictine monastery. You enter through a Norman arch to find a
heavily beamed bar with comfortable armchairs, old brass and lots of
character, while adjacent to it is the tiny Hogarth bar. The comfortable
bedrooms have been recently refurbished and vary from handsome,
traditionally furnished rooms in the inn and neighbouring Malt House to
more modern ones in an annexe. Children up to 14 stay free in parents'
room. Resort Hotels. *Rooms 36. Garden, croquet, pétanque. Access, Amex,
Visa,*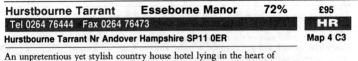

Hurstbourne Tarrant   Esseborne Manor   72%   £95

Tel 0264 76444   Fax 0264 76473   **HR**

Hurstbourne Tarrant Nr Andover Hampshire SP11 0ER   **Map 4 C3**

An unpretentious yet stylish country house hotel lying in the heart of
Watership Down country, set back off the A343 about a mile to the north
of Hurstbourne Tarrant. It displays obvious attention to detail both in the
public rooms and in the overnight accommodation, with fresh flowers,
carved ducks, glossy magazines, family ornaments and some antiques. All of
the twelve bedrooms have been decorated and furnished to a very high
standard in both fabrics and materials, enjoying views overlooking the
well-kept gardens or rich farmland beyond. The six most spacious rooms
are housed in a a converted stable block, just a short distance across a
courtyard. Extras provided include thick robes, books and fresh fruit.
Bathrooms benefit from full-length mirrors, spacious surfaces and vividly
coloured bath toys. No children under 12. No dogs. *Rooms 12. Garden,
tennis, croquet. Access, Amex, Visa,*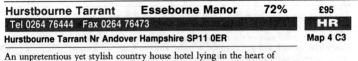

Restaurant   £76

A warm, cosy dining room with well-spaced tables, starched napery and
sparkling cutlery. Mark Greenfield's cooking is modern English in style;
lunch is usually a light affair with a choice of three dishes at each of the
two ("quickie") or three courses on a fixed-price menu – perhaps curried
parsnip soup followed by goujons of sole, with late-crop Hampshire
strawberries in a praline basket to finish. An alternative starter such as fish
marmite in saffron sauce might also make an appearance on the grander
(and considerably more expensive) five-course dinner menu as an
intermediary fish course; typical dishes might be a warm partridge and
pickled walnut salad followed by supreme of chicken on a sorrel sauce
with tomato coulis and an interesting selection of desserts (butterscotch ice
cream, lime mousseline with candied zests and dark chocolate or coconut
meringue with glazed pears and praline cream). Good selection of British
cheeses served with chilled grapes and celery. Family lunch with a
traditional roast on Sundays. Quietly efficient staff will even provide
gentlemen with a jacket, a formal touch decreed by the management.
*Seats 30. Parties 30. Private Room. L 12.30-2 D 7.30-9.30. Set L £15 Set D
£31.*

Hythe Hythe Imperial 71% £117

Tel 0303 267441 Fax 0303 264610 **H**

Princes Parade Hythe Kent CT21 6AE Map 7 C6

A large, family-run hotel set right on the seafront and surrounded by 50 acres of grounds. An imposing, cream-painted exterior of Victorian splendour belies the more classical air within. The polished mahogany reception area is adorned with brown leather chesterfield sofas and leads through to comfortable bars and lounges. All bedrooms have views of the sea or gardens and are mostly of good size with a mixture of quality period furniture, although some have more ordinary darkwood pieces. Excellent and very pleasant staff and leisure facilities that include go-karting and a children's play area with Scalextric. Families are particularly well catered for with baby-sitting, baby-listening and crèche facilities available. Current building includes a new children's playroom and two extensions to the conference rooms (which cater for up to 200 delegates). No dogs. ***Rooms 100.*** *Garden, coffee shop (8.30am-10.30pm), indoor swimming pool, gymnasium, spa bath, sauna, solarium, steam room, beauty & hair salons, squash, tennis, games room, 9-hole golf course, putting, dinner dance (weekly), helipad. Access, Amex, Visa,* Diners Club International

Hythe Stade Court 62% £80

Tel 0303 268263 Fax 0303 261803 **H**

West Parade Hythe Kent CT21 6DT Map 7 C6

A small, welcoming entrance hall opens out on to a bamboo-furnished bar, and there's an upstairs lounge looking out to sea. There are also Channel views from many of the traditionally styled bedrooms, the majority of which have little sun lounges. All the bedrooms are double-glazed. Free use of the extensive leisure facilities at the Hythe Imperial, excluding golf (for which a green fee is charged). ***Rooms 42.*** *Garden. Access, Amex, Visa,* Diners Club International

Hythe Places of Interest

Lympne Castle Tel 0303 267571.
Port Lympne Zoo Park Lympne Tel 0303 64646.

Ide Old Mill £55

Tel 0392 59480 **R**

20 High Street Ide Nr Exeter Devon EX2 9RN Map 3 D2

Set menus and à la carte are available both lunchtime and evening in the tranquil surroundings of a converted 16th-century mill, just off the A30 west of Exeter. Fish dishes feature prominently, with lobsters, fresh from the tank, prawn tails and lemon sole ever-popular choices. Lamb cutlets and chicken Piri Piri are familiar alternatives, with pavlovas, chocolate parfait and home-made ice creams to follow. ***Seats 32.*** *Parties 45. Private Room. L 12-1.30 D 7-9.30. Closed L Sat, all Sun, 25 & 26 Dec. Set L £9.95 Set D £14. Access, Amex, Visa.*

Ilkley Box Tree £70

Tel 0943 608484 Fax 0943 816793 **R**

29 Church Street Ilkley West Yorkshire LS29 9DR Map 10 C1

Sadly, all has changed at the long-established and renowned Box Tree and as we went to press its future was still unclear. Edward Denny (who achieved star recognition last year) has left to go to *Normandie* in Birtle, near Bury. ***Seats 50.*** *Parties 26. Private Room. L 12.30-2 (Sun to 2.30) D 7.30-9.45. Closed L Sat, D Sun, all Mon & Tue, 25 & 26 Dec, 1 Jan. Set L £11.95 Set D £16.95. Access, Amex, Visa,* Diners Club International

Ilkley   Rombalds Hotel   61%   £84

Tel 0943 603201   Fax 0943 816586   **H**

West View Wells Road Ilkley West Yorkshire LS29 9JG   Map 10 C1

A sand-coloured Victorian house in an attractive terrace, Rombalds stands
on a hill leading up to the famed Ilkley Moor. The personal domain since
1981 of Jill and Ian Guthrie, it is tended throughout with care and taste.
Gradual bedroom refurbishment has created stylish modern facilities on a
sympathetic and modish Victorian theme. Private rooms accommodate
dining for 50 and conferences up to 80. Excellent Sunday brunches (from
9am). Children under 12 stay free in parents' room. *Rooms 15. Garden.
Closed 27-30 Dec. Access, Amex, Visa,* **(I)** *Diners Club International*

Ilminster   Forte Travelodge   £40

Tel 0460 53748   **L**

A303 Southfield roundabout Horton Cross Ilminster
Somerset PA19 9PT   Map 3 E2

Located on the A303 at the intersection with the Ilminster bypass, west of
the town centre. *Rooms 32. Access, Amex, Visa.*

Ingatestone   Heybridge Moat House   68%   £101

Tel 0277 355355   Fax 0277 353288   **H**

Roman Road Ingatestone Essex CM4 9AB   Map 7 B4

Motel-style rooms stand round a central courtyard, and there are purpose-
built conference facilities for up to 600 delegates. Just off the A12.
Rooms 22. Closed 25 & 26 Dec. Access, Amex, Visa, **(I)** *Diners Club International*

Ipswich   Belstead Brook Hotel   68%   £74

Tel 0473 684241   Fax 0473 681249   **H**

Belstead Road Ipswich Suffolk IP2 9HB   Map 6 C3

On the southern outskirts of the city (ask for directions when booking), the
16th-century Belstead Brook is set in eight acres of gardens and woodland.
Public rooms and the four-poster honeymoon suite are in the original
house with most of the other well-appointed bedrooms in a modern
extension. The six best suites are in a secluded garden block. Children up to
16 stay free in parents' room. Purpose-built syndicate rooms cater for
meetings of upto 60. No dogs. *Rooms 92. Garden, croquet. Access, Amex,
Visa,* **(I)** *Diners Club International*

Ipswich   Forte Posthouse   63%   £67

Tel 0473 690313   Fax 0473 690412   **H**

London Road Ipswich Suffolk IP2 0UA   Map 6 C3

On the A12 two miles from the centre of Ipswich, this Posthouse offers
stylish public areas and decent-sized bedrooms. Families are well catered
for, with reduced rates and a playroom for children at weekends.
Rooms 112. Outdoor swimming pool, children's play area. Access, Amex, Visa,
(I) *Diners Club International*

Ipswich   Marlborough Hotel   65%   £113

Tel 0473 257677   Fax 0473 226927   **H**

73 Henley Road Ipswich Suffolk IP1 3SP   Map 6 C3

Peacefully located within walking distance of the town centre, the
Marlborough is a privately owned hotel run with care and enthusiasm by
manager David Brooks. The tasteful public areas and the comfortable
bedrooms (the best have antique furniture) are equally well kept. 24 hour
room service. *Rooms 22. Garden, croquet. Access, Amex, Visa,* **(I)** *Diners Club International*

Ipswich   Novotel   61%   NEW   £78

Tel 0473 232400   Fax 0473 232414

H

Greyfriars Road Ipswich Suffolk IP1 1UP   Map 6 C3

Five minutes walk from the pedestrianised town centre and only a brisk
ten from the station: purpose-built facilities include all-day grill,
conferences from 2 to 200 (banquets 180) and 4 bedrooms for the disabled.
Under-16s stay free in parents' room. **Rooms 101.** *Patio, coffee shop
(6am-midnight). Access, Amex, Visa,*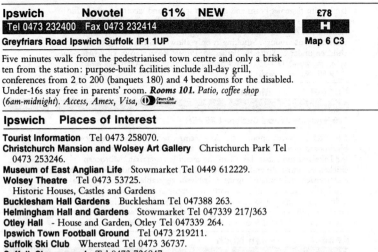

Ipswich   Places of Interest

Tourist Information   Tel 0473 258070.
Christchurch Mansion and Wolsey Art Gallery   Christchurch Park Tel
   0473 253246.
Museum of East Anglian Life   Stowmarket Tel 0449 612229.
Wolsey Theatre   Tel 0473 53725.
   Historic Houses, Castles and Gardens
Bucklesham Hall Gardens   Bucklesham Tel 047388 263.
Helmingham Hall and Gardens   Stowmarket Tel 047339 217/363
Otley Hall   - House and Garden, Otley Tel 047339 264.
Ipswich Town Football Ground   Tel 0473 219211.
Suffolk Ski Club   Wherstead Tel 0473 36737.
Suffolk Showground   Tel 0473 726847.

Ixworth   Theobalds   £60

Tel 0359 31707

R

68 High Street Ixworth Bury St Edmunds Suffolk IP31 2HJ   Map 6 C2

In a village seven miles north of Bury St Edmunds, Simon and Geraldine
Theobald set up their restaurant 12 years ago. Oak beams and log fires
make a traditional setting for enjoying Simon's capable and confident
cooking. Many of his dishes feature well-constructed sauces: port and
blackcurrant with a parfait of chicken livers, creamy tarragon with
steamed fillet of halibut, Calvados to accompany roast partridge with
apples. The price of a three-course meal is dictated by the price of the main
dish (an allowance is made for any course not required); at lunchtime there
is also a good-value table d'hote. Menus now always include a vegetarian
option. Keenly priced and well-compiled wine list with a good selection of
half bottles. No smoking – puffers can repair to the lounge. **Seats 36.**
*Parties 36. L 12-2 D 7-9.30 (Sat to 10). Closed L Sat, D Sun, all Mon, Bank
Holidays. Set L £15 Set D £22. Access, Visa.*

Jervaulx   Jervaulx Hall   70%   £91

Tel 0677 60235

H

Jervaulx Masham Nr Ripon North Yorkshire HG4 4PH   Map 15 B6

Enjoying an attractive spot next to the ruins of the 12th-century Abbey,
the Hall is run by the sociable John Sharp. A dignified yet homely
atmosphere prevails with watercolours, period furnishings, ornaments and
family photos in the quiet and appealing day rooms. Peace is the main
objective in the bedrooms, where no TVs or telephones intrude; an
abundance of quality toiletries in the carpeted bathrooms continues the
home-from-home appeal. **Rooms 10.** *Garden, croquet. Closed Dec-mid Mar.
No credit cards.*

Jevington   Hungry Monk Restaurant   £58

Tel 0323 482178

R

The Street Jevington Nr Polegate East Sussex BN26 5QF   Map 7 B6

The friendly atmosphere created by owners Nigel and Sue Mackenzie is
enhanced by the charming surroundings, which feature open fires and low
beamed ceilings. The fixed-price menu, which always includes some
vegetarian options, ranges from mulligatawny soup and rack of English

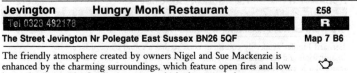

lamb with flageolet beans and garlic to spinach and ricotta cheese in filo
pastry with sweet pepper sauce, and fillets of brill or monkfish with
hollandaise. A good choice to finish might be Sussex pond pudding, tarte
tatin or a hot savoury. Smoking is only allowed in the sitting room. No
children under 3. **Seats 36.** Parties 36. Private Room. L Sun 12-2 (Mon-Sat
by arrangement) D 7-10. Closed Bank Holidays, 3 days Xmas. Set meals
£19.50. No credit cards.

Kendal   Moon   £35

Tel 0539 729254   **R**

129 Highgate Kendal Cumbria LA9 4EN   Map 13 D5

Eye-catching bistro opposite the Arts Centre, with a daily-changing
blackboard menu. Attention to quality and loyalty to local produce makes
for Lakeland food at its best; half the menu is vegetarian. Moroccan
chicken in cinnamon and prunes, beef, blackeyed bean and aubergine curry,
cod, spinach and tomato lasgane, Caribbean vegetable and okra gumbo,
lentil, Brie and hazelnut roast with red pepper and pesto sauce are typical
dishes. Children's portions. Sunday brunch. Once a month they have a
pudding club – one starter and five sweets! **Seats 78.** Parties 40. Private
Room. D only 6-9 (Fri & Sat to 10). Closed 25 Dec, 1 Jan. Access, Visa.

Kendal   Posh Nosh   £35

Tel 0539 725135   **R**

Yard 11 Stramongate Kendal Cumbria LA9 4BH   Map 13 D5

Sophisticated family restaurant with a dreadful name. Chef-patron Stephen
Burrows, a Miller Howe emigré, provides carefully-priced daytime and
nightime menus that range from home-made soups and Cumberland
sausage at lunchtime to pear and parmesan risotto and sautéed scallops in
lime, yoghurt and bacon sauce for dinner. British farmhouse cheeses served
with home-made sesame biscuits. Scones, cakes and teas at anytime Mon-
Thurs. **Seats 52.** Parties 38. Meals 9-6 (Fri & Sat 9-3 & 7-9). Closed
D Mon-Thu, all Sun, Bank Holidays. Access, Visa, **①** Diners Club International

Kendal   Woolpack Hotel   59%   £62

Tel 0539 723852   Fax 0539 728608   **H**

Stricklandgate Kendal Cumbria LA9 4ND   Map 13 D5

17th-century former coaching inn with old-fashioned original bedrooms
and a modern annexe. Once you've negotiated the one-way system you'll
find plenty of secure parking. Children up to 15 stay free in parents' room.
Conferences for up to 100. No dogs. **Rooms 54.** Access,
Amex, Visa, **①** Diners Club International

Kendal   Places of Interest

Tourist Information   Tel 0539 725758.
Levens Hall   Tel 05395 60321.
Sizergh Castle and Garden (NT)   Tel 05395 60070.
Kendal Ski Club   Tel 0539 33031.
   Museums and Art Galleries
Abbot Hall Art Gallery   Tel 0539 722464.
Abbot Hall Museum of Lakeland Life and Industry   Tel 0539 722464.
Kendal Museum of Natural History and Archaeology   Tel 0539 721374.

Kenilworth   Restaurant Bosquet   £72

Tel 0926 52463   **R**

97a Warwick Road Kenilworth Warwickshire CV8 1HP   Map 10 C4

Bernard Lignier's superbly consistent cooking has a sound classical base. His
imagination and obvious creative flair enhance daily fixed-price and
seasonal à la carte menus which are full of ambition and interest; the
translations from the French descriptions help considerably. Saucing is first-
rate as in the pear and pepper sauce that comes with the saddle of venison

or the beurre blanc with the feuilleté of asparagus. Jane Lignier's polite, efficient service complements the serious cooking. The 3-course, fixed-price dinner menu offers a choice of three dishes per courses – perhaps including confit of duck and pork salad or feuilleté of asparagus to start, followed by jugged hare, calf's liver with lime sauce or fish of the day. **Seats 26.** Parties 30. D only 7-9.30. Closed Sun & Mon, 1 week Xmas, 2 weeks Aug. Set D £19 (exc Sat). Access, Amex, Visa.

Kenilworth Clarendon House 60% £77
Tel 0926 57668 Fax 0926 50669 H
Old High Street Kenilworth Warwickshire CV8 1LZ Map 10 C4

The Lea family's friendly hotel stands at the heart of the town's conservation area and was originally built in 1430 as a tavern to serve the local community. Care has been taken to retain the original character, with panelling and exposed beams much in evidence. Bedrooms, which include some tiny singles, are furnished in a cosy, unfussy manner in a variety of styles. Each has its own en-suite bath or shower room. The hotel is not far from the NEC, and Birmingham, Leamington, Warwick, Stratford and Coventry are within easy reach. **Rooms 31.** Access, Visa.

Kenilworth De Montfort Hotel 63% £91
Tel 0926 55944 Fax 0926 57830 H
Kenilworth Warwickshire CV8 1ED Map 10 C4

Modern De Vere hotel with spacious day rooms and a good standard of accommodation. Banqueting facilities up to 200, conferences to 350. **Rooms 96.** Access, Amex, Visa, Diners Club International

Kenilworth Places of Interest

Royal Showground National Agricultural Centre, Stoneleigh Park Tel 0203 696969.

Kenton Travel Inn £42
Tel 081-907 1671 Fax 081-909 1604 L
Kenton Road Kenton Middlesex HA3 8AT Map 7 A4

Includes a function room; near Wembley Stadium and Arena. **Rooms 43.** Access, Amex, Visa, Diners Club International

Keswick Keswick Hotel 60% £75
Tel 076 87 72020 Fax 076 87 71300 H
Station Road Keswick Cumbria CA12 4NQ Map 13 C5

Solid Victorian hotel set in four acres of gardens, an easy walk from the town. Lakeland views. Families welcome, but also a business trade. A fine Victorian conservatory has a grapevine and is a fine place for afternoon tea. Guests can play golf free (Monday to Friday) at the Keswick Club. **Rooms 66.** Garden, croquet, putting. Access, Amex, Visa, Diners Club International

Keyston Pheasant Inn £55
Tel 080 14 241 R
Village Loop Road Keyston Nr Bythorn Cambridgeshire PE18 0RE Map 6 A2

Polished wooden tables, gleaming silverware and an intimate, friendly atmosphere characterise the Pheasant, a charming pub serving both bar and restaurant food. Owner-chef Nick Steiger's menu in the restaurant is interesting but never outlandish: smoked haddock and basil rillettes; gnocchi of polenta with wild mushrooms and crispy bacon; breast of chicken stuffed with salmon mousse served on sorrel sauce; fillet of beef with pink peppercorn sauce. Plainly cooked dishes on request. Bar snacks are above average. Good Sunday lunch. Keenly-priced and interesting wines listed by style. **Seats 30.** Parties 30. L 12-2 D 7-10. Closed D 25 & 26 Dec. Set L £14.95. Access, Amex, Visa, Diners Club International

Kidderminster   Stone Manor   65%   £92

H

Tel 0562 777555   Fax 0562 777834

Stone Nr Kidderminster Hereford & Worcester DY10 4PJ   Map 10 B4

Mock-Tudor in style, the Manor dates from 1926. Space is not in short supply; newer conference complex accommodates 150; Garden Room banqueting for up to 250. Some characterful bedrooms overlooking rose gardens and swimming pool include four with four-posters. Chidlren under 5 stay free in parents' room. *Rooms 52. Garden, croquet, outdoor swimming pool, putting, tennis, dinner dance (monthly Sept-May). Access, Amex, Visa,*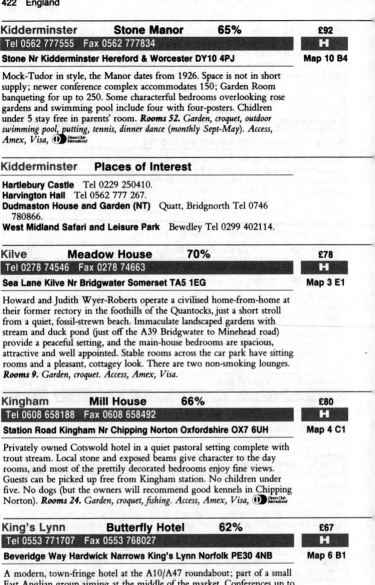

Kidderminster   Places of Interest

Hartlebury Castle   Tel 0229 250410.
Harvington Hall   Tel 0562 777 267.
Dudmaston House and Garden (NT)   Quatt, Bridgnorth Tel 0746 780866.
West Midland Safari and Leisure Park   Bewdley Tel 0299 402114.

Kilve   Meadow House   70%   £78

H

Tel 0278 74546   Fax 0278 74663

Sea Lane Kilve Nr Bridgwater Somerset TA5 1EG   Map 3 E1

Howard and Judith Wyer-Roberts operate a civilised home-from-home at their former rectory in the foothills of the Quantocks, just a short stroll from a quiet, fossil-strewn beach. Immaculate landscaped gardens with stream and duck pond (just off the A39 Bridgwater to Minehead road) provide a peaceful setting, and the main-house bedrooms are spacious, attractive and well appointed. Stable rooms across the car park have sitting rooms and a pleasant, cottagey look. There are two non-smoking lounges. *Rooms 9. Garden, croquet. Access, Amex, Visa.*

Kingham   Mill House   66%   £80

H

Tel 0608 658188   Fax 0608 658492

Station Road Kingham Nr Chipping Norton Oxfordshire OX7 6UH   Map 4 C1

Privately owned Cotswold hotel in a quiet pastoral setting complete with trout stream. Local stone and exposed beams give character to the day rooms, and most of the prettily decorated bedrooms enjoy fine views. Guests can be picked up free from Kingham station. No children under five. No dogs (but the owners will recommend good kennels in Chipping Norton). *Rooms 24. Garden, croquet, fishing. Access, Amex, Visa,*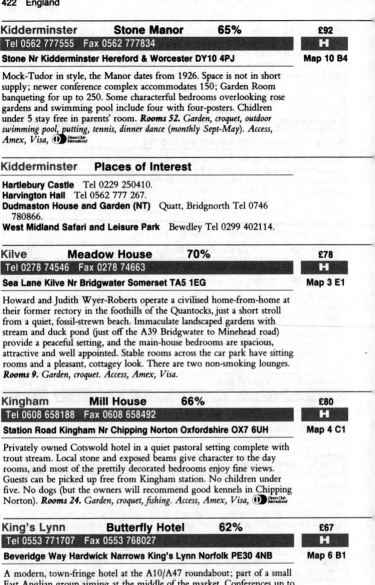

King's Lynn   Butterfly Hotel   62%   £67

H

Tel 0553 771707   Fax 0553 768027

Beveridge Way Hardwick Narrows King's Lynn Norfolk PE30 4NB   Map 6 B1

A modern, town-fringe hotel at the A10/A47 roundabout; part of a small East Anglian group aiming at the middle of the market. Conferences up to 50; private dining for 15; under-16s stay free in parents' room. *Rooms 50. Garden. Access, Amex, Visa,*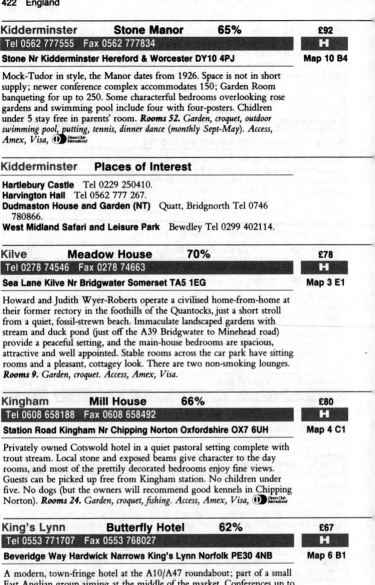

King's Lynn   Duke's Head   60%   £91

H

Tel 0553 774996   Fax 0553 763556

Tuesday Market Place King's Lynn Norfolk PE30 1JS   Map 6 B1

Forte Heritage hotel with an imposing 17th-century frontage. Singles, doubles and superior doubles. Conference facilites. *Rooms 71. Access, Amex, Visa,*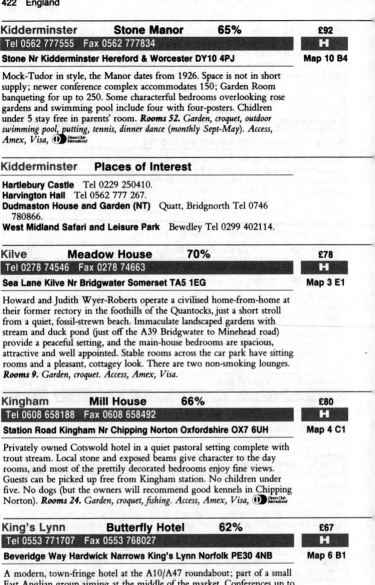

King's Lynn   Forte Travelodge   £40

Tel 0406 362230   **L**

A17 Wisbech Road Long Sutton Kings Lynn Norfolk PE12 9AG   Map 6 B1

On the A17 at the junction with the A1101, 12 miles west of King's
Lynn and 10 miles north of Wisbech. *Rooms 40. Access, Amex, Visa.*

King's Lynn   Places of Interest

Tourist Information   Tel 0553 763044.
Houghton Hall   Tel 0485 569.
Oxburgh Hall (NT)   Swaffham Tel 036621 258.
Sandringham House and Grounds   Sandringham Tel 0553 772675.
Peckover House and Garden (NT)   Wisbech Tel 0945 583463.
Hunstanton Beach *14 miles King's Lynn.*

Kington   Penrhos Court   £65

Tel 0544 230720   Fax 0544 230754   **R R**

Penrhos Kington Hereford & Worcester HR5 3LH   Map 4 A1

Martin Griffiths and Daphne Lambert's restaurant is in the beautifully
restored 13th-century Cruck Hall, complete with flagstone floors and
heavy beams – a characterful setting for occasional medieval banquets.
Daphne offers daily-changing menus with a short choice; perhaps smoked
breast of duck with orange salad or queen scallops grilled with a herb crust
to start, followed by beef in ale with mustard dumplings or medallions of
venison with Grand Veneur sauce. Simple, but well-executed, desserts such
as pear meringue, lemon tart and passion fruit water-ice. 2- or 3-course
Sunday lunches offer a small choice, but always includes a traditional roast.
*Seats 50. Parties 90. Private Room. L (Sun only) 12.30-3 D 7.30-9. Closed 25
& 26 Dec. Set L £10.50/£15.50. Access, Amex, Visa,* Diners Club International

Rooms   £110

Individually styled bedrooms, named after birds, show some fine taste. The
latest eight rooms are in converted Elizabethan barns and are expected to
come on line in spring '93; of a fair size, they use fine lightwood and
mahogany furniture, co-ordinated contemporary fabrics and bright, clean
decor. Bathrooms (some with shower/WC only) have attractive fittings
and quality toiletries. Limited hotel-style public areas, but high bedroom
standards. *19 rooms.*

Kington   Places of Interest

Hergest Croft Gardens   Tel 0544 230160.

Kintbury   Dundas Arms   £65

Tel 0488 58263   Fax 0488 58568   **I R**

53 Station Road Kintbury Nr Newbury Berkshire RG15 0UT   Map 4 C2

The Kennet and Avon canal runs by an 18th-century inn with roomy,
traditionally-styled accommodation in a converted livery and stable block.
Sliding picture windows offer access to a terrace with garden furniture; all
rooms enjoy views of the ducks at play. *Rooms 5. Closed 25 Dec. Access,
Amex, Visa.*

Restaurant   £65

A comfortable dining room with canal views is the stage for owner David
Dalzell-Piper's cooking. Fresh local ingredients are prepared with skill,
confidence and a notable lack of fuss – the food is cooked, put on a plate
and served. These talents show up well in dishes like paté-stuffed quail with
peppered red jelly, grilled red mullet with a lively citrus sauce or roast
partridge with fried cabbage and smoky bacon. Bread and butter pudding
and treacle tart are favourite old-fashioned desserts. Food is also served in
the bar (Mon-Sat, exc Mon D). Some keen prices on a good wine list, with
excellent clarets and burgundies. *Seats 50. Parties 20. Private Room.*

L 12.30-1.30 D 7.30-9.15. Closed Xmas/New Year, Sun & Mon,
Set L £16.50 Set D £24.

Kinver	Berkleys	£55

Tel 0384 873679	**R**
5 High Street Kinver West Midlands	Map 10 B4

In the Piano Room (a pianist plays Fri & Sat eves) Andrew Mortimer's
short menu, with explanatory notes, is cautiously contemporary: deep-fried
king prawns in filo pastry, quail's egg salad with ham croquette, breast of
guinea fowl baked with orange, honey and ginger. The bistro, with a
different selection of dishes, is now open lunchtime and evening. *Seats 35.*
Parties 40. D only 7-10 (Bistro also 12-2 & 7-10). Closed Sun, Bank Holidays,
2 weeks Feb. Access, Amex, Visa, 🄳 *Diners Club International*

Knapton	Knapton Hall	60%	£50

Tel 0263 720405 Fax 0263 721692	**H**
The Street Knapton North Walsham Norfolk NR28 0SB	Map 6 D1

Use the church at Knapton as a landmark to find the white-painted Hall
with its distinctive low-windowed frontage. There is no separate lounge as
such but an area off the convivial, slightly pubby, bar has some sofa seating.
Well-kept bedrooms are furnished mostly with antique or period pieces
and two have four-poster beds. No dogs. *Rooms 9. Garden, indoor swimming*
pool. Access, Amex, Visa, 🄳 *Diners Club International*

Knaresborough	Dower House	63%	£66

Tel 0423 863302 Fax 0423 867665	**H**
Bond End Knaresborough Nr Harrogate North Yorkshire HG5 9AL	Map 15 C6

An ivy-decked former dower house that retains a lot of traditional appeal
while moving with the times. Period furnishings and the Georgian staircase
in the lounge are examples of the former, while the leisure and conference
centres cater for modern-day requirements. Bedrooms vary in size, shape
and furniture; children stay free in parents' room. Dogs are allowed in four
annexe rooms only. Banqueting/conference facilities for 100/60. *Rooms 32.*
Inddor swimming pool, garden, spa bath, sauna, solarium, gymnasium. Access,
Amex, Visa, 🄳 *Diners Club International*

Knaresborough	Places of Interest

Allerton Park Tel 0423 330927.
Mother Shipton's Cave and Petrifying Well Tel 0423 864600 *Oldest*
   tourist attraction in Britain.

Knutsford	La Belle Epoque	£70

Tel 0565 633060 Fax 0565 634150	**RR**
60 King Street Knutsford Cheshire WA16 2DT	Map 10 B2

A flamboyant art nouveau restaurant with fancy table settings, parquet
flooring, cane chairs, marble columns and richly-coloured curtain drapes.
The cooking, from Graham Codd and David Mooney, matches the setting
with elaborate combinations in modern dishes such as fresh salmon lasagne,
lamb's kidneys wrapped in lettuce leaves, apple and tomato charlotte with
green lentils, fillet steak with shallot and honey purée, Gressingham duck
garnished with a sausage of leg meat and pear, and served with a Cassis
sauce. Good cheeses. Outdoor eating on the roof garden in fine weather.
1½ miles from J19 of the M6 and 3 miles from Manchester Airport.
Seats 65. Parties 22. Private Room. D only 7.30-10. Closed Sun, Bank
Holidays, 1 week Jan. Access, Amex, Visa, 🄳 *Diners Club International*

Rooms	£60

Seven charmingly decorated rooms with large floral prints and a mixture
of Edwardian and white reproduction furniture. All have en-suite
bathrooms. No children under 12 in rooms or restaurant.

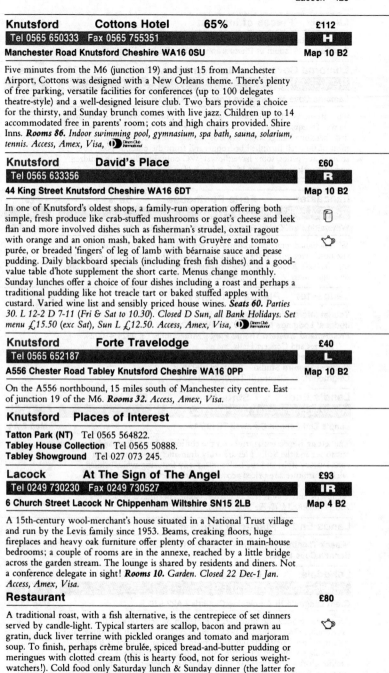

Knutsford — Cottons Hotel — 65% — £112

H

Tel 0565 650333   Fax 0565 755351

Manchester Road Knutsford Cheshire WA16 0SU — Map 10 B2

Five minutes from the M6 (junction 19) and just 15 from Manchester Airport, Cottons was designed with a New Orleans theme. There's plenty of free parking, versatile facilities for conferences (up to 100 delegates theatre-style) and a well-designed leisure club. Two bars provide a choice for the thirsty, and Sunday brunch comes with live jazz. Children up to 14 accommodated free in parents' room; cots and high chairs provided. Shire Inns. *Rooms 86. Indoor swimming pool, gymnasium, spa bath, sauna, solarium, tennis.* Access, Amex, Visa,

Knutsford — David's Place — £60

R

Tel 0565 633356

44 King Street Knutsford Cheshire WA16 6DT — Map 10 B2

In one of Knutsford's oldest shops, a family-run operation offering both simple, fresh produce like crab-stuffed mushrooms or goat's cheese and leek flan and more involved dishes such as fisherman's strudel, oxtail ragout with orange and an onion mash, baked ham with Gruyère and tomato purée, or breaded 'fingers' of leg of lamb with béarnaise sauce and pease pudding. Daily blackboard specials (including fresh fish dishes) and a good-value table d'hote supplement the short carte. Menus change monthly. Sunday lunches offer a choice of four dishes including a roast and perhaps a traditional pudding like hot treacle tart or baked stuffed apples with custard. Varied wine list and sensibly priced house wines. *Seats 60. Parties 30. L 12-2 D 7-11 (Fri & Sat to 10.30). Closed D Sun, all Bank Holidays. Set menu £15.50 (exc Sat), Sun L £12.50.* Access, Amex, Visa,

Knutsford — Forte Travelodge — £40

L

Tel 0565 652187

A556 Chester Road Tabley Knutsford Cheshire WA16 0PP — Map 10 B2

On the A556 northbound, 15 miles south of Manchester city centre. East of junction 19 of the M6. *Rooms 32.* Access, Amex, Visa.

Knutsford — Places of Interest

Tatton Park (NT)   Tel 0565 564822.
Tabley House Collection   Tel 0565 50888.
Tabley Showground   Tel 027 073 245.

Lacock — At The Sign of The Angel — £93

IR

Tel 0249 730230   Fax 0249 730527

6 Church Street Lacock Nr Chippenham Wiltshire SN15 2LB — Map 4 B2

A 15th-century wool-merchant's house situated in a National Trust village and run by the Levis family since 1953. Beams, creaking floors, huge fireplaces and heavy oak furniture offer plenty of character in main-house bedrooms; a couple of rooms are in the annexe, reached by a little bridge across the garden stream. The lounge is shared by residents and diners. Not a conference delegate in sight! *Rooms 10. Garden. Closed 22 Dec-1 Jan.* Access, Amex, Visa.

Restaurant — £80

A traditional roast, with a fish alternative, is the centrepiece of set dinners served by candle-light. Typical starters are scallop, bacon and prawn au gratin, duck liver terrine with pickled oranges and tomato and marjoram soup. To finish, perhaps crème brulée, spiced bread-and-butter pudding or meringues with clotted cream (this is hearty food, not for serious weight-watchers!). Cold food only Saturday lunch & Sunday dinner (the latter for residents only). *Seats 45. Parties 20. Private Room. L 1-1.30 D 7.30-8.15. Closed L Sat & Mon (including Bank Holidays), D Sun. Set L £16 Set D £22.50-£30.*

Lacock   Places of Interest

Lacock Abbey (NT)   Tel 024973 227.
Fox Talbot Museum of Photography (NT)   Tel 024 973 459.

Lamorna Cove   Lamorna Cove Hotel   67%   £75

Tel 0736 731411   **H**

Lamorna Cove Nr Penzance Cornwall TR19 6XH   Map 2 A4

On a steep, wooded hillside in eight acres of grounds with some stunning views. Tranquillity is a key attraction here. There are three lounges and a little bar; one lounge looks towards the sea. Views down the valley from most of the well-furnished bedrooms and from the outdoor pool. Four rooms have patios, some have shower/WC only. Families with children and pets welcome. *Rooms 18. Garden, outdoor swimming pool. Access, Amex, Visa,* ●

Lancaster   Forte Posthouse   69%   £67

Tel 0524 65999   Fax 0524 841265   **H**

Waterside Park Caton Road Lancaster Lancashire LA1 3RA   Map 13 D6

Well-designed, practical accommodation and smart public rooms in a low-rise hotel overlooking the river Lune. Banqueting and conference facilities for 100/120. *Rooms 110. Indoor swimming pool, gymnasium, spa bath, sauna, solarium. Access, Amex, Visa,* ●

Lancaster   Places of Interest

Tourist Information   Tel 0524 32878.
Judges' Lodgings Museum   Tel 0524 32808.
Frontierland Western Theme Park   Morecambe Tel 0524 410024.
   Theatres and Concert Halls
Dukes Theatre   Tel 0524 66645.
Nuffield Theatre Studio   Tel 0524 39026.
Leighton Hall   Carnforth Tel 0524 734474.

Land's End   State House   67%   £70

Tel 0736 871844   Fax 0736 871812   **H**

Land's End Sennen Cornwall TR19 7AA   Map 2 A4

The setting is spectacular, right on the clifftop at Land's End, and the views out to sea and the Scilly Isles are truly dramatic. Day rooms are in conservatory style, and the bedrooms, many featuring white-painted wicker furniture, are priced according to the view. Several rooms have four-posters, the majority are available for family use and children occupy parents' rooms free of charge. Conference/function facilities for 200+. *Rooms 34. Coffee shop. Access, Amex, Visa.*

Lands End   Places of Interest

Minack Theatre   Porthcurno Tel 0736 810471.
Sennen Cove Beach.

Langdale   Langdale Hotel   71%   £140

Tel 096 67 302   Fax 096 67 694   **H**

Great Langdale Nr Ambleside Cumbria LA22 9JD   Map 13 C5

An extensive hotel and timeshare complex in 35 acres of woodland overlooking Great Langdale Beck. Centrally, an open-plan bar-lounge and restaurant incorporate the old mill stream, while an adjacent pub bar features slate walls and a log fire. Accommodation comprises a number of satellite blocks, constructed in Lakeland stone, where there is plenty of room for families in the former self-catering chalets. Wet-weather provision includes fine leisure facilities, a supervised crèche, Lego table in

the bar and coffee shop seating by the large pool. No dogs. **Rooms 65.**
Garden, croquet, gymnasium, indoor swimming pool, spa bath, sauna, solarium,
beauty & hair salon, adventure trail, coffee shop (10am-10pm). Access, Amex,
Visa, (◑) 𝐷𝑖𝑛𝑒𝑟𝑠 𝐶𝑙𝑢𝑏

Langho   Northcote Manor   65%   £60

| Tel 0254 240555 Fax 0254 246568 | **H R** |

Northcote Road Langho Nr Blackburn Lancashire BB6 8BE   Map 10 B1

Just off the A59 and nine miles from the M6 (J31), Langho was once home
to a Victorian cotton luminary and today retains much of the atmosphere
of a lived-in family home. By day, large bay windows afford fine views of
the Ribble Valley, while on winter nights open log fires are warm and
welcoming. The first-floor bedrooms, reached by a carved oak staircase, are
attractive and homely, with characterful old-fashioned bathrooms; children
stay free in parents' room. **Rooms 6.** *Garden Access, Amex, Visa,* (◑) 𝐷𝑖𝑛𝑒𝑟𝑠 𝐶𝑙𝑢𝑏

Restaurant   £80

Classically based dishes refreshed with innovative touches run through
joint-owner Nigel Haworth's seasonal menus. Terrine of duckling
combines Oriental flavours with a beansprout salad; collops of venison
balance sweet potato and apple purée with a Calvados sauce; apple tart
"Michelle Darchi" is accompanied by apple and yoghurt sorbet. Good
farmhouse cheeses come in large or small portions; home-made breads and
amuse-gueule are classy touches. Something for everyone on the wine list.
Seats 50. Parties 65. Private Room. L 12-1.30 D 7-9.30 (Sat to 10). Closed
1 Jan. Set L £12.40.

Langley-on-Tyne   Langley Castle   65%   £70

| Tel 0434 688888 Fax 0434 684019 | **H** |

Langley-on-Tyne Nr Haydon Bridge Northumberland NE47 5LU   Map 15 B4

Surrounded by ten acres of woodland, this resplendent castle, built in 1350,
has walls that are seven feet thick and is full of architectural interest; the
main staircase houses some of the best-preserved 14th-century garderobes in
Europe and there's a chapel in the roof. Bedrooms are simply furnished but
given individuality by stylishly draped half-tester beds. One of the en-suite
bathrooms has a sauna and another a whirlpool bath. A large, lofty
drawing room boasts an open fireplace and antique furniture. **Rooms 8.**
Garden, clay-pigeon shooting. Access, Amex, Visa, (◑) 𝐷𝑖𝑛𝑒𝑟𝑠 𝐶𝑙𝑢𝑏

Lavenham   Great House   £45

| Tel 0787 247431 | **R R** |

Market Place Lavenham Suffolk CO10 9QZ   Map 6 C3

The Great House is 15th-century with a Georgian facade, and stands just
opposite Lavenham's historic Guildhall. Frenchman Régis Crépy provides
excellent food served in cosy surroundings on rural French and English
menus, applying a modern touch to the best local ingredients. Also lighter
lunchtime menus. No smoking. **Seats 40.** Parties 50. L 12-2.30 D 7-9.30
(Sat to 10.30). Closed D Sun, all Mon. Set L £10.90 Set D £14.95. Access,
Amex, Visa, (◑) 𝐷𝑖𝑛𝑒𝑟𝑠 𝐶𝑙𝑢𝑏

Rooms   £68

There are four charming bedrooms/suites. Thick beams, antique furniture
and floral fabrics create the look of village England.

Lavenham   The Swan   71%   £121

HR

Tel 0787 247477   Fax 0787 248286

High Street Lavenham Nr Sudbury Suffolk CO10 9QA   Map 6 C3

A splendid example of Elizabethan architecture, the Swan has been
welcoming guests since the 15th century. Bristling with timbers, the cosy
alcoves meander one into another, creating charming public areas. The
lounge has long been the setting for relaxing afternoon tea, while the
earthy real-ale bar has the warm feel of a much-loved local. Walkways
overlooking pretty little gardens lead to the variously sized bedrooms,
designed to retain the period feel; stylish furniture and extras like fruit and
chocolates set the the tone for the attention to detail in evidence
throughout the hotel. Breakfast is good and service is on the ball. Forte
Heritage. *Rooms 47. Garden. Access, Amex, Visa,*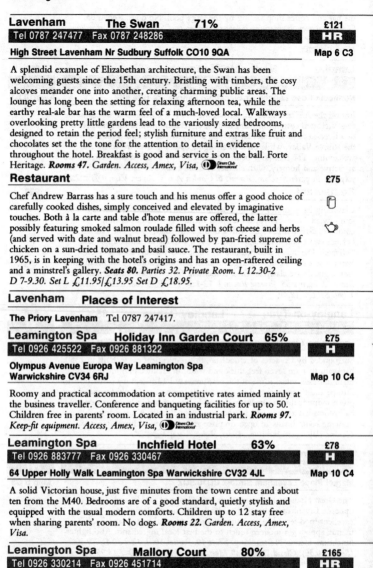

Restaurant   £75

Chef Andrew Barrass has a sure touch and his menus offer a good choice of
carefully cooked dishes, simply conceived and elevated by imaginative
touches. Both à la carte and table d'hote menus are offered, the latter
possibly featuring smoked salmon roulade filled with soft cheese and herbs
(and served with date and walnut bread) followed by pan-fried supreme of
chicken on a sun-dried tomato and basil sauce. The restaurant, built in
1965, is in keeping with the hotel's origins and has an open-raftered ceiling
and a minstrel's gallery. *Seats 80. Parties 32. Private Room. L 12.30-2
D 7-9.30. Set L £11.95/£13.95 Set D £18.95.*

Lavenham   Places of Interest

The Priory Lavenham   Tel 0787 247417.

Leamington Spa   Holiday Inn Garden Court   65%   £75

H

Tel 0926 425522   Fax 0926 881322

**Olympus Avenue Europa Way Leamington Spa
Warwickshire CV34 6RJ**   Map 10 C4

Roomy and practical accommodation at competitive rates aimed mainly at
the business traveller. Conference and banqueting facilities for up to 50.
Children free in parents' room. Located in an industrial park. *Rooms 97.
Keep-fit equipment. Access, Amex, Visa,*

Leamington Spa   Inchfield Hotel   63%   £78

H

Tel 0926 883777   Fax 0926 330467

64 Upper Holly Walk Leamington Spa Warwickshire CV32 4JL   Map 10 C4

A solid Victorian house, just five minutes from the town centre and about
ten from the M40. Bedrooms are of a good standard, quietly stylish and
equipped with the usual modern comforts. Children up to 12 stay free
when sharing parents' room. No dogs. *Rooms 22. Garden. Access, Amex,
Visa.*

Leamington Spa   Mallory Court   80%   £165

HR

Tel 0926 330214   Fax 0926 451714

**Harbury Lane Bishop's Tachbrook Leamington Spa
Warwickshire CV33 9QB**   Map 10 C4

Standing in 10 acres of beautifully landscaped gardens, Mallory Court has
an air of luxury and refinement. It's one of the original country house
hotels and still one of the very best, built in 1910 in the Elizabethan style
of tall chimneys and stone-mullioned windows with leaded lights. A small
entrance hall leads directly into the main lounge, complete with deep-
cushioned couches and armchairs, quality drapes, deep carpets and fine
period furniture; the drawing room boasts green leather chesterfields and
there's a delightful conservatory sun-trap. Bedrooms are generally of a
good size and impeccably designed, with stylish fabrics, light, fresh colours

and quality freestanding furniture; some have four-posters. Extras in the rooms include bath robes, mineral water, flowers and magazines. The Blenheim suite is nothing short of luxurious with its own balcony, two tubs in the bathroom and a painted ceiling. Attentive staff and highly efficient housekeeping. Unsuitable for children under the age of nine. No dogs – kennelling nearby. *Rooms 10. Garden, croquet, outdoor swimming pool, squash, all-weather tennis. Access, Visa,* ◖◗ *Diners Club International*

Restaurant ★ £115

The panelled dining room is at the very heart of Mallory Court, offering high-quality cooking with polished and professional service to match. Classical dishes sit harmoniously alongside more modern offerings, so grilled Dover sole with herb butter sits side-by-side with quail terrine spiked with dried apricots and garnished with pickled vegetables, as does rhubarb crumble with iced gingerbread and white chocolate terrine with prunes in red wine. The à la carte is most unusually priced with a minimum charge of £27.50 plus supplements for every dish – from £2.75 for melon pearls with blackcurrant sorbet to £14.50 for roast Cornish lobster with béarnaise sauce. The fixed-price, three-course table d'hote dinner has been reduced in price since last year and offers alternative dishes at each course, while more informal lunchtimes see only a 2- or 3-course fixed-price menu, but with a good choice of less involved dishes like fricassee of rabbit with mustard cream sauce or beer-battered fillet of cod with tartare sauce and chipped potatoes. "No service charge is made or expected." *Seats 50. Parties 26. Private Room. L 12.30-2 D 7.30-9.45 (Sat to 10, Sun to 9). Set L £20.50/£24.50 Set D £29.50.*

Leamington Spa	Regent Hotel	63%	£85

HR

Tel 0926 427231   Fax 0926 450728

77 The Parade Leamington Spa Warwickshire CV32 4AX — Map 10 C4

Privately-owned town-centre hotel with a handsome, white Regency facade that has graced the Parade since 1819 (when it was apparently the largest hotel in the world). An agreeably old-fashioned air pervades the roomy lounge, but bedrooms are more up to date. Many of the staff have seen long years' service, and general manager Vernon May retired only a couple of years ago after 36 years. Conference/banqueting facilities for 100/250. *Rooms 83. Games room. Access, Amex, Visa,* ◖◗ *Diners Club International*

Vaults Restaurant £66

A friendly basement restaurant offering fixed-price 2- or 3-course lunches and both fixed-price and à la carte dinners. The former might see kedgeree, a roast from the trolley and steamed sultana roll with custard, while the latter extends to warmed salad with smoked duck and mangetout, stuffed breast of duck with Calvados sauce and zabaglione with Marsala. *Seats 55. Parties 20. Private Room. L 12.30-2 D 7.30-10.45. Closed Bank Holidays, Sun. Set L £9.75/£11.75 Set D £16.50.*

Leamington Spa	Tuscany Hotel	66%	£85

H

Tel 0926 332233   Fax 0926 332232

34 Warwick Place Leamington Spa Warwickshire CV32 5DE — Map 10 C4

Billing itself as 'the Alternative Hotel', the Tuscany is a non-smoking establishment in a listed Regency building with crenellations. The owners' attention to detail runs to recycled stationery, non-chemically softened water, and organic produce for the kitchen. The lounge has a relaxing, club-like feel and bedrooms, smartly furnished in stained pine, have well-equipped bathrooms with baths and thermostatic showers. No dogs. *Rooms 10. Access, Amex, Visa,* ◖◗ *Diners Club International*

Leamington Spa   Places of Interest

Tourist Information   Tel 0926 311470.
Offchurch Bury Polo Club   Red House Farm, Campion Hills Tel 0926 882883.

Ledbury   The Feathers   £79

| Tel 0531 5266   Fax 0531 2001 | I |

High Street Ledbury Hereford & Worcester HR8 1DS   Map 4 B1

A classic timber-framed former coaching inn dating from 1565 with oddly-shaped, en-suite, double-glazed bedrooms (including one with a four-poster), uneven, creaky floors and drunken staircases. Remote-control TV, bedside tea-tray and hair-dryers are standard. Good snacks in the hop-bedecked Fuggles bar. Conference/banqueting facilities for 150/125.
Rooms 11. *Access, Amex, Visa,* Diners Club International

Ledbury   Hope End   70%   £115

| Tel 0531 3613   Fax 0531 5697 | HR |

Hope End Ledbury Hereford & Worcester HR8 1SQ   Map 4 B1

Elizabeth Barrett-Browning's former home, largely of 18th-century origin, is mellow rather than grand, nestling in 40 acres of wooded parkland and a Georgian landscaped garden which includes a temple, grotto and island ruin. Today's incumbents John and Patricia Hegarty run this haven of tranquillity in suitably informal fashion, setting piles of books by the deep sofas in front of the log-burning stoves. Simply decorated bedrooms have exposed beams along with country oak and antique stripped-pine furniture, fresh flowers and yet more books; nary a TV unless requested. Cork and tile bathrooms come with a selection of bath oils. No children under 12. No dogs. **Rooms 9.** *Garden. Closed mid Dec-mid Feb. Access, Visa.*

Restaurant   £70

Patricia Hegarty is the definitive home cook, her chutneys, breads and jellies as integral a part of production as her nightly fixed-price dinner. The kitchen garden provides vegetables, herbs and fruit for her naturally-flavoured sorrel and potato soup, salmis of duckling with damson relish and refreshingly different cottagers kale, Swiss chard or maybe cabbage with juniper which accompany. Salad and farmhouse cheeses then precede the likes of morello cherry and almond tart or baked custard and mulberries. An exceptional wine list is strongest in fine burgundies, best for value in the Rhone. No smoking. **Seats 18.** *Parties 6. D only 7.30-8.30. Closed Mon & Tue except residents. Set D £30.*

Ledbury   Places of Interest

Eastnor Castle   Tel 0531 2305/2894.

Leeds   Bhavani Junction   £24

| Tel 0532 468988 | R |

2 Eastgate Leeds West Yorkshire LS2 7JI   Map 10 C1

An exclusively vegetarian restaurant (on the top floor of Shabab) with an interesting range of northern thalis as a complement to their Moglai menu. Anarkali includes onion bhaji's, bhindian with fresh tomato, palak allo with methi, home-made paneer korma, raita, pillau rice, puri, fresh salad and gulab jamun, an excellent value combination. Bite-sized pani puri are filled with a mixture of chick peas and spicy potatoes. **Seats 50.** *Parties 100. Private Room. L 11.30-2.30 D 6.30-11.45. Closed L Sun, Bank Holidays. Set L from £4.50 Set D from £7.50. Access, Visa.*

Leeds　　　Brasserie Forty Four　　↑　　£50

Tel 0532 343232　Fax 0532 343332　　**R**

44 The Calls Leeds West Yorkshire LS2 7EW　　Map 10 C1

A stylishly converted grain mill (next to *42 The Calls* hotel – see entry)
houses an attractive riverside brasserie. A wide-ranging menu displays
numerous styles and influences with tempura seafoods sitting happily
alongside Yorkshire puddings. Lamb and apricot pie, veal kidneys with
brioche and a mustard sauce, oxtail casserole with butter beans, Irish
pickled salt beef, braised onion with spinach soufflé and sweet capsicum
with a cheese soufflé, and floating islands indicate the style – adventurous
and, more often than not, successful. Also available (to end a romantic
dinner?) is chocolate fondue for two, with marshmallows and pieces of
fruit for dipping. **Seats 125.** Parties 50. Private Room. L 12-2.30
D 6.30-10.30. Closed L Sat, all Sun. Set L £7.95. Access, Amex, Visa.

Leeds　　　Corner Café　　　£15

Tel 0532 623958　　**R**

83 Buslingthorpe Lane Leeds West Yorkshire　　Map 10 C1

A simple, inner-city unlicensed café run for many years by Mr Ghauri,
next door to the Skinner's Arms. The best nan and lamb kebab for miles
around. No tandoori dishes, but quality and value curries plus a vast
vegetable choice. **Seats 39.** Parties 30. Private Room. L 12-2.30 D 6-11. *No
credit cards.*

Leeds　　　Dawat　　　£30

Tel 0532 872279　　**R**

4-6 Leeds Road Kippax Nr Leeds West Yorkshire LS25 7LT　　Map 11 D1

Indian home cooking Delhi-style by Mrs Arora in two 19th-century
cottages. **Seats 26.** Parties 16. D only 6.30-11. Closed Sun, 25 & 26 Dec.
Access, Visa, Diners Club International

Leeds　　　42 The Calls　　　£115

Tel 0532 440099　Fax 0532 344100　　**PH**

42 The Calls Leeds West Yorkshire LS2 7EW　　Map 10 C1

Created from a derelict riverside grain mill, 42 The Calls provides a new
level of modern, sophisticated comfort for visitors to Leeds. Part of a
smaller-scale London Dockland-style residential development, it's the
brainchild of Jonathan Wix, whose idea has now blossomed. Its strong
point is the bedrooms: co-ordinated soft furnishings blend with the
building's original features like painted stone walls and warehouse beams.
Each room has a large work desk, three phones, a CD stereo system and
coffee percolator. Individual touches abound: 14 original paintings in one
room, a large basket of dried roses, a little basket of wrapped sweets.
Bathrooms are equally impressive. Minimal day rooms include a bright
foyer and small lounge. There's no restaurant, but direct billing is arranged
with a number of local restaurants that include *Brasserie Forty Four* next
door (see entry), in which Wix has an interest. Excellent staff impress
greatly. **Rooms 39.** Coarse fishing. Access, Amex, Visa, Diners Club International

Leeds　　　La Grillade　　　£30

Tel 0532 459707　　**R**

Wellington Street Leeds West Yorkshire LS1 4HJ　　Map 10 C1

Bustling basement French bistro serving snails to steaks and toasted goat's
cheese to Toulouse sausages. **Seats 65.** Parties 30. Private Room. L 12-2.30
D 7.30-11. Closed L Sat, all Sun, Bank Holidays, 1 week Xmas. Set meals
£10.80. Access, Visa.

Leeds   Haley's Hotel   74%   £112

Tel 0532 784446   Fax 0532 753342   **HR**

Shire Oak Road Headingley Leeds West Yorkshire LS6 2DE   **Map 10 C1**

Two miles from the city centre, on a leafy lane just off the A660 Otley
Road, stands a lovely Victorian house that has been transformed into a
stylish hotel. Although not large, the individually designed bedrooms are
well appointed with smart fabrics in varying styles; attention to detail
extends to a phone on both bedside and desk, shoe-cleaning service and
antique pieces. Bathrooms are bright and tiled, and quality toiletries and
bathrobes are provided. Smartly attired young staff; 24hr room service and
good breakfasts. The Bramley Room holds up to 30 delegates for small,
theatre-style conferences. *Rooms 22. Garden. Closed 26-31 Dec. Access,
Amex, Visa,* **(I)** *Diners Club International*

Restaurant   £52

A serious restaurant with a style and quality unusual for the Leeds area.
The refined, quietly elegant atmosphere is enhanced by neat table settings,
subtle lighting and smartly dressed staff. Chef Andrew Foster cooks in a
modern style, putting a classical training to good use as a foundation on
which to build. Fixed-price menus are offered for both lunch and dinner,
the former offering, perhaps, chilled pigeon terrine with pine nuts or crispy
smoked bacon and oyster mushroom salad followed by baked salmon,
braised chicken with creamed leek sauce or roast rib of beef served from a
trolley; desserts are straightforward – glazed summer fuits under Sauternes
sabayon or chocolate and orange terrine with coffee sauce. The seasonal
carte might cover a range from bourride with saffron and garlic
mayonnaise or purple onion soup with a puff pastry crust to trellised
salmon and brill, red mullet fillets, steamed breast of corn-fed chicken wih
truffle noodles, leeks and butter sauce, and calf's liver with grapes, sultanas,
almonds and Sauternes sauce. French and British cheeses with home-made
biscuits and walnut bread, plus wines by the glass. Opinionated notes do
little to enliven a rather dull wine list. *Seats 50. Parties 24. Private Room.
L 12.30-2 D 7.15-9.45. Closed L Sat, D Sun. Set L £14.75 Set D
£17.95/£22.50.*

Leeds   Hilton International   69%   £129

Tel 0532 442000   Fax 0532 433577   **H**

Neville Street Leeds West Yorkshire LS1 4BX   **Map 10 C1**

Escalators in glass 'antechambers' lead to the cool marble reception/lounge.
A modern, well-kept, well-run hotel. Conference/banqueting facilities for
400/290. *Rooms 210. Garage, coffee shop (10am-11pm). Access, Amex, Visa,*
(I) *Diners Club International*

Leeds   Holiday Inn   71%   £164

Tel 0532 442200   Fax 0532 440460   **H**

Wellington Street Leeds West Yorkshire LS1 4DL   **Map 10 C1**

Modern, redbrick, seven-storey hotel in the city centre, easily accessed from
the motorway network. A marble-floored foyer leads up to modern
meeting rooms on the mezzanine floor and the Roundhay lounge bar,
which overlooks the striking swimming pool. A club-like cocktail bar
adjoins Hamilton's restaurant and the lively Wig and Pen pub is also on the
ground floor. Bedrooms have at least one double bed, stylish furniture and
individual air-conditioning. There are many thoughtful extras included and
ample work space with easy chairs. Large mirrors, bathrobes, slippers and
toiletries in the bathrooms. Staff are young, smart and quietly efficient.
Conference/banqueting facilities for 200/250. Car park for 140 cars.
*Rooms 125. Indoor swimming pool, children's pool, spa bath, sauna, solarium,
beauty salon, snooker, keep-fit equipment, steam room. Access, Amex, Visa,*
(I) *Diners Club International*

Leeds   Low Hall   £50

Tel 0532 588221   R

Calverley Lane Horsforth Nr Leeds West Yorkshire LS18 4ES   Map 10 C1

Traditional and modern British cooking, from a bargain seasonal lobster menu to good-value tables d'hote – perhaps starting with a salad of smoked chicken and mango, followed by salmon trout with home-made pasta and light herb sauce. *Seats 80. Parties 120. Private Room. L 12-2 D 7-10. Closed L Sat, all Sun & Mon, Bank Holidays, 1 week Oct. Set L £12.95. Access, Visa.*

Leeds   Maxi's Chinese Restaurant   £40

Tel 0532 440552   Fax 0532 343902   R

Bingley Street Leeds West Yorkshire LS3 1LX   Map 10 C1

The largest purpose built Chinese restaurant in the North, serving Cantonese and Peking cuisine to over 300 diners. Hardly worthy of a foodie pilgrimage, but worth knowing about; plenty of room for families. *Seats 300. Parties 280. Private Room. Meals 12-12. Closed 25 & 26 Dec. Set meals from £13. Access, Amex, Visa,*  Diners Club International

Leeds   Merrion Hotel   £91

Tel 0532 439191   Fax 0532 423527   H

Merrion Centre Leeds West Yorkshire LS2 8NH   Map 10 C1

Modern city-centre hotel was undergoing major refurbishment as we went to press. Easy parking. Mount Charlotte Thistle. *Rooms 120. Access, Amex, Visa,* Diners Club International

Leeds   New Asia   £35

Tel 0532 343612   R

128 Vicar Lane Leeds West Yorkshire LS2 7NL   Map 10 C1

Mr Xuan Truong Hoang produces inexpensive Vietnamese specialities in slightly old-fashioned surroundings. Fine spring rolls made to order, mung bean flour (luk dao fan) noodles and char siu. There's a long list of seafood and over a dozen soups. *Seats 60. Parties 60. L 12-2 D 5-12. Set L from £4.25 set D from £9.50. Access, Visa.*

Leeds   Queen's Hotel   67%   £109

Tel 0532 431323   Fax 0532 425154   H

City Square Leeds West Yorkshire LS1 1PL   Map 10 C1

A grand hotel with a variety of function rooms catering for up to 650 conference delegates or banquet diners. Imposing facade, spacious bedrooms and smart bathrooms. Forte Grand. *Rooms 188. News kiosk, coffee shop (9.30am-11pm). Access, Amex, Visa,* Diners Club International

Leeds   Sang Sang   £50

Tel 0532 468664   R

7 The Headrow Leeds West Yorkshire   Map 10 C1

Over 200 dishes are listed on the long menu at this popular Chinese restaurant. All the favourites are represented including sizzling dishes, noodles with mixed meat and Peking duck. *Seats 110. Parties 80. Private Room. Meals 12-12. Closed Bank Holidays. Set meals from £12. Access, Amex, Visa,* Diners Club International

Leeds   Sous le Nez en Ville   £40
`Tel 0532 440108`   **R**

Basement Quebec House Quebec Street Leeds
West Yorkshire LS1 2HA   **Map 10 C1**

Basement bistro with the emphasis on fresh tastes (moules marinière, good
fresh fish), conviviality and better-than-average desserts. Great value early-
evening *menu du soir*. Tapas in the bar. *Seats 70. Parties 75. Private Room.
L 12-2.30 D 6-10.30. Closed L Sat, all Sun, Bank Holidays. Set D £10.95
(Mon-Sat 6-7.30pm). Access, Visa.*

Leeds   Thai Siam   £40
`Tel 0532 451608`   **R**

68-72 New Briggate Leeds West Yorkshire LS1 6NU   **Map 10 C1**

Friendly service from traditionally clad staff in simple, uncluttered first-
floor surroundings. Short menu, from tom yum goong soup to weeping
tiger (grilled sirloin steak with chili sauce) and Thai custard dessert with
palm sugar, egg and coconut milk. *Seats 60. Parties 20. L 12-2.30 D 6-11
(Sun 4-10.30). Set L from £5.50 Set D from £11. Access, Visa.*

Leeds   Places of Interest

Tourist Information   Tel 0532 478302.
Harewood House and Bird Garden   Tel 0532 886225/886238.
The Hollies Park   Tel 0532 782030.
Museum of Leeds   Tel 0532 478275
International Pool   Tel 0532 438696.
Headingley Cricket Ground   Tel 0532 787394.
Leeds United Football Ground   Tel 0532 716037.
Pontefract Park Racecourse   Tel 0977 703224.
Middleston Railway   Moor Road Railway Station Tel 0532 710320
   World's oldest railway.
   Theatres and Concert Halls
City Varieties Music Hall   Tel 0532 430808.
Civic Theatre   Tel 0532 462453.
Grand Theatre and Opera House   Tel 0532 459351.
Leeds Playhouse   Tel 0532 442141.

Leicester   Belmont Hotel   65%   £77
`Tel 0533 544773   Fax 0533 470804`   **H**

De Montfort Street Leicester Leicestershire LE1 7GR   **Map 11 D4**

In the same family ownership for more than 50 years, the Belmont stands
in a quiet street just off the A6. Good-quality darkwood furniture is used in
the bedrooms, the larger of which are designated Executives. Among the
day rooms are two bars: Olive's in the basement has a wine bar/bistro
atmosphere. *Rooms 68. Garden. Closed Xmas. Access, Amex, Visa,*

Leicester   Country Court   69%   £107
`Tel 0533 630066   Fax 0533 630627`   **H**

Braunstone Leicester Leicestershire LE3 2WQ   **Map 11 D4**

Ten minutes from the city centre, just off junction 21 of the M1, at the end
of the M69. A modern, business-oriented hotel offering good-sized
bedrooms (all rooms have either one or two double beds), extensive range
of conference facilities (for up to 90), leisure club and vastly reduced rates
at off-peak weekends when businessmen are thin on the ground. Children
up to 6 free in parents' room. *Rooms 141. Garden, indoor swimming pool, spa
bath, sauna, solarium, steam room, beautician, gymnasium. Access, Amex, Visa,*

Leicester	Curry Pot	£45
Tel 0533 538256		**R**
78 Belgrave Road Leicester Leicestershire		**Map 11 D4**

Tandoori restaurant offering a short menu of Indian favourites that are a cut above the standard suggested by the dull exterior. Particularly good samosas, chicken tikka and masala, plus lamb shahi korma. *Seats 55. Parties 30. Private Room. L 12-2 (Sat to 1.30) D 6-11 (Sat to 11.30). Closed Sun, 4 days Xmas, 1 Jan. Set meals from £14.50. Access, Amex, Visa,*

Leicester	Forte Posthouse	62%	£67
Tel 0533 630500 Fax 0533 823623			**H**
Braunston Lane East Leicester Leicestershire LE3 2FW			**Map 11 D4**

Equidistant from junction 21 of the M1 and the town centre, this modern low-rise hotel has recently benefited from complete refurbishment. Conference/banqueting facilities for 80. *Rooms 172. Garden. Access, Amex, Visa,*

Leicester	Granada Lodge	£43
Tel 0530 244237 Fax 0530 244580		**L**
M1/A50 junction 22 Markfield Leicester Leicestershire LE6 0PP		**Map 11 D3**

Rooms 39. Access, Amex, Visa,

Leicester	Grand Hotel	66%	£106
Tel 0533 555599 Fax 0533 544736			**H**
Granby Street Leicester Leicestershire LE1 6ES			**Map 11 D4**

A city-centre Victorian building with ample parking close to the station. Public rooms and bedrooms are stylish and of a good size. Three themed bars; vast banqueting and conference facilities for up to 450. 24hr room service. Jarvis Hotels. *Rooms 92. Coffee shop (10am-6pm Mon-Sat), dinner dance (Sat). Access, Amex, Visa,*

Leicester	Holiday Inn	72%	£113
Tel 0533 531161 Fax 0533 513169			**H**
129 St Nicholas Circle Leicester Leicestershire LE1 5LX			**Map 11 D4**

At the hub of a major road interchange, near junction 21 of the M1, Leicester's Holiday Inn is a tall building reaching high over the city. The marbled reception area makes a splendid first impression, and the lounge area that adjoins it is no less appealing. The rustic-style Hayloft restaurant with beams and agricultural accoutrements is an interesting contrast to the otherwise modern decor. Bedrooms provide plenty of space, large beds, fitted units and good tiled bathrooms. 65 are designated non-smoking. The leisure centre is a great family attraction at weekends. Free covered parking for residents. Conference facilities for 300. *Rooms 188. Indoor swimming pool, sauna, solarium, spa bath, steam room, news kiosk, coffee shop (7am-10.15pm). Access, Amex, Visa,*

Leicester	Leicester Forest Moat House	58%	£73
Tel 0533 394661 Fax 0533 394952			**H**
Hinckley Road Leicester Leicestershire LE3 3GH			**Map 11 D4**

Alongside the A47 four miles from the city centre, 3 miles from junction 21 interchange of M69 and M1 (but still close to the latter). Well-equipped bedrooms, a choice of bars and conference rooms for up to 65. Weekend rates are considerably reduced. *Rooms 34. Garden. Access, Amex, Visa,*

Leicester　　Man Ho　　£40

Tel 0533 557700　　R

16 King Street Leicester Leicestershire LE1 6RJ　　Map 11 D4

Comprising two houses in a low Georgian terrace behind New Walk Centre, Man Ho probably offers the best Chinese cooking in Leicester. Space, comfort and tastefully modern decor make a fine setting in which smartly-suited waitresses serve a mix of Peking, Cantonese and Szechuan cooking. Good choice of iron-plated sizzling dishes (including oysters and stuffed rainbow trout), fresh fish (grey mullet, sea bass, Dover sole), crispy aromatic duck and lamb, plus lettuce-wrapped minced chicken and seafood. *Seats 130. Parties 60. Private Room. L 12-2.30 D 5.30-11.30 (Sat & Sun 12-11.30). Set L from £6.50 Set D from £10. Access, Amex, Visa.*

Leicester　　Park International　　61%　　£82

Tel 0533 620471　Fax 0533 514211　　H

Humberstone Road Leicester Leicestershire LE5 3AT　　Map 11 D4

Large, tall and modern hotel with a choice of bars and five conference suites (for up to 400), but no leisure facilities. *Rooms 209. Coffee shop (7am-10pm, from 8am weekends). Access, Amex, Visa,* ◑ *Diners Club International*

Leicester　　Rise of the Raj　　£35

Tel 0533 553885　　R

6 Evington Road Leicester Leicestershire LE2 1HF　　Map 11 D4

Curiously old-fashioned in a reassuring way, offering much better than average north Indian cooking in a cosy setting on two floors. Good-value thali set meals (meat or vegetarian). *Seats 72. Parties 40. Private Room. L 12-2 D 6-11.45. Closed 25 Dec. Set meals from £8.50.* ◑ *Diners Club International*

Leicester　Places of Interest

Tourist Information Tel 0533 511300/511301.
Haymarket Theatre Tel 0533 539797
Phoenix Arts Theatre Tel 0533 554854.
Bosworth Battlefield Visitor Centre & Country Park Market Bosworth
　Tel 0455 290429.
Leicester Cathedral Tel 0533 625294.
The Leicestershire Museum and Art Gallery New Walk Tel 0533
　554100.
Leicestershire Museum of Technology Tel 0530 510851.
Grace Road Cricket Ground Tel 0533 831880.
Leicester City Football Ground Tel 0533 555000.
Leicester Racecourse Tel 0533 716515.
Outdoor Pursuits Centre Dry Ski Slope Tel 0533 681426.
Braunstone Park Showground Tel 0509 231665.
Mallory Park Motor Racing Circuit Tel 0455 842931.

Leighton Buzzard　　The Swan　　64%　　£80

Tel 0525 372148　Fax 0525 370444　　H

High Street Leighton Buzzard Bedfordshire LU7 7EA　　Map 5 E1

Recently acquired by Resort Hotels, a handsome Georgian coaching inn in the centre of town. Bedrooms vary in both size and decor with a mix of pine and reproduction furniture and colourful fabrics. Bathrooms are neat and unfussy. The Hunter's bar has rustic appeal with hunting prints, guns and fishing rods on the walls, and a carved-oak counter. There is also a comfortable lounge. *Rooms 38. Access, Amex, Visa,* ◑ *Diners Club International*

Leighton Buzzard   Places of Interest

Library Theatre Tel 0525 378310.
Ascott (NT) House & Garden Wing Tel 0296 688242.

Lenham   Chilston Park   71%   £92

Tel 0622 859803   Fax 0622 858588

H

Sandway Lenham Nr Maidstone Kent ME17 2BE   Map 7 C5

Four miles from junction 8 of M20, between Ashford and Maidstone.
Judith and Martin Miller, publishers of *Miller's Antiques Price Guide*, run
this remarkable hotel set in 250 acres complete with a lake. The 17th-
century Grade I house contains a treasure trove of antique furniture, oil
paintings, water colours, rugs and objets d'art. Over 200 candles are lit
throughout the public areas at dusk, evoking a sense of the past. The
Marble Hall and Drawing Room are fine examples of elegant comfort and
each bedroom in the house has its own very individual style and character;
some have open fires. The Hogarth Room has an 18th-century four-poster
and a splendid view of the lake. Bedrooms in the stable block are simpler
but not without charm. A new orangery has been added to enhance the
lounge accommodation. Characterful conference and meeting rooms (for
up to 120). *Rooms 40. Garden, tennis, croquet, clay-pigeon shooting, coarse
fishing, snooker. Access, Amex, Visa,*

Letchworth   Broadway Toby Hotel   59%   £56

Tel 0462 480111

H

The Broadway Letchworth Hertfordshire SG6 3NZ   Map 6 A3

1½ miles from junction 9 of the M1, a smartly-kept hotel with a friendly,
non-chain feel (even though it is in the Toby and Osprey chain). Well-
furnished bedrooms and a calm cocktail bar-cum-lounge. Conference and
banqueting facilities for up to 180. Children up to 12 stay free in parents'
room. *Rooms 35. Access, Amex, Visa,*

Lewdown   Lewtrenchard Manor   72%   £95

Tel 056 683 256   Fax 056 683 332

HR

Lewtrenchard Lewdown Nr Okehampton Devon EX20 4PN   Map 2 C2

Mature grounds and a dovecote add to the mellow charm of this early
17th-century manor house, once the home of the Rev Sabine Baring-
Gould, who wrote the hymn *Onward Christian Soldiers*. Fine architectural
features include massive wood and stone fireplaces, panelling and ornate
ceilings. The entrance hall serves as a sitting room, and a fine oak staircase climbs to an antique-lined corridor off which the bedrooms lead. These are
individual in style, with pretty floral fabrics and plenty of thoughtful
extras. Very friendly owners and staff. No children under eight. *Rooms 8.
Garden, croquet, putting, clay-pigeon shooting, coarse fishing. Access, Amex,
Visa,*

Restaurant   £70

A huge log fire, dark panelling hung with ancestral portraits, crisp white
linen, candles and flowers make a splendid setting for new chef Patrick
Salvadori's cooking. The à la carte menu is supplemented by a four-course
table d'hote dinner with no choice – from a chicken and chanterelle
galantine to wild salmon fillet and crab mousse, good cheeses and a trio of
seasonal fruit tarts. *Seats 35. Parties 25. Private Room. L 12.30-2
D 7.15-9.30. Closed L Mon-Sat. Set L £16 Set D £24.50.*

438   England

Lewes   Shelleys Hotel   60%   £116

Tel 0273 472361   Fax 0273 483152   **H**

High Street Lewes East Sussex BN7 1XS   Map 7 B6

One of the original Mount Charlotte hotels, Shelleys is located on the main
road through Lewes. Dating from the 17th century, it retains some old-
world charm and elegance. *Rooms 21. Garden. Access, Amex, Visa,*

Lewes   Places of Interest

Historic Houses, Castles and Gardens
Bateman's (NT)   Burwash Tel 0435 882302 *Rudyard Kipling lived here.*
Charleston Farmhouse   Fircle Tel 032 183 265 *Home of Vanessa and
    Clive Bell and Duncan Grant, leaders of the Bloomsbury movement.*
Firle Place   Tel 0273 858335.
Glynde Place   Tel 0273 858337.
Monk's House   Rodmell Tel 0273 479274 *Cottage home of Virginia and
    Leonard Woolf.*
Wilmington Priory and Long Man   Nr Newhaven Tel 0323 870537 *10
    miles.*
Borowski Centre Dry Ski Slope   Newhaven Tel 0273 515402.
Drusillas Zoo   Alfriston Tel 0323 870656.

Leyland   Leyland Resort Hotel   65%   £80

Tel 0772 422922   Fax 0772 622282   **H**

Leyland Way Leyland Lancashire PR5 2JX   Map 10 B1

Formerly the Penguin, located a short drive from the M6 at junction 28.
Meeting room with 220 capacity and banqueting for up to 180. Disabled
and non-smoking bedrooms. Health club promised for early 1993.
Rooms 93. Access, Amex, Visa,

Lichfield   George Hotel   59%   £88

Tel 0543 414822   Fax 0543 415817   **H**

Bird Street Lichfield Staffordshire WS13 6PR   Map 10 C3

Regency style survives in the spacious, peaceful day rooms and the pastel-
decorated bedrooms of this Jarvis hotel. The ballroom can accommodate
up to 100 guests for a banquet or conference. Children up to 12 stay free in
parents' room. *Rooms 38. Access, Amex, Visa,*

Lichfield   Places of Interest

Tourist Information   Tel 0543 252109.
Hanch Hall and Garden   Tel 0543 490308.
Lichfield Cathedral   Tel 0543 256120.
Samuel Johnson Birthplace Museum   Tel 0543 264972.
Lichfield Heritage Exhibition Treasury and Muniment Room   Tel 0543
    256611.

Lifton   Arundell Arms   65%   £86

Tel 0566 784666   Fax 0566 784494   **H**

Lifton Devon PL16 0AA   Map 2 C2

Ann Voss-Bark's lovely old creeper-covered inn has for more than 50 years
been a leading fishing hotel, with 20 miles of its own water on the Tamar
and its tributaries. Public areas include a warm, old-fashioned sitting room,
a bar, a games room and a skittle alley. Bedrooms are light and cheerful,
with soft colours and solid furnishings. *Rooms 29. Garden, fishing. Closed
3 days Xmas. Access, Amex, Visa,*

Lifton   Places of Interest

Launceston Castle   Launceston Tel 0566 2365.

Lincoln **D'Isney Place**	£61

Tel 0522 538881   Fax 0522 511321

PH

Eastgate Lincoln Lincolnshire LN2 4AA   Map 11 E2

A delightful garden surrounds D'Isney Place, an 18th-century building by
the Cathedral offering an exceptionally warm and comfortable atmosphere.
David and Judy Payne run it as an up-market bed and breakfast hotel.
Well-loved antique furniture abounds and there's a homely feel
throughout. The rooms vary from large, with four posters and spa baths or
steam showers, to compact but charming singles, one with shower/WC
only. Also available is a cottage with double en-suite bedrooms, living
room, dining room and kitchen. All the bedrooms have tables and
breakfast is served to order in the rooms. Parking within the grounds.
Rooms 17. Garden. Access, Amex, Visa,

Lincoln **Forte Crest** 63%	£88

Tel 0522 520341   Fax 0522 510780

H

Eastgate Lincoln Lincolnshire LN2 1PN   Map 11 E2

A modern hotel right beside the cathedral. Well-equipped bedrooms and
extensive 24hr room service add to the convenience. Conference and
function facilities for up to 80. *Rooms 70. Garden. Access, Amex, Visa,*

Lincoln **White Hart** 69%	£116

Tel 0522 526222   Fax 0522 531798

H

Bailgate Lincoln Lincolnshire LN1 3AR   Map 11 E2

An old Forte Heritage hotel in the heart of the city on a site where there
has been an inn for over 600 years. Secure parking available opposite.
Conference facilities for up to 160. *Rooms 50. Roof-top garden, orangery
coffee shop (9.30am-5.30pm). Access, Amex, Visa,*

Lincoln   Places of Interest

Tourist Information   Tel 0522 529828.
  Theatre Royal   Tel 0522 23303.
  Historic Houses, Castles and Gardens
Doddington Hall   Doddington Tel 0522 694308.
Lincoln Castle   Castle Hill Tel 0522 511068.
Tattershall Castle (NT)   Tattershall, Nr Woodhall Spa Tel 0526 42543.
The Old Hall   Gainsborough Tel 0427 612669.
Lincoln Cathedral   Tel 0522 530320.
City and County Museum   Tel 0522 530401.
Usher Gallery   Tel 0522 527890.
Market Rasen Racecourse   Tel 0673 843434 *16 miles.*
Cadwell Park Motor Racing Circuit   Nr Louth Tel 0507 343248.
Grange-de-Lings Showground   Tel 0522 522900.

Linton **Wood Hall** 80%	£84

Tel 0937 587271   Fax 0937 584353

HR

Linton Nr Wetherby West Yorkshire LS22 4JA   Map 10 C1

It's hard not to be impressed when first sighting this magnificent Georgian
house (with an older, Jacobean wing), set in 100 acres of rolling parkland.
Day rooms exude elegance, from the polished flagstone floor to the
panelled bar and sumptuously furnished lounge – all appointed with great
taste. Supremely comfortable, spacious bedrooms, individually styled and
beautifully decorated, are furnished with bold fabrics and freestanding,
painted furniture. Extras provided include sherry, fruit, mineral water and

a teddy bear. Carpeted bathrooms have power showers, huge towels, quality toiletries and telephone extensions. 22 new bedrooms have been added, along with a new leisure centre. **Rooms 44.** *Garden, croquet, coarse fishing, indoor swimming pool, spa bath, solarium, beauty salon, steam room, gymnasium, games room, snooker. Access, Amex, Visa,*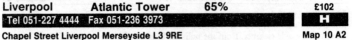

Restaurant
£80

An elegant restaurant where chef Simon Wood cooks in a style that is best described as light, modern English, with no heavily-reduced or cream sauces in evidence. An extensive wine list, albeit at stiff prices. **Seats 65. Parties 45.** *Private Room. L 12.30-2 D 7-9.30 (Sun to 9, Fri & Sat to 10). Closed L Sat. Set L £14.95 (£12.95 Sun).*

Liskeard   Well House   74%
£109
HR
Tel 0579 342001

St Keyne Liskeard Cornwall PL14 4RN
Map 2 C3

Three miles south of Liskeard off the B3254, the Well House is a tranquil spot set in small landscaped gardens that include an enchanting duck pond. Owner Nick Wainford and his charming staff are unfailingly helpful and discreet, guaranteeing that a stay here really is a tonic. Off the tiled hall are a relaxing drawing room and an inviting little bar; across the hall, the dining room has magnificent bay windows overlooking the sun terrace and lawns. Individually designed bedrooms and well-equipped bathrooms are immaculately kept. First-rate breakfasts. **Rooms 7.** *Garden, croquet, outdoor swimming pool, tennis. Access, Visa.*

Restaurant
£65

Daily menus at fixed prices offer four or five choices for each course, featuring what's best and freshest from the local markets. Marinated salmon and mackerel tartare followed by sautéed guinea fowl with tarragon cream make a suitably light lunch; for dinner, perhaps hot venison samosa with Cumberland sauce, red mullet with basil sauce and leeks, then English farmhouse cheeses with walnut bread, cherry Bakewell tart or marbled chocolate marquise. Decent wine list with standard 'names' and a good selection of half bottles. **Seats 32. Parties 30.** *L 12.30-2 D 7.30-9. Set L £21 Set D £24.95.*

Liskeard   Places of Interest

Thorburn Museum and Gallery   Tel 0579 20325/21129 *Audio-visual gallery.*

Liverpool   Armadillo
£60
R
Tel 051-236 4123

20-22 Mathew Street Liverpool Merseyside L2 6RE
Map 10 A2

A cheerfully informal restaurant with a particularly good-value lunchtime/early supper menu that might include garlic bread with melted cheese and toasted nuts, fettuccine with pesto and sun-dried tomatoes, seafood cassoulet and spiced lamb and spinach meatloaf. From 7.30pm the main dinner menu brings fillets of salmon stuffed with prawns, pork fillet en croute and beef poulette. There are always a couple of interesting vegetarian choices too. Well-chosen wines include plenty of half bottles. **Seats 60. Parties 25.** *L 12-3 D 7.30-10.30 Early supper Tue-Fri 5-6.30). Closed Sun & Mon, Bank Holidays. Access, Visa.*

Liverpool   Atlantic Tower   65%
£102
H
Tel 051-227 4444   Fax 051-236 3973

Chapel Street Liverpool Merseyside L3 9RE
Map 10 A2

A high-rise city-centre hotel, resembling a great liner's bow in outline, whose various public areas include a bar inspired by Nelson's *Victory* in addition to a smart cocktail bar. Well-equipped bedrooms make good-sized singles but rather compact doubles and twins, with no space between beds in the latter. Corner rooms are larger and there are eight full suites. There's free garage parking just behind the hotel. Conference/banqueting facilities for 140/120. Mount Charlotte Thistle. *Rooms 226. Garage. Access, Amex, Visa,* (❶) *Diners Club International*

Liverpool	**Britannia Adelphi Hotel**	68%	£102
Tel 051-709 7200	Fax 051-708 8326		**H**
Ranelagh Place Liverpool Merseyside L3 5UL			Map 10 A2

Leisure facilities and a health club, conferences for up to 900 delegates, six bars and a night club are among the amenities of a large hotel with many grand original Edwardian features. Bedrooms range from singles to suites and jacuzzi rooms. *Rooms 391. Indoor swimming pool, sauna, spa bath, squash, hairdressing & beauty salon, snooker, coffee shop (11am-2am Mon-Sat). Access, Amex, Visa,* (❶) *Diners Club International*

Liverpool	**Campanile Hotel**		£36
Tel 051-709 8104	Fax 051-709 8725		**L**
Chaloner Street Queen's Dock Liverpool Merseyside L3 4AJ			Map 10 A2

Just outside the city centre. *Rooms 82. Access, Amex, Visa,* (❶) *Diners Club International*

Liverpool	**Forte Crest**	58%	£87
Tel 051-709 7050	Fax 051-709 2193		**H**
Lord Nelson Street Liverpool Merseyside L3 5QB			Map 10 A2

Grey-brick hotel by Lime Street station, with ample car parking, a vast range of conference and meeting rooms (handling up to 600 delegates) and membership of a local sports club. 24hr room food service, a lounge bar serving light meals and a choice of bars. *Rooms 154. Access, Amex, Visa,* (❶) *Diners Club International*

Liverpool	**Moat House**	67%	£112
Tel 051-709 0181	Fax 051-709 2706		**H**
Paradise Street Liverpool Merseyside L1 8JD			Map 10 A2

Spacious bedrooms, large beds, smart public areas and a leisure centre with swimming pool. Conference/banqueting for 400/200. *Rooms 251. Indoor swimming pool, sauna, spa bath, solarium, gymnasium, coffee shop (11am-midnight). Access, Amex, Visa,* (❶) *Diners Club International*

Liverpool	**St George's Hotel**	60%	£91
Tel 051-709 7090	Fax 051-709 0137		**H**
St John's Precinct Lime Street Liverpool Merseyside L1 1NQ			Map 10 A2

Modern hotel in a central location opposite Lime Street station. Banquets/conferences up to 300. Free overnight parking in adjacent NCP. Forte Heritage. *Rooms 155. Access, Amex, Visa,* (❶) *Diners Club International*

Liverpool   Places of Interest

Tourist Information Tel 051-709 3631.
Croxteth Hall & Country Park Tel 051-228 5311.
Speke Hall (NT) Tel 051-427 7231.
Liverpool Cathedral Tel 051-709 6271.
Metropolitan Cathedral of Christ the King Tel 051-709 9222.
Aigburth Cricket Ground Tel 051-427 2930.
Everton Football Ground Goodison Park Tel 051-521 2020.
Liverpool Football Ground Anfield Park Tel 051-263 2361.
Aintree Racecourse Tel 051-523 2600.
Liverpool Aquarium Tel 051-207 0001.
Knowsley Safari Park Prescot Tel 051-430 9009.
Mersey Ferries Tel 051-630 1030.
Beatles Story Albert Dock Tel 051-709 1963.

Theatres and Concert Halls
Empire Theatre   Tel 051 709 1555.
Everyman Theatre   Tel 051 709 4776.
Liverpool Playhouse   Tel 051 709 8478/9.
Neptune Theatre   Tel 051 709 7844.
Museums and Art Galleries
Liverpool Museum and Planetarium   Tel 051-207 0001.
Merseyside Maritime Museum   Tel 051-207 0001.
Walker Art Gallery   Tel 051-207 0001.
Tate Gallery Liverpool   Tel 051-709 3223.
Pilkington Glass Museum   St. Helens Tel 0744 692014.

Lockington Hilton National E Midlands Airport   69%   £118

Tel 0509 674000 Fax 0509 672412	**H**
Derby Road Lockington Leicestershire DE7 2RH	Map 11 D3

Near junction 24 of the M1 and just 1½ miles from the airport;
Donnington Park race track is also nearby. A modern low-rise hotel with
conference facilities for up to 250 and an unusual Japanese teppanyaki grill
restaurant. *Rooms 151. Indoor swimming pool, sauna, solarium, spa bath,
gymnasium, beautician, coffee shop (10am-6pm). Access, Amex, Visa,*

Lolworth   Forte Travelodge   £40

Tel 0954 781335	**L**
A604 Huntingdon Road Lolworth Bar Hill Cambridgeshire CB3 8DR	Map 6 B3

On the A604 northbound, 3 miles north of junction 14 on the M11, 5
miles north of Cambridge. *Rooms 20. Access, Amex, Visa.*

Long Melford   Black Lion   65%   £65

Tel 0787 312356 Fax 0787 74557	**H**
The Green Long Melford Sudbury Suffolk CO10 9DN	Map 6 C3

Count the Toby jugs and admire the maps and copper collection or relax
in deep sofas in the charming lounge. Bedrooms are bright and
comfortable, attractive fabrics complementing neutral walls and carpets.
Each room has antique pine furniture and an easy chair or sofa. *Rooms 9.
Garden. Closed 23 Dec-2 Jan. Access, Visa.*

Long Melford   Bull Hotel   65%   £96

Tel 0787 78494 Fax 0787 880307	**H**
Hall Street Long Melford Suffolk CO10 9JG	Map 6 C3

Built by a wealthy wool merchant in the 15th century, becoming a posting
house with the arrival of the coaching era, the real-Tudor Bull is now a
Forte Heritage hotel combining character with comfort. *Rooms 25. Access,
Amex, Visa,*

Long Melford   Chimneys   £75

Tel 0787 79806	**R**
Hall Street Long Melford Sudbury Suffolk CO10 9JR	Map 6 C3

Sam Chalmers' delightful beamed restaurant offers monthly menus full of
interest and cooking in a modern style. For starters pigeon breast in flaky
pastry with basil sauce and monkfish tail in a light curry; to follow, red
mullet in Oriental spices and calf's kidneys with red cabbage and grain
mustard sauce. Some simpler cooking at lunchtimes with traditional
English puddings. Good selective wine list strong on Alsace and the New
World. Dinner club with substantial discounts. *Seats 40. Parties 40. L 12-2
D 7-9. Closed D Sun. Set L £13.95 Set D £27.50. Access, Visa,*

Long Melford   Places of Interest

Kentwell Hall (House, Garden & Maze)   Long Melford Tel 0787 310207.
Melford Hall (NT) House & Garden   Long Melford Tel 0787 880286.

| Longham | Bridge House | 61% | £75 |

Tel 0202 578828   Fax 0202 572620   **H**

2 Ringwood Road Longham Nr Wimborne Dorset BH22 9AN   **Map 4 C4**

Anna Joannides is Greek Cypriot and her riverfront hotel has a distinctly Mediterranean air; the sunny reception and lounge have white walls with tiles depicting Greek goddesses and the large bar opens onto a terrace overlooking the water. Bedrooms have plain white walls and pink draylon headboards; some large rooms have canopied or four-poster beds. Several conference suites are available for up to 70 delegates. No dogs. *Rooms 37. Garden, coarse fishing, children's play area. Access, Amex, Visa.*

| Longhorsley | Linden Hall | 73% | £110 |

Tel 0670 516611   Fax 0670 88544   **H**

Longhorsley Nr Morpeth Northumberland NE65 8XF   **Map 14 B3**

Four miles from the A1, through the village on the A697, a long tree-lined drive runs up to a Georgian country house. Elegant and restful public rooms include a lofty inner hall with a splendid sweeping staircase, an antique-furnished drawing room and two bars, one the Linden Pub in the old converted granary. Bedrooms are of a reasonable size and individual in style; they range from singles to doubles, twins, four-posters and family rooms. A swimming pool is planned for 1993. *Rooms 45. Garden, tennis, putting, croquet, sauna, solarium, beautician & hair salon, snooker, coarse fishing, mountain bikes, cricket pitch. Access, Amex, Visa,* **①** Diners Club International

| Longridge | Heathcote's | ★ | £76 |

Tel 0772 784969   **R**

104-106 Higher Road Longridge Nr Preston Lancashire PR3 3SY   **Map 10 B1**

A spotless whitewashed cottage at the higher end of Longridge with muted blue and pink decor plus relaxed and professional staff combining to produce a first-rate atmosphere for Paul Heathcote's considerable skills (ably assisted by "head chef" Andrew Barnes). He is meticulous in seeking out the very best produce from local growers and farmers (free-range wherever possible) for his exciting menu: Dornoch beef (garnished with braised oxtail, wild mushrooms and burgundy sauce), local duckling (crisply roasted and served with potato and apple rösti, cabbage, smoked bacon, quenelle of pea purée and a salad made from the leg), Goosnargh corn-fed chicken (with wild mushrooms and basil-scented jus). Starters might range from layered chicken, foie gras and truffle terrine with lentils and hazelnut vinaigrette to hot and cold salad of smoked salmon roses with roast scallops on a bed of vegetables and basil vinaigrette; desserts are equally involved – gratin of Henry Pickton plums and lychees glazed with elderflower sabayon and blackcurrant sorbet, hot raspberry soufflé with almond ice cream, or millefeuille of caramelised apples and blueberries with rosemary-scented cream. Tip-top British cheeses plus a choice of savoury cheese dishes. The five-course gourmet menu is sensational stuff: herb gnocchi with foie gras and Madeira sauce; salmon with ginger, leeks and coriander; smoked chicken and watercress soup; lamb cutlet with baked garlic and button onions; sultana soufflé with ice cream (or cheese), culminating with petits fours and coffee. Three beamed rooms on split levels provide a delightful setting in which to enjoy the professionalism of such a shining young star. However, the pricing of wines appears to be inconsistent. *Seats 40. Parties 16. L (Fri & Sun only) 12-2 D 7-9.30. Closed Mon, 1 & 2 Jan. Set L £15 Set D £30. Access, Visa.*

Looe   Talland Bay Hotel   67%   £120

Tel 0503 72667   Fax 0503 72940   **H**

Talland Bay Nr Looe Cornwall PL13 2JB   Map 2 C3

Take the Polperro road from Looe and turn left, after two miles, at the hotel sign at a crossroads. A mile down the lane you'll come to a fine hotel standing in beautiful gardens overlooking Talland Bay. Parts date back to the 16th century and the two lounges are appropriately traditional with loose-covered settees and armchairs and good paintings on the walls; there's also a small bar decorated with Gurkha mementoes from the owner's regimental days. All ground-floor rooms open on to the garden; one of the nicest is a single with its own secluded patio. Good-quality darkwood furniture, chintzy furnishings, fresh flowers and pot-pourri in all the rooms make them homely and comfortable. *Rooms 23. Garden, outdoor swimming pool, sauna, solarium, keep-fit equipment, snooker, croquet, putting. Closed Jan. Access, Amex, Visa,*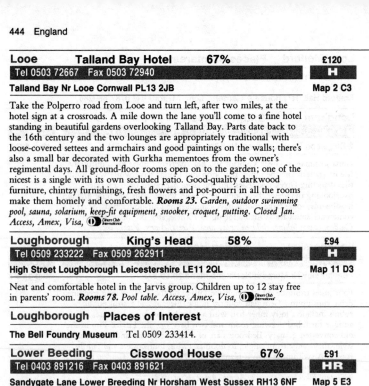

Loughborough   King's Head   58%   £94

Tel 0509 233222   Fax 0509 262911   **H**

High Street Loughborough Leicestershire LE11 2QL   Map 11 D3

Neat and comfortable hotel in the Jarvis group. Children up to 12 stay free in parents' room. *Rooms 78. Pool table. Access, Amex, Visa,*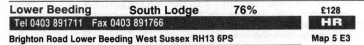

Loughborough   Places of Interest

The Bell Foundry Museum   Tel 0509 233414.

Lower Beeding   Cisswood House   67%   £91

Tel 0403 891216   Fax 0403 891621   **HR**

Sandygate Lane Lower Beeding Nr Horsham West Sussex RH13 6NF   Map 5 E3

A mock-Tudor mansion built in the 1920s for the then chairman of Harrods, using many Harrods craftsmen. The reception area features ornamental pargeting and timbers of oak, the same wood that panels a smart lounge. Bedrooms, except for a few singles, are spacious and bright, with breakfast tables and writing surfaces. Three bedrooms have spa baths. A fairly new feature is the Courtyard Suite of conference and banqueting rooms, catering for up to 200. No children under 12. No dogs. *Rooms 34. Garden, croquet, indoor swimming pool, keep-fit equipment, sauna. Closed Xmas/New Year. Access, Amex, Visa,*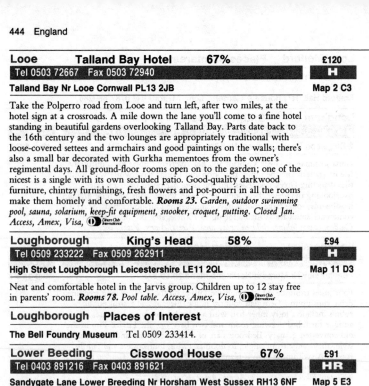

Restaurant   £50

Chef-patron Othmar Illes's menus are based on French classical traditions with nothing very elaborate and everything prepared with skill and assurance. The choice encompasses moules marinière, sole Colbert, halibut steak hollandaise, gigot of lamb and medallions of venison with poached pear in a rich red wine sauce. For dessert perhaps a pancake filled with home-made walnut ice cream and topped with chocolate sauce. The dining room setting is plush, with peaceful garden views through the leaded windows. *Seats 60. Parties 150. Private Room. L 12.15-2 D 7-9 (Sat to 10). Set L £14.50 Set D £22.50/£27.50*

Lower Beeding   South Lodge   76%   £128

Tel 0403 891711   Fax 0403 891766   **HR**

Brighton Road Lower Beeding West Sussex RH13 6PS   Map 5 E3

Solicitous staff make a refreshing welcome at this grand, wisteria-clad Victorian country house set in 90 acres of parkland. An abundance of fresh flowers from the gardens adorns the day rooms, which include an inviting lounge with heavily-carved wood panelling, ornate ribbed ceiling, chandeliers and glass-fronted cabinets filled with porcelain and silver objets d'art. Individually designed bedrooms are furnished with a variety of reproduction and original antiques and have luxurious Italian marble bathrooms with a host of extras from bathrobes to cotton buds. 14 large rooms with beamed ceilings are in a converted stable block that surrounds an indoor garden. Guests using the conference facilities (up to 80 delegates) are kept apart from individual guests. *Rooms 39. Access, Amex, Visa,*

Restaurant   £92

A decorative Victorian dining room is the classic setting for the skilled execution of an interesting à la carte and signature menus from Anthony Tobin. Modern touches include a timbale of crab and lobster with a watercress and a coriander purée, rack of South Downs lamb with a fresh basil mousse and poached pear and butterscotch in a light puff pastry with lime custard. The signature menu offers no choice but a finely balanced meal of three to five courses (your choice). Elaborate dado panelling and wooden sideboards display a collection of decorative plates and there are views over the South Downs from the window tables. Good all-round wine list, though there are some naughty prices among the vintage clarets. *Seats 40. Parties 8. Private Room. L 12-2.30 D 7.30-10. Set L £15 (Sun £17.50). Set D £25-£32.*

Lower Slaughter	Lower Slaughter Manor	77%	£100

Tel 0451 820456   Fax 0451 882150

H R

Lower Slaughter Nr Bourton-on-the-Water Gloucestershire GL54 2HP   Map 4 C1

Now under new owners, Peter and Audrey Marks and their daughter Jane, formerly owners of *Rookery Hall* in Nantwich. In one of the area's prettiest villages, the imposing 17th-century, mellow-stoned manor house stands in its own immaculate walled gardens. Its interior offers a haven of relaxation. The entrance hall with its elegant red decor sets the tone and is furnished with comfortable seating and period pieces. Two lounges, one with a wonderful ornate ceiling, employ soft colours, plum-cushioned seating and pretty floral fabrics; fine fireplaces and floral displays complete the elegant dayroom settings. Bedrooms, named after girls' names and trees, are in both the main house and coach house and decorated in restful pastel shades, with complementary soft furnishings, period furniture and thoughtful extras including a decanter of sherry. Many improvements have accompanied the new owners, not least real linen sheets and personal service. No children under 10. *Rooms 19. Garden, indoor swimming pool, sauna, solarium, tennis, croquet, fishing. Access, Amex, Visa,*

Restaurant   £85

Dining in the elegant setting of the restaurant epitomises English country house living, and the mainly British dishes receive Gallic touches from chef Serge Puyal. Prices have actually come down from last year and the fixed-price menus offer splendid value – Evesham asparagus with hollandaise sauce or country quail salad; millefeuille of Scottish salmon with basil or braised guinea fowl with baby root vegetables. Enticing desserts might include a hot passion fruit soufflé, and a marbled chocolate marquise. Excellent British farmouse cheeses. *Seats 26. L 12.30-2 D 7-9.30. Set L £14.95 Set D £25.*

Lower Swell	Old Farmhouse	£63

Tel 0451 30232

I

Lower Swell Stow-on-the-Wold Gloucestershire GL54 1LF   Map 4 C1

A very relaxed, laid-back place with everything under the personal supervision of Dutch owner Erik Burger. The premises were a working farm until the 1960s, and the original farmhouse contains the bar-lounge and restaurant. Above are neat country-style bedrooms, two of which share a bathroom. Further bedrooms are in former stables opening onto the car park; best rooms are in the old coach house, where there's also a quiet residents' lounge with TV, magazines and board games. *Rooms 14. Garden, Access, Visa.*

Ludlow   Dinham Hall   66%   £83

Tel 0584 876464   Fax 0584 876019   **H**

off Market Square Ludlow Shropshire SY8 1EJ   **Map 10 A4**

A pale-stone Georgian town house, dating from 1792, adjacent to the castle
and lovingly restored. Public areas include a cosy drawing room and
comfortable lounge with an extravagant, carved wood fireplace and deep-
cushioned couches. The bedrooms vary in size and are comfortably
appointed with matching floral fabrics; one has a four-poster. Well-lit,
fully tiled bathrooms complete the picture. Children up to 12 stay free in
parents' room. Polished service with a human touch. *Rooms 13. Garden,
sauna, keep-fit equipment. Access,Amex, Visa.*

Ludlow   Feathers Hotel   69%   £98

Tel 0584 875261   Fax 0584 876030   **H**

Bull Ring Ludlow Shropshire SY8 1AA   **Map 10 A4**

The magnificent timbered and gabled facade of this historic hotel makes a
fine first impression. Dating from 1603, it is near the old Covegate, one of
seven gates that used to protect Ludlow. Inside, the bedrooms (some of
which have four-posters) are decorated in bright floral fabrics and contrast
greatly with the public rooms, which have plenty of period charm but
little style. A notable Jacobean lounge has wood panelling, intricate plaster
ceiling and a large, carved wood mantelpiece above the fireplace. No dogs.
Characterful meeting rooms for up to 80. *Rooms 40. Snooker. Access,
Amex, Visa,* (I) *Diners Club International*

Ludlow   Forte Travelodge   £40

Tel 058 472 695   **L**

A49 Woofferton Ludlow Shropshire SY8 4AL   **Map 10 A4**

On the A49, 4 miles south of Ludlow at the junction of the A456 and the
B4362. 8 miles north of Leominster. *Rooms 32. Access, Amex, Visa.*

Ludlow   Places of Interest

Ludlow Racecourse   Tel 0584 77221.

Luton   Forte Crest   60%   £87

Tel 0582 575911   Fax 0582 581859   **H**

Waller Avenue Luton Bedfordshire LU4 9RU   **Map 5 E1**

Halfway between the M1 (junction 11) and Luton town centre. Caters
well for families; also popular for functions and conferences (up to 250).
Rooms 91. Access, Amex, Visa, (I) *Diners Club International*

Luton   Forte Posthouse   57%   £67

Tel 0582 575955   Fax 0582 490065   **H**

641 Dunstable Road Luton Bedfordshire LU4 8RQ   **Map 5 E1**

Practical accommodation (mostly single rooms) in a modern building at
junction 11 of the M1. Family oriented at weekends, when a playroom is
available. *Rooms 117. Access, Amex, Visa,* (I) *Diners Club International*

Luton   Hotel Ibis   60%   £55

Tel 0582 424488   Fax 0582 455511   **H**

Spittlesea Road Luton Bedfordshire LU2 9NZ   **Map 5 E1**

Purpose-built, redbrick hotel opposite Luton airport's main runway. No
frills, clean accommodation at a budget price, with many rooms suitable
for family use. *Rooms 98. Coffee shop (noon-10.30pm). Access, Amex, Visa,*
(I) *Diners Club International*

Luton   Leaside Hotel   55%

£50

Tel 0582 417643   Fax 0582 419676

H

72 New Bedford Road Luton Bedfordshire LU3 1BT

Map 5 E1

Near the town centre but a touch tricky to find, Leaside is a modest but
very agreeable little hotel run by Carole and Martin Gillies. The building
is Victorian, and a certain period charm survives in the panelled bar. In the
club room guests can relax over a frame of snooker. Many bedrooms are
smallish singles, but the basic needs are supplied and housekeeping is good.
Ask for precise directions when booking. *Rooms 13. Closed 26 Dec, 1 Jan.
Access, Amex, Visa,* **(1)** *Diners Club International*

Luton   Strathmore Thistle   63%

£102

Tel 0582 34199   Fax 0582 402528

H

Arndale Centre Luton Bedfordshire LU1 2TR

Map 5 E1

High-rise hotel next to town-centre shopping and railway station.
Banqueting facilities for up to 250, conferences to 300. *Rooms 150. Coffee
shop (11am-11pm 6 days). Access, Amex, Visa,* **(1)** *Diners Club International*

Luton   Places of Interest

Tourist Information   Tel 0582 401579.
St. Georges Theatre   Tel 0582 21628.
Luton Hoo   Tel 0582 22955.
Luton Museum and Art Gallery   Tel 0582 36941.
Stockwood Craft Museum and Gardens   Tel 0582 38714.
Luton Town Football Ground   Tel 0582 411622.

Lutterworth   Denbigh Arms   66%

£79

Tel 0455 553537   Fax 0455 556627

H

High Street Lutterworth Leicestershire LE17 5AD

Map 11 D4

An extended Georgian coaching inn right on the high street just over a
mile from junction 20 and the M1. Three meeting rooms with a total
capacity of 60 (banquets up to 50). Several ground floor bedrooms open on
to a rear courtyard: good housekeeping and pleasant friendly staff. Resort
hotels. *Rooms 34. Access, Amex, Visa,* **(1)** *Diners Club International*

Lutterworth   Places of Interest

Stanford Hall   Tel 0788 860250.

Lyme Regis   Alexandra Hotel   58%

£82

Tel 0297 442010   Fax 0297 443229

H

Pound Street Lyme Regis Dorset DT7 3HZ

Map 3 E2

A wide, airy sun lounge gives on to 1½ acres of gardens leading down
towards the seafront at this family-run hotel where all but five of the
bedrooms overlook Lyme Bay and the Cobb. *Rooms 26. Garden. Closed
Xmas-early Feb. Access, Amex, Visa,* **(1)** *Diners Club International*

Lymington   Gordleton Mill   65%

£80

Tel 0590 682219   Fax 0590 683073

HR

Silver Street Hordle Nr Lymington Hampshire SO41 6DJ

Map 4 C4

The food comes first at this idyllic, creeper-clad converted mill alongside a
mill stream on which Canada geese and water lilies float gently. There's no
formal reception and you have to ring to announce your arrival. There is
no bar but drinks are served on either the terrace or in two
interconnecting lounges, one of which is non-smoking. Bedrooms, all en-
suite (one with only a shower), are of a good size and are all identically
furnished with honey-coloured units and pretty floral fabrics; fresh fruit
and mineral water are provided, room service is not. One has a terrace
overlooking the river and gardens while another two share a

spacious, sunny roof terrace. Breakfast is a highlight. No children under 7.
Rooms 7. Closed 1-3 Jan. Access, Amex, Visa,

Provence Restaurant ★   £100

Narrow wooden footbridges lead from the car park to the restaurant and
gardens to the rear of the mill. The old building has been extended to
create a bright, spacious and well-appointed dining-room. Decor is mainly
in soft beiges and muted pinks with ample but discreet lighting and
generously sized, well spaced tables. Chef Jean-Christophe Novelli is
extremely ambitious and enthusiastic, and seemingly in possession of
boundless energy. Much of this energy is expended in the manipulation of
foods on the plate with almost all his dishes being very fanciful in concept,
artistic in presentation and generous in portion. Typical is a braised
artichoke bottom infused with olive oil and lime, filled with anchovy
mayonnaise, crab meat and avocado, and encased in smoked salmon, then
topped with a gently poached quail's egg. Offal is a particular favourite.
Desserts are magical creations (see Dessert of the Year award). A good
French wine list also finds room for some interesting New World
offerings. *Seats 45. Parties 14. Private Room. L 12.30-2.30 (Sun to 3)
D 7.30-10 (Sat to 10.30). Closed D Sun, all Tue. Set meals £20.*

Lymington   Passford House   70%   £97

Tel 0590 682398 Fax 0590 683494	**H**

Mount Pleasant Lane Lymington Hampshire SO41 8LS   Map 4 C4

On the edge of the New Forest between Lymington (2 miles) and Sway,
this elegant white house was originally the home of Lord Arthur Cecil.
Two bedroom wings and a leisure centre have since been added, but the
traditional look survives in the lounges – one oak-panelled with an open
fire, another with French windows opening onto a patio and ornamental
pool. Upstairs there are bright and airy bedrooms with mostly white
furniture; carpeted bathrooms have showers and useful toiletries. There are
eight 'deluxe' rooms. Purpose-built Dolphin leisure centre has a good range
of facilities. Children are catered for admirably, with cots, high chairs, a
separate play area and separate meal times. *Rooms 56. Garden, indoor &
outdoor swimming pools, sauna, solarium, spa bath, keep-fit equipment, tennis,
putting, croquet, games room, snooker, pool table. Access, Amex, Visa.*

Lymington   Stanwell House   65%   £98

Tel 0590 677123 Fax 0590 677756	**H**

High Street Lymington Hampshire SO41 9AA   Map 4 C4

The hotel dates from the 18th century, but careful modernisation has
extended its scope. Attractive day rooms include a smart cocktail bar and a
chintzy lounge. Behind the restaurant is a paved garden which opens on to
a small function/conference suite. Well-equipped bedrooms (including one
with a four-poster) are named after Bordeaux wine chateaux. No dogs.
Rooms 35. Garden. Access, Visa.

Lymington   Places of Interest

Spinners Garden   Tel 0590 673347.

Lympsham   Batch Farm   56%   £56

Tel 0934 750371	**H**

Lympsham Nr Weston-super-Mare Somerset BS24 0EX   Map 3 E1

Lympsham is easy to find, only some three miles from junction 22 of the
M5. The hotel, with its 50-acre garden, stands in open farmland through
which the river Axe flows. Origins of the former farmhouse are evident in
the beams which adorn the bar and residents' lounges, while the neat
practical bedrooms in an extension benefit from panoramic views of either
the Mendip or Quantock hills. The adjoining Somerset Suite is a popular
venue for functions up to 100. No dogs. *Rooms 8. Garden, croquet, coarse
fishing. Access, Amex, Visa,* Diners Club International

Lympsham   Places of Interest

Taunton Vale Polo Club   Southlands, Berrow Road, Burnham on Sea Tel 0278 782266.

Lympstone   River House   £88

Tel 0395 265147   **RR**

The Strand Lympstone Devon EX8 5EY   Map 3 E3

There are lovely views over the river Exe to Powderham Castle from both the ground-floor bar and restaurant above at Michael and Shirley Wilkes's restaurant with rooms. Dinner is the main attraction, offering two to five courses at various fixed prices: perhaps devilled kidneys with fresh pasta, soufflé suissesse on a bed of spinach or lovage, cheese, onion and cream tart to start, followed by quail stuffed with smoked oyster and herbs, crisp honey-roast duck with orange liqueur sauce or a three-fish dish of salmon, plaice and brill. Fish dishes are always particularly good. At least five different vegetables, prepared in an interesting and varied manner, accompany main courses. Vegetarians are well catered for (£22.50/£28 for 2/3 courses). Puddings offer a good choice; home-made fudge, praline and chocolates are a treat with coffee. Sunday lunch is a popular affair, with a choice of four dishes per course (always including a roast); weekday lunches (except Mon) see simpler fare (minimum charge £9.25). *Seats 34. Private Room. L 12-1.30 D 7-9.30 (Sat to 10.30). Closed D Sun, all Mon, Bank Holidays. Set L Sun £16/£20 Set D £29.75-£46.50. Access, Amex, Visa.*

Rooms   £81

Pretty bedrooms have en-suite bathrooms and many thoughtful extras. No children under six. No dogs. *Sea fishing.*

Lyndhurst   The Crown   65%   £87

Tel 0703 282922   Fax 0703 282751   **H**

High Street Lyndhurst Hampshire SO43 7NF   Map 4 C4

A solid gabled building in the high street opposite the church. Ample lounge areas provide space to relax with pleasant views of the gardens; the bar is a fine period piece with library-style wood panelling. Decent-sized bedrooms have stylish repro furniture and good bathrooms. Children under 16 are accommodated free when they share a room with a parent. No dogs. *Rooms 40. Garden. Access, Amex, Visa,* **① Diners Club International**

Lyndhurst   Lyndhurst Park   61%   £60

Tel 0703 283923   Fax 0703 283019   **H**

High Street Lyndhurst Hampshire SO43 7NL   Map 4 C4

The Forestdale Group's much-extended Georgian mansion set in spacious grounds has a popular conference facility accommodating 200, with banqueting for up to 300. Bedrooms have freestanding furniture and small tiled bathrooms. Day rooms include a cocktail bar and little lounge. Summer activity for families centres round the pool and playground. There's a nominal charge for children sharing parents' room. *Rooms 59. Garden, outdoor swimming pool, tennis, sauna, games room, playroom & playground. Access, Amex, Visa,* **① Diners Club International**

Lyndhurst   Parkhill Hotel   67%   £104

Tel 0703 282944   Fax 0703 283268   **H**

Beaulieu Road Lyndhurst Hampshire SO4 7FZ   Map 4 C4

Secluded in parkland on the edge of the New Forest, Parkhill was built in 1740 as the country home of the Duke of Clarence. Restored in 1850, it retains a civilised, peaceful atmosphere, with antiques, ornaments, oil paintings and flowers. Spacious and comfortable bedrooms are furnished with solid period-style pieces; the best rooms have views across the lawns to the forest. A self-contained bungalow comprises double/twin bedroom, dressing room, lounge and bathroom, plus a walled garden. *Rooms 20. Garden, outdoor swimming pool, croquet, tennis. Access, Amex, Visa,* ⓘ ●Diners Club International

Lyndhurst   Places of Interest

Rhinefield (New Forest) Polo Club   Manor Farm Cottage, Minstead Tel 0703 813678.
New Park Showground   Brockenhurst Tel 0590 22400.

Lynmouth	Rising Sun Inn	£76
Tel 0598 53223 Fax 0598 53480		■
Harbourside Lynmouth Devon EX35 6EQ		Map 3 D1

Medieval character survives in a 14th-century thatched inn overlooking the harbour: oak panelling in the restaurant and bar, uneven floors, crooked ceilings, open fires. Bedrooms are in keeping, being snug and cottagey. Shelley's cottage, where the poet spent his honeymoon, consists of a double bedroom with four-poster bed, a sitting room and a private garden. There's another literary connection: RS Blackmore wrote part of *Lorna Doone* here. The inn owns a stretch of river for salmon fishing. No children under five. *Rooms 16. Garden, fishing. Access, Amex, Visa,* ⓘ ●Diners Club International

Lynton	Lynton Cottage	65%	£79
Tel 0598 52342 Fax 0598 52597			ᴴ
North Walk Lynton Devon EX35 6ED			Map 3 D1

Spectacular sea views are enjoyed from the day rooms (and all but three bedrooms) at a family-run hotel on the cliff 500 feet above Lynmouth Bay. Well modernised and smartly kept, it's a warm, friendly place, particularly the bar, with comfortable, old-fashioned seats and Victorian pine panelling. Bedrooms are individually decorated and range from cosy and small to airy and spacious. Well-appointed bathrooms. No children under ten. *Rooms 17. Garden, bar billiards. Closed Jan. Access, Amex, Visa,* ⓘ ●Diners Club International

Lytham	Clifton Arms	63%	£87
Tel 0253 739898 Fax 0253 730657			ᴴ
West Beach Lytham Lancashire FY8 5QJ			Map 10 A1

Best bedrooms at this redbrick Victorian building are the 'Executives' at the front, overlooking the Ribble Estuary; standard rooms are smaller. Winged armchairs and settees fill the lounge. Children up to 12 free in parents' room. Conference/banqueting facilities for 300/200. Lansbury Hotels. *Rooms 41. Sauna, solarium, spa bath, keep-fit equipment. Access, Amex, Visa,* ⓘ ●Diners Club International

Lytham St. Anne's   Places of Interest

Church Road Cricket Ground   Tel 0253 733422.

Macclesfield	Sutton Hall	£85
Tel 0260 253211 Fax 0260 252538		■
Bullocks Lane Sutton Macclesfield Cheshire SK11 0HE		Map 10 B2

First a 16th-century baronial residence, later a convent, Sutton Hall is now a hotel, public house and restaurant full of old-world atmosphere. Exposed beams, flagstones and open log fires characterise the day rooms, and bedrooms feature four-posters, Gothic windows and sturdy English furniture. *Rooms 10. Garden. Access, Amex, Visa.*

Macclesfield   Topo's

`Tel 0625 422231`

15 Church Street Macclesfield Cheshire SK11 6LB

£45

R

Map 10 B2

Once you get to grips with the confusing array of options – various set-price menus, an à la carte and a large blackboard of *Stop Press* offerings (fresh game from Sept-Feb) – you can enjoy an unusual mix of French and Italian dishes at this lively bistro packed with tables. Good-value pizza and pasta dishes. No children under 10. *Seats 55. Parties 50. L 12-2 D 7.30-10 (Sat to 10.30). Closed Sun & Mon, Bank Holidays. Set meals £10.95. Access, Amex, Visa,* *Diners Club International*

Macclesfield   Places of Interest

Tourist Information Tel 0625 21955.
Macclesfield Silk Museum and Heritage Centre Tel 0625 613210.
Paradise Mill Silk Museum Tel 0625 618228.
  Historic Houses, Castles and Gardens
Capesthorne Hall and Gardens Tel 0625 861221.
Gawsworth Hall Tel 0260 223456.
Hare Hill Garden (NT) Hare Hill, Over Alderley Tel 0625 828981.
Jodrell Bank Arboretum Tel 0477 71339.

Madingley   Three Horseshoes

`Tel 0954 210221`

High Street Madingley Cambridge Cambridgeshire CB3 8AB

£50

R

Map 6 B3

Chef-patron Eamonn Webster runs a busy, cheerful country inn serving bar snacks and grills and a restaurant menu which updates traditional cuisine. Smoked mackerel mousse with lemon cream, pigeon breasts in puff pastry on red cabbage with caraway seeds, and fillet of beef with a Meaux mustard sauce show the style. Home-made bread and ice creams. Excellent wines by the glass or bottle. *Seats 50. Parties 100. Private Room. L 12-2 (Sun to 2.30) D 7-10 (Sun to 9). Set L £15.75 Set D £22.50. Access, Amex, Visa,* *Diners Club International*

Maiden Newton   Maiden Newton House   73%

`Tel 0300 20336   Fax 0300 21021`

Maiden Newton Nr Dorchester Dorset DT2 0AA

£112

HR

Map 4 B4

Right in the centre of the village, the manor house of Maiden Newton is set in 21 acres of parkland with a stream running through the gardens. The experience is one of staying with friends. Wooden floors in the entrance hall gleam by dint of good housekeeping and the drawing room is a model of informal English country comfort. Next door is a charming little library. Roomy individually decorated bedrooms are very comfortable and come with a battery of cosseting extras. Two rooms have four-posters, another a hand-painted half tester. No children under 12. *Rooms 6. Garden, croquet, game fishing. Closed 1st 3 weeks Dec. Access, Visa.*

Restaurant

£70

Dinner is an elegant affair, taken *en famille* with Elizabeth and Brian Ferriss at a polished mahogany dining table. There is no choice. A typical meal could comprise tagliatelle with basil and pine nut sauce, braised pheasant breast with Madeira sauce, and rhubarb fool. The finale is a selection of West Country cheeses. Excellent wines by the glass are served with each course. Booking essential. *Seats 16. D only at 8. Set D £25.*

Maiden Newton   Le Petit Canard   £50

R

Tel 0300 20536

56 Dorchester Road Maiden Newton Dorset DT2 OBE   Map 4 B4

Canadians Lin and Geoff Chapman relocated to this former fish café after
working for several years on the fringe of North America's second-largest
China town in Vancouver. Both French and Oriental styles influence
Geoff's intuitive cooking on a fixed-price, three-course affair: stir-fried
rabbit with sweet ginger, green onion and noodles; confit of duck on a bed
of tarragon-scented lentils; roast rack of lamb with hoisin on a nest of
beansprouts; almond tuile with vanilla parfait and lychees. Lin compiles the
short, mainly French, wine list with helpful tasting notes and also handles
service with cheery enthusiasm. No-smoking area. *Seats 28. Parties 30.
Private Room. D only 7-9. Closed Sun & Mon. Set D £17.95. Access, Visa.*

Maidenhead   Fredrick's   76%   £155

HR

Tel 0628 35934   Fax 0628 771054

Shoppenhangers Road Maidenhead Berkshire SL6 2PZ   Map 5 E2

Leave the M4 at junction 8/9 to find this luxury redbrick hotel in a well-
to-do residential road geared mainly to the needs of senior executives. The
style of the public areas is aptly sleek and glitzy. Futuristic chandeliers
dominate the foyer, where guests are given a glass of champagne at check-
in; the Winter Garden lounge opens on to neat grounds and the cocktail
bar is a veritable pot-pourri of decorative styles. Good bedrooms are strong
on modern comforts, well-kept bathrooms. Highly efficient staff led by
Fredrick Losel, here since 1977. Above-average breakfast. No dogs.
Rooms 38. Garden, croquet. Closed 24-30 Dec. Access, Amex, Visa,

Restaurant   £90

Brian Cutler's cooking is traditional French with modern overtones, and
the panelled dining room is an elegant setting. A four-course table d'hote
dinner might comprise grilled salmon and scallop salad followed by cream
of parsnip and honey soup and fillet of venison with cinnamon and port
wine sauce or lemon sole meunière with mussels; tiramisu with poached
pear to finish. The à la carte is an appealing mix of tradition and fashion:
supreme of pigeon on braised lentils sits alongside noisettes of venison
grand veneur. The wine list is concise, but broadly based. Open for
Christmas lunch, even though the hotel is closed. *Seats 60. Parties 15.
Private Room. L 12-2 D 7-9.45. Closed L Sat. Set L £19.50 Set D £28.50.*

Maidenhead   Holiday Inn   66%   £136

H

Tel 0628 23444   Fax 0628 770035

Manor Lane Maidenhead Berkshire SL6 2RA   Map 5 E2

Set in 18 acres of grounds close to junction 8/9 of M4. Top-notch
conference and banqueting facilities (for up to 400) include the
characterful, reconstructed Elizabethan Shoppenhangers Manor house in the
grounds. Straightforward accommodation, but good leisure facilities.
Playroom provided for children at weekends. *Rooms 189. Garden, indoor
swimming pool, spa bath, sauna, solarium, squash, gymnasium, snooker, croquet,
coffee shop (9am-11pm). Access, Amex, Visa,*

Maidenhead   Places of Interest

Cliveden (NT)   Taplow, Nr Burnham Tel 0628 605069.
Stanley Spencer Gallery   King's Hall, Cookham-on-Thames Tel 062 85
   20890/20043.
Courage Shire Horse Centre   Maidenhead Thicket Tel 0628 824848.

Maidstone   Larkfield Priory   62%   £96

Tel 0732 846858   Fax 0732 846786   **H**

812 London Road Maidstone Kent ME20 6HJ   Map 7 B5

Leave the M20 at junction 4 taking the A228 Tonbridge road, then the
Maidstone road from the first roundabout, to find a Forte Heritage hotel
centred around a Victorian priory. A popular conference venue with
facilities for up to 80 delegates. *Rooms 52. Garden. Access, Amex, Visa,*

Maidstone   Mandarin Chef   £35

Tel 0622 755917   **R**

35 Lower Stone Street Maidstone Kent   Map 7 B5

Friendly service and sound Chinese cooking by chef Ken Lai make this a
popular place with a regular clientele. Peking and Cantonese regions are
well represented with dishes such as braised beef fillet, sweet and sour pork,
hot and sour soup, pickled cabbage, diced chicken with cashew nuts in
yellow bean sauce and baked crab in ginger and spring onion sauce. Town-
centre site with modern decor in assorted blues. Ring ahead for an off-the-
menu feast of specials. *Seats 75. Parties 14. L 12-2.15 D 5.30-11.30 (Sun to
11.15). Closed 3 days Xmas. Set L from £7 Set D from £13.50. Access,
Amex, Visa,*

Maidstone   Stakis Country Court Hotel   69%   NEW   £109

Tel 0622 34322   Fax 0622 34600   **H**

Bearsted Weavering Maidstone Kent ME14 5AA   Map 7 B5

New, purpose-built hotel with conference and banqueting facilities for
90/60 and good leisure amenities. Vastly reduced rates Fri-Sun. *Rooms 139.
Garden, indoor swimming pool, spa bath, sauna, solarium, gymnasium. Access,
Amex, Visa,*

Maidstone   Places of Interest

Tourist Information   Tel 0622 673581.
Hazlitt Theatre   Tel 0622 58611.
Boughton Monchelsea Place   Boughton Monchelsea Tel 0622 743120.
Leeds Castle and Culpeper Gardens   Tel 0622 765400.
Tyrwhitt-Drake Museum of Carriages   Tel 0622 54497.
The Moat Cricket Ground   Tel 0622 54545.
Kent County Showgrounds   Tel 0622 30975.
Leeds Castle   Aviaries Leeds Castle Tel 0622 65400.
Mereworth Parrot Park   Seven Mile Lane, Mereworth Tel 0622 812045.

Maldon   Blue Boar   59%   £82

Tel 0621 852681   Fax 0621 856202   **H**

3 Silver Street Maldon Essex CM9 7QE   Map 7 C4

A 16th-century inn located just off the High Street, notable for its elegant
Georgian facade, heavy oak beams, open fires and timbered wings
overlooking a stable yard. Rooms refurbished two years ago. Conference
and banqueting facilities for up to 100. Forte Heritage. *Rooms 28. Garden.
Access, Amex, Visa,* (D) Diners Club International

Maldon   Francine's   £50
`Tel 0621 856605`   **R**
1a High Street Maldon Essex CM9 7PB   Map 7 C4

An unpretentious restaurant, sited in one of Maldon's oldest buildings. The
minuteness of John Brotherton's kitchen is not something he lets constrain
him. Care is taken over the preparation of distinctly modern, unfussy
dishes, the produce is fresh, seasonings and flavourings are accurately
applied and sauces are faultless. At front of house John's wife Sara reaps the
benefit when customers compliment their menu (which changes on the
first Tuesday of each month); Sara also cooks a set Thai menu twice a
month. The menu might include Norfolk crab salad with beetroot and
curd cheese or baked avocado with Stilton and bacon followed by poached
fillets of sole with a sauce of wild mushrooms or fillet of lamb with honey
and sherry sauce, out of four choices at each course. Car parking to the
rear. *Seats 24. Parties 24. D only 7.30-9.15. Closed Sun & Mon, Bank
Holidays, 2 weeks Feb, 2 weeks Aug. Access, Visa.*

Maldon   Places of Interest

Tourist Information Tel 0621 856503.
Oakwood Arts Centre Tel 0621 56503.

Malmesbury   Old Bell Hotel   64%   £88
`Tel 0666 822344   Fax 0666 825145`   **H**
Abbey Row Malmesbury Wiltshire SN16 0BW   Map 4 B2

Hard by the abbey, the Old Bell dates back to 1210 and therefore has
claims to being England's oldest hostelry. Its wisteria-clad facade is more
than a match for its spiritual neighbour. Public rooms comprise two oak-
beamed bars and two lounge areas, one with a famous 800-year-old
chimney. Bedrooms in the main building come in all shapes and sizes,
while those in the converted stables are more uniformly modern. Families
are well catered for; children up to 10 stay free in parents' room. No dogs.
Clipper Hotels. *Rooms 37. Garden. Access, Visa.*

Malvern   Abbey Hotel   62%   £85
`Tel 0684 892332   Fax 0684 892662`   **H**
Abbey Road Malvern Hereford & Worcester WR14 3ET   Map 4 B1

A mix of impressive, ivy-clad exterior and modern bedrooms in an
extension block. Conference/banqueting facilities for up to 350/200.
Children under 14 accommodated free in parents' room. De Vere Hotels.
Rooms 107. Access, Amex, Visa, **Diners Club**

Malvern   Anupam   £40
`Tel 0684 573814`   **R**
85 Church Street Malvern Hereford & Worcester WR14 2AE   Map 4 B1

Ever-popular for its dependable South Indian cooking and efficient service;
hot minced lamb and potato ranga kebab, joypuri chicken with coriander,
ground almonds and fresh ginger, dry-fried spicy biran trout and tandoori
mushroom in almond-based masala are recent additions to the menu.
*Seats 50. Parties 50. L 12-2.30 D 6-12. Closed 25 Dec. Set meals from
£11.95. Access, Amex, Visa,* **Diners Club**

Malvern   Colwall Park Hotel   62%   £77
`Tel 0684 40206   Fax 0684 40847`   **H**
Colwall Malvern Hereford & Worcester WR13 6QG   Map 4 B1

In the centre of Colwall village, on the B4218 between Malvern and
Ledbury, this mock-Tudor hotel offers simple, well-kept accommodation.
Public rooms include a street-facing lounge bar with comfortable chairs
and sofas, and a quiet, traditionally furnished lounge. Bedrooms are light

and spacious, with quality furniture and functional bathrooms without frills. Families are well catered for. **Rooms 20.** *Garden, croquet. Access, Amex, Visa.*

Malvern   Cottage in the Wood   65%

Tel 0684 573487   Fax 0684 560662

Holywell Road Malvern Wells Hereford & Worcester WR14 4LG

£87

HR

Map 4 B1

A family-owned and operated hotel with arguably "the best view in England" looking out over the Severn Plain from high on the steep wooded slopes of the Malvern Hills. It comprises three distinct buildings; the public rooms and eight cottagey bedrooms are in a fine Georgian dower house, with the remaining accommodation (of a more functional nature) in the nearby Coach House and Beech Cottage. Private conference room for up to 14 boardroom style. No dogs in the main house. **Rooms 20.** *Garden. Access, Amex, Visa.*

Restaurant

£65

Traditional English cooking with intrusive hints of modernism – melon with crème de menthe sorbet; avocado with soured cream and strawberry sauce; kidneys with juniper berries, gin and mint; bacon-wrapped, Stilton-stuffed pork fillet roulade; strawberry and cream-filled choux pastry with chocolate mallow sauce. Light bite options at lunchtime; good English cheeseboard. A dozen or more English bottles and a Chinese chardonnay are included on the varied wine list. No smoking. **Seats 50.** *Parties 20. L 12.30-2 D 7-9 (Sun to 8.30).*

Malvern   Croque-en-Bouche   ★

Tel 0684 565612

221 Wells Road Malvern Wells Hereford & Worcester WR14 4HF

£82

R

Map 4 B1

A glance at the wine list will show the seriousness of Robin and Marion Jones's restaurant, a winner for the second time of our Cellar of the Year Award. Marion's cooking, once influenced mainly by French country cuisine, now expands to take in, for example, some Japanese and exotic touches. Salmon, smoked by the restaurant, is sautéed and served hot with spinach and a sorrel-infused beurre blanc. Wild rabbit is marinated with cumin and coriander, braised with root vegetables and tomato, and served with couscous and preserved lemon. Salads are usually dressed in Oriental style. Desserts are well nigh impossible to resist – apricot and almond tart with a glass of prunelle de Bourgogne, frozen ginger meringue, melon and champagne sorbet. If you enjoy wine, arrive early and enjoy reading this fascinating, dedicated, unbelievable value wine list. Mr Jones is a wine genius so, if he offers, let him choose. Be adventurous; you won't regret it. The wine list is one of the country's greatest *and* reasonably priced. 25 house wines under £14 offer superb value. **Seats 24.** *Parties 6. Private Room. D only 7.30-9.15. Closed Sun-Tue, Xmas/New Year. Set D from £31. Access, Visa.*

Malvern   Foley Arms   61%

Tel 0684 573397   Fax 0684 569665

14 Worcester Road Great Malvern Hereford & Worcester WR14 4QS

£85

H

Map 4 B1

Said to be the town's oldest hotel (built as a coaching inn in 1810), the Foley Arms stands at the top of the town, commanding magnificent views over the Severn valley. Sympathetically upgraded, the public areas include two homely lounges (one non-smoking), a pubby bar and a summer dining terrace. Good-sized bedrooms, the best with fine views, are comfortable and unfussy, with duvets and freestanding units. Under-16s stay free in parents' room. Three function suites accommodate conferences up to 50; banqueting for 80. **Rooms 28.** *Garden, giant chess. Access, Amex, Visa,*

Malvern   Places of Interest

Tourist Information   Tel 0684 892289.
Little Malvern Court   Nr Great Malvern Tel 0684 892988.

Manchester   Britannia Hotel   66%   £123
Tel 061-228 2288   Fax 061-236 9154   **H**

Portland Street Manchester Greater Manchester M1 3LA   Map 10 B2

Converted from a cotton warehouse and resplendent with its over-the-top
furnishings, the Britannia is a peculiar mix of rather gaudy, gilt-decorated
public rooms and simply decorated bedrooms. Fancier suites are split-level
and bedecked in floral prints. Two discos, together with numerous bars
and restaurants, keep up the lively pace. *Rooms 362. Indoor swimming pool,
sauna, solarium, keep-fit equipment, beauty & hair salons, coffee shop
(11am-2am). Access, Amex, Visa,*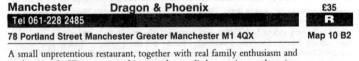

Manchester   Charterhouse Hotel   72%   £122
Tel 061-236 9999 Fax 061-236 0674   **H**

Oxford Street Manchester Greater Manchester M60 7HA   Map 10 B2

Formerly the distinctive Refuge Assurance building, adjacent to the BBC
and Palace Theatre, two minutes from Oxford Road railway station. Much
of the original Victorian architecture – ornate plasterwork, intricate
cornicing, lofty columns and stained-glass windows – has been retained,
especially in the vast open-plan public areas which feature contemporary
seating, heavy drapes and much greenery in modern country house style.
Bedrooms vary in size and are individually decorated (tastefully, though
not too luxuriously) with co-ordinated fabrics and contract furniture. Fully
carpeted bathrooms with gold taps, low basins, thoughtlessly positioned
shaving mirrors and good-quality toiletries. There's fresh milk in the mini-
bars, complimentary chocolates, mineral water and three telephones (bed,
desk and bathroom) per room. Conference and banqueting facilities for
150/120. Hidden Hotels. *Rooms 58. Coffee shop (10am-11pm). Access,
Amex, Visa,*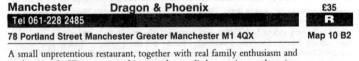

Manchester   Copthorne Hotel   70%   £115
Tel 061-873 7321   Fax 061-873 7318   **H**

Clippers Quay Salford Quays Manchester Greater Manchester M5 3DL   Map 10 B2

Standing next to the quays in the Salford Docks redevelopment area (just a
mile from the city centre) is a modern redbrick hotel. A high ceiling,
exposed brickwork and polished tile floor combine to give an up-to-date
feel to the foyer, with other day rooms continuing the contemporary
theme. The Clippers Bar has tinted mirror walls and is a genuinely
comfortable place to relax. The most popular bedrooms overlook the quay
and have large bay windows, allowing in plenty of natural light; coloured-
wood furniture and bathrooms tiled in two colours continue the bright
theme. Six bedrooms are specifically adapted for use by wheelchair-bound
guests. 24hr room service. Conference and function facilities for up to 150.
*Rooms 166. Terrace, indoor swimming pool, sauna, solarium, spa bath, keep-fit
equipment. Access, Amex, Visa,*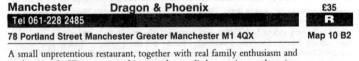

Manchester   Dragon & Phoenix   £35
Tel 061-228 2485   **R**

78 Portland Street Manchester Greater Manchester M1 4QX   Map 10 B2

A small unpretentious restaurant, together with real family enthusiasm and
predominantly Vietnamese cooking, proves a little gem in an otherwise
mediocre area for dining out. The deft use of spicing like lemon grass, chili
and ginger helps give an interesting alternative to the otherwise Cantonese
dishes. *Seats 45. L 12-3 D 7-12 (Fri & Sat 6-3). Closed Sun. Set L from
£3.50. Access, Visa.*

Manchester   Forte Posthouse   60%   £67

Tel 061-998 7090   Fax 061-946 0139   **H**

Palatine Road Northenden Manchester Greater Manchester M22 4EH   **Map 10 B2**

Mid-70s, high-rise hotel, 3 miles from the airport, 7 miles from the city centre, close to junction 9 of M63. Cosy day rooms and comfortable bedrooms. Banqueting/conference facilities for 100/120. *Rooms 190. Garden. Access, Amex, Visa,*

Manchester   Gaylord   £35

Tel 061-832 6037   **R**

**Amethyst House Spring Gardens Manchester
Greater Manchester M2 1EA**   **Map 10 B2**

Tandoori, Mughlai and Kashmiri cuisine finds an authentic home in Manchester's best Indian restaurant. The Gaylord empire stretches round the world, with outlets in Frankfurt, Delhi, Hong Kong and San Francisco. Outstanding dishes include home-made cottage cheese (in Kebabs, in pakoras, with spinach or with tomatoes and cream), lamb korma badami, and a splendidly rich chicken tikka masala. Lotus roots are an unusual item in the vegetable section. In the city centre, but not too easy to find (approach via King Street if coming by car, as it's half a block from the Market Street precinct). *Seats 85. Parties 30. L 12-3 D 6-11.30. Set L £5.95 Set D from £10.95. Access, Amex, Visa,*

Manchester   Granada Lodge   £43

Tel 061-410 0076   Fax 061-655 3358   **L**

M62 junction 18/19 Birch Manchester Greater Manchester OL10 2QH   **Map 10 B2**

Rooms 37. Access, Amex, Visa,

Manchester   Holiday Inn Crowne Plaza   73%   £147

Tel 061-236 3333   Fax 061-228 2241   **H**

Peter Street Manchester Greater Manchester M60 2DS   **Map 10 B2**

A grand town-centre hotel (adjacent to the G-Mex centre) restored at great expense to its past glory with ornate ceilings, arches and pillars. The foyer area is vast, with a glass roof and hanging plants crowning white columns. Cane chairs and comfortable couches adorn the adjoining terrace lounge. The high-ceilinged Octagon, one of three bars, is decorated in similar style; there are also three restaurants. Corridors that lead to the bedrooms are wide and reminiscent of a former age of spacious and luxurious hotels. Bedrooms are generously sized and have a high standard of decor, with tiled bathrooms throughout. Extensive conference and banqueting (including kosher) facilities for up to 500. *Rooms 303. Indoor swimming pool, sauna, solarium, spa bath, keep-fit equipment, squash, news kiosk. Access, Amex, Visa,*

Manchester   Little Yang Sing   £42

Tel 061-228 7722   **R**

17 George Street Manchester Greater Manchester M1 4HE   **Map 10 B2**

Basement Chinatown restaurant with a vast menu based on Cantonese cooking. Besides the usual range of seafood, pork, beef and poultry dishes there's an exceptional choice for vegetarians and vegans. Dim sum include some unusual items such as chicken's feet with black beans and chili sauce, ox tripe with ginger and spring onion or sweet water chestnut cake, plus Sunday specials. *Seats 90. Meals 12-11.30. Closed 25 Dec. Set D from £15. Access, Amex, Visa.*

Manchester	Market Restaurant	£60

Tel 061-834 3743   **R**

104 High Street Smithfield City Centre Manchester
Greater Manchester M4 1HQ   Map 10 B2

A homely restaurant situated in the back streets of Manchester, close to
Smithfield Market. An authentic 1940s' ambience is evoked by period
music, slightly faded decor, sewing-machine tables, an oddment of
antique crockery and 30s' milk bottles used for serving the house wine.
Menus with middle- and far-eastern inspiration change monthly and offer
something for everyone – perhaps lettuce soup, Claudia Roden's Israeli
mixed salad or an unusual light smoked venison and potato salad to start,
followed by shami kebab, pork tapénade with a fresh tomato sauce or a
classic fillet of beef with béarnaise sauce. Vegetables seem a poor relation
and can sometimes be overcooked, oversauced and generally overworked.
Decent sweets might include a cherry ratafia cream or rich chocolate
praline terrine. English farmhouse cheeses, so-so coffee and reasonably-
priced wines that are carefully chosen to complement the menu. Note the
thirty or so bottled Continental beers. *Seats 40. D only 6-9.30 (Sat from 7).*
Closed Sun & Mon, 1 week Xmas, 1 week Easter, Aug. Access, Amex, Visa,

Manchester	Novotel	62%	£82

Tel 061-799 3535   Fax 061-703 8207   **H**

Worsley Brow Worsley Manchester Greater Manchester M28 4YA   Map 10 B2

Modern hotel in its own grounds by junction 13 of the M62. Ample free
parking. Banqueting/conferences for up to 160/220. Novotel policy is that
two children under 16 are accommodated free, with breakfast included,
when sharing their parents' room. *Rooms 119. Garden, outdoor swimming
pool. Access, Amex, Visa,*

Manchester	Penang Village	£45

Tel 061-236 2650   **R**

56 Faulkner Street Manchester Greater Manchester   Map 10 B2

Hot, rich and spicy dishes run the gamut of Malaysian cuisine in a first-
floor restaurant on the south corner of Chinatown. Satay is a popular
prelude to a wide range of main courses including, as specialities, grilled
king prawns or fish fillets topped with sambal sauce, spicy deep-fried
chicken and Penang-style curry. Plenty of vegetarian options. Charming
service from sarong-clad waitresses. *Seats 70. Parties 80. L 12-2 D 5.30-12
(Sat & Sun 12-12). Closed 25 & 26 Dec, 1 Jan. Set meals from £15. Access,
Amex, Visa,*

Manchester	Hotel Piccadilly	73%	£138

Tel 061-236 8414   Fax 061-236 2533   **H**

Piccadilly Plaza Manchester Greater Manchester M60 1QR   Map 10 B2

Above a shopping centre, this high-rise hotel gives a vastly misleading
impression from the exterior. Fast lifts lead up to an elegant reception area,
with an expanse of sparkling, coloured-marble flooring, and a smart coffee
house on the second floor, both of which set the standard for decor
throughout and more than compensate for any misapprehensions. A bar
and restaurant are on the open-plan third floor. In the basement a well-
equipped leisure club is centred around a good-sized pool. Bedrooms are
also generously sized with darkwood furniture contrasting against lighter,
contemporary colour schemes and well-lit bathrooms. The top,
Ambassador floor, has eight suites, its own check-in and a butler.
Conference and banqueting facilities for up to 800. Jarvis Hotels.
*Rooms 271. Indoor swimming pool, gymnasium, spa bath, sauna, solarium,
steam room, beauty salon, coffee shop (9am-6pm). Access, Amex, Visa,*

Manchester   Portland Thistle   69%   £130

Tel 061-228 3400   Fax 061-228 6347   **H**

Portland Street Manchester Greater Manchester M1 6DP   **Map 10 B2**

In the heart of the city overlooking Piccadilly Gardens, the Portman is
within easy reach of most of the city's amenities. Parlour plants decorate a
sometimes chaotic foyer, but one can always retire to the bars, one of
which features a wall of whisky bottles. The Executives are the best of the
bedrooms. Conference rooms hold up to 300. Valet parking. 24hr room
service. *Rooms 205. Indoor swimming pool, sauna, solarium, keep-fit equipment.*
Access, Amex, Visa,  Diners Club International

Manchester   Quan Ju De   £60

Tel 061-236 5236   **R**

44 Princess Street Manchester Greater Manchester M1 6DE   **Map 10 B2**

Perhaps not yet in a position to challenge Yang Sing for Manchester's top
Chinese spot, this authentic Peking restaurant is definitely one to watch.
The new chef and his team come from the parent restaurant in Peking.
Despite the bright, simplistic decor and trendy modern artwork, the menu
has plenty of traditional dishes with roasted duck and crispy aromatic duck
as the specialities. Fried seaweed with grated scallop, Szechuan beef and
turnip soup, prawns in ginger and garlic and teppan beef served on a
sizzling platter also feature on a balanced menu of commendable brevity.
Good spicing and competent handling of raw materials are the hallmarks.
Tempting banquets for two or more include a vegetarian version. Pianist
Tues-Sat eves. *Seats 120. Parties 80. Private Room. L 12-2.30 D 6-11.30*
(Sun 12-11.30). Closed Bank Holidays. Set L from £4.80 Set D from £16.
Access, Amex, Visa.

Manchester   Rajdoot   £40

Tel 061-834 2176   **R**

Carlton House 18 Albert Square Manchester
Greater Manchester M2 5PR   **Map 10 B2**

Rajdoot is a small chain of restaurants serving well-prepared Indian food in
comfortable surroundings. The range of tandoori dishes is fairly standard,
though mackerel, lobster and lamb's kidneys are a little out of the ordinary.
Also at: Birmingham & Dublin (see entries). *Seats 67. Parties 70. L 12-2.30*
D 6.30-11.30. Closed L Sun & Bank Holidays, 25 & 26 Dec. Set L from £8
Set D from £14.50. Access, Amex, Visa, Diners Club International

Manchester   Ramada Renaissance   73%   £116

Tel 061-835 2555   Fax 061-835 0731   **H**

Blackfriars Street Manchester Greater Manchester M3 2EQ   **Map 10 B2**

The foyer of this tall hotel looks good in marble, and off it the large and
sumptuous lounge provides a haven from the bustle of city life. The muted,
pastel-shaded bedrooms are all spacious (mini-suite size), with seating areas,
desk space, all the expected modern accessories and bright, well-equipped
bathrooms. Children up to 16 stay free in parents' room. There are
extensive conference and banqueting facilities (maximum capacity 400).
Rooms 200. Gift shop, coffee shop (9.30am-1am). Access, Amex, Visa,
Diners Club International

Manchester   Sachas Hotel   64%   £121

Tel 061-228 1234   Fax 061-236 9202   **H**

Tib Street Piccadilly Manchester Greater Manchester M4 1PQ   **Map 10 B2**

Formerly a C&A store, now a brash hotel with a stuffed polar bear in the
entrance hall. Bedrooms vary from inner ones with neither windows nor
natural light to superior versions with whirlpool baths and four-poster
beds. There are lively eating and drinking spots in the basement and a
variety of conference and banqueting suites catering for up to 650

delegates. Sister hotel to the *Britannia*. **Rooms 223.** *Indoor swimming pool, sauna, solarium, keep-fit equipment, beauty & hair salons, coffee shop (11am-2am), night club. Access, Amex, Visa,* ⓘ Diners Club International

---

Manchester	Siam Orchid	£45
Tel 061-236 1388		**R**
54 Portland Street Manchester Greater Manchester M1 4QU		Map 10 B2

A friendly Thai restaurant on the edge of Manchester's Chinatown. A long à la carte menu (13 pages!) covers the whole Thai range from soups and satay to fish cakes, spicy salads, curries of several hues, noodle platters, rice platters and many variations on pork, chicken, crab, fish, prawns, lobster, squid and eggs. There's plenty of choice, too, for vegetarians, plus a business lunch menu and other set menus for four or more. **Seats 60.** *Parties 60. L 11.30-2.30 D 6.30-11.30 (Fri & Sat from 6, Sun 5-11). Closed L Sat, Sun & Bank Holidays. Set L from £5 Set D from £16. Access, Visa,* ⓘ Diners Club International

---

Manchester	Sonarga	£45
Tel 061-861 0334		**R**
269 Barlow Moor Road Chorlton-cum-Hardy Manchester Greater Manchester		Map 10 B2

On the edge of south Manchester's residential fringe at Chorlton-cum-Hardy, the broad-fronted, Sonarga is more Armani than original Veeraswamy, presenting much more than the oft-seen good shopfitting job. A well-judged modern style of Bangladeshi cooking and service is offered and the kitchen appears eager to offer new ideas without forsaking traditional values. Good thalis, unusually excellent dhal and six hours' notice required for house specialities like Pashoree beef or lobster Lahare. Undoubtedly one of the best Indian restaurants in the area. Fried chicken and chips appears in a short section of the menu wittily labelled "exotic dishes". **Seats 62.** *Parties 70. L 12-2.30 D 6-11 (Sat 1-11.30, Sun 1-10.30). Closed L Fri. Set L from £4.50. Access, Visa.*

Manchester	That Café	£42
Tel 061-432 4672		**R**
1031 Stockport Road Levenshulme Manchester Greater Manchester M19 2TB		Map 10 B2

Home cooking (minted lamb casserole, spicy vegetable brochettes, pineapple crush) comes in generously sized portions at a restaurant alongside the A6, to the south of the city. The short set-price menu always includes a vegetarian option. **Seats 90.** *Parties 25. Private Room. L Sun 12.30-2.30 other days by arrangement D 7-10.30. Closed D Sun & Mon, 2 weeks Aug. Set L £10.95 Set D £12.95. Access, Amex, Visa,* ⓘ Diners Club International

---

Manchester	Woodlands	£55
Tel 061-336 4241		**R**
33 Shepley Road Audenshaw Manchester Greater Manchester M34 5DJ		Map 10 B2

Chef Mark Jackson trained at the *Savoy* and *Claridge's* so it's not surprising that the menu in this solid Victorian house is based on classic French tradition. Rich sauces are part of many dishes – warm butter with steamed asparagus, cheese with poached brill on a bed of spinach, Madeira with medallions of fillet steak, black cherry with breast of duck. Descriptive, mainly French wine list. **Seats 40.** *Parties 12. L 12-2 D 7-9.30 (Sat to 10). Closed L Sat, all Sun & Mon, Xmas/New Year, 1 week Easter, 2 weeks Aug. Set L £14.65 Set D £16.65. Access, Visa.*

Manchester   Yang Sing   ★   £50

Tel 061-236 2200   Fax 061-236 5934   **R**

34 Princes Street Manchester Greater Manchester M1 4JY   **Map 10 B2**

Booking is still essential at this basement restaurant on the edge of
Chinatown, serving the best Chinese food that Manchester has to offer.
Tables are squeezed tightly together and the decor is a mite dated,
providing a nondescript background for the fine food that is prepared in an
open-to-view kitchen. Slow-cooked brisket of beef and steamed chicken
with wine-dried sausage are definite highlights from the enormous (and
almost daunting) Cantonese-inspired menu that also offers interesting daily
specials like Dover sole with asparagus. A wide range of pastries and cakes,
from the bakery across the road, is on display to complete a meal. Dim
sum is popular at lunchtimes and unusually, through into the evening.
*Seats 140. Parties 330. Private Room. Meals 12-11. Closed 25 Dec. Access,
Amex, Visa.*

Manchester   Places of Interest

Tourist Information   Tel 061-234 3157/3158.
G-Mex Centre   Tel 061-832 9000
Manchester Cathedral   Tel 061-773 2959.
Heaton Hall   Tel 061-236 9422.
Warwick Road Cricket Ground   Old Trafford Tel 061-848 7021.
Oldham Ski Centre   Tel 061-678 4055.
  Theatres and Concert Halls
Contact Theatre   Tel 061-274 4400.
Library Theatre   Tel 061-236 7110.
Manchester Opera House   Tel 061-831 7766.
Palace Theatre   Tel 061-236 9922.
Royal Exchange   Tel 061-833 9833.
  Museums and Art Galleries
City Art Gallery   Tel 061-236 5244.
Gallery of English Costume   Tel 061-224 5217.
The Museum of Science and Industry   Tel 061-832 2244.
Manchester Museum   Tel 061-275 2634.
Whitworth Art Gallery   Tel 061-273 4865.
Art Gallery   Oldham Leisure Services Tel 061-678 4651.
  Football Grounds
Manchester City   Tel 061-226 1191.
Manchester United   Tel 061-872 1661.
Oldham Athletic   Tel 061-624 4972.

Manchester Airport   Etrop Grange   67%   NEW   £102

Tel 061-499 0500   Fax 061-499 0790   **HR**

Etrop Green Manchester Greater Manchester M22 5NR   **Map 10 B2**

Unusually for an airport hotel, this privately-owned and extended 18th-
century Georgian house is set in landscaped gardens. Public areas are
comfortably and traditionally furnished, though the conservatory has
contemporary decor. Bedrooms are mostly on the small side, but offer
adequate facilities, though despite double-glazing some rooms suffer from
traffic noise. Some bathrooms have no shower over the bath. Hiccups in
maintenance and service keep the grading from being higher. *Rooms 41.*
Access, Amex, Visa,

Restaurant   £70

Diners will discover that Raymond Sharp's cooking, English in character, is
rather better than the unnecessarily flowery and fruity menu descriptions
indicate. The number of courses you eat determines the price that you pay,
and there are sufficient choices in each section to satisfy all tastes, say, a
chilled melon soup, timbale of seafood, loin of lamb and rice pudding.
Good British farmhouse cheeses, keenly served in chi-chi surroundings,
where candles are lit in broad daylight. *Seats 60. Parties 80. Private Room.
L 12-3 D 7-10. Set L £11.50 Set D £19.50.*

Manchester Airport   Forte Crest   65%   £97

Tel 061-437 5811   Fax 061-436 2340   **H**

Ringway Road Wythenshawe Greater Manchester M22 5NS   Map 10 B2

Formerly the Excelsior. Between terminals A & B, 8 miles from the city
centre. Banqueting and conference facilities for 200, plus a leisure centre.
*Rooms 297. Garden, indoor swimming pool, gymnasium, sauna, coffee shop
(9am-10pm). Access, Amex, Visa,* Diners Club International

Manchester Airport   Four Seasons Hotel   68%   £115

Tel 061-904 0301   Fax 061-980 1787   **H**

Hale Road Hale Barns Nr Altrincham Greater Manchester WA15 8XW   Map 10 B2

A privately owned hotel two miles from the airport (leave the M56 at
junction 6). Smart modern bedrooms overlook central courtyard gardens.
Well geared up for business people with up-to-date conference facilities (for
up to 160) and secretarial support services available. Bright, conservatory
brasserie and Mulligans snug bar for entertaining after business hours.
Rooms 94. Business centre, car hire desk. Access, Amex, Visa, Diners Club International

Manchester Airport   Hilton International 71%   £162

Tel 061-436 4404   Fax 061-436 1521   **H**

**Outwood Lane Ringway Manchester Airport
Greater Manchester M22 5WP**   Map 10 B2

Convenient for both the airport and the motorway network, this modern
hotel caters admirably for travellers and general businessmen alike with its
good business and meeting facilities (for up to 200). An unusual feature is a
fountain that leads into a fish-filled pond in one corner of a lounge area.
Plaza bedrooms are larger and more impressive than the standard rooms,
but all are smartly furnished with contemporary fabrics and have
surprisingly spacious bathrooms. Double-glazing features throughout, so
noise is not a problem, despite the location. Small leisure pool. *Rooms 223.
Garden, indoor swimming pool, children's pool, keep-fit equipment, spa bath,
sauna, steam bath, coffee shop (8am-midnight). Access, Amex, Visa,* Diners Club International

Manchester Airport   Moss Nook   £80

Tel 061-437 4778   **RR**

Ringway Road Moss Nook Manchester Greater Manchester M22 5NH   Map 10 B2

Red suede walls, heavy drapes, stained glass, lots of silver plate (in need of a
bit of polish), heavy crystal glassware, and lace slips over the tablecloths, all
add up to a rather ostentatious opulence. The French-style à la carte menu
is supplemented by a *menu surprise* (five small courses at lunchtime, seven
in the evening). Cooking is generally acceptable if not quite managing to
live up to the surroundings. Service can be overly deferential. *Seats 60.
Parties 10. L 12-1.30 D 7-9.30 Closed L Sat, all Sun & Mon, Bank Holidays,
2 weeks Xmas. Set L £16.50 Set D £26. Access, Amex, Visa,* Diners Club International

Room   £90

An adjacent, self-contained cottage has a double bedroom with en-suite
bathroom and lounge. The makings of a continental breakfast are provided.
Room 1.

Market Drayton   Corbet Arms   £50

Tel & Fax 0630 652037   **I**

High Street Market Drayton Shropshire TF9 1LL   Map 10 B3

A creeper-clad 16th-century coaching inn retaining exposed timbers (and
creaky floorboards) in smartly decorated bedrooms. Period ballroom for
up to 140 revellers, and smaller private conference rooms. Cheerful staff.
Rooms 11. Access, Amex, Visa, Diners Club International

Market Drayton   Goldstone Hall   60%

£75

Tel 0630 86202   Fax 0630 86585

Goldstone Market Drayton Shropshire TF9 2NA   Map 10 B3

Set in five acres of gardens, the hall is an accumulation of centuries of
building, with possible Anglo-Saxon origins, and is furnished with the
family collection of antiques. Bedrooms are individually designed with
period furniture and several have large Victorian brass bedsteads. Separate
conference rooms accommodate 70, with banqueting for 100. Five miles
from Market Drayton – follow the signs to Goldstone from Hinstock on
the A41. *Rooms 8. Garden, snooker. Closed 26 Dec. Access, Amex, Visa.*

Market Drayton   Places of Interest

Market Drayton Pool   Tel 0630 652619.

Market Harborough   Three Swans Hotel   65%

£77

H

Tel 0858 466644   Fax 0858 433101

21 High Street Market Harborough Leicestershire LE16 7NJ   Map 11 D4

Charles I slaked his thirst here in 1645, by when this splendid coaching inn
was already more than 200 years old. Several bars ensure that today's
visitors don't go thirsty, and there's an attractive conservatory/lounge and a
patio. Bedrooms are in the main building or a block across the courtyard.
All are of a good size, decorated in restful pastels and furnished with smart
modern units; all have private bathrooms with tubs, shower and toiletries.
Friendly staff. Banquets (for up to 95) and conferences (up to 75) catered
for. No dogs. *Rooms 37. Access, Amex, Visa,*

Market Harborough   Places of Interest

Deene Park House and Gardens   Nr Corby Tel 078085 278 or 361.
Kirby Hall   Nr Corby Tel 0536 203230.
Rockingham Castle   Corby Tel 0536 770240.
Rutland Polo Club   Barnsdale House, Great Easton Tel 0536 770238.

Markington   Hob Green   70%

£75

H

Tel 0423 770031   Fax 0423 771589

Markington Nr Harrogate North Yorkshire HG3 3PJ   Map 15 B6

A long winding drive leads to a mellow stone-built hotel set in over 800
acres of farm and woodland. The gardens are regular winners of local
awards, and there are pleasant views of the rolling Yorkshire countryside.
The garden room is bright and summery, while the hall and drawing
room have a traditional appeal that's helped along by antiques and log fires.
Books, magazines and games are available for relaxation. Bedrooms are
individually appointed in homely style and furniture is an agreeable mix of
period and modern. Most have a little sitting area. *Rooms 12. Garden,
croquet. Access, Amex, Visa,* Diners Club International

Marlborough   Ivy House   61%

£76

H

Tel 0672 515333   Fax 0672 515338

High Street Marlborough Wiltshire SN8 1HJ   Map 4 C2

The Grade II Georgian house faces St Peter's Church, where Charles
Wesley was ordained. Once a boarding school for boys, it is now a modest
hotel comprising a dozen neat bedrooms in the main house and 16 in a
modern conference centre to the rear; both are interlinked by a cobbled
courtyard to the restaurant, bistro and sun terrace. Six further bedrooms in
country cottage style are in an annexe across the High Street.
Banqueting/conferences for 70/50. No children under 3. Under-10s stay
free in parents' room. *Rooms 32. Closed 2 weeks Xmas/New Year. Access,
Amex, Visa,* Diners Club International

Marlow   Compleat Angler Hotel   73%   £161

Tel 0628 484444   Fax 0628 486388   **H**

Marlow Bridge Marlow Buckinghamshire SL7 1RG   Map 5 E2

A famous Marlow landmark in a glorious riverside setting by the weir.
Said to be where Izaak Walton wrote his definitive angling work (after
which the hotel is named), it dates in part back to the 16th century, but has
been extended over the years. The latest extension houses eighteen
bedrooms, twelve of which overlook the river. Creaking floorboards
feature in the original rooms, which include riverside rooms at a
supplement to already high tariffs. On the ground floor the marble-floored
foyer leads to a panelled bar with a conservatory, opening onto a small
balcony that also overlooks the river. Overall, it's expensive for what is on
offer. Forte Grand. *Rooms 64. Access, Amex, Visa,* (**1**) *Diners Club International*

Marlow   Places of Interest

Bisham Abbey Sports Centre   Tel 0627 476911.

Marston   Forte Travelodge   £40

Tel 0234 766755   **L**

M1/A421 Beancroft Road Marston Moretaine Bedfordshire MK43 0PZ   Map 5 E1

On the A421 northbound, 3 miles from junction 13 of the M1, 6 miles
south west of Bedford. *Rooms 32. Access, Amex, Visa.*

Matlock   Riber Hall   71%   £107

Tel 0629 582795   Fax 0629 580475   **H R**

Matlock Derbyshire DE4 5JU   Map 10 C2

Housekeeping is first-class throughout at this dark stone Elizabethan manor
house which sports antiques, beams and fresh flowers; there's also a lovely
conservatory and walled garden. Bedrooms are located in converted stables
across a courtyard where the original beams and rough stone walls remain;
all are filled with thoughtful extras, centrally heated and have period four-
poster or half-tester beds. Best rooms face south and east and overlook the
large garden. Bathrooms are well equipped, neat and warm. A tennis
trainer ball machine is available on the all-weather tennis court. No dogs.
Rooms 11. Tennis, clay-pigeon shooting. Access, Amex, Visa, (**1**) *Diners Club International*

Restaurant   £66

An interesting selection of dishes (on both an extensive dinner and more
limited lunch menus) is well served in two elegant dining rooms. Space is
limited, so booking is essential. Terrine of rabbit with wild mushrooms
and hazelnuts, turban of salmon and sole with champagne sauce, noisettes
of venison with damson gin, breast of corn-fed chicken with stir-fried
vegetables are typical dishes. There's also usually a good choice on the
pudding and separate vegetarian menus. Good ingredients and presentation
throughout. The fixed-price lunch offers five or so choices at each course.
Seats 45. Parties 34. Private Room. L 12-1.30 D 7-9.30. Set L £14.50

Matlock   Places of Interest

Gullivers Kingdom Matlock Bath   Tel 0629 580540.

Matlock Bath	New Bath Hotel	63%	£111

Tel 0629 583275   Fax 0629 580268   **H**

New Bath Road Matlock Bath Derbyshire DE4 3PX   Map 10 C2

Tucked away down a narrow, twisting gorge, the New Bath is set in five
acres of landscaped gardens overlooking the river Derwent. Good leisure
facilities include an outdoor swimming pool fed by a thermal spring.
Conference/banqueting for 150/200. Forte Heritage. *Rooms 55. Garden,
indoor & outdoor swimming pools, sauna, solarium, tennis, putting. Access,
Amex, Visa,*

Mawnan Smith	Budock Vean Hotel	65%	£145

Tel 0326 250288   Fax 0326 250892   **H**

Mawnan Smith Nr Falmouth Cornwall TR11 5LG   Map 2 B4

Sport and leisure rank highly at Budock Vean, which has a private
foreshore to the Helford River. 65 acres of sub-tropical gardens proliferate
around the hotel, while the fine leisure facilities even extend to a log fire in
the unusually large indoor pool room. Public areas include a cane
furniture-filled conservatory, cocktail bar (jackets and ties after 7pm) and
several lounges. Spacious bedrooms include some with sitting rooms.
*Rooms 58. Garden, indoor swimming pool, tennis, 9-hole golf course, putting,
table tennis, coarse fishing, snooker. Closed 3 Jan-Feb. Access, Amex, Visa,*

Mawnan Smith	Meudon Hotel	69%	£130

Tel 0326 250541   Fax 0326 250543   **H**

Mawnan Smith Nr Falmouth Cornwall TR11 5HT   Map 2 B4

The Pilgrim family, owners since 1966, put the accent on peace, quiet and
personal service, with no conference or even large parties to intrude. Large
sub-tropical gardens, laid out by 'Capability' Brown, are at their flowering
best between March and June, and lead down to a private beach. The
house itself was built at the turn of the century, and the new wing,
connected at first-floor level, is in matching stone. The main lounge is very
comfortable and appealing, with paintings, photographs, fresh flowers and
antiques. Bedrooms are individually appointed in elegant style, with
furnishings and fittings of a uniformly high standard; all overlook the
gardens. Residents can enjoy free golf at the Falmouth course (two miles
away). No children under 5. *Rooms 32. Garden, fishing. Closed Jan & Feb.
Access, Visa,*

Mawnan Smith	Nansidwell	71%	£140*

Tel 0326 250340   Fax 0326 250440   **HR**

Mawnan Smith Nr Falmouth Cornwall TR11 5HU   Map 2 B4

Surrounded by miles of National Trust coastline and walks down the
Helford river, Nansidwell stands at the head of a wooded valley sloping
down to the sea: its five acres of sub-tropical gardens are ablaze with
colour from spring to late autumn. Paintings, antiques, fresh flowers and a
blazing winter fire add great charm to the drawing room which is both
tastefully decorated and marvellously comfortable, and great attention is
paid to personal service, making it very easy to feel at home. Bedrooms are
immaculate, individually decorated and well stocked with good books and
magazines. Views down to the sea are superb. *Half-board terms only.
Rooms 12. Garden, croquet, boules, tennis. Closed Jan. Access, Visa,

Restaurant   £60

Nightly table d'hote menus are supplemented by Tony Alcott's special
suggestions, which include home-smoked salmon with horseradish cream,

loin of rabbit with chestnut and sage mousse and Bramley and ginger
crumble. Puddings are a strong point, as is chef's granary bread with the
local cheeses. Inclusive Sunday lunch; lighter lunches weekdays, with
minimum charge to non-residents. Booking advised. *Seats 30. Parties 10.
L 12.30-1.45 D 7-9 (Sun to 8.30). Set L £14.75 Set D
£20.*

Mawnan Smith   Places of Interest

Glendurgan Garden (NT)   Helford River Tel 0208 74281.
Trebah Garden   Tel 0326 250448.

Medmenham   Danesfield House   79%   £166

| Tel 0628 891010   Fax 0628 890408 | **HR** |

Medmenham Marlow Buckinghamshire SL7 3ES   Map 5 D2

Set in 65 acres of woodlands and formal gardens, with panoramic views
over the River Thames, Danesfield is the third property to have been built
on this outstanding site. The present house only dates from the turn of the
century, but it already has a chequered history and even a ghost, the Grey
Lady of Danesfield Park. The reception area is surprisingly small for a big
house and the Grand Drawing Room, although impressive in scale, is
inappropriately furnished with leather and chintzy seating and lacks overall
decorative impact. The rest of the hotel is disappointingly institutional in
style. Although well-furnished and in some cases lifted by having
wonderful views over the river, the bedrooms are all decorated in one of
four pastel colour themes and are very much alike, with only small details
varying slightly according to the particular theme. Smartly uniformed staff
offer high levels of service from the moment of arrival, when porters are
on hand to open car doors and take care of both luggage and parking.
*Rooms 93. Garden, croquet, tennis, outdoor swimming pool. Access, Amex,
Visa,*

Oak Room & Loggia   £80

Where there were formerly four restaurants here, there are now just two:
the panelled Oak Room offering a fixed-price menu that ranges from
warm quail salad and grilled fillet of beef to a mousse of scallops on a
tomato and herb vinaigrette, and bacon and parsley stuffed saddle of rabbit
with braised garlic and herb sauce, and The Loggia with a short but varied
Italian à la carte. Unless you know your wines the list does not offer much
help, except for the house selection and cellarmaster's choice. *Seats 35.
Parties 30. Private Room. L 12-2 D 7-10. Set L £18.50 Set D £35.*

Melbourn   Pink Geranium   £85

| Tel 0763 260215 | **R** |

Station Road Melbourn Nr Royston Hertfordshire SG8 6DX   Map 6 B3

Set in an early 16th-century thatched cottage, Steven and Sally Saunders'
pretty restaurant combines a homely atmosphere with some sophisticated
cooking. Chef John Curtis produces a variety of menus that range from
relatively straightforward lunches (warm duck confit salad, supreme of
chicken with crab and sticky toffee pudding) to a three-course *menu
gourmande* (escalope of salmon with vodka and lemon beurre blanc, venison
steak with celeriac purée and port sauce, cripsy mango tart with vanilla
crème anglaise and blueberries). The carte is involved with dishes like
morel-studded terrine of guinea fowl with toasted sesame brioche and
breast of Bresse chicken filled with salmon mousseline and served with a
Szechuan peppercorn sauce. Crispy duck with citrus fruits and a saké sauce
(for two) is a house speciality. French or English cheeses served with home-
made walnut bread. Chauffeur service for those who wish to enjoy the
wine list *and* not drive home. *Seats 72. Parties 100. Private Room. L 12-2
D 7-10 (Sat to 10.30). Closed L Sat, D Sun, all Mon. Set L
£12.95/£15.95 (£16.95 Sun) Set D £24.95. Access, Amex, Visa,*

Melbourn   Places of Interest

Bassingbourn Ski Club   Royston Tel 0462 34107.

Melksham   King's Arms   £55

Tel 0225 707272   Fax 0225 702085   I

Market Place Melksham Wiltshire SN12 6EX   Map 4 B3

A cobbled courtyard lit by coaching lamps brighten up the front of a
traditional inn built from Bath stone, situated in the town's market square.
Heavy carved-oak furniture and a beamed ceiling decorate the residents'
lounge and a lounge bar is warmed by an open fire. Bedrooms are bright,
pleasant and simply furnished; four singles share two bathrooms. Children
up to 12 stay free in parents' room. *Rooms 14. Access, Amex, Visa,*
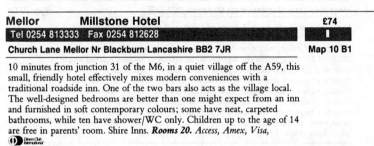 *Diners Club International*

Melksham   Places of Interest

Devizes Tourist Information   Tel 0380 729408.

Mellor   Millstone Hotel   £74

Tel 0254 813333   Fax 0254 812628   I

Church Lane Mellor Nr Blackburn Lancashire BB2 7JR   Map 10 B1

10 minutes from junction 31 of the M6, in a quiet village off the A59, this
small, friendly hotel effectively mixes modern conveniences with a
traditional roadside inn. One of the two bars also acts as the village local.
The well-designed bedrooms are better than one might expect from an inn
and furnished in soft contemporary colours; some have neat, carpeted
bathrooms, while ten have shower/WC only. Children up to the age of 14
are free in parents' room. Shire Inns. *Rooms 20. Access, Amex, Visa,*
Diners Club International

Melmerby   Village Bakery   £30

Tel 0768 881515   R

Melmerby Penrith Cumbria CA10 1HE   Map 13 D4

A converted barn with a bright, airy conservatory and pine furniture, run
for a decade by Andrew and Lis Whitley, and overlooking the green of a
windswept village near Penrith. The owners are committed to providing
food produced by organic methods, with free-range eggs and home-reared
lamb and pork on the restaurant menu. Breakfast (including a vegetarian
fried version with aduki bean pattie) is served until 11am; lunch (12-2) is
followed by marvellous afternoon teas with bread and cakes from their
own brick-built oven. Children's portions. No smoking. *Egon Ronay's Just
a Bite Guide* Tea Place of the Year 1992. *Seats 46. Parties 46. Meals 8.30-5
(Mon to 2.30 in winter, Sun from 9.30). Closed all Sun in Jan & Feb, 25 &
26 Dec. Access, Visa,* *Diners Club International*

Melton Mowbray   George Hotel   57%   £58

Tel 0664 62112   Fax 0664 410457   H

High Street Melton Mowbray Leicestershire LE13 0TR   Map 11 D3

The entrance hall at this very old former coaching inn was once the
archway through which the stage coaches drove. The arrival and departure
clock still stands on display, and another traditional touch is provided by
four-posters in some of the bedrooms. Children up to 10 stay free in
parents' room. There are two bars, one with beams and hunting prints, and
a patio. *Rooms 22. Access, Amex, Visa,* *Diners Club International*

Mere — Old Ship Hotel £52

Tel 0747 860258   Fax 0747 860501 | **I**

Castle Street Mere Wiltshire BA12 6JE | **Map 4 B3**

A splendid 17th-century inn with flagstones, exposed brick and stonework, log fires, panelling and beamed ceilings. Period oak furniture in the three characterful bars and the quiet residents' lounge complements the ancient fabric of the building. Bedrooms in the main house have traditional furnishings while ten in the annexe are more compact and modern. Eight bedrooms not en suite share three bathrooms. This is a popular base for touring, walking and riding. Families are well catered for. *Rooms 23. Baby-sitting, baby-listening. Access, Visa.*

Mere   Places of Interest

Stourhead (NT)   Stourton Tel 0747 840348.
Stourton House Garden   Stourton Tel 0747 840417.

Meriden — Forest of Arden Hotel   70% £120

Tel 0676 22335   Fax 0676 23711 | **H**

Maxstoke Lane Meriden West Midlands CV7 7HR | **Map 10 C4**

Just over a mile off the A45 (west of Coventry), near the M6/M42 intersection, this purpose-built hotel stands at the end of a country lane in 400 acres of rolling countryside. A Mediterranean feel to the interior is achieved by using archways, tapered white columns, rough-plastered white walls and terracotta tiles throughout the lounge and reception areas. Bedrooms are not large, but are comfortable and furnished with taste in contemporary fashion; bathrooms are carpeted and have good-quality showers. Leisure facilities are housed in an impressive Country Club and include a large pool. *Rooms 152. 2 golf courses, indoor swimming pool, sauna, steam room, spa bath, solarium, squash, tennis, snooker, fitness studio, beauty salon, dance studio, fishing. Access, Amex, Visa,*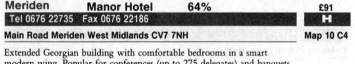

Meriden — Manor Hotel   64% £91

Tel 0676 22735   Fax 0676 22186 | **H**

Main Road Meriden West Midlands CV7 7NH | **Map 10 C4**

Extended Georgian building with comfortable bedrooms in a smart modern wing. Popular for conferences (up to 275 delegates) and banquets (up to 220). De Vere. *Rooms 74. Access, Amex, Visa,*

Mickleton — Three Ways Hotel   59% £63

Tel 0386 438429   Fax 0386 438118 | **H**

Mickleton Nr Chipping Campden Gloucestershire GL55 6SB | **Map 4 C1**

A privately-run hotel built from mellow, local stone, standing at the heart of the village by the B4632 (formerly the A46) Stratford to Broadway road. Bedrooms are practical rather than luxurious with modest en-suite facilities. Although the decor is dated, cleanliness is usually a strong point. Friendly and relaxing atmosphere. Three conference/function suites, one opening onto a patio. *Rooms 40. Garden. Access, Amex, Visa,*

Middle Wallop — Fifehead Manor   61% £75

Tel 0264 781565   Fax 0264 781400 | **H**

Middle Wallop Nr Stockbridge Hampshire SO20 8EG | **Map 4 C3**

Beside the busy A343 between Andover and Salisbury, the manor house stands in 3½ acres of land and has origins going back to the Middle Ages. Central to the house is the medieval dining hall with its mullioned windows and there is a small bar plus a lounge with a rather unused air. Large bedrooms in the main house have good-size bathrooms complete with resident plastic ducks; smaller singles (with showers only) are in an annexe, but have the attraction of leading out onto the rear lawn. Subdued fabrics and colour schemes are used throughout, and the furniture is mostly modern, although a few antiques help contribute to the friendly and informal atmosphere. Fine cooked breakfasts, but little choice for the more health-conscious. *Rooms 16. Garden, croquet. Closed 2 weeks Xmas/New Year. Access, Amex, Visa,* ①

Middlecombe   Periton Park   66%   £88

Tel 0643 706885   Fax 0643 702698   **H**

Periton Road Middlecombe Nr Minehead Somerset TA24 8SW   **Map 3 D1**

Time stands still at Periton Park, a handsome late-Victorian country residence nestling in its own woodland and gardens on the northern edge of Exmoor National Park. For total relaxation, guests feel quite at home in the stylish drawing room warmed by a log fire in winter; more energetic pursuits include fly fishing, and riding from stables adjacent to the hotel. Each bedroom (all en suite) has its own character and all enjoy splendid views; two are for non-smokers, and one ground-floor room, with French windows opening on to the garden, allows dogs. No children under 12. *Rooms 8. Garden, shooting, riding, fishing. Access, Amex, Visa.*

Middlesbrough   Hotel Baltimore   62%   £88

Tel 0642 224111   Fax 0642 226156   **H**

250 Marton Road Middlesbrough Cleveland TS4 2EZ   **Map 15 C5**

Popular businessman's hotel within a mile of the town centre. Bedrooms are double-glazed. Children up to 12 stay free in parents' room. Reduced prices at weekends. *Rooms 31. Solarium. Access, Amex, Visa,* ①

Middlesbrough   Hospitality Inn   59%   £91

Tel 0642 232000   Fax 0642 232655   **H**

Fry Street Middlesbrough Cleveland TS1 1JH   **Map 15 C5**

High-rise hotel in the town centre. Five banqueting and conference suites have a maximum capacity of 400. Mount Charlotte Thistle. *Rooms 180. Access, Amex, Visa,* ①

Middlesbrough   Places of Interest

Tourist Information   Tel 0642 243425.
Ormesby Hall (NT)   Tel 0642 324188.
Middlesbrough Football Ground   Ayresome Park Tel 0642 819659.
Redcar Racecourse   Redcar Tel 0642 484068.
   Theatres and Concert Halls
Little Theatre   Tel 0642 818971.
Redcar Bowl   Tel 0642 231212.
Town Hall Crypt   Tel 0642 221866.
   Museums and Art Galleries
Captain Cook Birthplace Museum   Tel 0642 311211.
Cleveland Crafts Centre   Tel 0642 226351.
Cleveland Gallery   Tel 0642 225408.
Guisborough Priory   Guisborough Tel 0287 38301.
Middlesbrough Art Gallery   Linthorpe Road Tel 0642 247445.

Middleton Stoney   Jersey Arms   £60

Tel 086 989 234   Fax 086 989 234   **I**

Middleton Stoney Nr Bicester Oxfordshire OX6 8SE   **Map 5 D1**

A Cotswold stone inn alongside the A43 that offers comfortable accommodation in cottagey style. Bedrooms are divided between the main house (where wooden beams and creaking floors abound) and the courtyard, where they are a little more up-to-date. Day rooms include a low-ceilinged bar warmed by an open fire and a new lounge with half panelling and comfortable seating. The new M40 has taken the pressure off the A43, making a stay here more restful than it used to be. *Rooms 16. Access, Amex, Visa,*

Middleton-in-Teesdale   Teesdale Hotel   58%   £61

Tel 0833 40264   **H**

Middleton-in-Teesdale Durham DL12 0QG   Map 15 B5

A former coaching inn run by Dieter and Audrey Streit since 1977.
Pleasantly unpretentious and a convenient base for touring the beautiful
surrounding countryside. Bedrooms are not large but are clean and
comfortable with bold wallpapers, matching fabrics and mainly white
furniture; modest bathrooms have either bath or shower. Four self-catering
cottages are to the rear around a courtyard. *Rooms 14. Access, Visa,*
 *Diners Club International*

Midhurst   Spread Eagle   69%   £80

Tel 0730 816911   Fax 0730 815668   **H**

South Street Midhurst West Sussex GU29 9NH   Map 5 E3

The characterful 15th- and 17th-century buildings combine here with
friendly staff and pleasing decor to form a most appealing hotel. The
lounge bar with log fire, old timbers and fresh flowers has great charm, as
do the other public areas, including the residents' lounge with its high
beamed ceiling. Bedrooms are individually decorated with quiet good taste
and are furnished with a mixture of reproduction and antique pieces.
Many, including the five four-poster rooms, have old exposed timbers or
mellow wood panelling. Four large family rooms are in the old Market
House across the road; baby sitting and baby listening can be arranged.
Smart bathrooms offer huge towels and good toiletries. The 17th-century
Jacobean Hall is a characterful setting for banquets and meetings (for
around 100). *Rooms 41. Garden. Access, Amex, Visa,* *Diners Club International*

Midhurst   Places of Interest

Petworth House (NT)   Petworth Tel 0798 42207.
Cowdray Park Polo Club   Cowdray Estate Office Tel 0730 812423.

Milford-on-Sea   Rocher's   £60

Tel 0590 642340   **R**

69-71 High Street Milford-on-Sea Hampshire SO41 0QG   Map 4 C4

Chef patron Alain Rocher spent two years just down the road at *Chewton
Glen* before opening his own restaurant in 1988. It's an unassuming,
comfortable establishment and the food on offer is commendable. Alain's
style is classical with modern touches and his cooking is characterised by
full flavours and excellent saucing with smooth textures, fine seasoning and
first-rate consistencies. Excellent meals are complemented by smart,
friendly service headed by Alain's wife Rebecca. Exclusively French wine
list with helpful notes. *Seats 26. Parties 30. L 12.30-2.30 D 7-9. Closed Mon
& Tue, 2 weeks Jan, 2 weeks Jun. Set L £12.50 Set D £15.20. Access, Visa.*

Milford-on-Sea   South Lawn   66%   £84

Tel 0590 643911   Fax 0590 644820   **H**

Lymington Road Milford-on-Sea Nr Lymington Hampshire SO41 0RF   Map 4 C4

The high proportion of repeat business here says much for the standards of
maintenance, service and hospitality provided by Ernst and Jennifer Barten,
owners since 1971 of this rambling black-and-white former dower house.
Fresh flowers make a colourful show both outside and in the roomy
lounge, and the bedrooms have views over paddocks and garden. No
children under seven. No dogs. *Rooms 24. Garden. Closed Xmas/New Year.
Access, Visa.*

Milton Keynes   Forte Crest   68%   £98

Tel 0908 667722   Fax 0908 674714

H

500 Saxon Gate Milton Keynes Buckinghamshire MK9 2HQ

Map 5 E1

Modern hotel in the centre of town. Banqueting facilities for up to 110, conferences to 150. *Rooms 151. Gymnasium, sauna, solarium, indoor swimming pool, coffee shop (6.30am-10.30pm). Access, Amex, Visa,* 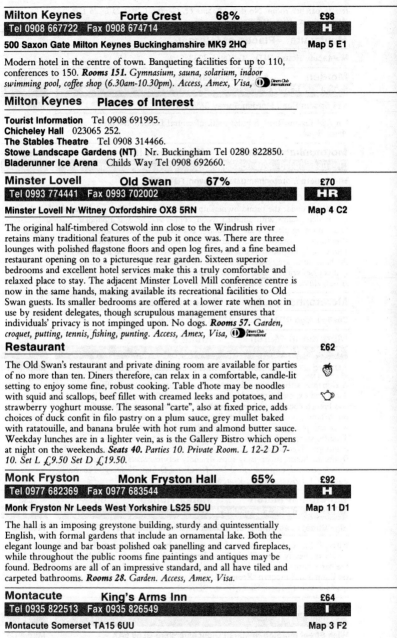 Diners Club International

Milton Keynes   Places of Interest

Tourist Information   Tel 0908 691995.
Chicheley Hall   023065 252.
The Stables Theatre   Tel 0908 314466.
Stowe Landscape Gardens (NT)   Nr. Buckingham Tel 0280 822850.
Bladerunner Ice Arena   Childs Way Tel 0908 692660.

Minster Lovell   Old Swan   67%   £70

Tel 0993 774441   Fax 0993 702002

HR

Minster Lovell Nr Witney Oxfordshire OX8 5RN

Map 4 C2

The original half-timbered Cotswold inn close to the Windrush river retains many traditional features of the pub it once was. There are three lounges with polished flagstone floors and open log fires, and a fine beamed restaurant opening on to a picturesque rear garden. Sixteen superior bedrooms and excellent hotel services make this a truly comfortable and relaxed place to stay. The adjacent Minster Lovell Mill conference centre is now in the same hands, making available its recreational facilities to Old Swan guests. Its smaller bedrooms are offered at a lower rate when not in use by resident delegates, though scrupulous management ensures that individuals' privacy is not impinged upon. No dogs. *Rooms 57. Garden, croquet, putting, tennis, fishing, punting. Access, Amex, Visa,* Diners Club International

Restaurant   £62

The Old Swan's restaurant and private dining room are available for parties of no more than ten. Diners therefore, can relax in a comfortable, candle-lit setting to enjoy some fine, robust cooking. Table d'hote may be noodles with squid and scallops, beef fillet with creamed leeks and potatoes, and strawberry yoghurt mousse. The seasonal "carte", also at fixed price, adds choices of duck confit in filo pastry on a plum sauce, grey mullet baked with ratatouille, and banana brulée with hot rum and almond butter sauce. Weekday lunches are in a lighter vein, as is the Gallery Bistro which opens at night on the weekends. *Seats 40. Parties 10. Private Room. L 12-2 D 7-10. Set L £9.50 Set D £19.50.*

Monk Fryston   Monk Fryston Hall   65%   £92

Tel 0977 682369   Fax 0977 683544

H

Monk Fryston Nr Leeds West Yorkshire LS25 5DU

Map 11 D1

The hall is an imposing greystone building, sturdy and quintessentially English, with formal gardens that include an ornamental lake. Both the elegant lounge and bar boast polished oak panelling and carved fireplaces, while throughout the public rooms fine paintings and antiques may be found. Bedrooms are all of an impressive standard, and all have tiled and carpeted bathrooms. *Rooms 28. Garden. Access, Amex, Visa.*

Montacute   King's Arms Inn   £64

Tel 0935 822513   Fax 0935 826549

I

Montacute Somerset TA15 6UU

Map 3 F2

A 16th-century hamstone inn that was once an ale-house owned by the abbey; today's comfortable little inn offers characterful accommodation in 11 en-suite rooms, one with a four-poster bed. The Windsor room is a relaxing lounge; the Pickwick Bar remains the centre of village life. Follow a relaxing night with a decent buffet-style breakfast. Children stay free in parents' room. No dogs. **Rooms 11.** *Garden. Closed 25 & 26 Dec. Access, Amex, Visa,*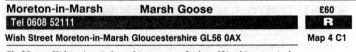

Montacute   Places of Interest

Montacute House (NT)   Tel 0935 823289.

Morden   Forte Travelodge   £40

| Tel 081-640 8227 | **L** |

A24 Epsom Road Morden Surrey SM4 5PH   Map 5 E2

On A24 Epsom Road, 8 miles south of central London. **Rooms 32.** *Access, Amex, Visa.*

Moretonhampstead   White Hart Inn   £63

| Tel 0647 40406   Fax 0647 40565 | **I** |

The Square Moretonhampstead Devon TQ13 8NF   Map 3 D2

Formerly a Georgian posting house, the White Hart offers traditional hospitality under the proud ownership of Peter Morgan. The oak-beamed bar, which gleams with polished wood, copper and brass, is a popular locals' meeting place, while the lounge is a cosy setting for residents' afternoon tea. Bulging walls add character to the bedrooms, which are comfortably furnished in old-fashioned style. New-fashioned additions in the bathrooms are power showers and telephone extensions. There are 15 golf courses within 30 miles. No children under ten. **Rooms 20.** *Garden. Access, Amex, Visa,*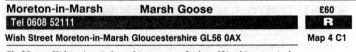

Moretonhamptstead   Places of Interest

Castle Drogo (NT)   Chagford Tel 064743 3306.

Moreton-in-Marsh   Annie's   £60

| Tel 0608 51981 | **R** |

3 Oxford Street Moreton-in-Marsh Gloucestershire GL56 0LA   Map 4 C1

A romantic setting of candle-light and soft music, framed by flagstone floors and exposed Cotswold stonework. David Ellis's self-styled English and French country cooking is without pretension: warm salad of mushrooms, bacon and chicken livers in sherry; roast poussin with lemon sauce and pistachios; oven-roasted salmon with lobster cream sauce. Traditional spotted Dick or wickedly rich rum truffle cake among the puddings. Fixed-price Sunday lunch offer a choice of roasts. Annie herself fronts the house, supervising super-friendly service. **Seats 28.** *Parties 30. Private Room. L Sun only 12-2 D 7-10. Closed D Sun, 27 Jan-10 Feb. Set Sun L £15. Access, Amex, Visa,*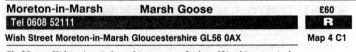

Moreton-in-Marsh   Manor House   66%   £83

| Tel 0608 50501   Fax 0608 51481 | **H** |

High Street Moreton-in-Marsh Gloucestershire GL56 0LJ   Map 4 C1

Parts of this roadside, Cotswold-stone manor house date back to 1545, but others are nearly new. The hall and lounge both have a period feel, while the bar is more modern. Even in the bedrooms there's a choice between traditional and modern. **Rooms 37.** *Garden, putting, indoor swimming pool, spa bath, sauna. Access, Amex, Visa,*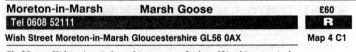

Moreton-in-Marsh   Marsh Goose   £60

| Tel 0608 52111 | **R** |

Wish Street Moreton-in-Marsh Gloucestershire GL56 0AX   Map 4 C1

Chef Sonya Kidney is quietly making a name for herself in this attractively refurbished restaurant that was once a stable block. Bare stonework contrasts happily with elegant Villeroy and Boch china, as does a simple spicy carrot soup with grilled scallops and nuggets of foie gras with radishes, spring onions and orange segments or fillet of beef with morels and Madeira sauce thickened with duck liver parfait. Sonya's style is in a modern mode (marinated salmon with sweet mustard sauce, grilled tuna with tomato jelly, olives and mixed leaves) but never leaves classic concepts far behind. The fixed-price menus change daily, so an excellent dish like jugged hare can appear in season; nevertheless, there is always a good choice (seven or so dishes at each course) and much to excite – right through to the desserts (mincemeat and almond strudel with coconut ice cream, black coffee jelly in a brandy snap basket with butterscotch sauce, clotted cream and caramelised pecans); a good choice of dessert wines is offered by the glass, but at a price. Realistically priced lunch menus include a choice of starters that can also be ordered as light meal dishes, but also extends to à la carte main courses; the same interesting desserts are offered as at dinner. James White apple juices (Bramley, Cox and Russett) feature on the wine list as suitable non-alcoholic accompaniments. *Seats 60. Parties 20. L 12.15-2.30 D 7.30-9.45. Closed D Sun, all Mon. Set Sun L £14.50 Set D £19.90. Access, Visa.*

Moreton-in-Marsh   Redesdale Arms   £50
Tel 0608 50308   Fax 0608 51843   **I**
High Street Moreton-in-Marsh Gloucestershire GL56 0AW   Map 4 C1

Once a stopping point on the Lincoln-Bath coach run, the Redesdale retains some period touches, including flagstones and Queen Anne panelling. Relaxation is easy in the bar and in the cane-furnished conservatory lounge. Bedrooms come in various shapes and sizes; six are in an annexe and three have patios and kitchenettes. *Rooms 17. Garden.Access, Visa.*

Morley   Breadsall Priory   69%   £102
Tel 0332 832235   Fax 0332 833509   **H**
Moor Road Morley Nr Derby Derbyshire DE7 6DL   Map 10 C3

A second 18-hole golf course is now open at this large stone mansion house hotel (just off the A38 to the north of Derby), which is aimed squarely at the conference (up to 150 delegates) and leisure markets. A parquet-floored foyer with stone columns and archways has a period feel, but there is little period atmosphere elsewhere. Both the main building and modern extension bedrooms are uniform in design, but comfortable. No dogs. Country Club Hotels. *Rooms 91. Garden, indoor swimming pool, sauna, solarium, squash, gymnasium, snooker, beautician, two 18-hole golf courses, golf driving range & putting green, tennis, helipad. Access, Amex, Visa,* **(D)** Diners Club International.

Morley   Places of Interest
American Adventure Theme Park   Nr Ilkeston Tel 0773 531521.

Morston   Morston Hall   72% NEW   £120*
Tel &   Fax 0263 741041   **HR**
Morston Holt Norfolk NR25 7AA   Map 6 C1

One of the country's very smallest hotels has instantly established itself as one of Norfolk's very best, and with good reason. Owners Galton and Tracy Blackiston and Justin Fraser are enthusiastic and totally dedicated hosts who will purposefully cross the garden, hoe in hand, to greet arriving guests. Their home is delightfully lived-in, the garden aspect of its day rooms reflected by abundant fresh flowers and floral drapes. The four spacious bedrooms are individually furnished and immaculately kept, the result of careful thought and thoughtful care whereby each used bathrobe or discarded towel is replaced while house guests are at dinner. A first-class breakfast follows a truly restful night. *Half-board terms only. Rooms 4. Access, Amex, Visa.*

Restaurant   ↑   £60

Galton Blackiston's nightly menu offers a choice only at the dessert stage, though immaculate care is taken in the garnishing of ingredients and total balancing of flavours. The four courses might run through local pullet's egg on watercress salad with chive hollandaise, halibut with red pepper, celery and apple coated with mature Cheddar, and roast breast of duck on red and blackcurrant purée; one or other of your hosts may be seen also running through the garden to gather one final herbaceous garnish for the garden gooseberry fool or *coeur à la crème* with summer fruits. Carefully selected wines are sensibly listed by grape variety. No smoking in the dining room; children under 8 are discouraged at dinner. *Seats 30. Parties 30. L 12.30 for 1 D 7.30 for 8. Closed L Mon-Thu, D Sun. Set L £12 Set D £21.*

Mottram St Andrew   Mottram Hall   70%   £140

Tel 0625 828135   Fax 0625 829284   **H**

Mottram St Andrew Prestbury Cheshire SK10 4QT   Map 10 B2

De Vere Hotels' impressive Georgian mansion, adjacent to the A538, stands in 270 acres of mature parkland. Extensive leisure facilities now include a championship golf course and clubhouse. Spacious day rooms in the original Mottram Hall feature restored Adam ceilings and fine panelling. Most of the bedrooms are in newer extensions. *Rooms 133. Garden, indoor swimming pool, spa bath, sauna, solarium, beautician, gymnasium, squash, snooker, games room, tennis, 18-hole golf course. Access, Amex, Visa,*

Moulsford-on-Thames   Beetle & Wedge   67%   £85

Tel 0491 651381   Fax 0491 651376   **HR**

Moulsford-on-Thames Oxfordshire OX10 9JF   Map 5 D2

Once home of Jerome K Jerome (who wrote Three Men in a Boat), Richard and Kate Smith's picturesque Thameside Victorian hotel really is a home from home. Guests, who are treated as personal friends, can relax in comfortable surroundings – in front of a real fire in the cosy lounge, or wallow in old-fashioned cast-iron bath tubs, perhaps with a glass of champagne. The refurbished bedrooms, most overlooking the river, have been tastefully designed with excellent fabrics and furniture and many personal touches from Kate – note the wall stencilling and indulgent bathroom extras. The old beamed Boat House, with its own terrace, serves as the informal bar, and the Watergarden (complete with lily pond) is the perfect summer setting for afternoon tea or salad lunches on fine days. Terrific English breakfasts. *Rooms 10. Garden, croquet, fishing. Access, Amex, Visa,*

Dining Room   ↑   £70

Happily, the dining room does not fall into the trap of so many riverside restaurants by being too chi-chi, rather, its elegant and tranquil setting perfectly matches the understated yet sophisticated cooking of Richard Smith. Always taking advantage of the best possible fresh produce, his dishes actually taste of their ingredients' fine flavours – thinly-sliced baked salmon (cooked on the plate) with a smooth chive butter sauce, a perfectly cooked fillet of red mullet with noodles and squid, or an escalope of tender veal with girolles and sweetbreads. Unfussy vegetables are served crisp, and desserts include a heavenly chocolate and rum truffle cake with coffee parfait glacée, or a more traditional summer pudding and apple and blackcurrant crumble. A selection of farmhouse cheeses is always offered. Three-course Sunday lunches also offer a good choice that might include roast rib of beef with Yorkshire pudding or roast best end of lamb with herb crust and braised endive, as well as a good selection of fish. Kate oversees the first-class service, and is responsible for a sensibly priced and carefully compiled wine list, as well as explaining the restaurant's policy on wine price mark-ups. *Seats 40. Parties 65. Private Room. L 12.30-2 D 7.30-10. Closed 25 Dec. Set Sun L £24.50*

Boathouse Brasserie   £55

The wood-framed, riverside brasserie is more informal than the hotel restaurant, with lower prices to match the setting but with the same emphasis on quality ingredients. The chargrill is put to good use in dishes like calf's kidneys and black pudding with a green herb mustard sauce, whole sea bass with fresh herbs and Pernod, and escalope of halibut with scallops and béarnaise. Seafood and shellfish are always a strong point (Irish oysters, moules marinière à la crème, poached lemon and prawns and chives) alongside ploughman's lunches with good cheeses and interesting salady selections. Tip-top puddings. On fine summer days a few tables are set on the riverside terrace.

Moulton — Black Bull — £56

Tel 0325 377289 — **R**

Moulton Nr Richmond North Yorkshire DL10 6QJ — **Map 15 B5**

Good fresh fish is the foundation of the Black Bull's reputation, nurtured by the Pagendam family for nearly 30 years, that extends far beyond North Yorkshire. Grilled Dover sole, poached salmon with hollandaise sauce, and queenie scallops in garlic butter typify the generally simple style. For meat-eaters there are Aberdeen Angus steaks and the likes of rack of lamb with Provencal herbs. A number of different eating areas include a conservatory (complete with huge grapevine) and one of the original Pullman carriages, vintage 1932, from the *Brighton Belle*. Good-value fixed-price lunch – perhaps Bayonne ham with melon and figs followed by crab-stuffed plaice fillets with hollandaise and chives, and a rice terrine with dried fruit compote. *Seats 100. Parties 30. Private Room. L 12-2 D 7-10.15. Closed Sun (except bar), 23-31 Dec. Set L £11.75. Access, Amex, Visa.*

Moulton — Places of Interest

North Yorkshire County Showground East Cowton Tel 0609 773429.
Catterick Bridge Racecourse Tel 0748 811478.

Mousehole — Lobster Pot — 57% — £73

Tel 0736 731251 Fax 0736 731140 — **H**

Mousehole Nr Penzance Cornwall TR19 6QX — **Map 2 A4**

Perched over the small, bustling harbour, the Lobster Pot scores on character if not on size. Four cottages on either side of a street just one car wide provide neat, recently refurbished accommodation. The lounge, cocktail bar, restaurant and several bedrooms enjoy views over the bustling harbour. Family facilities include rooms with an adjoining bunk bedroom, high tea and baby listening. A 5% service charge is automatically added to all bills. *Rooms 25. Closed 2-31 Jan & Mon-Wed in Feb. Access, Visa.*

Much Birch — Pilgrim Hotel — 64% — £85

Tel 0981 540742 Fax 0981 540620 — **H**

Much Birch Nr Hereford Hereford & Worcester HR2 8HJ — **Map 4 A1**

Set back from the A49, this much extended former rectory stands in four acres of grounds with views over Golden Valley and the Black Mountains. Stone walls, oak furniture and a long stove give character to the bar, and the bedrooms have good-quality furnishings, armchairs and useful desk space. Children under 10 accommodated free in parents' room. *Rooms 20. Garden, 3-hole pitch & putt. Access, Amex, Visa,*

Mudeford — Avonmouth Hotel — 59% — £101

Tel 0202 483434 Fax 0202 479004 — **H**

95 Mudeford Christchurch Dorset BH23 3NT — **Map 4 C4**

Forte Heritage hotel with a private jetty, slipway and moorings at the end of lawns leading down to Christchurch Harbour. Best bedrooms (with a small supplement) have balconies and/or sea views. *Rooms 41. Garden, outdoor swimming pool, games room. Access, Amex, Visa,*

Mullion   Polurrian Hotel   65%   £168*

Tel 0326 240421   Fax 0326 240083   **H**

Mullion Helston Cornwall TR12 7EN   **Map 2 B4**

A large, white-painted hotel in a commanding position atop 300-ft-high cliffs. Its interior decor is in carefully muted colours and there are unparalleled westerly views from both lounge and dining room. Children's amenities are a great draw for family holidays, with an under-7s' playroom in the leisure club, adventure playground in the garden, and safe bathing cove, approached by a winding cliff path; baby-sitting is also available. * Half-board terms only, plus self-catering family apartments. *Rooms 40. Garden, indoor & outdoor swimming pools, sauna, solarium, spa bath, keep-fit equipment, tennis, squash, badminton, putting, sea fishing, boating, snooker, coffee shop (7.30am-10pm). Closed Nov-Mar. Access, Amex, Visa,*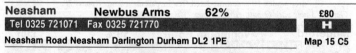

Nantwich   Rookery Hall   79%   £118

Tel 0270 610016   Fax 0270 626027   **HR**

Worleston Nr Nantwich Cheshire CW5 6DQ   **Map 10 B3**

The hotel gained its schloss-style outline in mid-Victorian times, having been built fifty years earlier as a country house. Surrounded by extensive grounds, with some lovely walks by the river, the old Hall retains the spacious reception rooms with character highlighted by moulded ceilings, fine antiques and panelling. Stylish additions of recent years are the Coach House, a self-contained conference centre (for up to 80 delegates) converted from Georgian stables with bedrooms built around the courtyard, and the west wing. All bedrooms are luxuriously furnished and offer fresh flowers, fruit and sherry to greet guests on arrival plus well-designed bathrooms with excellent overhead showers, good toiletries, and smart bathrobes. *Rooms 45. Garden, tennis, croquet, putting, coarse fishing, clay-pigeon shooting, helipad. Access, Amex, Visa,* (D) *Diners Club International*

Restaurant   £88

The cooking is modern, but disciplined, so the results on the plate are invariably successful. Two very different dining rooms, one mahogany-panelled, the other in more traditional country house style, share lovely garden views. Dishes such as ravioli of seafood in an armagnac-flavoured Cornish crab and caviar bisque, and roast quail salad with eggs, wild mushrooms and Puy lentils catch the eye among the starters and best end of Welsh lamb topped with a pesto crust on a bed of braised leeks from the main dishes. A fine wine list (though there are some silly prices) with renowned Burgundy growers, lots of classic Bordeaux and a good selection of half bottles. *Seats 80. Parties 40. Private Room. L 12-1.45 D 7-9.30 (Sat to 10). Set L £16.50 Set D £30.*

Nantwich   Places of Interest

Crewe Tourist Information Centre   Tel 0270 583191
Lyceum Theatre   Heath Street, Crewe Tel 0270 211149.

Neasham   Newbus Arms   62%   £80

Tel 0325 721071   Fax 0325 721770   **H**

Neasham Road Neasham Darlington Durham DL2 1PE   **Map 15 C5**

A pleasant, informal and very friendly establishment, the creeper-clad Newbus Arms dates from the 1780s. Day rooms include a panelled lounge and an attractive bar. Bedrooms are modest with no frills, but are well kept and comfortable; decor is light and unfussy with solid traditional furniture and mainly floral fabrics. Bathrooms are equally simple. Conferences/banqueting for 110/70. Children up to 15 stay free in parents' room. *Rooms 15. Garden, squash. Access, Amex, Visa,* (D) *Diners Club International*

Needham Market Pipps Ford 60% £52 H
Tel 044 979 208 Fax 044 979 561

Needham Market Nr Ipswich Suffolk IP6 8LJ Map 6 C3

Mrs Hackett-Jones welcomes guests personally to her 16th-century
farmhouse in a delightful garden just off the A45/A140 roundabout.
Winter log fires burn in huge inglenooks, and a fine breakfast featuring
home-produced honey, eggs and bread is served in the plant-filled
conservatory. Bedrooms are split between the house and adjacent Stables
Cottage, where two small singles share a shower room. No phones or TV.
No children under 5. No dogs. *Rooms 6. Garden, croquet, outdoor swimming
pool, tennis, coarse fishing. Closed mid Dec-mid Jan. Visa,*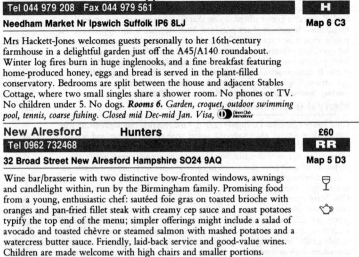

New Alresford Hunters £60 RR
Tel 0962 732468

32 Broad Street New Alresford Hampshire SO24 9AQ Map 5 D3

Wine bar/brasserie with two distinctive bow-fronted windows, awnings
and candlelight within, run by the Birmingham family. Promising food
from a young, enthusiastic chef: sautéed foie gras on toasted brioche with
oranges and pan-fried fillet steak with creamy cep sauce and roast potatoes
typify the top end of the menu; simpler offerings might include a salad of
avocado and toasted chèvre or steamed salmon with mashed potatoes and a
watercress butter sauce. Friendly, laid-back service and good-value wines.
Children are made welcome with high chairs and smaller portions.
*Seats 30. Parties 80. Private Room. L 12-2 D 7-10. Closed D Sun, 24-27
Dec. Access, Visa,*

Rooms £48

Three rooms in an old Georgian building, all with shower and WC en
suite. No phones in rooms. *Rooms 3.*

New Barnet Mims Restaurant £58 R
Tel 081-449 2974

63 East Barnet Road New Barnet Hertfordshire EN4 8RN Map 7 B4

Given an unpromising location, next to a petrol station in a rather dowdy
street, and modest interior decoration, chef Ismail Al-Sersy's refined, skilful
cooking comes as a most agreeable surprise and has attracted a loyal
following – some regulars travelling from quite far afield to dine here. The
minimum price is fixed (for two courses) at both lunch and dinner, with
the former being half the price of the latter. Baked skate with baby fennel
and braised calf's tongue with coriander catch the eye among the starters
followed by the likes of red mullet with cumin and tomato vinaigrette or
braised rabbit with lemon and dill. Friendliness makes up for a certain lack
of polish in the service. *Seats 50. Parties 50. Private Room. L 12-3 D 6.30-
11 (Sun 12-10.30). Closed L Sat, all Mon, 25-30 Dec. Set L £8.50 Set D
£17. Access, Visa,*

New Milton Chewton Glen 89% £206 HR
Tel 0425 275341 Fax 0425 272310

Christchurch Road New Milton Hampshire BH25 6QS Map 4 C4

Martin and Brigitte Skan's magnificent hotel justly enjoys a worldwide
reputation not only for what it offers today, but for consistently
maintaining the highest standards for more than 25 years. Great hotels rely
on the quality of their staff and here they are unquestionably professional,
courteous and efficient, superbly directed by the Skans and managing
director Robin Hutson. Over the years the hotel has evolved into one of
the country's finest, pioneering styles and setting standards that others have
followed, the most recent example being the stunningly designed leisure
and health club whose centrepiece swimming pool epitomises the quality
to be found throughout. It is hard to imagine that the leisure facilities here
can be bettered anywhere else in the UK. The newest garden bedrooms

with balconies and terraces are equally luxurious, complementing those that guests have relaxed in for many years, with high-quality fabrics, beautiful colour schemes, period furniture and bathrooms, complete with fresh flowers; it goes without saying that fruit, sherry, mineral water, home-made biscuits et al are provided. Such elegance is also apparent in the public areas where the tastefully decorated rooms with their exquisite antiques, fine paintings and memorabilia still provide the atmosphere of a large private house. No children under seven. No dogs. *Rooms 58. Garden, indoor & outdoor swimming pools, solarium, sauna, steam room, spa bath, gymnasium, 9-hole golf course, indoor & outdoor tennis, putting, croquet, snooker, valeting, boutique, helipad. Access, Amex, Visa,* ⓓ Diners Club International

Marryat Room Restaurant ★ £98

Chef Pierre Chevillard is highly skilled, handling first-rate ingredients with admirable assurance and producing sauces with subtle flavours and perfect textures. Both lunch and dinner see fixed-price and à la carte menus offered, but lighter dishes like New Forest sausages and creamed potato, carpaccio of fresh tuna marinated in coconut milk or vegetarian risotto of wild mushrooms and Gruyère cheese feature at the former; all menus are refreshingly written in unpretentious English. Dinner extends to show Chevillard's prowess at combining complementary flavours: confit of salted monkfish dressed with truffle oil on a salad of baby spinach leaves, pastry case filled with casserole of snails and celery, and crab soup flavoured with pesto are among the starters. Dover sole may be accurately and simply grilled or served Georges Rebeiz-style with Sevruga caviar; a simple ingredient such as corn-fed chicken breast may be stuffed with foie gras and cooked with a salted thyme crust. Boned Norfolk squab pigeon with bulgar wheat galette and mild garlic sauce; braised leg and sautéed breast of duck with pear and blackcurrants in red wine sauce – exciting dishes, invariably well executed. Vegetarian options are equally good: farmhouse Brie samosas with frisée and sun-dried tomatoes; "nage" of asparagus, morel mushrooms, globe artichokes and tomatoes, or fresh truffle risotto with Parmesan. Even the petits fours served with coffee are a work of art. Cheeses are both English and French. Desserts are tempting to the point of indulgence: iced hazelnut and pistachio parfait with caramel sauce, hot raspberry soufflé, vanilla millefeuille with black cherry sauce, ultra-fine pastry parcel of apple with walnut sauce and more... Summer eating here is delightful, both on an outdoor terrace area and an airy conservatory. Be guided by Gérard Basset, a truly masterful head sommelier, when selecting wines from a quite outstanding, albeit pricy, list – winner of our Cellar of the Year South of England regional award. *Seats 120. Parties 12. Private Room. L 12.30-2 (Sun to 2.30) D 7.30-9.30. Set L £22.50 Set D £39.*

Newark   Forte Travelodge   £40

Tel 0636 703635	**L**
A1 North Muskham Newark Nottinghamshire NG23 6HT	Map 10 C2

Situated on the A1 southbound close to Nottingham, Leicester and Lincoln. *Rooms 30. Access, Amex, Visa.*

Newark-on-Trent   Grange Hotel   58%   £53

Tel 0636 703399 Fax 0636 702328	**H**
73 London Road Newark-on-Trent Nottinghamshire NG24 1RZ	Map 11 D3

An unassuming, family-run Victorian hotel on the edge of town. Homely and friendly. No dogs. *Rooms 15. Garden. Closed Xmas/New Year. Access, Visa.*

Newbury	Chequers Hotel	66%	£106

Tel 0635 38000   Fax 0635 37170   **H**

Oxford Street Newbury Berkshire RG13 1JB   Map 5 D2

A handsome Georgian facade conceals an even older town-centre coaching inn. Today's travellers can be sure of up-to-date standards of comfort and modern amenities. Forte Heritage. *Rooms 56. Garden. Access, Amex, Visa,* ⓘ *Diners Club International*

Newbury	Foley Lodge	71%	£123

Tel 0635 528770   Fax 0635 528398   **H**

Stockcross Newbury Berkshire RG16 8JU   Map 5 D2

Just over a mile from Newbury, off the A4 to Hungerford (take M4 J13), this former Victorian hunting lodge has a cream-coloured exterior with louvre-shuttered windows and is approached via a winding, tree-lined drive. The entrance is through a glass conservatory with black-and-white tiled floor and wicker chairs, overlooking the landscaped gardens. A modern Victorian ambience is cleverly created in both the public rooms and bedrooms by using fringed floral drapes and smart reproduction antiques. There is a high standard of accommodation throughout, with rooms in a new block being equally comfortable. A bright and airy octagonal pagoda is an unusual setting for the bubbling, circular swimming pool. Meeting rooms for up to 250 persons. Children up to the age of 14 free in parents' room; cots, baby-sitting and baby-listening available. *Rooms 69. Garden, indoor swimming pool, coffee shop (7am-11pm). Access, Amex, Visa,* ⓘ *Diners Club International*

Newbury	Hilton National	69%	£127

Tel 0635 529000   Fax 0635 529337   **H**

Pinchington Lane Newbury Berkshire RG14 7HL   Map 5 D2

Modern low-rise hotel one mile south of Newbury with a variety of conference rooms (catering for up to 200) and a leisure complex. Best of the bedrooms are the Plaza rooms, with bigger beds and more accessories than the others; non-smoking rooms available. *Rooms 104. Indoor swimming pool, keep-fit equipment, sauna, solarium, steam room, dinner dance (monthly). Access, Amex, Visa,* ⓘ *Diners Club International*

Newbury	Millwaters	67%	£114

Tel 0635 528838   Fax 0635 523406   **H**

London Road Newbury Berkshire RG13 2BY   Map 5 D2

The rivers Kennet and Lambourn meet in the 8 acres of grounds of this charming hotel on the A4. The Georgian house has rustic extensions containing public rooms and bedrooms that offer homely touches like scatter cushions, fresh fruit and plants. Some bathrooms feature corner or whirlpool baths and one tub is big enough for a whole family (although children under 12 are accommodated only by arrangement). *Rooms 32. Garden, fishing. Access, Amex, Visa,* ⓘ *Diners Club International*

Newbury   Regency Park Hotel   70%   £103

Tel 0635 871555   Fax 0635 871571   **H**

Bowling Green Road Thatcham Newbury Berkshire RG13 3RP   **Map 5 D2**

Standing in its own grounds just five minutes from Newbury (signposted off the A4 Reading road), the original Edwardian house is now rather lost within more modern extensions. Spacious bedrooms offer guests comfortable, carefully planned accommodation in rooms that are light and well appointed. Picture windows in the sun lounge overlook the patio and an ornamental fountain. A separate purpose-built conference centre has rooms for up to 65 people. Keen, helpful management. *Rooms 50. Garden, dinner dance (fortnightly). Access, Amex, Visa,* ◑ *Diners Club International*

Newbury   Stakis Newbury Hotel   67%   £109

Tel 0635 247010   Fax 0635 247077   **H**

Oxford Road Newbury Berkshire RG16 8XY   **Map 5 D2**

Just off junction 13 of the M4, the Stakis Newbury is well designed for business people. Bedrooms feature good desk/work space, and there are four conference/seminar rooms with up-to-date equipment. *Rooms 112. Indoor swimming pool, gymnasium, spa bath, sauna, steam room, solarium, dinner dance (Saturday). Access, Amex, Visa,* ◑ *Diners Club International*

Newbury   Places of Interest

Tourist Information   The Wharf Tel 0635 30267.
Watermill Theatre   Bagnor Tel 0635 45834.
Westridge Open Centre   Tel 0635 253322.
Highclere House   Tel 0635 253210.
Sandham Memorial Chapel (NT)   Burghclere, Nr Newbury Tel 063527 394/292.
Newbury Racecourse   Tel 0635 40015.
Chieveley Showground   Tel 0635 247111.

Newby Bridge   The Swan 61%   £80

Tel 053 95 31681   Fax 053 95 31917   **H**

Newby Bridge Nr Ulverston Cumbria LA12 8NB   **Map 13 D6**

Attractively situated opposite the bridge over the river Leven by Windermere's southern shore, the Swan is comfortable rather than elegant; its former identity as coaching inn has long since ceded to family hotel and fisherman's haunt. In addition to one suite and four de luxe bedrooms with balconies, there are some spacious family rooms and bright, neatly-kept bathrooms throughout. Children's menu. No dogs. Facilities for small conferences of up to 60 delegates. *Rooms 36. Garden, coarse fishing, mooring, coffee shop (11am-11pm), helipad. Closed 3-13 Jan. Access, Amex, Visa,* ◑ *Diners Club International*

Newby Wiske   Solberge Hall   69%   £75

Tel 0609 779191   Fax 0609 780472   **H**

Newby Wiske Nr Northallerton North Yorkshire DL7 9ER   **Map 15 C6**

Leisure and business visitors are both well looked after at the Hall, a country mansion dating from 1824 and set in 16 acres of gardens and woodland. The views are impressive and inside there's a delightful panelled and wood-floored foyer with a blue and white tiled fireplace, a homely lounge and a comfortable bar. Bedrooms are good-sized, some having four-posters, with plenty of thoughtful extras. Children under 16 stay free in parents' room. Banqueting/conference facilities for 100/80. *Rooms 25. Garden, croquet, clay-pigeon shooting. Access, Amex, Visa,* ◑ *Diners Club International*

Newby Wiske   Places of Interest

Thirsk Racecourse Tel 0845 522276.

Newcastle-under-Lyme   Clayton Lodge   60%   £97

Tel 0782 613093   Fax 0782 711893   **H**

Clayton Road Newcastle-under-Lyme Staffordshire ST5 4AF   Map 10 B3

Jarvis-owned conference and meeting hotel with views over the Lyme
Valley. The largest of the several conference rooms can accommodate 270.
Well-equipped bedrooms, where children up to 16 stay free with parents.
On the A519, a mile from the M6 (J15). *Rooms 50. Access, Amex, Visa,*

Newcastle-under-Lyme   Forte Posthouse   60%   £67

Tel 0782 717171   Fax 0782 717138   **H**

Clayton Road Newcastle-under-Lyme Staffordshire ST5 4DL   Map 10 B3

100 yards from junction 15 of the M6, this Posthouse provides decent
modern accommodation, keep-fit amenities and conference facilities for up
to 70. *Rooms 126. Indoor swimming pool, keep-fit equipment, sauna, coffee shop
(10am-6pm). Access, Amex, Visa,*

Newcastle-under-Lyme   Places of Interest

Tourist Information Tel 0782 711964.
New Victoria Theatre Tel 0782 717954.

Newcastle-upon-Tyne   Airport Moat House   62%   £79

Tel 0661 24911   Fax 0661 860157   **H**

Woolsington Newcastle-upon-Tyne Tyne & Wear NE13 8DJ   Map 15 B4

Low-riser just north of the Tyne Tunnel. Conference/banqueting facilities
for 400/350. Children up to the age of 12 are accommodated free in
parents' room. Queens Moat Houses. *Rooms 100. Access, Amex, Visa,*

Newcastle-upon-Tyne   Campanile Hotel   NEW   £36

Tel 081-569 6969 (Head Office)   **L**

Emerson Road Washington Nr Newcastle-upon-Tyne Tyne & Wear   Map 15 B4

Close to A1(M)/A195 intersection. Opening late '92. *Rooms 77. Access,
Amex, Visa,*

Newcastle-upon-Tyne   County Thistle   68%   £98

Tel 091-232 2471   Fax 091-232 1285   **H**

Neville Street Newcastle-upon-Tyne Tyne & Wear NE99 1AH   Map 15 B4

A handsome Victorian building opposite the station. Popular for
conferences (up to 200). Choice of restaurants and bars. Decent bedrooms,
studios being the best equipped. Monthly dinner dance in summer.
Rooms 115. Access, Amex, Visa,

Newcastle-upon-Tyne   Fisherman's Lodge   £82

Tel 091-281 3281   Fax 091-281 6410   **R**

7 Jesmond Dene Jesmond Newcastle-upon-Tyne
Tyne & Wear NE7 7BQ   Map 15 B4

In a deep wooded valley, yet just minutes from the city centre. One menu
offers traditional favourites of the restaurant and another presents more
innovative dishes; the latter is shorter and changes daily with the likes of
pig's trotter with veal sweetbreads, lemon sole and crab soufflé with crab
and ginger sauce. Seafood is the high point, being of top quality and

beautifully cooked, fine examples being lobster, surf'n'turf and a trio of fresh salmon – grilled with a scallop, poached with a herb crust and a lobster and salmon mousse. Also meat and game dishes. The fixed-price lunch menu changes weekly and offers a choice of four dishes per course. Good puds. There's a separate vegetarian menu. No smoking; no children under 10. *Seats 65. Parties 12. Private Room. L 12-2 D 7-11. Closed L Sat, all Sun, Bank Holidays. Set L £16. Access, Amex, Visa,*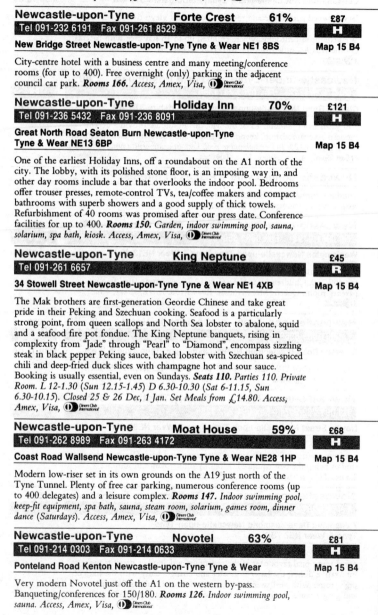

Newcastle-upon-Tyne · Forte Crest · 61% · £87

Tel 091-232 6191   Fax 091-261 8529   **H**

New Bridge Street Newcastle-upon-Tyne Tyne & Wear NE1 8BS   **Map 15 B4**

City-centre hotel with a business centre and many meeting/conference rooms (for up to 400). Free overnight (only) parking in the adjacent council car park. *Rooms 166. Access, Amex, Visa,*

Newcastle-upon-Tyne · Holiday Inn · 70% · £121

Tel 091-236 5432   Fax 091-236 8091   **H**

Great North Road Seaton Burn Newcastle-upon-Tyne Tyne & Wear NE13 6BP   **Map 15 B4**

One of the earliest Holiday Inns, off a roundabout on the A1 north of the city. The lobby, with its polished stone floor, is an imposing way in, and other day rooms include a bar that overlooks the indoor pool. Bedrooms offer trouser presses, remote-control TVs, tea/coffee makers and compact bathrooms with superb showers and a good supply of thick towels. Refurbishment of 40 rooms was promised after our press date. Conference facilities for up to 400. *Rooms 150. Garden, indoor swimming pool, sauna, solarium, spa bath, kiosk. Access, Amex, Visa,*

Newcastle-upon-Tyne · King Neptune · £45

Tel 091-261 6657   **R**

34 Stowell Street Newcastle-upon-Tyne Tyne & Wear NE1 4XB   **Map 15 B4**

The Mak brothers are first-generation Geordie Chinese and take great pride in their Peking and Szechuan cooking. Seafood is a particularly strong point, from queen scallops and North Sea lobster to abalone, squid and a seafood fire pot fondue. The King Neptune banquets, rising in complexity from "Jade" through "Pearl" to "Diamond", encompass sizzling steak in black pepper Peking sauce, baked lobster with Szechuan sea-spiced chili and deep-fried duck slices with champagne hot and sour sauce. Booking is usually essential, even on Sundays. *Seats 110. Parties 110. Private Room. L 12-1.30 (Sun 12.15-1.45) D 6.30-10.30 (Sat 6-11.15, Sun 6.30-10.15). Closed 25 & 26 Dec, 1 Jan. Set Meals from £14.80. Access, Amex, Visa,*

Newcastle-upon-Tyne · Moat House · 59% · £68

Tel 091-262 8989   Fax 091-263 4172   **H**

Coast Road Wallsend Newcastle-upon-Tyne Tyne & Wear NE28 1HP   **Map 15 B4**

Modern low-riser set in its own grounds on the A19 just north of the Tyne Tunnel. Plenty of free car parking, numerous conference rooms (up to 400 delegates) and a leisure complex. *Rooms 147. Indoor swimming pool, keep-fit equipment, spa bath, sauna, steam room, solarium, games room, dinner dance (Saturdays). Access, Amex, Visa,*

Newcastle-upon-Tyne · Novotel · 63% · £81

Tel 091-214 0303   Fax 091-214 0633   **H**

Ponteland Road Kenton Newcastle-upon-Tyne Tyne & Wear   **Map 15 B4**

Very modern Novotel just off the A1 on the western by-pass. Banqueting/conferences for 150/180. *Rooms 126. Indoor swimming pool, sauna. Access, Amex, Visa,*

Newcastle-upon-Tyne   Swallow Hotel   63%

£82

H

Tel 091-232 5025   Fax 091-232 8428

2 Newgate Arcade Newcastle-upon-Tyne Tyne & Wear NE1 5SX

Map 15 B4

City-centre hotel with large car park and panoramic bar.
Banqueting/conferencing facilities for 100/120. Dinner dance (Saturdays).
Ample parking. **Rooms 94.** *Access, Amex, Visa,*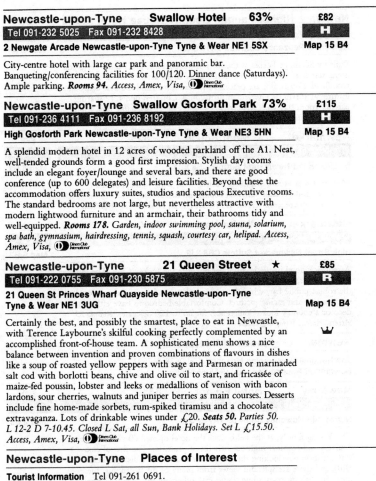

Newcastle-upon-Tyne   Swallow Gosforth Park   73%

£115

H

Tel 091-236 4111   Fax 091-236 8192

High Gosforth Park Newcastle-upon-Tyne Tyne & Wear NE3 5HN

Map 15 B4

A splendid modern hotel in 12 acres of wooded parkland off the A1. Neat,
well-tended grounds form a good first impression. Stylish day rooms
include an elegant foyer/lounge and several bars, and there are good
conference (up to 600 delegates) and leisure facilities. Beyond these the
accommodation offers luxury suites, studios and spacious Executive rooms.
The standard bedrooms are not large, but nevertheless attractive with
modern lightwood furniture and an armchair, their bathrooms tidy and
well-equipped. **Rooms 178.** *Garden, indoor swimming pool, sauna, solarium,
spa bath, gymnasium, hairdressing, tennis, squash, courtesy car, helipad. Access,
Amex, Visa,*

Newcastle-upon-Tyne   21 Queen Street   ★

£85

R

Tel 091-222 0755   Fax 091-230 5875

**21 Queen St Princes Wharf Quayside Newcastle-upon-Tyne
Tyne & Wear NE1 3UG**

Map 15 B4

Certainly the best, and possibly the smartest, place to eat in Newcastle,
with Terence Laybourne's skilful cooking perfectly complemented by an
accomplished front-of-house team. A sophisticated menu shows a nice
balance between invention and proven combinations of flavours in dishes
like a soup of roasted yellow peppers with sage and Parmesan or marinaded
salt cod with borlotti beans, chive and olive oil to start, and fricassée of
maize-fed poussin, lobster and leeks or medallions of venison with bacon
lardons, sour cherries, walnuts and juniper berries as main courses. Desserts
include fine home-made sorbets, rum-spiked tiramisu and a chocolate
extravaganza. Lots of drinkable wines under £20. **Seats 50.** *Parties 50.
L 12-2 D 7-10.45. Closed L Sat, all Sun, Bank Holidays. Set L £15.50.
Access, Amex, Visa,*

Newcastle-upon-Tyne   Places of Interest

Tourist Information   Tel 091-261 0691.
Gulbenkian Studio Theatre   Tel 091-232 9974.
Theatre Royal   Tel 091-232 2061.
Tyne Theatre   Tel 091-232 1551.
Seaton Delaval Hall and Gardens   Whitley Bay Tel 091-237 3040/1493.
Newcastle Cathedral   Tel 091-232 1939.
Newcastle United Football Ground   St. James' Park Tel 091-232 8361.
Newcastle Racecourse   Tel 091-236 2020.
Whitley Bay Ice Rink   Tel 091-252 6240.
Cullercoats Beach 7 *Miles.*
    Museums and Art Galleries
Trinity Maritime Centre   Tel 091-261 4691.
Laing Art Gallery   Tel 091-232 7734.
Hancock Museum   Tel 091-222 7418.
Hunday National Tractor and Farm Museum   Newton Tel 0661 842553.
Cherryburn, Berwick Museum   Mickley, Nr Stocksfield Tel 0661
    843276 *Thomas Berwick Birthplace Trust.*

Newlyn　Higher Faugan Country House Hotel　62%

£70

H

Tel 0736 62076　Fax 0736 51648

Newlyn Nr Penzance Cornwall TR18 5NS

Map 2 A4

Built by Stanhope Forbes at the turn of the century, this sturdy greystone house stands at the end of a winding drive in 10 acres of lawns and woodland. Day rooms are peaceful and traditional, and the best bedrooms feature Victorian or Edwardian furnishings. Children under 12 sharing parents' room stay free. *Rooms 12. Garden, outdoor swimming pool, tennis, putting, solarium, snooker. Access, Amex, Visa,* ⓘ Diners Club International

Newmarket　Moat House　62%

£78

H

Tel 0638 667171　Fax 0638 666533

Moulton Road Newmarket Suffolk CB8 8DY

Map 6 B2

Modern Moat House originally built as flats, with well-appointed bedrooms and versatile function rooms (up to 150 for banquets/conferences). *Rooms 47. Kiosk. Access, Amex, Visa,* ⓘ Diners Club International

Newmarket　White Hart　60%

£62

H

Tel 0638 663051　Fax 0638 667284

High Street Newmarket Suffolk CB8 8JP

Map 6 B2

A redbrick hotel in the High Street opposite the Jockey Club. The lounge bar with its cane furniture, mirrors, plants and muted lights, complements the robust public bar, which has stained-glass panels, deep sofas, a panelled serving area and racing pictures. Comfortable bedrooms have either an art deco or a country look. Conferences for up to 120 delegates. *Rooms 23. Access, Amex, Visa,* ⓘ Diners Club International

Newmarket　Places of Interest

The National Horseracing Museum　Tel 0638 667333.
Newmarket Racecourse　Tel 0638 663482.

Newquay　Hotel Bristol　64%

£80

H

Tel 0637 875181　Fax 0637 879347

Narrowcliff Newquay Cornwall TR7 2PQ

Map 2 B3

The Young family, at the helm since the hotel opened 60 years ago, put courtesy and comfort high on their list of priorities. The Bristol enjoys a fine situation overlooking the sea and the beach (some distance below the cliff), and there are splendid views from many of the bedrooms; these come in various styles, some traditional, others more modern. There are also some self-catering houses. Day rooms provide ample space to relax over a drink, a chat or one of the board games available from reception. Conferences (for up to 180 delegates) and banquets (up to 265) are catered for. *Rooms 76. Indoor swimming pool, sauna, solarium, beauty and hair salon, games room, dinner dance (weekly in summer). Access, Amex, Visa,* ⓘ Diners Club International

Newquay　Hotel Riviera　63%

£78

H

Tel 0637 874251　Fax 0637 850823

Lusty Glaze Road Newquay Cornwall TR7 3AA

Map 2 B3

Popular for family holidays, functions and conferences (for around 150), this well-appointed modern hotel overlooks a lovely stretch of coastline. Three bars, a lounge and a garden provide plenty of space to relax, and in summer there's evening entertainment. Most of the bedrooms enjoy sea views. *Rooms 50. Outdoor swimming pool, games room, snooker, sauna, squash, racquetball, children's playroom and play area. Access, Amex, Visa.*

Newquay   Places of Interest

Trerice (NT)   Tel 0637 875404.

Newton Abbot   Passage House   65%   £85

Tel 0626 55515   Fax 0626 63336   **H**

Hackney Lane Kingsteignton Newton Abbot Devon TQ12 3QH   **Map 3 D3**

The Inn has been a popular watering hole for years, and the modern hotel
next door enjoys panoramic views down the Teign estuary; follow the
Racecourse signs from the A380 to find it. Extended recently to include a
purpose-built spa and conference facilities (for up to 60 delegates), the
marriage is an uneasy one. Contemporary decor, spacious bedrooms and
friendly staff afford the trappings of luxury, but are tempered by ragged
facilities at the original inn and rumbling InterCity encroachments from
the railway line. *Rooms 40. Garden, indoor swimming pool, sauna, steam
room, solarium, spa bath, keep-fit equipment, coarse fishing. Access, Amex, Visa,*
◑ *Diners Club International*

Newton Abbot   Places of Interest

Ugbrooke House   Chudleigh Tel 0626 852179.
Outdoor Seasonal Pool   Tel 0626 61101.
Newton Abbot Racecourse   Tel 0626 53235.
Shaldon Wildlife Trust   Shaldon Tel 0626 872234 *7 miles.*
Teignmouth and Meadfoot Beaches.

Newton Solney   Newton Park   67%   £116

Tel 0283 703568   Fax 0283 703214   **H**

Newton Solney Burton-on-Trent Derbyshire DE15 0SS   **Map 10 C3**

Three miles from the centre of Burton-on-Trent, the 17th-century, creeper-
clad Newton Park enjoys a peaceful setting in landscaped grounds
overlooking the river. Conference facilities for up to 140 delegates. Jarvis
Hotels. *Rooms 51. Garden, dinner dance (monthly). Access, Amex, Visa,*
◑ *Diners Club International*

Nidd   Nidd Hall   77%   £140

Tel 0423 771598   Fax 0423 770931   **H**

Nidd Nr Harrogate North Yorkshire HG3 3BN   **Map 15 B6**

A solid stone mansion set in 45 acres of grounds to the north of Harrogate,
whose true splendour lies in its public areas. An octagonal entrance hall
with exquisite plasterwork, statuary and glass cupola high above leads on
to the even more impressive galleried inner hall which includes red marble
columns and some very fine, intricate wrought-iron work on the stairs
amongst many notable features. A large, elegant drawing room boasts an
ornate plastic ceiling and pair of splendid matching fireplaces. There is also
a mahogany panelled library. Bedrooms are individually decorated in some
style and furnished with a mixture of antique and reproduction pieces plus
comfortable sofas and armchairs. Good bathrooms all have bidets and most
have separate shower cubicles in addition to the bath tub. Main-house
rooms are to be preferred to the 'courtyard' bedrooms. Levels and quality
of service do not quite manage to live up to the surroundings. There are
conference facilities for up to 250 delegates. Children stay free in parents'
room. No dogs. *Rooms 59. Garden, indoor swimming pool, gymnasium, sauna,
solarium, beauty & hair salon, squash, tennis, snooker, boating. Access, Amex,
Visa,* **◑** *Diners Club International*

North Huish   Brookdale House   72%

£95

HR

Tel 0548 82402   Fax 0548 82699

North Huish South Brent Devon TQ10 9NR

Map 3 D3

Hidden down country lanes just minutes from the A38, the secluded
Tudor Gothic-style mansion stands in four acres of gardens and woodland.
Built as a rectory in the mid-19th century, it has a calm and peaceful air.
Proprietors Carol and Charles Trevor-Roper are truly at the heart of things
here, impeccable as hosts and attentive to every detail. The bedrooms are a
delight, individually furnished with a variety of rattan, pine and antiques,
and contain personal touches such as mineral water and flowers, with huge
bath sheets and quality toiletries in the bathrooms. No children under 10.
No dogs. *Rooms 8. Garden, croquet. Closed 3 weeks Jan. Access, Visa.*

Restaurant

£70

Local, additive-free, organically-produced ingredients are used wherever
possible – from free-range quail, guinea fowl and Aylesbury ducks to
naturally-reared pigs that produce the pork and apple sausages for breakfast.
The fixed-price, four-course menu always offers a good choice, perhaps
starting with a filo pastry parcel of scallops and strips of vegetables and
ginger with a vermouth sauce, followed by medallions of pork fillet with
aubergine charlotte and sweet pepper sauce, unpasteurised farmhouse
cheeses and a brandy snap basket of orange yoghurt mousse with poached
rhubarb. Excellent range of pudding wines served by the glass. The wine
list contains a good selection of wines listed, unusually, by character rather
than by growing area. *Seats 24. Parties 16. Private Room. L by arrangement
D 7.15-9.15. Set D £28.*

North Petherton   Walnut Tree Inn   65%

£63

H

Tel 0278 662255   Fax 0278 663946

Fore Street North Petherton Nr Bridgwater Somerset TA6 6QA

Map 3 E2

A carefully modernised 18th-century coaching inn whose conference and
function facilities accommodate up to 90 guests. Business types will
appreciate the good work space in both standard and larger executive
bedrooms, while more romantically inclined weekenders may plump for
one of the spacious four-poster suites. Friendly service from resident
proprietors. Children under 12 stay free in parents' room. *Rooms 28.
Garden, solarium. Closed 25 & 26 Dec. Access, Amex, Visa,* ◑ Diners Club International

North Stifford   Moat House   61%

£103

H

Tel 0375 390909   Fax 0375 390426

High Street North Stifford Nr Grays Essex RM16 1UE

Map 7 B4

Just off one of the inner ring roads, with a good variety of leisure facilities.
The new Garden Suite holds 30 bedrooms and a function room.
Banqueting/conference facilities for 120/150. *Rooms 126. Garden, sauna,
beauty salon, massage, tennis. Closed 27-30 Dec. Access, Amex, Visa,* ◑ Diners Club International

North Stoke   Springs Hotel   70%

£113

H

Tel 0491 36687   Fax 0491 36877

Wallingford Road North Stoke Oxfordshire OX9 6BE

Map 5 D2

The Springs is midway between the M4 (leave at junction 8/9) and the
M40 (exit 6), a mock-Tudor building dating from 1874, which stands in
30 acres of gardens and grounds complete with spring-fed lake. Public areas
include a panelled lounge of old-world appeal and a small cosy bar. Three
separate meeting rooms hold up to 50 theatre-style and 30 for private
dining. Bedrooms generally are spacious and pleasantly appointed with
quality fabrics, smart furniture and subtle colours: best are those with
private balconies. No dogs. *Rooms 37. Garden, outdoor swimming pool,
sauna, tennis, croquet, putting. Access, Amex, Visa,* ◑ Diners Club International

Northampton   Forte Travelodge   £40

Tel 0604 758395

L

A45 Upton Way Northampton Northamptonshire NN5 6EG   Map 5 D1

On the western outskirts of Northampton, on the ring road off the A45.
Located 3 miles from junction 16 on the M1. *Rooms 40. Access, Amex,
Visa.*

Northampton   Holiday Inn Garden Court   65%   £75

Tel 0604 22777   Fax 0604 35454

H

Bedford Road Northampton Northamptonshire NN4 0YF   Map 5 D1

Five minutes from junction 15 of the M1, just off the A45 alongside the
A428, one mile from the town centre. Large bedrooms, competitively
priced – even more so at weekends. Modern meeting rooms for up to 30.
Plenty of free parking. *Rooms 104. Keep-fit equipment, coffee shop
(7am-10.15pm). Access, Amex, Visa,* 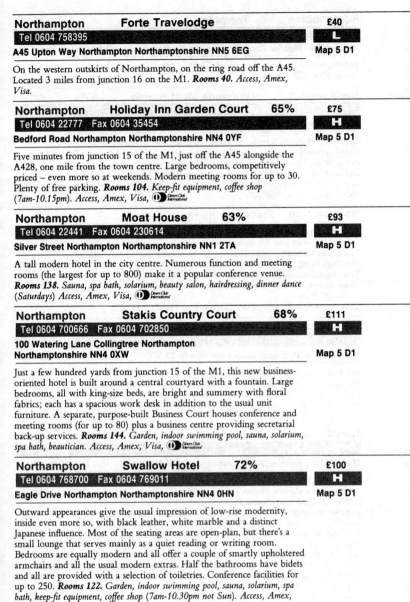 *Diners Club International*

Northampton   Moat House   63%   £93

Tel 0604 22441   Fax 0604 230614

H

Silver Street Northampton Northamptonshire NN1 2TA   Map 5 D1

A tall modern hotel in the city centre. Numerous function and meeting
rooms (the largest for up to 800) make it a popular conference venue.
*Rooms 138. Sauna, spa bath, solarium, beauty salon, hairdressing, dinner dance
(Saturdays) Access, Amex, Visa,* *Diners Club International*

Northampton   Stakis Country Court   68%   £111

Tel 0604 700666   Fax 0604 702850

H

100 Watering Lane Collingtree Northampton
Northamptonshire NN4 0XW   Map 5 D1

Just a few hundred yards from junction 15 of the M1, this new business-
oriented hotel is built around a central courtyard with a fountain. Large
bedrooms, all with king-size beds, are bright and summery with floral
fabrics; each has a spacious work desk in addition to the usual unit
furniture. A separate, purpose-built Business Court houses conference and
meeting rooms (for up to 80) plus a business centre providing secretarial
back-up services. *Rooms 144. Garden, indoor swimming pool, sauna, solarium,
spa bath, beautician. Access, Amex, Visa,* *Diners Club International*

Northampton   Swallow Hotel   72%   £100

Tel 0604 768700   Fax 0604 769011

H

Eagle Drive Northampton Northamptonshire NN4 0HN   Map 5 D1

Outward appearances give the usual impression of low-rise modernity,
inside even more so, with black leather, white marble and a distinct
Japanese influence. Most of the seating areas are open-plan, but there's a
small lounge that serves mainly as a quiet reading or writing room.
Bedrooms are equally modern and all offer a couple of smartly upholstered
armchairs and all the usual modern extras. Half the bathrooms have bidets
and all are provided with a selection of toiletries. Conference facilities for
up to 250. *Rooms 122. Garden, indoor swimming pool, sauna, solarium, spa
bath, keep-fit equipment, coffee shop (7am-10.30pm not Sun). Access, Amex,
Visa,* *Diners Club International*

Northampton   Travel Inn
£42
L

Tel 0604 832340   Fax 0604 831807

Harpole Turn Weedon Road Northampton Northamptonshire NN7 4DD   Map 5 D1

Meeting rooms available, 2 miles off the M1 (J16). *Rooms 51. Access,
Amex, Visa,* (●) Diners Club International

Northampton   Westone Moat House   59%
£77
H

Tel 0604 406262   Fax 0604 415023

Ashley Way Weston Favell Northampton Northamptonshire NN3 3EA   Map 5 D1

Built in 1914 by the founder of Trueform shoes, the Westone is a warm
honey-coloured stone mansion set in its own grounds off the A4500 to the
east of town. Public rooms have some interesting architectural features and
bedrooms are well-equipped with modern comforts. *Rooms 66. Garden,
croquet, putting, sauna, solarium, keep-fit equipment. Closed Xmas/New Year.
Access, Amex, Visa,* (●) Diners Club International

Northampton   Places of Interest

Tourist Information   Tel 0604 22677.
Central Museum and Art Gallery   Guildhall Road Tel 0604 39415.
The Canal Museum   Stoke Bruerne, Nr Northampton Tel 0604 862229.
Wantage Road Cricket Ground   Tel 0604 32917.
Towcester Racecourse   Tel 0327 50969.
Skew Bridge Ski School   Rushden, Nr Wellingborough Tel 0933
59939/53808.
CLA Game Fair Showground   Castle Ashby Tel 071 235 0511.

Northleach   Old Woolhouse
£85
R

Tel 0451 60366

Market Place Northleach Gloucestershire GL54 3EE   Map 4 C2

Just four tables in Jacques and Jenny Astic's tiny restaurant, and they don't
encourage single diners. A short set-price menu offers French cooking of a
high standard, with classic sauces and a largely traditional repertoire.
*Seats 18. Parties 18. D only 8.15-9.30. Closed Sun & Mon, 1 week Xmas.
Set D £30. No credit cards.*

Northleach   Wickens
£55
R

Tel 0451 60421

Market Place Northleach Gloucestershire GL54 3EJ   Map 4 C2

On one side of the square in this very English village stands Chris and
Joanna Wickens's very English restaurant. Exposed Cotswold-stone walls,
low ceilings and subtle lighting create an intimate setting for unfussy,
patriotic cooking: pan-fried black pudding and bacon salad dressed in
walnut oil, casseroled Cotswold lamb in cider with winter vegetables plus
herb and horseradish dumplings; roast duck with a prune and apple
stuffing and port gravy. Joanna both produces the puddings (perhaps
chocolate marquise with an orange cream sauce or sticky toffee pudding)
and handles front of house in an admirably homely fashion. Well-kept
British farmhouse cheeses are served with fruit and celery. Dinner is a
fixed-price, 3- or 4-course affair offering a good choice; menus change
weekly. Helpful notes on a carefully compiled wine list with strength in
the New World; good prices. *Seats 38. Parties 20. L 12.15-1.45
D 7.15-8.45. Closed Sun & Mon, Bank Holidays. Set L £10.50 Set D
£19.75. Access, Amex, Visa.*

Northleach   Places of Interest

Cotswold Countryside Collection   Fossewa Tel 0451 60715.

Northwich   Hartford Hall   63%   £70
Tel 0606 75711   Fax 0606 782285   **H**

School Lane Hartford Northwich Cheshire CW8 1PW   Map 10 B2

Mock-Victorian is the style of the day rooms at this 16th-century gabled
house just off the A556. Good desk space in the bedrooms. Beamed
conference room for up to 30. One of Sottish and Newcastle Brewery's
Mulberry Inns. *Rooms 20. Garden, Access, Amex, Visa,* 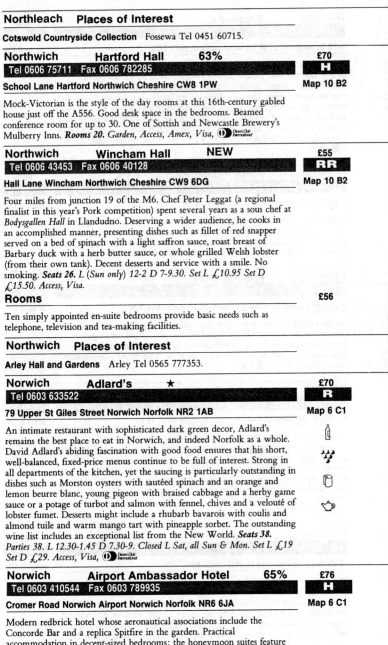 *Diners Club International*

Northwich   Wincham Hall   NEW   £55
Tel 0606 43453   Fax 0606 40128   **RR**

Hall Lane Wincham Northwich Cheshire CW9 6DG   Map 10 B2

Four miles from junction 19 of the M6. Chef Peter Leggat (a regional
finalist in this year's Pork competition) spent several years as a sous chef at
Bodysgallen Hall in Llandudno. Deserving a wider audience, he cooks in
an accomplished manner, presenting dishes such as fillet of red snapper
served on a bed of spinach with a light saffron sauce, roast breast of
Barbary duck with a herb butter sauce, or whole grilled Welsh lobster
(from their own tank). Decent desserts and service with a smile. No
smoking. *Seats 26. L (Sun only) 12-2 D 7-9.30. Set L £10.95 Set D
£15.50. Access, Visa.*

Rooms   £56

Ten simply appointed en-suite bedrooms provide basic needs such as
telephone, television and tea-making facilities.

Northwich   Places of Interest

Arley Hall and Gardens   Arley Tel 0565 777353.

Norwich   Adlard's   ★   £70
Tel 0603 633522   **R**

79 Upper St Giles Street Norwich Norfolk NR2 1AB   Map 6 C1

An intimate restaurant with sophisticated dark green decor, Adlard's
remains the best place to eat in Norwich, and indeed Norfolk as a whole.
David Adlard's abiding fascination with good food ensures that his short,
well-balanced, fixed-price menus continue to be full of interest. Strong in
all departments of the kitchen, yet the saucing is particularly outstanding in
dishes such as Morston oysters with sautéed spinach and an orange and
lemon beurre blanc, young pigeon with braised cabbage and a herby game
sauce or a potage of turbot and salmon with fennel, chives and a velouté of
lobster fumet. Desserts might include a rhubarb bavarois with coulis and
almond tuile and warm mango tart with pineapple sorbet. The outstanding
wine list includes an exceptional list from the New World. *Seats 38.
Parties 38. L 12.30-1.45 D 7.30-9. Closed L Sat, all Sun & Mon. Set L £19
Set D £29. Access, Visa,* *Diners Club International*

Norwich   Airport Ambassador Hotel   65%   £76
Tel 0603 410544   Fax 0603 789935   **H**

Cromer Road Norwich Airport Norwich Norfolk NR6 6JA   Map 6 C1

Modern redbrick hotel whose aeronautical associations include the
Concorde Bar and a replica Spitfire in the garden. Practical
accommodation in decent-sized bedrooms; the honeymoon suites feature
four-poster beds and jacuzzis. Purpose-built facility for conferences and
banquets (up to 450/350). *Rooms 108. Gymnasium, indoor swimming pool,
sauna, steam room, whirlpool bath. Access, Amex, Visa,* *Diners Club International*

Norwich   Brasted's   £60

Tel 0603 625949   **R**

8-10 St Andrew's Hill Norwich Norfolk NR2 1DS   Map 6 C1

A cosy little restaurant tucked away in the old part of the city. Candy-
striped fabrics cover the ceiling and walls to create an intimate effect.
Sensibly short menus testify to careful shopping and thoughtful
combinations. Oriental spices enliven crispy lamb salad; salmon caviar and
smoked salmon sauce accompany the cauliflower terrine – to be followed
perhaps by sauté of monkfish and courgettes or fillet of Welsh rabbit with
a confit of the leg on red cabbage salad. *Seats 22. Parties 22. L 12-2 D 7-10.
Closed Sun, Bank Holidays. Set L from £16.50. Access, Amex, Visa,*
Diners Club International

Norwich   Forte Posthouse   63%   £67

Tel 0603 56431   Fax 0603 506400   **H**

Ipswich Road Norwich Norfolk NR4 6EP   Map 6 C1

In secluded grounds just off the A10 to the south of town. The largest of
several conference rooms can hold up to 100 delegates theatre-style.
*Rooms 113. Garden, indoor swimming pool, sauna, spa bath, solarium,
gymnasium, coffee shop (9am-10.30pm). Access, Amex, Visa,* Diners Club International

Norwich   Friendly Hotel   60%   £78

Tel 0603 741161   Fax 0603 741500   **H**

2 Barnard Road Bowthorpe Norwich Norfolk NR5 9JB   Map 6 C1

Modern hotel 4 miles west of the city centre, on the A47, with modest,
plain accommodation. Fully equipped leisure centre; conference and
banqueting facilities for up to 200. *Rooms 80. Indoor swimming pool,
gymnasium, spa bath, sauna, steam room, solarium, baby-sitting, baby-listening.
Access, Amex, Visa,* Diners Club International

Norwich   Greens Seafood Restaurant   £60

Tel 0603 623733   **R**

82 Upper St Giles Street Norwich Norfolk NR2 1LT   Map 6 C1

Local supplies of fresh fish form the basis of the menu at Dennis
Crompton's popular restaurant with appropriate nautical decor. Whitebait,
prawns with herb butter or fish soup could start the meal, with a grilled
Dover sole or something sauced from the daily specials for a main course.
French apple tart continues the unfussy theme into the sweets, and there are
some well-chosen, well-priced wines to accompany a meal. *Seats 48. Parties
50. L 12.15-2.15 D 7-10.45. Closed L Sat, all Sun & Mon, Bank Holidays,
1 week Xmas. Set L £14 Set D £26. Access, Visa.*

Norwich   Marco's   £80

Tel 0603 624044   **R**

17 Pottergate Norwich Norfolk NR2 1DS   Map 6 C1

23 years now on the same site, Marco Vessalio still greets diners from the
door of his kitchen, the master of all he surveys; his is quintessential
provincial Italian food, steadfastly untrendy, with wonderful ingredients
unfailingly well cooked. Helpfully described on the menu are the regional
origins and constituents of five dishes such as *fettuccine Laguna Nera* (made
with cuttlefish ink) and *cervo alla piemontese* served with Barolo red wine
sauce. Marco's *gelato al miele* is topped with chocolate sauce, and *panettone
alla genovese* served with a glass of Asti Spumante. An extensive Italian
wine list, equally well described, is arranged by colours and regions. No
smoking. *Seats 20. Parties 10. L 12.30-2 D 7.30-10. Closed Sun & Mon,
Bank Holidays. Set L £16. Access, Amex, Visa,* Diners Club International

Norwich   Hotel Nelson   65%   £83

Tel 0603 760260   Fax 0603 620008   **H**

Prince of Wales Road Norwich Norfolk NR1 1DX   **Map 6 C1**

A modern red-brick hotel alongside the river Wensum. Picture windows
in the spacious lounge overlook the water and one of the two bars displays
memorabilia of Nelson's flagship Victory. Best bedrooms include a sitting
area and some have private balconies. The largest of five conference rooms
can accommodate up to 90 delegates. *Rooms 121. Garden. Access, Amex,
Visa,* (I) *Diners Club International*

Norwich   Hotel Norwich   62%   £71

Tel 0603 787260   Fax 0603 400466   **H**

121 Boundary Road Norwich Norfolk NR3 2BA   **Map 6 C1**

Modern redbrick hotel on the outer ring road north-east of the city.
Roomy, well-equipped bedrooms with ample writing surfaces.
Conference/banqueting facilities for 340/300. Sister establishment to the
Hotel Nelson (see entry). *Rooms 108. Indoor swimming pool, spa bath, sauna,
solarium, keep-fit equipment, coffee shop (10am-6pm). Access, Amex, Visa,*
(I) *Diners Club International*

Norwich   Norwich Sport Village Hotel   63%   £69

Tel 0603 788898   Fax 0603 406845   **H**

Drayton High Road Hellesdon Norwich Norfolk NR6 5DU   **Map 6 C1**

Practical, roomy bedrooms are at the centre of a very extensive sports
complex situated just off the outer Norwich ring road on the A1067 to
Fakenham. All the rooms have en-suite facilities, half showers, half tubs.
Sporting facilities are the most impressive feature. They include seven
squash courts and no less than a dozen tennis courts, seven of them indoors.
Hotel guests share the lively open-plan bar, bistro and restaurant with the
other users of the complex. No dogs. Conference facilities for 2000.
*Rooms 55. Garden, indoor swimming pool, steam baths, whirlpool bath, sauna,
solarium, gymnasium, multi-sports hall, aerobics, beauty clinics, hairdressing,
squash, tennis, badminton, snooker, coffee shop (10am-10.30pm). Access, Amex,
Visa,* (I) *Diners Club International*

Norwich   Sprowston Manor   69%   £88

Tel 0603 410871   Fax 0603 423911   **H**

Wroxham Road Sprowston Nr Norwich Norfolk NR7 8RP   **Map 6 C1**

Built around a 16th-century manor house, once the house of the Gurney
banking family, this newly extended hotel by the A115 contains a wealth
of up-to-date facilities. A new leisure club is at the heart of the new
development, resplendent with palms and stone balustrades. Meeting and
conference rooms are kept discreetly apart from the main hotel day rooms,
with a separate entrance to the ballroom (banquets up to 90). Bedrooms
benefit from views of the surrounding parkland, home to the adjacent
Sprowston Golf Club; they also combine stylish fitted furniture and floral
fabrics with up-to-date accessories including mini-bars and wall safes. Older
manor house bedrooms are currently being restyled to a similar standard.
Children under 16 stay free in parents' room. *Rooms 97. Garden, spa bath,
sauna, solarium, beauty salon, gymnasium, outdoor chess, coffee shop
(7.30am-9pm). Access, Amex, Visa,* (I) *Diners Club International*

Norwich   Places of Interest

Tourist Information   Tel 0603 666071.
Norwich Cathedral   Tel 0603 626290
Norwich City Football Ground   Carrow Road Tel 0603 612131.
Fakenham Racecourse   Nr Norwich Tel 0328 862388.
Norfolk Ski Club   Tel 0692 650442.
Royal Norfolk Showground   New Costessey Tel 0603 748931.

Theatres and concert halls
Norwich Puppet Theatre Tel 0603 615564.
Theatre Royal Tel 0603 623562.
Little Theatre Sheringham Tel 0263 822347.
Historic Houses, Castles and Gardens
Blickling Hall (NT) Aylsham Tel 0263 733084.
The Fairhaven Garden Trust South Walsham Tel 060549 449.
Felbrigg Hall (NT) Cromer Tel 026 375 444.
Mannington Hall Saxthorpe Tel 026 387 4175.
Norwich Castle Tel 0603 222222.
Raveningham Hall Gardens Raveningham Tel 050846 206.
Museums and Art Galleries
Colman's Mustard Museum Tel 0603 627889.
Norwich Castle Museum Tel 0603 223624.
Sainsbury Centre for Visual Arts University of East Anglia Tel 0603 592470.

Nottingham   Forte Crest   70%   £87

Tel 0602 470131   Fax 0602 484366   **H**

St James's Street Nottingham Nottinghamshire NG1 6BN   Map 11 D3

Large city-centre hotel whose bedrooms employ bold, up-to-date fabrics,
smart, freestanding furniture and restful colour schemes; higher-floor
rooms have good views. Bathrooms are fully tiled and well lit, with
showers as well as tubs. Public areas include a striking foyer with white
floor tiles and contrasting black woodwork. Conference and function
rooms for up to 450. *Rooms 130. Access, Amex, Visa,*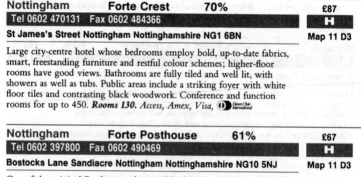

Nottingham   Forte Posthouse   61%   £67

Tel 0602 397800   Fax 0602 490469   **H**

Bostocks Lane Sandiacre Nottingham Nottinghamshire NG10 5NJ   Map 11 D3

One of the original Posthouses, close to J25 of the M1. Last year some
bedrooms were converted to expand the range of meeting rooms, which
now cater for up to 70 delegates. *Rooms 91. Garden, coffee shop (10am-7pm).
Access, Amex, Visa,*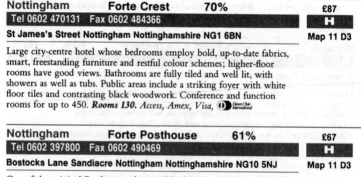

Nottingham   Higoi   £50

Tel 0602 423379   **R**

57 Lenton Boulevard Nottingham Nottinghamshire NG7 2FQ   Map 11 D3

Japanese chef Mr Kato, assisted by his English wife, continues to educate
customers in the delights of his native cooking. Helpful and informative
staff will guide you through the complete range of specialities and menus,
including good-value vegetarian, children's (£3.99) and *dombure* one-pot
lunches and a bento box dinner. Teriyaki, shogoyaki and tempura dinners
are preceded by selected hors d'oeuvre; special set meals for four or more
include up to five main dishes. Kaiseki dinners (served Tues-Thurs only,
for two or more: £28.50 per person) require 2 days' notice. *Seats 35.
Parties 35. Private Room. L 12-2 D 6.30-10.30. Closed L Sun-Tue, all Bank
Holidays. Set L from £5.90 Set D from £15.95. Access, Visa,*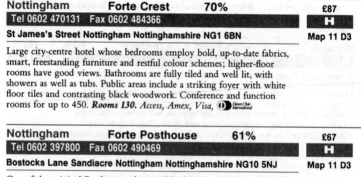

Nottingham   Holiday Inn Garden Court   65%   £70

Tel 0602 500600   Fax 0602 500433   **H**

Castle Marina Park, Nottingham Nottinghamshire NG7 1GX   Map 11 D3

Spacious rooms with large beds are a big plus at this bright modern hotel
off the A6005, near the marina; good value, too – particularly for families,
as the room price covers up to four occupants. *Rooms 100. Access, Amex,
Visa,*

Nottingham   Loch Fyne Oyster Bar   £25

Tel 0602 508481   **R**

17 King Street Nottingham Nottinghamshire   **Map 11 D3**

Produce from its illustrious Scottish progenitor (see under Cairndow,
Argyll, Scotland) appears not to suffer unduly from its overnight journey
south. Loch Fyne oysters and shellfish take their place alongside more
humble offerings of mussel stew and Arbroath smokies, with Cheddar,
Bonnet and Dunsyre Blue to follow. *Also at:* near Peterborough, Elton
Dairy, Elton (0832) 280298. *Seats 40. Parties 20.* Meals 9-8 (*Thu-Sat to
10.30*). *Closed Sun, Bank Holidays. Access, Amex, Visa.*

Nottingham   Moat House   59%   £82

Tel 0602 602621   Fax 0602 691506   **H**

Mansfield Road Nottingham Nottinghamshire NG5 2BT   **Map 11 D3**

A modern hotel to the north of the city centre. The 40 recently
refurbished Executive bedrooms are the ones to ask for.
Conferences/banqueting for up to 200/160. *Rooms 172.* Closed 25 & 26
Dec. Access, Amex, Visa, ⏺ *Diners Club International*

Nottingham   Noble House   £60

Tel 0602 501105   **R**

31 Greyfriar Gate Nottingham Nottinghamshire NG9 1EF   **Map 11 D3**

Friendly and helpful service complemented by stylish, swish black and pink
decor all add to the ambience of this sophisticated Peking-style restaurant.
An extensive menu (including some sixteen 'sizzling' dishes) is based on
good raw materials that are well handled in choices like sweet and sour
fish, fried beef with pickled cabbage, peppered salted scallops or squid, and
lamb with yellow bean sauce. *Seats 80. Parties 12.* L 12-2 D 6-11.30 (*Sun
12-11.30*). *Closed 3 days Xmas. Set L from £6 Set D from £14. Access,
Amex, Visa,* ⏺ *Diners Club International*

Nottingham   Novotel   62%   £70

Tel &   Fax 0602 720106   **H**

Bostocks Lane Long Eaton Nottingham Nottinghamshire NG10 4EP   **Map 11 D3**

Practical, modern accommodation just off junction 25 of the M1. Up to
two children under 16 stay free of charge (inc breakfast) when sharing
their parents' room. Greatly reduced rates at weekends. Conference facilities
for up to 200. *Rooms 112. Garden, outdoor swimming pool, coffee shop
(6am-midnight). Access, Amex, Visa,* ⏺ *Diners Club International*

Nottingham   Ocean City   £40

Tel 0602 410041   Fax 0602 240369   **R**

100-104 Derby Road Nottingham Nottinghamshire NG1 5FB   **Map 11 D3**

A cavernous restaurant just out of the city centre; highly popular with the
local Chinese community, especially for the dim sum on Sundays. The long
Cantonese menu is strong on sizzling dishes and assorted seafood that
includes lobster, crab and monkfish; these are well complemented by some
more unusual and rarely seen dishes on the freshly cooked lunchtime dim
sum selection. *Seats 250. Parties 12. Private Room.* L 12-2.30 (*Mon & Tue to
4*) D 6-12 (*Mon-Fri*), Sat 12-12, Sun 12-10.30. *Closed 25 Dec. Set L from
£5.30 Set D from £11. Access, Amex, Visa,* ⏺ *Diners Club International*

Nottingham   Royal Moat House   70%   £100

Tel 0602 414444   Fax 0602 475667   **H**

Wollaton Street Nottingham Nottinghamshire NG1 5RH   **Map 11 D3**

A long, verdant atrium, off which are the various bars and restaurants, is a
major attraction at this strikingly modern city-centre hotel next to the
Theatre Royal. There is also a sunken lounge off the black marble foyer

and the Penthouse Bar offers panoramic views over the city. Bedroom size varies from roomy doubles and twins to rather more compact singles. Decor is light and contemporary in style and all rooms have a mini-bar and the usual modern comforts. No dogs. Conference facilities for up to 600 delegates. *Rooms 201. Gymnasium, squash, hairdressing, kiosk, coffee shop (10am-6pm). Access, Amex, Visa,*

Nottingham · Rutland Square Hotel · 72% · £98
Tel 0602 411114   Fax 0602 410014
HR

St James Street Nottingham Nottinghamshire NG1 6FJ — Map 11 D3

The impressive, city-centre Rutland Square hotel was, unusually, converted from a warehouse into a quality hotel. Its day rooms have an elegant, contemporary feel. The bright, impressive foyer features a marble-tiled floor and a smart, if somewhat cramped, lounge area with glass roof adjoins the clubby bar. Bedrooms are quite small but are tastefully and stylishly appointed with limed oak units and harmonious fabrics. The white marble-tiled bathrooms are also well equipped, with powerful showers and well-lit mirrors. Conference and banqueting facilities for 200/140. Children up to the age of 5 free in parents' room. *Rooms 104. Access, Amex, Visa,*

Elliott's Restaurant — £50

Unadventurous menu – from trio of melon pearls to steamed salmon, profiteroles and Cheddar cheese – given a lift by a few attempts at modern cooking – mixed seafood broth, tandoori chicken salad, breast of chicken filled with avocado and wild mushroom mousse and accompanied by smoked bacon and port wine sauce. Simpler offerings from the chargrill are probably the best bet. Mixed fare with mixed results. *Seats 84. Parties 20. Private Room. L 12.30-2 (Sun to 3) D 7-10 (Sun to 9.30). Closed L Sat, 25 & 26 Dec, 1 Jan.*

Nottingham · Sonny's · £50
Tel 0602 473041
R

3 Carlton Street Hockley Nottingham Nottinghamshire NG1 1NL — Map 11 D3

Plenty of fresh fish (chargrilled salmon with salsa verde) and interesting vegetarian options (steamed mushroom pudding with onion gravy) bring a refreshing touch of Cajun-influenced French-American cooking to Nottingham. Sensibly priced dishes, mainly based round the chargrill, are capably cooked. Smart but informal atmosphere; friendly service. *Seats 65. Parties 30. L 12-2.30 D 7-10.30 (Fri & Sat to 11). Closed Sun, Bank Holidays. Set L £9.50/£12.50 Set D £12.50. Access, Visa.*

Nottingham · Stakis Victoria Hotel · 62% · £69
Tel 0602 419561   Fax 0602 484736
H

Milton Street Nottingham Nottinghamshire NG1 3PZ — Map 11 D3

19th-century Edwardian building in a central position. Accommodation ranges from singles to family rooms and suites. Nine conference rooms handle from 6 to 200 delegates. *Rooms 166. Access, Amex, Visa,*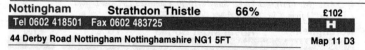

Nottingham · Strathdon Thistle · 66% · £102
Tel 0602 418501   Fax 0602 483725
H

44 Derby Road Nottingham Nottinghamshire NG1 5FT — Map 11 D3

Neat, practical bedrooms and stylish day rooms in a modern hotel on the edge of the city centre, directly opposite the Albert Hall conference (up to 650 delegates) and exhibition centre and Playhouse theatre. Banqueting in the hotel for up to 150. Choice of bars and 24hr room service. Children up to 14 free in their parents' room. *Rooms 69. Access, Amex, Visa,*

Nottingham   Places of Interest

Tourist Information Tel 0602 470661.
Nottingham Playhouse Tel 0602 419419.
Theatre Royal Tel 0602 482626.
Newstead Abbey Tel 0623 793557 *Home of the poet Byron.*
Wollaton Hall Tel 0602 281333/281130.
Nottingham Forest Football Ground City Ground Tel 0602 822202.
Notts County Football Ground Meadow Lane Tel 0602 861155.
Holme Pierrepoint National Water Sports Centre Adbolton Lane Tel 0602 821212.
Nottingham Racecourse Tel 0602 580620.
Nottingham Ice Stadium Tel 0602 484526.
Nottingham Sutton Centre Ice Rink Sutton-in-Ashfield, Nr Nottingham. Tel 0623 554554.
Carlton Forum Ski Slope Tel 0602 872333.
  Museums and Art Galleries
D H Lawrence Birthplace Museum Tel 0773 763312.
The Lace Centre Nottingham Tel 0602 413539.
Museum of Costume and Textiles Tel 0602 483504.
Nottingham Castle Museum Tel 0602 483504.

Nuteaton	Forte Travelodge	£40
		L

Tel 0203 382541

A444 Bedworth Nuneaton Coventry Warwickshire CV12 0BN   Map 10 C4

On the A444 in close proximity to junction 3 of the M6 and NEC.
Rooms 40. *Access, Amex, Visa.*

Nuneaton	Travel Inn	£42
		L

Tel 0203 343584   Fax 0203 327156

Coventry Road Nuneaton Warwickshire CV10 7PJ   Map 10 C4

Situated 20 minutes drive from Birmingham International Airport with conference facilities available. ***Rooms 30.*** *Access, Amex, Visa,*

Nutfield	Nutfield Priory	70%	£114
			H

Tel 0737 822072   Fax 0737 823321

Nutfield Redhill Surrey RH1 4EN   Map 5 F3

Ten minutes from J6 & 8 of the M25 (8 miles from Gatwick Airport), built in high Victorian Gothic style by an MP in 1872, the Priory stands on a ridge enjoying panoramic views across the Surrey and Sussex countryside. Roomy public areas boast fine architectural features including a stone-vaulted cloister restaurant, high stained-glass windows, a panelled library and even an old pipe organ in the galleried grand hall. Bedrooms (nine of which were added recently) are individually decorated in some style with matching fabrics, often with elaborate bedhead drapes, and freestanding furniture varying from oak or yew to rattan. Extras include mineral water, fresh fruit and room safes. Beds are turned down at night; room service, although available, is deliberately not advertised (indicative of the management style). Smart bathrooms are decorated to match individual bedrooms. Conferences (of up to 60 delegates) are an important part of the business, with executives' leisure time well catered for by the Fredericks sports complex. Supervised crèche during weekdays; cots and baby-sitting available. No dogs. ***Rooms 52.*** *Garden, indoor swimming pool, sauna, solarium, spa bath, steam room, gymnasium, beauty salon, badminton, squash, snooker, croquet. Access, Amex, Visa,*

Oakham   Barnsdale Lodge   65%

£70

H

Tel 0572 724678   Fax 0572 724961

The Avenue Rutland Water Nr Oakham Leicestershire LE15 8AB

Map 11 E3

Converted from a 16th-century farmhouse and outbuildings, furnished with practical antiques and period touches from the Edwardian age, like quilted eiderdowns. A flagstone-floored bar has pastel yellow walls and solid oak furniture, while a small lounge has more prints and ornaments from the era. Bedrooms vary from one with a four-poster and views over Rutland Water to five single rooms with just shower/WC. Alongside the A606, two miles east of Oakham. Three conference rooms cater for up to 80. *Rooms 17. Access, Amex, Visa,* 🌑 *Diners Club International*

Oakham   Hambleton Hall   84%

£120

HR

Tel 0572 756991   Fax 0572 724721

Hambleton Nr Oakham Leicestershire LE15 8TH

Map 11 E3

At the forefront of country house hotels since its creation in 1979, Tim and Stefa Hart's elegant and imposing Victorian house is a haven of quiet luxury, but at the same time with the feel of a private home where customers are welcomed and treated as old friends. One mile east of Oakham on the A606, signposted Hambleton village, the setting is spectacular, atop mature and terraced grounds that lead down to Rutland Water. The lovely gardens provide many of the blooms that Anne Taylor blends into magnificent flower arrangements throughout the hotel with the grandest of all occupying pride of place in the entrance hall below the fine oak staircase. Elegant day rooms include the drawing room with beautiful views, fine drapes, an ornately painted ceiling, antiques, pictures, an open fire, and the refurbished bar with its fine inglenook fireplace. Nina Campbell, the celebrated interior designer, masterminded the decoration of the house at the outset and continues to lend her ideas, illustrated by the luxurious bedrooms furnished with antiques and quality fabrics with an acute eye for detail. Guests want for nothing – remote-control TV, portable radio, home-made biscuits, mineral water, books and magazines, and sumptuous bathrooms, each with a large deep bath, jet shower, bidet, Molton Brown toiletries and huge towels and bathrobes that pamper to the full. Beds are turned down at night, linen and dirty towels changed – an example of caring and efficient service carried out by enthusiastic staff under the watchful eye of general manager Jeffrey Crockett. Meeting room facilities for up to 30. *Rooms 15. Garden, outdoor swimming pool, tennis. Access, Visa.*

Restaurant   ★ ↑

£70

If illustration were needed that our top chefs are getting younger, Aaron Patterson, who succeeds Brian Baker and Nick Gill, both previous stars here, is not yet 25. Upholding the Hambleton tradition of outstanding cooking, Aaron first trained at the hotel, followed by stints with Blanc, Mosimann, and Koffmann (have any top British chefs not learnt from these masters?) and he leads an equally young and committed kitchen brigade that really does achieve what it sets out to. Two dining rooms, beautifully done out in shades of cream, offer sensational food, polished service, comfort, refinement and superb views. The à la carte menu is short, but always includes Hambleton's new speciality: honey-roasted Gressingham duck on a bed of dried lime, orange, ginger and lemon grass (for two). As an alternative to the daily carte, a four-course £40 set menu might offer a terrine of locally farmed lamb served with a tomato chutney, marinated fennel and a saffron vinaigrette, a slice of gently steamed wild salmon, a selection of British, French and Irish cheeses served with walnut bread, and a caramelised lemon tart with poached pears and red wine sauce. Though the restaurant offers fresh fish daily, it relies on what the fishmonger has, but on Thursdays it makes its own trip to Billingsgate, so that's the night for specialities. Excellent wine list includes three pages listing 30 wines that are drinking especially well, categorised by price.

*Seats 50. Parties 60. Private Room. L 12-1.45 D 7-9.30. Set L from £19.50
Set D £39.50.*

Oakham   Whipper-In Hotel   70%   £80

Tel 0572 756971   Fax 0572 757759   **H**

Market Place Oakham Rutland Leicestershire LE15 6DT   Map 11 E3

Standing in the market square of Rutland's old county town, this relaxed,
rural hotel dates back to the 17th century. A flagstone-floored foyer leads
through to a low-beamed bar-lounge that is popular with the locals.
Bedrooms, two of which boast four-poster beds, are neat and individually
decorated with comfortable seating areas and a few antiques. Children up
to 14 free in parents' room. Meeting rooms for up to 50. Sister hotel to the
Royal Oak in Sevenoaks, Kent. **Rooms 25.** *Access, Visa,* **(D)** Diners Club International

Odiham   George Hotel   £68

Tel 0256 702081   Fax 0256 704213   **I**

High Street Odiham Nr Basingstoke Hampshire RG25 1LP   Map 5 D3

First granted a licence in 1540, the George has kept a good deal of its
period character. Timber framing can be seen throughout, and in the Oak
Room – a popular place for afternoon tea or private parties – the wattle
and daub walls are exposed. The oak-panelled, flagstone-floored restaurant
was at one time an assize court. Main-house bedrooms have creaking floors,
beams and antiques, while rooms in the converted barn and coach house
are modern behind original exteriors. One mile from the M3 (junction 5).
Rooms 18. *Garden. Access, Amex, Visa,* **(D)** Diners Club International

Okehampton   Forte Travelodge   £40

Tel 0837 52124   **L**

A30 Sourton Cross Nr Okehampton Devon EX20 4LY   Map 3 D2

On the A30, 4 miles west of Okehampton. 22 miles north of Plymouth.
Rooms 32. *Access, Amex, Visa.*

Old Burghclere Dew Pond   £70

Tel 0635 27408   **R**

Old Burghclere Newbury Berkshire RG15 9LH   Map 5 D3

At the foot of Watership Down, six miles south of Newbury, off the A34.
The feeling of dining in someone's front room is inescapable as the
Marshall and Roberts families cook and serve in their 16th-century
extended cottage. Careful cooking from Keith Marshall with few frills or
spills on a fixed-price, 3-course menu with dishes like twice-baked soufflé
with wild mushrooms, trio of salmon (marinated, mousse and poached),
feuilleté of lightly curried mussels with asparagus, roast partridge with
glazed baby onions, smoked bacon and savoy cabbage, and corn-fed
chicken breast with leek purée and Madeira sauce are served in sensible
portions with clear flavours. Straightforward desserts (crème brulée, bread-
and-butter pudding) and home-made petits fours served with Colombian
coffee. The wine list has been improved in the last year and now includes
several wines at £15 or under and a good selection of half bottles and
New World wines. **Seats 40.** *Parties 50. L 12-2 D 7-10. Closed Sun & Mon,
2 weeks Jan, 2 weeks Aug. Set L £19.50 Set D £23. Access, Visa.*

Old Harlow   Travel Inn

£42

L

Tel 0279 442545   Fax 0279 452169

Cambridge Road Old Harlow Essex CM20 2EP

Map 7 B4

Pretty riverside location, 15 miles from Stanstead Airport. *Rooms 38.*
Access, Amex, Visa,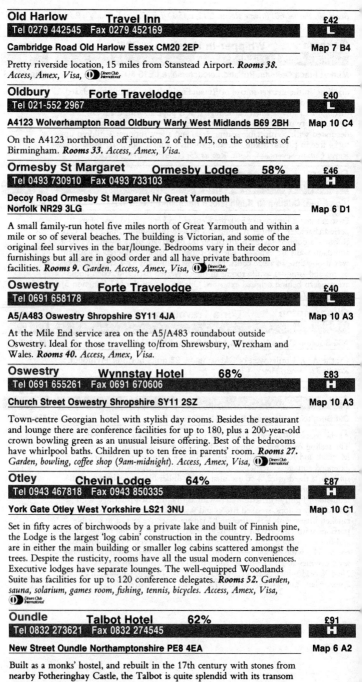

Oldbury   Forte Travelodge

£40

L

Tel 021-552 2967

A4123 Wolverhampton Road Oldbury Warly West Midlands B69 2BH

Map 10 C4

On the A4123 northbound off junction 2 of the M5, on the outskirts of
Birmingham. *Rooms 33. Access, Amex, Visa.*

Ormesby St Margaret   Ormesby Lodge   58%

£46

H

Tel 0493 730910   Fax 0493 733103

**Decoy Road Ormesby St Margaret Nr Great Yarmouth
Norfolk NR29 3LG**

Map 6 D1

A small family-run hotel five miles north of Great Yarmouth and within a
mile or so of several beaches. The building is Victorian, and some of the
original feel survives in the bar/lounge. Bedrooms vary in their decor and
furnishings but all are in good order and all have private bathroom
facilities. *Rooms 9. Garden. Access, Amex, Visa,*

Oswestry   Forte Travelodge

£40

L

Tel 0691 658178

A5/A483 Oswestry Shropshire SY11 4JA

Map 10 A3

At the Mile End service area on the A5/A483 roundabout outside
Oswestry. Ideal for those travelling to/from Shrewsbury, Wrexham and
Wales. *Rooms 40. Access, Amex, Visa.*

Oswestry   Wynnstay Hotel   68%

£83

H

Tel 0691 655261   Fax 0691 670606

Church Street Oswestry Shropshire SY11 2SZ

Map 10 A3

Town-centre Georgian hotel with stylish day rooms. Besides the restaurant
and lounge there are conference facilities for up to 180, plus a 200-year-old
crown bowling green as an unusual leisure offering. Best of the bedrooms
have whirlpool baths. Children up to ten free in parents' room. *Rooms 27.*
Garden, bowling, coffee shop (9am-midnight). Access, Amex, Visa,

Otley   Chevin Lodge   64%

£87

H

Tel 0943 467818   Fax 0943 850335

York Gate Otley West Yorkshire LS21 3NU

Map 10 C1

Set in fifty acres of birchwoods by a private lake and built of Finnish pine,
the Lodge is the largest 'log cabin' construction in the country. Bedrooms
are in either the main building or smaller log cabins scattered amongst the
trees. Despite the rusticity, rooms have all the usual modern conveniences.
Executive lodges have separate lounges. The well-equipped Woodlands
Suite has facilities for up to 120 conference delegates. *Rooms 52. Garden,*
sauna, solarium, games room, fishing, tennis, bicycles. Access, Amex, Visa,

Oundle   Talbot Hotel   62%

£91

H

Tel 0832 273621   Fax 0832 274545

New Street Oundle Northamptonshire PE8 4EA

Map 6 A2

Built as a monks' hostel, and rebuilt in the 17th century with stones from
nearby Fotheringhay Castle, the Talbot is quite splendid with its transom
windows and bell-capped gables. Inside is the very staircase descended by
Mary Queen of Scots on the day of her execution. The best bedrooms

enjoy the best garden views. Conference/banqueting facilities for up to 100.
Forte Heritage. **Rooms 40.** *Garden. Access, Amex, Visa,* (D) *Diners Club International*

Oxford	Al-Shami	£30
Tel 0865 310066		**R**
25 Walton Crescent Oxford Oxfordshire OX1 2JH		Map 5 D2

Between Somerville and Worcester Colleges, a Lebanese restaurant open
long hours serving authentic dishes including charcoal grills of lamb,
chicken and minced meat and their usual wide range of hot and cold hors
d'oeuvre. The short wine list includes four vintages from Chateau Musar.
Seats 70. *Meals 12-12.* (D) *Diners Club International*

Oxford	Bath Place Hotel & Restaurant	£65
Tel 0865 791812 Fax 0865 791834		**RR**
4 & 5 Bath Place Holywell Street Oxford Oxfordshire OX1 3SU		Map 5 D2

Down a cobbled courtyard, off Holywell Street, in the oldest part of
Oxford, is this cosy clutter of 17th-century cottages run by the Fawsitt
family. The style of cooking is light (pan-fried veal with mushrooms in a
Madeira-scented jus) with modern touches (wood pigeon salad dressed in
balsamic vinegar), competitively priced and served in an unpretentious
manner. Three-course Sunday lunches are popular and offer a choice of
four dishes at each course; a smaller choice is offered at weekday lunches.
Dinners see a short à la carte or fixed-price, three-choice-per-course menus.
Desserts are expensive but can be involved – like a roast conference pear in
a lime sorbet-lined feuilleté case accompanied by a ginger-scented crème
anglaise. All non-smoking. Inexpensive wines on a short list. **Seats 35.**
*L 12-2 D 7-10 (Fri & Sat to 10.30). Closed L Tue, D Sun, all Mon. Set L
£12.95 (Sun £15.50) Set D £21.95. Access, Amex, Visa,* (D) *Diners Club International*

Rooms   £99

More a restaurant with rooms than a hotel, because facilities are lacking.
Small bedrooms, but neat and smartly furnished with useful accessories to
justify the price; day rooms are almost non-existent, with both the tiny
residents' lounge and bar doubling up for use by the restaurant's patrons.
Rooms 10.

Oxford	Browns	£30
Tel 0865 511995 Fax 0865 52347		**R**
5-11 Woodstock Road Oxford Oxfordshire OX2 6HA		Map 5 D2

All-day value-for-money eating in one of Oxford's most popular
restaurants. Spaghetti, salads, savoury pies, steaks, burgers and hot
sandwiches are the basis of the menu, the last including double egg and
bacon, club and vegetarian. Lots of puddings, late-morning breakfasts,
traditional teas and a children's menu. **Seats 250.** *Parties 50. Private Room.
Meals 11am-11.30pm (Sun from 12). Access, Visa.*

Oxford	Cherwell Boathouse	£44
Tel 0865 52746 Fax 0865 391459		**R**
Bardwell Road Oxford Oxfordshire OX2 6SR		Map 5 D2

Park your car or moor your punt, and enjoy a leisurely meal in the
friendly surroundings of a converted boathouse on the river Cherwell. The
three-course menu changes weekly and the starters and mains always
include a dish for vegetarians. Typical choices run from courgette soup and
mussels in cream and wine to mustard-sauced mullet, grilled pigeons and
vegetable Wellington. Sticky toffee pudding is a regular favourite dessert,
alongside the likes of good British cheeses and home-made ice creams. The
food is generally less remarkable than the wine list which still offers class
bottles at cheap prices, so take the opportunity to drink a better-than-
average bottle or two! **Seats 50.** *Parties 50. L 12-2 D 7-10 (Sat to 10.30).
Closed L in winter, D Sun & Mon, Bank Holidays, Xmas. Set D from £15.
Access, Amex, Visa,* (D) *Diners Club International*

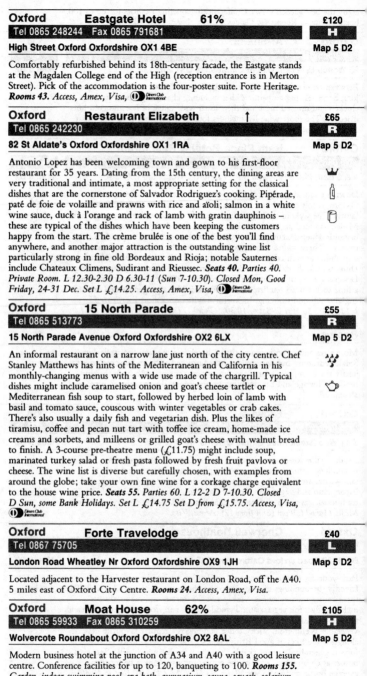

Oxford	Eastgate Hotel	61%	£120

Tel 0865 248244   Fax 0865 791681   **H**

High Street Oxford Oxfordshire OX1 4BE   Map 5 D2

Comfortably refurbished behind its 18th-century facade, the Eastgate stands
at the Magdalen College end of the High (reception entrance is in Merton
Street). Pick of the accommodation is the four-poster suite. Forte Heritage.
Rooms 43. Access, Amex, Visa, ◉ Diners Club International

Oxford	Restaurant Elizabeth	↑	£65

Tel 0865 242230   **R**

82 St Aldate's Oxford Oxfordshire OX1 1RA   Map 5 D2

Antonio Lopez has been welcoming town and gown to his first-floor
restaurant for 35 years. Dating from the 15th century, the dining areas are
very traditional and intimate, a most appropriate setting for the classical
dishes that are the cornerstone of Salvador Rodriguez's cooking. Pipérade,
paté de foie de volaille and prawns with rice and aïoli; salmon in a white
wine sauce, duck à l'orange and rack of lamb with gratin dauphinois –
these are typical of the dishes which have been keeping the customers
happy from the start. The crème brulée is one of the best you'll find
anywhere, and another major attraction is the outstanding wine list
particularly strong in fine old Bordeaux and Rioja; notable Sauternes
include Chateaux Climens, Sudirant and Rieussec. *Seats 40. Parties 40.
Private Room. L 12.30-2.30 D 6.30-11 (Sun 7-10.30). Closed Mon, Good
Friday, 24-31 Dec. Set L £14.25. Access, Amex, Visa,* ◉ Diners Club International

Oxford	15 North Parade		£55

Tel 0865 513773   **R**

15 North Parade Avenue Oxford Oxfordshire OX2 6LX   Map 5 D2

An informal restaurant on a narrow lane just north of the city centre. Chef
Stanley Matthews has hints of the Mediterranean and California in his
monthly-changing menus with a wide use made of the chargrill. Typical
dishes might include caramelised onion and goat's cheese tartlet or
Mediterranean fish soup to start, followed by herbed loin of lamb with
basil and tomato sauce, couscous with winter vegetables or crab cakes.
There's also usually a daily fish and vegetarian dish. Plus the likes of
tiramisu, coffee and pecan nut tart with toffee ice cream, home-made ice
creams and sorbets, and milleens or grilled goat's cheese with walnut bread
to finish. A 3-course pre-theatre menu (£11.75) might include soup,
marinated turkey salad or fresh pasta followed by fresh fruit pavlova or
cheese. The wine list is diverse but carefully chosen, with examples from
around the globe; take your own fine wine for a corkage charge equivalent
to the house wine price. *Seats 55. Parties 60. L 12-2 D 7-10.30. Closed
D Sun, some Bank Holidays. Set L £14.75 Set D from £15.75. Access, Visa,*
◉ Diners Club International

Oxford	Forte Travelodge		£40

Tel 0867 75705   **L**

London Road Wheatley Nr Oxford Oxfordshire OX9 1JH   Map 5 D2

Located adjacent to the Harvester restaurant on London Road, off the A40.
5 miles east of Oxford City Centre. *Rooms 24. Access, Amex, Visa.*

Oxford	Moat House	62%	£105

Tel 0865 59933   Fax 0865 310259   **H**

Wolvercote Roundabout Oxford Oxfordshire OX2 8AL   Map 5 D2

Modern business hotel at the junction of A34 and A40 with a good leisure
centre. Conference facilities for up to 120, banqueting to 100. *Rooms 155.
Garden, indoor swimming pool, spa bath, gymnasium, sauna, squash, solarium,
snooker, putting, coffee shop (7am-11pm). Closed Xmas/New Year. Access,
Amex, Visa,* ◉ Diners Club International

Oxford   Munchy Munchy   £30

Tel 0865 245710   **R**

6 Park End Street Oxford Oxfordshire OX1 1HH   Map 5 D2

Tony and Ethel Ow's Indonesian restaurant is long established and now
well known, making booking almost essential. Ethel prepares a short (just
seven or so dishes), oft-changing menu in an open-plan kitchen, offering
dishes like spicy lamb with celery seeds, paprika, lemon grass, lemon balm,
mango purée and sour cream or king prawns with poppy seeds, fenugreek,
fennel seeds, cinnamon, fresh turmeric, lemon grass in coconut milk and
chopped cashew nuts. Spicy, but seriously nicey and not particularly pricy.
*Seats 60. Parties 10. L 12-2 D 5.30-10. Closed Sun & Mon, Bank Holidays,
3 weeks Aug/Sep, 3 weeks Xmas. No credit cards.*

Oxford   Old Parsonage   70%   £105

Tel 0865 310210   Fax 0865 311262   **H**

1 Banbury Road Oxford Oxfordshire OX2 6NN   Map 5 D2

At the city end of Banbury Road, the extended Old Parsonage dates from
1660 and underwent a major transformation in order to open as a quality
hotel a couple of years ago. Great style and taste have been employed in its
refurbishment, creating an effect easy on the eye. Bedrooms, though not
large, are stylishly appointed with striking soft furnishings, muted colours
and harmonious fittings. Stunning marble-fitted bathrooms have two
showers, soft towels, fine toiletries and good lighting. A clubby bar has
walls hung with hundreds of pictures and there's a small lounge. Young,
efficient staff. No dining room as such, but light meals are served in the
bar – typically, bagel with smoked salmon and cream cheese, moules
marinière or venison casserole with dauphinoise potatoes; *Browns* restaurant
(under the same ownership as the hotel) is two minutes away. *Rooms 30.
Garden, punting. Closed 24-26 Dec. Access, Amex, Visa,*

Oxford   Randolph Hotel   68%   £148

Tel 0865 247481   Fax 0865 791678   **H**

Beaumont Street Oxford Oxfordshire OX1 2LN   Map 5 D2

With neo-Gothic facade facing the Ashmolean museum, the Randolph is
Oxford's best-known hotel. The grand, oak-panelled foyer with high
vaulted ceiling and sweeping staircase, sets the tone for the day rooms,
which include an elegant, chandeliered lounge, clubby bar with red leather
armchairs, and Spires restaurant where good breakfasts are served under a
splendid plasterwork ceiling. Bedrooms, now all refurbished, vary in size
from small to spacious and include a number of suites. A fairly extensive
room-service menu is available throughout the day and evening.
Guaranteed free parking for residents. Forte Grand. *Rooms 109. Kiosk,
coffee shop (10-8). Access, Amex, Visa,*

Oxford   Places of Interest

Tourist Information   Tel 0865 726871.
Oxford United Football Ground   Manor Ground Tel 0865 61503.
Kirtlington Park Polo Club   Bicester Tel 0869 50777.
Oxford University Polo Club   c/o Wolfson College Tel 0865 274100.
Oxford Ice Rink   Tel 0865 248076.
Oxford Cathedral   Tel 0865 276155.
  Theatres and Concert Halls
Apollo Theatre   Tel 0865 244554.
Pegasus Theatre   Tel 0865 722851.
Oxford Playhouse   Tel 0865 247134.
  Historic Houses, Castles and Gardens
Waterperry Gardens   Nr Wheatley Tel 0844 339226.
Kingston House   Kingston Bagpuiz, Nr Abingdon Tel 0865 820259.
  Museums and Art Galleries
The Ashmolean Museum of Art and Archaeology   Tel 0865 278000.

Museum of Modern Art   Tel 0865 722733.
Museum of Oxford   Tel 0865 815559.
The Oxford Story   Tel 0865 728822.
The Pitt Rivers Museum   Tel 0865 270927.

Padstow	Seafood Restaurant	★	£77
Tel 0841 532485 Fax 0841 533344			**RR**
Riverside Padstow Cornwall PL28 8BY			Map 2 B3

One of the very best fish restaurants in the country, not least because the
raw products appear on the doorstep, ensuring their freshness. Rick Stein
has run this bustling, informal quayside restaurant for 17 years, offering à
la carte and three-course fixed-price menus (now both lunch and dinner).
The light and airy room is decorated in pastel colours with greenery
abounding in hanging baskets; cane furniture and cheerful pictures on the
walls complete the picture. Aperitifs are served with harbour views and
amuse-gueule in the conservatory at the front of the building. Fish and
shellfish soup with rouille and Parmesan, squab with stir-fried cabbage and
garlic chives, steamed langoustines, Helford oysters, crab pancakes with
lemon grass and coriander, fried scallops with lentils du Puy to start; roast
turbot with hollandaise, fruits de mer platter, chargrilled rib of beef with
béarnaise sauce, lobster with fine herbes, John Dory with olives, capers and
lavender, and chargrilled red mullet fillets with wild mushrooms, rocket
and sun-dried tomatoes are typical main courses. Simple sweets, with only a
small choice – tiramisu, baked pears with crème brulée ice cream, warm
date and apple pudding with hot fudge sauce; good cheeses (Cornish Yarg,
Epoisses, Devon Blue). The business now extends to a delicatessen (try the
fish soup and proper Cornish pasties), bakery and wine shop (upstairs)
tucked away in the old back streets of town. No minimum charge at
lunchtime, so you can drop in for just a bowl of soup or half-a-dozen
oysters. **Seats 70.** L 12.30-2 D 7-10 *(Sat to 10.30). Closed Sun, late Dec-end
Jan. Set L £17.50 Set D £24.50. Access, Visa,* **()** Diners Club International

Rooms	£73

Ten bedrooms above the restaurant are decorated in light colours and have
modern en-suite bathrooms and most hotel conveniences; chilled half
bottles of white wine in the fridges are a nice touch. All rooms are
centrally heated amd some have balconies overlooking the harbour.
Children under six stay free with their parents; others are offered special
rates. Sunday cold supper (smoked salmon, lobster and crème brulée)
served in the rooms when restaurant is closed. Good breakfasts. Special
break prices (min 2 nights) at start and end of season.

Padstow	Places of Interest

Polzeath Beach.

Paignton	Palace Hotel	60%	£96
Tel 0803 555121 Fax 0803 527974			**H**
Esplanade Road Paignton Devon TQ4 6BJ			Map 3 D3

Traditional seaside hotel overlooking the pier and Torbay beyond. Good
leisure amenities and conference facilities for up to 50. Forte Heritage.
*Rooms 52. Garden, outdoor swimming pool, tennis, keep-fit equipment, spa bath,
sauna, solarium, beautician, hair salon, pool table. Access, Amex, Visa,*
() Diners Club International

Paignton	Redcliffe Hotel	60%	£92
Tel 0803 526397 Fax 0803 528030			**H**
Marine Drive Paignton Devon TQ3 2NL			Map 3 D3

A round tower is the central feature of this distinctive turn-of-the-century
hotel by the sea. Day rooms enjoy the view, as do some of the bedrooms,
which include seven low-ceilinged rooms of character in the tower. A

private tunnel leading to the beach is of particular appeal to children (who stay free in parents' room if under 5). **Rooms 59.** *Outdoor swimming pool, putting, games room, hairdressing. Access, Visa.*

Paignton   Places of Interest

Tourist Information   Tel 0803 558383.
Compton Castle   Tel 0803 872112.
Paignton Zoo   Tel 0803 557479.
Paignton sands Beach.

Painswick   Painswick Hotel   70%   £85

Tel 0452 812160   Fax 0452 812059

H

Kemps Lane Painswick Gloucestershire GL6 6YB   Map 4 B2

Somerset and Helene Moore have elegantly refurbished a refined Georgian house in the heart of 'the queen of the Cotswolds', next to the church. All the bedrooms are now stylishly decorated and the very best have stunning views over the Severn Valley. Restyled day rooms include some exquisite antique pieces, comfortable seating and painted panelling. **Rooms 15.** *Garden, croquet. Access, Amex, Visa,*

Pangbourne   Copper Inn Restaurant   £70

Tel 0734 842244   Fax 0734 845542

R

Church Road Pangbourne Berkshire RG8 7AR   Map 5 D2

In a 19th-century mock-Tudor building next to the village church Paul Webster cooks with care and an artistic touch, offering both familiar and innovative dishes. Typifying the latter are sautéed chicken livers in a puff-pastry cushion with a morel cream sauce and poached salmon with shredded celeriac, yoghurt and basil. To finish there are good puds and, usually, a range of seven well-kept British cheeses. Terrace seating in good weather. Oft-changing table d'hote menus offer four choices at each course. Over-expensive wine list. **Seats 50.** *Parties 20. Private Room. L 12.30-2 (Sun to 2.30) D 7.30-9 (Fri & Sat to 10). Closed L Sat. Set L from £13.95 Set D from £16.95. Access, Amex, Visa,*

Pangbourne   Places of Interest

Basildon Park (NT)   Tel 0734 843040.

Parkgate   Ship Hotel   58%   £76

Tel 051-336 3931   Fax 051-353 0051

H

The Parade Parkgate The Wirral Cheshire L64 6SA   Map 10 A2

A small stone-fronted Forte hotel overlooking the Dee estuary; the Birdwatchers bar has picture windows from which to observe the wildlife on the salt marshes. The two front bedrooms have four-poster beds and the best views. Forte Heritage. **Rooms 26.** *Access, Amex, Visa,*

Parkham   Penhaven Country House   64%   £87

Tel 0237 451388   Fax 0237 451878

H

Parkham Nr Bideford Devon EX39 5PL   Map 2 C2

Maxine and Alan Wade are the friendly hosts at a small 19th-century hotel whose setting in the Devon countryside includes 11 acres of gardens and a nature trail. Inside, all is spick and span, from the bar with its log fire to the bedrooms – these range from standard to 'super-de-luxe' and six cottage suites. All rooms have both bath and shower. No smoking in the restaurant. No children under ten. **Rooms 12.** *Garden. Access, Amex, Visa,*

Paulerspury   Vine House   £55

Tel 032 733 267   Fax 032 733 309   **RR**

High Street Paulerspury Northamptonshire NN12 7NA   Map 5 D1

A rural restaurant in a small village off the A5 (3 miles from Towcester)
where Marcus and Julie Springett offer fixed-price lunch and dinner menus
(with a choice of four or five dishes at each course) that change daily and
are inspired by the freshest ingredients available. Marcus is an enthusiastic
and self-taught chef making as much on the premises as possible (including
breads and sweetmeats) and producing dishes like crab and smoked salmon
fish cakes with lemon butter sauce, pot-roasted loin of pork with a truffle
juice served with lentils and button onions or confit of Norfolk duck with
red cabbage, lardons of bacon and roasted garlic. Desserts range from
banana wrapped in filo with caramel sauce and peanut brittle ice cream to
the more traditional apple and rhubarb crumble with custard. Higgledy-
piggledy wine list. Non-smoking area. *Seats 45. Parties 25. Private Room.
L 12-2.30 D 7-10. Closed L Mon & Sat, D Sun (except for residents). Set L
from £13.95 Set D £19.50 (Mon-Thurs) £23.50 (Fri & Sat). Access, Visa.*

Rooms   £62

The six cottagey bedrooms have been completely redecorated in the last
year and are kept in good order. One room has a delightful floral-draped
four-poster and all have en suite facilities and modern hotel conveniences.

Penkridge   William Harding's House   £45

Tel 078 571 2955   **R**

Mill Street Penkridge Stafford Staffordshire ST19 5AY   Map 10 B3

Built as a stable in 1693 and occupied by Cromwell's men during the Civil
War, this is a small, cottagey restaurant run by Fiona and Eric Bickley.
Some dishes on Eric's frequently changing fixed-price menu have an old-
fashioned ring, while others are modern: pancake of sea fish with
vermouth and cream sauce; feathered fowlie and vegetable pottage; roast
breast of wood pigeon on warmed tayberries, collops of pork tenderloin
with mushroom sauce. Puddings and British cheeses are served from this
sideboard. *Seats 24. Parties 14. L (Sun only) 12.30-1.45 D 7.30-9.30. Closed
D Sun & Mon, Bank Holidays. Set D £17.65. Access, Visa.*

Penrith   Forte Travelodge   £40

Tel 0768 66958   **L**

A66 Redhills Penrith Cumbria CA11 0DT   Map 13 D5

¼ mile west of junction 40 of the M6, 15 miles east of Keswick. *Rooms 32.
Access, Amex, Visa.*

Penrith   North Lakes Gateway Hotel   71%   £100

Tel 0768 68111   Fax 0768 68291   **H**

Ullswater Road Penrith Cumbria CA11 8QT   Map 13 D5

A stern-looking hotel, by junction 40 of the M6, which comfortably
divides its time between mid-week conferences and a weekend base for
Lakeland visitors. Facilities for both categories are purpose-built around a
central lodge of local stone and massive railway-sleeper beams, which
houses bar, lounges and coffee shop. Newest Executive-style bedrooms have
raised work areas with fold-away beds, while interconnecting syndicate
rooms convert handily for family use at holiday times. Children up to 12
free in parents' room. Conference and banqueting facilities for 200. Shire
Inns. *Rooms 85. Garden, indoor swimming pool, sauna, spa bath, solarium,
gymnasium, squash, snooker, coffee shop (noon-11pm). Access, Amex, Visa,*

Penrith Places of Interest

Acorn Bank Garden (NT) Temple Sowerby Tel 07683 61893.
Dalemain Dacre Tel 07684 86450.

Penzance	Abbey Hotel	67%	£75

Tel 0736 66906   Fax 0736 51163 **HR**

Abbey Street Penzance Cornwall TR18 4AR Map 2 A4

One of the South-West's most individual hotels, the Abbey is perched
above and overlooks the quay in a quiet backwater of town. Jean and
Michael Cox describe themselves as the decorators, but this understates the
case: their house is a model of good taste, replete with their collections of
antiques and fine art, deep armchairs and abundant reading material. Stylish
bedrooms retain the building's uniqueness and charm, using colour and
light to great advantage where space is limited. *Rooms 7. Garden, croquet.*
Access, Amex, Visa,

Restaurant £58

Do book as, with only six tables, non-residents are only welcomed as space
allows, but don't expect any great sense of occasion. A table d'hote offers
three choices per course nightly, with vegetarian alternatives always
available. Thus a starter may be carrot and cardamom soup or quenelles of
salmon à la crème followed by poussin marinated in fresh basil and lemon
with a red wine sauce, lemon sole with capers or a stir-fry of mixed
vegetables and nuts. *Seats 18. Parties 8. D only 7.30-8.30. Set D £21.50.*

Penzance	Berkeley Restaurant	£50

Tel 0736 62541 **R**

Abbey Street Penzance Cornwall TR18 4AW Map 2 A4

On a hillside above the harbour, this tiny first-floor restaurant run by Ian
and Denise Morris is part of the Club Zero night club. The food is well
prepared and cooked to order – from lemon sole to steaks and chicken.
Dishes like *scallopine al geo* and *mushrooms alla romana* show a leaning
towards Italy where the owners spent some time. There's never a rush as a
table is allocated for the whole evening, and diners may dance in the club
until 1am. *Seats 34. Parties 40. D 7.30-10.30. Closed D Sun & Mon in*
summer (also Tue & Wed in winter), 25 & 26 Dec. Access, Amex, Visa.

Penzance	Harris's	£66

Tel 0736 64408 **R**

46 New Street Penzance Cornwall TR18 2LZ Map 2 A4

The separate fish menu, which comes along with the short hand-written à
la carte, is the thing to go for here: grilled fillets of red mullet, John Dory
with white wine and saffron sauce, Dover sole meunière. There is also a
light supper menu with dishes at about £6. Lunch is an informal affair
served in the upstairs bar. *Seats 30. Parties 25. Private Room. L 12-2 D 7-10.*
Closed L Sun, all Mon, 25 & 26 Dec, 1 Jan, 2 weeks Nov. Access, Amex,
Visa,

Penzance Places of Interest

Tourist Information Tel 0736 62207.
The Acorn Theatre Tel 0736 65520.
St. Michael's Mount (NT) Marazion Tel 0736 710507.
Trengwainton Garden (NT) Tel 0736 63021.
Penzance and District Museum and Art Gallery Tel 0736 63625.
Porthmeor Beach *5 miles NW Penzance.*

Peterborough   Butterfly Hotel   63%   £70

Tel 0733 64240   Fax 0733 65538   **H**

**Thorpe Meadows Longthorpe Parkway Peterborough
Cambridgeshire PE3 6GA**   Map 6 A2

One of a small chain of modern, low-rise East Anglian hotels (the others
are in Bury St Edmunds, Colchester and King's Lynn). Peterborough's
Butterfly sits at the water's edge, overlooking a rowing lake. Neat, practical
accommodation ranges from studio singles to four suites. Children up to
eight stay free in parent's room. *Rooms 70. Access, Amex, Visa,* ⓘ *Diners Club International*

Peterborough   Forte Posthouse   60%   £67

Tel 0733 240209   Fax 0733 244455   **H**

**Great North Road Norman Cross Peterborough Cambridgeshire PE7
3TB**   Map 6 A2

Business hotel at the Norman Cross roundabout on the A1. Good leisure
facilities and the usual good Forte value. Meeting rooms for up to 45.
*Rooms 93. Indoor swimming pool, spa bath, solarium, sauna, beautician,
gymnasium, baby listening. Access, Amex, Visa,* ⓘ *Diners Club International*

Peterborough   Forte Travelodge   £40

Tel 0733 231109   **L**

A1 Alwalton Village Nr Peterborough Cambridgeshire PE7 3UR   Map 6 A2

On the A1 Great North Road southbound, 3 miles from the centre of
Peterborough. *Rooms 32. Access, Amex, Visa.*

Peterborough   Moat House   64%   £91

Tel 0733 260000   Fax 0733 262737   **H**

Thorpe Wood Peterborough Cambridgeshire PE3 6SG   Map 6 A2

Two miles west of the city centre by the Thorpe Wood golf course, a
modern redbrick hotel offering extensive leisure and air-conditioned
conference facilities; the largest room can take up to 400 delegates.
*Rooms 129. Indoor swimming pool, spa bath, sauna, solarium, gymnasium,
dinner dance (Sat). Access, Amex, Visa,* ⓘ *Diners Club International*

Peterborough   Swallow Hotel   69%   £99

Tel 0733 371111   Fax 0733 236725   **H**

Lynch Road Peterborough Cambridgeshire PE2 0GB   Map 6 A2

Modern, low-rise hotel by the A605, two minutes from the A1. Spacious
public areas are bright and airy. Extensive leisure and conference facilities.
*Rooms 163. Garden, indoor swimming pool, spa bath, sauna, solarium, steam
room, beauty and hair salon, keep-fit equipment, coffee shop (7am-10.30pm).
Access, Amex, Visa,* ⓘ *Diners Club International*

Peterborough   Places of Interest

Tourist Information   Tel 0733 317336.
Key Theatre   Tel 0733 52439.
Lady Lodge Arts Centre   Tel 0733 237073.
Peterborough Cathedral   Tel 0733 43342.
Peterborough Museum and Art Gallery   Tel 0733 43329.
East of England Ice Rink   Tel 0733 260222.
East of England Showground   Tel 0733 234451.
Peakirk Wildfowl Trust   Tel 0733 252271.

Petersfield — Langrish House — 63% — £73
H

Tel 0730 66941   Fax 0730 60543

Langrish Petersfield Hampshire GU32 1RN — Map 5 D3

Built around the heart of a 16th-century farmhouse, the house stands in rolling countryside three miles out of Petersfield off the A272. Bedrooms have peaceful pastoral views, traditional furnishings and a few homely extras. The basement bar was reputedly excavated by Royalist prisoners taken at the Civil War's Battle of Cheriton after which they ended up in their own prison! The lack of leisure facilities is reflected in the price. 17 miles from Portsmouth. *Rooms 18. Garden. Closed 25 Dec-1 Jan. Access, Amex, Visa,*

Pitton — Silver Plough — £55
R

Tel 0722 72266

Pitton Nr Salisbury Wiltshire SP5 1DZ — Map 4 C3

An object lesson in good pub-keeping, where a young and professional team are dedicated to quality food, wines and beers. Talented chef Joanne Docherty sets out daily dishes on blackboards, adding a printed set dinner menu. Choices are wide and adventurous: fillet of shark with soy sauce or ragout of lamb's kidneys and snails in balsamic sauce. The main restaurant is in a lower level extension of the original farmhouse, though part of the bar has attractively clothed tables, cosily clustered around the open fire in the winter. Several good wines at bargain prices. *Seats 32. Parties 34. Private Room. L 12-2 D 7-10. Closed D Sun, 25 Dec, Jan & Feb. Set meals £10.95/£12.95. Access, Amex, Visa,*

Plumtree — Perkins Bar Bistro — £50
R

Tel 0602 373695

Old Railway Station, Station Road Plumtree Nottinghamshire NG12 5NA — Map 11 D3

Tony and Wendy Perkins bought an old railway station in 1982, and their conversion work has added a delightful conservatory. France is the main influence on the kitchen, which includes fried baby squid with rémoulade sauce, blanquette of lamb with veal quenelles, ballotine of tarragon chicken béarnaise and sticky toffee pudding in its repertoire. Traditional values (properly made stocks and sauces) ally with modern presentation. *Seats 75. Parties 30. Private Room. L 12-2 D 7-9.45. Closed Sun & Mon, 25 & 26 Dec, 1 Jan, Easter Monday. Access, Amex, Visa.*

Plymouth — Astor Hotel — 58% — £69
H

Tel 0752 225511   Fax 0752 851994

14 Elliott Street The Hoe Plymouth Devon PL1 2PS — Map 2 C3

Victorian hotel handy for the Hoe and the city centre. Children up to the age of 14 free in parents' room. Mount Charlotte Thistle. *Rooms 56. Access, Amex, Visa,*

Plymouth — Boringdon Hall — 70% — £90
H

Tel 0752 344455   Fax 0752 346578

Colebrook Plympton Plymouth Devon PL7 4DP — Map 2 C3

Based on a Grade 1 listed mansion, where the first Queen Elizabeth may have stayed, a hotel with epic intentions has been hewn out of the hall and historic outbuildings. A spectacular bar in the Great Hall provides a focal point, overlooked by both restaurant and minstrel's gallery. Above, tower bedrooms feature carved four-posters and period furniture designed to match. Recently completed extensions, externally clad in original stone, stand around a courtyard alongside the leisure spa; though lacking the charm of the older rooms, the newer rooms compensate with better bathrooms. Conference/banqueting facilities for 110/100. Children up to the age of 16 free in parents' room. *Rooms 40. Garden, 9-hole pitch & putt, indoor swimming pool, sauna, solarium, gymnasium, tennis. Access, Amex, Visa,* ⓓ *Diners Club International*

Plymouth   Campanile Hotel   £36
Tel 0752 601087   Fax 0752 223213   **L**

Marsh Mills Longbridge Road Plymouth Devon PL6 8LD   Map 2 C3

Off the A38, heading towards Cornwall. *Rooms 50. Access, Amex, Visa,* ⓓ *Diners Club International*

Plymouth   Chez Nous   ★   £92
Tel 0752 266793   **R**

13 Frankfort Gate Plymouth Devon PL1 1QA   Map 2 C3

For the past dozen years the charming Marchals have put their personal stamp on a tiny piece of France in a modest, tree-lined shopping precinct. Jacques' "Cuisine Spontanée" is truly of the moment, relying entirely on the best local produce in its season, and his specialities from the blackboard menu (admirably translated by Suzanne) are models of consistency. Coquilles St Jacques with ginger, venison medallions poivrade and chateaubriand béarnaise are representative dishes. Fine nougat glacé with raspberry coulis, French cheeses, a well-balanced list of mainly French wines with decent house selections and good half bottles. Mostly French wines, though the small New World selection offers good value. *Seats 28. Parties 22. L 12.30-2 D 7-10.30. Closed Sun & Mon, Bank Holidays, 3 weeks Feb, 3 weeks Sep. Set meals from £24.50. Access, Amex, Visa,* ⓓ *Diners Club International*

Plymouth   Copthorne Hotel   70%   £106
Tel 0752 224161   Fax 0752 670688   **H**

Armada Way Plymouth Devon PL1 1AR   Map 2 C3

Follow the signs for the city centre, then signs for the ferry port. It's an attractive hotel, with the light and elegant decor in the foyer setting the overall tone; other public areas include a restaurant, café-bar, Gallery cocktail bar and lounge. Bedrooms include Classic, Connoisseur and suites all with contemporary fitted furniture and plenty of writing space; there are rooms for the disabled and for non-smokers; tiled bathrooms have good counter space and large, well-lit mirrors. Ample free parking. Greatly reduced weekend rates (Fri-Sun). Facilities for banquets and conferences (up to 80). *Rooms 135. Indoor swimming pool, gymnasium, sauna, solarium, kiosk, dinner dance (monthly). Access, Amex, Visa,* ⓓ *Diners Club International*

Plymouth   Forte Crest   65%   £87
Tel 0752 662828   Fax 0752 660974   **H**

Cliff Road The Hoe Plymouth Devon PL1 3DL   Map 2 C3

High-riser with fine views from its prime position on the Hoe. Formerly the Mayflower Posthouse. Conferences for up to 100, banqueting to 140. *Rooms 106. Garden, outdoor swimming pool. Access, Amex, Visa,* ⓓ *Diners Club International*

Plymouth   Moat House   70%   £98
Tel 0752 662866   Fax 0752 673816   **H**

Armada Way Plymouth Devon PL1 2HJ   Map 2 C3

Day rooms at this high-rise hotel, in particular the penthouse restaurant and bar, command spectacular views of the Hoe and Plymouth Sound. So do many of the good-sized, picture-windowed bedrooms, which have double beds (twins have two double beds), seating areas and plenty of writing space. On the ground floor the large, bright reception area includes a relaxing lobby bar. Conference and banqueting facilities for up to 500. Children under 14 are accommodated free if sharing their parents' room. *Rooms 217. Gymnasium, indoor swimming pool, spa bath, sauna, solarium, games room. Access, Amex, Visa,* ⓓ *Diners Club International*

Plymouth Novotel 62% £68

H

Tel 0752 221422 Fax ext 126

Marsh Mills Roundabout Plymouth Devon PL6 8HN Map 2 C3

Practical modern accommodation and conference/banqueting facilities (for up to 240 delegates) on the A38 two miles from the town centre. **Rooms 101.** *Garden. Access, Amex, Visa,*

Plymouth Places of Interest

Tourist Information Tel 0752 264849.
Athenaeum Theatre Tel 0752 266079.
Theatre Royal Tel 0752 668.
City Museum and Art Gallery Tel 0752 264878.
Plymouth Argyle Football Ground Home Park Tel 0752 562561.
Dartmoor Wildlife Park Sparkwell Tel 0755 37209.
  Historic Houses, Castles and Gardens
Saltram House (NT) Tel 0752 336546.
Antony House, Woodland Garden and Natural Woods(NT) Torpoint
  Tel 0752 812191.
Mount Edgcumbe House & Country Park Tel 0752 822236.

Pocklington Feathers Hotel £50

I

Tel 0759 303155 Fax 0759 318947

Market Place Pocklington Humberside YO4 2UN Map 11 E1

A friendly market-town inn, 15 minutes drive from York, useful to know in an area with a dearth of decent accommodation. Main-house rooms include a residents' lounge and new conservatory, and a bridal suite with a half-tester bed. Six rooms with bow-fronted windows are in the stone-clad annexe. Function room for conferences (max 300 and banqueting up to 60). No dogs. Mulberry Inns Group. **Rooms 12.** *Garden. Access, Amex, Visa,*

Podimore Forte Travelodge £40

L

Tel 0935 840074

A303 Podimore Nr Yeovil Somerset BA22 8JG Map 4 B3

On the A303, 6 miles north of Yeovil and adjacent to the junction with the A37. **Rooms 31.** *Access, Amex, Visa.*

Polperro Kitchen at Polperro £55

R

Tel 0503 72780

The Coombs Polperro Cornwall PL13 2RQ Map 2 C3

Park in the village car park and walk down to Ian and Vanessa Bateson's lovely little restaurant. The cooking is enjoyable and unpretentious, the menus interesting and varied and always with seafood at centre stage. Lobster (order by Thursday for the weekend) and crab are the real specialities, but you'll also find healthy vegetarian options, Cornish smoked cider sausage, cardamom nushrooms, oriental duck with pineapple sauce and breast of duck with blueberry and Drambuie sauce. Short, helpfully descriptive wine list. Simple, but satisfying. **Seats 24,** *Parties 6. D only 7-9.30. Closed Tue in summer, Sun-Thu in winter, 25 & 26 Dec, Jan. Set D £19.50. Access, Visa,*

Pool-in-Wharfedale Pool Court ★ £85

RR

Tel 0532 842288 Fax 0532 843115

Pool Bank Pool-in-Wharfedale Otley West Yorkshire LS21 1EH Map 10 C1

The dedication of owners Michael and Hanni Gill is as great today as when they started out in 1966, and with Yorkshireman David Watson heading a talented brigade, Pool Court remains one of the county's premier restaurants. Menus, priced according to choice of main course, offer a wide selection and consistently excellent results show a timeless style that pays little heed to modernistic fads. Salad of corn-fed chicken with lobster and leeks or a hot pike mousse could precede soup (creamy parsnip with curried almonds) or a citrus sorbet. Roast saddle of hare with confit of the leg and Scottish salmon with tapénade typify the main-course offerings. Delicious sweets or British cheeses follow. The owners' personal selections precede a well-rounded wine list with a good selection of half bottles. *Seats 65. Parties 72. Private Room. D only 7-9.30. Closed Sun & Mon, Bank Holidays, 2 weeks Xmas. Set D £24-£31.50. Access, Amex, Visa,* (●)*Diners Club International*

Rooms   £109

Six splendid bedrooms are individually designed and furnished with rich, quality fabrics and solid period pieces. Housekeeping is immaculate and long-serving staff extend many an old-fashioned courtesy. Fruit, flowers, magazines, wall safe, bar fridge. *Rooms 6.*

Poole	Haven Hotel	66%	£136
Tel 0202 707333 Fax 0202 708796			**H**
Banks Road Sandbanks Poole Dorset BH13 7QL			Map 4 C4

Four miles from Poole Old Town, following the signs for the Swanage ferry, which docks by the sea wall. Such is the coastline here that on three sides there are sea views, of which bedroom balconies take full advantage. Bleached oak and bright contemporary fabrics contribute a spacious feeling to surprisingly roomy superior rooms. Comprehensive leisure facilities and purpose-built conference centre (for up to 150) are conspicuously well kept and clearly well run. Not suitable for children under the age of 5. Beauty treatments include aromatherapy. *Rooms 95. Indoor & outdoor swimming pools, sauna, solarium, spa bath, steam room, gymnasium, beauty salon, hairdressing, squash, tennis. Access, Amex, Visa,* (●)*Diners Club International*

Poole	Hospitality Inn	63%	£101
Tel 0202 666800 Fax 0202 684470			**H**
The Quay Poole Dorset BH15 1HD			Map 4 C4

Many rooms overlook the harbour at this modern two-storey, red-brick hotel. Neat practical bedrooms. Children under 14 stay free in parents' room. Conference facilities for up to 80 delegates. Mount Charlotte Thistle. *Rooms 68. Access, Amex, Visa,* (●)*Diners Club International*

Poole	Mansion House	74%	£95
Tel 0202 685666 Fax 0202 665709			**HR**
11 Thames Street Poole Dorset BH15 1JN			Map 4 C4

Facing St James Church across a tiny square, the marble-pillared portico and tall, arched windows of the Mansion House epitomise Georgian elegance. It is only a stone's throw from bustling Poole quay, yet it affords an oasis of calm within. The best bedrooms are generously proportioned and airy, although some others are rather less so. Each is decorated in individual style and furnished with fine antiques, to which today's more modern necessities have been sympathetically added. More thoughtful, homely extras extend to mineral water, fresh fruit and boiled sweets in the rooms plus complimentary early morning tea tray and choice of newspaper. Children up to 12 stay free in parents' room. Banqueting for up to 110; meetings for 30. No dogs. *Rooms 28. Access, Amex, Visa,* (●)*Diners Club International*

Restaurant   £62

A smart dining club, also open to the public, where hotel residents receive the same generous discounts as club members on the well-balanced table d'hote menu. Local seafood is well represented alongside such dishes as pigeon breast in puff pastry with red wine and juniper berry sauce, fillet of beef with oxtail sauce, and pan-fried calf's liver with onions. The clubby atmosphere successfully avoids stuffiness and service is good. *Seats 95.*

Parties 40. Private Room. L 12.30-2.15 D 7.30-9.30 (Sun to 9). Closed L Sat,
1 Jan, Easter Monday. Set L £17.75 Set D £23.50.

Poole	Sandbanks Hotel	59%	£110

Tel 0202 707377   Fax 0202 708885   **H**

15 Banks Road Sandbanks Poole Dorset BH13 3PS   Map 4 C4

Ideal for families, with an attractive patio and garden leading onto the
surprisingly clean sandy beach (winner of an EEC Blue Flag Award), and
complete holiday services that include organised activities and a nursery.
Four tiers of balconied bedrooms look either out to sea or across Poole
Bay. Winter trade is boosted by conference business (up to 170 delegates)
when the open-plan bar, vast sun lounge and dining rooms afford little
privacy for individual hotel guests. 20 larger rooms in the original hotel
building are designated as family rooms. No dogs. Children under the age
of 12 accommodated free in parents' room (except in high season – July to
Sept); separate children's restaurant. *Rooms 105. Garden, indoor swimming
pool, sauna, steam room, solarium, spa bath, gymnasium, crèche (daily in
summer). Access, Amex, Visa,* (❶) *Diners Club International*

Poole   Places of Interest

Tourist Information   Tel 0202 673322.
Poole Arts Centre   Tel 0202 685222.
Guildhall Museum   Tel 0202 675151.
Waterfront Poole   Tel 0202 675151/683138.
Icetrax Ice Rink   Tel 0202 716000.
Sandbanks Beach.

Porlock	Oaks Hotel	65%	£70

Tel 0643 862265   **HR**

Porlock Somerset TA24 8ES   Map 3 D1

A fine elevated position gives Tim and Anne Riley's Edwardian house
great views over Porlock sweeping down to the beach and sea. It's a
friendly, homely spot, with a lounge full of flowers, books and magazines
and an even more intimate bar. Bedrooms are light and pretty with a mix
of pine and some nice old-fashioned bedroom pieces. Service is a strong
point and the whole place is kept crisp and fresh. *Rooms 10. Garden,*
(❶) *Diners Club International*

Restaurant   £44

Anne's daily-changing menus are unpretentious, but offer fine value. Start
with soup (carrot and orange or tomato and basil) or smoked salmon
roulade, follow with a no-choice fish course (seafood medley or poached
scallops with lime and ginger); main courses might be beef stroganoff,
pork tenderloin with prunes or roast chicken with tarragon and orange
stuffing. Simple puddings: ginger surprise, rhubarb fool, ice creams, sorbets
and local cheeses. Fair prices on a concise wine list. *Seats 24. Parties 10.*
D only 7-8.30. Set D £17.50.

Portloe	Lugger Hotel	59%	£92

Tel 0872 501322   Fax 0872 501691   **H**

Portloe Truro Cornwall TR2 5RD   Map 2 B3

At the water's edge in a tiny cove, the Lugger was a smugglers' haunt in its
early days. Its attractions are now very much above board and the Powell
family, resident owners for more than 40 years, extend the warmest of
welcomes. The scale may be small in the bar and older bedrooms, but this
just adds to the cosiness. Roomiest accommodation is in a modern building.
No children under 12. *Rooms 19. Closed Dec & Jan. Access, Amex, Visa,*
(❶) *Diners Club International*

Portsmouth Forte Crest 65% £87

Tel 0705 827651   Fax 0705 756715 **H**

Pembroke Road Southsea Portsmouth Hampshire PO1 2TA **Map 5 D4**

Near the Hovercraft terminal at Southsea, a modern hotel with leisure and
business centres (conferences for up to 220, banqueting up to 180).
*Rooms 163. Indoor swimming pool, gymnasium, spa bath, sauna, steam room,
solarium. Access, Amex, Visa,*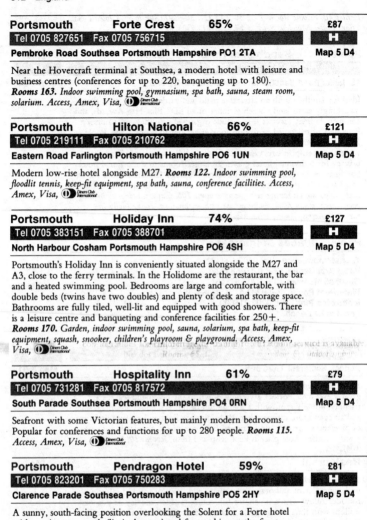

Portsmouth Hilton National 66% £121

Tel 0705 219111   Fax 0705 210762 **H**

Eastern Road Farlington Portsmouth Hampshire PO6 1UN **Map 5 D4**

Modern low-rise hotel alongside M27. *Rooms 122. Indoor swimming pool,
floodlit tennis, keep-fit equipment, spa bath, sauna, conference facilities. Access,
Amex, Visa,*

Portsmouth Holiday Inn 74% £127

Tel 0705 383151   Fax 0705 388701 **H**

North Harbour Cosham Portsmouth Hampshire PO6 4SH **Map 5 D4**

Portsmouth's Holiday Inn is conveniently situated alongside the M27 and
A3, close to the ferry terminals. In the Holidome are the restaurant, the bar
and a heated swimming pool. Bedrooms are large and comfortable, with
double beds (twins have two doubles) and plenty of desk and storage space.
Bathrooms are fully tiled, well-lit and equipped with good showers. There
is a leisure centre and banqueting and conference facilities for 250+.
*Rooms 170. Garden, indoor swimming pool, sauna, solarium, spa bath, keep-fit
equipment, squash, snooker, children's playroom & playground. Access, Amex,
Visa,*

Portsmouth Hospitality Inn 61% £79

Tel 0705 731281   Fax 0705 817572 **H**

South Parade Southsea Portsmouth Hampshire PO4 0RN **Map 5 D4**

Seafront with some Victorian features, but mainly modern bedrooms.
Popular for conferences and functions for up to 280 people. *Rooms 115.
Access, Amex, Visa,*

Portsmouth Pendragon Hotel 59% £81

Tel 0705 823201   Fax 0705 750283 **H**

Clarence Parade Southsea Portsmouth Hampshire PO5 2HY **Map 5 D4**

A sunny, south-facing position overlooking the Solent for a Forte hotel
with a private car park (limited spaces) and free parking at the front.
Rooms 49. Patio. Access, Amex, Visa,

Portsmouth Places of Interest

Tourist Information Tel 0705 832464.
Kings Theatre Tel 0705 820527.
New Theatre Royal Tel 0705 864611.
Portsmouth Cathedral Tel 0705 823300.
Portsmouth Football Ground Fratton Park Tel 0705 731204.
  Museums and Art Galleries
Charles Dickens' Birthplace Museum Tel 0705 827261.
HMS Victory HM Naval Base Tel 0705 819604.
Mary Rose Ship Hall and Exhibition HM Naval Base Tel 0705 750521.
The Royal Naval Museum HM Naval Base Tel 0705 733060.
D-Day Museum Tel 0705 827261.
HMS Warrior 1860 HM Naval Base Tel 0705 291379.

Powburn   Breamish House   67%   £65

Tel 066 578 266   Fax 066 578 500   **HR**

Powburn Alnwick Northumberland NE66 4LL   Map 15 B3

Originally a 17th-century farmhouse, converted to hunting lodge in the 1800s. Breamish House is an elegant Georgian-style building standing in five acres of colourful gardens just off the A697. Each bedroom is individually decorated and named after trees from the surrounding woodland: abundant peace and quiet are among the amenities promised by resident owners Doreen and Alan Johnson. No children under 12. *Rooms 11. Garden. Closed Jan-mid Feb. No credit cards.*

Powerstock   Three Horseshoes Inn   £50

Tel 0308 85328   **RR**

Powerstock Bridport Dorset DT6 3TF   Map 4 A4

The Three Horseshoes is a stone and thatch country inn with simple country furnishings and open fires, reached by narrow winding lanes. Its restaurant comprises two pine-panelled rooms, one small and cosy, the other more roomy and airy. Fish is what chef-licensee Pat Ferguson is best known for, and the blackboard menu can include anything from freshly boiled crab or grilled lobster to fish pie, bourride and sea bass cooked in a paper bag. Meat and game dishes, too: garlic-studded rack of lamb, kidneys turbigo, venison pie; plus traditional British puddings. Must book for busy Sunday lunches in winter. Tables in the garden for summer eating. *Seats 60. Private Room. L 12-2 D 7-10 (Sun 7.30-8.30). Set L £7.50 & £10.50 (Sun only). Access, Amex, Visa.*

Rooms   £55

Large, traditionally styled rooms have central heating, en-suite bathrooms and lovely views. Delightful garden. Families with children are welcome, with cots available. *Rooms 4.*

Prestbury   Bridge Hotel   63%   £84

Tel 0625 829326   Fax 0625 827557   **H**

New Road Prestbury Nr Macclesfield Cheshire SK10 4DQ   Map 10 B2

Old-world charm and modern convenience meet in a privately owned hotel in the centre of a pretty village. Day rooms retain some feel of the 17th-century origins, while most of the bedrooms are in a modern redbrick extension overlooking the River Bollin. Children up to 12 stay free in parents' room. *Rooms 23. Garden, dinner dance (Sat). Access, Amex, Visa,*

Preston   Forte Crest   63%   £87

Tel 0772 59411   Fax 0772 882955   **H**

The Ringway Preston Lancashire PR1 3AU   Map 10 B1

Tall redbrick hotel with neatly designed bedrooms, and conference facilities for up to 120. Free parking for guests' cars in an adjacent multi-storey. *Rooms 126. Access, Amex, Visa,*

Preston   Novotel   62%   £64

Tel 0772 313331   Fax 0772 627868   **H**

Reedfield Place Walton Summit Preston Lancashire PR5 6AB   Map 10 B1

Practical modern accommodation and conference facilities for 120. Handy for the motorway network. *Rooms 100. Outdoor swimming pool. Access, Amex, Visa,*

Preston   Travel Inn   £42

Tel 0772 720476   Fax 0772 729971   **L**

Blackpool Road Lea Preston Lancashire PR4 0XL   **Map 10 B1**

En route to the Lake District, 20 minutes drive from the seaside resort of
Blackpool. **Rooms 40.** *Access, Amex, Visa,*

Preston   Places of Interest

Tourist Information   Tel 0772 53731.
Hoghton Tower   Tel 025 485 2986.
Harris Museum and Art Gallery   Tel 0772 58248.
Camelot Theme Park   Chorley Tel 0257 455044.

Puckrup   Puckrup Hall   70%   £78

Tel 0684 296200   Fax 0684 850788   **HR**

Puckrup Tewkesbury Gloucestershire GL20 6EL   **Map 4 B1**

On the A38, close to junction 1 of the M50, Puckrup Hall is a Regency
building standing in 140 acres of parkland, many of which have recently
been turned into an 18-hole golf course. The house retains a period
elegance, best displayed in the tranquil lounge, with its soft decor,
comfortable sofas and fine plasterwork. The bar overlooks the croquet
lawn and has a clubby atmosphere. Bedrooms, named after months and
seasons, have decor and soft furnishings inspired by their names. Carpeted
bathrooms, with shower fittings, have copious towels and Taylor's "green"
toiletries. Keen management leads efficient staff. **Rooms 16.** *Garden, golf,
putting, croquet, fishing. Access, Amex, Visa,*

Restaurant   £85

An elegant dining room with fine plasterwork is the setting for chef Geoff
Balharrie's balanced and structured cooking. His menu displays a number
of styles, from classical *magret de canard Chimay* or veal cutlet flamed with
truffle and chanterelles in brandy to a couple of more radical vegetarian
dishes (curd cheese and spinach parcels with sweet pepper marmalade and
walnut salad) and more modern offerings – perhaps collops of beef fillet
with oysters, smoked bacon and a dry sherry and black bean sauce. The
more modern style shines brightly, but traditionalists are unlikely to be
disappointed, with natural flavours carefully enhanced by distinctive
saucing. Good sweets or British cheeses. **Seats 34.** *Parties 10. L 12.30-2
D 7-9.30 (Fri & Sat to 10). Set L £13.50 Set D £18.50.*

Puddington   Craxton Wood   70%   £100

Tel 051-339 4717   Fax 051-339 1740   **HR**

Parkgate Road Puddington South Wirral Cheshire L66 9PB   **Map 10 A2**

Old-fashioned standards of service and comfort hold sway at Craxton
Wood, where Mr Petranca celebrated his 25th year as owner/manager last
year. Extensive wooded grounds, lawns and rose gardens provide a peaceful
setting and the spacious bedrooms are reassuringly traditional, with
reproduction furniture, conservative decor and neat, bright bathrooms. By
contrast, the bar is done out in modern greys, pinks and pastel blues,
though the main feature here is the splendid view that can be had of the
gardens. The lounge is more traditional in style and very formal, with the
highly polished furniture that characterises the bedrooms. No dogs.
Rooms 14. *Garden. Closed 1 week Xmas, 2 weeks Aug, Bank Holidays, Sun.
Access, Amex, Visa,*

Restaurant   £70

French menu with English translations, bright Continental service and
competent cooking of fresh ingredients. Stuffed quail on a bed of cherries,
feuilleté of scallops and chicory, and fillet of beef with a parfait of foie gras
demonstrate the style. Fixed-price menus at lunch and dinner for table
parties only; à la carte menu priced as a three course meal by choice of

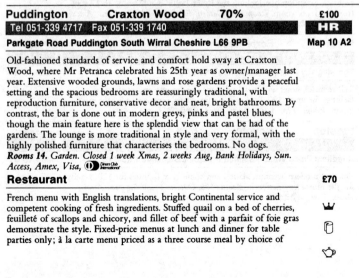

main dish. Both the menus and wine list are priced without the inclusion of VAT. *Seats 85. Parties 50. Private Room. L 12.30-2 D 7.30-10. Set D £25.85*

Puddington   Places of Interest

Ness Gardens   Liverpool Botanic Gardens Between Neston and Burton Tel 051 336 7769.

Pulborough	Chequers Hotel	61%	£65

Tel 0798 872486   Fax 0798 872715

Church Place Pulborough West Sussex RH20 1AD   Map 5 E3

A small, family-run hotel in a picturesque village (just north of the village centre, at the top of the hill, opposite the church). John and Ann Searancke have been here since 1960 yet they are still continuing to make improvements – this last year has seen new public toilets and a new floodlit car park added to the coffee shop and conservatory extension added the year before. Favoured accommodation is a little panelled bedroom with a half-tester bed and a dressing area through a low doorway; alternatively, there's a more spacious room with a four-poster bed and window seat. Dog owners will be delighted to find a 9-acre meadow right outside the front door. Children under 12 accommodated free in their parents' room. *Rooms 11. Garden, coffee shop (9.30am-5.30pm). Access, Amex, Visa,*

Diners Club International

Pulborough	Stane Street Hollow		£56

Tel 0798 872819   **R**

Codmore Hill Pulborough West Sussex RH20 1BG   Map 5 E3

Converted from two 16th-century cottages, René and Ann Kaiser's long-established, charming restaurant is built of solid Sussex stone. René's cooking is as reliably solid and resilient as the setting, with a menu that changes in its entirety every four weeks. Even after 15 years Swiss influences are in evidence (perhaps a *Schwarzwalder Kirsch torte* – chocolate truffle-topped chocolate sponge with cherries and kirsch), but the main theme is French, from *potage de gibier, soufflé jurasienne* (with leeks and bacon) and salad of home-smoked chicken with gherkins and apples to guinea fowl casseroled with Alsace wine, smoked boned leg of duckling with a coarse pork stuffing and turkey escalopes with mushroom and cream sauce and straw potatoes. There's a choice of seven dishes at each course including *assiette René* which offers a taster in miniature of four of the desserts. Lunch is a simpler, fixed-price 2-course affair. The wine list includes some splendid wines at giveaway prices a good selection of half bottles, strong French names from Bordeaux and Burgundy and Dole wines from Switzerland. *Seats 34. Parties 20. Private Room. L 12.30-1.15 D 7.30-9.15. Closed L Sat, all Sun-Tue, 1 week Xmas, 1 week May, 2 weeks Oct. Set L £8.25. No credit cards.*

Pulborough   Places of Interest

Parham Elizabethan House & Gardens   Parham Park Tel 0903 742021.

Purton	Pear Tree	74%	£92

Tel 0793 772100   Fax 0793 772369   **HR**

Church End Purton Nr Swindon Wiltshire SN5 9ED   Map 4 C2

A former vicarage, set in seven acres, on the road out of Purton towards Lydiard Millicent. The latest bedrooms are built around a central atrium to give light and space, and the decoration is of high standard with charming fabrics, ruched blinds, paintings and a wealth of extras such as mineral water, fruit and biscuits. Three have four-posters, and some beds are canopied; the bathrooms are carpeted and tiled, and boast showers plus good toiletries. The comfortable lounge opens on to the gardens and there's a bright, smart lounge bar with plants, sofas and stylish fabrics. Anne and

Francis Young and their smart, friendly staff offer exceptional standards of service. No dogs. *Rooms 18. Garden, croquet. Access, Amex, Visa,*

Restaurant   £65

Two matching conservatories make a delightful setting in which to enjoy the lively cooking of Janet Pichel-Juan. Perhaps sole, watercress and saffron terrine with chervil mayonnaise or a salad of Parma ham, water chestnuts and palm hearts in elderflower dressing to start, followed by pan-fried medallions of Wiltshire pork with apple and banana compote on a mild curry sauce, deep-fried conference pears filled with cream cheese, walnuts and chives on an orange sauce or poached Looe turbot in mushroom and cream sauce with pastry crescents. Puddings might include Mrs Collet's Dorset treacle pie or poppy seed and vanilla ice cream with kiwi fruit coulis – typical dishes on a far from ordinary menu. Lunchtime brings slightly less choice, although an equally interesting selection. There's normally a choice of three farmhouse cheeses. Good cooking, good value, good service, and good wines by the glass on a good list with personal notes on each wine. *Seats 60. Parties 50. Private Room. L 12-2 D 7-9.30. Closed L Sat. Set L £15 Set D £25.*

Quorn   The Quorn   72%   £102
| Tel 0509 415050   Fax 0509 415557 | **H** |

66 Leicester Road Quorn Leicestershire LE12 8BB   Map 11 D3

Alongside the A6 and with gardens reaching down to the river Soar, the Quorn offers ease of access with a touch of the country thrown in. The mahogany-panelled entrance hall with its flagstones, Oriental rugs and carved stone fireplace, has a very welcoming look, and a splendid wooden staircase featuring oil paintings and a brass chandelier heightens the country house feel. Bedrooms in a modern purpose-built part are prettily decorated and tastefully furnished; appointments include air-conditioning, two armchairs and remote-control TV (some with teletext). Staff are very jolly and friendly. *Rooms 19. Garden, coarse fishing. Access, Amex, Visa,*

Quorn   Quorn Grange   67%   £94
| Tel 0509 412167   Fax 0509 415621 | **HR** |

Wood Lane Quorn Leicestershire LE12 8DB   Map 11 D3

A short drive off the A6 brings you to this extended, ivy-clad Victorian house. The addition of new rooms and self-contained function facilities (for up to 120) has lifted it to hotel status. Twelve stylish new bedrooms offer garden views and are tastefully appointed using contemporary fabrics offset against plain walls. Impressive, brightly lit bathrooms have huge mirrors, marble surrounds and powerful showers. Original bedrooms are more individual, but with simpler bathrooms. A bar-lounge is housed in a bright, plant-filled conservatory. *Rooms 17. Garden. Access, Amex, Visa,*

Restaurant   £60

Dining room windows are hung with Austrian blinds – a quietly elegant setting for chef Gordon Lang's serious cooking. Fixed-price menus are along traditional British lines (watercress soup, medallions of venison with wild mushrooms and a choice of sweets) and there's also a short carte that covers a range from warm salad of smoked chicken, bacon and walnuts to Barbary duckling with bubble and squeak, celery and orange essence; vegetarians are usually offered a good choice of dishes. *Seats 50. Parties 10. Private Room yes. L 12-2.30 D 7-9.30 (Sat to 10, Sun to 9). Closed L Sat. Set meals from £15.95.*

Ramsbottom   Village Restaurant   £80

Tel 0706 825070   R

16 Market Place Ramsbottom Nr Bury Greater Manchester BL0 9HT   Map 10 B1

A six-course, no-choice dinner is cooked by Ros Hunter and served by
Chris Johnson in a style they describe as "extended dinner party". Every
care is taken in shopping and preparation of fresh Fleetwood fish, locally
picked garden produce and fine unpasteurised British cheeses. Results are
commendable in the Stilton, onion and parsley soup, baby halibut with
banana and lime sauce, and locally reared chicken prepared two ways and
served with six seasonal vegetables – all of which which typify the style.
The wine list is laid out by grape variety and the wines have been expertly
chosen: Chris, a teetotaller, offers a nightly "by the glass" selection to
complement Ros's menu. No smoking. *Seats 20. Parties 14. Private Room.
D only at 8 for 8.30. Closed Sun & Mon, 1 Jan. Set D £29.50. Access, Visa.*

Ravenstonedale   Black Swan Inn   £57

Tel 053 96 23204   I

Ravenstonedale Nr Kirkby Stephen Cumbria CA17 4NG   Map 13 D5

A turn-of-the-century, Lakeland-stone inn, six minutes from the M6
(junction 38) and a mere half an hour from Ullswater, useful as a base for
walking and fishing. Main bedrooms in traditional style are supplemented
by more modern additions in the old stables, where ramps and wide
doorways offer good access for disabled guests. ***Rooms 16.*** *Garden, lake and
river fishing, tennis. Access, Amex, Visa,*

Reading   Caversham Hotel   71%   £119

Tel 0734 391818   Fax 0734 391665   H

Richfield Avenue Caversham Bridge Reading Berkshire RG1 8BD   Map 5 D2

Right on the edge of the river Thames, by the side of Caversham Bridge,
this three-storey hotel is ultra modern in design with a mixture of red
brick and sloping roofs. Large, open-plan public rooms include a cocktail
bar in the sunken lounge, and a spotless white marble foyer. Limed
lightwood furniture graces the uniformly decorated bedrooms. Eight suites
have private balconies with river views, good-sized sitting rooms and
better quality furnishings. Centrepiece of the hotel is a restaurant with a
glass pyramid roof and doors that open on to a riverside verandah.
Uniformed staff show an admirable willingness to help when required.
Rooms 114. *Indoor swimming pool, sauna, solarium, keep-fit equipment, dinner
dance (fortnightly). Access, Amex, Visa,*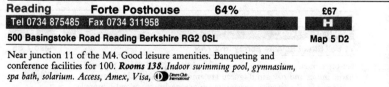

Reading   Forte Posthouse   64%   £67

Tel 0734 875485   Fax 0734 311958   H

500 Basingstoke Road Reading Berkshire RG2 0SL   Map 5 D2

Near junction 11 of the M4. Good leisure amenities. Banqueting and
conference facilities for 100. ***Rooms 138.*** *Indoor swimming pool, gymnasium,
spa bath, solarium. Access, Amex, Visa,*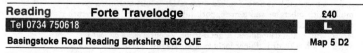

Reading   Forte Travelodge   £40

Tel 0734 750618   L

Basingstoke Road Reading Berkshire RG2 0JE   Map 5 D2

Located next to the Harvester restaurant on the A33 southbound, close to
Reading town centre. 1 mile north of junction 11 on the M4. ***Rooms 36.***
Access, Amex, Visa.

Reading   Ramada Hotel   70%   £121

`Tel 0734 586222   Fax 0734 597842`   **H**

Oxford Road Reading Berkshire RG1 7RH   Map 5 D2

In the town centre but not far from the M4, the Ramada is a large modern
hotel in red brick. Good-sized bedrooms range from singles to a
presidential suite; up-to-date accessories include individual air-conditioning.
Among the public areas are a comfortable sunken lounge, a stylish piano
bar, the lively Continental-style *Froggies* bar-café and two restaurants (one
open long hours). There are five syndicate rooms, a large conference suite
(capacity 200+) and a well-appointed health and leisure centre. Children
under 16 stay free in parents' room. *Rooms 196. Indoor swimming pool,
keep-fit equipment, sauna, sun beds, hair salon. Access, Amex, Visa,*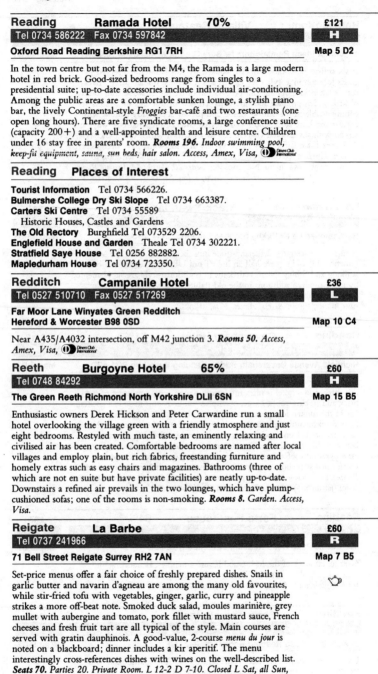

Reading   Places of Interest

Tourist Information   Tel 0734 566226.
Bulmershe College Dry Ski Slope   Tel 0734 663387.
Carters Ski Centre   Tel 0734 55589
   Historic Houses, Castles and Gardens
The Old Rectory   Burghfield Tel 073529 2206.
Englefield House and Garden   Theale Tel 0734 302221.
Stratfield Saye House   Tel 0256 882882.
Mapledurham House   Tel 0734 723350.

Redditch   Campanile Hotel   £36

`Tel 0527 510710   Fax 0527 517269`   **L**

Far Moor Lane Winyates Green Redditch
Hereford & Worcester B98 0SD   Map 10 C4

Near A435/A4032 intersection, off M42 junction 3. *Rooms 50. Access,
Amex, Visa,*

Reeth   Burgoyne Hotel   65%   £60

`Tel 0748 84292`   **H**

The Green Reeth Richmond North Yorkshire DLII 6SN   Map 15 B5

Enthusiastic owners Derek Hickson and Peter Carwardine run a small
hotel overlooking the village green with a friendly atmosphere and just
eight bedrooms. Restyled with much taste, an eminently relaxing and
civilised air has been created. Comfortable bedrooms are named after local
villages and employ plain, but rich fabrics, freestanding furniture and
homely extras such as easy chairs and magazines. Bathrooms (three of
which are not en suite but have private facilities) are neatly up-to-date.
Downstairs a refined air prevails in the two lounges, which have plump-
cushioned sofas; one of the rooms is non-smoking. *Rooms 8. Garden. Access,
Visa.*

Reigate   La Barbe   £60

`Tel 0737 241966`   **R**

71 Bell Street Reigate Surrey RH2 7AN   Map 7 B5

Set-price menus offer a fair choice of freshly prepared dishes. Snails in
garlic butter and navarin d'agneau are among the many old favourites,
while stir-fried tofu with vegetables, ginger, garlic, curry and pineapple
strikes a more off-beat note. Smoked duck salad, moules marinière, grey
mullet with aubergine and tomato, pork fillet with mustard sauce, French
cheeses and fresh fruit tart are all typical of the style. Main courses are
served with gratin dauphinois. A good-value, 2-course *menu du jour* is
noted on a blackboard; dinner includes a kir aperitif. The menu
interestingly cross-references dishes with wines on the well-described list.
*Seats 70. Parties 20. Private Room. L 12-2 D 7-10. Closed L Sat, all Sun,
Bank Holidays (open Good Friday), 25-27 Dec. Set L £9.90/16.95 Set D
£25.95/£28.95 (with house wine). Access, Amex, Visa,*

Reigate   Bridge House   61%   £91

H

Tel 0737 246801   Fax 0737 223756

Reigate Hill Reigate Surrey RH2 9RP   Map 7 B5

Just off junction 8 of the M25, 15 minutes from Gatwick Airport. High on
Reigate Hill, a modern hotel with impressive views across the valley.
Bedrooms are of a good size, with smart darkwood units; the best rooms
have south-facing balconies and good views, while rear rooms have poor
outlooks. Children up to 4 stay free in parents' room; special rates for
families of four (with children under 15) using one or two rooms. No
dogs. *Rooms 37. Dinner dance (Fri & Sat). Access, Amex, Visa,*  *Diners Club International*

Renishaw   Sitwell Arms   61%   £116

H

Tel 0246 435226   Fax 0246 433915

39 Station Road Renishaw Nr Eckington Derbyshire S31 9WE   Map 11 D2

18th-century inn with many extensions and a purpose-built bedroom
block. One mile from the M1 (junction 30). *Rooms 30. Garden, dinner
dance (weekly Nov-Jan). Access, Amex, Visa,* *Diners Club International*

Retford   Forte Travelodge   £40

L

Tel 0777 838091

Al Markham Moor Nr Retford Nottinghamshire DN22 0QU   Map 11 D2

On the A1(M) northbound, 14 miles north of Newark-on-Trent, 25 miles
south-east of Sheffield with access from both north and southbound
carriageways. *Rooms 40. Access, Amex, Visa.*

Richmond   Petersham Hotel   64%   £120

HR

Tel 081-940 7471   Fax 081-940 9998

Nightingale Lane Richmond Surrey TW10 6UZ   Map 7 A5

A distinctive mid-Victorian confection in French Gothic style overlooking
the Thames, right next to the 2,500 acres of Royal Richmond Park. The
hotel's grand staircase (the longest unsupported Portland stone flight in
England) winds through five floors to bedrooms in a mish-mash of styles
and sizes. The best have reproduction furniture, spacious bathrooms and
stunning river views; the cramped singles elsewhere don't match up.
Receptions, conferences and private dining for 20-70 people. Children stay
free in parents' room. No dogs. *Rooms 54. Coffee shop (9am-11pm). Access,
Amex, Visa,* *Diners Club International*

Nightingales   £65

Decorated in attractive pale pink tones, with glorious river views from a
few tables, Nightingales derives its name from the nearby grassy
carriageway of Victorian times. Classical origins equally permeate Tim
Richardson's thoughtful menus, his cooking a mixture of the traditional
and the innovative. Favourites on the 3-course lunchtime menu include
duck and wood pigeon terrine, calf's liver with bubble and squeak and
bread-and-butter pudding. Specialities from the carte may be ravioli of
lobster with baby leeks and his signature dish of brill and salmon gateau
with scampi, seaweed and saffron mousse and champagne sauce.
Richardson's fixed-price 4-course "taste of England today" dinner menu
invokes poetic licence by offering a range from grilled fresh sardines with
mustard seed dressing to char-grilled fish kebab and white chocolate and
mint parfait with Tia Maria-flavoured dark chocolate sauce. *Seats 60.
Parties 30. Private Room. L 12.15-2.15 D 7-9.45. Closed 25 & 26 Dec. Set L
£17 (£20 Sun) Set D £22.*

Richmond　　Richmond Gate Hotel　　65%　　£105

Tel 081-940 0061　Fax 081-332 0354　　**H**

Richmond Hill Richmond Surrey TW10 6RP　　Map 7 A5

High up on Richmond Hill (opposite the Royal Star and Garter Home), almost overlooking the Thames, the hotel was originally a collection of four 18th-century buildings. The original, Morshead House, contains intimate public rooms and eight luxury double rooms of grand proportions. In a newer extension, to the rear, bedrooms are equally attractive and comfortable,though more uniform in design. Under-7s stay free in parents' room. Adaptable meeting and dining rooms accommodate up to 70 people. No dogs. *Rooms 53. Garden, squash. Access, Amex, Visa,*

Richmond　　Wine & Mousaka　　£25

Tel 081-940 5696　　**R**

12 Kew Green Richmond Surrey TW9 3BH　　Map 7 A5

Sensibly-priced Greek restaurant overlooking Kew Green offering the usual favourites, including a good meze. See also entry under London W5 (Ealing). *Seats 52. Parties 20. L 12-2.30 D 6-11. Closed Sun, Bank Holidays. Access, Amex, Visa,* ⓘ

Ridgeway　　Old Vicarage　　★　　£80

Tel 0742 475814　　**R**

Ridgeway Moor Ridgeway Nr Sheffield Derbyshire S12 3XW　　Map 10 D2

Tessa Bramley has tried to move up a gear this year in terms of cooking skills, service and all-round value-for-money; less butter is now used in sauces, the use of olive oil and nut oils follows the contemporary culinary styles set elsewhere; similarly, expensive ingredients are used less and the kitchen skills themselves made more of a feature. Certainly, the lower-priced set meals are more instantaneous in concept (cannelloni of spinach, leeks and pine kernels with spring herb soufflé, honey-roast duckling with caramelised apple tart, baked chocolate pudding with hot fudge sauce and English custard), but not to the detriment of the overall quality of the dishes produced. Imagination is much in evidence and her food *is* exciting (as well as technically sound), as she wants it to be. The full-price menu includes amuse-gueule and a light intermediate course as well as, perhaps, a starter combining beef satay, Thai-spiced fish cakes and filo packets of monkfish and lemon balm, followed by roast local duckling on a bed of cabbage with garlic and juniper plus the legs served as Peking duck pancakes with hoi sin sauce – both evolved and involved dishes. Front of house is now run by owner Tessa's son Andrew and his fiancée. The wine list is well thought out and well-chosen, with some classic gems at reasonable prices; ask for advice and you'll get it. *Seats 50. Parties 40. Private Room. L 12.30-3 D 7-11. Closed D Sun, all Mon, Bank Holiday Mons, 27-30 Dec. Set meals £18.50 & £27.50. Access, Amex, Visa.*

Ripley　　Michels'　　£83

Tel 0483 224777　　**R**

13 High Street Ripley Surrey GU23 6AQ　　Map 5 E3

Chic decor and polished service complement Erik Michel's sophisticated and inventive cooking. Pressed terrine of ratatouille and langoustines, with a red pepper sauce, best end of lamb wrapped with potato, roasted and served with creamed parsley and mushrooms, and frozen soufflé of candied carrots with passion fruit juice show the style. Unusually, the price of the dessert includes a cheese course and there's good coffee and varied petits fours to finish. *Seats 50. Parties 12. Private Room. L 12.30-1.45 D 7.30-9 (Sat 7-9.30). Closed L Sat, D Sun, all Mon, 25 & 26 Dec, 1 Jan. Set L £20 Set D £27. Access, Amex, Visa,* ⓘ

Ripon   Ripon Spa Hotel   62%   £70

Tel 0765 602172   Fax 0765 690770   **H**

Park Street Ripon North Yorkshire HG4 2BU   Map 15 C6

A comfortable hotel dating from 1909, with good staff and commendably
high standards of housekeeping. The prize-winning gardens, which extend
to seven acres, are a major plus, and the setting is secluded considering its
proximity to the city centre. Another asset comes in the shape of the high-
ceilinged bedrooms. Rooms are individually decorated and furnished, and
two have four-posters. One de luxe room has a whirlpool bath. Children
up to 14 stay free in parents' room. *Rooms 40. Garden. Access, Amex, Visa,*
 Diners Club International

Ripon   Places of Interest

Fountains Abbey & Studley Royal Gardens (NT)   Tel 0765 86333.
Newby Hall & Gardens   Nr Ripon Tel 0423 322583.
Ripon Cathedral   Tel 0765 2072.
Ripon Racecourse   Tel 0765 602165.
Lightwater Valley Action Park   Tel 0765 85321.

Roade   Roadhouse   £55

Tel 0604 863372   **R**

16 High Street Roade Northamptonshire NN7 2NW   Map 5 D1

Chris Kewley runs a leisurely village restaurant. He cooks a short menu
with about six choices per course in a sound, ungimmicky style and
without undue attention to calorie-counting. Duck liver paté with port,
bacon and brandy; feuilleté of asparagus with beurre blanc sauce; sautéed
pigeon breasts with kumquats and red wine sauce; strawberries baked on
brioche and served with vanilla ice cream. Informal service suits the
surroundings. Short, varied wine list with a good selection of half bottles.
*Seats 32. Parties 20. L 12.30-1.45 D 7-10. Closed L Sat, Sun & Mon, Bank
Holidays, 2 weeks Jul/Aug. Set L £13.70 Access, Visa.*

Rochester   Forte Crest   62%   £87

Tel 0634 687111   Fax 0634 684512   **H**

Maidstone Road Rochester Airport Rochester Kent ME5 9SF   Map 7 B5

Up-to-date comfort on the A229 near junction 3 of the M2.
Conference/banqueting facilities for 40/80. *Rooms 105. Indoor swimming
pool, gymnasium, spa bath, sauna, solarium, beautician, coffee shop (10am-6pm)
Access, Amex, Visa, Diners*

Rochester   Places of Interest

Tourist Information   Tel 0634 843666.
Cobham Hall   Cobham Tel 0472 823371.
Rochester Castle (EH)   Tel 0634 402276.
Rochester Cathedral   Tel 0634 43366.
Charles Dickens Centre   Tel 0634 844176.
Alpine Ski Centre   Chatham Tel 0634 827979.
Sheerness Beach 22 miles.

Oast House Theatre   Gillingham Tel 0634 372121.
Doddington Place Gardens   Sittingbourne Tel 079586 385.
The Ice Bowl   Gillingham Tel 0634 388477.

Rolleston-on-Dove   Brookhouse Hotel   62%   £75

Tel 0283 814188   Fax 0282 813644   **H**

**Brookside Rolleston-on-Dove Nr Burton-on-Trent
Staffordshire DE13 9AA**   Map 10 C3

Standing by the village brook, the William and Mary listed building was
built around 1690 and converted to a hotel in 1976. Bedrooms are all

individually styled with antique furniture, many with four-posters, half-tester or Victorian brass beds: several are in an adjacent converted barn. Private meetings and dining room for up to 14. No children under 12. *Rooms 19. Garden. Access, Amex, Visa,*

Romsey   Old Manor House   ↑   £90

Tel 0794 517353   **R**

21 Palmerston Street Romsey Hampshire SO51 8GF   **Map 4 C3**

In cottagey surroundings that are staunchly and traditionally old English, Mauro Bregoli has made his mark with the cuisine both of his native Italy and of France. He tracks down wild mushrooms, shoots a lot of game, smokes his own meat, makes his own foie gras, salami and pasta. Table settings are impeccable and amuse-gueule interesting – a taste of promising things to follow. Suckling pig and lobster are seasonal favourites and on a recent visit pastry-topped fish soup, grilled sea bass with courgettes and a black peppercorn crust, and pear feuilleté were notably good, so too the warm escalope of goose liver with a cold goose liver terrine. Good breads, cheeses (a fine French selection), petits fours and coffee. Lunchtime sees a choice of particularly good-value menus with an established repertoire of dishes like wild mushroom risotto or confit of duck. An extraordinary selection of clarets accompany a meticulously chosen list that is forty pages long and has depth everywhere you look. Prices are generally high, though the house choices provide good value. *Seats 42. Parties 10. Private Room. L 12-2 D 7-9.30. Closed D Sun, all Mon, 1 week Xmas. Set L £17.50 Set D £33. Access, Visa.*

Romsey   White Horse Hotel   63%   £96

Tel 0794 512431   Fax 0794 517485   **H**

Market Place Romsey Hampshire SO5 8ZJ   **Map 4 C3**

Georgian facade, oak beams, bedrooms (both period and modern) in a Forte hotel right on the market place. Courtyard seating. Banqueting facilities for 90, conferences up to 40. *Rooms 33. Access, Amex, Visa,*

Romsey   Places of Interest

Paultons Romany and Village Life Museums and Theme Park   Paultons Park, Ower Tel 0703 814442.
   Historic Houses, Castles and Gardens
Broadlands   Tel 0794 516878 *Home of Lord Mountbatten.*
Hillier Gardens and Arboretum   Ampfield Tel 0794 68787.
Mottisfont Abbey Garden (NT)   Mottisfont Tel 0794 41220/40757.

Rosedale Abbey   Milburn Arms   60%   £70

Tel &   Fax 075 15 312   **H**

Rosedale Abbey Nr Pickering North Yorkshire YO18 8RA   **Map 15 C5**

Tranquil surroundings in the beautiful North Yorks moors are the big attraction of Terry and Joan Bentley's delightful country hotel. Plants, ornaments, books and games make the lounge a nice place to spend an hour or two, and the bar is also the village local. Most of the bedrooms have good views. Dogs in ground-floor annexe rooms only. *Rooms 11. Garden. Access, Visa.*

Ross-on-Wye   Chase Hotel   64%   £75

Tel 0989 763161   Fax 0989 768330   **H**

Gloucester Road Ross-on-Wye Hereford & Worcester HR9 5LH   **Map 4 B1**

Old world charm almost blends with the modern decor at this restored Georgian mansion, standing in 11 acres of manicured grounds only a short walk from the town centre. Recent alterations have increased conference/banqueting capacity to 250 without undue intrusion.

Comfortable furniture and appealing fabrics impart a certain country house
appeal to the restyled bedrooms whose up-to-date amenities remain
practical and unobtrusive. No dogs. *Reduced rates at weekends.* **Rooms 39.**
Access, Amex, Visa.

Ross-on-Wye	**Pengethley Manor**	**67%**	**£114**

Tel 0989 87211 Fax 0989 87238	**H**

Harewood End Ross-on-Wye Hereford & Worcester HR9 6LL   Map 4 B1

Fifteen acres of estate with pitch-and-putt golf course, trout lake and
landscaped gardens enhance Pengethley's tranquil country setting: while
there is plenty of activity for sportsmen and families (under-14s staying
free in parents' room). There is also purpose-built accommodation for
disabled guests in the converted stables. Banqueting for up to 85 and
conference rooms accommodating 60 are kept discreetly separate.
Rooms 24. *Garden, croquet, outdoor swimming pool, snooker, outdoor chess,
9-hole improver's golf course, fishing. Access, Amex, Visa,*  Diners Club International

---

Ross-on-Wye	**Pheasants**	**£55**

Tel 0989 65751	**RR**

52 Edde Cross Street Ross-on-Wye Hereford & Worcester HR9 7BZ   Map 4 B1

A dozen neatly space tables occupy the front rooms of this former pub
alongside a tiny bar-lounge comprising four easy chairs, window seat and
open fire. Eileen Brunnarius has created an informal, home-from-home
atmosphere, which is reflected in the studied simplicity of her best dishes:
rabbit and gammon brawn, strudel of courgettes and feta cheese, baked
gurnard with anchovy gusto, and free-range chicken served "abreast of the
thyme". There are over 30 wines (including dessert wines) available by the
glass on a very personal wine list compiled by Adrian Wells who looks
after front of house. Splendid selection, super value. **Seats 22.** *Parties 40.
Private Room. L 12-2 D 7-10. Closed Sun & Mon, Bank Holidays, 1 week
Xmas. Access, Amex, Visa.*

Rooms   £36

Guests occupying the two cottagey bedrooms (one double, one twin) share
a bathroom with Eileen, her cheese plant and a china hippopotamus.
Splendid country breakfasts.

Ross-on-Wye   Places of Interest

Tourist Information   Tel 0989 62768.
Goodrich Castle   Tel 0600 890538.
Hill Court Gardens   Hom Green Tel 0989 763123.

Rotherham	**Campanile Hotel**	**£36**

Tel 0709 700255 Fax 0709 545169	**L**

**Lowton Way off Denby Way Hellaby Ind. Est. Rotherham
S. Yorks S66 8RY**   Map 11 D2

Off M18 junction 1, past M1 junction 32. **Rooms 50.** *Access, Amex, Visa,*
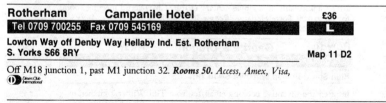 Diners Club International

---

Rotherham	**Moat House**	**69%**	**£86**

Tel 0709 364902 Fax 0709 368960	**H**

Moorgate Road Rotherham South Yorkshire S60 2BG   Map 11 D2

By the A618, south of town. Leisure facilities (no pool) and conference
suites (for up to 250 delegates). **Rooms 83.** *Spa bath, sauna, solarium, keep-fit
equipment, dinner dance (Fri & Sat). Access, Amex, Visa,* Diners Club International

Rotherham   Travel Inn   £42
| Tel 0709 543216   Fax 0709 531546 | **L** |

Bawtry Road Rotherham South Yorkshire S65 3JB   Map 11 D2

3 miles off the M1 (J33), 10 minutes from Sheffield and Doncaster.
Rooms 37. Access, Amex, Visa, (⬦)

Rotherham   Places of Interest

Tourist Information   Tel 0709 823611.
Rotherham Arts Centre   Tel 0709 373866.

Rotherwick   Tylney Hall   77%   £108
| Tel 0256 764881   Fax 0256 768141 | **HR** |

Rotherwick Nr Hook Hampshire RG27 9AJ   Map 5 D3

Well signed from the B3349, just off junction 5 of the M3, this imposing
mansion is of palatial proportions. A boarding school until 1984, it stands
in 66 acres of mature grounds with lakes and formal gardens. The original
carved oak panelling and high, moulded ceilings indicate that no expense
was spared when the house was built in Victorian times. Large day rooms
have recently been smartened up, but the bedrooms remain a mix of
varying sizes and styles. Although all is grand and comfortable (with
appropriate service to match), it doesn't quite achieve luxury status.
Banqueting and conference facilities for around 100. *Rooms 91. Garden,
indoor & outdoor swimming pools, keep-fit equipment, spa bath, sauna, tennis,
snooker. Access, Amex, Visa,* (⬦)

Restaurant   £85

An adventurous, wide-ranging carte is complemented by a fixed-price
menu of 'traditional English fayre' and both try hard to match the grand,
candlelit setting. Admirably attentive and friendly service. *Seats 100.
Parties 10. Private Room. L 12.30-2 D 7.30-9.30. Set L £19 Set D £27.*

Rothley   Rothley Court   67%   £100
| Tel 0533 374141   Fax 0533 374483 | **H** |

Westfield Lane Rothley Leicestershire LE7 7LG   Map 11 D3

By the B5328 west of Rothley (six miles outside Leicester), this imposing
13th-century manor stands in six acres of grounds, surrounded by lawns
and open farmland. Much historical character is retained, including an
11th-century chapel built by the Holy Order of the Knights Templar. Day
rooms feature some fine oak panelling, buttoned-leather chairs, exposed
floorboards and stone fireplaces, while the main staircase boasts two fine
stained-glass windows. Manor bedrooms vary in size with antique
furniture and subdued colour schemes, while annexe rooms are more
uniform; feature rooms, like the King Henry III suite in a separate cottage,
attract a justifiable 20% supplementary charge. Characterful meeting rooms
for up to 100. Forte Heritage. *Rooms 36. Garden, croquet. Access, Amex,
Visa,* (⬦)

Rowde   George & Dragon   NEW   £30
| Tel 0380 723053 | **R** |

High Street Rowde Wiltshire SN10 2PN   Map 4 B3

Inspired and inventive cooking emanates from Tim Withers's kitchen in
the humblest surroundings of a Wadworths village pub. Dishes run from
baked eggs to lobster soufflé, plus finest fresh fish from Falmouth (steamed
cod with lemon grass and coriander, fillet of grey mullet with leeks) and
English-only cheeses, beers and mineral waters. Remarkably, any one of
over 40 wines on the list is available by the glass. Booking is always
advised, at least one week in advance for tables at weekends. *Seats 35.
Parties 32. Private Room. L 12-2 D 7-10. Closed D Sun, all Mon, 25 & 26
Dec, 1 Jan. Set L £10 (Sun £12.50). Access, Visa.*

Rowsley	Peacock Hotel	64%	**£75**

Tel 0629 733518   Fax 0629 732671   **H**

Rowsley Matlock Derbyshire DE4 2EB   **Map 10 C2**

Trout and grayling fishing on the river Derwent that runs along the
bottom of the garden (and an additional 12 rods on the Wye) make this
17th-century hotel a popular fisherman's haunt. Mellow, antique-filled
public rooms include a beamed bar with rough stone walls, while
individually decorated bedrooms offer all the usual modern comforts.
Jarvis Hotels. *Rooms 14. Garden, coarse & game fishing. Access, Amex, Visa,*

Ruckhall	Ancient Camp Inn	**£58**

Tel 0981 250449   **I**

Ruckhall Nr Eaton Bishop Hereford & Worcester HR2 9QX   **Map 4 A1**

On the site of a former Iron Age fort, the inn stands atop an escarpment
overlooking a wide bend in the river Wye. Conversion by owners David
and Nova Hague retains original stonework and flagstone floor to create an
intimate atmosphere, cheered in winter by huge log fires. Nova's home-
made pub lunches and informal dinners make this a popular haunt. Three
neat bedrooms to the rear have showers/WC only; of two at the front one
has a private sitting room, the other an en-suite bath elevated to maximise
its river view. No children under 8. No dogs. *Rooms 5. Garden, fishing.
Access, Visa.*

Rugby	Periquito Hotel	**£56**

Tel 0788 544585   Fax 0788 546097   **I**

Sheep Street Rugby Warwickshire CV21 3BX   **Map 11 D4**

Formerly the *Three Horse Shoes*, this 18th-century coaching inn has
recently been acquired by Periquito Hotels, who plan major refurbishment.
Children stay free in parents' room. *Rooms 35. Access, Amex, Visa,*

Rugeley	Forte Travelodge	**£40**

Tel 0889 570096   **L**

A51/B5013 Western Springs Road Rugeley Staffordshire WS15 2AS   **Map 10 C3**

On the A51/B5013, 6 miles east of Stafford in the centre of the town, next
to the bus station. Close to Lichfield, Stoke-on-Trent and junctions 13/14
of the M6. *Rooms 32. Access, Amex, Visa.*

Runcorn	Campanile Hotel	**£36**

Tel 0928 581771   Fax 0928 581730   **L**

Lowlands Road Runcorn Cheshire WA7 5TP   **Map 10 A2**

Take junction 12 off the M56 to the A557 ring road. Close to the station.
Rooms 53. Access, Amex, Visa,

Runcorn	Forte Crest	62%	**£88**

Tel 0928 714000   Fax 0928 714611   **H**

Wood Lane Beechwood Runcorn Cheshire WA7 3HA   **Map 10 A2**

A modern hotel not far from the M56 (junction 12), with ample free car
parking, a leisure club and a very extensive conference facilities (a choice of
19 rooms holding up to 500 delegates theatre-style). *Rooms 134. Indoor
swimming pool, gymnasium, spa bath, sauna, solarium, steam room, beauty &
hair salon, 24hr lounge service, dinner dance (Sat). Access, Amex, Visa,*

Rushden   Forte Travelodge   £40
`Tel 0933 57008`   **L**
A45 Saunders Lodge Rushden Hertfordshire   **Map 11 E4**

Located on the A45 near Rushden, 14 miles east of Northampton and 10
miles south of Kettering. *Rooms 40. Access, Amex, Visa.*

Rusper   Ghyll Manor   68%   £116
`Tel 0293 871571   Fax 0293 871419`   **H**
High Street Rusper Nr Horsham West Sussex RH12 4PX   **Map 5 E3**

Surrounded by 40 acres of gardens on the main road to Rusper, two miles
east of the A24 from Dorking. Bedrooms are split between the main,
original house, two cottages and a converted stable mews set around a
cobbled courtyard and high-beamed banqueting/conference room (catering
for up to 110). Those in the extensions are modern and larger than those in
the house, which have a few antiques and period detail. A comfortable, if
slightly cramped, library acts as a sitting room and features an open fire;
there is also an adjacent, tiny bar. Children up to 16 accommodated free in
parents' room; cots and baby-listening available. Forte Heritage. *Rooms 27.
Garden, croquet, sauna, solarium, tennis court, outdoor heated swimming pool
(May-October). Access, Amex, Visa,*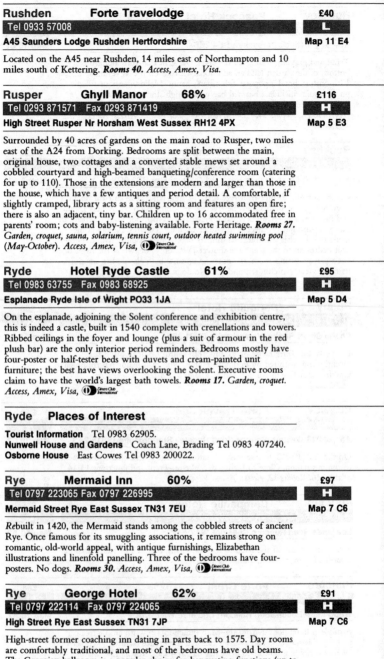

Ryde   Hotel Ryde Castle   61%   £95
`Tel 0983 63755   Fax 0983 68925`   **H**
Esplanade Ryde Isle of Wight PO33 1JA   **Map 5 D4**

On the esplanade, adjoining the Solent conference and exhibition centre,
this is indeed a castle, built in 1540 complete with crenellations and towers.
Ribbed ceilings in the foyer and lounge (plus a suit of armour in the red
plush bar) are the only interior period reminders. Bedrooms mostly have
four-poster or half-tester beds with duvets and cream-painted unit
furniture; the best have views overlooking the Solent. Executive rooms
claim to have the world's largest bath towels. *Rooms 17. Garden, croquet.
Access, Amex, Visa,*

Ryde   Places of Interest

Tourist Information   Tel 0983 62905.
Nunwell House and Gardens   Coach Lane, Brading Tel 0983 407240.
Osborne House   East Cowes Tel 0983 200022.

Rye   Mermaid Inn   60%   £97
`Tel 0797 223065 Fax 0797 226995`   **H**
Mermaid Street Rye East Sussex TN31 7EU   **Map 7 C6**

Rebuilt in 1420, the Mermaid stands among the cobbled streets of ancient
Rye. Once famous for its smuggling associations, it remains strong on
romantic, old-world appeal, with antique furnishings, Elizabethan
illustrations and linenfold panelling. Three of the bedrooms have four-
posters. No dogs. *Rooms 30. Access, Amex, Visa,*

Rye   George Hotel   62%   £91
`Tel 0797 222114   Fax 0797 224065`   **H**
High Street Rye East Sussex TN31 7JP   **Map 7 C6**

High-street former coaching inn dating in parts back to 1575. Day rooms
are comfortably traditional, and most of the bedrooms have old beams.
The Georgian ballroom is a popular choice for banqueting functions (up to
100) and conferences (up to 80). Forte Heritage. *Rooms 22. Access, Amex,
Visa,*

Rye   Landgate Bistro   £48
Tel 0797 222829   **R**

5/6 Landgate Rye East Sussex TN31 7LH   Map 7 C6

Converted from two tiny Landgate shops, this long-standing and popular
bistro is brick-lined and cottagey, with plastic table-cloths setting the tone
of presentation, but not the quality of cooking. Toni Ferguson-Lees'
cooking is intelligently constructed, effortlessly simple and strong on fish:
moules marinière, smoked haddock fishcakes with parsley sauce, crab
terrine, scallops and brill with vermouth and orange sauce, fillet of turbot
and tarragon sauce. Nevertheless, leek and Roquefort tart, duck liver and
pepper salad, wild rabbit, jugged hare, lamb leg steak with flageolet beans
and guinea fowl help balance the menu. A 3-course, fixed-price menu is
offered from Tuesday to Thursday only, perhaps encompassing chicken
quenelles with mushroom sauce, lamb's kidneys with grain mustard sauce
and chocolate marquise; the price includes coffee and service. *Seats 34.
Parties 8. D only 7-9.30 (Sat to 10). Closed Sun & Mon, Xmas, 1 week Jun,
1 week Oct. Set D £13.50. Access, Visa,*

Rye   Places of Interest

Tourist Information   Tel 0797 226696.
Lamb House   Tel 0797 226696 *Home of Henry James.*
Camber Sands Beach *3 miles E of Rye.*

Saffron Walden   Saffron Hotel   58%   £68
Tel 0799 522676   Fax 0799 513979   **HR**

10-18 High Street Saffron Walden Essex CB10 1AY   Map 6 B3

A family-run hotel in the centre of town with new owners this year.
There's an old-fashioned panelled bar with exposed brickwork and timbers.
Bedrooms, a few with four-posters, vary in size and style, but their decor
and appointments are generally quite modest. Some rooms are reached by
winding passages with head-threatening beams. It's best to discuss your
room requirements when booking. *Rooms 24. Garden. Access, Amex, Visa,*

Restaurant   £40

A bright and airy conservatory dining room is the setting for sound,
traditional cooking. Choose from à la carte or 2- or 3-course fixed-price
table d'hote menus. *Seats 50. Parties 20. Private Room. L 12-2 D 7-9. Closed
L Sat, D Sun. Set L £13.50 Set D £16.50.*

Saffron Walden   Places of Interest

Audley End House and Park (EH)   Tel 0799 22399.
Mole Hall Wildlife Park   Widdington, Newport Tel 0799 40400.

St Albans   Noke Thistle   68%   £102
Tel 0727 54252   Fax 0727 41906   **H**

Watford Road St Albans Hertfordshire AL2 3DS   Map 5 E2

Practical accommodation in what was once the farm of Burston Manor.
Set in its own grounds near M1, M10 and M25. Banqueting for up to 60,
conferences to 70. *Rooms 111. Garden. Access, Amex, Visa,*

St Albans   Sopwell House   65%   £115
Tel 0727 864477   Fax 0727 44741   **H**

Cottonmill Lane Sopwell St Albans Hertfordshire AL1 2HQ   Map 5 E2

A new country club is the centrepiece of this much extended 18th-century
house. Conferences for up to 300 delegates. *Rooms 84. Garden, gymnasium,
indoor swimming pool, sauna, solarium, spa bath, steam room, beautician,
hairdressing, snooker. Access, Amex, Visa,*

St Albans   St Michael's Manor   63%   £88

Tel 0727 864444   Fax 0727 48909

Fishpool Street St Albans Hertfordshire AL3 4RY   Map 5 E2

The manor house, which dates from the 16th century, overlooks beautiful
gardens and a lake. Well-proportioned day rooms have a traditional feel,
particularly the Oak Lounge, part of the original Tudor structure, with
fine plastered ceilings dated 1586. The restaurant has a bright conservatory
that's popular for private parties. The grounds contain many specimen
trees, after which all the bedrooms are named. Best of the rooms are
doubles with four-posters and garden views. *Rooms 26. Garden. Closed
3 days Xmas. Access, Amex, Visa,*

St. Albans   Places of Interest

Tourist Information   Tel 0727 864511.
Abbey Theatre   Tel 0727 57861.
The Gardens of the Rose   Chiswell Green Tel 0727 50461.
St. Albans Cathedral   Tel 0727 60780.
Dunstable Road Showground   Redbourne Tel 0582 792626.
   Museums and Art Galleries
St. Albans Organ Museum   Tel 0727 51557/73896.
The Verulamium Museum   St. Michael's Tel 0727 54659 or 866100 Ext
   2912.
The Mosquito Aircraft Museum   Salisbury Hall, London Colney Tel
   0727 22051.

St Austell   Boscundle Manor   65%   £110

Tel 0726 813557   Fax 0726 814997

Tregrehan St Austell Cornwall PL25 3RL   Map 2 B3

Secluded grounds make a peaceful setting for this lovely little 18th-century
manor house, whose owners Andrew and Mary Flint have been in
residence since 1978. Seven bedrooms are in the main house, one in the
Garden Room above the swimming pool and two in a cottage at the top of
the garden; all the doubles (8) have spa baths. A new practice golf area has
a golf net, two greens, several teeing positions, a lake, pond and a grassed
area for practising shots. *Rooms 10. Garden, golf practice area, outdoor
swimming pool, helipad, keep-fit equipment. Closed mid Oct-Easter. Access, Visa.*

St Austell   White Hart   £60

Tel 0726 72100   Fax 0726 74705

Church Street St Austell Cornwall PL25 4AT   Map 2 B3

Dating back to 1735, the White Hart stands in the centre of town.
Upgrading has kept day rooms and accommodation abreast of the times
and there are meeting facilities for up to 50. *Rooms 18. Access, Amex, Visa,*

St Ives   Slepe Hall   61%   £65

Tel 0480 63122   Fax 0480 300706

Ramsey Road St Ives Cambridgeshire PE17 4RB   Map 6 B2

An intimate hotel, housed in what was once a small private boarding
school for girls, kept in good order by the house-proud Stapleton family.
Several bedrooms feature four-poster beds and all but a couple have en-
suite bathrooms. The Brunel Suite and conference room provide adaptable
facilities for up to 220. Children stay free in parents' room. *Rooms 16.
Closed 25 & 26 Dec. Access, Amex, Visa,*

St Ives   Garrack Hotel   61%   £78

Tel 0736 796199   Fax 0736 798955   **H**

Burthallan Lane St Ives Cornwall TR26 3AA   Map 2 A3

The Kilby family have been running this creeper-clad hotel since 1965.
The main lounge is a cluttered, family room with games and books, and
there are two other more formal lounges plus a pleasant cocktail bar.
Rooms in the main house are period in style; those in the extension are
more modern with superb views over the sweeping bay in the distance. A
leisure centre in the two acres of gardens make a small pool and coffee bar.
Rooms 18. *Garden, indoor swimming pool, sauna, solarium, whirlpool bath,
coffee shop (11am-10.30pm). Access, Amex, Visa,*

St. Ives   Places of Interest

Tourist Information   Tel 0736 796297.
The Barbara Hepworth Museum   (The Tate Gallery) Tel 0736 796226.
Paradise Park   Hayle Tel 0736 753365.
Porthmeor Beach *10 miles.*

St Margaret's   Wallett's Court   60%   £45

Tel 0304 852424   **H**

West Cliffe St Margaret's Dover Kent CT15 6EW   Map 7 D5

Chris and Lea Oakley came here in 1980 to run a small, personal hotel
based around their 17th-century family home. Exposed brickwork and
beams in the foyer set the old-world rural tone and the lounge is splendid,
with beams, a brick fireplace and antique furniture. Three spacious rooms
in the main house have freestanding furniture, simple fabrics and tiled
bathrooms; those in the converted barn on the other side of the car park
are smaller but just as comfortable. Children up to the age of 7 stay free in
parents' room. No dogs. **Rooms 7.** *Garden, tennis. Closed Xmas, 1 week Jan,
1 week Nov. Access, Visa.*

St Martin's   St Martin's Hotel   69%   £196*

Tel 0720 22092   Fax 0720 22298   **H R**

St Martin's Isles of Scilly TR25 0QW   Map 2 A2

Hotel launch and Land Rover provide transport for arrivals, so make your
travel arrangements when booking. St Martin's provides the ultimate
escape for solitude seekers; an equally novel activity centre for families
(under-14s stay free in parents' room); and the last word in privacy for a
conference (max 100) or private dinner (up to 50). Public rooms include
the first-floor sunset lounge which affords wonderful views westward
towards Tresco. Under the same ownership as the Polurrian Hotel in
Mullion, Cornwall – Francis Family Hotels. *Half-board terms only.
Rooms 24. *Garden, croquet, indoor swimming pool, fishing, snooker, sailing and
scuba-diving instruction, baby-sitting, baby-listening. Closed Nov-Mar. Access,
Amex, Visa,*

Restaurant   £55

Table d'hote dinners make good use of fish and shellfish, game and home-
grown vegetables. Many special dishes, such as sautéed scampi tails with
orange beurre blanc or collops of crawfish with timbale of Scilly crab and
Pernod cream sauce attract a supplement to the fixed-price menus. Simple
sweets – pear crumble, profiteroles, baked cherry cheesecake. Lighter bar
lunches. **Seats 80.** *Parties 80. Private Room. D 7.15-9. Set D £22.*

St Mary's   Hotel Godolphin   58%   £92*

Tel 0720 22316   Fax 0720 22252   **H**

Church Street St Mary's Isles of Scilly TR21 0JR   Map 2 A2

Surrounded by a delightful town-house garden filled with sub-tropical
plants, the hotel has a welcoming, homely appearance and is just a minute
from the harbour beach. The friendly feel continues inside, where a

panelled entrance hall leads to a comfortable lounge area with gold velour seating around a marble fireplace. There is also a cosy bar. Most of the simply furnished bedrooms have functional bathrooms without showers; three are not en suite and four are suitable for family use. No dogs. *Half board terms; B&B rates on application. **Rooms 31.** Garden, sauna. Closed mid Oct-mid Mar. Access, Visa.

St Mary's   Tregarthen's Hotel   60%   £118*
Tel 0720 22540   Fax 0720 22089   **H**
St Mary's Isles of Scilly TR21 0PP   Map 2 A2

Founded in 1840 by a Captain Tregarthen, the hotel stands in terraced gardens overlooking the harbour. The foyer-lounge is mid-70s in style: chairs upholstered in oatmeal fleck, wood strip-panelled walls. The bar is more modern, with tasteful blue and grey seating and walls hung with limited edition prints. Bedrooms, some looking out to sea, are neat and comfortable, with up-to-date bathrooms. One bathroom boasts a Victorian cast-iron tub. * Half-board terms only. No dogs. **Rooms 29.** Garden. Access, Amex, Visa, ○ Diners Club International

St Mawes   Idle Rocks Hotel   61%   £108
Tel 0326 270771   Fax 0326 270062   **H R**
Tredenham Road St Mawes Cornwall TR2 5AN   Map 2 B4

Uninterrupted views of the harbour and Carrick Rocks are enjoyed from a water's-edge terrace, and through picture windows fronting the bar and lounge. Public rooms have a comfortable, if somewhat cluttered, feel. Contemporary fabrics and bright colour schemes enhance stylish bedrooms, which sport draped beds and antique furniture. Front rooms have beautiful views and are to be preferred to those in the annexe, although the complete hotel has been refurbished in the last year. **Rooms 23.** Access, Amex, Visa, ○ Diners Club International

Water's Edge Restaurant   £55

Alan Vickops (formerly at Alverton Manor in Truro) offers a good choice of standard favourites with a particular emphasis on seafood: crab tartlet with mango and light mint dressing, brioche bun with lobster, shallots and a tomato and courgette coulis, Fowey sea trout, fish ragout, brill with spring onion and ginger butter sauce, lobster salad. **Seats 65.** Parties 20. L 12-2.30 D 7-9.15.

St Mawes   Rising Sun   62%   £58
Tel 0326 270233   **H**
The Square St Mawes Truro Cornwall TR2 5DJ   Map 2 B4

Popular and lively, with a harbour-view terrace that attracts the crowds when the sun shines. The small conservatory frontage houses a lounge bar, and there's a public bar that's a favourite with the locals. Residents can retreat to their own little lounge at the back (six seats, with TV). Bedrooms are smart and simple, with pine furniture and neat, practical bathrooms; three rooms are not en suite. **Rooms 12.** Access, Amex, Visa, ○ Diners Club International

St Mawes   Hotel Tresanton   69%   £78
Tel 0326 270544   Fax 0326 270002   **H**
Lower Castle Road St Mawes Cornwall TR2 5DR   Map 2 B4

A sun terrace makes the most of the setting overlooking the Fal estuary, and the garden boasts many exotic plants and trees. In cooler weather, the drawing room, with its open fire and inviting sofas, is definitely the place to be. Bedrooms all have sea views and private bathrooms, most of which are across a corridor. Four rooms have little balconies. Room price includes Cornish afternoon tea. No children under ten. **Rooms 21.** Garden. Closed Nov-Feb (open Xmas). Access, Amex, Visa, ○ Diners Club International

Salcombe   Marine Hotel   71%

£142

Tel 0548 844444   Fax 0548 843109

H

Cliff Road Salcombe Devon TQ8 8JH

Map 3 D3

Primarily a holiday town hotel, where most rooms have a balcony and a view of the Salcombe estuary with its sandy beaches and the rolling coastal hills beyond. Situated in the heart of the town, perched right on the water's edge, the dining room, lounge and other public rooms have large picture windows. A book-lined library section of the lounge is particularly quiet and restful. Carpeted bathrooms enhance the comfortable feel of the bedrooms, with the better rooms having polished wood, smarter units and a few more extras like a decanter of sherry. Large rooftop sundeck, poolside brasserie and other good leisure facilities. Tends to be a family hotel during the high summer months with an older clientele out of season. No dogs. Children up to 7 stay free when sharing with two adults. *Rooms 51. Garden, indoor swimming pool, sauna, solarium, spa bath, gymnasium, keep-fit equipment, beauty salon, hairdressing, sea fishing, mooring, games room. Access, Amex, Visa,*

Salcombe   Soar Mill Cove   65%

£128

Tel 0548 561566   Fax 0548 561223

HR

Soar Mill Cove Salcombe Devon TQ7 3DS

Map 3 D3

Spectacular coastal location and unrivalled sea views make for a memorable holiday hotel. The closeness of 14 bedrooms, all at ground level with neighbouring patios, readily engenders a house party atmosphere, much in keeping with the Makepeace family's philosophy, and to which the staff contribute willingly. Thoroughly comfortable bedrooms, close-carpeted through to equally adequate bathrooms, provide essential ingredients for a peaceful stay. The National Trust beach and cliff walks prove highly popular diurnal activities. Families with young children are admirably catered for; high tea between 5 and 5.30pm is designed to leave residents in peace in the dining room during dinner. *Rooms 14. Garden, indoor & outdoor swimming pools, tennis, putting, games room, laundry room. Closed Jan-mid Feb. Access, Amex, Visa.*

Restaurant

£70

Residents order in advance from their rooms, arriving for the main event at immaculately prepared tables in the dining room. A typical menu might offer a choice of four dishes at each course – hot terrine of veal and mushroom with a dill sauce, followed by tenderloin of pork glazed with a light Stilton sabayon. Laden dessert and cheese trolleys, followed by coffee in the lounge, continue the communal flavour. *Seats 40. L 12.30-2 D 7.30-9.30. Set D £28.*

Salcombe   South Sands   61%

£138*

Tel 0548 843741   Fax 0548 842112

H

Cliff Road Salcombe Devon TQ8 8LL

Map 3 D3

New owners (the same as the Tides Reach) have taken over this well-maintained holiday hotel, which stands directly on a sandy South Sands beach, a mile south of the town. Public areas include a bar/lounge with log-burning stove and a popular buttery bar. Pine-furnished bedrooms include several that interconnect for family use. Families are well catered for, with high tea, baby-listening and a supervised crèche in high season. *Half-board terms only, but B&B in early and late season. *Rooms 32. Indoor swimming pool, solarium whirlpool bath, steam bath, moorings, coffee shop (noon-8.30pm). Access, Visa.*

Salcombe   Spinnakers   £50
Tel 0548 843408   R
Fore Street Salcombe Devon TQ8 8JG   Map 3 D3

A picturesque waterside location where most of the tables have views of
the estuary. David and Sandra May serve up informal bar and patio meals
at lunchtime, with a more formal service in the evenings. There's always
an unpretentious atmosphere, a fixed-price dinner menu with a choice of
three dishes per course (perhaps home-cured beef with potato salad
followed by fidget pie with gammon, apple and cider, plus apple and
orange pie to finish), a variety of fresh local fish (from Brixham) and a few
vegetarian options. The carte ranges from crab croquettes with prawn
sauce or seafood pancake to Oxford John (lamb steak cooked with onions,
mushrooms, potatoes and white wine) and breast of duck with orange and
Grand Marnier. *Seats 60. Private Room. L 12-2.30 D 7-9.30. Closed D Sun,
also all Mon & Tue in winter, all Dec & Jan. Set D £12.95. Access, Visa.*

Salcombe   Tides Reach   71%   £162*
Tel 0548 84 3466   Fax 0548 84 3954   H
South Sands Salcombe Devon TQ8 8LJ   Map 3 D3

Nestling in the valley behind South Sands beach, with clear views over the
estuary and the Bolt Head, the Tides Reach celebrated its 25th anniversary
last year. All the elegant public areas – the marble-floored conservatory-
style entrance, the lounge in restful blue, the stylish Aquarium Bar – enjoy
sea views, as do all but three bedrooms. These range from five singles with
small double beds to junior and family suites. The sunbathing deck next to
the pool and a grass area around an ornamental pond are both glorious
suntraps in good weather. Very friendly and willing staff. A small public
ferry chugs its way from South Sands beach into the town and there are
spectacular coastal walks straight from the hotel. No children under 8.
*Rooms 39. Garden, indoor swimming
pool, sauna, solarium, keep-fit equipment, beauty and hairdressing salons, snooker,
squash, sailing, windsurfing (with tuition), water skiing, moorings, boat house &
dinghy park. Closed Nov-Feb. Access, Amex, Visa,*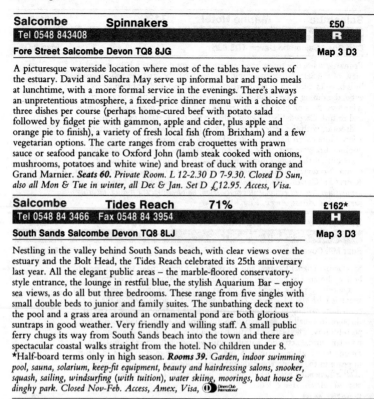

Salcombe   Places of Interest

Overbecks Museum and Garden (NT)   Tel 054884 2893.

Salisbury   Rose & Crown   56%   £96
Tel 0722 327908   Fax 0722 339816   H
Harnham Road Harnham Salisbury Wiltshire SP2 8QJ   Map 4 C3

A 13th-century, half-timbered inn whose gardens border the river Avon.
Public areas and some characterful bedrooms are in the original building,
other rooms are in a modern extension. Queens Moat Houses. *Rooms 28.
Garden. Access, Amex, Visa,*

Salisbury   White Hart   63%   £106
Tel 0722 327476   Fax 0722 412761   H
1 St John Street Salisbury Wiltshire SP1 2SD   Map 4 C3

City-centre hotel with an impressive pillared portico and elegant Georgian
facade, but dated bedrooms. Forte Heritage. *Rooms 68. Access, Amex, Visa,*

Salisbury   Places of Interest

Tourist Information   Tel 0722 334956.
  Theatres and Concert Halls
Medieval Hall   Tel 0980 610304.
Salisbury Arts Centre   Tel 0722 21744.
Salisbury Playhouse   Tel 0722 20333.

Historic Houses, Castles and Gardens
Fitz House Garden Tel 0722 716257.
Heale Gardens and Plant Centre Tel 0722 73504.
The King's House Tel 0722 332151.
Old Sarum Tel 0722 335398.
Wilton House Wilton Tel 0722 743115.
Stonehenge Nr Amesbury.
Salisbury Cathedral Tel 0722 22457.
Salisbury and South Wiltshire Museum and Stonehenge Gallery
    Tel 0722 332151.
Salisbury Racecourse Tel 0722 326461.

Saltash	**Granada Lodge**	£43
Tel 0752 848408 Fax 0752 848346		**L**
A38 bypass Saltash Cornwall PL12 6LF		**Map 2 C3**

Rooms 31. Access, Amex, Visa,

Samlesbury	**Swallow Trafalgar**	**64%**	£82
Tel 0772 877351 Fax 0772 877424			**H**
Preston New Road Samlesbury Lancashire PR5 0UL			**Map 10 B1**

Practical, well-run hotel on the A677, east of the M6 (junction 31). Good
leisure facilities and conference/banqueting facilities for 150/200. Children
up to 16 free in parents' room. *Rooms 78. Garden, indoor swimming pool, spa
bath, sauna, solarium, keep-fit equipment, squash. Access, Amex, Visa,*

Samlesbury	**Tickled Trout**	**63%**	£85
Tel 0772 877671 Fax 0772 847463			**H**
Preston New Road Samlesbury Nr Preston Lancashire PR5 OUJ			**Map 10 B1**

A modern hotel on the banks of the Ribble, west of junction 31 of the M6.
Good accommodation, a comfortable lounge bar with Victorian artefacts
and a decent leisure area are among the attractions. Quiet bedrooms (most
overlook the river) have fitted furniture, modern fabrics and the usual
accessories including trouser press. Small tiled bathrooms have baths plus
showers and hairdryers. Dinner dances every Friday and Saturday night.
Rank Hotels. *Rooms 72. Indoor swimming pool, fishing. Access, Amex, Visa,*

Sandbach	**Chimney House**	**61%**	£85
Tel 0270 764141 Fax 0270 768916			**H**
Congleton Road Sandbach Cheshire CW11 0ST			**Map 10 B2**

Although only moments from the M6 (junction 17) the mock-Tudor
Chimney House has a remarkably peaceful rural setting within eight acres
of wooded grounds. Open-plan public areas focus on a back-to-back pair of
original fireplaces; bedrooms favour pastel shades. Conference facilities for
up to 100 theatre-style. No dogs. *Rooms 48. Garden, sauna, solarium. Access,
Amex, Visa,*

Sandiway	**Nunsmere Hall**	**75%**	£125
Tel 0606 889100 Fax 0606 889055			**HR**
Tarporley Road Sandiway Cheshire CW8 2ES			**Map 10 B2**

Standing on a peninsula, surrounded by woods and a 60-acre lake,
Nunsmere is an elegant Victorian-built hall once the home of Sir Aubrey
Brocklebank, director of the Cunard-Brocklebank shipping line. Now
restored to its former glory and extended to double its original size and
housing a hotel with modern facilities including a fine, oak-panelled
cocktail bar, smart boardroom and conference facilities (for up to 48
delegates), with two floors of spacious bedrooms above. Luxury standards
apply: generous seating, vanitory and desk space plus top-quality
furnishings; stylish fabrics are used throughout. Victorian-style bathroom

recreations are nonethless state-of-the-art: all contain bidets and most a separate shower. **Rooms 32.** *Garden, croquet, keep-fit equipment, snooker, clay-pigeon shooting, archery, golf practice net, helipad. Access, Amex, Visa,*

Restaurant   £75

Plush decor and table settings in the stylish restaurant are complemented by cooking of convoluted extravagance. Chef Paul Kitching offers a variety of menus: simple, short-choice fixed-price lunches (terrine of salmon with saffron and tomato mayonnaise followed by braised leg of Cumberland lamb with black pudding, sausage and creamed potatoes and chocolate chiffon pie), plus à la carte, table d'hote and dégustation in the evening. The carte has effusive descriptions of the admittedly involved dishes (roast saddle of wild Scottish venison is served with fresh chestnuts, sautéed duck foie gras, steamed wild rice, and a game stock-based sauce spiked with red peppercorns and red wine vinegar) and the seven-course, no-choice dégustation runs the gamut from confit of duck and pork with foie gras to Brixham scallops, River Dart salmon, Scottish beef, wild mushrooms, farmhouse cheeses and chocolate marquise. A harpist plays on Saturday night. Well-balanced wine list with plenty of choice around the world. No smoking. **Seats 48.** *Parties 60. Private Room. L 12.30-2 (Sun 12-2.30) D 7.30-10 (Sat to 10.30). Set L £12.95/£17.25 (£16.50 Sat & Sun) Set D from £25.*

Saunton	Saunton Sands	67%	£124
Tel 0271 890212 Fax 0271 890145			**H**
Saunton Nr Braunton Devon EX33 1LQ			Map 2 C1

An ideal, family-oriented resort hotel, where you may park your car for a week and never need to use it; Saunton Sands commands panoramic views over the North Devon coastline. Five miles of golden sands stretch past the door; within, the leisure facilities are as abundant as are the sporting and aquatic activities without. Bedrooms are neat, light and airy, with Laura Ashley-style fabrics. Childrens' facilities include crèche, play areas, plenty of cots, baby-sitting, baby-listening and high teas. Three conference suites accommodate 20-200. No dogs. **Rooms 96.** *Garden, tennis, squash, indoor swimming pool, spa bath, sauna, solarium, snooker, hairdressing. Access, Amex, Visa,*

Sawbridgeworth	Manor of Groves	74%	£90
Tel 0279 600777 Fax 0279 600374			**H**
High Wych Sawbridgeworth Hertfordshire CM21 OLA			Map 7 B4

Off junction 7 of the M11 (following the signs to Harlow and then Bishops Stortford), a country manor, golf and country club converted and extended by Stuart and Wendy Sharer from a Georgian manor house. Surrounded by landscaped gardens and the original walled kitchen garden, with a further 150 acres transformed into an 18-hole golf course. Day rooms are generally comfortable, with restful colours and rich fabrics, including plump-cushioned seating in the drawing room. Most impressive, though, is the long, glazed and colonnaded loggia with check-tiled flooring, wicker furniture and parlour plants; snacks are served here. Bedrooms are tastefully gracious and stylish with soft, carefully co-ordinated fabrics and furnishings; the Coach House has duplex suites. Wonderful bathrooms with marble tiling, bright lighting and splendid, deep baths. Conference/banqueting facilities for 35/150. **Rooms 39.** *Garden, croquet, outdoor swimming pool, tennis, snooker, gymnasium, sauna, solarium, coffee shop (8am-late evening). Access, Amex, Visa,*

Scalby	Wrea Head	65%	£90
Tel 0723 378211 Fax 0723 371780			**H**
Scalby Nr Scarborough North Yorkshire YO13 0PB			Map 15 D5

Built in 1881, Wrea Head stands in 14 acres of wooded and landscaped gounds. It's signposted off the A171 and reached by a narrow driveway. A fine panelled hall features a wall-long stained glass window, while the bar is notable for an unusual terracotta frieze. Bedrooms are generally neat and comfortable, with delightful views. No dogs. **Rooms 21.** *Garden. Closed 4 days Xmas. Access, Amex, Visa,*

Scarborough   The Crown   63%   £91

Tel 0723 373491   Fax 0723 362271   **H**

Esplanade Scarborough North Yorkshire YO11 2AG   **Map 15 D6**

A splendid South Cliff setting just above the Spa Conference Centre. In-house conferences for up to 200. Forte Heritage. **Rooms 78.** *Snooker, hair & beauty salon. Access, Amex, Visa,*

Scarborough   Holbeck Hall   65%   £110

Tel 0723 374374   Fax 0723 351114   **H**

Seacliff Road South Cliff Scarborough North Yorkshire YO11 2XX   **Map 15 D6**

Located at the southern end of South Cliff, with views over the harbour, Holbeck Hall was built in 1886 and converted to hotel use in 1930. The most impressive features are the oak-panelled reception hall with its imposing baronial fireplace, the carved pine staircase and the minstrel's gallery. Recently restyled and redecorated bedrooms are smartly contemporary, enjoying either garden or sea views. Adjacent conference suites accommodate up to 160 delegates theatre-style. **Rooms 30.** *Garden. Access, Amex, Visa,*

Scarborough   Lanterna   £45

Tel 0723 363616   **R**

33 Queen Street Scarborough North Yorkshire YO11 1HQ   **Map 15 D6**

Established for 20 years, a straightforward Italian with a selection of chicken, veal and steak dishes as well as snails, spaghetti and scampi. **Seats 36.** *D only 7-9.30. Closed Sun & Mon. Access, Visa,*

Scarborough   Places of Interest

Tourist Information   Tel 0723 373333.
Royal Opera House   Tel 0723 36999.
St. Joseph Theatre in the Round   Tel 0723 370541.
Whitby Abbey   Whitby Tel 0947 603568.
Filey Bay Beach *7 miles from Scarborough.*

Scole   Scole Inn   £62

Tel 0379 740481   Fax 0379 740762   **I**

Norwich Road Scole Nr Diss Norfolk IP21 4DR   **Map 6 C2**

Built in 1655 by a wool merchant, this red-brick inn is Grade I listed for its architectural interest. Splendid brick gables front and rear show the Dutch influence that was then prevalent. Bedrooms in the Georgian stable block are quieter that in the main building, which face a busy lorry route. Main-house rooms, though, are full of character, many having carved oak doors, old timbers and fireplaces plus four-poster half-tester beds. The bar also has plenty of atmosphere. **Rooms 23.** *Garden. Access, Amex, Visa,*

Scotch Corner	**Forte Travelodge**	£40

Tel 0748 3768   **L**

A1 Scotch Corner Skeeby Nr Richmond North Yorkshire DL10 5EQ   **Map 15 B5**

On the A1 northbound, ½ mile south of Scotch Corner. *Rooms 40. Access, Amex, Visa.*

Seahouses	**Olde Ship Hotel**	£62

Tel 0665 720200   Fax 0665 721383   **I**

9 Main Street Seahouses Northumberland NE66 7RD   **Map 14 B2**

Alan and Jean Glen have emphasised the nautical charm of their characterful old inn overlooking the picturesque harbour and Farne Islands. The tiny cabin bar and handsome saloon bar house marine antiques, while the long gallery lounge has a collection of model ships. It's very much a traditional pub, a social centre for regulars and locals. Homely bedrooms; two have four-poster beds. No children under 10. No dogs. *Rooms 15. Garden, spa bath, putting. Closed Dec & Jan. Access, Visa.*

Seahouses   Places of Interest

Beadnell Bay Beach *4 miles South.*

Seale	**Hog's Back Hotel**	**64%**	£106

Tel 025 18 2345   Fax 025 18 3113   **H**

Seale Nr Farnham Surrey GU10 1EX   **Map 5 E3**

A tile-hung, gable-fronted hotel on the A31, with day rooms smart in pastel and pale wood, a leisure centre and conference facilities for up to 120. The pick of the accommodation size-wise is the most recent extension of 25 rooms. Children up to 14 stay free in parents' room. No dogs. Jarvis Hotels. *Rooms 75. Garden, indoor swimming pool, keep-fit equipment, spa bath, sauna, solarium, snooker. Access, Amex, Visa,*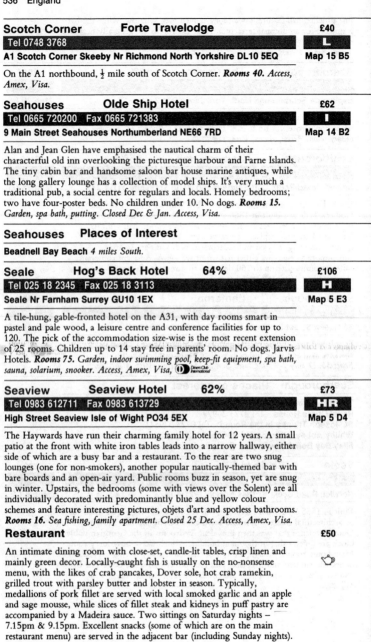

Seaview	**Seaview Hotel**	**62%**	£73

Tel 0983 612711   Fax 0983 613729   **HR**

High Street Seaview Isle of Wight PO34 5EX   **Map 5 D4**

The Haywards have run their charming family hotel for 12 years. A small patio at the front with white iron tables leads into a narrow hallway, either side of which are a busy bar and a restaurant. To the rear are two snug lounges (one for non-smokers), another popular nautically-themed bar with bare boards and an open-air yard. Public rooms buzz in season, yet are snug in winter. Upstairs, the bedrooms (some with views over the Solent) are all individually decorated with predominantly blue and yellow colour schemes and feature interesting pictures, objets d'art and spotless bathrooms. *Rooms 16. Sea fishing, family apartment. Closed 25 Dec. Access, Amex, Visa.*

Restaurant   £50

An intimate dining room with close-set, candle-lit tables, crisp linen and mainly green decor. Locally-caught fish is usually on the no-nonsense menu, with the likes of crab pancakes, Dover sole, hot crab ramekin, grilled trout with parsley butter and lobster in season. Typically, medallions of pork fillet are served with local smoked garlic and an apple and sage mousse, while slices of fillet steak and kidneys in puff pastry are accompanied by a Madeira sauce. Two sittings on Saturday nights – 7.15pm & 9.15pm. Excellent snacks (some of which are on the main restaurant menu) are served in the adjacent bar (including Sunday nights). *Seats 32. Parties 32. L 12-2 D 7.30-9.30. Closed D Sun.*

Seavington St Mary   The Pheasant   69%   £70
Tel 0460 40502   Fax 0460 42388   **H**
Water Street Seavington St Mary Nr Ilminster Somerset TA19 0QH   Map 4 A4

A setting of landscaped gardens with abundant trees and shrubs imbues the Paolonis' 17th-century former farmhouse with distinctive charm and character. Look for signs from the South Petherton end of the A303 Ilminster bypass. Hand-crafted reproductions of 18th- and 19th-century fine wood furniture feature in all the individually styled bedrooms: two in the main house with beams galore, the rest in cottages across the garden. Children under 2 stay free. No dogs. 10% service charge is added to your bill. *Rooms 10. Garden. Closed 26 Dec-10 Jan. Access, Amex, Visa,*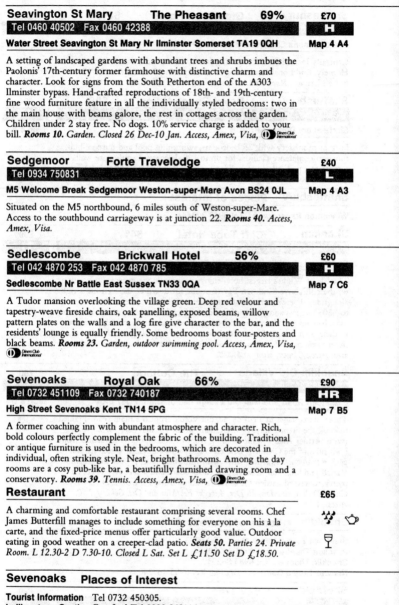

Sedgemoor   Forte Travelodge   £40
Tel 0934 750831   **L**
M5 Welcome Break Sedgemoor Weston-super-Mare Avon BS24 0JL   Map 4 A3

Situated on the M5 northbound, 6 miles south of Weston-super-Mare. Access to the southbound carriageway is at junction 22. *Rooms 40. Access, Amex, Visa.*

Sedlescombe   Brickwall Hotel   56%   £60
Tel 042 4870 253   Fax 042 4870 785   **H**
Sedlescombe Nr Battle East Sussex TN33 0QA   Map 7 C6

A Tudor mansion overlooking the village green. Deep red velour and tapestry-weave fireside chairs, oak panelling, exposed beams, willow pattern plates on the walls and a log fire give character to the bar, and the residents' lounge is equally friendly. Some bedrooms boast four-posters and black beams. *Rooms 23. Garden, outdoor swimming pool. Access, Amex, Visa,*

Sevenoaks   Royal Oak   66%   £90
Tel 0732 451109   Fax 0732 740187   **HR**
High Street Sevenoaks Kent TN14 5PG   Map 7 B5

A former coaching inn with abundant atmosphere and character. Rich, bold colours perfectly complement the fabric of the building. Traditional or antique furniture is used in the bedrooms, which are decorated in individual, often striking style. Neat, bright bathrooms. Among the day rooms are a cosy pub-like bar, a beautifully furnished drawing room and a conservatory. *Rooms 39. Tennis. Access, Amex, Visa,*

Restaurant   £65

A charming and comfortable restaurant comprising several rooms. Chef James Butterfill manages to include something for everyone on his à la carte, and the fixed-price menus offer particularly good value. Outdoor eating in good weather on a creeper-clad patio. *Seats 50. Parties 24. Private Room. L 12.30-2 D 7.30-10. Closed L Sat. Set L £11.50 Set D £18.50.*

Sevenoaks   Places of Interest

Tourist Information Tel 0732 450305.
Lullingstone Castle Eynsford Tel 0322 862114.
  Historic Houses, Castles and Gardens
Emmetts Garden Tel 073275 429.
Great Comp Borough Green Tel 0732 882669.
Ightham Mote (NT) Ivy Hatch, Ightham Tel 0732 810378.
Knole (NT) Tel 0732 450608.
Chartwell (NT) Tel 0732 866368 *Home of Winston Churchill.*
Squerryes Court Westerham Tel 0959 62345.

Shaftesbury   Grosvenor Hotel   62%   £86

Tel 0747 52282   Fax 0747 54755   **H**

The Commons Shaftesbury Dorset SP7 8JA   Map 4 B3

Centrally located former coaching inn based around a cobbled courtyard.
Homely, traditional feel. Conference/banqueting facilities for 150/120.
Forte Heritage. *Rooms 41. Access, Amex, Visa,*

Shaftesbury   Royal Chase Hotel   60%   £84

Tel 0747 53355   Fax 0747 51969   **H**

Shaftesbury Dorset SP7 8DB   Map 4 B3

Former monastery with 35 bedrooms, swimming pool and purpose-built
function/conference facilities for up to 190 delegates. Families are well
catered for, particularly in holiday periods. *Rooms 35. Garden, indoor
swimming pool, solarium, steam room. Access, Amex, Visa,*

Shaftesbury   Places of Interest

Wincanton Racecourse   Tel 0963 32344.

Shanklin   Cliff Tops Hotel   64%   £99

Tel 0983 863262   Fax 0983 867139   **H**

Park Road Shanklin Isle of Wight PO37 6BB   Map 5 D4

The Isle of Wight's largest hotel enjoys panoramic views from its position
on the cliff above Sandown Bay (a public lift down to the seafront is right
alongside). There's a choice of bars, a leisure club, conference rooms for up
to 350 delegates and plenty of facilities for children. Most of the bedrooms
have balconies. Children up to 14 stay free in parents' room (50% discount
in their own room). *Rooms 88. Indoor swimming pool, gymnasium, sauna,
steam room, spa bath, solarium, beauty & hair salon, snooker, children's play
area. Access, Amex, Visa,*

Shanklin Old Village   The Cottage   £50

Tel 0983 862504   **R**

8 Eastcliff Road Shanklin Old Village Isle of Wight PO37 6AA   Map 5 D4

Three old cottages in a cul de sac, but visible from the main road. Trained
to cook the French way, Neil Graham, in the kitchen here for 20 years
(with partner Alan Priddle running front of house), draws influences from
both sides of the Channel: Brie en croute with a devilled sauce, venison
paté, sole quenelles, grilled lamb with mint béarnaise, pepper steak flambé.
Varied puddings and desserts, plus cheeseboard and a savoury. There's a
pretty courtyard garden for summer eating. *Seats 32. L 12-2 D 7.30-9.45.
Closed D Sun, all Mon, 26 Dec, 4 weeks Feb/Mar and Oct. Set L £7.50.
Access, Visa.*

Shanklin   Places of Interest

Sandown Tourist Information   Tel 0983 403886.
Pavillion Theatre   Tel 0983 402295.
Shanklin Theatre   Tel 0983 862739.
Nunwell House Gardens   Brading Tel 0983 407240.

Sheffield   Bay Tree   £20

Tel 0742 759254   **R**

119 Devonshire Street Sheffield South Yorkshire S3 7SB   Map 10 C2

Vegetarian and fish dishes with generous portions in informal setting.
Typical choices include fennel goulash, green peppercorn roulade with
salads, and cod and prawn pie. *Seats 50. Parties 12. D Thu & Fri 6.30-9
Meals 9.30-3 (Sat 9.30-4). Closed L Sun, D Sat-Wed, Bank Holidays,*

Sheffield	**Charnwood Hotel**	67%	**£90**
Tel 0742 589411 Fax 0742 555107			**H**
10 Sharrow Lane Sheffield South Yorkshire S11 8AA			**Map 10 C2**

Val and Chris King and their young, friendly staff are ambitiously improving an extended Georgian building. The latest additions are the re-siting of the à la carte restaurant and the creation of a stylish brasserie adjoining the main hotel. The popular conservatory lounge is bright, in contrast to the two quiet drawing rooms with period furniture. Bedrooms are warm and comfortable with subdued colour schemes, dark units and thoughtful extras. The compact bathrooms are neat and well lit. *Rooms 21. Access, Amex, Visa,*

Restaurant

New chef Kevin Hensby (who has worked under Paul Bocuse and also had his own restaurant – *The Elizabethan* – in Brixham, Devon) arrived last May to oversee both the Charnwood's restaurants: the smart, formal **Henfry's** and the stylishly informal **Brasserie Leo**. The latter offers a good-value blackboard menu and particularly good 'light bites' and a speciality dish of fresh shellfish. *Closed Bank Holidays. Access, Amex, Visa,*

Sheffield	**Forte Crest**	65%	**£88**
Tel 0742 670067 Fax 0742 682620			**H**
Manchester Road Sheffield South Yorkshire S10 5DX			**Map 10 C2**

An undistinguished, concrete 60s' building refurbished up to acceptable standards. Half the rooms are non-smoking. Good leisure facilities and conference/banqueting amenities for 300/200. *Rooms 136. Indoor swimming pool, spa bath, sauna, solarium, keep-fit equipment, coffee shop (24hr). Access, Amex, Visa,*

Sheffield	**Grosvenor House**	67%	**£75**
Tel 0742 720041 Fax 0742 757199			**H**
Charter Square Sheffield South Yorkshire S1 3EH			**Map 10 C2**

Modern multi-storey hotel with direct access from its own car park. Rooms on the higher floors have good views over the city. Conference/banqueting facilities for 500/450; two boardrooms seat up to 20. Forte. *Rooms 103. Access, Amex, Visa,*

Sheffield	**Holiday Inn Royal Victoria**	67%	**£108**
Tel 0742 768822 Fax 0742 724519			**H**
Station Approach Sheffield South Yorkshire S4 7XE			**Map 10 C2**

Large redbrick Victorian building with well-proportioned, high-ceilinged day rooms. Conference and banqueting facilities for up to 300. Ample free car parking. *Rooms 100. Access, Amex, Visa,*

Sheffield	**Moat House**	71%	**£100**
Tel 0742 375376 Fax 0742 378140			**H**
Chesterfield Road South Sheffield South Yorkshire S8 8BW			**Map 10 C2**

A modern redbrick hotel situated alongside the A61, just south of the ring road, offering the businessman numerous up-to-date facilities. Its day rooms are tastefully styled with an impressive foyer that has polished marble floors and good space. The adjoining lounge area is fashionably and comfortably furnished but the main bar lacks atmosphere. Bedrooms are uniform in both size and design with lightwood units, contemporary fabrics and plenty of work space. Neat, but cold bathrooms are rather small. Well-equipped leisure centre. Conference/banqueting facilities for 500/300. *Rooms 95. Garden, indoor swimming pool, spa bath, sauna, solarium, beauty salon, keep-fit equipment. Access, Amex, Visa,*

Sheffield   Nirmal's   £40

Tel 0742 724054   **R**

193 Glossop Road Sheffield South Yorkshire S10 2GW   Map 10 C2

Arguably the best Indian restaurant in Sheffield, though the high prices of
vegetarian specialities may raise a few eyebrows. Look forward, however,
to superior North Indian cooking, refreshingly restrained in the use of oil
and ghee, in Nirmal's exclusive dishes from the specials board, in the well-
spiced daily-changing dals and the splendid home-made paneer. Good-value
set lunch, ambitious feasts for two or more and two days notice required
for the lamb masallam for six people. *Seats 80. Parties 50. Private Room.
L 12-2.30 D 6-12 (Fri & Sat to 1). Closed L Sun, all 25 & 26 Dec. Set L
£6.95 Set D (for 2) from £24. Access, Amex, Visa.*

Sheffield   St George Swallow Hotel   64%   £92

Tel 0742 583811   Fax 0742 500138   **H**

Kenwood Road Sheffield South Yorkshire S7 1NQ   Map 10 C2

Up-to-date accommodation, conference facilities (for up to 250) and a
smart leisure club in a much-extended country house. Set in 11 acres of
landscaped gardens (including an ornamental lake), two miles from the city
centre. *Rooms 141. Garden, indoor swimming pool, steam room, spa bath,
sauna, solarium, keep-fit equipment, coffee shop (10am-10pm). Access, Amex,
Visa,* **❶** Diners Club International

Sheffield   Places of Interest

Tourist Information   Tel 0742 734671/734672.
Sheffield Cathedral   Tel 0742 753434.
Sheffield United Football Ground   Bramhall Lane Tel 0742 738955.
Sheffield Wednesday Football Ground   Hillsborough Tel 0742 343122.
Don Valley Athletics Stadium   Tel 0742 789199.
  Theatres and Concert Halls
Crucible Theatre   Tel 0742 79922.
Leadmill   Tel 0742 754500.
Merlin Theatre   Tel 0742 551638.
  Museums and Art Galleries
Graves Art Gallery   Tel 0742 734781.
Kelham Island Industrial Museum   Tel 0742 722106.
Mappin Art Gallery   Tel 0742 726281.
Ruskin Gallery   Tel 0742 734781.

Shepperton   Moat House   61%   £103

Tel 0932 241404   Fax 0932 245231   **H**

Felix Lane Shepperton Middlesex TW17 8NP   Map 5 E2

A peaceful location by the Thames is a big plus at this modern hotel with
conference facilities for up to 300 delegates. *Rooms 180. Sauna, solarium,
keep-fit equipment, snooker, putting, mooring. Closed 1 week Xmas. Access,
Amex, Visa,* **❶** Diners Club International

Shepperton   Warren Lodge   £82

Tel 0932 242972   Fax 0932 253883   **I**

Church Square Shepperton Middlesex TW17 0JZ   Map 5 E2

In the corner of a pretty village square, this 18th-century inn offers clean,
basic accommodation in a picturesque setting. There are views of the river
not only from the wood-beamed bar but also from six rooms in a new
wing which lead on to a courtyard, motel-style. Bedrooms are modestly
decorated and kept in good order. A handsome old walnut tree dominates
the cool and shady garden that leads down to the banks of the Thames.
Rooms 52. Access, Amex, Visa, **❶** Diners Club International

Shepton Mallet   Blostin's Restaurant   £45

Tel 0749 343648   **R**

29 Waterloo Road Shepton Mallet Somerset BA4 5HH   **Map 4 B3**

Dark and candle-lit bistro where Nick Reed produces consistently well-cooked meals with 2- or 3-course fixed-price menus supplemented by an additional list of à la carte seasonal specialities. Gazpacho, local asparagus, gravad lax with avocado, guinea fowl with apples and cider brandy, fillet of hake with tomatoes and basil and home-made desserts (lemon tart, crème brulée, chocolate St Emilion) show the style. *Seats 32. Parties 28. D only 7-9.30. Closed Sun & Mon, 2 weeks Jan, 1 week Jun, 1 week Nov. Set D £13.50/£14.50. Access, Visa,* Diners Club International

Shepton Mallet   Places of Interest

Tourist Information   Tel 0749 345258.
Wookey Hole Caves and Mill Wookey Hole   Nr Shepton Mallet.
Royal Bath & West Showground   Tel 0749 823211.

Sherborne   Eastbury Hotel   67%   £98

Tel 0935 813131   Fax 0935 817296   **H**

Long Street Sherborne Dorset DT9 3BY   **Map 4 B3**

Built in 1740, the Eastbury is a fine Georgian town house with well-proportioned rooms. Public areas comprise an elegant entrance hall, a comfortably furnished lounge, a library amd an intimate cocktail bar with an ornately carved counter. Bedrooms, three of which are in an adjacent building, have smart polished-wood furniture and pretty fabrics. Bathrooms offer showers and tubs, plus good soaps and toiletries. No dogs. Families are well catered for – children up to 10 stay free in parents' room. Clipper Hotels. *Rooms 15. Garden. Access, Visa.*

Sherborne   Forte Posthouse   58%   £67

Tel 0935 813191   Fax 0935 816493   **H**

Horsecastles Lane Sherborne Dorset DT9 6BB   **Map 4 B3**

Low-rise hotel set in its own grounds on the A30 just outside Sherborne. *Rooms 59. Golf driving net, croquet, children's playroom, playground. Access, Amex, Visa,* Diners Club International

Shifnal   Park House   71%   £85

Tel 0952 460128   Fax 0952 461658   **H**

Park Street Shifnal Nr Telford Shropshire TF11 9BA   **Map 10 B4**

Originally two adjacent country houses of completely different architectural styles, Park House has nevertheless managed to retain much of the atmosphere of a private house. An elegant garden suite and individually stylish private rooms accommodate conferences and catering from 20 to 250. Bedrooms use quality furniture and fabrics, and plentiful extras include decanters of sherry and baskets of fresh fruit. Children under eight stay free in parents' room. This Rank hotel is near junction 4 of the M54. *Rooms 54. Garden, indoor swimming pool, spa bath, sauna, solarium, fishing. Access, Amex, Visa,* Diners Club International

Shifnal   Places of Interest

Boscobel House   Tel 0902 850244.
Weston Park   Weston-under-Lizard Tel 095276 207.

Shinfield   L'Ortolan   ★★★   £140

Tel 0734 883783   Fax 0734 885391   **R**

Old Vicarage Church Lane Shinfield Nr Reading Berkshire RG2 9BY   **Map 5 D2**

Five minutes off junction 11 of the M4, John and Christine Burton-Race's
former vicarage is a tranquil haven of culinary excellence, perhaps the
nearest thing to one of France's outstanding country restaurants that you'll
find in the UK. John's pedigree in the kitchen is well documented (time
spent at *Chewton Glen* and with Raymond Blanc at *Quat' Saisons* in
Summertown, Oxford, which he later ran himself) and Christine runs
front of house with charm and panache. A drink before your meal can be
taken on the garden lawn or the conservatory, while enjoying some of the
best amuse-gueule offered anywhere; sadly, if the restaurant is really busy
and everyone arrives at once, these rooms get overcrowded and so you
might get shown straight to your table. The choice of dining areas is
between a pair of rooms inside the house and an airy conservatory leading
off, overlooking the lawn; the latter is obviously the favourite in summer,
so book well ahead. The three-course fixed-price *menu du jour* might offer a
choice of four or five dishes per course, perhaps starting with heart of
Brittany artichoke topped with a crab mousse wrapped in smoked salmon
or potted mince of duck bound with pork and scented with herbs, served
with a Madeira jelly, followed by red mullet steamed with basil, its juices
bound in olive oil, laced with a tomato coulis, or local wild pigeon breast
marinated in cream, grilled, resting on a watercress coulis and garnished
with fresh pasta. English menu descriptions (translated from French) can
occasionally go over the top, but then so much work goes into the
preparation of the dishes that flowery descriptions can be excused. The
£48 dinner menu includes *spécialités du jour* that might include a raviolo
filled with light chicken mousseline bound with foie gras and truffles, or
lobster soufflé wrapped in a fillet of sole lined with courgette; carpaccio of
salmon trout and sea bass, feuilleté of rabbit with creamed sweetcorn – the
choice is always exciting and unusual. A dish of Scottish wild salmon
marinated in Chinese spices then dry-grilled in the skin and served on a
bed of shredded red cabbage shows that Burton-Race and his team (which
now includes sous-chef Nigel Marriage) are never content to stand still
when they could usefully be creating new taste combinations, or carefully
stuffing the flower of a baby courgette with asparagus mousse. The wide
selection of French cheeses is expertly described (and always in superb
condition); desserts are as involved as the main courses (*soufflé chaud
démoulé au chocolat, chartreuse citronelle, dome de mousse caramel brulée*).
Splendid breads are served with Echiré butter, and the petits fours that
accompany coffee and infusions are quite wonderful. An excellent wine list,
albeit with some gaps, has plenty of half bottles; best value are the French
regional wines. **Seats 60.** Parties 30. Private Room. L 12.15-2.15
D 7.15-10.30. Closed D Sun, all Mon, last 2 weeks Aug, last 2 weeks Feb.
Set L (weekday lunches) & D (Tues-Fri) £29.50/£38.75 Set D £48. Access,
Amex, Visa, ⓓ *Diners Club International*

Shipdham   Shipdham Place   64%   £60

Tel 0362 820303   **H**

Shipdham Nr Thetford Norfolk IP25 7LX   **Map 6 C2**

On the A1075, half way between East Dereham and Watton. Although
Georgian at first sight, parts of this old rectory date back to 1630 and
there's a Victorian addition, too. Day rooms include an elegant morning
room, and a TV lounge in the old part has stripped pine panelling. Good
breakfasts are served in the delightful old kitchen. More old pine, antiques
and rattan easy chairs characterise the pretty bedrooms. **Rooms 8.** Garden.
Access, Amex, Visa, ⓓ *Diners Club International*

Shipley   Aagrah   £25

Tel 0274 594660   R

27 Westgate Shipley West Yorkshire   Map 10 C1

Branch of the popular Bradford Indian chain. See further entries under
Bradford (Pudsey) and Skipton. *Seats 45. Parties 45. D only 6-12.15 (Fri &
Sat to 1.15). Closed 25 Dec. Access, Amex, Visa,* **①** *Diners Club International*

Shorne   Inn on the Lake   61%   £78

Tel 0474 823333   Fax 0474 823175   H

Shorne Nr Gravesend Kent DA12 3HB   Map 7 B5

A modern stopover set in landscaped grounds with ornamental lakes. Two
lounge bars open off the reception area, one quieter with settees, the other
with conference chairs and often occupied for that purpose. Of the pleasant
and practical bedrooms, a few on the first floor overlook the lakes and
have balconies. No dogs. Banqueting/conference facilities for 400/500.
Rooms 78. Garden, dinner dance (Saturdays). Access, Amex, Visa, **①** *Diners Club International*

Shrewsbury   Lion Hotel   62%   £91

Tel 0743 353107   Fax 0743 352744   H

Wyle Cop Shrewsbury Shropshire SY1 1UY   Map 10 A3

A town-centre Forte Heritage hotel with characterful, beamed bedrooms
and other period features amid the modern day rooms and conference
facilities (for up to 200). *Rooms 59. Access, Amex, Visa,* **①** *Diners Club International*

Shrewsbury   Prince Rupert Hotel   64%   £83

Tel 0743 236000   Fax 0743 357306   H

Butcher Row Shrewsbury Shropshire SY1 1UQ   Map 10 A3

Recently refurbished Queens Moat Houses hotel in the centre of the
historic city. Bedrooms include two four-poster suites. Conference facilities
for up to 100. Valet parking. *Rooms 65. Access, Amex, Visa,* **①** *Diners Club International*

Shrewsbury   Places of Interest

Tourist Information   Tel 0743 50761.
The Music Hall   The Square Tel 0743 50671.
Quarry Swimming Centre   Tel 0743 236583.
   Historic Houses, Castles and Gardens
Attingham Park (NT)   Attingham Tel 0743 77 203.
Hodnet Hall Gardens   Hodnet Tel 063 084 202.
Pitchford Hall   Condover Tel 06944 205.
Shipton Hall   Much Wenlock Tel 074 636 225.

Sidmouth   Belmont Hotel   63%   £106

Tel 0395 512555   Fax 0395 579154   H

The Esplanade Sidmouth Devon EX10 8RX   Map 3 E2

Standing in substantial grounds on the seafront, the Belmont, built as a
private residence in 1820, enjoys views over the bay from its roomy
lounges and from many of its bedrooms. Some rooms have private
balconies, and de luxe rooms offer numerous cosseting extras. Guests have
free use of the leisure facilities of the neighbouring sister hotel, the *Victoria*.
No dogs. *Rooms 54. Garden, putting, dinner dance (Saturdays). Access, Amex,
Visa,* **①** *Diners Club International*

| Sidmouth | Fortfield Hotel | 59% | £91 |

Tel & Fax 0395 512403

Station Road Sidmouth Devon EX10 8NU | **H** / **Map 3 E2**

New owners Mr & Mrs Torjusson have refurbished the bedrooms and
lounges at their Edwardian redbrick building overlooking a cricket pitch
and the sea beyond. A light, sunny lounge makes the most of the location,
and a number of bedrooms have balconies. *Rooms 55. Garden, putting,
indoor swimming pool, sauna, solarium. Access, Amex, Visa,* ⓄDiners Club International

| Sidmouth | Hotel Riviera | 64% | £106 |

Tel 0395 515201   Fax 0395 577775

The Esplanade Sidmouth Devon EX10 8AY | **H** / **Map 3 E2**

A handsome Regency facade fronts a terrace of three-storey houses in the
middle of the esplanade. Day rooms have recently been redecorated: the
Regency Bar is a relaxing spot for a drink, while cream teas can be enjoyed
in the lounge or out on the patio. There are various little extras in the
bedrooms, most of which overlook Lyme Bay. *Rooms 31. Access, Amex,
Visa,* ⓄDiners Club International

| Sidmouth | Victoria Hotel | 67% | £120 |

Tel 0395 512651   Fax 0395 579154

The Esplanade Sidmouth Devon EX10 8RY | **H** / **Map 3 E2**

Named after Queen Victoria, a frequent visitor to her neighbouring
residence, the hotel was actually opened early in the reign of Edward VII.
Lounges are roomy and relaxing, and most of the well-appointed bedrooms
face the sea (many have French windows leading to private balconies).
Families are well catered for with good leisure facilities, babysitting and
considerations for children in the dining room. Room service is available at
any hour. No dogs. *Rooms 65. Garden, putting, indoor & outdoor swimming
pools, keep-fit equipment, squash, tennis, spa bath, sauna, solarium, snooker &
games room, hairdressing, dinner dance (Saturdays), lock-up garages. Access,
Amex, Visa,* ⓄDiners Club International

Sidmouth   Places of Interest

Jacobs Ladder Beach.

| Silchester | Romans Hotel | 64% | £76 |

Tel 0734 700421   Fax 0734 700691

Little London Road Silchester Nr Reading Hampshire RG7 2PN | **H** / **Map 5 D3**

Built in the early years of this century, this handsome Lutyens house stands
amid trim lawns and mature grounds. Inside, polished floors, oak panelling
and ornate mouldings take the eye in the day rooms, while bedrooms in
the main house have space, comfort and mainly period furniture. Extension
rooms are smaller. *Rooms 23. Garden, outdoor swimming pool, tennis. Closed
Xmas/New Year. Access, Amex, Visa,* ⓄDiners Club International

| Silloth-on-Solway | Skinburness Hotel | 67% | £78 |

Tel 069 73 32332   Fax 069 73 32549

Silloth-on-Solway Nr Carlisle Cumbria CA5 4QT | **H** / **Map 13 C4**

Somewhat off the beaten track, a recent Victorian-style restoration
featuring brass lamps and ceiling fans, cane furniture and a picturesque
conservatory – creating a harmonious interior to what might otherwise be
considered as a rather solid redbrick period piece. Accommodation is
divided between plainly decorated Green Rooms and generally more
comfortable Red Rooms which provide the extra space required by
vacationing families. 200 yards from the beach from where there are views
across the Solway Firth to Scotland. Special terms for golfers who wish to
play at the local championship course. *Rooms 25. Garden, sauna, solarium,
keep-fit equipment, croquet, snooker. Access, Amex, Visa,* ⓄDiners Club International

Simonsbath — Simonsbath House — 64% — £84

Tel 064 383 259

H

Simonsbath Somerset TA24 7SH

Map 3 D1

Owned and run by the Burns family, Simonsbath dates from 1654. Right in the centre of Exmoor, its location is tranquil; inside you'll find oak panelling and velvet drapes, log fires, fresh flowers, comfortable sofas and plenty of books. Individually decorated bedrooms contain a mixture of modern pieces and the occasional four-poster. No children under 10. No dogs. *Rooms 7. Garden. Closed Dec & Jan. Access, Amex, Visa,* 🛈 *Diners Club International*

Sindlesham — Reading Moat House — 70% — £132

Tel 0734 351035   Fax 0734 666530

H

Mill Lane Sindlesham Nr Wokingham Berkshire RG11 5DF

Map 5 D2

Late-80s hotel standing in its own grounds near the M4 (junction 10 is closest). There's no lack of style – from a pine-panelled, marble-floored foyer and roomy lounge bar to smartly appointed bedrooms and bathrooms. The traditional, free-house Poachers pub and a night club are located in the old mill house next to the main building. *Rooms 96. Garden, gymnasium, sauna, solarium, steam room, dinner dance (Friday). Access, Amex, Visa,* 🛈 *Diners Club International*

Sissinghurst — Rankins — £65

Tel 0580 713964

R

The Street Sissinghurst Kent TN17 2JH

Map 7 C5

A charming, white clapboard cottage is the setting for Hugh Rankin to produce enjoyable, varied and interesting dishes such as rich crab soup decorated with spicy white meat, salad of leeks, prawns, apple and celery with an olive oil and soy dressing; steamed brill and salmon with braised fennel and dill butter sauce, pot-roast lamb shoulder and dry-fried duck breast, bacon and green peppercorns. Puddings are simple, but interesting: rhubarb and orange crumble, mango and lychee sorbets, jellied terrine of berry fruits. No children under eight in the evening. *Seats 30. Parties 20. L Sun only 12.30-1.30 D 7.30-9. Closed D Sun-Tue, Bank Holidays, 1 week Oct, 1 week May. Access, Visa.*

Six Mile Bottom — Swynford Paddocks — 74% — £107

Tel 063 870 234   Fax 063 870 283

H

Six Mile Bottom Nr Newmarket Cambridgeshire CB8 0UE

Map 6 B3

Previous owners of this country mansion standing in a 60-acre stud farm include Augusta Leigh (Lord Byron's half sister) and Lord and Lady Halifax. It was converted into a luxurious hotel in 1976. The dado-panelled and galleried hall/reception sets the period tone and from there you can progress to a large bar/lounge with stylishly draped curtains, comfortable easy chairs and a grand piano. The bedrooms have attractive matching bedcovers and curtains and many extras, including books and mini-bars; four 'superior' rooms are particularly spacious with bigger bathrooms and showers as well as tubs. *Rooms 15. Garden, croquet, all weather tennis, putting, giant chess. Closed Xmas/New Year. Access, Amex, Visa,* 🛈 *Diners Club International*

Skipton — Aagrah — £25

Tel 0756 790807

R

Unit 5 Unicorn House Devonshire Place Keighly Road Skipton West Yorkshire

Map 10 C1

Branch of the popular Indian chain, based around Bradford. See further entries under Bradford (Pudesy) and Shipley. *Seats 45. Parties 20. D only 6-11.30 (Fri & Sat to 12). Closed 25 Dec. Access, Amex, Visa,* 🛈 *Diners Club International*

Skipton Forte Travelodge £40

Tel 0756 798091 **L**

A65/A59 Gargrave Road Skipton North Yorkshire BD23 1UD Map 10 C1

At the roundabout junction of the A65 and A59. Easy access to Bradford
and Leeds. *Rooms 32. Access, Amex, Visa.*

Skipton Randell's Hotel 65% £95

Tel 0756 700100 Fax 0756 700107 **H**

Keighley Road Snaygill Skipton North Yorkshire BD23 2TA Map 10 C1

A purpose-built hotel, just south of the town centre, standing by the
Liverpool to Leeds canal. Spacious bedrooms are light and contemporary
with fully-tiled private facilities. Day rooms include an open-plan lobby
and a first-floor bar. There's also a well-equipped leisure centre,
conference/banqueting facilities for 400/330 and a terrace overlooking the
canal. Splendid facilities for youngsters, including the Playzone supervised
crèche. *Rooms 61. Indoor swimming pool, gymnasium, spa bath, sauna,
solarium, beautician, hair salon, squash, snooker, coffee shop (7am-10pm). Access,
Amex, Visa,*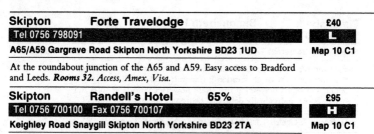

Slaidburn Hark to Bounty Inn £45

Tel 020 06 246 **I**

Slaidburn Nr Clitheroe Lancashire BB7 3AQ Map 10 B1

Set in the heart of the Forest of Bowland, Slaidburn's stone-built village inn
is an ideal touring base. Dating in parts from the 14th century, it contains a
remarkable courtroom which kept that function until 1937. Nowadays it's
used for banquets (up to 70) or conferences (up to 100 theatre-style).
Bedrooms are modest and cottagey in style; one has WC/shower only.
Under-5s stay free in parents' room. *Rooms 8. Garden. Access, Amex, Visa,*

Sleaford Forte Travelodge £40

Tel 0529 414752 **L**

A17/A15 Holdingham Sleaford Lincolnshire NG34 8PN Map 11 E3

On the roundabout at the junction of the A17/A15, one mile north of
Sleaford on the bypass. Less than 16 miles from Lincoln, Grantham, Boston
and Newark-on-Trent. *Rooms 40. Access, Amex, Visa.*

Slough Copthorne Hotel 71% £127

Tel 0753 516222 Fax 0753 516237 **H**

Cippenham Lane Slough Berkshire SL1 2YE Map 5 E2

Conveniently situated next to junction 6 of the M4, the Copthorne owes
80% of its trade to corporate business. All the elegant public areas – the
polished granite-floored reception area, the comfortable spacious lounge
and relaxing bar – are Art Deco in style; so, too, the variously sized
conference rooms. All bedrooms are decorated to the same high standard
with lightwood units and co-ordinating fabrics. Tiled bathrooms offer
showers and tubs, plus good soaps and toiletries. First-rate fitness centre.
*Rooms 219. Indoor swimming pool, gymnasium, steam bath, spa bath, sauna,
solarium, snooker, news kiosk. Access, Amex, Visa,*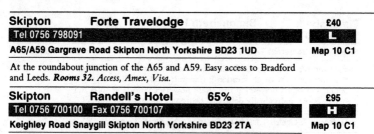

Slough Heathrow/Slough Marriott Hotel 73% £157

Tel 0753 544244 Fax 0753 540272 **H**

Ditton Road Langley Slough Berkshire SL3 8PT Map 5 E2

Formerly the Holiday Inn Slough/Windsor, now metamorphosed into a
Marriott with 50 new bedrooms added last year. Next to junction 5 of the
M4, it's a purpose-built hotel with good modern leisure and conference
(for up to 300) facilities plus stylish day rooms. Bedrooms have at least one

double bed and are decorated in soft shades with lightwood units. All have tiled, if rather small, bathrooms. Staff are civil and smart. *Rooms 352. Indoor swimming pool, steam room, spa bath, sauna, solarium, beauty & hair salons, gymnasium, games room, all-weather floodlit tennis, coffee shop (11am-11pm), courtesy airport coach. Access, Amex, Visa,* 🔘 *Diners Club International*

Slough   Place of Interest

Ice Arena   Montem Lane Tel 0753 821555.

Solihull	George Hotel	65%	£109
Tel 021-711 2121 Fax 021-711 3374			**H**
The Square Solihull West Midlands B91 3RF			**Map 10 C4**

Edge-of-town site (take junction 5 from the M42), closer to the National Exhibition Centre than the town centre. A modernised coaching inn with quiet bedrooms away from the road overlooking an ancient bowling green. Children up to 12 free in parents' room. Conference/banqueting faciliies for 200. Jarvis Hotels. *Rooms 78. Access, Amex, Visa,* 🔘 *Diners Club International*

Solihull	Liaison		£90
Tel 021-743 3993			**R**
761 Old Lode Lane Solihull West Midlands B92 8JE			**Map 10 C4**

Owner-chef Lorenzo Lee's experience in the kitchens of *Le Talbooth* in Essex and *The Capital* in London makes Liaison one of the most interesting restaurants in the area. His cooking puts a French accent on an English menu offering enjoyable, well-constructed dishes like warm duck mousse with ceps and Jerusalem artichokes, langoustines and scallops poached in vin jaune, or rump steak with wild mushrooms, garlic, roquefort and a red wine sauce. There's a separate, weekly-changing vegetarian menu, and a dessert list that tempts with the likes of pears wrapped in pastry served with caramel and custard sauces. A mainly French wine list includes plenty of half-bottles. *Seats 30. Parties 8. L 12-2 D 7.30-11. Closed Sun & Mon, 25 Dec, 2 weeks Aug. Set L £17 Set D £19.50. Access, Amex, Visa,* 🔘 *Diners Club International*

Solihull	Moat House	69%	£113
Tel 021-711 4700 Fax 021-711 2696			**H**
Homer Road Solihull West Midlands B91 3QD			**Map 10 C4**

Purpose-built in 1990, this large hotel stands just out of the town centre. A marble-floored entrance hall leads to the reception area, main lounge and a raised bar area. Light decor throughout, with seating comfortable and contemporary in both design and colour. Bedrooms are equally stylish, using co-ordinating fabrics and mainly darkwood freestanding furniture. Modern health and fitness club. Conference and banqueting facilities for up to 200. *Rooms 115. Indoor swimming pool, gymnasium, spa bath, sauna, solarium. Access, Amex, Visa,* 🔘 *Diners Club International*

Solihull	Regency Hotel	64%	£94
Tel 021-745 6119 Fax 021-733 3801			**H**
Stratford Road Shirley Solihull West Midlands B90 4EB			**Map 10 C4**

The luxurious leisure club is a major feature at a business-oriented hotel on the A34, one mile from junction 4 of the M42. Baby-sitting and baby-listening services available. *Rooms 112. Garden, indoor swimming pool, spa bath, gymnasium, solarium, sauna, coffee shop (10am-10pm). Access, Amex, Visa.*

Solihull	**St John's Swallow Hotel**	63%	£108

Tel 021-711 3000   Fax 021-705 6629 · **H**

651 Warwick Road Solihull West Midlands B91 1AT · Map 10 C4

A comfortable, well-appointed hotel with distinctive gabled facade and massive conference (up to 800 delegates) and good leisure facilities. Parking for 400 cars. **Rooms 206.** *Indoor swimming pool, spa bath, sauna, solarium, steam room, keep-fit equipment. Access, Amex, Visa,*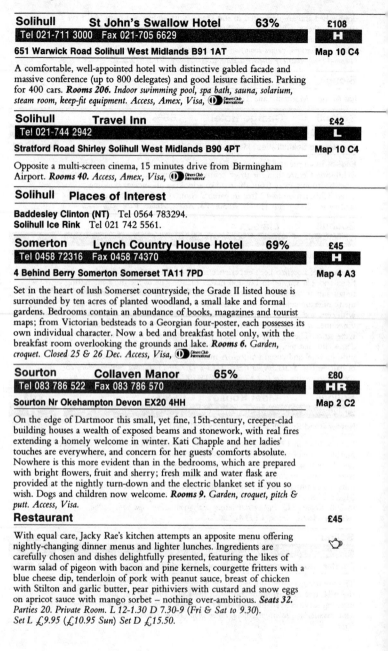

Solihull	**Travel Inn**		£42

Tel 021-744 2942 · **L**

Stratford Road Shirley Solihull West Midlands B90 4PT · Map 10 C4

Opposite a multi-screen cinema, 15 minutes drive from Birmingham Airport. **Rooms 40.** *Access, Amex, Visa,*

Solihull   Places of Interest

Baddesley Clinton (NT)   Tel 0564 783294.
Solihull Ice Rink   Tel 021 742 5561.

Somerton	**Lynch Country House Hotel**	69%	£45

Tel 0458 72316   Fax 0458 74370 · **H**

4 Behind Berry Somerton Somerset TA11 7PD · Map 4 A3

Set in the heart of lush Somerset countryside, the Grade II listed house is surrounded by ten acres of planted woodland, a small lake and formal gardens. Bedrooms contain an abundance of books, magazines and tourist maps; from Victorian bedsteads to a Georgian four-poster, each possesses its own individual character. Now a bed and breakfast hotel only, with the breakfast room overlooking the grounds and lake. **Rooms 6.** *Garden, croquet. Closed 25 & 26 Dec. Access, Visa,*

Sourton	**Collaven Manor**	65%	£80

Tel 083 786 522   Fax 083 786 570 · **HR**

Sourton Nr Okehampton Devon EX20 4HH · Map 2 C2

On the edge of Dartmoor this small, yet fine, 15th-century, creeper-clad building houses a wealth of exposed beams and stonework, with real fires extending a homely welcome in winter. Kati Chapple and her ladies' touches are everywhere, and concern for her guests' comforts absolute. Nowhere is this more evident than in the bedrooms, which are prepared with bright flowers, fruit and sherry; fresh milk and water flask are provided at the nightly turn-down and the electric blanket set if you so wish. Dogs and children now welcome. **Rooms 9.** *Garden, croquet, pitch & putt. Access, Visa.*

Restaurant   £45

With equal care, Jacky Rae's kitchen attempts an apposite menu offering nightly-changing dinner menus and lighter lunches. Ingredients are carefully chosen and dishes delightfully presented, featuring the likes of warm salad of pigeon with bacon and pine kernels, courgette fritters with a blue cheese dip, tenderloin of pork with peanut sauce, breast of chicken with Stilton and garlic butter, pear pithiviers with custard and snow eggs on apricot sauce with mango sorbet – nothing over-ambitious. **Seats 32.** *Parties 20. Private Room. L 12-1.30 D 7.30-9 (Fri & Sat to 9.30). Set L £9.95 (£10.95 Sun) Set D £15.50.*

South Cave   Forte Travelodge   £40

Tel 0430 424455   **L**

A63 Beacon service area South Cave Hull Humberside   Map 11 E1

Located at the Beacon service area on the eastbound carriageway of the A63, 12 miles west of Kingston-upon-Hull and 4 miles east of junction 38 of the M62. *Rooms 40. Access, Amex, Visa.*

South Godstone   La Bonne Auberge   £75

Tel 0342 893184   Fax 0342 893435   **R**

Tilburstow Hill South Godstone Surrey RH9 8JY   Map 7 B5

Set in a large Victorian house overlooking a circular lawn and two-acre lake. Many of the attractively presented dishes have a French regional or modern ring, ranging from potted rabbit paté with rocket salad and crispy pieces of rabbit tenderloin, or boned chicken leg rolled in oats and filled with rosemary and mushroom forcemeat to steamed fillet of zander with shredded vegetables and clams or asparagus ravioli with a mild Roquefort sauce. Cheeses are exclusively French; desserts chosen and served from a trolley. A five-course *menu surprise* is also offered except on Saturdays. Three-course, fixed-price dinner menus are for two or more diners and include a bottle of wine. Separate banqueting facilities in converted stables. The all-French wine list has some keenly priced bottles. *Seats 60. Parties 100. Private Room. L 12-2 D 7-10. Closed D Sun, all Mon, Bank Holidays. Set L £17.50 Set D £26/£29.90. Access, Amex, Visa,*

South Milford   Forte Posthouse Leeds/Selby   65%   £67

Tel 0977 682711   Fax 0977 685462   **H**

South Milford Nr Leeds North Yorkshire LS25 5LF   Map 11 D1

At the junction of the A1 and A63, between York and Leeds. Modern hotel with good conference facilities (for up to 300). *Rooms 105. Indoor swimming pool, sauna, 9-hole pitch & putt, tennis. Access, Amex, Visa,*

South Mimms   Forte Posthouse   60%   £67

Tel 0707 43311   Fax 0707 46728   **H**

Bignells Corner South Mimms Nr Potters Bar Hertfordshire EN6 3NH   Map 5 E2

Up-to-date accommodation at the South Mimms service area on the M25. A room is set aside for children at weekends and there's also a playground. *Rooms 123. Gymnasium, spa bath, sauna, solarium, pool table. Access, Amex, Visa,*

South Mimms   Forte Travelodge   £40

Tel 0707 665440   **L**

M25 Bignells Corner South Mimms Nr Potters Bar Hertfordshire EN6 3QQ   Map 5 E2

Located at junction 23 of the M25 at the South Mimms Welcome Break service area. Central London 15 miles. *Rooms 52. Access, Amex, Visa.*

South Molton   Whitechapel Manor   76%   £130

Tel 0769 573377   Fax 0769 573797   **HR**

South Molton Devon EX36 3EG   Map 3 D2

John and Patricia Shapland's peaceful Elizabethan country manor house is set above 14 acres of terraced garden, surrounded by wooded valleys, rolling pasture and arable land. Only ten minutes from the A361: take j27 of the M5, signposted to Barnstaple, then last turning off second roundabout, signposted to Whitechapel; from there you might have to ask for further directions. A magnificent Jacobean oak screen separates the entrance hall from the Great Hall drawing room – one of the comfortable day rooms that feature handsome, early 18th-century panelling and warming log fires. The style is carefully low-key – colours are gentle, and several bedrooms have old paintings above their fireplaces, as well as chintzy curtains and antique pieces. Some rooms are large, others intimate, and thoughtful touches extend to the splendid bathrooms. *Rooms 10. Garden, croquet, stabling. Access, Amex, Visa,*

Restaurant   ★ ↑   £75

The dining room is simple and discreet, the cooking serious and correct. Thierry Lepretre-Granet's cooking is top-notch, with interesting menus based on prime seasonal produce. A 3- or 4-course, fixed-price menu with good choice is served in the evening, although the choice is less, but equally interesting, at lunchtime. Pepper and beef kebab, savoury choux bun and anchovy puff are among first-rate amuse-gueule. Typical dishes might include a classical consommé, poached skate salad or brandy-soaked raisin-and sultana-studded foie gras served with brioche, lamb's lettuce and a glass of sweet Loire wine to start; calf's sweetbreads served with red cabbage, braised lentils and mustard seed sauce, breast of wood pigeon with beetroot purée and fried leeks, braised leg of hare with fresh pasta, or fillet of seabass with julienne of vegetables and red wine sauce to follow. Hot plum soufflé and iced plum sorbet and exceptional, individual hot apple tart with caramel ice cream and sugared walnuts (well worth the 25 minutes wait) show that M. Lepretre-Granet has a passion for desserts. Miniature oatcakes and walnut bread accompany a good selection of English cheeses. Enjoy good petits fours with coffee in the drawing room. Service is quietly efficient and friendly. No smoking. Reasonable prices on a concise wine list. *Seats 24. Parties 24. Private Room. L 12.30-2 D 7-8.45. Set L from £15 Set D from £26.*

South Normanton   Swallow Hotel   69%   £92

Tel 0773 812000   Fax 0773 580032   **H**

Carter Lane East South Normanton Derbyshire DE55 2EH   Map 11 D3

Modern, low-rise hotel near junction 28 of the M1 with spacious public areas and large, up-to-date conference facilities for a maximum of 220 delegates. Two of the bedrooms have been specially designed for disabled guests. *Rooms 161. Indoor swimming pool, sauna, solarium, spa bath, steam room, keep-fit equipment. Access, Amex, Visa,*

South Normanton   Places of Interest

Sherwood Forest Visitor Centre   Tel 0623 824490.

South Witham   Forte Travelodge   £40

Tel 057 283 586   **L**

A1 New Fox South Witham Colsterworth Lincolnshire LE15 8AU   Map 11 E3

Northbound on the A1, 9 miles south of Grantham. *Rooms 32. Access, Amex, Visa.*

South Wootton   Knights Hill Hotel   64%   NEW   £81
`Tel 0553 675566    Fax 0553 675568`   **H**

Knights Hill Village South Wootton King's Lynn Norfolk PE30 3HQ   Map 6 B1

At the junction of the A148 and A149 at Rising Chase, Knights Hill stands
in 11 acres of parkland overlooking King's Lynn and the Wash.
Sympathetic conversion of a collection of 17th-century farm buildings has
produced a village complex of hotel, pub, leisure club and
conference/banqueting centre (max 400) in the spectacularly converted
Knights Barn. Accommodation is in up-to-date bedrooms in a stylish new
extension or in more modest (and older) courtyard apartments with
private entrances. *Rooms 58. Indoor swimming pool, spa bath, sauna, solarium,
gymnasium, snooker, tennis, steam room, jogging circuit, helipad. Access, Amex,
Visa,* **(I)** *Diners Club International*

Southall   Asian Tandoori Centre   £15
`Tel 081-574 2597`   **R**

114 The Green Southall Middlesex   Map 7 A4

Simple Indian canteen serving hearty, unsophisticated food throughout the
day. Particularly good peshwari stuffed nan. Unlicensed; non-smoking area.
*Also at: 157 The Broadway, Southall. Tel 081-574 3476. Seats 65. Meals
9am-10.30pm (Fri & Sat to 11pm).*

Southampton   Browns Brasserie   £74
`Tel 0703 332615`   **R**

**Frobisher House Nelson Gate Commercial Road
Southampton Hampshire SO1 0GX**   Map 5 D4

In a neighbourhood of unfashionable eating houses close to the Mayflower
Theatre, there's an air of enthusiastic amateurism here that seems to work.
An adventurous menu includes the likes of crab soufflé, venison boudins,
panaché of seafoods, pigeon breast en croute, wild mushroom ravioli, prune
and armagnac parfait and baked pears. *Seats 24. Parties 50. L 12-2.30 D 7-
11 (Sat to 11.30). Closed Sun, 25 & 26 Dec, 1 Jan. Set D from £14.95.
Access, Amex, Visa,* **(I)** *Diners Club International*

Southampton   Dolphin Hotel   60%   £86
`Tel 0703 339955    Fax 0703 333650`   **H**

High Street Southampton Hampshire SO9 2DS   Map 5 D4

Modernised high-street coaching inn with a restaurant and cocktail bar.
Free use of nearby Posthouse health and fitness club.
Banqueting/conferences for 120/75. Forte. *Rooms 73. Access, Amex, Visa,*
(I) *Diners Club International*

Southampton   Forte Posthouse   58%   £67
`Tel 0703 330777    Fax 0703 332510`   **H**

Herbert Walker Avenue Southampton Hampshire SO1 0HJ   Map 5 D4

Ten-storey tower-block hotel with views of the liners' berths from some
rooms. Redecorated bedrooms, spacious nautical bar, children's playroom
and playground. *Rooms 128. Indoor swimming pool, gymnasium, spa bath,
sauna, solarium. Access, Amex, Visa,* **(I)** *Diners Club International*

Southampton   Hilton National   68%   £127
`Tel 0703 702700    Fax 0703 767233`   **H**

Bracken Place Chilworth Southampton Hampshire SO2 4HB   Map 5 D4

Up-to-date facilities by the A33 and M27 (approach from junction 5).
Regular weekend dinner dance. *Rooms 135. Indoor swimming pool,
gymnasium, spa bath, sauna, steam room, beauty salon, business centre. Access,
Amex, Visa,* **(I)** *Diners Club International*

Southampton   Kuti's   £45

Tel 0703 221585   **R**

70 London Road Southampton Hampshire SO1 2AJ   **Map 5 D4**

Plush and pristine Indian restaurant off the Avenue by the new Law
Courts. Low lit, with comfortable seating and friendly staff. The kitchen
puts good raw materials to excellent use in a range of lamb, chicken and
prawn dishes that include house specialities served with pilau rice and nan
bread. Onion bhaji and vegetable side dishes are also first-rate. Finish a fine
meal with traditional gulab jamun or cool, fresh mango. Good value thalis,
buffet lunches and fixed-price dinners. *Seats 66. Parties 30. L 12-2.15
D 6-11.30. Closed 25 & 26 Dec. Set L from £7.50 Set D from £10.95.
Access, Amex, Visa.*

Southampton   Novotel   62%   £74

Tel 0703 330550   Fax 0703 222158   **H**

1 West Key Road Southampton Hampshire SO1 0RA   **Map 5 D4**

Very modern hotel convenient for ferries and Ocean Village. Geared to
business use in the week (with conference facilities for up to 450,
banqueting up to 350), families at weekends. *Rooms 121. Indoor swimming
pool, keep-fit equipment, sauna. Access, Amex, Visa,*

Southampton   Polygon Hotel   65%   £72

Tel 0703 330055   Fax 0703 332435   **H**

Cumberland Place Southampton Hampshire SO9 4DG   **Map 5 D4**

Close by the civic centre, an Edwardian structure in red brick overlooking
Watts Park. Banqueting/conference facilities for 400/500. Free use of Forte
Posthouse health and fitness club in Herbert Walker Avenue. Forte Crest.
Rooms 119. Access, Amex, Visa,

Southampton   Southampton Park Hotel   64%   £60

Tel 0703 223467   Fax 0703 332538   **H**

12 Cumberland Place Southampton Hampshire SO9 4NY   **Map 5 D4**

Functional modern building overlooking Watts Park. Well-equipped
bedrooms (front ones have balconies), roomy lounge areas, two restaurants,
a cocktail bar, conference rooms and a leisure club. Conference facilities for
up to 200, banqueting for 150. *Rooms 71. Indoor swimming pool, keep-fit
equipment, spa bath, sauna, solarium, steam room. Access, Amex, Visa,*

Southampton   Places of Interest

Tourist Information   Tel 0703 832615.
Exbury Gardens   Exbury Tel 0703 891203.
Southampton City Art Gallery   Tel 0703 231375.
Northlands Road Cricket Ground   Tel 0703 333788.
Southampton Football Ground   The Dell Tel 0703 220505.
Calshort Activities Centre   Fawley Tel 0703 891380/892077.
Southampton Ski Centre   Bassett Tel 0703 760604.
  Theatres and Concert Halls
Mayflower Theatre   Tel 0703 330083.
Mountbatten Theatre   Tel 0703 832453.
Nuffield Theatre   Tel 0703 671771.

Southport   New Bold Hotel   58%   £50

Tel 0704 532578   Fax 0704 532528   **H**

Lord Street Southport Merseyside PR9 0BE   **Map 10 A1**

Family-owned and family-run, the Bold stands on the town's leafy main
boulevard. Modernised bedrooms include two for family use and a bridal
suite with sunken bath; back rooms are the quietest. A public bar serves

traditional beers and Raphael's bar/café has long-hours opening and live entertainment. Reception is upstairs, and the front door leads straight into the bar. **Rooms 23.** *Access, Amex, Visa,* (D) *Diners Club International*

Southport   Prince of Wales Hotel   65%   £65

Tel 0704 536688   Fax 0704 543488   **H**

Lord Street Southport Merseyside PR8 1JS   **Map 10 A1**

On Southport's tree-lined main street, with modern amenities and some of Southport's Victorian atmosphere remaining both inside and out. Conferences are well catered for, with a maximum capacity of 450 theatre-style. Forte Grand. **Rooms 104.** *Garden, 24hr lounge service. Access, Amex, Visa,* (D) *Diners Club International*

Southport   Places of Interest

Tourist Information   Tel 0704 533333.
Atkinson Art Gallery   Tel 0704 533133.
Rufford Old Hall (NT)   Rufford Tel 0704 821254.
Martin Mere Wildfowl Trust   Tel 0704 895181 *6 miles.*
Trafalgar Road Cricket Ground   Birkdale Tel 0704 69951.
Southport Zoo   Tel 0704 538102.

Southsea   Bistro Montparnasse   £55

Tel 0705 816754   **R**

103 Palmerston Road Southsea Hampshire PO5 3PS   **Map 5 D4**

Careful cooking and attractive presentation bring the regulars back to a warm and welcoming French bistro close to Southsea's main shopping area. Irish chef Michael Weir offers a well-thought-out and often inventive choice on his fixed-price menus, which change monthly. Moist chunks of various smoked fish in a filo pastry cup with a gently complementary curry sauce, cassoulet of rabbit with leeks and blackberries, and breast of duck filled with orange and ginger mousse should tempt most palates. Warm lemon tart with crisp pastry and piped meringue reflects the enthusiasm of the kitchen. **Seats 38.** *Parties 35. D only 7-10. Closed Sun & Mon, Bank Holidays, 3 weeks Jan. Set D £15.90. Access, Amex, Visa,* (D) *Diners Club International*

Southwell   Saracen's Head   62%   £86

Tel 0636 812701   Fax 0636 815408   **H**

Market Place Southwell Nottinghamshire NG25 0HE   **Map 11 D3**

Recent renovations at this 16th-century half-timbered inn have revealed an original Elizabethan wall painting, still in excellent condition; another claim to fame is that Charles 1 stayed here in 1646 just before surrendering to the Scottish Commissioners. Today's guests can enjoy the characterful public areas before retiring to bedrooms that offer all the usual modern comforts and conveniences. Forte Heritage. **Rooms 27.** *Access, Amex, Visa,* (D) *Diners Club International*

Southwell   Places of Interest

Southwell Minster   Tel 0636 812649.

Southwold   The Crown   £63

Tel 0502 722275   Fax 0502 722740   **R**

90 High Street Southwold Suffolk IP18 6DP   **Map 6 D2**

Southwold brewers, Adnams, take credit for the restoration of their town-centre Georgian inn: to the front, facing the High Street, the Parlour serves as half lounge, half coffee shop, while the front bar and attendant restaurant exude refinement. Bedrooms are well equipped, with antique or decent reproduction pieces and bright fabrics and furnishings: all have private bathrooms though three are not strictly en suite. **Rooms 12.** *Closed 1 week Jan. Access, Amex, Visa.*

Restaurant   £48

Menus are produced daily with an accent on fresh fish, and simpler dishes
are the best bet. For starters, try red mullet Oriental-style or smoked fish
with dill mayonnaise. Main courses offer the likes of pan-fried monkfish
with fresh herbs and cream and beef stroganoff with saffron rice. Also
lighter bar meals and vegetarian alternatives. Twenty wines by the glass,
from a list selected monthly by Simon Loftus, are kept in peak condition
by the Cruover machine. Winner of our 1993 Wine Cellar of the Year
East of England Regional award. *Seats 40. Parties 25. Private Room.
L 12.30-1.45 D 7.30-9.30. Set L £14.75 Set D £18.50.*

Southwold   The Swan   65%   £82
Tel 0502 722186   Fax 0502 724800   **HR**
Market Place Southwold Suffolk IP18 6EG   Map 6 D2

The ancient Swan (rebuilt in 1660 and remodelled in the 1820s) faces the
market place of a most charming seaside town. An old long-case clock and
fresh flowers grace the flagstoned foyer and an abundance of sofas the
period drawing room. Main-house bedrooms are traditional in style with
freestanding furniture, including the odd antique, while simpler chalet-style
rooms surround a garden to the rear. An adjacent brewery can occasionally
disturb the peace during the day. Banquets/conferences for up to 50.
Rooms 45. Access, Amex, Visa.

Restaurant   £65

An elegant, pink dining room and a choice of fixed-price only menus
offering an interesting mix ranging from chicken and bacon terrine on a
green herb sauce to sautéed Cromer skate wing with mixed pepper sauce
and spotted dick with clotted cream. *Seats 50. Private Room. L 12.15-1.45
(Sun to 1.30) D 7-9.30 (Sun to 9). Closed D 3rd Sun in Jan. Set L
£10.50/£13.95 Set D £15.95-£25.50*

Southwold   Place of Interest

Southwold Beach.

Spark Bridge   Bridgefield House   60%   £82
Tel 0229 85239   Fax 0229 85379   **HR**
Spark Bridge Ulverston Cumbria LA12 8DA   Map 13 C6

To describe Bridgefield House as modest is to decry neither its homeliness
nor the warmth of the proprietors' welcome. A decade of steady
improvements has established a hotel of some charm in a superb location
overlooking the Crake valley. Bedrooms, though spacious, are modestly
appointed with mostly freestanding furniture, telephones and clock radios;
TVs there are not. *Rooms 5. Garden. Access, Visa.*

Restaurant   £70

Dinner at candle-lit dark mahogany tables is courteously overseen by
David Glister. His wife Rosemary's daily-changing menus offer a choice of
starters and sweets but a fixed main course, and the robustness indicated by
guinea fowl with juniper berries and white wine or salmon with vermouth
and ginger sauce generally succeeds. Good cheeses, coffee and truffles. A
long wine list, strangely but not greedily priced, with a good world-wide
choice. No smoking. Booking essential. *Seats 30. Parties 24. D only 7.30 for
8. Set D from £24.*

Staddle Bridge   McCoy's   70%   £109

HR

Tel 060 982 671   Fax 060 982 660

**The Cleveland Tontine Staddle Bridge Nr Northallerton
North Yorkshire DL6 3JB**

Map 15 C5

At the intersection of the busy A19 and A172 stands the McCoy brothers' unusual establishment. The 30s' decor won't please everyone, but there's no doubting its originality. The mix of open fires, slightly worn couches, brightly coloured cushions and rug-covered floorboards displays a mild, tongue-in-cheek eccentricity. In the evenings, subtle lighting and music from the 30s seem highly appropriate and not the least bit out of place. Large parlour plants and bold-patterned paper help create the comfortable style of the bar. Bedrooms are best described as cosy, with Givenchy wall coverings and double-glazing to keep out traffic noise. The overall informal style is suitably enhanced by chatty, yet efficient young staff. The day starts with a memorable breakfast. *Rooms 6. Garden. Closed 25 & 26 Dec, 1 Jan. Access, Amex, Visa,*

Restaurant   ★↑   £90

In an eccentric and flamboyantly furnished setting with parasols, parlour plants and Oriental-style wall-coverings, McCoy's continues to please by not taking itself too seriously. Although the menu doesn't change very often, Tom McCoy's cooking is exciting and uninhibited, yet quintessentially English. It commands attention with rich combinations of ingredients like duckling with Toulouse sausage, loin of lamb with red capsicum tart and truffle sauce and Bresse pigeon with lentils and foie gras. Equally tempting desserts include the original "Crepe San Lorenzo" with vanilla ice, amaretti and Grand Marnier. The wine list is arranged by style with helpful notes; careful selection with some unusual offerings. Both the magical atmosphere and the marvellously informal service play their part in making McCoy's a must for lovers of seriously good food. *Seats 45. Parties 12. Private Room. D only 7-10 (Bistro: 12-2, 7-10.30). Closed Mon.*

Stafford   Tillington Hall   63%   £95

H

Tel 0785 53531   Fax 0785 59223

Eccleshall Road Stafford Staffordshire ST16 1JJ

Map 10 B3

Half a mile from the M6 (J14), this modern De Vere hotel adds good leisure and conference facilities (200 maximum) to decent bedrooms that range from singles to four-poster rooms. Children up to 14 share adult accommodation free. *Rooms 90. Garden, indoor swimming pool, gymnasium, spa bath, sauna, solarium, beauty salon, tennis, snooker. Closed 28 & 29 Dec. Access, Amex, Visa,*

Stafford   Places of Interest

Tourist Information   Tel 0785 40204.
Shugborough (NT) House & Garden & Staffordshire County Museum & Park Farm   Tel 0889 881388.
Wolseley Garden Park   Wolseley Bridge Tel 0889 574888.
County Showground   Weston Road Tel 0785 58060.

Stamford   The George of Stamford   72%   £90

HR

Tel 0780 55171   Fax 0780 57070

71 St Martins Stamford Lincolnshire PE9 2LB

Map 11 E3

A gallows sign above the road announces the George, in a position where a hostelry has stood for over 900 years. Rugs cover a long, flagstoned entrance hallway, either side of which are the dark-panelled London Room and York Bar where travellers used to wait for highway coaches. Comfortable day rooms include a beamed cocktail bar, a cosy lounge with easy couches and armchairs, an open fire and fine exposed stone walls and a bright, covered Garden Lounge filled with wrought-iron garden furniture and plants. The age of the building dictates that sizes and shapes of the

bedrooms are varied, but most are well proportioned. Ivy surrounds the
windows of the quietest rooms overlooking a cobbled courtyard. A
converted livery stable houses a business centre that caters for conferences
of up to 50 delegates. *Rooms 47. Garden, beautician, hair salon, bookshop,
coffee shop (7am-midnight). Access, Amex, Visa,*

Restaurant   £85

An elegant setting with polished tables, gleaming silverware and oak
panelling. The à la carte dinner menu is essentially traditional, with a few
modern touches: tortellini of snail and basil; smoked sweetbreads and forest
mushroom salad; scallop, sea bream, red snapper, parrot fish and crayfish
pan-fried with a red wine sauce – a few unusual dishes, in contrast to the
silver-domed carving wagons offering traditional roast sirloin of Scotch
beef and a further daily roast. Trolleys, trolleys, everywhere: smoked
salmon is sliced at the table; even the cheese is trundled to your table, as
are the desserts. Quick, fixed-price lunch menu offers a good choice of any
two from a list of starter-style dishes, plus dessert or cheese. A super wine
list, expertly compiled, with as reasonable prices as you'll find anywhere.
Private dining rooms at no extra charge. *Seats 80. Parties 90. Private Room.
L 12.30-2.30 D 7-10.30 (Garden Lounge 8am-11pm). Set L £15.50
(Mon-Sat).*

Stamford   Places of Interest

Tourist Information Tel 0780 55611.
Burghley House Tel 0780 52451.
Stamford Brewery Museum Tel 0780 52186.
Tallington Dry Ski Slope Tel 0788 344990.

Standish   Almond Brook Moat House   63%   £90

Tel 0257 425588   Fax 0257 427327   **H**

Almond Brook Road Standish Nr Wigan Greater Manchester WN6 0SR   **Map 10 B1**

Two hundred yards from junction 27 of the M6, this Moat House includes
conference rooms (for up to 150) and a leisure centre among its facilities.
Bedrooms are smallish but adequate. Families are well catered for; under-
14s sharing with parents are free. *Rooms 126. Garden, indoor swimming pool,
sauna, solarium, keep-fit equipment, night club. Closed 24-30 Dec. Access,
Amex, Visa,*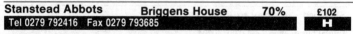

Standish   Places of Interest

Wigan Pier Wigan Tel 0942 323666 *4 miles.*
Wigan International Pool Wigan Tel 0942 43345.

Stanstead Abbots   Briggens House   70%   £102

Tel 0279 792416   Fax 0279 793685   **H**

Stanstead Road Stanstead Abbots Nr Ware Hertfordshire SG12 8LD   **Map 7 B4**

A large, stately home-from-home, a few miles off the M11, set in 45 acres
of grounds with its own 9-hole golf course. High standards of service are
typified by the smart, uniformed doormen. A magnificent carved wood
staircase leads up from the entrance hall with its glass chandelier to 22
bedrooms in the main house; 32 more are in the converted coach house
and have lower ceilings, but all are equally tastefully decorated with a good
range of extras included as standard. Swagged drapes and elegant
reproduction antiques give an elegant air. In summer, tables are set on the
expansive lawns outside the French windows leading off the lounge.
Conference and banqueting facilities for up to 100. Queens Moat Houses.
*Rooms 54. Garden, outdoor swimming pool, tennis, 9-hole golf course, croquet,
bowls, fishing. Closed 1 wk Xmas. Access, Amex, Visa,*

Stanstead Abbots   Places of Interest

Hill House Ware Tel 0920 870013.
Trading Places Gallery New Road, Ware Tel 0920 469620.

Stanton St Quintin   Stanton Manor   64% NEW   £78
Tel 0666 837552   Fax 0666 837022   **HR**

Stanton St Quintin Nr Chippenham Wiltshire SN4 6DQ   Map 4 B2

This 19th-century stone manor house, recently extended to provide further bedrooms, inherits some 900 years of continuous habitation; a unique 14th-century dovecote still stands in the five acres of grounds. Just two minutes from the M4 (at junction 17), it's the home of enthusiastic young proprietors Philip and Elizabeth Bullock, who go out of their way to make guests welcome. Delegates attending private conferences of up to 20 are assured similar levels of personal service. *Rooms 8. Garden, croquet. Closed 26 Dec-2 Jan, 2 weeks end Jul. Access, Amex, Visa.*

Restaurant   £50

Simpler dishes are the best bet on a short à la carte, to which the manor's own kitchen garden contributes seasonal fruit and vegetables. Informal service is relaxed and friendly. *Seats 30. Parties 50. Private Room. L 12-2 D 7-9. Closed all Sun (dinner residents only).*

Stapleford   Stapleford Park   86%   £141
Tel 057 284 522   Fax 057 284 651   **HR**

Stapleford Nr Melton Mowbray Leicestershire LE14 2EF   Map 11 D3

This majestic stately house set in 500 acres of mature parkland was transformed into a sumptuous country house hotel by Chicago Pizza Pie entrepreneur Bob Payton. Its welcomimg air of freshness and spontaneity owes much to its creator, who with his carefully chosen young staff idiosyncratically cuts out the snobbery. The result is casual luxury at its best, evident throughout day rooms that exude quality and style and in bedrooms individually designed by such luminaries as David Hicks and Lindka Cierach. The splendid library, lounge and galleried salon abound in beautiful fabrics, oil paintings and ornaments; each bedroom sharing this style in sumptuous comfort with wonderful marble-tiled bathrooms and numerous thoughtful extras. Conference, meeting and private function rooms are equally superb, accommodating up to 200 guests in luxurious yet informal surroundings. Children up to 10 stay free in parents' room. *Rooms 35. Garden, croquet, fishing, tennis, pitch & putt, basketball, clay-pigeon shooting, horseshoes. Access, Amex, Visa,*

Restaurant   £70

Stapleford's restaurant never takes itself too seriously and isn't afraid to serve French fries when appropriate. Lunch menus feature Caesar salad, grilled chicken with French fries and lemon broth, and cheeseburgers. At dinnertime strong Mediterranean flavours will balance a rocket salad with warm goat's cheese and penne rigate with asparagus, tomato and saffron broth. Steamed Scottish salmon with cherry tomato salsa and fettuccine and medallions of lamb with pesto mashed potato restate the theme among the main courses. Black Bottom and pecan pies add a transatlantic twist to the dessert menu while, unsurprisingly, Californian wines make a strong showing on the well-described wine list, which is listed by style. *Seats 70. Parties 150. Private Room. L 12-3 (Sun to 3.30) D 7-10 (Sat to 10.30, Sun to 9.30). Set D £19.92.*

Steeple Aston   Hopcrofts Holt Hotel   63%   £80

Tel 0869 40259   Fax 0869 40865

H

Steeple Aston Oxfordshire OX5 3QQ   Map 5 D1

Once a coaching inn, the hotel has now expanded its role with executive accommodation and purpose-built conference rooms. Just off the A4260 between Banbury and Oxford. Mount Charlotte Thistle. *Rooms 85. Access, Amex, Visa,*

Stevenage   Novotel   60%   £80

Tel 0438 742299   Fax 0438 723872

H

Knebworth Park Stevenage Hertfordshire SG1 2AX   Map 6 B3

Modern, open-plan hotel at junction 7 of the A1(M). Banqueting facilities for up to 110, conferences up to 150. *Rooms 100. Outdoor swimming pool. Access, Amex, Visa,* ①

Stevenage   Places of Interest

Tourist Information   Tel 0438 369441.
Gordon Craig Theatre   Tel 0438 316291.
Benington Lordship Gardens   Tel 0438 85668.
Shaw's Corner (NT)   Ayot St. Lawrence Tel 0438 820307 *Home of George Bernard Shaw.*
Welwyn Roman Baths   Tel 0707 271362.
Knebworth House   Knebworth Tel 0438 812661.
Stevenage Ice Rink   Tel 0438 740750.
Welwyn Garden City Ski Centre   Tel 0707 331056/330780.
Silver Leys Polo Club Troopers   Drivers End. Codicote Tel 0438 820414.

Stilton   Bell Inn   £62

Tel 0733 241066   Fax 0733 245173

IR

Great North Road Stilton Nr Peterborough Cambridgeshire PE7 3RA   Map 6 A2

Reputedly the oldest coaching inn on the Great North Road, the Bell boasts a Roman well in the courtyard and an impressive 15th-century stone frontage. 1990 additions include hotel reception glassed in under the original archway and two rear wings of bedrooms with today's trappings, tokens of antiquity sadly confined to the odd four-poster bed. Separate conference/banqueting in the Marlborough Suite accommodates up to 100. No dogs. *Rooms 19. Garden, croquet. Access, Amex, Visa,* ①

Restaurant   £45

The galleried restaurant with vaulted ceiling and exposed rafters is more in character with the original Old Bell. Weekly table d'hote menus and "creations" à la carte (lamb niçoise, Marlborough duck) conclude with good Stilton cheese, plum bread and vintage port. *Seats 40. Parties 64. Private Room. L (2nd week Dec-1st week Jan only) 12-2 (Sun from 12.30) D 7-9.30 (Sun to 9). Set D £14.50.*

Stockbridge   Grosvenor Hotel   57%   £80

Tel 0264 810606   Fax 0264 810747

H

High Street Stockbridge Hampshire SO20 6EU   Map 4 C3

On the A30 in the village centre, the Grosvenor (in the Lansbury group) has kept many of its original Georgian features. The bar lacks period appeal, but is one of the focal points of Stockbridge life. Bedrooms in the original house are larger than those in the converted stables. No dogs. Banqueting and conference facilities for around 70. *Rooms 25. Garden, sauna, snooker. Access, Amex, Visa,* ①

Stockbridge   Places of Interest

Houghton Lodge House and Gardens   Tel 0264 810177.
Museum of Army Flying   Middle Wallop Tel 0264 384421.

Stockport   Alma Lodge   61%   £98
Tel 061-483 4431   Fax 061-483 1983   **H**

149 Buxton Road Stockport Greater Manchester SK2 6EL   Map 10 B2

Two miles from the M6 (junction 12) on the A6 to the south of Stockport,
an early Victorian house has been greatly extended to create this business-
oriented hotel. Some original features of the old house – wood panelling
and open fires – survive in the public rooms. Function facilities for up to
250. Children up to 16 accommodated free in parents' room. Jarvis Hotels.
Rooms 56. *Access, Amex, Visa,* 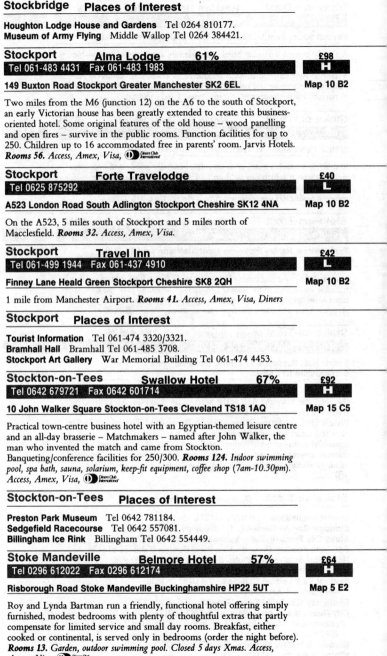 Diners Club International

Stockport   Forte Travelodge   £40
Tel 0625 875292   **L**

A523 London Road South Adlington Stockport Cheshire SK12 4NA   Map 10 B2

On the A523, 5 miles south of Stockport and 5 miles north of
Macclesfield. ***Rooms 32.*** *Access, Amex, Visa.*

Stockport   Travel Inn   £42
Tel 061-499 1944   Fax 061-437 4910   **L**

Finney Lane Heald Green Stockport Cheshire SK8 2QH   Map 10 B2

1 mile from Manchester Airport. ***Rooms 41.*** *Access, Amex, Visa, Diners*

Stockport   Places of Interest

Tourist Information   Tel 061-474 3320/3321.
Bramhall Hall   Bramhall Tel 061-485 3708.
Stockport Art Gallery   War Memorial Building Tel 061-474 4453.

Stockton-on-Tees   Swallow Hotel   67%   £92
Tel 0642 679721   Fax 0642 601714   **H**

10 John Walker Square Stockton-on-Tees Cleveland TS18 1AQ   Map 15 C5

Practical town-centre business hotel with an Egyptian-themed leisure centre
and an all-day brasserie – Matchmakers – named after John Walker, the
man who invented the match and came from Stockton.
Banqueting/conference facilities for 250/300. ***Rooms 124.*** *Indoor swimming
pool, spa bath, sauna, solarium, keep-fit equipment, coffee shop (7am-10.30pm).
Access, Amex, Visa,* Diners Club International

Stockton-on-Tees   Places of Interest

Preston Park Museum   Tel 0642 781184.
Sedgefield Racecourse   Tel 0642 557081.
Billingham Ice Rink   Billingham Tel 0642 554449.

Stoke Mandeville   Belmore Hotel   57%   £64
Tel 0296 612022   Fax 0296 612174   **H**

Risborough Road Stoke Mandeville Buckinghamshire HP22 5UT   Map 5 E2

Roy and Lynda Bartman run a friendly, functional hotel offering simply
furnished, modest bedrooms with plenty of thoughtful extras that partly
compensate for limited service and small day rooms. Breakfast, either
cooked or continental, is served only in bedrooms (order the night before).
Rooms 13. *Garden, outdoor swimming pool. Closed 5 days Xmas. Access,
Amex, Visa,* Diners Club International

Stoke-on-Trent   Haydon House Hotel   65%   £65
Tel 0782 711311   Fax 0782 717470   H
Haydon Street Basford Stoke-on-Trent Staffordshire ST4 6JD   Map 10 B3

A family owned Victorian hotel with friendly atmosphere, dependable
accommodation and six de-luxe suites in adjacent Glebe Mews. Classy
Victorian-style day rooms with antique clock collection. Stands on A54 at
Basford. Banqueting and conferences up to 80. Children under 12 stay free
in parents' room. *Rooms 30. Access, Amex, Visa,*

Stoke-on-Trent   North Stafford Hotel   61%   £86
Tel 0782 744477   Fax 0782 744580   H
Station Road Stoke-on-Trent Staffordshire ST4 2AE   Map 10 B3

Red-brick Victorian hotel with cheerful, generally good-sized bedrooms
and a ballroom which can hold up to 450 for a conference. More
bedrooms due before we publish. Children up to 14 stay free in parents'
room. *Rooms 69. Dinner dances. Access, Amex, Visa,*

Stoke-on-Trent   Stakis Grand Hotel   68%   £96
Tel 0782 202361   Fax 0782 286464   H
Trinity Street Hanley Stoke-on-Trent Staffordshire ST1 5NB   Map 10 B3

Based at Hanley town centre and close to Stoke Festival Park, the recently
remodelled Grand combines conference trade (max 300) with good family
facilities and leisure club. *Rooms 128. Indoor swimming pool, spa bath, sauna,
steam room, solarium, keep-fit equipment, baby-listening, crèche (mid-July to end
Aug, weekends and school holidays) Access, Amex, Visa,*

Stoke-on-Trent Moat House   70%NEW   £99
Tel 0782 219000   Fax 0782 284500   H
Etruria Hall, Festival Way Etruria Stoke-on-Trent
Staffordshire ST1 5BQ   Map 10 B3

Ten minutes drive from the M6, and equidistant from junctions 15 and 16,
the hotel stands by the A53 at the heart of the 1986 Garden Festival park.
Extensive conference and banqueting facilities for up to 500 are housed in
Etruria Hall, the former home of Josiah Wedgwood. Day rooms, leisure
club and smart up-to-date bedrooms are in a sympathetically designed
stone-clad complex which reflects within it many of the original hall's
features. *Rooms 147. Indoor swimming pool, spa bath, sauna, solarium, beauty
salon, gymnasium, snooker, coffee shop (8am-10pm). Access, Amex, Visa,*

Stoke-on-Trent   Places of Interest

Tourist Information   Tel 0782 411222.
Biddulph Grange Garden (NT)   Biddulph Tel 0782 517999.
Stoke City Football Club   Victoria Ground Tel 0782 413511.
Port Vale Football Ground   Vale Park, Burslem Tel 0782 814134.
North Staffordshire Ski Club   Kidsgrove Tel 0782 784908.
Alton Towers   Alton Tel 0538 702200.
Festival Park Leisure Complex   Tel 0782 283838.
   Museums and Art Galleries
Chatterley Whitfield Mining Museum   Tel 0782 813337.
City Museum and Art Gallery   Tel 0782 202173.
Wedgwood Museum   Josiah Wedgwood and Sons Ltd Tel 0782
   204218/204141.
Gladstone Pottery Museum   Tel 0782 319232.
Minton Museum   Tel 0782 744766.
Sir Henry Doulton Gallery   Tel 0782 575454.

Stokesley   Chapters   64%   £57

HR

Tel 0642 711888   Fax ext 223

27 High Street Stokesley North Yorkshire TS9 5AD   Map 15 C5

Alan Thompson relocated Chapters restaurant in the former Golden Lion
hotel a couple of years ago and embarked on a total transformation. Red-
tiled floors and light, bright furnishings lend the ground floor a
contemporary feel, with a popular new café-bar at the front.
Refurbishment of the generally modest bedrooms continues with
expected completion by the end of 1992. *Rooms 13. Garden, coffee shop
(9am-10.30pm). Access, Amex, Visa,* **① Diners Club International**

Restaurant   £40

Yellow decor, white wicker furniture and tiled floors have given a
summery lift to the restaurant, and there's a Mediterranean air to many of
the menu's best dishes: hot spinach soufflé with tapénade and anchovy
sauce, or San Daniele ham with fresh figs and Reggiano cheese for starters.
Monkfish baked with a pesto rosso on mussel and red pepper sauce shows a
similar slant. Follow with a citrus trio of lemon tart, lime mousse and
grapefruit sorbet on a bed of orange sauce, and a cup of excellent
cappuccino. *Seats 62. Parties 54. Private Room. L by arrangement D 7-9.30
(Sat to 10). Closed Sun.*

Ston Easton   Ston Easton Park   87%   £152

HR

Tel 0761 241631   Fax 0761 241377

Ston Easton Nr Bath Avon BA3 4DF   Map 4 B3

An immaculately restored, Grade I listed Palladian mansion built in 1740
and set in a marvellous Humphry Repton landscape. Superb pictures,
priceless porcelain and fine antiques (of which a museum would be proud)
are complemented by wonderful floral displays. In the salon, ornate
plasterwork and trompe l'oeil murals are used to stunning effect and the
library is graced by listed mahogany bookcases. Bedrooms are decorated in
exquisite taste, with an array of pictures and fine furniture; several have
four-posters of the Chippendale and Hepplewhite periods. The bathrooms
are of a similarly high standard, most having marbled tiles and vanitory
units; all offer showers and baths. No children under 12. *Rooms 21.
Garden, croquet, snooker, tennis, helipad, hot air ballooning. Access, Amex, Visa,*
① Diners Club International

Restaurant   £90

In contrast to the rest of the house, the restaurant is more informal, with
bamboo furniture and drag-painted, off-white panelling. Chef Mark
Harrington's cooking is "updated classical", with interesting combinations,
and assertive flavours: roulade of rabbit, spinach and walnuts with a peach
chutney; noisette of Welsh lamb on a garlic croute and pine kernel and
rosemary crust; terrine of white chocolate and rosewater marshmallow on
a kumquat coulis. Nevertheless, the traditional is still well represented by
the likes of chicken liver parfait studded with smoked foie gras and truffles,
rondel of Scotch beef "Wellington style", and sablé biscuits with a lemon
and lime bavarois. Lunchtime brings an equally traditional choice and
there's always a vegetarian choice – perhaps a feuilleté of globe artichoke
filled with leek and Roquefort mousseline, dressed with lemon butter.
Clearly laid-out wine list shows good balance, and is particularly easy to
use for those who know their vintages. *Seats 40. Parties 26. Private Room.
L 12.30-2 D 7.30-9.30 (Fri & Sat to 10). Set L £24 Set D £35.*

Stonehouse   Stonehouse Court   68%   £98

Tel 0453 825155   Fax 0453 824611   **H**

Bristol Road Stonehouse Gloucestershire GL10 3RA   Map 4 B2

Conveniently situated about a mile from junction 3 of the M5, Stonehouse Court is an imposing 17th-century building set in 6 acres of mature gardens. Accommodation is split between spacious rooms with mullioned windows in the main house and more uniform, characterless ones in redbrick extensions. Day rooms include a large panelled lounge with fine carved stone fireplace, abundant seating and a bar with green leather chesterfield sofas. Friendly management. Clipper Hotels. *Rooms 37. Garden, croquet, putting, snooker, fishing, helipad. Access, Visa,*

Stonehouse   Places of Interest

Slimbridge Wildfowl Trust   Tel 0453 890333.

Stonham   Mr Underhill's   ★   £70

Tel 0449 711206   **R**

Stonham Nr Stowmarket Suffolk IP14 5DW   Map 6 C3

Chris and Judy Bradley's delightful restaurant stands north of Ipswich on the A140. Much like the decor, Chris's French-influenced cooking is in the modern idiom, with carefully chosen, balanced ingredients and imaginative combinations that are neither fussy nor fanciful. New-style evening menus offer three or four courses at fixed prices: compote of roasted sweet pepper paired with confit of Barbary duck and Provençal olives, or fillet of brill with tomato and olives preceding rack of lamb with herbes de Provence. Choose then between classic pecan and apple tart, Creole coffee parfait and the superb cheeseboard. True value, too, for 2- or 3-course Sunday lunches. There are helpful guidance notes on the world-wide wine list that includes many interesting bottles. *Seats 24. Parties 24. Private Room. L by arrangement D 7.30-9. Closed Sun & Mon, Bank Holidays (open 25 & 26 Dec). Set L £15/£19.95 Set D from £18.95/£21.95. Access, Amex, Visa,*

Stonor   Stonor Arms   £80

Tel 0491 63345   Fax 0491 638863   **RR**

Stonor Nr Henley-on-Thames Oxfordshire RG9 6HE   Map 5 D2

Two levels of food in an attractively converted, 16th-century village former pub: informal, daily-changing à la carte in the flagstoned bar area, and more formal (but not overly ambitious) menus in the elegant restaurant proper and conservatory room. Aperitifs and canapés are served in a spacious drawing room graced with antiques and comfortable sofas. Stephen Frost uses fresh produce from local sources, fish from Cornwall (perhaps fillet of hake with a green mustard sauce or brill with a fondue of tomatoes and a butter sauce) and some meats and vegetables from their own farm or estates in Scotland. A clear fish and shellfish soup shows off his classical technique, while oxtail casserole and hot apricot soufflé with Amaretto ice-cream show that currently fashionable ingredients are not overlooked. Desserts are particularly strong and cheeses well kept, served with oatcakes, apples and grapes. The reasonably priced wine list includes classic clarets and burgundies as well as a range of French country wines and the award-winning Noble Bacchus Chiltern Valley English dessert wine. *Seats 40. Parties 24. Private Room. Bar: L & D 7 days, Restaurant: L Sun only (set menu) 12-1.45 D 7-9.30. Closed D Sun. Set D £19.75. Access, Amex, Visa.*

Rooms   £104

A wing of bedrooms, now numbering nine (including two suites), is furnished to a high standard with some antiques. Cots and Z-beds for children are additional charges, as are cooked breakfasts (£5.50). Enquire about special Dinner, Bed & Breakfast. No dogs. *Rooms 9.*

Storrington   Abingworth Hall   71%   £96

| Tel 0798 813636   Fax 0798 813914 | **HR** |

Thakeham Road Storrington West Sussex RH20 3EF   Map 5 E3

2 miles north of Storrington on the B2139. There's a pretty lake within
the eight acres of grounds surrounding Abingworth Hall, which has had a
succession of colourful owners, including Sir Oswald Mosley. Built in the
1930s, the white-painted house has been extended to include 21 bedrooms,
all with immaculate en-suite bathrooms and decorated with a range of
furnishings from antique to cane. An oak-panelled drawing room and
rattan-furnished conservatory look out on to the lawned garden and are
peaceful and tranquil, as is the whole setting. Housekeeping standards and
repair are maintained at a high level throughout by the considerate owners
Mr and Mrs Bulman. No children under ten. No dogs. *Rooms 21. Outdoor
swimming pool, helipad, garden, tennis, croquet, putting, coarse fishing. Closed
2 weeks Jan. Access, Visa,*

Restaurant   £65

Tasteful decor, large, well-spaced tables with crisp linen and high-quality
cooking from Peter Cannon guarantee an enjoyable meal. His style is
modern but with a conservative streak, offering both à la carte and table
d'hote menus at lunch (3-course) and dinner (4-course). Typical dishes
might include baked field mushrooms and glazed goat's cheese or a duck
and sultana paté with orange and redcurrant sauce and hot brioche to start,
followed by poached, foie gras-stuffed supreme of chicken with an oyster
mushroom sauce or sautéed lamb cutlets in a sherry vinegar, tomato and
tarragon sauce. Desserts range from roast almond and toffee ice cream with
chocolate sauce to warm strawberries in orange and peppercorn sauce.
There are several gaps in the rather erratic wine list. Gentlemen are
requested to wear a jacket and tie for dinner. *Seats 50. Parties 54. Private
Room. L 12.30-1.45 D 7.15-9. Closed 2 weeks Jan. Set L £15/£12.50 (Sun)
Set D £28.*

Storrington   Little Thakeham   78%   £150

| Tel 0903 744416   Fax 0903 745022 | **HR** |

Merrywood Lane Storrington West Sussex RH20 3HE   Map 5 E3

A fine example of a Sir Edward Lutyens manor house standing in
delightful gardens designed in the style of Gertrude Jekyll. Tim and
Pauline Ractliff have furnished their beautiful house in a style sympathetic
to its architectural features; the minstrel's gallery, mullioned windows,
polished stone floors and oak doors are complemented by period furniture
in leather and oak, arts and crafts-designed chairs and sideboards, and
pictures, flowers and ornaments. The bedrooms are spacious (although not
always furnished in keeping with the country house style), with garden
views, period Liberty prints, some lovely oak pieces and personal touches
such as pot pourri, books and magazines. Bathrooms are a slight
disappointment by comparison. Little Thakeham seems to be run more as a
country house than as a hotel. No dogs. Children by arrangement.
*Rooms 9. Garden, outdoor swimming pool, tennis, croquet, helipad. Closed
2 weeks Xmas/New Year. Access, Amex, Visa,*

Restaurant   £90

The short, four-course, fixed-price menu offers a safe choice of
uncomplicated cooking, but at a fairly hefty price. Melon with Parma
ham, grilled goat's cheese and avocado or fricassée of scallops and spiced
tomato soup with cream and croutons are hardly exciting starters, but cater
for their guests who "enjoy the change from ambitious restaurant menus".
Main course dishes like roast duck with apple and calvados sauce and rack
of Southdown lamb with redcurrant sauce are also straightforward but still
no match for the elegant dining room. Several classics on the wine list at
reasonable prices. *Seats 30. Parties 14. Private Room. L 12.30-2 D 7.30-9.
Closed D Sun. Set L £14.50 Set D £32.50.*

Storrington   Manley's   £90

Tel 0903 742331   **RR**

Manleys Hill Storrington West Sussex RH20 4BT   Map 5 E3

A sharp appetite is a must when visiting this attractive, low-beamed Sussex-
stone restaurant, where Karl Löderer cooks hearty Continental dishes with
care and presents them with flair. *Petit gateau aux poissons à la crème de
ciboulette* – layers of sole, sea bass, scallops and crab topped with puff pastry
and served with a light chive sauce and tomato concassé – makes a pretty,
well-balanced first course, while *magret de canard mariné et grillé au chou
blanc au gingembre* – marinated duck breast, grilled and served with ginger-
flavoured cabbage – is an interesting and very satisfying main course.
Locally grown vegetables are good, as are details like bread, canapés and
amuse-gueule; pretty, involved desserts like poached pear and almond
cream in a puff pastry case with Amaretto sauce and Salzburger nockerln (a
lemon and orange-flavoured soufflé cooked in honey and rum) reflect
Löderer's Austrian background. A good wine list, with good German
examples; friendly, efficient service and delightful fresh flower
arrangements all add to the enjoyment. Sunday lunches are popular,
offering a short carte that might include roast rib of beef and Yorkshire
pudding. No service charge is added to the bill. *Seats 48. Parties 10. Private
Room. L 12-2 D 7-9.30. Closed D Sun, D 25 & 26 Dec, all Mon, Bank
Holidays except Good Friday, 1st 2 weeks Jan. Set L £18.60 (£24.50 Sun)
Set D £26. Access, Amex, Visa,* ⓘ *DinersClub International*

Room   £87

A handsome suite overlooking the downs is available for restaurant guests
who wish to stay overnight. No children or dogs.

Storrington   Old Forge   £55

Tel 0903 743402   **R**

6a Church Street Storrington West Sussex RH20 4LA   Map 5 E3

A converted beamed forge is the relaxing setting for adventurous cooking
from Clive Roberts, who offers monthly-changing menus. Inspiration for
dishes is taken from many countries: sliced sea bass in vanilla-flavoured
Provençal olive oil, shrimp, pepper and onion brochette with tabbouleh,
ox tongue and celeriac in filo pastry with Bourgogne mustard sauce.
British produce is not overlooked, though, with Scottish smoked salmon
bisque, steamed suet pudding of beef, Guinness, kidney and oysters and
farmhouse cheeses served with hazelnut and smoked cheese bread. Home-
made ice creams and sorbets and perhaps a rich hazelnut chocolate cream
accompanied by brandy snaps filled with praline mousse among the
desserts, ably complemented by a varied selection of sweet wines by the
glass. *Seats 22. Parties 12. Private Room. L 12.30-1.30 D 7.30-9. Closed
L Sat, D Sun, all Mon, Bank Holidays, 3 weeks Oct. Set L £13 Set D
£18.50. Access, Visa,* ⓘ *DinersClub International*

Storrington   Places of Interest

St. Mary's House and Gardens   Bramber Tel 0903 816205.

Stourbridge   Talbot Hotel   59%   £65

Tel 0384 394350   Fax 0384 371318   **H**

High Street Stourbridge West Midlands DY8 1DW   Map 10 B4

A coaching inn pedigree is evident in many places, including the original
heavy doors to the coach entrance and signs of what were once galleries.
The mellow lounges sport some old timbers, a feature echoed in some of
the bedrooms, which are reached by a marvellous old winding staircase.
Some rooms have antiques, others freestanding pine, while the smaller
singles use fitted units. Informal, friendly service. *Rooms 25. Coffee shop
(9am-11pm). Access, Amex, Visa.*

Stourbridge Places of Interest

Hagley Hall Nr Stourbridge Tel 0562 882408.
Broadfield House Glass Museum Barnett Lane, Kingswinford Tel 0384
252401.

Stourport-on-Severn	Moat House	62%	£69
Tel 0299 827733 Fax 0299 878520			**H**
Hartlebury Road Stourport-on-Severn Hereford & Worcester DY13 9LT			Map 10 B4

Well set up for business or pleasure, the Moat House stands in a wooded
23-acre site. Conferences up to 350 delegates. *Rooms 68. Garden, outdoor
swimming pool, keep-fit equipment, sauna, squash, tennis, snooker. Access,
Amex, Visa,*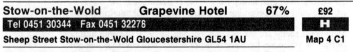

Stourport Place of Interest

Eastgrove Cottage Garden Nursery Sankyns Green, Nr Shrawley Tel
0299 896389.

Stow Bardolph	Hare Arms	£50
Tel 0366 382229		**R**
Stow Bardolph Nr Downham Market Norfolk PE34 3HT		Map 6 B2

The restaurant of David and Tricia McManus's picturesque country pub is
a charming room whose panelled walls are painted to look like marble. A
simple table d'hote menu (prawn mousse, egg mayonnaise, chicken breast
chasseur, rump steak with onion rings) is offered from Mon-Thurs;
straightforward à la carte only on Friday and Saturday, with the likes of
smoked snails, deep-fried goat's cheese, skate wing with black butter and
capers, and pork medallions with Marsala. *Seats 60. Parties 40. Private
Room. D only 7.30-9.30. Closed Sun, 25 & 26 Dec. Set D £14.50
(Mon-Thurs). No credit cards.*

Stow-on-the-Wold	Fosse Manor	60%	£90
Tel 0451 30354 Fax 0451 32486			**H**
Fosse Way Stow-on-the-Wold Gloucestershire GL54 1JX			Map 4 C1

Long-standing resident proprietors Bob and Yvonne Johnston and their
loyal staff run a family haven that attracts many repeat visits. Built in the
style of a Cotswold manor house, it stands in its ivy coat in grounds set
back from the A429. Bedrooms (including ten equipped for family use)
overlook colourful gardens and the Fosse Way; the bright look of the day
rooms is enhanced throughout by potted plants, fresh flowers and spotless
housekeeping. Family facilities include supervised play times for children in
a playroom and playground on high days and holidays. *Rooms 20. Garden,
croquet, sauna, solarium, spa bath, beauty salon. Closed 22-30 Dec. Access,
Amex, Visa,* (D)

Stow-on-the-Wold	Grapevine Hotel	67%	£92
Tel 0451 30344 Fax 0451 32278			**H**
Sheep Street Stow-on-the-Wold Gloucestershire GL54 1AU			Map 4 C1

All the bedrooms at Sandra Elliott's well-run hotel are comfortable and
well equipped. Main-house rooms are generally smaller and cottagey; best
are the four-poster rooms and the six stylish garden rooms. It's a genuinely
welcoming place, from the foyer through day rooms given character by
exposed stone and beams. High standards of housekeeping. *Rooms 23. Patio.
Access, Amex, Visa,* (D)

Stow-on-the-Wold　　　Unicorn Hotel　　59%　　£95
Tel 0451 30257　Fax 0451 31090　　　　　　H
Sheep Street Stow-on-the-Wold Gloucestershire GL54 1HQ　　Map 4 C1

17th-century origins with some period appeal (steep tiled roof, dormer
windows and original beams). Forte. *Rooms 20. Access, Amex, Visa,*
Diners Club International

Stow-on-the-Wold　　　Wyck Hill House　　75%　　£95
Tel 0451 31936　Fax 0451 32243　　　　　　HR
Burford Road Stow-on-the-Wold Gloucestershire GL54 1HY　　Map 4 C1

Perched on a hillside, this fine Cotswold-stone manor stands among 100
acres of parkland (by the A424) and is almost worth a visit just for the
magnificent views over the Windrush valley. Dating from 1790, it retains
a relaxed, eminently civilised atmosphere with smart day rooms that
include a stylish and impressive library-lounge with original cedar
panelling and a high-ceilinged bar with rich club-like decor. 16 main-house
bedrooms are well appointed, with antique furniture, bold-patterned fabrics
and seating areas. Further bedrooms in a coach house and orangery have
exposed stonework and a summery feel. Up-to-date and well-lit bathrooms
throughout. Keen management and motivated staff. No dogs. *Rooms 31.*
Garden, croquet, riding. Access, Amex, Visa, **Diners Club International**

Restaurant　　　　　　　　　　　　　　　£85

Smart decor and a splendid conservatory give the restaurant an elegant
interior air to enhance the fine views. Chef Ian Smith offers an à la carte
with a good choice, ranging from a pressed terrine of leeks, king prawns
and tomato with a beetroot dressing, traditional bouillabaisse, or Cornish
crab and spinach lasagne with a two-caviar sauce, to a pavet of Cornish
monkfish, wild rabbit casserole and medallions of local venison (served on
a juniper, celeriac and pickled pear sauce). Puddings and vegetarian dishes
(with a particularly good choice) are equally interesting: perhaps crème
brulée mousse with apple and blackcurrant compote and brandy snap
twists or coconut soufflé and warm pineapple coulis. British farmhouse
cheeses served with warm chive and onion bread. An improving wine list.
Seats 30. Parties 20. Private Room. L 12.30-2 D 7.30-9.30 (Sat to 10). Set L
£16.95.

Stowmarket　　　Forte Travelodge　　　　　£40
Tel 0449 615347　　　　　　　　　　　L
A45 Stowmarket Suffolk IP14 3PY　　　　　　Map 6 C3

On the A45 northbound, 12 miles north of Ipswich with Bury St
Edmunds also within easy reach. *Rooms 40. Access, Amex, Visa.*

Stratfield Turgis　　　Wellington Arms　　　£75
Tel 0256 882214　Fax 0256 882934　　　　　I
Stratfield Turgis Basingstoke Hampshire RG27 0AS　　Map 5 D3

This Georgian-fronted hostelry began life as a farmhouse, and was a
coaching inn before becoming the smart, well-run establishment it is today.
Set just back from the A33, it offers high standards of accommodation.
Main-house rooms are spacious and individually decorated with quality
fabrics. Newer rooms have pretty Laura Ashley wall coverings and pine
furniture. There's a Georgian-style lounge and a flagstoned 'Green Wellie'
bar. *Rooms 35. Garden, game fishing. Access, Amex, Visa,* **Diners Club International**

Stratford-upon-Avon   Alveston Manor   65%   £112

Tel 0789 204581   Fax 0789 414095   **H**

Clopton Bridge Stratford-upon-Avon Warwickshire CV37 7HP   Map 4 C1

A Midsummer Night's Dream was first performed in the seven acres of
gardens of this manor house, behind whose gabled exterior there remains a
good deal of period charm in the day rooms. Bedrooms, though, are
mainly modern. Forte Grand. *Rooms 108. Garden, pitch & putt. Access,
Amex, Visa,* **(i)** Diners Club International

Stratford-upon-Avon   Billesley Manor   76%   £128

Tel 0789 400888   Fax 0789 764145   **HR**

Billesley Alcester Nr Stratford-upon-Avon Warwickshire B49 6NF   Map 4 C1

Three miles from Stratford-upon-Avon, the centuries-old stone manor
house stands in 11 acres of typically English gardens. Within, its public
rooms are impressive, with oak panelling, leather seating and open log fires
in the cocktail bar, plus polished mahogany tables and fine garden views
through stone-mullioned windows in the restaurant. More panelling,
period furniture and some four-poster beds imbue main-house bedrooms
with the most character; the remainder are housed in two modern blocks
with a high degree of comfort. Housekeeping throughout is good, staff are
polite and efficient. Conferences accommodated (up to 100 delegates). No
dogs. Queens Moat Houses. *Rooms 41. Garden, croquet, tennis, pitch & putt,
indoor swimming pool. Access, Amex, Visa,* **(i)** Diners Club International

Restaurant   £90

Daily shopping in Evesham and London assures the freshness and quality of
all ingredients. Mark Naylor produces a confident combination of balanced
textures and well-defined flavours. Salad of John Dory, figs and hazelnuts
with a port dressing; marinated duck breast with an orange juniper gin
sauce; and warm mango tart with lime and ginger sauce show the style of
his à la carte menus. *Seats 40. Private Room. L 12.30-2 D 7.30-9.30. Set L
£17 Set D £25.*

Stratford-upon-Avon   Dukes Hotel   65%   £65

Tel 0789 269300   Fax 0789 414700   **H**

Payton Street Stratford-upon-Avon Warwickshire CV37 6UA   Map 4 C1

Two Georgian town houses dating from 1820 make up a civilised hotel
not far from the centre, the shops and the theatres. Well-worn armchairs,
antique furniture and ornaments make a homely, lived-in lounge, and
there's a small bar. Bedrooms are neat and comfortable with period pieces;
there are four-poster rooms and suites. No children under 12. No dogs.
Rooms 22. Garden. Closed 10 days Xmas/New Year. Access, Amex, Visa,
(i) Diners Club International

Stratford-upon-Avon   Ettington Park   76%   £140

Tel 0789 450123   Fax 0789 450472   **H**

Alderminster Stratford-upon-Avon Warwickshire CV37 8BS   Map 4 C1

An imposing neo-Gothic stately home with a Grade 1 preservation listing.
It stands five miles south of Stratford on the A34 to Oxford, in mature
parkland by the Stour. The interior of the house fully lives up to the
promise of the setting. Notable features include a lovely plant-filled
conservatory entrance, a fine Victorian drawing room, a richly panelled
library bar and a very elegant and relaxing lounge. Bedrooms are no less
impressive, with plenty of space, well-chosen antiques, light, restful colour
schemes and all sorts of little personal touches. The majority of rooms
enjoy fine country views. The Long Gallery is one of the most characterful
meeting rooms in the country, with book-lined walls and a high, wood-
panelled vaulted ceiling; it holds up to 60 delegates. Similarly, there are
other interesting rooms like the 14th-century chapel with stained-glass
windows, suitable for private dining and board meetings. No dogs.   *See over*

Rooms 48. Garden, croquet, tennis, helipad, indoor swimming pool, sauna, solarium, whirlpool bath, coarse fishing, riding, clay-pigeon shooting. Access, Amex, Visa,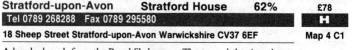

Stratford-upon-Avon　　Falcon Hotel　　63%　　£94

Tel 0789 205777　Fax 0789 414260　　H

Chapel Street Stratford-upon-Avon Warwickshire CV37 6HA　　Map 4 C1

Behind a classic timbered facade there's a blend of old and new. The beamed and panelled Oak Bar is as old as the building (1640), while the conference rooms (for up to 200) are thoroughly up-to-date. 20 bedrooms, including a four-poster suite, are in the original part, the rest in a modern section. Ample car parking. Queens Moat Houses. *Rooms 73. Garden. Access, Amex, Visa,*

Stratford-upon-Avon　　Forte Posthouse　　59%　　£67

Tel 0789 266761　Fax 0789 414547　　H

Bridgefoot Stratford-upon-Avon Warwickshire CV37 7LT　　Map 4 C1

Popular tourist, family and business base overlooking the river Avon, opposite the theatre. *Rooms 60. Children's playground. Access, Amex, Visa,*

Stratford-upon-Avon　　Moat House International　71%　　£120

Tel 0789 414411　Fax 0789 298589　　H

Bridgefoot Stratford-upon-Avon Warwickshire CV37 6YR　　Map 4 C1

A purpose-built, modern hotel close to the centre of town with a wealth of facilities to keep the conference trade happy. Spacious public rooms include a simply furnished residents' lounge and another that overlooks the river Avon. The Tavern Bar is pub-like and The Actors night club opens six nights a week. Bedrooms have the usual uniformity of chain hotels but are of a good size and comfortable, with smart dark furniture. Some of the rooms have views of the Royal Shakespeare Theatre and river. The Warwick Grill opens only for dinner and Sunday lunch; a Carvery also overlooks the river. Superb Metropolitan health and fitness centre. Conference and banqueting facilities for up to 450. *Rooms 247. Garden, gymnasium, indoor swimming pool, spa bath, sauna, steam room, solarium, beautician, hairdressing, mooring, helipad, disco, shopping arcade, news kiosk. Access, Amex, Visa,*

Stratford-upon-Avon　　Shakespeare Hotel　　69%　　£116

Tel 0789 294771　Fax 0789 415111　　H

Chapel Street Stratford-upon-Avon Warwickshire CV37 6ER　　Map 4 C1

A Forte Heritage hotel with a central location and a long history. The gabled and timbered facade is typical of its 17th-century origins, and inside are beams and flagstones, open fires and period furnishings. Floral fabrics and smart darkwood furniture are used in the bedrooms, which include suites and four-posters. Function facilities for up to 120. *Rooms 63. Garden, bar billiards. Access, Amex, Visa,*

Stratford-upon-Avon　　Stratford House　　62%　　£78

Tel 0789 268288　Fax 0789 295580　　H

18 Sheep Street Stratford-upon-Avon Warwickshire CV37 6EF　　Map 4 C1

A hundred yards from the Royal Shakespeare Theatre and the river Avon, this quiet little hotel in a Georgian house is a comfortable, friendly home from home. An open fire warms the lounge, and there's a bright conservatory restaurant and bar. In warm weather the walled garden comes into its own. Neat bedrooms use floral fabrics and darkwood units. *Rooms 11. Garden. Closed 4 days Xmas. Access, Amex, Visa,*

Stratford-upon-Avon   Welcombe Hotel   74%   £140

Tel 0789 295252   Fax 0789 414666   **H**

Warwick Road Stratford-upon-Avon Warwickshire CV37 0NR   Map 4 C1

The parkland surrounding this extensive, handsome Jacobean-style mansion
includes two lakes and an 18-hole, par 70 golf course, whose clubhouse is a
popular spot for a drink or a snack. A comfortable alternative in the main
building is the oak-panelled bar, named after sometime owner Sir George
Trevelyan. In the lounge, deep sofas and armchairs provide abundant
comfort, and a log fire burns in the ornate black marble fireplace.
Individually furnished bedrooms in the main house have antiques and
period pieces, plus marble bathrooms with separate showers. Some of the
suites are most impressive – the Lady Caroline (Trevelyan) comprises four-
poster bedroom, drawing room, study and luxurious bathroom. Rooms in
a garden wing are smaller but equally comfortable. Conference facilities for
up to 120, banqueting up to 180. *Rooms 76. Garden, golf course, tennis.
Closed 1 wk Xmas. Access, Amex, Visa,*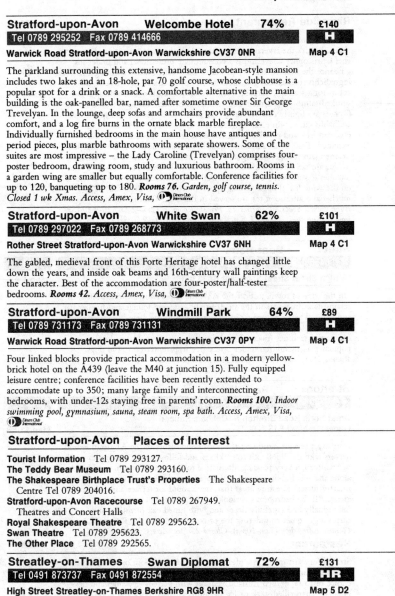

Stratford-upon-Avon   White Swan   62%   £101

Tel 0789 297022   Fax 0789 268773   **H**

Rother Street Stratford-upon-Avon Warwickshire CV37 6NH   Map 4 C1

The gabled, medieval front of this Forte Heritage hotel has changed little
down the years, and inside oak beams and 16th-century wall paintings keep
the character. Best of the accommodation are four-poster/half-tester
bedrooms. *Rooms 42. Access, Amex, Visa,*

Stratford-upon-Avon   Windmill Park   64%   £89

Tel 0789 731173   Fax 0789 731131   **H**

Warwick Road Stratford-upon-Avon Warwickshire CV37 0PY   Map 4 C1

Four linked blocks provide practical accommodation in a modern yellow-
brick hotel on the A439 (leave the M40 at junction 15). Fully equipped
leisure centre; conference facilities have been recently extended to
accommodate up to 350; many large family and interconnecting
bedrooms, with under-12s staying free in parents' room. *Rooms 100. Indoor
swimming pool, gymnasium, sauna, steam room, spa bath. Access, Amex, Visa,*

Stratford-upon-Avon   Places of Interest

Tourist Information   Tel 0789 293127.
The Teddy Bear Museum   Tel 0789 293160.
The Shakespeare Birthplace Trust's Properties   The Shakespeare
   Centre Tel 0789 204016.
Stratford-upon-Avon Racecourse   Tel 0789 267949.
   Theatres and Concert Halls
Royal Shakespeare Theatre   Tel 0789 295623.
Swan Theatre   Tel 0789 295623.
The Other Place   Tel 0789 292565.

Streatley-on-Thames   Swan Diplomat   72%   £131

Tel 0491 873737   Fax 0491 872554   **HR**

High Street Streatley-on-Thames Berkshire RG8 9HR   Map 5 D2

In a delightful setting on the banks of the Thames, an attractive, efficiently
run hotel. Bedrooms are spacious and elegantly furnished with traditionally
styled mahogany pieces; decor is light, restful and modern. Over half the
rooms have balconies and river views, and day rooms like the panelled bar
and comfortable lounge also enjoy the views. The old Magdalen College
barge, fully restored to its 19th-century splendour, is an unusual venue for
drinks or meetings. *Rooms 45. Garden, indoor swimming pool, sauna,
solarium, keep-fit equipment, beautician, croquet, rowing boats, moorings. Access,
Amex, Visa,*

see over

Riverside Restaurant

£80

Something of a garden house feel here with trellis ceiling and faux-rattan chairs, but it's the riverside setting that's still the main attraction. Executive chef Christopher Cleveland is a consummate professional and under his guidance the kitchen reliably produces well-crafted dishes utilising first-rate ingredients such as foie gras included in both a mixed hors d'oeuvre comprising scallops, Barbary duck, woodland mushrooms, asparagus and smoked salmon and a main-course fillet of Scotch beef with truffle sauce. Oysters are lightly cooked and served on a bed of noodles and spinach with a Chablis sauce, while calf's sweetbreads and scallops are served with creamed leek and celeriac and a red wine sauce – modern ideas, well executed. Traditional skills are never overlooked, however, ensuring that steamed jam sponge, meringue, a vanilla and coffee bavarois and orange parfait appear among the choice of desserts. The three-course table d'hote includes less involved but equally well-executed dishes. Some good names on the wine list, though pricing appears inconsistent. Breakfast, light lunches and afternoon tea are served in the Duck Room, which also has river views. *Seats 80. Parties 45. Private Room. L 12.30-2 D 7.30-9.30 (Sat from 7, Sun to 9). Closed L Sat, 1 week Jan. Set L £19.50 Set D £23.50.*

Street   Bear Hotel   63%

£60

Tel 0458 42021   Fax 0458 840007

H

53 High Street Street Somerset BA16 0EF

Map 4 A3

On the edge of town, just off the A39, the late-Victorian stone-built Bear retains its intimate air in the small fire-lit residents' lounge and livelier bar and patio. There's a sturdy, old-fashioned feel to the main-house bedrooms; five in the Rose Cottage annexe are more modern. Well-equipped conference facilities (max 80) and functions for up to 110 make this a popular place. Children under 5 stay free in parents' room. No dogs. *Rooms 15. Closed 4 days Xmas. Access, Amex, Visa.*

Stretton   Ram Jam Inn

£57

Tel 0780 410776   Fax 0780 410361

IR

Great North Road Stretton Nr Oakham Rutland
Leicestershire LE15 7QX

Map 11 E3

Hard by a service station on the northbound lanes of the A1 (southbound drivers take the B668 exit to Oakham and follow signs), nine miles north of Stamford, a very pleasing alternative to the mass of commercial hotels along the A1. Public rooms are devoted completely to informal, yet smartly furnished eating areas (bar, snack, outdoor terrace and restaurant areas). All the bedrooms overlooking the garden and orchard are individually and tastefully decorated with limed oak furniture, and surprisingly quiet considering the proximity to the road. *Rooms 10. Garden, coffee shop (7am-10pm). Closed 25 Dec. Access, Amex, Visa.*

Restaurant

£35

Straightforward menu in a pleasingly light dining room overlooking the orchard. Home-made soup, half a pint of prawns with crusty bread, a choice of pasta, braised Rutland venison with glazed vegetables and new potatoes, chargrilled steak or leg of lamb, stir-fried pork and good desserts like treacle tart with praline ice cream or blackberry and apple compote with a pastry hat and custard. Well-priced wines with regular bin ends and useful tasting notes. Great snacks in an informal snack area include breakfast from 7am, one-inch-thick home-made burgers, giant granary baps and home-baked cookies. On a road dominated by fast food outlets, it's well worth slowing down for the extraordinary Ram Jam Inn. *Seats 40. Parties 40. Private Room. L 12-2.30 D 7-10 (light meals 7am-10pm).*

Stroud   Oakes   ★   £80

Tel 0453 759950   **R**

169 Slad Road Stroud Gloucestershire GL5 1RG   **Map 4 B2**

On the B4070 just out of town, Oakes is an early 19th-century Cotswold stone house that was once a school for young ladies. It is now a restaurant of renown, with Chris Oakes preparing memorable meals from the finest fresh produce. Many of his suppliers are local, and the menu gives them generous individual credit. His technique is sure and sound throughout menus where the choice is short but difficult: fish terrine with avocado and a lemon vinaigrette; venison sausage served on mixed lettuces with bacon, quail's eggs and a creamy garlic dressing; roast cutlets of lamb with parsnips "Molly Parkin" and a rosemary sauce; fillet of brill on rösti with braised onions. Don't miss out on superb desserts like chocolate and coffee terrine with orange sauce or hot cinnamon soufflé with Drambuie cream. *Seats 40. Parties 30. Private Room. L 12.30-1.45 D 7.30-9.30. Closed D Sun, all Mon, Bank Holidays, 2 weeks Aug, 4 weeks Xmas. Set L £16 Set D £34. Access, Visa.*

Stroud   Places of Interest

Tourist Information   Tel 0453 765768.
Misarden Park Gardens   Tel 028582 309.
Painswick Rococo Garden   Painswick Tel 0452 813204.

Stuckton   The Three Lions   £60

Tel 0425 652489   **R**

Stuckton Nr Fordingbridge Hampshire SP6 2HF   **Map 4 C3**

The long-standing reputation for good, confident cooking remains high in this converted pub with a relaxed, informal ambience. Locals and visitors from further afield crowd round the blackboard menus, a feature of the dining room along with pine tables, pewter plates and corn dollies. The choice, which changes only rarely, is typified by Swedish herrings, French onion soup, terrine of leeks with hot duck liver, sea bream with herb butter, lamb sweetbreads with a shellfish sauce and bratwurst with sauerkraut. *Seats 55. Parties 40. L 12.15-1.30 D 7.15-9 (Sat to 9.30). Closed Sun & Mon, Bank Holidays, 10 days Xmas/New Year, 2 weeks summer. Access, Visa.*

Stuckton   Places of Interest

Rockbourne Roman Villa   Nr Fordingbridge Tel 072 53 541.

Studland Bay   Knoll House   61%   £154★

Tel 092 944 251   Fax 092 944 423   **H**

Studland Bay Nr Swanage Dorset BH19 3AH   **Map 4 C4**

Progeny-free holidaymakers and families are equally well catered for at the Fergusons' hotel, which recently won the Family Hotel of the Year award in Egon Ronay's Heinz Guide *...and Baby Comes Too.* There's an adventure playground, indoor play rooms, family suites with interconnecting rooms and even a children's dining room with a separate kitchen to keep the little ones happy, while the wooded grounds, a nearby bird sanctuary and a safe, sandy beach provide peaceful diversions for other guests. There's plenty of comfortable lounge space, and bedrooms – neither large nor small – are plain and practical. TVs may be hired. ★Half-board terms only. *Rooms 80. Garden, outdoor swimming pool, sauna, solarium, whirlpool bath, steam room, keep-fit equipment, tennis, 9-hole golf course, boutique. Closed Nov-Easter. No credit cards.*

Studland Bay   Place of Interest

Swanage Beach.

Sturminster Newton   Plumber Manor   £52

| Tel 0258 72507   Fax 0258 73370 | RR |

Hazelbury Bryan Road Sturminster Newton Dorset DT10 2AF   Map 4 B4

The Prideaux-Brune family has been here since the Manor was built in
1665. The location is ideal for exploring Hardy country. Two fixed-price
menus offer a good choice of dishes marrying English produce with French
ideas – carré of lamb with onion and mint soubise with Shrewsbury sauce,
beef Wellington or chateaubriand, and smoked salmon paupiettes and
smoked trout mousseline are typical dishes. Vegetarian options are a feature
where otherwise tradition rules. Good wines. *Seats 60. Parties 40. Private
Room. D only 7-9.30. Closed Feb. Set D from £19.50. Access, Amex, Visa,*
Diners Club International

Rooms   £80

The rooms are spacious and well appointed, most having antique furniture.
Six are in the main house; stable-block rooms are more modern and even
larger. No children under 12. *Rooms 16.*

Sudbury   Mabey's Brasserie   £45

| Tel 0787 74298 | R |

47 Gainsborough Street Sudbury Suffolk CO10 7SS   Map 6 C3

Robert Mabey, formerly at Hintlesham Hall, is cooking an eclectic mix at
this informal and friendly split-level brasserie frequented mainly by locals.
Pew seating is in booths and the short menu is written on a large
blackboard. Home-grown salads and home-made ice creams complement
dishes as diverse as Japanese giant prawn tempura with dipping sauce,
crispy-cooked duck leg on a bed of apple, and traditional summer pudding
with vanilla sauce. Good-value wines. *Seats 36. Parties 40. L 12-2 D 7-10.
Closed Sun & Mon, Bank Holidays. Access, Visa.*

Sudbury   Mill Hotel   58%   £78

| Tel 0787 75544   Fax 0787 73027 | H |

Walnut Tree Lane Sudbury Suffolk CO10 6BD   Map 6 C3

The old mill overlooks the river Stour and a large mill pond. Recently
redecorated bedrooms are either old-fashioned or extension-modern. Note
the old millwheel in the bar-lounge. *Rooms 50. Coarse fishing. Access,
Amex, Visa,* Diners Club International

Sudbury   Places of Interest

Tourist Information   Tel 0787 881320.
Gainsborough's House   Gainsborough Street Tel 0787 72958.
Colne Valley Railway   Castle Hedingham Tel 0787 61174.
  Historic Houses, Castles and Gardens
Hedingham Castle   Castle Hedingham Tel 0787 60261.

Sunderland   Swallow Hotel   £92

| Tel 091-529 2041   Fax 091-529 4227 | H |

Queen's Parade Seaburn Sunderland Tyne & Wear SR6 8DB   Map 15 C4

A seafront hotel with up-to-the-minute leisure facilities in a glass-domed
club. The major refurbishment was completed too late for grading this
year. *Rooms 66. Indoor swimming pool, keep-fit equipment, spa bath, sauna,
solarium. Access, Amex, Visa,* Diners Club International

Sunderland   Places of Interest

Tourist Information   Tel 091-565 0960/0990.
Sunderland Empire Theatre   Tel 091-514 2517.
Hylton Castle   Tel 091-548 0152.
Washington Old Hall (NT)   Washington Tel 091-416 6879.
Sunderland Football Ground   Roker Park Tel 091-514 0332.
Sunderland Ice Rink and Leisure Centre   Tel 091-514 2511.
Silksworth Dry Ski Slope   Tel 091-522 9119.
Washington Waterfowl Park   Washington Tel 091-416 5454.

Surbiton   Chez Max   £65

Tel 081-399 2365   **R**

85 Maple Road Surbiton Surrey KT6 4AW   Map 5 E2

Chef-patron Max Markarian's conservatory-roofed suburban restaurant is a
haven for francophiles; well-conceived dishes of meat, fish and fowl come
across with clear, positive flavours. Spicy duck in pastry with apricot sauce;
egg and cheese soufflé with spinach; and roulade of smoked haddock and
salmon precede *les plats de résistance*: monkfish fillet in chive sauce; guinea
fowl with vermouth and garlic; beef medallions sauced with red and green
peppers. The full à la carte is available for Saturday dinner only, but there's
still a choice of six or so dishes per course on the fixed-price, two-course
dinner menu during the week; desserts are charged as taken (£2.75-
£4.85). Prix fixe menu at lunchtime, plus 12½% service charge. *Seats 40.
Parties 50. L 12.30-2 D 7.30-10. Closed L Sat, all Sun & Mon (open
Mothering Sunday), Bank Holidays. Set L £18.50 Set D £15.95 (Tues-Fri).
Access, Amex, Visa,*

Sutton   Holiday Inn   70%   £140

Tel 081-770 1311   Fax 081-770 1539   **H**

Gibson Road Sutton Surrey SM1 2RF   Map 5 E3

A new, redbrick town-centre hotel (overshadowing the Secombe Centre
next door) with ample parking. Practical and convenient accommodation
rather than luxurious; well laid-out bedrooms have the usual Holiday Inn
virtues of large beds, plenty of well-lit work space and good easy chairs
around a substantial breakfast table. Bathrooms are user-friendly, too, with
thermostatically-controlled showers over tubs, good shelf space and large
towels. Executive rooms have various extras and include seven Study
Rooms equipped with fax machines. Public areas are fairly plain although
the colourful waistcoats or braces of the keen young staff brighten things
up. Good breakfasts. Modern conference facilities for up to 200.
*Rooms 116. Indoor swimming pool, spa bath, sauna, solarium, steam room,
beautician, keep-fit equipment, snooker, coffee shop (9am-6pm). Access, Amex,
Visa,*

Sutton   Partners Brasserie   £55

Tel 081-644 7743   **R**

23 Stonecot Hill Sutton Surrey SM3 9HB   Map 5 E3

In a shopping parade on the busy A24, Partners is not like a brasserie to
look at with its pale-green rag-painted walls. Neither is the menu ordinary
brasserie fare but a selection of sophisticated, well-prepared dishes such as
leek and potato soup with nutmeg croutons, leaf salad with scallops and
mussels, guinea fowl with braised cabbage and marjoram, and steak with a
red wine and mushroom sauce. Crème brulée with poached pears is a
typical dessert. Wines are sensibly priced. *Seats 32. Parties 30. L 12-2
D 7-9.30. Closed L Sat, D Sun, all Mon, Bank Holidays, 2 weeks Aug. Access,
Amex, Visa,*

Sutton   Places of Interest

Epsom Polo Club   Tel 0372 362593.
Epsom Racecourse   Tel 0372 726311.

Sutton Coldfield   Forte Travelodge   £40

Tel 021-355 0017   **L**

Boldmere Road Sutton Coldfield West Midlands B72 5UP   Map 10 C4

4 miles from both junctions 5 and 6 of the M6. Situated on Boldmere
Road (B4142), off the A452. 2 miles from Sutton Coldfield and 6 miles
from Birmingham. *Rooms 32. Access, Amex, Visa.*

Sutton Coldfield   Moor Hall   62%   £88

Tel 021-308 3751   Fax 021-308 8974   **H**

Moor Hall Drive Four Oaks Sutton Coldfield West Midlands B75 6LN   Map 10 C4

In a rural setting, but handy for the motorway network, the extended
Edwardian building is surrounded by a golf course. It has its own leisure
centre, plus facilities for up to 200 delegates. There are two bars, and the
bedrooms include suites and Executive rooms. *Rooms 75. Garden, indoor
swimming pool, gymnasium, sauna, solarium, beauty salon. Access, Amex, Visa,*
Diners Club International

Sutton Coldfield   New Hall   78%   £129

Tel 021-378 2442   Fax 021-378 4637   **HR**

Walmley Road Sutton Coldfield West Midlands B76 8QX   Map 10 C4

Twenty-six acres of beautiful grounds surround New Hall, said to be the
country's oldest moated building. Dating from the 13th century, the
sympathetically restored house is now a luxury hotel of some note. Though
owned corporately by Mount Charlotte Thistle, it is run along personal
lines by Ian and Caroline Parkes, who have an obvious love of the house.
Day rooms include an elegantly furnished new lounge and feature
panelling, ornate ceilings and latticed windows. Bedrooms in the main
house are largest and most are sumptuously appointed, but the majority of
rooms are in an unobtrusive modern wing built around a courtyard. There
is generally a high standard of decor and furnishing; all the bathrooms are
luxuriously appointed. Immaculately turned-out, professional staff. No
children under eight. A choice of sumptuous meeting rooms can
accommodate up to 40 delegates. No dogs. *Rooms 60. Garden, golf driving
net, putting, croquet, helipad. Access, Amex, Visa,* Diners Club International

Restaurant   £90

The elegant, panelled dining room is in the oldest part of the house. Chef
Glenn Purcell cooks in an "unmistakably English" style, with innovation
and attractive presentation enhancing many classic dishes. Typically, roasted
quail is served on a bed of savoy cabbage and raisins with a truffle jus,
while rack of lamb is garnished with tomato and basil-filled morels and a
light Madeira jus. Prime produce is meticulously handled and desserts, like
butterscotch soufflé (with orange and cinnamon ice cream) or a trio of
English pear tartlet, mousse and poire William ice cream, are truly
wonderful. Clearly laid-out wine list with several house wines and good
choices wherever you look. *Seats 60. Parties 8. Private Room. L 12.30-2
(Sun to 2.15) D 7-10 (Sun to 9.30). Closed L Sat. Set D £24.95.*

Sutton Coldfield   Penns Hall   66%   £132

Tel 021-351 3111   Fax 021-313 1297   **H**

Penns Lane Walmley Sutton Coldfield West Midlands B76 8LH   Map 10 C4

Converted 17th-century house by a fishing lake. Banqueting and
conference facilities for 600. *Rooms 114. Garden, gymnasium, spa bath,
sauna, solarium, beauty salon, steam room, children's playground. Access, Amex,
Visa,* Diners Club International

Sutton Scotney North	**Forte Travelodge**	**£40**
Tel 0962 761016		**L**
A34 Sutton Scotney North Nr Winchester Hampshire SO21 3JY		**Map 5 D3**

At the Northside Welcome Break service area on the A34 northbound, 8 miles north of Winchester city centre. Easy access to M3 and M4. *Rooms 31. Access, Amex, Visa.*

Sutton Scotney South	**Forte Travelodge**	**£40**
Tel 0962 760779		**L**
A34 Sutton Scotney South Nr Winchester Hampshire SO21 3JY		**Map 5 D3**

At the Southside Welcome Break service area on the A34 southbound, 8 miles north of Winchester city centre. *Rooms 40. Access, Amex, Visa.*

Swavesey	**Forte Travelodge**	**£40**
Tel 0954 789113		**L**
A604 Cambridge Road Swavesey Nr Cambridge Cambridgeshire		**Map 6 B2**

8 miles north-west of Cambridge on the eastbound carriageway of the A604. *Rooms 36. Access, Amex, Visa.*

Sway	**The Tower** NEW	**£98**
Tel 0590 682117 Fax 0590 683785		**H**
Sway Hampshire SO4		**Map 4 C4**

Built in the 1880s by the eccentric judge Andrew Peterson communicating with the spirit of Sir Christopher Wren, this 218ft tower was once the tallest concrete building in the world. It has now been cleverly refurbished by its present owners Paul and Julie Atlas who have introduced modern comforts without altering its charm and history – staying here feels like being invited into a friend's home. Climbing the narrow, bare stone spiral staircase may put you out of breath but the result is well worth the effort. The bright and attractive bedrooms (one per floor!) benefit from stunning views through windows facing east, south and west to Hampshire and across the Solent to the Isle of Wight. Each is individually decorated with antique furniture but they also have modern facilities such as a mini-bar, satellite television and an answerphone. Downstairs, the dining room and lounge are full of character with neo-Gothic arches, wall tapestries and more antique furniture from the owners' collection. Dinner is only open to non-residents by prior arrangement. No children under 12. No smoking. *Rooms 4. Garden, croquet, indoor swimming pool, tennis.*

Swindon	**Blunsdon House** 69%	**£93**
Tel 0793 721701 Fax 0793 721056		**H**
Blunsdon Swindon Wiltshire SN2 4AD		**Map 4 C2**

A farm guest house in 1958, a country club in 1960, and a fully licensed hotel since 1962 – and the Clifford family have been here from the beginning. It's a popular conference rendezvous (up to 300 delegates) with extensive leisure club facilities. Guests are provided with a good standard of comfort in the form of gardens, formal and casual bars, a residents' lounge, two restaurants and porterage. All the bedrooms are reasonably roomy and many have pleasant views. Decoration and appointments are of smart modern business standard, and bathrooms all have shower attachments and ample toiletries; some have spa baths. Latest opening date for the nine-hole golf course is Jan 1993. Families are well catered for; children up to 13 stay free in parents' room. No dogs. *Rooms 88. Garden, tennis, croquet, putting, indoor swimming pool, squash, sauna, solarium, gymnasium, spa bath, beautician, hairdressing, games room, snooker, crèche. Access, Amex, Visa,* ⑩ Diners Club International

Swindon De Vere Hotel 69% NEW £110

Tel 0793 878785 Fax 0793 877822 **H**

Shaw Ridge Leisure Park Whitehill Way Swindon Wiltshire SN5 7DW **Map 4 C2**

Follow the signs to Shaw Ridge Leisure Park, some 2½ miles from the M4 (junction 16). Brick-built and fronted by a clock tower and futuristic leisure club, its cavernous conference facilities have their own, lower-level entrance. Wilton Suite conference rooms can accommodate 340 theatre-style; banquet seating for up to 290. Two floors of bedrooms with executive-style facilities are built around a central courtyard; day rooms, however, are rather lacking in intimacy for the individual guest. ***Rooms 154.*** *Indoor swimming pool, spa bath, sauna, solarium, beauty salon, gymnasium, snooker, coffee shop (8am-10pm). Access, Amex, Visa,* Diners Club International

Swindon Forte Crest 62% £88

Tel 0793 831333 Fax 0793 831401 **H**

Oxford Road Stratton St Margaret Swindon Wiltshire SN3 4TL **Map 4 C2**

Modern low-rise hotel on the A420, near the A419 roundabout. Very much geared-up to the need of the business traveller with secretarial services, in-house pager facilities, 24hr room service and meeting rooms for up to 50 people theatre-style. ***Rooms 97.*** *Snooker. Access, Amex, Visa,* Diners Club International

Swindon Forte Posthouse 63% £67

Tel 0793 524601 Fax 0793 512887 **H**

Marlborough Road Swindon Wiltshire SN3 6AQ **Map 4 C2**

70s' hotel set in five acres of grounds between junction 15 of the M4 and the town centre. Conference facilities for 80. Popular with families at weekends. ***Rooms 100.*** *Indoor swimmimg pool, keep-fit equipment, garden, spa bath, sauna, solarium. Access, Amex, Visa,* Diners Club International

Swindon Swindon Marriott 71% £121

Tel 0793 512121 Fax 0793 513114 **H**

Pipers Way Swindon Wiltshire SN3 1SH **Map 4 C2**

Formerly the Holiday Inn, a modern purpose-built hotel standing in mature woodland next to a golf course. It's easily found when approaching from junction 15 of the M4, yet only half a mile from the Old Town. Scandinavian-influenced public areas overlook the Leisure Club and are open-plan, with central beams and pine ceilings. Contemporary-style bedrooms have plenty of natural light, individual temperature control and good beds; bathrooms are on the small side. Conferences and banqueting for up to 280. ***Rooms 153.*** *Indoor swimming pool, steam bath, spa bath, sauna, solarium, beauty and hair salons, keep-fit equipment, squash, tennis, shop. Access, Amex, Visa,* Diners Club International

Swindon Wiltshire Hotel 62% £100

Tel 0793 528282 Fax 0793 541283 **H**

Fleming Way Swindon Wiltshire SN1 1TN **Map 4 C2**

Swindon's only central hotel, a short walk from bus and railway stations and with ample free parking. Meeting rooms from 22 to 230, with banqueting for up to 200. Mount Charlotte Thistle. ***Rooms 95.*** *Access, Amex, Visa,* Diners Club International

Swindon   Places of Interest

Tourist Information Tel 0793 530328/526161.
Wyvern Theatre Tel 0793 24481.
Buscot Park (NT) Faringdon Tel 0367 240786.
Great Western Railway Museum Tel 0793 526161.
Swindon Town Football Ground County Ground Tel 0793 430430.
Ice Rink Link Centre Tel 0793 871212.
Oulton Park Motor Racing Circuit Little Budworth Tel 0829 760301.

Swinfen   Swinfen Hall   70%   £85

Tel 0543 481494   Fax 0543 480341   **H**

Swinfen Nr Lichfield Staffordshire WS14 9RS   Map 10 C4

Set back from the A38 two miles south of Lichfield, the present Hall was
completed in 1757, a wing being added in the Edwardian period. The
grand entrance hall with its minstrel's gallery, Corinthian columns and
stuccoed ceiling carved by Italian craftsmen, makes a good first impression,
and other notable day rooms include a handsome banqueting hall and bar.
The cocktail bar has French windows opening on to a balustraded terrace,
with an ornamental fountain beyond. Spacious bedrooms range from
singles to suites; rooms on the second floor are particularly bright and airy,
with pastel shades and light oak furniture. Banquets up to 150, conferences
to 200 theatre-style. *Rooms 19. Garden, croquet. Closed 4 days end Dec.*
Access, Amex, Visa, ⑪ *Diners Club International*

Tamworth   Granada Lodge   £43

Tel 0827 260123   Fax 0827 260145   **L**

M42/A5 junction 10 Tamworth Staffordshire B77 5PH   Map 10 C4

Rooms 63. Access, Amex, Visa, ⑪ *Diners Club International*

Taplow   Clivenden   90%   £234

Tel 0628 668561   Fax 0628 661837   **HR**

Taplow Nr Maidenhead Buckinghamshire SL6 0JF   Map 5 E2

Former home of a Prince of Wales, several dukes and the Astor family,
Cliveden has been at the centre of Britain's social and political life for over
three centuries. Overlooking the Thames, it is set in 376 acres of National
Trust private gardens and parkland and is Britain's only hotel that is also a
stately home. Much of the original mansion remains to this day – witness
the terrace, the dominant feature of the south facade overlooking the
parterre, one of the finest hotel views in England, the main staircase, the
Great Hall and the library. These are public areas on a grand scale,
featuring magnificent antiques, paintings and tapestries (the Orkney
tapestries in the Great Hall celebrate the Duke of Marlborough's victory at
Blenheim), while the stylish bedrooms are exquisitely and individually
decorated to the very highest standard and stunning bathrooms provide for
every conceivable need. A hotel since 1986, it lacks nothing in modern
amenities, and the sport and leisure facilities are outstanding. The Pavilion,
situated within the original walled garden, houses a luxurious complex,
including specially designed rooms for massage, health and beauty, while
for outdoor enthusiasts the hotel has its own horses, two Edwardian river
launches and an electric canoe. Situated in the privacy of the Garden wing
is the state-of-the-art and fully air-conditioned Churchill boardroom that
opens directly on to its own terrace. *Rooms 31. Garden, indoor and outdoor
swimming pools, saunas, solarium, whirlpool bath, steam room, hairdressing,
gymnasium, indoor and outdoor tennis, squash, badminton, snooker, croquet,
riding, coarse fishing, boats, valeting, laundry service. Access, Amex,*
Visa, ⑪ *Diners Club International*

Terrace Dining Room   £120

The most majestic of dining rooms (undoubtedly one of the finest settings
in England), overlooking extensive formal gardens. Fine, personalised   ♛

Spode china and linen complete smart table settings and a French-influenced menu offers a choice of dishes that ranges from potted shrimps with deep-fried langoustines in filo pastry to creamed lentil soup with spring vegetables, Cliveden mixed grill and smoked braised oxtails with olives and roast seasonal vegetables. Good half-bottle selection, and lots of pudding wines on the extensive, but still pricy list that spans the world. Prices include a £3 donation per head to the National Trust. *Seats 70. Parties 12. Private Room. L 12.30-2 D 7.30-9.30. Set L from £24.*

Waldo's   £110

In an elegant, air-conditioned London club-like setting with panelled stained-pine walls lined with bookcases, Ron Maxfield presents his distinctive modern cooking. Set dinners of four or five courses provide a small choice of carefully executed dishes like warm terrine of foie gras, potato and bacon with a lentil dressing, lasagne of lobster and langoustine, magret of duck with Chinese spices and roast fillet of venison with a walnut and Madeira sauce. No choice on the six-course Waldo's menu. Same wine list as in the Terrace dining room. No smoking. *Seats 28. Parties 6. Private Room. D only 7.30-10. Closed Sun & Mon. Set D £47, £55 & £60.*

Taunton	Castle Hotel	76%	£125

Tel 0823 272671 Fax 0823 336066   **HR**

Castle Green Taunton Somerset TA1 1NF   Map 3 E2

Understated Englishness is the wisteria-clad Castle's greatest strength: look no further than the foyer and staircase to absorb its history echoed by chiselled stonework, wrought iron and English oak, given warmth by rich oils, tapestries and floral displays. Such a building necessarily imposes limitations on modernisation, thus some single rooms are on the small side. A fine hotel, nevertheless, carefully balancing the old and new with a worthy reputation for accommodation and service; nowhere is this more apparent than in the plush garden suites, whose deep sofas, comfortable canopied beds and spacious, well-appointed bathrooms remain as luxurious as ever. *Rooms 35. Garden, lock-up garaging with car-wash service. Access, Amex, Visa,* Diners Club International

Restaurant   ★ ↑   £80

Gone is the expensive à la carte in favour of fixed-price menus that "include all the frills" (canapés, petits fours and coffee or tea) and vary according to the number of courses taken. Chef Phil Vickery gives due recognition on his menus to the first-rate suppliers who provide tip-top produce on a daily basis in order to satisfy the daily-changing menus. The restaurant at the Castle has been at the forefront of the revival of interest in English culinary traditions for ten years now with a succession of chefs (John Hornsby, Chris Oakes, Gary Rhodes) consistently turning out fine meals. The traditional repertoire surfaces in dishes like boiled collar of bacon with split peas, steamed English asparagus in a puff pastry case with tarragon butter sauce, almond blancmange with rose petal syrup or baked egg custard tart with nutmeg ice cream, while more modern, Mediterranean influences are exhibited in steamed lobster sausage with couscous, chick pea soup with olive oil, marinated vegetables with garlic toasts and cherry tomatoes. The likes of potted wood pigeon and rabbit with Cumberland sauce, toasted walnut and raisin bread, tournedos Rossini, grilled John Dory with mushroom butter sauce, wild rice and deep-fried parsley, baked apple with candied lemon tart and caramel ice cream, plus fine cheeses complete the picture. Sunday lunch is a traditional three-course affair, perhaps with roast forerib of beef in a salt crust and Yorkshire pudding. The outstanding wine list wins our 1993 Cellar of the Year West Country regional award; over thirty house wines, mostly under £12 a bottle; see further details at back of Guide under Cellar of the Year Regional Winners. *Seats 60. Parties 125. Private Room. L 12.30-2 D 7.30-9. Set L £13.50/£14.90 & £24.50/£28.50 (Sun £14.90) Set D £17.90/£21.90 & £28.50.*

Taunton   County Hotel   61%   £86

H

Tel 0823 337651   Fax 0823 334517

East Street Taunton Somerset TA1 3LT

Map 3 E2

A white-fronted former coaching inn offering comfortable Superior rooms, more functional Standards, a town-centre location and convenient free parking. Extensive conference facilities seating up to 400, and banqueting for up to 350. Forte Heritage. *Rooms 66. Access, Amex, Visa,*

Taunton   Forte Posthouse   66%   £67

H

Tel 0823 332222   Fax 0823 332266

Deane Gate Avenue Taunton Somerset TA1 2UA

Map 3 E2

Two miles from the town centre, close to junction 25 of the M5. Modern conference facilities for up to 200. *Rooms 97. Keep-fit equipment, sauna. Access, Amex, Visa,*

Taunton   Porters Wine Bar   £40

R

Tel 0823 256688

49 East Reach Taunton Somerset TA1 3EX

Map 3 E2

Joanne Porter's cosmopolitan menu changes daily with typical lunches of cream of fennel soup and pasta carbonara supplemented at night by trout with gooseberry sauce, spiced vegetable fritters and chargrilled steaks. Three vegetarian dishes every day and around a dozen wines available by the glass. Courtyard and non-smoking area. *Seats 50. Parties 30. L 12.30-2 D 7.30-10. Closed L Sat, all Sun, Bank Holidays. Access, Visa.*

Taunton   Travel Inn   £42

L

Tel 0823 321112   Fax 0823 322054

81 Bridgwater Road Taunton Somerset TA1 2DU

Map 3 E2

Its close proximity to M5 (J25) makes it ideal for stops on the way to Devon and Cornwall. *Rooms 40. Access, Amex, Visa,*

Taunton   Places of Interest

Tourist Information   Tel 0823 274785.
Brewhouse Theatre   Tel 0823 83244.
Forde Abbey and Gardens   Nr Chard Tel 0460 20231.
Hestercombe House and Gardens   Cheddon Fitzpaine Tel 0823 337222.
Somerset County Museum   Tel 0823 255504.
County Cricket Ground   Tel 0823 272946.
Royal Naval Equestrian Association   Orchard House, Hatch Beauchamp Tel 0823 480223.
Taunton Racecourse   Tel 0823 337172.
Wellington Sports Centre   Wellington Tel 0823 473010.
Cricket St. Thomas Wildlife Park   Chard Tel 0460 30755.

Teffont Evias   Howard's House   68%   £85

HR

Tel 0722 716392   Fax 0722 716820

Teffont Evias Dinton Nr Salisbury Wiltshire SP3 5RJ

Map 4 C3

In a sleepy hamlet of medieval origins the families Firmin and Ford have studiously converted their Tudor stone farmhouse into a very comfortable private house hotel. Downstairs is dominated by the restaurant and smaller lounge; there's no bar but drinks are served at any time. Gracious living is exemplified by top-quality linen in the bedrooms and mushroom tartlets with poached eggs and hollandaise for breakfast. A little gem of a place, high up the value-for-money ladder. *Rooms 8. Garden, croquet. Access, Amex, Visa.*

Restaurant £75

You are unlikely to stay in the hotel and think of dining elsewhere. Paul Firmin's home-baked anchovy amuse-gueule and dinner rolls show that as much attention to detail is paid to his fixed-price dinner menu as to the accommodation. Six or more choices per course include a good selection of game in winter and fish in spring. Pan-fried scallops with lentils and coriander, salmon and crab fishcakes with parsley sauce, guinea fowl with compote of grapefruit and oranges and fillet of brill with hazelnut mousseline and lime sauce are all confidently prepared and interestingly presented. If you can resist a steamed treacle pudding with ginger custard or hot passion fruit soufflé then a selection of unpasteurised French cheeses might be just the thing. *Seats 34. Parties 40. L (Sun only) 12.30-2 D 7-10. Set L £16.50 Set D £27.50.*

Teignmouth   Thomas Luny House £55

Tel 0626 772976   **PH**

Teign Street Teignmouth Devon TQ14 8EG   Map 3 D3

Built by the marine artist Thomas Luny in the early 1800s, this small Georgian town house has been charmingly restored by the Allens, who now run it as a Wolsey Lodge. This means that one is essentially a guest in their home, socialising with them and fellow guests in the well-appointed drawing room that displays family photos, and sharing the evening meal around a large polished dining table. The simple, carefully prepared set dinner (for residents and their guests only) is a joint effort by John and Alison Allen and there is a short, modestly-priced list of wines from which to choose. Four antique-furnished bedrooms have been decorated with great style and quality and have excellent co-ordinating bathrooms (one has shower and WC only). All rooms have direct-dial telephones and remote-control TV. It all adds up to a delightful alternative to a conventional hotel. *Rooms 4. Garden. Closed mid Dec-mid Jan. No credit cards.*

Telford   Forte Travelodge £40

Tel 0952 251244   **L**

Admaston Road Shawbirch Telford Shropshire TF1 3QA   Map 10 B3

On the A5223 at the junction of the A442 and B5063, 2 miles from junction 6 of the M54. 1 mile north-west of Telford. *Rooms 40. Access, Amex, Visa.*

Telford   Holiday Inn   68% £104

Tel 0952 292500   Fax 0952 291949   **H**

St Quentin Gate Telford Shropshire TF3 4EH   Map 10 B3

With easy access to the M54 (junction 4) and town centre, this modern low-riser is adjacent to Telford Racquet and Exhibition Centre. Business centre serves conferences (max 290) and banqueting up to 180. Health and leisure club. *Rooms 100. Indoor swimming pool, gymnasium, spa bath, sauna, solarium, steam room. Access, Amex, Visa,*

Telford   Madeley Court   66% £95

Tel 0952 680066   Fax 0952 684275   **HR**

Madeley Telford Shropshire TF7 5DW   Map 10 B3

A striking Elizabethan manor house in extensive grounds just off the A442, recently restored to create an attractive hotel of much character and with serious ambitions. Further restoration of the 17th-century mill will result in a conference centre for 200 and 15 more bedrooms are to be added. The original 13th-century hall now houses the (non-smoking) hotel restaurant, when not required by function business, and a brasserie is located in the undercroft. *Rooms 32. Access, Amex, Visa,*

Telford	Moat House	67%	£95

Tel 0952 291291   Fax 0952 292012   **H**

Foregate Telford Shropshire TF3 4NA   **Map 10 B3**

Modern hotel with good conference (12 rooms catering for up to 400 delegates) and leisure facilities. Comfortable atrium lounge and Forgegate bar. Children up to 16 free in parents' room. *Rooms 148. Indoor swimming pool, spa bath, sauna, solarium, dinner dance (Sat). Access, Amex, Visa,* 🅞 *Diners Club International*

Telford	Telford Hotel	64%	£89

Tel 0952 585642   Fax 0952 586602   **H**

Great Hay Sutton Hill Telford Shropshire TF7 4DT   **Map 10 B3**

Standing south of the town centre above Ironbridge Gorge, the hotel combines comfortable, modern accommodation with golf and country club facilities and a state-of-the-art conference centre (for up to 300). Under-12s stay free in parents' room. Queens Moat Houses. *Rooms 86. Garden, indoor swimming pool, gymnasium, golf course, golf driving range, spa bath, sauna, solarium, steam room, coffee shop (9am-9.30pm), dinner dance (weekly Nov-Feb). Access, Amex, Visa,* 🅞 *Diners Club International*

Telford   Places of Interest

Tourist Information Tel 0952 291370.
Benthall Hall (NT) Broseley Tel 0952 882159.
Ironbridge Gorge Museum Tel 0952 453522.
Telford Ice Rink Tel 0952 291511.
Telford Ski Slope Tel 0952 586791.

Tetbury	Calcot Manor	74%	£106

Tel 0666 890391   Fax 0666 890394   **H**

Tetbury Gloucestershire GL8 8YJ   **Map 4 B2**

By the junction of the A4135 and A46, three miles west of Tetbury. The Ball family converted several Cotswold-stone farm buildings (circa 14th century) creating a unique and peaceful hostelry where Brian Ball puts his many years in the hotel industry to good effect. A long drawing room has stone fireplaces at each end and enjoys views over the gardens. Three bedrooms in adjoining outbuildings have exposed beams and first-rate bathrooms. Period furniture features in the rest of the comfortable bedrooms, split between the main house and further outbuildings. Professional staff, led by Brian's son Richard, are polished yet retain a sense of humour. No children under ten. *Rooms 14. Garden, croquet, outdoor swimming pool, clay-pigeon shooting. Access, Amex, Visa,* 🅞 *Diners Club International*

Tetbury	The Close	75%	£75

Tel 0666 502272   Fax 0666 504401   **HR**

8 Long Street Tetbury Gloucestershire GL8 8AQ   **Map 4 B2**

Echoes of a former Cistercian monastery lend the 400-year-old Close a special feel and atmosphere apposite to its name. Today's identity is that of a refined, relaxed town house, epitomised by ubiquitous books and board games in the sitting room and croquet in the walled rear garden. Bedrooms are individually named and each one has its own style, from Elizabethan (the First) to Art Deco. Evening turn-down, early morning tea and complimentary newspaper are the oft-neglected touches which turn closeness into comfort. No children under 10. No dogs. *Rooms 15. Garden. Closed 1 week Jan. Access, Amex, Visa,* 🅞 *Diners Club International*

Restaurant   £75

A new format of menus offers a set dinner of seasonal produce – asparagus with basil butter, Cotswold chicken with herb mousse and a Pimms and summer fruit jelly – alongside a more involved à la carte. Lighter lunches are available daily; other highlights include fresh lobster from the salt-water tank and a leisurely Sunday brunch running well into the afternoon. Unusually, wines are listed alphabetically by grape variety – OK if you know what you're looking for; nevertheless, it's an excellent list, with an extensive selection of fine clarets and burgundies. The garden is floodlit at night, providing a romantic view from the beautifully appointed dining room. No smoking. **Seats 65. Parties 24. Private Room.** L 12.30-2 D 7.30-10 (Sun to 9.30). Set L £16 Set D £19.

Tetbury   Snooty Fox Hotel   69%   £85

| Tel 0666 502436   Fax 0666 503479 |

Market Place Tetbury Gloucestershire GL8 8DD   Map 4 B2

A mellowed 16th-century building with steep stone gables and original wooden pillars, the Snooty Fox stands in the square of a picturesque Cotswold market town not far from M4 and M5. Lounge space is plentiful and the two rooms (one for non-smokers) are peaceful and traditional in character with deep sofas, magazines, oil paintings and prints of the Beaufort Hunt. The bar, with its imposing copper fire hood, is a contrastingly lively spot. Family antiques and portraits continue the period tone in the individually designed bedrooms – all of which are upstairs – where little extras like a basket of fruit and bottles of mineral water are typical thoughtful touches. The bathrooms are carpeted and light, and boast luxurious bathrobes and towels. No dogs. Executive meeting facilities for up to 30. **Rooms 12.** Access, Amex, Visa, Diners Club International

Tetbury   Places of Interest

Tourist Information Tel 0666 503552.
Chavenage House Tel 0666 502329.
Beauford Polo Club Down Farm, Westonbirt Tel 0666 88214.

Tewkesbury   Bell Hotel   60%   £70

| Tel 0684 293293   Fax 0684 295938 |

Church Street Tewkesbury Gloucestershire GL20 5SA   Map 4 B1

Half-timbered former posting house, thought to be even older that the 1696 carved on the exterior. Original beams and panelling give considerable character to the day rooms. **Rooms 25.** Garden. Access, Amex, Visa, Diners Club International

Tewkesbury   Royal Hop Pole   66%   £101

| Tel 0684 293236   Fax 0684 296680 |

Church Street Tewkesbury Gloucestershire GL20 5RT   Map 4 B1

One of the smaller hotels in the Forte chain, with a charm all its own. Walled rose gardens run down to the Avon and the hotel's own mooring. Sympathetic conversion has provided an elegant drawing room and rear-facing bar. Best of the bedrooms feature a four-poster and executive extras, but many may plump for the oak-beamed character of the older rear bedrooms, where bathroom space is at a premium. **Rooms 29.** Garden, mooring. Access, Amex, Visa, Diners Club International

Tewkesbury   Tewkesbury Park   62%   £89

| Tel 0684 295405   Fax 0684 292386 |

Lincoln Green Lane Tewkesbury Gloucestershire GL20 7DN   Map 4 B1

Built around an 18th-century mansion, but the atmosphere today is more country club than country house and conferences (up to 150 people) are big business. Well-appointed bedrooms afford views of the Malvern Hills. Good facilities for families with a supervised crèche in the leisure club at weekends. Children's playroom and playground. No dogs. Country Club Hotels. **Rooms 78.** Garden, indoor swimming pool, keep-fit equipment, spa bath, sauna, solarium, squash, tennis, golf, beautician, hairdressing, snooker, coffee shop (10am-10.30pm). Access, Amex, Visa, Diners Club International

Thame   Spread Eagle   63%   £84

H

Tel 0844 213661   Fax 0844 261380

Cornmarket Thame Oxfordshire OX9 2BW   Map 5 D2

Standing square and proud in the town centre, the 16th-century Spread
Eagle offers period charm and a variety of accommodation that includes
suites and family rooms. Also banqueting suites and syndicate rooms. No
dogs. **Rooms 33.** *Access, Amex, Visa,* ⓘ *Diners Club International*

Thetford   The Bell   62%   £91

H

Tel 0842 754455   Fax 0842 755552

King Street Thetford Norfolk IP24 2AZ   Map 6 C2

An old coaching inn overlooking the Ouse with many architectural
features dating back to the 15th century. Bedrooms in the main part are
beamed, several boasting four-posters; wing rooms are more up to date.
The function facility houses banqueting for 75, conferences up to 90. Forte
Heritage. **Rooms 47.** *Garden. Access, Amex, Visa,* ⓘ *Diners Club International*

Thetford   Places of Interest

Euston Hall   Thetford Tel 0842 766377.
Kilverstone Wildlife Park   Tel 0842 755369.
Snetterton Motor Racing Circuit   Snetterton Tel 095 387 303.

Thornaby-on-Tees   Forte Posthouse   59%   £67

H

Tel 0642 591213   Fax 0642 594989

**Low Lane By Stainton Village Nr Thornaby-on-Tees
Cleveland TS17 9LW**   Map 15 C5

An older-style Posthouse in the village of Stainton. Conferences for up to
120 delegates. **Rooms 135.** *Garden, sauna, solarium. Access, Amex, Visa,*
ⓘ *Diners Club International*

Thornbury   Thornbury Castle   82%   £145

HR

Tel 0454 418511   Fax 0454 416188

Thornbury Nr Bristol Avon BS12 1HH   Map 4 B2

A Tudor castle dating back to 1511 when it was built by Edward Stafford,
3rd Duke of Buckingham. After his execution it became the Royal
Demesne of Henry VIII, who stayed here in 1535 with Anne Boleyn. The
interior has been luxuriously restored, befitting its royal patronage. There
are bed chambers fit for a king, dark oak panelling, leaded mullion
windows, and tapestries, portraits and heraldic shields adorning the walls.
Comforts include leather wing chairs in the library and deep sofas in the
lounge. Tower bedrooms and the tiny Jewel room retain their character
among the battlements, while suites in the north wing are furnished in
evocative Tudor style. Housekeeping is impressive (as are the welcoming
touches of sherry and fruit) and the staff are charming. No children under
12. No dogs. **Rooms 18.** *Garden, croquet, helipad. Closed 10 days Jan. Access,
Amex, Visa,* ⓘ *Diners Club International*

Restaurant   £75

The two baronial, panelled dining rooms, candlelit at night, are appositely
grand. Fixed-price menus, written daily, balance perceived English Country
House style with both Oriental and transatlantic influences which gain
approval from a truly international clientele. While chicken liver salad is
sharpened with grapefruit (and salmon enhanced by vegetable ribbons and
hollandaise), the smoked salmon with capers and fillet steak with a carrot
and potato rösti and two creamed sauces are bound to satisfy more catholic
tastes. The classic English cheeseboard remains peerless; treacle tart with
Cornish cream is also likely to be in constant demand without unduly
taxing the skill or ingenuity of the kitchen. **Seats 60.** *Parties 26. L12-2
D 7-9.30 (Sun to 9). Closed Xmas (open to residents only). Set L £17.75
Set D £29.50.*

Thornton Heath   Mamma Adele   £50

`Tel 081-683 2233`   **R**

23 Brigstock Road Thornton Heath Surrey CR4 7JJ   Map 7 B5

A modestly presentable little family restaurant with a real taste of Italy,
based on dishes from Mamma's home region of Marche. *Pasta all'adriatico,
vitello alla pizzaiola* and Mamma's brandy-sauced steaks are all reliable fare.
Husband Kam Memon runs front of house with urbane good humour.
Open lunchtimes by prior arrangement only. *Seats 32. Parties 35. L by
arrangment with 24 hours notice D 6-10.30 (Sat 7-11.30). Closed Sun, Bank
Holidays, all Jan. Access, Visa.*

Thornton-le-Fylde   River House   £100

`Tel 0253 883497   Fax 0253 892083`   **IR**

Skippool Creek Thornton-le-Fylde Nr Blackpool Lancashire FY5 5LF   Map 10 A1

Built in 1830 for a gentleman farmer, the River House lies four miles from
Blackpool close to Skippool Creek. Bill and Carole Scott create a home-
from-home atmosphere with antiques, fresh flowers and log fires, and a
tranquil air. The Victorian-style conservatory is particularly attractive.
Bedrooms include the Pink Room with a half four-poster and views over
the Wyre Estuary. Each double room now has its own bathroom, two
with grand Victorian hooded baths. *Rooms 4. Garden. Access, Visa.*

Restaurant   £68

Bill Scott retains his tireless enthusiasm for cooking, insisting on the
freshest of fish landed at Fleetwood and game from nearby moors in
season. Produce may be local, but his influences are more diverse: fillet of
beef is prepared Japanese-style with Oriental vegetables and a cup of saké,
lobster is lightly spiced with Muscat de Beaumes de Venise and Mrs
Sykes's duck is served with apple and potato rösti and a honey and
armagnac sauce. Goat's cheese soufflé, mushroom, York ham and Gruyère-
filled crepes, locally smoked salmon, beef stroganoff, pan-fried fillet of
salmon with chive and Noilly Prat sauce, venison two ways (roasted loin
with port sauce and civet), assiette gourmande (beef, veal and lamb), and
chateaubriand exemplify his style. Desserts might include cabinet pudding,
three chocolate terrine, lemon and passion fruit mousse and "ticky tacky
pudding – the original hot date and walnut pudding with butterscotch
sauce". Unusual selection of teas and infusions. Some good wines, especially
German, on an erratically presented list; check out the bin ends for good
value. *Seats 40. Parties 40. Private Room. L by arrangement D 7.30-9.30.
Closed D Sun, some Bank Holidays.*

Thrapston   Forte Travelodge   £40

`Tel 0801 25199`   **L**

A14 Thrapston bypass Thrapston Northamptonshire   Map 11 E4

On the A14 (the new A1/M1 link road), 8 miles east of Kettering. Corby
8 miles, Wellingborough 10 miles. *Rooms 40. Access, Amex, Visa.*

Thrussington   Forte Travelodge   £40

`Tel 0664 424525`   **L**

**A46 Thrussington Green Acres filling stations Thrussington
Leicestershire LE7 8TF**   Map 11 D3

On the A46 southbound, close to Derby and Nottingham. 8 miles north of
Leicester city centre. *Rooms 32. Access, Amex, Visa.*

Thundridge   Hanbury Manor   81%   £150

`Tel 0920 487722   Fax 0920 487692`   **HR**

Thundridge Nr Ware Hertfordshire SG12 0SD   Map 5 F1

In 200 acres of parkland by the A10, Hanbury Manor is a late 19th-century house built in the Jacobean style, recently converted from a girls' convent into a fine, modern country house hotel and sporting complex. The style and character of the old building have been greatly enhanced with well-chosen fabrics and furnishings. Wonderful carved panelling and wall tapestries in the Oak Hall give a real taste of the past, while an elegant and comfortable cocktail bar features a hand-painted ceiling. The Library also has a fine marble fireplace and views over the golf course. Sumptuous furnishings, fine-quality fabrics, period furniture and marble bathrooms make the bedrooms exceptional. Superb leisure facilities, including a palatial swimming pool and a magnificent 18-hole golf course. No dogs. Conference and banqueting facilities for up to 138 in a selection of ten rooms including the unusual Poles Hall. A Rockresort hotel. *Rooms 96. Garden, golf, tennis, squash, croquet, putting, indoor swimming pool, spa bath, sauna, solarium, snooker, gymnasium, riding, beautician, crèche, news kiosk, helipad. Access, Amex, Visa,*

Zodiac Room and Conservatory   ↑   £115

The Zodiac Room is formal and elegant (complete with silver cloches), while the more informal Conservatory is light and airy with views over the golf course. Chef Rory Kennedy (in consultation with Albert Roux) offers a good value menu du jour (perhaps crab bisque or carpaccio of smoked duck followed by sea bass with aubergine, tomato and thyme or mignons of venison with cranberry compote and sauce poivrade and iced Grand Marnier soufflé to finish), a complex à la carte (with more than the odd touch from *Le Gavroche*) and a six-course menu gourmand. A 'safe' list, short on half bottles, with few bargains. *Seats 40. Parties 8. Private Room. L 12-3 D 7-10. Closed D Sun. Set L £19.50 Set D £22.50.*

Thurlestone   Thurlestone Hotel   69%   £152

`Tel 0548 560382   Fax 0548 561069`   **H**

Thurlestone Kingsbridge Devon TQ7 3NN   Map 3 D3

The elegance of the 20s combines with the amenities of the 90s in a handsome family-owned hotel in a lovely setting with spectacular sea views. Splendidly geared to family holidays, it also has an off-peak trade in small conferences (for up to 100). Day rooms make the most of the location, likewise half the smart, well-equipped bedrooms. Children up to 16 can stay free of charge in their parents' room. *Rooms 68. Garden, 9-hole golf course, putting, tennis, badminton, indoor & outdoor swimming pools, keep-fit equipment, squash, sauna, solarium, beauty salon, hairdressing, games room, coffee shop (8am-10pm). Access, Visa.*

Thurrock   Granada Lodge   £52

`Tel 0708 891111   Fax 0708 860971`   **L**

M25 junction 30/31 Dartford Crossing Thurrock Essex RM16 3BG   Map 7 B5

Rooms 35. Access, Amex, Visa,

Tickton   Tickton Grange   62%   £73

`Tel 0964 543666   Fax 0964 542556`   **H**

Tickton Nr Beverley Humberside HU17 9SH   Map 11 E1

A family-owned Georgian house standing in 3½ acres of rose gardens, where afternoon teas are served in the summer. Day rooms retain a traditional appeal, and bedrooms are decorated in a fresh, light style. There are two suites, one with a Georgian four-poster bed. Tickton truffles are offered as a welcome. The Whymant family run the hotel along friendly and informal lines. *Rooms 16. Garden. Access, Amex, Visa,*

Tiverton — Forte Travelodge — £40
Tel 0884 821087   **L**

**Sampford Peverell Service Area M5 Junction 27 Nr Tiverton
Devon EX16 4LY**   **Map 3 D2**

At junction 27 of the M5 next to the Little Chef. 7 miles east of Tiverton.
Rooms 40. Access, Amex, Visa.

Tiverton — Lowman Restaurant — £48
Tel 0884 257311   **R**

45 Gold Street Tiverton Devon EX16 6QB   **Map 3 D2**

Friendly market town restaurant taking its name from the river passing its
door. Two cosy dining rooms in pretty pink are the setting for
uncomplicated dishes prepared by Jane Hall. Venison and red wine pie,
very good roast pheasant with Madeira sauce and rack of lamb scented
with orange and garlic are good choices, but the menus change every two
months. Home-made ice creams are popular sweets. Book at weekends
when there's a good value Sunday lunch. *Seats 40. Parties 40. Private Room.
L 12-2 D 6-9 (Fri & Sat to 9.30). Closed D Sun, all Mon, Xmas/New Year.
Access, Visa,*

Toddington — Granada Lodge — £43
Tel 052 587 3881   Fax 052 587 5358   **L**

**Toddington service area M1 Southbound Nr Dunstable
Bedfordshire LU5 6HR**   **Map 5 E1**

Rooms 43. Access, Amex, Visa,

Tonbridge — Rose & Crown — 59% — £91
Tel 0732 357966   Fax 0732 357194   **H**

125 High Street Tonbridge Kent TN9 1DD   **Map 7 B5**

A 16th-century coaching inn with traditionally furnished bedrooms in the
old part, modern rooms in the garden wing. Conference/banqueting
facilities for 110/80. Forte Heritage. *Rooms 50. Garden. Access, Amex, Visa,*

Torquay — Grand Hotel — 67% — £105
Tel 0803 296677   Fax 0803 213462   **H**

Sea Front Torquay Devon TQ2 6NT   **Map 3 D3**

Commanding a superb position overlooking Torbay, the Grand is an
impressive, turreted Edwardian building whose grounds include a lido
with heated swimming pool. Not all the bedrooms enjoy sea views but
those that do have balconies and are generally the roomiest. Furnishings are
mainly modern and simple. *Rooms 101. Garden, indoor & outdoor swimming
pools, tennis, keep-fit equipment, spa bath, sauna, solarium, hair salon, coffee shop
(10.30-6.30). Access, Visa,*

Torquay — Homers Hotel — 63% — £66
Tel 0803 213456   Fax 0803 213458   **H**

Warren Road Torquay Devon TQ2 5TN   **Map 3 D3**

Pamela and Derek Oatley are former regular guests who bought the hotel
in 1989, and have carefully refurbished the interior in an individual
comfortable style. Chandeliers and gilt cornices reflect the building's
Victorian origins, and the residents' bar in a recessed alcove adds an
intimate atmosphere. Though many bathrooms are a bit small, the
bedrooms, one with a fine four-poster, are generally good-sized; best of all
are those with splendid views over Torbay. Private conference/dining
facilities for up to 50. No children under 12. *Rooms 15. Garden.
Closed 4 Jan-4 Feb. Access, Amex, Visa,*

Torquay   Imperial Hotel   81%   £150

Tel 0803 294301   Fax 0803 298293

H

Parkhill Road Torquay Devon TQ1 2DG

Map 3 D3

Opened as a resort hotel in 1866, and much favoured by royalty in the
years that followed, the Imperial still operates on a grand scale. From the
pink-pillared foyer, through palatial lounges to the Pool Terrace,
overlooking the sweep of Torbay, both decor and appointments set out to
impress. The hotel attracts many regulars and the Torbay suite is
increasingly popular for conferences and banqueting with a capacity of
350. Light, bright bedrooms contain good-quality furniture and fabrics:
most have sea views and private balconies. Leisure facilities are extensive,
and there's dancing six nights a week to a resident band. *Rooms 167.
Garden, indoor & outdoor swimming pools, sauna, solarium, whirlpool bath,
gym, tennis, squash, snooker, hairdressing. Access, Amex, Visa,*  Diners Club International

Torquay   Livermead Cliff Hotel   60%   £86

Tel 0803 299666   Fax 0803 294496

H

Sea Front Torquay Devon TQ2 6RQ

Map 3 D3

Right by the sea, with direct access to the beach and popular for family
holidays. Also geared up to the conference trade (for up to 60 delegates), so
it's quite a busy place all year round. Picture windows in the lounge look
out to sea. Parents with offspring are well catered for with cots, baby-
sitting, baby-listening and children's high tea available. Good housekeeping,
friendly staff. *Rooms 64. Garden, outdoor swimming pool, solarium, laundry
room. Access, Amex, Visa,* Diners Club International

Torquay   Livermead House   60%   £82

Tel 0803 294361   Fax 0803 200758

H

Sea Front Torquay Devon TQ2 6QJ

Map 3 D3

A popular guest house in the last century, where author Charles Kingsley
once stayed. Today's Livermead House, under the personal direction of the
Rew family, lives on as a thoroughly modern hotel. Picture windows
afford panoramic sea views beyond the pool and tennis court, and there's
plenty of activity indoors on rainy days. Conferences (max 100) and
banqueting are kept discreetly separate from private guests. No dogs.
*Rooms 63. Garden, outdoor swimming pool, sauna, solarium, keep-fit equipment,
putting, snooker. Access, Amex, Visa,* Diners Club International

Torquay   Osborne Hotel   65%   £102

Tel 0803 213311   Fax 0803 296788

H

Hesketh Crescent Meadfoot Beach Torquay Devon TQ1 2LL

Map 3 D3

Careful renovation has kept some of the original feel at the Osborne,
which stands at the centre of Torquay's best example of Regency
architecture. Day rooms include a high-ceilinged lounge bar, a long-hours
brasserie/wine bar and a library that's used for meetings. Bedrooms –
named not numbered – are smart and spacious, with seating areas and
plenty of creature comforts. As well as the bedrooms there are several
luxury apartments. No dogs. *Rooms 23. Garden, indoor & outdoor swimming
pools, sauna, spa bath, solarium, keep-fit equipment, tennis, brasserie
(10.30am-11pm). Access, Visa.*

Torquay   Palace Hotel   68%   £128

Tel 0803 200200   Fax 0803 299899

H

Babbacombe Road Torquay Devon TQ1 3TG

Map 3 D3

A much-extended Victorian hotel set in 25 acres of gardens and woodland
running down to the sea. Very much a family holiday place in summer, it's
more concerned with conferences (for up to 350 delegates) at other times.
Public rooms are vast, with elegant pillars and moulded ceilings. Six large
suites have splendid views, individual decor and good-quality furniture;

ordinary rooms are simple but comfortable, with handsome period
bathrooms. Children up to 12 stay free in parents' room. No dogs.
*Rooms 140. Garden, indoor & outdoor swimming pools, sauna, hairdressing,
indoor & outdoor tennis, squash, 9-hole golf course, snooker, children's play room,
nanny (resident in high season). Access, Visa,*

Torquay   Table Restaurant   £68

Tel 0803 324292   **R**

135 Babbacombe Road Babbacombe Torquay Devon TQ1 3SR   Map 3 D3

A tiny restaurant run by Trevor Brooks and Jane Corrigan on the outskirts
of town. The menu – fixed-price with choices – offers the likes of Brixham
fish soup with saffron, crepinette of pig's trotters and ham with a caper and
preserved lemon vinaigrette or confit of duck with lentils to start, followed
by a choice of fresh fish dishes (perhaps roasted sea bass, grilled John Dory
and wing of skate), pheasant with air-dried ham, rib of beef with
mushrooms, shallots and bone marrow and best end of lamb with fennel
ratatouille. Desserts could include cinnamon rice brulée with tropical fruit
coulis; mocha and cardamom mousse, or poached pear with ginger ice
cream plus an orange and honey sauce. Cheeses are traditional farmhouse.
*Seats 20. Parties 21. D only 7.30-10 (Sun to 9.30). Closed Mon, Bank
Holidays, 2 weeks Feb, 2 weeks Sept. Set D £24. Access, Visa.*

Torquay   Places of Interest

Tourist Information   Tel 0803 297428.
Torre Abbey   Tel 0803 293593 *Includes Dame Agatha Christie Memorial
    Room.*
Wessex Ski Club   Tel 0803 313350.
Oddicombe, Anstey's Cove and Meadfoot Beaches.

Towcester   Forte Travelodge   £40

Tel 0327 359105   **L**

A43 East Towcester bypass Towcester Northamptonshire NN12 0DD   Map 5 D1

On the A43, 8 miles south of Northampton. 18 miles south-east of Rugby
town centre, 8 miles east of Coventry. *Rooms 33. Access, Amex, Visa.*

Tresco   Island Hotel   67%   £170*

Tel 0720 22883   Fax 0720 23008   **H R**

Tresco Isles of Scilly TR24 0PU   Map 2 A2

Tresco, England's "Island of Flowers", is privately owned and maintained
with, incidentally, a total ban on cats and dogs. Guests arriving at the quay
or heliport (from Penzance) are transported by tractor-drawn charabanc to
the island's only hotel, set in beautifully tended gardens. Picture windows
make the most of this spectacular location and the panoramic sea views:
should the mists close in there's a Terrace Bar and a Quiet Room stacked
with books, magazines and games. Under-14s stay free in parents' room.
Special holiday packages for gardeners. *Half-board terms only. *Rooms 40.
Garden, croquet, outdoor swimmimg pool, fishing, boating, bowling green, games
room. Closed 6 weeks Oct/Nov. Access, Amex, Visa.*

Restaurant   £60

Table d'hote and à la carte menus place strong emphasis on local seafood
(Scillonian scallops, Bryher crab), and there's Devonshire beef and veal
from the grill. Traditional farmhouse cheeses. Luxurious Sunday buffet
(including lobster). Children can eat half-price from the carte. No smoking.
Seats 95. Parties 40. L 12-2 D 7-9.30. Set D £22.50.

Tresco   Places of Interest

Tresco Abbey Gardens   Tel 0720 22849.

Tring   Travel Inn   £42

Tel 0442 824819   Fax 0442 890787   **L**

Tring Hill Tring Hertfordshire HP23 4LD   Map 5 E2

12 miles from M1 and M25, a short drive from Whipsnade Zoo and Luton Airport. *Rooms 30. Access, Amex, Visa,* ●)) *Diners Club International*

Troutbeck   Mortal Man Inn   £104*

Tel 053 94 33193   Fax 053 94 31261   **I**

Troutbeck Nr Windermere Cumbria LA23 1PL   Map 13 D5

A bright, well-cared-for inn of 17th-century origins, with an established reputation for hospitality. Join the regulars in the Village bar or relax in the residents' bar and sunny lounge overlooking the Troutbeck Valley. Bedrooms are smart, bathrooms compact and housekeeping praiseworthy. No children under five. * Half-board terms only. *Rooms 12. Garden. Closed mid Nov-mid Feb. No credit cards.*

Troutbeck   Places of Interest

Holebird Garden   Tel 09662 6238.

Truro   Alverton Manor   75%   £65

Tel 0872 76663   Fax 0872 222989   **H**

Tregolls Road Truro Cornwall TR1 1XQ   Map 2 B3

For a property so grand (a grade II listed building, and former convent of Sisters of the Epiphany) Alverton has an immediate charm deriving from a warm lived-in feel. There's gracious elegance in the foyer and mahogany-lined stairwells, and a timeless comfort in the lounge, which opens on to the gardens. In stark contrast is the Gothic-style former chapel, which makes a spectacular exhibition or conference hall. Bedrooms, individually decorated, range from suites in the grand mode to several singles high in the tower, which have showers only; bathrooms elsewhere are spacious and well lit. *Rooms 25. Garden, games room. Access, Amex, Visa,* ●)) *Diners Club International*

Truro   Places of Interest

Tourist Information   Tel 0872 74555.
City Hall   Tel 0872 76461.
Trelissick Garden (NT)   Tel 0872 862090.
Trewithen House and Gardens   Probus Tel 0726 882764.
Truro Cathedral   Tel 0872 76782.
Flambards Theme Park   Culdrose Manor Tel 0326 574549.

Tuckenhay   Maltsters Arms   £80

Tel 0803 732350   **R**

Bow Creek Tuckenhay Totnes Devon TQ9 7EQ   Map 3 D3

TV chef Keith Floyd's busy pub is located down the narrow country lanes outside Totnes, at the head of a pretty tidal creek surrounded by trees. The layout has recently changed with a larger 'Canteen' eating area on the first floor (at road level) utilising pine tables and simple French bar-style table settings; window tables have views overlooking the creek. A long bar/bistro menu runs the gamut from cockles to caviar and liver and bacon to lobster, Thai-spiced chicken and more. The ground floor was being converted into a smarter restaurant area as we went to press. Barbecue in good weather on the quay where the boats tie up. *Seats 34. Parties 8. Private Room. L 12-3 D 6-9.30 (Sun from 7). Access, Visa.*

Tunbridge Wells   Cheevers   £60

Tel 0892 545524   **R**

56 High Street Tunbridge Wells Kent TN1 1XF   **Map 7 B5**

Cool decor, crisp white tablecloths, good tableware and quiet, professional
service create the ambience, while Tim Cheevers provides the good food to
complement it. He sticks to what he knows best and carefully sources
ingredients for dishes that are both fresh and imaginative: spinach-wrapped
crab mousse, terrine of duck livers and pigeon with toasted brioche, mussel
and fennel broth, crisply roast duckling with spring onion and ginger,
quickly-fried Scotch fillet with a yoghurt, garlic and fresh coriander
dressing. Invention extends to the desserts with unusual apple, whisky and
marmalade ice cream, gin and grapefruit sorbet. A la carte at lunchtime,
fixed-price menu at dinner; both menus offer a good choice of around six
dishes per course. Short, mixed-up wine list with a first-rate choice of half
bottles. Martin Miles runs front-of-house with a smile for everyone.
Seats 32. Parties 12. L 12.30-2 (Sat to 1.45) D 7.30-10.30. Closed Sun &
Mon, Bank Holidays, 2 weeks Jan. Set D £22.50. Access, Visa, Diners Club International

Tunbridge Wells   Downstairs at Thackeray's   £45

Tel 0892 537559   **R**

85 London Road Tunbridge Wells Kent TN1 1EA   **Map 7 B5**

Downstairs, with its own courtyard entrance, this delightful little place
with cosy, close-set tables and fresh flowers has the friendly relaxed feel of
a bistro. Dishes are varied and imaginative, ranging from crispy crab
pancakes and Piedmont peppers to lamb's kidneys with hot onion
marmalade and honey-roast duck with lemon sauce; banoffi pie and
mascarpone with apricots for dessert. Value new age selection of 15 wines
under £15. Excellent service; booking advised. *Seats 30. Parties 12.*
L 12.30-2.30 D 7.30-9.30. Closed Sun & Mon, Bank Holidays, 1 week Xmas.
Set L £6.75/£8.75. Access, Visa.

Tunbridge Wells   Eglantine   £55

Tel 0892 524957   **R**

65 High Street Tunbridge Wells Kent TN1 1XX   **Map 7 B5**

Chef-patronne Susan Richardson is now well established at her appealing
restaurant tucked away in the Pantiles part of town. Fixed-price menus
(one can choose just two courses at lunchtime) are short on choice but full
of interest with the likes of shallot and parsley soup to start and roasted
fillets of monkfish served with a mustard and tarragon sauce among the
main dishes; vegetarian options are always included. Attention to detail
extends to home-made bread and petits fours. 10% service is added to the
fixed-price menus. *Seats 40. Parties 16. L 12.15-1.45 D 7.15-9.30 (Sat to*
10). Closed Sun & Mon, 24-28 Dec, 1 Jan. Set L £10.50/£13 Set D
£20.50. Access, Amex, Visa.

Tunbridge Wells   Royal Wells Inn   64%   £65

Tel 0892 511188   Fax 0892 511908   **H**

Mount Ephraim Tunbridge Wells Kent TN4 8BE   **Map 7 B5**

The royal coat of arms atop the family-run Royal Wells is a proud
memento of the days when, during her childhood, Queen Victoria used to
stay here. Inside, there's a stylish reception/lounge with columns, marble-
effect wallcoverings and matching fabrics as well as a light and attractive
bar area. Best bedrooms are on the top floor – these have brass beds,
quality pine furniture, Laura Ashley fabrics and up-to-date, tiled bathrooms;
two rooms have four-posters. The hotel bus is a 1909 Commer. *Rooms 22.*
Access, Amex, Visa, Diners Club International

Tunbridge Wells   Spa Hotel   72%   £84

Tel 0892 520331   Fax 0892 510575   **HR**

Mount Ephraim Tunbridge Wells Kent TN4 8XJ   **Map 7 B5**

Sister hotel to *The Goring* in London, an 18th-century Spa in 15 acres of
grounds that has been run as a hotel by the same family since 1880. The
foyer opens on to a spacious lounge with Corinthian columns, darkwood
panelling and a gas log fire at each end; half is reserved for non-smokers.
Bedrooms vary in size and decor, the older ones having woodchip
wallpaper, but all feature freestanding furniture (many finished in burr-
walnut). De luxe rooms have king-sized beds and tend to be larger, with
views across several acres of informal parkland gardens. Although
conferences (for up to 350) form most of the weekday business, there is an
atmosphere of a moderately grand hotel run along traditional lines, with
fine leisure facilities and an emphasis on good service from friendly staff.
Children up to 16 free in parents' room. *Rooms 76. Garden, indoor
swimming pool, gymnasium, spa bath, sauna, solarium, beauty clinic, hair salon,
tennis, games room, children's adventure playground, croquet, dinner dance
(monthly). Access, Amex, Visa,* **Diners Club** International.

Chandelier Restaurant   £60

Large, high-ceilinged Regency dining room where good-quality produce is
best enjoyed in the simpler dishes and lunchtime roasts carved and served
formally from a trolley. Lighter, individually-priced dishes are also served
at lunchtime in the lounge and Equestrian Bar, catering mainly for local
businessmen; more elaborate, but limited, à la carte and table d'hote dinner
menus . *Seats 90. Parties 14. Private Room. L 12.30-2.30 D 7-9.30. Closed
L Sat. Set L £17.50 Set D £20.50.*

Tunbridge Wells   Thackeray's House   ★   £90

Tel 0892 511921   **R**

85 London Road Tunbridge Wells Kent TN11 1EA   **Map 7 B5**

In the green and white clapboard house that was once Thackeray's home,
chef Bruce Wass presents his carefully prepared versions of classical dishes
to an ever-increasing circle of aficionados. Daily written menus give a wide
choice of spending options with star-rated dishes not characterised simply
by price. Textures throughout are well judged and presentation is equally
appealing in the likes of skate and scallop salad with black bean sauce,
breast and ballotine of guinea fowl with sun-dried tomatoes, basil and pine
kernels, and chocolate Armagnac loaf with coffee sauce. Fine cheeses and
comprehensive tea selection. Well-chosen wine list with several bottles
under £20 and many half bottles. *Seats 36. Parties 40. Private Room
(Downstairs at Thackeray's). L 12.30-2.30 D 7-10 (Downstairs open all day
daily). Closed Sun & Mon, Bank Holidays, 1 week Xmas. Set L £14.75 Set D
£19.85. Access, Visa.*

Tunbridge Wells   Places of Interest

Tourist Information   Tel 0892 515675.
Assembly Hall   Tel 0892 30613.
Trinity Arts Centre   Tel 0892 44699.
Neville Road Cricket Ground   Tel 0892 20846.
Bowles Outdoor Pursuits Centre   Tel 0892 64127.
    Historic Houses, Castles and Gardens
Scotney Castle Garden (NT)   Lamberhurst Tel 0892 890651.
Penshurst Place   Penshurst, Tonbridge Tel 0892 870307.
Moorlands Gardens   Friars Gate, Nr Crowborough Tel 0892 652474.

Turners Hill   Alexander House   79%   £185

Tel 0342 714914   Fax 0342 717328   **HR**

East Street Turners Hill West Sussex RH10 4QD   **Map 7 B5**

A retirement home for the clergy between 1953 and 1984, this imposing
country mansion stands in 135 acres on the B2110. Distinguished buildings
have occupied the site since the 14th century and the oldest part of the
present house dates from the early 17th century. Numerous grand day
rooms feature many high-quality antiques, paintings (including *A Jamaica
Bay* by Noel Coward) and other decorative features like the painted silk
chinoiserie panels in the main salon and a pair of ornate French ormolu
lamps in the foyer. Many bedrooms have traditional yew furniture and
boast original paintings plus many little extras like fresh flowers, fruit and
magazines. Smart, friendly staff. *Rooms 14. Garden, croquet, tennis,
clay-pigeon shooting, hairdressing, valeting, snooker, limousine service, helipad.*
Access, Amex, Visa, ① Diners Club International

Restaurant   £110

David Needham's à la carte menu is high French with English translations;
his skilled execution of it makes for consistently enjoyable eating, enhanced
by fine, formal service and a lofty, elegant setting that overlooks gardens.
Paté de canard au foie gras, vichyssoise, homard Thermidor, supreme de
volaille savoyarde, steak Diane, soufflé au Grand Marnier and sablé aux
fraises show the range. Fish and shellfish (including the crayfish that appear
as a starter with home-made noodles and light cheese sauce as well as a
main course of wild salmon with white wine sauce) are kept in oxygenated
tanks to ensure maximum freshness. Predictably pricy wines on a mostly
French list. *Seats 60. Parties 60. Private Room. L 12.30-2 D 7-9.30 (Sun to
9). Set L £22.50*

Tutbury   Ye Olde Dog & Partridge Inn   £60

Tel 0283 813030   Fax 0283 813178   **I**

High Street Tutbury Nr Burton-on-Trent Staffordshire DE13 9LS   **Map 10 C3**

Much of the original (15th-century) building remains, its half-timbered
frontage bedecked in summer with flower tubs and hanging baskets. The
main public area, all alcoves and partitions, is mainly given over to the
buffet and carvery operation. A pianist plays nightly. Three bedrooms with
black-and-white panelling and creaking floorboards are in the main
building, the rest in an adjacent Georgian property with a four-floor spiral
staircase. No children under 5, but 5-12 year olds stay free in parents'
room. No dogs. *Rooms 17. Garden. Closed 25 & 26 Dec.* Access, Amex,
Visa, ① Diners Club International

Twickenham   Café Cézanne   £50

Tel 081-892 3526   **R**

68 Richmond Road Twickenham Middlesex TW1 3BE   **Map 7 A5**

Tim Jefferson runs a bright, informal restaurant with a keenly-priced menu
offering a good range – from fish and shellfish chowder, spinach and feta
filo parcels with orange mayonniase or warm onion and cream tartlet to
monkfish with julienne of vegetables and lemon-scented rice, magret of
duck with port and pepper sauce, fillet of lamb en croute with mint pesto
and 'steak, frites, salade'. Tarte tatin with thick cream, bread-and-butter
pudding with Cointreau cream and redcurrant and raspberry soufflé keep
the interest alive to the very end. Very short wine list. *Seats 38. Parties 50.
L 12.30-2 D 7-10.30 (Fri & Sat to 11). Closed L Sat, all Sun, Bank Holidays.*
Access, Amex, Visa, ① Diners Club International

Twickenham   Hamiltons   £50

R

Tel 081-892 3949

43 Crown Road St Margarets Twickenham Middlesex TW1 3EJ   Map 7 A5

Anglo-French food – from smoked trout with apple and horseradish mayonnaise and salmon and herb fishcakes to pan-fried pigeon breasts with wild mushrooms and blackcurrant sauce and duck sausages with mashed potatoes and a Madeira and orange sauce. Tuesday to Friday lunchtimes see a fixed-price menu with soup or salad to start followed by just one daily-changing dish (perhaps supreme of chicken with mango and a lime and ginger sauce or lamb and mint sausages). Live jazz during family Sunday lunchtimes when the good choice usually includes three roasts. *Seats 40. Parties 50. Private Room. L 12-2.30 D 7-11. Closed L Sat, D Sun, all Mon, 1 week New Year. Set L £9.95 (£14.50 Sun). Access, Visa.*

Twickenham   McClements   £70

R

Tel 081-755 0176

12 The Green Twickenham Middlesex TW2 5AA   Map 7 A5

John McClements works virtually single-handed in the kitchen of his intimate French restaurant opposite Twickenham Green. A superb appetiser of lobster risotto in a light mousse shell and a little lemon tartlet among the petits fours were examples of John's keen attention to detail. Technically, dishes like grilled sea scallops with bacon, hot black pudding in flaky pastry, sea bass topped with sole mousse and grilled breast of duck with caramelised apple and juniper berry sauce are all faultlessly executed. *Seats 14. Parties 14. Private Room. L 12-2.30 D 7-10 (Sat to 10.30). Closed L Sat, all Sun, 2 weeks Xmas. Set L & D £18.50. Access, Visa.*

Uckfield   Horsted Place   79%   £135

HR

Tel 0825 750581   Fax 0825 750459

Little Horsted Uckfield East Sussex TN22 5TS   Map 7 B6

A splendid Victorian mansion, with distinctive chequered brickwork, just off the A26 to the south of Uckfield and set in grounds designed by Geoffrey Jellico. For opera lovers Glyndebourne is only a few minutes away and golfers will appreciate the view across the East Sussex National course. Luxurious day rooms are furnished in fine country-house style with chintz fabrics and well-chosen antiques. Bedrooms, reached via a magnificent carved oak staircase by Pugin, are equally sumptuous and come with a host of extras such as fruit, flowers, books, mineral water and sweets. Smart meeting rooms for up to 35. No children under seven. No dogs. *Rooms 17. Garden, indoor swimming pool, tennis, croquet. Closed 10 days Jan. Access, Amex, Visa,*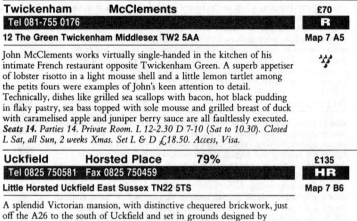

Dining Room   £95

A sensibly short menu – about six options per course – enables Allan Garth to concentrate all his considerable skills on just a few well-conceived dishes, with predictably pleasing results. A ballotine of foie gras accompanied by onion bread or marinated salmon flavoured with orange and coriander and served with a yoghurt dressing, might be followed by sea bass on a bed of spinach with basil sauce, or a simple roast sirloin of beef with Yorkshire pudding. No smoking in the dining room. Service is not included on the fixed-price menus. An unexceptional wine list, despite the imposing foreword. *Seats 30. Parties 8. Private Room. L 12.30-2 D 7.30-9.15. Closed L Sat. Set L £16.50/20.50 Set D £32.50.*

Uckfield   Places of Interest

Sheffield Park Garden (NT)   Tel 0825 790655.
Bluebell Railway   Sheffield Park Station Tel 0825 722370 *Talking
Timetable 3777.*

| Ullswater | Leeming House | 77% | £139 |

Tel 076 84 86622   Fax 076 84 86443   **HR**

Watermillock Ullswater Cumbria CA11 0JJ   Map 13 D5

A friendly country house atmosphere and stunning views of the lake and
fells contribute equally to Leeming House's special allure. Another major
plus is the 20 acres of landscaped gardens and natural woodland in which it
stands. The new library, two elegant lounges and an intimate panelled bar
are a measured blend of comfort and practicality, while a striking
conservatory (forming a link to the recently added east wing) makes a
splendid setting for light snacks or full afternoon tea. Front-facing,
balconied bedrooms in the main house retain their elegantly proportioned
Georgian appeal, sporting huge bathrooms and feature baths; the east wing
makes virtues both of its purpose-built furniture and fittings and of the
tranquillity of the location. Ever-efficient staff are always on hand without
ever being obtrusive, providing testimony to the assured direction of
manager Chris Curry. Forte Grand. *Rooms 40. Garden. Access, Amex, Visa,*
Diners Club International.

Restaurant   £75

One of the area's most memorable settings is well served by Jon Reed's six-
course dinners, commendably cooked and graciously served. Nightly
menus balance a certain conservatism (evidenced by soup, a roast,
traditional pudding and English cheeseboard) with more adventurous
dishes like noisettes of venison with redcurrant and port wine sauce or
escalope of Scottish salmon with sole mousse. The style is essentially
modern, showing perhaps rather more confidence than flair; though truly
noteworthy are the classic desserts, home-made jams and chutneys, faultless
breads and brioches and formidable country house breakfasts. There's also a
full Sunday lunch and a lighter à la carte mid-week. Starter dishes and open
sandwiches are also served in the Conservatory. No smoking. *Seats 80.
Parties 20. Private Room. L 12.30-1.45 D 7.30-8.45. Set L £15.75 (Sun)
Set D £27.50/£34.50.*

| Ullswater | Old Church Hotel | 67% | £120 |

Tel 076 84 86204   Fax 076 84 86368   **HR**

Watermillock Penrith Cumbria CA11 0JN   Map 13 D5

A stylish water's-edge hotel where residents are greeted very much as
Kevin and Maureen Whitemore's house guests. Both lounges are built for
relaxation and packed with board games and periodicals; in the library a
TV rarely comes into play. Maureen's bold colour schemes brighten the
bedrooms (priced according to the view), with crown canopies and half-
testers framing really comfortable beds. By contrast, bathrooms are on the
cramped side. Breakfasts deserve to be taken seriously, ranging from
Lakeland yoghurts and home-made muesli to Manx kippers, Cumberland
sausage and mixed grill with black pudding. No dogs. *Rooms 10. Garden,
croquet, fishing, boating. Closed Dec-Feb. Visa.*

Restaurant   £70

The smaller lounge doubles as an aperitif bar where guests gather prior to
dinner at 8 (non-residents must book). There's a limited choice of first and
main courses, four dishes at each stage, with perhaps mushrooms with
Stilton and port sauce or grilled goat's cheese with mustard and fried apples
followed by noisettes of lamb with parsley pepper crust and rosemary
gravy or roast loin of pork with sage stuffing, crackling and plum sauce.
An inter-course dish of soup (typically Norman potato and shallot soup
with shredded carrot) is optional. Kiwi fruit and plum pavlova or black

cherry and almond frangipane might be among the traditional desserts given a modern twist. Well-chosen English cheeses. Lighter lunches are also served daily. A carefully selected wine list with some excellent burgundies. **Seats 30.** Parties 10. Private Room. L 12.30-1.45 D 7.30 for 8. Set D £28.50.

Ullswater   Rampsbeck Country House Hotel   65%   £72

Tel & Fax 076 84 86442   **HR**

Watermillock Ullswater Nr Penrith Cumbria CA11 0LP   Map 13 D5

Rampsbeck's lakeside garden is filled with rhododendron bushes and the backdrops of the fells make for a spectacular location, to which Robin and Marion Gibb add just the right touch of Lakeland hospitality. The grandfather clocks, open log fire and profusion of flowers bring serenity to the panelled lounge: the bar's much livelier and opens on to a patio and the garden. Enlarged (and much improved) bedrooms are immaculately kept; those guests lying in will enjoy the luxury of their not-so-early-morning tea tray. The fresh, crisp bed linen is turned down in the evening. Not suitable for young children. **Rooms 21.** Garden, croquet, spa bath, fishing, mooring. Closed 6 weeks Jan/Feb. Access, Visa.

Restaurant   £55

Andrew McGeorge's modern classical cooking is never dull and abounds with experimental combinations of texture and flavour. The four-course table d'hote dinner menu might offer sliced bacon-wrapped pork fillet with veal jus and caraway seeds, French onion soup, baked Scottish salmon with basil butter sauce and strawberries with a white wine sabayon and tuile basket of vanilla ice cream. A la carte is more involved – from quail lasagne with woodland mushrooms to baked oyster samosa with cucumber spaghetti or Cumbrian lamb with feuilleté of calf's sweetbreads and Dublin Bay prawns. Vegetarians are particularly well catered for. Fixed-price lunch on Sundays; bar lunches only Mon-Sat. **Seats 36.** Parties 20. Private Room. L 12-1.45 D 7-8.45. Set L £17.95 Set D £23.

Ullswater   Sharrow Bay   81%   £236*

Tel 076 84 86301   Fax 076 84 86349   **HR**

Ullswater Howtown Nr Penrith Cumbria CA10 2LZ   Map 13 D5

On the shore of Lake Ullswater, this is perhaps the daddy of the English country house hotels. It's run by Francis Coulson and Brian Sack, now in their 45th season, and their manager Nigel Lawrence. Relaxation is the keynote, and the 12 acres of peaceful gardens around the main house (built in 1840) offer it in abundance. Public areas are festooned with objets d'art, valuable porcelain and handsome antiques. Comfortable lounges and drawing room provide lovely views over the water, and there's a sunny conservatory. Sharrow Bay has grown considerably from its small beginnings in 1948 and in addition to the main house there is accommodation in Bank House (a converted farmhouse with a magnificent refectory breakfast room, in a quiet, elevated position a mile distant); Thwaite Cottage in a small village four miles away; and the Lodge Gatehouse and Garden Cottage in the grounds. All the rooms are finished and decorated to a high standard and are charmingly old-fashioned. Housekeeping throughout is exemplary. Wonderful breakfasts, as one might expect from a kitchen of this stature. No children under 12. *Half-board terms only. **Rooms 28.** Closed Dec-Feb. No credit cards.

Restaurant   ★   £95

Two separate dining rooms, each with its own distinctive charm and appeal; one, with views out over Ullswater, polished Regency-style tables and chairs and an antique dresser, the other windowless but elegant, with fine panelling and a handsome fireplace. Both rooms are graced with antique porcelain and objets d'art. The cooking is at heart traditional British but some Continental touches and modern influences are apparent on the extensive-choice menus (fixed-price) that kick off in fine style with around a dozen starters followed by a fish course (typically fillet of Aberdeen sole with cheese soufflé suissesse and crayfish sauce), sorbet, a wide choice of main courses and both hot and cold desserts. There's a single sitting for each meal where the selection could contain some of the following: cream of pea and ham soup; tartlet of wild mushrooms; West Cumberland ham; sautéed scallops with a red pepper mousse and tomato sauce with aubergines, garlic and courgettes; Dover sole with a champagne and chive sauce; Old English Regency syllabub; fresh fruits set in apple jelly. The style is reminiscent of a bygone era and the element of theatre is always strong, notably in Brian Sack's presentation of the dessert trolley in the evening. Good British cheeses finish a memorable experience. Staff, many of whom are long-standing, provide courteous and willing service. An easy-to-use wine list with French classics at predictably high prices, though there's better value elsewhere. No children under 12. No smoking. **Seats 65.** Parties 10. L 1-1.45 D 8-8.45. Set L £28.50 Set D £38.50.

Ulverston   Bay Horse Inn & Bistro   £57
Tel 0229 53972   **RR**

Canal Foot Ulverston Cumbria LA12 9EL   Map 13 C6

1½ miles from Ulverston, an old pub with sympathetic conversion that includes an intimate conservatory restaurant with picturesque views over the Leven estuary. Chef Robert Lyons gives full rein to his wide-ranging repertoire; once the protegé of co-owner John Tovey at Miller Howe, he's equally at home with a deceptively simple salad or a balanced soup of broccoli, Stilton and Guinness, as with elaborate dishes typified by fillets of lemon sole stuffed with sliced leeks, prawns and water chestnuts, lightly poached and served with a white wine and fresh herb cream sauce. Complimentary coffee is served in the lounge. Lunch offers a limited choice of two dishes per course plus a few more sweets. There's a feature wine list with a fine selection of New World (mainly Antipodean) wines, with little over £20. No children under 12. No smoking. **Seats 50.** Parties 40. L 12-2 D 7.30 for 8. Closed L Mon, all Sun, Jan. Set L £14.85. Access, Visa.

Rooms   £121*

Overnight accommodation is provided in six attractive en-suite bedrooms, five of which open on to a small terrace with a view of the estuary. "A surcharge of 10% is added to all final accounts in lieu of service charge." *Half-board terms only (above price includes the surcharge). Light afternoon tea is served.

Ulverston   Place of Interest

The Laurel and Hardy Museum   Tel 0229 52292.

Umberleigh   Rising Sun Inn   £55
Tel 0769 60447   Fax 0769 60764   **I**

Umberleigh Devon EX37 9DU   Map 3 D2

After a day fishing the Taw, salmon and trout anglers will find racks for rods and drying cabinets in this 17th-century roadside inn. Six charming bedrooms have cottagey pine furniture; bathrooms with hand shower sets are simple and neat. A new extension built last year houses two new bedrooms, plus a new restaurant and kitchen. Children up to three free in parents' room. **Rooms 8.** Garden, game fishing. Access, Visa.

Upper Slaughter   Lords of the Manor   73%   £98
Tel 0451 20243   Fax 0451 20696   **HR**

Upper Slaughter Nr Bourton-on-the-Water Gloucestershire GL54 2JD   Map 4 C1

For 200 years the Lords of the Manor were the Witts family, rectors of the parish. The handsome 17th-century Cotswold-stone house stands in eight acres of grounds which include a lake stocked with brown trout (guests can catch their own dinner and have the chef prepare it). Victorian additions to the original building retained the country house feel that prevails today. Reception rooms feature chintzy furnishings, antiques and family portraits. Bedrooms, whether in the main house or converted outhouses, are notably comfortable and stylish, with pretty fabrics, soft colour schemes and fine pieces of period furniture including some splendid old beds. Bathrooms are tiled and carpeted, with good showers and quality toiletries. *Rooms 29. Garden, croquet, fishing. Access, Amex, Visa,* **()** *Diners Club International*

Restaurant   £90

The setting is formal, with period furniture and candle-light, and gentlemen are requested to wear jackets and ties in the evening. The menus have a modern ring, typified by Thai-flavoured ravioli accompanied by a compote of cucumber and mint on a sweet red pepper coulis, or roast breast of Gressingham duck with a liver timbale, the leg confit placed on an orange-flavoured sauce. Lighter luncheon menu. The wine list includes some good house recommendations; it's well annotated and has big names but few bargains. *Seats 45. Parties 10. Private Room. L 12.30-2 D 7.30-9.30. Set L £10.95 Set D £28*

Uppingham   Forte Travelodge   £40
Tel 0572 87719   **L**

A47 Glaston Road Morcott Nr Uppingham Leicestershire LE15 8SA   Map 11 E4

On the A47 eastbound, 4 miles east of Uppingham. Close to Peterborough and Leicester. *Rooms 40. Access, Amex, Visa.*

Uppingham   The Lake Isle   £50
Tel 0572 822951   Fax 0572 822951   **RR**

16 High Street East Uppingham Leicestershire LE15 9PZ   Map 11 E4

Reached via a flower-bedecked yard just off the town centre, the Whitfields' charming restaurant is homely and welcoming. David gathers the ingredients for his short multi-course menus from near and far with twice-weekly deliveries from the Paris Rungis market, fish from Grimsby and Cornwall, plus herbs from his own walled garden. Dishes such as pistachio and chicken terrine with a fromage frais and tarragon sauce, stuffed poussin with wild mushrooms, and individual summer pudding all demonstrate a sure touch in the kitchen. Good-value lunches; dinner extends to five courses, but with only a small choice of dishes. There is a splendid selection of half bottles on the excellent wine list, which is presented in two sections – everyday and fine wines. *Seats 40. Parties 20. Private Room. L 12.30-1.45 (Sun to 2) D 7.30-9.30 (Sat 7-10, Sun 7.30-8.30). Closed L Mon, D Sun except to residents. Set L from £9.75 Set D from £19.50. Access, Amex, Visa,* **()** *Diners Club International*

Rooms   £64

Bedrooms vary in size and style but all have direct-dial phones, colour TVs and thoughtful extras like fruit, mineral water and a decanter of sherry. *Rooms 11.*

Uttoxeter   Forte Travelodge   £40
Tel 0889 562043   **L**

A50/A5030 Ashbourne Road Uttoxeter Staffordshire ST14 5AA   Map 10 C3

On the outskirts of Uttoxeter, 5 miles south of Alton Towers Leisure Park, 14 miles east of Stoke-on-Trent and 16 miles west of Derby. *Rooms 32. Access, Amex, Visa.*

Uttoxeter   White Hart   £54

| Tel &   Fax 0889 562437 | **I** |

Carter Street Uttoxeter Staffordshire ST14 8EU   Map 10 C3

An old town-centre coaching inn owned by Ansell's Brewery. Adequate
overnight accommodation; 15 of the bedrooms have en-suite facilities.
Two meeting rooms for up to 50 people. *Rooms 26. Access, Amex, Visa,*

Uttoxeter   Place of Interest

Uttoxeter Racecourse   Tel 0889 562561.

Ventnor   Royal Hotel   60%   £76

| Tel 0983 852186   Fax 0983 855395 | **H** |

Belgrave Road Ventnor Isle of Wight PO38 1JJ   Map 5 D4

Neat gardens and a small children's swimming pool front this Victorian
sandstone hotel owned by Forte. The rattan-furnished conservatory
entrance hall is a favourite seating area, as is a cosy bar. Elderly lightwood
fitted units and rather neutral colour schemes in the bedrooms are
enlivened only by a variety of colourful floral curtains. Children are well
catered for with a games room, ice cream parlour and nanny during school
summer holidays. *Rooms 54. Garden, croquet, outdoor swimming pool, games
room. Access, Amex, Visa,*

Ventnor   Places of Interest

Tourist Information   Tel 0983 853625.
The Winter Gardens   Tel 0983 855111.
Appuldercombe House   (Ruins and Park) Wroxall Tel 0983 852484.

Veryan   Nare Hotel   70%   £122

| Tel 0872 501279   Fax 0872 501856 | **HR** |

Carne Beach Veryan Nr Truro Cornwall TR2 5PF   Map 2 B3

Standing above the mile-long sandy Carne Beach, the Nare has been
transformed from a simple, seaside family hotel to a model of good taste
and a haven of tranquillity. Lounges and drawing room face extensive
patios and garden and have country house appeal with antique furniture
pieces. The very best of the bedrooms have easy chairs and sofas, with
beautiful views out to sea and over the hotel lawns from picture windows
and balconies. Expect fruit and flowers on arrival and join fellow guests for
complimentary afternoon tea. Not really a young person's hotel out of
season; in season the good sports amenities are a main attraction.
Concessionary vouchers are given to guests who wish to play golf at Truro
Golf Club. Families are well catered for, but at a price. *Rooms 39. Garden,
outdoor swimming pool, sauna, solarium, tennis, keep-fit equipment, snooker,
sports boat, sail boards. Access, Visa.*

Restaurant   £65

Appealing bay views through windows with swathed pelmets; standard
fare served in healthy-sized portions. Flambé dishes are popular and hors
d'oeuvre, desserts and cheese are served on well-laden trolleys. A light
lunch is served in the Gwendra Room and adjacent terrace during the
week; traditional Sunday lunch is in the dining room. Jacket and tie
preferred in the evening. No children under 7 in the dining room at night;
an early children's dinner is offered instead. *Seats 80. L Sun only 12.30-2
D 7.15-9.30. Set D £22.*

Wadhurst   Spindlewood   60%   £68

Tel 0580 200430   Fax 0580 201132   **HR**

Wallcrouch Wadhurst East Sussex TN5 7JG   Map 7 B6

Set in five acres of gardens, ponds and woodland, Victorian Spindlewood is
an easy drive from several historic castles and stately homes. Public rooms
are semi-grand but informal. A half-panelled, parquet-floored lounge
doubles as a conference room (capacity 20) and there's a bay-windowed bar
overlooking the gardens. Individually decorated bedrooms have mainly
period furniture. The hotel has been under the personal care of the
Fitzsimmons family since 1979. No dogs. *Rooms 9. Garden. Closed 4 days
Xmas. Access, Visa,* (I) Diners Club International

Restaurant   £62

In a peaceful and charming French Provincial-style dining room Harvey
Aram continues to cook in fine form. Typical choices could include pea,
lemon and mint soup (served hot or cold), salmon with spinach and a coral
sauce, rare breast and crispy leg of duck with citrus sauce, and loin of pork
studded with black pudding served with a Calvados and apple cream sauce.
Good-quality fresh ingredients, clear flavours, well-made sauces. *Seats 40.
Parties 60. Private Room. L 12.15-1.30 D 7.15-9. Closed L Bank Holidays.
Set L £14.95 Set D £22.95.*

Wakefield   Campanile Hotel   NEW   £36

Tel 081-569 6969   **L**

Monckton Road Wakefield West Yorkshire   Map 10 C1

Canalside location, 15 minute drive outside Leeds. Nearest motorway
junction is J39 from the M1, taking A636 Denby Dale road. Opening late
'92. *Rooms 77. Access, Amex, Visa,* (I) Diners Club International

Wakefield   Cedar Court   59%   £86

Tel 0924 276310   Fax 0924 280221   **H**

Denby Dale Road Calder Grove Wakefield West Yorkshire WF4 3QZ   Map 10 C1

Modern, purpose-built business hotel by junction 39 of the M1, 12 miles
south of Leeds. Open-plan day rooms, practical accommodation; phone
extensions in bathrooms; some whirlpool baths. Conference/banqueting
facilities for 350/300. No dogs. *Rooms 151. Garden. Access, Amex, Visa,*
(I) Diners Club International

Wakefield   Forte Posthouse   64%   £67

Tel 0924 276388   Fax 0924 276437   **H**

Queen's Drive Ossett Wakefield West Yorkshire WF5 9BE   Map 10 C1

Modern low-rise hotel near junction 40 of the M1. Facilities for up to 160
delegates in the largest of several conference rooms. *Rooms 99. Garden,
coffee-shop (7am-10.30pm). Access, Amex, Visa,* (I) Diners Club International

Wakefield   Granada Lodge   £43

Tel 0924 830569   Fax 0924 830609   **L**

M1 junction 38/39 Woolley Edge Wakefield West Yorkshire WF4 4LQ Map 10 C1

Rooms 31. Access, Amex, Visa, (I) Diners Club International

Wakefield   Swallow Hotel   58%   £86

Tel 0924 372111   Fax 0924 383648   **H**

Queen Street Wakefield West Yorkshire WF1 1JU   Map 10 C1

A tall hotel, with splendid views from bedrooms on the upper floors, near
the Cathedral in the city centre. Public rooms are on the 1st and 2nd
floors. The largest of several conference rooms can take up to 150
delegates. Parking for 40 cars. *Rooms 64. Access, Amex, Visa,* (I) Diners Club International

Wakefield   Places of Interest

Theatre Royal and Opera House   Drury Lane Tel 0924 366556.
Nostell Priory (NT)   Tel 0924 863892.
Wakefield Cathedral   Tel 0924 373923.
   Museums and Art Galleries
Wakefield Art Gallery   Wentworth Terrace Tel 0924 375402 or 295796.
Yorkshire Mining Museum and Underground Tours   Caphouse Colliery,
   New Road, Overton Tel 0924 848806.
Yorkshire Sculpture Park   Bretton Hall, West Bretton Tel 0924
   830579/830302.

Walberton	Avisford Park	66%	£106
Tel 0243 551215 Fax 0243 552485			**H**
Yapton Lane Walberton Arundel West Sussex BN18 0LS			Map 5 E4

From Arundel, follow the A27 towards Chichester and turn left on to the
B2132 to find this Georgian manor house set in 62 acres of grounds. The
day rooms at this former boys' school are on a big scale and might swamp
the individual guest, as might the swarms of conference delegates. The new
Garden Lodge Business Centre is linked by an enclosed walkway and
comprises a Grand Hall (holding up to 350 conference delegates), 24
Executive bedrooms, two suites and an Italian restaurant. No dogs.
*Rooms 126. Garden, indoor swimming pools, sauna, solarium, snooker, 9-hole
golf course, tennis, squash. Access, Amex, Visa,* ⓘ *Diners Club International*

Walkington	Manor House	72%	£93
Tel 0482 881645 Fax 0482 866501			**HR**
Northlands Walkington Beverley Humberside HU17 8RT			Map 11 E1

In a wonderfully peaceful location surrounded by the Yorkshire Wolds, 3
minutes from Beverley, is this late-Victorian house run by Derek and Lee
Baugh along the lines of a private house with family guests. The bedrooms,
all with king-size beds, offer fine country views and are decorated in soft
tones. Comfortable seating, flowers, magazines and ornaments add to the
homely appeal. Bathrooms squeeze with difficulty into 19th-century
rooms, but are well equipped. Day rooms include an elegant drawing room
with fine antiques, oil paintings and seating made for relaxation. Friendly
staff and notably good housekeeping. *Rooms 6. Garden. Access,
Visa,* ⓘ *Diners Club International*

Restaurant   £75

An elegant blue dining room and adjoining conservatory provide a choice
of environments in which to enjoy Derek Baugh's cooking. The fixed-
price, four-course dinner menu has over-the-top descriptions of the good
selection of dishes in both English and French. Classical with fashionable
touches is the style: "our now famous deep-fried knapsack of prawns in a
sherry and lobster coulis set on a glazed, feathered sauce", salad of smoked
bacon and chicken with croutons, avocado and marbled quail's eggs, and
goujons of maize-fed chicken with stir-fried vegetables in a curried cream
sauce are typical starters, followed by the likes of rendez-vous of calf's liver,
kidneys and sweetbreads in a tarragon mustard sauce, "pillows of fresh fish
from faraway places grilled in butter on a golden wine sauce", and roast
pigeon breasts on cabbage and apple with a Madeira sauce. A good-value,
nightly table d'hote offers simpler fare. Lee Baugh lends a more-than-
capable hand to the patisserie and baking, her forte. New World wines
offer best value on an excellent all-round wine list. *Seats 50. Parties 50.
Private Room. D only 7.30-9.30. Closed Sun. Set D £15.*

Wallingford   George Hotel   62%   £106

Tel 0491 36665   Fax 0491 25359

High Street Wallingford Oxfordshire OX10 0BS   Map 5 D2

Dick Turpin took rooms at this historic coaching inn and during the Civil
War Royalist troops were billeted here. Now, in a less turbulent phase, the
George mixes tradition with basic modern hotel amenity. A self-contained
suite can accommodate up to 120 conference delegates. Mount Charlotte
Thistle. *Rooms 39. Access, Amex, Visa,*

Wallingford   Shillingford Bridge Hotel   58%   £60

Tel 086 732 8567   Fax 086 732 8636

Ferry Road Shillingford Nr Wallingford Oxfordshire OX10 8LX   Map 5 D2

Riverside hotel made up of several buildings, the oldest dating from the
16th century. The hotel owns a stretch of river frontage, and fishing,
moorings and boat hire (nearby) are offered. Practical accommodation; five
rooms are in a bungalow, others in an annexe. Forestdale Hotels.
*Rooms 31. Garden, outdoor swimming pool, squash, coarse fishing, dinner dance
(Sat). Access, Amex, Visa,*

Wallingford   Places of Interest

Corn Exchange   Market Place Tel 0491 39336.

Walsall   Forte Posthouse   61%   £67

Tel 0922 33555   Fax 0922 612034

Birmingham Road Walsall West Midlands WS5 3AB   Map 10 C4

Take junction 7 of the M6, then A34 to ring road intersection to find a
modern block on four floors without many of the usual Posthouse
amenities. *Rooms 98. Access, Amex, Visa,*

Walsall Wood   Baron's Court   62%   £65

Tel 0543 452020   Fax 0543 361276

Walsall Wood Walsall West Midlands WS9 9AH   Map 10 C4

Mock-Tudor styling and fittings feature throughout the ground-floor areas
of this unusual hotel on the A461. Bedrooms employ Queen Anne-style
furniture and soft decor. Executive rooms are larger and have whirlpool
baths. Dinner dance every Saturday. *Rooms 100. Indoor swimming pool,
sauna, solarium, spa bath, steam room, keep-fit equipment. Access, Amex, Visa,*

Walsall   Places of Interest

Museum and Art Gallery and Garman Ryan Collection   Tel 0922
653135.
Walsall Leather Centre Museum   Tel 0922 721153.

Wansford-in-England   Haycock Hotel   70%   £90

Tel 0780 782223   Fax 0780 783031

Wansford-in-England Peterborough Cambridgeshire PE8 6JA   Map 6 A2

A lovely 17th-century honey-coloured stone coaching inn just off the A1.
It has been much extended, in sympathetic style, the most recent additions
being a large conference/ballroom and the stone-walled Orchard Room
with all-day bar and coffee-shop menu. Other day rooms include a pubby
bar and two traditional lounges. Bedrooms in the older parts of the
building are full of character, but all have been decorated with great style
and flair by Julia Vanocci using high-quality fabrics and furnishings.
Bathrooms are equally luxurious. Extensive grounds include award-
winning gardens which stretch along the banks of the river Nene and the

village cricket pitch. Poste Hotels. *Rooms 51. Garden, fishing, pétanque, dinner dance (Fri), coffee shop (7.30am-10.30pm). Access, Amex, Visa,*
Diners Club International

Restaurant £70

Candelabras and highly polished silver add to the mellow, traditional atmosphere of the twin dining rooms here. Richard Brandrick's menu is pretty traditional too, with the likes of steak and kidney pie, venison casserole and the roast sirloin of prime English beef that always features on the silver trolley. Slightly less standard offerings might include baked herring roes with Meaux mustard sauce and a skewer of monkfish and salmon with a light orange sauce. The dessert trolley comes with Devon clotted cream. *Seats 100. Parties 28. Private Room. L 12-2 D 7-10.15.*

Wantage	Bear Hotel	58%	£72
Tel 02357 66366 Fax 02357 68826			**H**
Market Square Wantage Oxfordshire OX12 8AB			Map 5 D2

Since the 16th century the Bear has been a notable feature on the market square of the town where Alfred the Great was born (his statue is another landmark). The cobbled courtyard evokes some of the atmosphere of the past, and a few of the bedrooms are furnished with some older pieces, including brass bedsteads. The Ascot Suite provides conference facilities for up to 80. No dogs. *Rooms 38. Access, Amex, Visa,* Diners Club International

Wareham	Priory Hotel	72%	£75
Tel 0929 551666 Fax 0929 554519			**H**
Church Green Wareham Dorset BH20 4ND			Map 4 B4

Trim lawns and immaculate gardens reach down to the river Frome (which leads into Poole Harbour), making a lovely setting for the former priory of Lady St Mary, which dates from the early 16th century. Two beautifully decorated lounges overlook the gardens, and there is a traditional bar. Bedrooms vary in size but all are thoughtfully equipped: each has mineral water, fresh fruit, books and magazines, plus bathrobes, clothes brushes and hairdryers. One room has a four-poster and a whirlpool bath and all feature handsome antique furniture. The Boathouse, converted from a 16th-century clay barn, contains two bedrooms and two luxurious suites. Moorings are available for guests arriving by boat. No dogs. *Rooms 19. Garden, croquet, coarse & game fishing. Access, Amex, Visa,*
Diners Club International

Wareham	Springfield Country Hotel	59%	£80
Tel 0929 552177 Fax 0929 551862			**H**
Grange Road Stoborough Nr Wareham Dorset BH20 5AL			Map 4 B4

Set in 6 acres of stylishly landscaped gardens off the A351, a pleasant redbrick hotel with an appealing modern exterior. The spacious foyer is dominated by a splendid stag's head and there are two cosy bars. Agreeable bedrooms, decorated in pink, include doubles, twins and singles, plus a number of family rooms and suites. Two small meeting rooms. No children under two. The large games room includes bar billiards, table tennis, pool and table football. *Rooms 32. Garden, outdoor swimming pool, tennis, games room, snooker, solarium. Access, Amex, Visa,* Diners Club International

Wareham   Place of Interest

Swanage Beach *9 miles SE of Wareham.*

Warminster   Bishopstrow House   79%   £123

HR

Tel 0985 212312   Fax 0985 216769

Boreham Road Warminster Wiltshire BA12 9HH

Map 4 B3

Built in 1817, Bishopstrow is an elegant house in a lovely setting. The
entrance hall, morning room and dining rooms are stylish and formal,
with fine oil paintings, French and English antiques, Persian carpets and
deep, inviting armchairs. Flower displays add splendid splashes of colour.
Spacious bedrooms are in three places: main house, garden rooms and
courtyard rooms reached by long corridors. Rooms are either standard or
de luxe. Fruit, biscuits, plants and magazines are provided and some of the
bedrooms feature spa baths or separate showers. A stunning indoor
swimming pool looks out on to the gardens. Conference facilities for up to
70. **Rooms 32.** *Garden, indoor & outdoor swimmimg pools, game fishing,
helipad. Access, Amex, Visa,* ⑩ *Diners Club International*

Restaurant   £80

Garden views accompany inventive modern cooking by Chris Suter.
Typifying his style are spinach and mussel tartlet with parsley sauce,
Yorkshire pudding filled with onion marmalade and foie gras, lemon sole
stuffed with crab mousseline and fillet of beef with morels. British and
French farmhouse cheeses. Mixed berries in red wine is a popular dessert in
its season; chocoholics should enjoy a pecan and chocolate muffin with
chocolate sauce and vanilla ice cream. "Light refreshment" menu (carpaccio
of beef, haddock and cheese bake, duck confit with red cabbage salad) also
available. **Seats 60.** *Parties 20. Private Room. L 12.30-2 D 7.30-9 (Fri & Sat
to 9.30). Set L £15 Set D £31/£36*

Warminster   Granada Lodge   £43

L

Tel 0985 219639   Fax 0985 214380

A36/A350 Warminster Wiltshire BA12 7RU

Map 4 B3

Rooms 31. *Access, Amex, Visa,* ⑩ *Diners Club International*

Warminster   Place of Interest

Longleat House and Wildlife Park   Tel 09853 551/328.

Warrington   Holiday Inn Garden Court   65%   £73

H

Tel 0925 838779   Fax 0925 838859

Woolston Grange Avenue Woolston Warrington Cheshire

Map 10 B2

By junction 21 of the M6, one of the new 'junior' Holiday Inns offering
good bedrooms, limited public areas and minimal service. The room price
covers up to four occupants. **Rooms 100.** *Keep-fit equipment. Access, Amex,
Visa,* ⑩ *Diners Club International*

Warrington   Lord Daresbury Hotel   67%   £115

H

Tel 0925 267331   Fax 0925 265615

Chester Road Daresbury Warrington Cheshire WA4 4BB

Map 10 B2

Conveniently located by junction 11 of the M56, this modern, conference-
oriented hotel offers extensive leisure amenities. Meeting rooms for up to
400 delegates. De Vere Hotels. **Rooms 141.** *Garden, indoor swimming pool,
spa bath, sauna, steam bath, solarium, gymnasium, beautician, squash, snooker,
games room, dinner dance (monthly), coffee shop (9.45am-9.45pm). Access,
Amex, Visa,* ⑩ *Diners Club International*

Warrington   Travel Inn   £42

| Tel 0582 482224   Fax 0582 405680 |

L

Winwick Road Warrington Cheshire   Map 10 B2

Just off M62 (J9), 30 minutes from Manchester Airport. Opened August
'92; phone numbers are for Travel Inns central reservations. *Rooms 40.*
Access, Amex, Visa,

Warrington   Places of Interest

Tourist Information   Tel 0925 36501.
Museum & Art Gallery   Tel 0925 44400/30550.

Warwick   Hilton National   66%   £139

| Tel 0926 499555   Fax 0926 410020 |

H

Stratford Road Warwick Warwickshire CV34 6RE   Map 10 C4

Conferences for up to 500 are catered for at this low-rise modern hotel at
the junction of the A46 and the M40. Accommodation includes 31 rooms
in a new extension. Regular Saturday night dinner dances. *Rooms 181.*
Indoor swimming pool, keep-fit equipment, sauna, steam room, pool table. Access,
Amex, Visa,

Warwick   Places of Interest

Tourist Information   Tel 0926 492212.
Doll Museum   Tel 0926 495546.
Warwickshire Museum   Tel 0926 410410 ext 2021.
Warwick Racecourse   Tel 0926 491553.
  Historic Houses, Castles and Gardens
Charlecote Park (NT)   Tel 0789 470277.
Warwick Castle   Tel 0926 495421.
Packwood House (NT)   Hockley Heath Tel 0564 782024.

Washington   Forte Posthouse   59%   £67

| Tel 091-416 2264   Fax 091-415 3371 |

H

Emerson District 5 Washington Tyne & Wear NE37 1LB   Map 15 B4

Practical modern hotel that's popular with business visitors, who obviously
appreciate the conference and banqueting facilities for up to 100 delegates.
Rooms 138. 18-hole pitch & putt, children's playroom & playground. Access,
Amex, Visa,

Washington   Granada Lodge   £43

| Tel 091-410 0076   Fax 091-410 0057 |

L

A1(M) Washington Tyne & Wear DH3 2SJ   Map 15 B4

Rooms 35. Access, Amex, Visa,

Washington   Moat House   66%   £94

| Tel 091-417 2626   Fax 091-415 1166 |

H

Stone Cellar Road District 12 Washington Tyne & Wear NE37 1PH   Map 15 B4

First-class leisure facilities are the main attraction at a modern Moat House
standing on a championship golf course. Large bedrooms have all the usual
modern accessories. Conference/banqueting suites for 200/180. *Rooms 106.*
Garden, indoor swimming pool, 18-hole golf course, pitch & putt, golf driving
range, spa bath, sauna, solarium, keep-fit equipment, squash, snooker. Access,
Amex, Visa,

| Waterhouses | Old Beams | £85 |

Tel 0538 308254   Fax 0538 308157

RR

Leek Road Waterhouses Staffordshire ST10 3HW

Map 10 C3

A charming restaurant with rooms, on the A523 Leek-Ashbourne road. Inside, oak beams, an open fire, fresh flowers, a grand piano and good-quality place settings are matched by Nigel Wallis' fine cooking and attentive service led by Ann. Dishes on the fixed-price menu often have a luxury ring: soufflé of Dublin Bay prawns and freshwater crayfish, tournedos Rossini, millefeuille of calf's sweetbreads on a Madeira sauce. Half bottles to the fore on the helpful list that shows great balance. No smoking. *Seats 50. Parties 30. Private Room. L 12-2 D 7-10. Closed L Sat, D Sun, all Mon, Bank Holidays, 2 weeks Jan. Set L £16.50 Set D £30. Access, Amex, Visa,* Diners Club International

Rooms   £68

Five of the six bedrooms are in a building across the road and are quite superb in every way, with hand-made beds, Egyptian cotton sheets and most luxurious marble bathrooms. No smoking.

| Wateringbury | Wateringbury Hotel | 59% | £80 |

Tel 0622 812632   Fax 0622 812720

H

Tonbridge Road Wateringbury Nr Maidstone Kent ME18 5NS

Map 7 B5

Twelve bedrooms have been added to the tally at this tile-hung roadside inn. Rooms range from singles to a four-poster suite. There's a cane-furnished conservatory, a cocktail bar and two function rooms (catering for conferences of up to 80). *Rooms 40. Garden, sauna. Access, Amex, Visa,* Diners Club International

| Watford | Hilton National | 64% | £109 |

Tel 0923 235881   Fax 0923 220836

H

Elton Way Watford Hertfordshire WD2 8HA

Map 5 E2

Practical accommodation, a leisure centre and extensive conference facilities (for up to 350). Children under the age of 14 are accommodated free in parents' room, but their time in the leisure centre is limited. *Rooms 198. Gymnasium, indoor swimming pool, spa bath, sauna, steam room, beautician. Access, Amex, Visa,* Diners Club International

Watford   Places of Interest

Palace Theatre   Tel 0923 235455.
Watford Football Ground   Vicarage Road Tel 0923 230933.
Watford Ski School   Garston Tel 0923 676559.

| Wath-in-Nidderdale | Sportsman's Arms | £60 |

Tel 0423 711306

RR

Wath-in-Nidderdale Pateley Bridge Nr Harrogate
North Yorkshire HG3 5PP

Map 15 B6

Roy Carter and Chris Williamson put prime English produce to excellent use in this very cheerful inn dating from the 17th century. Their network of suppliers guarantees the best raw materials for dishes like fillet of Nidderdale trout in a nettle cream sauce, breast of chicken with lemon, parsley and garlic butter, and roast best end of lamb with whole roast garlic in a leek and tomato jus. Summer pudding has for many years been the favourite dessert. Separate cheese list. *Seats 50. Parties 60. Private Room. L (Sun only) 12-2 D 7-9.30. Closed D Sun, 25 Dec. Set L from £12.50. Access, Visa.*

Rooms   £50

Seven rooms (five of which are not en suite) offer comfortable accommodation.

Watlington   Well House   £55

Tel 0491 613333   **RR**

34-40 High Street Watlington Oxfordshire OX9 5PY   **Map 5 D2**

In a quiet village 12 miles south-east of Oxford, five little properties, some
dating back to the 15th century, have been carefully altered to produce a
delightful restaurant with rooms. Owners Patricia and Alan Crawford are
particularly friendly hosts and meals in the beamed dining room, with its
exposed brick fireplace and well-spaced tables, are very relaxed affairs.
Patricia's cooking is sound and very straightforward, typified by twice-
baked soufflé, fish soup with saffron, filo parcels of pork and ginger, chive-
sauced red mullet and lamb pie with apricots and spices. Simpler snacks at
lunchtime in the small bar. The wine list includes a good range of half
bottles. *Seats 40. Parties 25. L 12.30-2 D 7-9.15 (Sat to 9.30). Closed L Sat,
D Sun, all Mon, most Bank Holidays except 25 Dec eve. Set meals from
£12.90. Access, Amex, Visa,*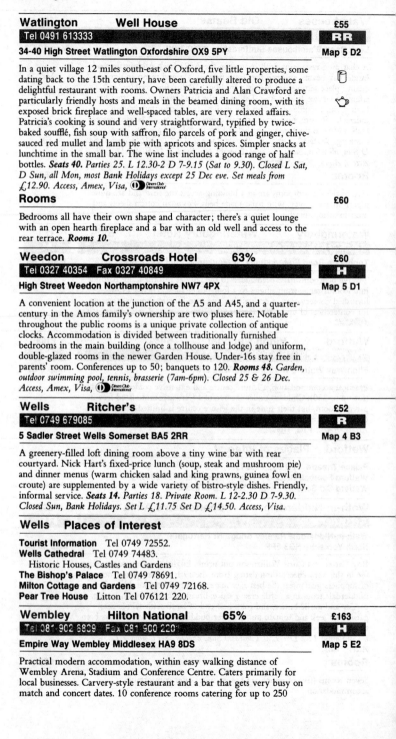

Rooms   £60

Bedrooms all have their own shape and character; there's a quiet lounge
with an open hearth fireplace and a bar with an old well and access to the
rear terrace. *Rooms 10.*

Weedon   Crossroads Hotel   63%   £60

Tel 0327 40354   Fax 0327 40849   **H**

High Street Weedon Northamptonshire NW7 4PX   **Map 5 D1**

A convenient location at the junction of the A5 and A45, and a quarter-
century in the Amos family's ownership are two pluses here. Notable
throughout the public rooms is a unique private collection of antique
clocks. Accommodation is divided between traditionally furnished
bedrooms in the main building (once a tollhouse and lodge) and uniform,
double-glazed rooms in the newer Garden House. Under-16s stay free in
parents' room. Conferences up to 50; banquets to 120. *Rooms 48. Garden,
outdoor swimming pool, tennis, brasserie (7am-6pm). Closed 25 & 26 Dec.
Access, Amex, Visa,*

Wells   Ritcher's   £52

Tel 0749 679085   **R**

5 Sadler Street Wells Somerset BA5 2RR   **Map 4 B3**

A greenery-filled loft dining room above a tiny wine bar with rear
courtyard. Nick Hart's fixed-price lunch (soup, steak and mushroom pie)
and dinner menus (warm chicken salad and king prawns, guinea fowl en
croute) are supplemented by a wide variety of bistro-style dishes. Friendly,
informal service. *Seats 14. Parties 18. Private Room. L 12-2.30 D 7-9.30.
Closed Sun, Bank Holidays. Set L £11.75 Set D £14.50. Access, Visa.*

Wells   Places of Interest

Tourist Information   Tel 0749 72552.
Wells Cathedral   Tel 0749 74483.
    Historic Houses, Castles and Gardens
The Bishop's Palace   Tel 0749 78691.
Milton Cottage and Gardens   Tel 0749 72168.
Pear Tree House   Litton Tel 076121 220.

Wembley   Hilton National   65%   £163

Tel 081-902 8806   Fax 081-900 2201   **H**

Empire Way Wembley Middlesex HA9 8DS   **Map 5 E2**

Practical modern accommodation, within easy walking distance of
Wembley Arena, Stadium and Conference Centre. Caters primarily for
local businesses. Carvery-style restaurant and a bar that gets very busy on
match and concert dates. 10 conference rooms catering for up to 250

delegates, supported by a business centre. **Rooms 300.** *News kiosk. Access, Amex, Visa,* **(I)** *Diners Club International*

Wentbridge   Forte Travelodge £40

| Tel 0977 620711 | L |

A1 Barnsdale Bar Wentbridge Nr Pontefract West Yorkshire WS8 3JB   Map 11 D1

Located southbound at the Barnsdale Bar service area. 6 miles south of junction 33 of the M62, 8 miles north of Doncaster. **Rooms 56.** *Access, Amex, Visa.*

Wentbridge   Wentbridge House   63% £71

| Tel 0977 620444   Fax 0977 620148 | H |

Wentbridge Nr Pontefract West Yorkshire WF8 3JJ   Map 11 D1

Creeper-clad Wentbridge House sits in 15 acres of wooded grounds in the beautiful Went Valley. Built in 1700, it has a period feel reinforced by suits of armour hanging in the main stairwell. Bedrooms, including the four-poster Oak Room, are individually furnished in traditional style. Popular for conferences; the largest of several meeting rooms can take up to 120 people theatre-style. No dogs. **Rooms 12.** *Garden, croquet. Access, Amex, Visa,* **(I)** *Diners Club International*

West Bexington   Manor Hotel   59% £75

| Tel 0308 897785   Fax 0308 897035 | H |

Beach Road West Bexington Nr Bridport Dorset DT2 9DF   Map 4 B4

"Where country meets coast", says their literature, and indeed Richard and Jayne Childs' small stone house stands in a garden on a gentle slope near the famous Chesil Bank shingle beach. Stone walls and oak panelling are much in evidence. Day rooms include lounge/reading room, cellar bar, restaurant and conservatory. Pretty, cottagey bedrooms, most with sea views, are furnished with old pine and enhanced with books and ornaments. Families are very well catered for. **Rooms 13.** *Garden, children's playground. Access, Amex, Visa,* **(I)** *Diners Club International*

West Bromwich   Moat House   59% £80

| Tel 021-553 6111   Fax 021-525 7403 | H |

Birmingham Road Bromwich West Midlands B70 6RS   Map 10 C4

A modern hotel with good-sized bedrooms and conference facilities. M5, junction 1. **Rooms 172.** *Coffee shop (8am-4pm), news kiosk. Access, Visa,* **(I)** *Diners Club International*

West Bromwich   Places of Interest

Art Gallery and Museum   Wednesbury Tel 021-556 0683.
West Bromwich Albion Football Ground   The Hawthorns Tel 021-525 8888.

West Chiltington   Roundabout Hotel   61% £76

| Tel 0798 813838   Fax 0798 812962 | H |

Monkmead Lane West Chiltington Nr Pulborough West Sussex RH20 2PF   Map 5 E3

A Tudor-style hotel with leaded windows, whitewashed walls and attractive, cottagey exterior. A cartwheel chandelier in the entrance hall, fairy lights over the bar and armchairs upholstered in tapestry style all characterise the public rooms. Attractive oak furniture neatly offsets the very English, rose-patterned bedcovers and curtains in the bedrooms. More spacious rooms are classified as executive (although decorated in essentially the same style) and some have four-poster beds. Tiled bathrooms are modest, but well kept. **Rooms 24.** *Garden. Access, Amex, Visa,* **(I)** *Diners Club International*

West Runton   The Links   62%

£150

H

Tel 0263 838383   Fax 0263 838265

Sandy Lane West Runton Nr Cromer Norfolk NR27 9QH

Map 6 C1

Privately owned, the Links is a large Edwardian mock-Tudor building extended by eight bedrooms and a function suite. Conferences and banquets (up to 200) are a growing part of the business, but private guests are well looked after in comfortable day rooms and decently equipped bedrooms (satellite TV, baby listening, 24hr room service) Midway between Sheringham and Cromer on the A149. *Rooms 40. Garden, tennis, 9-hole golf course. Access, Visa,*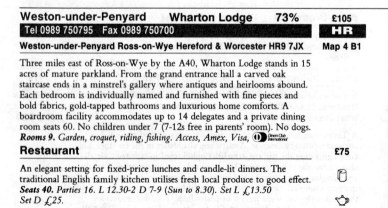

Weston-on-the-Green   Weston Manor   61%

£100

H

Tel 0869 50621   Fax 0869 50901

Weston-on-the-Green Oxfordshire OX6 8QL

Map 5 D1

2 miles from junction 9 of the M40, on the B430 six miles morth of Oxford, a manor house standing in 13 acres of gardens and grounds. Accommodation is divided between the main house and smaller, more modern rooms in the former coach house. Most characterful of the day rooms is the Baronial Hall dining room complete with minstrel's gallery. Themed party weekends are a regular feature. The hotel is part of the Hidden Hotel group. *Rooms 37. Garden, croquet, outdoor swimming pool, squash. Access, Amex, Visa,*

Weston-super-Mare   Grand Atlantic   64%

£96

H

Tel 0934 626543   Fax 0934 415048

Beach Road Weston-super-Mare Avon BS23 1BA

Map 4 A3

Modernised Victorian hotel standing in pleasant gardens across from sandy bay and new pleasure beach (but a little bit staid for younger families). Winter conference trade. Forte Heritage. *Rooms 76. Outdoor swimming pool, tennis, children's playground & playroom. Access, Amex, Visa,*

Weston-Super-Mare   Places of Interest

Clevedon Court (NT)   Nr Clevedon.
The Manor House   Walton-in-Gordano Tel 0272 872067.
Weston-Super-Mare Beach.
Avon Ski Centre   Churchill Tel 0934 852335.

Weston-under-Penyard   Wharton Lodge   73%

£105

HR

Tel 0989 750795   Fax 0989 750700

Weston-under-Penyard Ross-on-Wye Hereford & Worcester HR9 7JX

Map 4 B1

Three miles east of Ross-on-Wye by the A40, Wharton Lodge stands in 15 acres of mature parkland. From the grand entrance hall a carved oak staircase ends in a minstrel's gallery where antiques and heirlooms abound. Each bedroom is individually named and furnished with fine pieces and bold fabrics, gold-tapped bathrooms and luxurious home comforts. A boardroom facility accommodates up to 14 delegates and a private dining room seats 60. No children under 7 (7-12s free in parents' room). No dogs. *Rooms 9. Garden, croquet, riding, fishing. Access, Amex, Visa,*

Restaurant

£75

An elegant setting for fixed-price lunches and candle-lit dinners. The traditional English family kitchen utilises fresh local produce to good effect. *Seats 40. Parties 16. L 12.30-2 D 7-9 (Sun to 8.30). Set L £13.50 Set D £25.*

Weston-under-Redcastle   Hawkstone Park   59%

£110

H

Tel 0939 200611   Fax 0939 200311

Weston-under-Redcastle Shrewsbury Shropshire SY4 5UY

Map 10 B3

Sandy Lyle learned his game here, and the two 18-hole golf courses remain
a great attraction. Many other sport and leisure facilities are available, both
indoors and out, and for après sport there's a pub, a cocktail bar, a lounge
and two restaurants. Day rooms and bedrooms (all with fully-tiled
bathrooms) are part of an ongoing improvement programme which will
also involve the splendid monuments and follies in the grounds.
Conference facilities for up to 200 delegates. Children up to 14 stay free in
parents' room. No dogs. *Rooms 59. Garden, croquet, outdoor swimming pool,
golf, putting, tennis, clay-pigeon shooting, sauna, solarium. Access, Amex, Visa,*
Diners Club International

Westonbirt   Hare & Hounds   59%

£74

H

Tel 066 688 233   Fax 066 688 241

Westonbirt Nr Tetbury Gloucestershire GL8 8QL

Map 4 B2

A former farmhouse built of Cotswold stone and standing in wooded
grounds by the A433. Jeremy and Martin Price have run it for 40 years,
and its old-fashioned charm and homely atmosphere remain a great appeal.
Sturdy oak and leather are used for furnishings, and some of the bedrooms
have four-posters. Five rooms are in the garden cottage, with their own
adjacent parking. *Rooms 30. Garden, croquet, tennis, squash, putting, snooker.
Access, Amex, Visa,* Diners Club International

Wetheral   The Crown   70%

£106

H

Tel 0228 561888   Fax 0228 561637

Wetheral Nr Carlisle Cumbria CA4 8ES

Map 13 D4

The Crown stands above the river Eden, tucked away from the village
itself, yet only minutes from junction 43 of the M6 (via the A69). Despite
its somewhat austere appearance, it's a warm and welcoming hotel and the
staff are excellent. *Waltons*, the pubby bar, exudes atmosphere while the
garden-facing lounge is suitably relaxing. Bedroom accommodation is
attractive and well-maintained with bright modern bathrooms. Both the
conference facilities (catering for up to 200) and the well-equipped leisure
club are purpose-built and discreetly separate. Children under 14 stay free
in parents' room. Shire Inns. *Rooms 49. Garden, indoor swimming pool,
sauna, solarium, whirlpool bath, keep-fit equipment, squash, snooker. Access,
Amex, Visa,* Diners Club International

Wetherby   Sheba

£35

R

Tel 0937 583694

Swan Cottage 36 North Street Wetherby West Yorkshire

Map 11 D1

Reliable Bangladeshi restaurant using no animal fats. Speciality home-style
pasanda and tikkas. *Seats 40. Parties 40. D only 6-11.30 (Fri & Sat to 12).
Closed 25 Dec. Access, Visa.*

Weybourne   Gasché's

£50

R

Tel 026 370 220

The Street Weybourne Holt Norfolk NR25 7SY

Map 6 C1

Reverting to the name it bore before Swiss Restaurant, Gasché's has new
owners but the same chef (Nigel Massingham), who's been here for 37
years. The fixed-price only menus generally stick to tried and trusted
favourites like melon boats, cream of vegetable soup, Norfolk duckling
with apple sauce, chicken chasseur and rainbow trout with almonds. No
smoking except in the lounge. 2- or three-course lunches offer a good
choice; the additional "Cottage lunch" budget menu is served Tues-Sat
only. *Seats 50. Parties 30. L 12-2 D 7-9 (Sat to 9.30). Closed D Sun, all
Mon, Bank Holidays. Set L £10.70/£12.30 Set D £15.45-£20.45. Access,
Amex, Visa,* Diners Club International

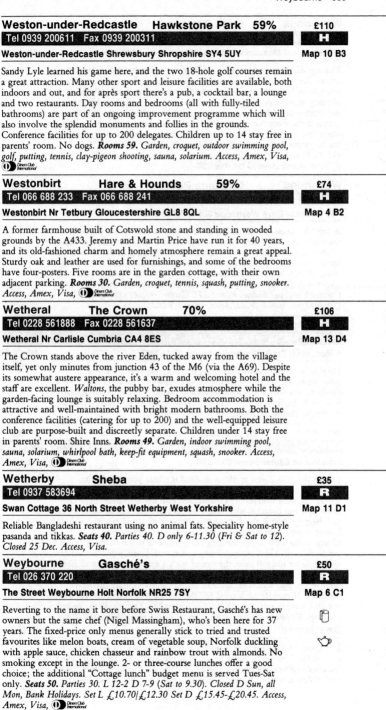

Weybridge   Casa Romana   £65

Tel 0932 843470   **R**

2 Temple Hall Monument Hill Weybridge Surrey KT13 8RH   Map 5 E3

Etchings of old Rome adorn the walls of a comfortable Italian restaurant
where diners sit on colourful striped chairs. The menu offers a lengthy
selection of hors d'oeuvre, which could precede a fish special, a steak or one
of many ways with chicken or veal (veal casanova is cooked with oysters
in a brandy and lobster sauce and topped with melted mozzarella). Set
menus include one for vegetarians. Good-value, fixed-price lunches offer a
reasonable choice. Good Italian wines, though vintages are rarely shown on
the list; some fine French bin ends. *Seats 90. Parties 100. L 12.15-2.15
D 7-10.45 (Sun to 10). Closed L Sat, 25 & 26 Dec. Set L £12.95 Set D
£16.50. Access, Amex, Visa,*

Weybridge   Oatlands Park   69%   £128

Tel 0932 847242   Fax 0932 842252   **H**

146 Oatlands Drive Weybridge Surrey KT13 9HB   Map 5 E3

A late 18th-century mansion, in 10 acres of parkland, whose porticoed
entrance leads into a most impressive galleried lounge with trompe l'oeil
marble columns and tapestry hangings under a large glass dome. Bedrooms
feature mahogany furniture, but sizes vary considerably and a few 'budget'
rooms do not live up to the generally good standard. Weekly residential
conferences (for up to 300) are the main business. Sister hotel to the Swiss
Cottage Hotel in London. *Rooms 131. Garden, croquet, coffee shop
(10am-11pm), tennis. Access, Amex, Visa,*

Weybridge   Ship Thistle   63%   £116

Tel 0932 848364   Fax 0932 857153   **H**

5 Monument Green Weybridge Surrey KT13 8BQ   Map 5 E3

Originally an 18th-century coaching inn but much extended and
refurbished with conference/banqueting facilities for up to 120. Open-plan
public rooms with a few antiques adding period character. Unremarkable
modern bedrooms are housed in extensions at the back. Reduced rates at
weekends. *Rooms 39. Access, Amex, Visa,*

Whimple   Woodhayes Hotel   75%   £80

Tel 0404 822237   **HR**

Whimple Nr Exeter Devon EX5 2TD   Map 3 E2

Just off the A30 Exeter to Honiton Road is where you will find the
winner of our *1992 Host of the Year* award. Katherine Rendle and her
family run their delightfully situated Georgian home-from-home with
great style and panache. Surrounded by park-like gardens, an apple orchard
and sheep grazing in the distance, the setting is rural and peaceful, although
Exeter is only eight miles away. The guests' wishes come first, and
afternoon tea with mouthwatering cakes included in the tariff is a typically
personal touch. There are two lounges, one with green, pale blue and
apricot decor and soft sofas, the second with a grey scheme, a small library
and even deeper sofas. For a peaceful drink, head for the flagstoned bar
with its old pine furniture. Spacious bedrooms have solidly traditional
furniture. Housekeeping is good and the breakfasts are excellent. An adult,
friendly country retreat, with no children under 12 to disturb the peace.
No dogs. *Rooms 6. Garden, tennis, croquet. Access, Amex, Visa,*

Restaurant   £62

Katherine discusses her menus with guests and special diets are gladly
catered for. Dinners are party occasions in the lovely dining room (where
French doors lead out on to a terrace), and the six courses could include
such dishes as terrine of vegetables with a tomato coulis, prawn bisque,

poached fillet of sea bass on frisée with olive oil, lemon and herb dressing, roasted guinea fowl with cider and juniper berries, and crème brulée, praline parfait with fruit salad or lemon tart. First-rate, unpasteurised mature local Cheddar is served with oat biscuits, grapes and walnuts. *Seats 18. Parties 6. L by arrangement for residents D 7-9.30. Set D £25.*

Whitewell   Inn at Whitewell   £57

| Tel 020 08 222 | I |

Whitewell Forest of Bowland Nr Clitheroe Lancashire BB7 3AT   Map 10 B1

Amid the wild beauty of North Lancashire, an ancient stone inn overlooking the River Hodder. Richard Bowman and his staff imbue the place with warmth, personality and a pleasing quirkiness. A stone-floored tap room and a library with good books and pictures are mellow and civilised. Bedrooms feature luxurious fabrics and Bang & Olufsen music systems. Telephones available on request. Good breakfasts. "No moody dogs in the public rooms." *Rooms 9. Garden, coarse & game fishing, pool table. Access, Amex, Visa,* Diners Club International

---

Whitwell-on-the-Hill   Whitwell Hall   66%   £95

| Tel 065 381 551   Fax 065 381 554 | H |

Whitwell-on-the-Hill Nr York North Yorkshire YO6 7JJ   Map 15 C6

Ivy-clad Whitwell Hall enjoys very fine views from its lofty position in 18 acres of parkland just off the A64. It's run with authority by Commander Milner and his wife, along with very pleasant staff. Public rooms lead off a splendid galleried hall; pride of place goes to the drawing room, where guests can relax in deep-cushioned settees while admiring the paintings. There's also a more modern orangery and a small bar. Bedrooms are mostly furnished in a quaint, old-fashioned style. No children under 12. Dogs are allowed in coach house rooms only. *Rooms 23. Garden, croquet, putting, tennis, indoor swimming pool, sauna. Access, Amex, Visa,* Diners Club International

---

Wickham   Old House Hotel   66%   £85

| Tel 0329 833049   Fax 0329 833672 | HR |

The Square Wickham Hampshire PO17 5JG   Map 5 D4

A splendid Georgian town house overlooking the village square. It's run with dedication by Richard and Annie Skipwith, who have created a civilised and unpretentious hotel. Polished wood floorboards, rugs and period furniture grace the two lounges, one of which is panelled; solid period pieces are also to be found in the warm, comfortable and prettily decorated bedrooms. Children stay free in parents' room. No dogs. *Rooms 12. Garden. Closed 2 wks Xmas, 2 wks Aug. Access, Amex, Visa,* Diners Club International

Restaurant   £65

Classical and modern elements meet in the kitchen, and Annie Skipwith's background in Provence is a major influence on chef Nick Harman. The surroundings are relaxed and friendly, and the short menu, which changes weekly, offers dishes such as ox tongue with a sauce of walnuts, garlic, olive oil and cream, Camembert and champagne soup, pot-roasted pigeon or fillet of beef en croute with a Madeira sauce. Tarte tatin and home-made ices tempt among the desserts. *Seats 40. Parties 35. Private Room. L 12.30-1.45 D 7.30-9.45. Closed Bank Holidays, L Sat-Mon, D Sun. Set meals £19/£23*

Willerby   Grange Park   67%   £87

| Tel 0482 656488   Fax 0482 656848 | H |

Main Street Willerby Nr Hull Humberside HU10 6EA   Map 11 E1

Four miles from Hull and four from Beverley, Grange Park is a much-extended Victorian house standing in 12 acres of grounds. Besides comfortable modern accommodation it offers extensive purpose-built

conference facilities (for up to 550) and a fine health and leisure centre
(Club Tamarisk). Families are well catered for with crèche facilities and a
children's playground; children's accommodation is free with two adults.
*Rooms 109. Garden, indoor swimming pool, gymnasium, sauna, steam room,
solarium, beautician, hair salon, helipad. Access, Amex, Visa,*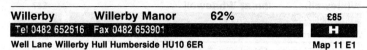

| Willerby | Willerby Manor | 62% | £85 |

Tel 0482 652616   Fax 0482 653901 — **H**

Well Lane Willerby Hull Humberside HU10 6ER   Map 11 E1

Part of a local family-owned wine merchant business, this Victorian house
stands in three acres of landscaped gardens. Everglades Bar is conservatory
in style and overlooks the garden; there are also two restaurants and a
number of rooms for conferences and banquets (catering for up to 450
delegates). Most of the bedrooms are in a modern annexe, and half have
king-size beds. *Rooms 36. Garden, croquet. Access, Amex, Visa.*

| Williton | White House | | £60 |

Tel 0984 32306 — **RR**

Williton Nr Taunton Somerset TA4 4QW   Map 3 E1

Engaging hosts Dick and Kay Smith are celebrating 25 years of personal
entertaining here, and still gaining new friends. Their nightly-changing
dinners are based on the best local produce, with a limited choice of three
courses at a set price. Withycombe asparagus, omelette bénédictine; beef
fillet rolled around fresh herbs or salmon with sorrel sauce; hot fruit brulée
or Kay Smith's chocolate pudding. Naturally flavoured soups and local
cheeses with home-made oatcakes are optional extras. No smoking. An
interesting wine list, lots of half bottles, some helpful notes and fair prices.
Seats 36. D only 7.30-8.30. Set D £21. Closed Nov-May. No credit cards.

Rooms   £60

Residents may choose between a bedroom in the main house or those in
the former stables with individual access. *Rooms 12.*

| Wilmington | Home Farm | 58% | £56 |

Tel 040 483 278 — **H**

Wilmington Nr Honiton Devon EX14 9JR   Map 3 E2

A thatched former farmhouse with a cobbled courtyard, a flagstoned bar
and a homely lounge with piano, books and board games. Bedrooms are
divided between the main house and the Garden and Courtyard wings.
Seven rooms do not have en-suite facilities. *Rooms 13. Garden. Access,
Amex, Visa.*

| Wilmslow | Harry's | | £48 |

Tel 0625 528799 — **R**

70 Grove Street Wilmslow Cheshire   Map 10 B2

Harry Yeung, chef/owner of Manchester's *Yang Sing*, also runs this notable
establishment. A simple, single doorway leads up to the first floor location
where those in the know enjoy excellent Cantonese-inspired dishes – from
a range of dim sum-style starters to stir-fried king prawn with glazed
walnuts, Singapore noodles and braised veal – all good examples of the
kitchen at its best. Friendly and helpful service. Ask for Harry's list of
specialities. *Seats 90. Parties 140. Private Room. D only 6-11. Closed Mon, 25
Dec. Set D from £16. Access, Amex, Visa.*

Wilmslow Moat House 58%

£103

H

Tel 0625 529201   Fax 0625 531876

Altrincham Road Wilmslow Cheshire SK9 4LR

Map 10 B2

A modern hotel in Swiss chalet style (although the original window shutters have now been removed) offering modest accommodation, with good leisure club facilities and a nightclub. Courtesy coaches to Manchester Airport, five minutes away. Free long-term parking (up to two weeks) for overnight guests on production of flight tickets. Vastly reduced weekend 2-night rates. Ongoing refurbishment programme. **Rooms 125.** *Indoor swimming pool, spa bath, sauna, solarium, beautician, gymnasium, squash. Access, Amex, Visa,*

Wilmslow Stanneylands 70%

£103

HR

Tel 0625 525225   Fax 0625 537282

Stanneylands Road Wilmslow Cheshire SK9 4EY

Map 10 B2

Set in a semi-rural location, hidden in the Bollin Valley, but with easy access from the A34 and close to Manchester Airport (10 minutes away). Two acres of picturesque gardens surround the redbrick house, and the interior is more modern than the Edwardian exterior might suggest, mainly due to modernisation in order to cater for conferences of up to 80. Original day rooms include an oak-panelled lounge and a cosy bar-lounge with an open fire. Individually decorated bedrooms with solid, free-standing furniture benefit from pleasant views. Two characterful private dining rooms cater for up to 100. Weekend rates are greatly reduced. **Rooms 33.** *Garden. Access, Amex, Visa,*

Restaurant

£70

New chef Steven Kitchen has instilled a new enthusiasm since stepping into his predecessor's shoes last year. The dining room is elegant with well-spaced tables and an imaginative à la carte augmented by twice-weekly market specials (perhaps mussel and saffron soup, Manx scallops with aromatic vegetables or tournedos of venison with chanterelles and oyster mushrooms) and a 6-course "menu of interesting tastes and textures" that changes weekly. Typical dishes from the new-style carte might be salt-cured fillets of lamb with a wood-mushroom and sweetbread fritter, chicken and leek consommé garnished with prunes, rice and sliced chicken breast, hazelnut crepes layered with Paris mushrooms and spinach glazed with a tofu veneer; Lunedale duck roasted with mulled pears and a thyme and walnut stuffing, and stroganoff of veal with spätzle. A lunchtime table d'hote offers lighter dishes. Sunday lunch is a popular, family affair. Good depth in an excellent wine list with something for everyone. *Seats 80. Parties 25. Private Room. L 12.30-2 D 7-10. Closed 1 Jan, Good Friday, D Sun (except to residents). Set L £11.50 Set D £25.*

Wilmslow Places of Interest

Quarry Bank Mill, Museum of the Cotton Textile Industry Styal
   Tel 0625 527468.

Wimborne Les Bouviers

£60

R

Tel 0202 889555

Oakleigh Hill Merley Wimborne Dorset BH21 1RJ

Map 4 C4

Chef-patron James Coward presents an enterprising French and English menu in a cottagey and sunny restaurant with ceiling fans, floral drapes and a conservatory. Local produce is used whenever possible, and everything fron bread to sorbets and petits fours is made on the premises. Some typical choices: terrine of confit of duck, double-baked cheese soufflé, rabbit with braised shallots and capers, noisettes of lamb with a crab mousse and curry sabayon, steamed ginger and cinnamon pudding with butterscotch sauce. No smoking. *Seats 40. L 12-2.15 D 7-10 (Sat from 6.45). Closed L Sat, all Sun, 1 week Xmas, 2 weeks Jan. Set L £7.95/£10.75 & £14.95 Set D from £17.95. Access, Amex, Visa,*

Wimborne   Places of Interest

Wimborne Minster   Tel 0202 884753.
  Historic Houses, Castles and Gardens
Cranborne Manor Gardens   Cranborne Tel 07254 248.
Edmondsham House and Gardens   Cranborne Tel 07254 207.
Kingston Lacey (NT)   Tel 0202 883402.

Winchester	Forte Crest	69%	£97
Tel 0962 861611 Fax 0962 841503			**H**
Paternoster Row Winchester Hampshire SO23 9LQ			Map 5 D3

A modern hotel just across from the cathedral. Among the day rooms are a
coffee shop with lots of light pine, a lounge with dark leather seating and a
cocktail bar. Bedrooms boast smart Italian furniture and Executive rooms
overlook the cathedral. **Rooms 94.** *Access, Amex, Visa,*

Winchester	Lainston House	75%	£134
Tel 0962 863588 Fax 0962 72672			**H**
Sparsholt Winchester Hampshire SO21 2LJ			Map 5 D3

63 acres of majestic parkland surround Lainston House, an elegant William
and Mary building dating from 1668. That it's an impressive establishment
is clear from the moment you enter the parquet-floored foyer, which is
dominated by a large fireplace decorated with fine Delft tiles. Flowers,
paintings, books and ornaments make the comfortable lounge homely and
relaxing and there's a splendid bar panelled with carved cedar. Main-house
bedrooms are of grand proportions, with quality soft furnishings, period
furniture and harmonious colour schemes; annexe rooms in Chudleigh
Court are smaller but have been refurbished this year. **Rooms 32.** *Garden,
tennis, croquet, coarse fishing, helipad. Access, Amex, Visa,*

Winchester	Royal Hotel	67%	£102
Tel 0962 840840 Fax 0962 841582			**H**
St Peter Street Winchester Hampshire SO22 8BS			Map 5 D3

Hidden away just 100 yards from the High Street, this former Benedictine
convent conceals behind a modest frontage a secluded walled garden
overlooked by lounge, bar terrace and a modern extension of smart, up-to-
date bedrooms. A striking marble-floored foyer leads to separate function
and meeting rooms accommodating up to 120 delegates. The terrace
barbecue is a popular summer feature. Under-14s stay free in parents'
room. *Garden.* **Rooms 75.** *Access, Amex, Visa,*

Winchester	Wykeham Arms		£70
Tel 0962 853834 Fax 0962 854411			**IR**
75 Kingsgate Street Winchester Hampshire SO23 9PE			Map 5 D3

Tucked away down narrow back streets, hard by the cathedral close, the
Jamesons have turned the 200 year old 'Wyk' into one of the finest
hostelries in the land. The main bar has old-fashioned schoolroom desks
with integral seats, some authentically carved with the initials of inattentive
pupils from years gone by. Collections of hats, mugs and fascinating old
prints and cartoons adorn six other interconnecting rooms, all set up for
eating. Individually decorated bedrooms have stylish matching bedcovers
and curtains and mostly honeyed pine furniture. All have mini-bars,
television and telephones plus homely extras like fresh flowers, books,
magazines and pot-pourri. Modern en-suite bathrooms, all with showers
over tubs, boast quality toiletries. First-rate breakfasts begin with freshly
squeezed orange juice and are served in a charming period breakfast room
on the first floor. **Rooms 7.** *Garden, sauna. Amex.*

Restaurant   £50

A blackboard menu changes daily offering unusual, but invariably
successful, combinations of flavours like ginger mousse with chicken breast,
thyme and horseradish sauce with rack of lamb, or their renowned Stilton
and quince paté; an excellent sauce béarnaise would put many more
pretentious restaurants to shame. Lunchtime sees a menu encompassing
sandwiches (some toasted), ploughman's, a good choice of starters (pork and
apricot terrine or Stilton & gooseberry paté) and popular hot dishes such as
Wyk potted haddock smokie and Thai chicken curry with coconut and
rice. Carrot and ginger pudding with butterscotch sauce and caramelised
apple sponge might be among the desserts. Twenty of the wines, from a
well-chosen list, are also available by the glass. For summer eating and
drinking there is a neat walled garden. Booking essential. No-smoking area.
Seats 50. Parties 8. L 12-2.30 D 6.30-8.45. Closed D Mon, all Sun, 25 Dec.

Winchester   Places of Interest

Tourist Information   Tel 0962 840500/848180.
Theatre Royal   Tel 0962 842122.
Avington Park   Tel 0962 78202.
Hinton Ampner (NT)   Nr New Alresford Tel 0962 771305.
Winchester Cathedral   Tel 0962 53137.
   Museums and Art Galleries
Winchester Cathedral Triforium Gallery
Winchester City Museum   Tel 0962 848269.
Guildhall Gallery   Tel 0962 52874.

Windermere   Holbeck Ghyll   68% NEW   £110*

| Tel 053 94 32375   Fax 053 94 34743 | |

Holbeck Lane Windermere Cumbria LA23 1LU   Map 13 D5

If approaching from Windermere on the A591, take the right turning
signposted Troutbeck *after* the Brockhole Visitor Centre (coming from
Ambleside, it's the first Troutbeck sign to the left). Once the hunting lodge
of Lord Lonsdale, the first president of the Automobile Association, and the
man who bequeathed the Lonsdale Belt to British boxing champions, the
house commands a majestic view over Lake Windermere. There's a
wonderful smell of polish in the oak-panelled entrance hall with its
inglenook fireplace, and the comfortable lounges and billiard room are
traditionally furnished in country-house style. Lots of attention to detail in
the individually designed bedrooms including a decanter of sherry, flowers
and home-made biscuits with early morning tea. Good bathrooms with
excellent water pressure (from their own spring) provide large bathrobes
and Potter & Moore toiletries. Caring service under the watchful eyes of
owners Patricia and David Nicholson. Small boardroom seats 16. Families
with young children are well catered for. *Half-board terms only.
Rooms 14. Garden, putting, snooker. Access, Amex, Visa.

Restaurant   £55

An oak-panelled restaurant serving a five-course menu of traditional
English-style dishes ranging from strips of calf's liver pan-fried with bacon
and shallots in a cream sauce with a dariole of saffron rice, to cream of
courgette and fennel soup, fillet of brill baked in the Aga and served on
bean sprouts with a light lemon and chive sauce, and individual queen of
puddings. Centre table of farmhouse cheeses and desserts. Perhaps too
liberal in their seasoning, the ladies in the kitchen nevertheless perform
creditably. Fairly priced wines and attentive service. No smoking. *Seats 30.
Parties 12. Private Room. D only 7-8.45. Set D £25.*

Windermere   Miller Howe   72%   £158★

Tel 053 94 42536   Fax 053 94 45664   HR

Rayrigg Road Windermere Cumbria LA23 1EY   Map 13 D5

Renowned the world over, John Tovey's Edwardian hotel is a delight to
visit: panoramic views of the lakes and fells; beautifully tended gardens in
which to stroll or simply admire; and charming staff. John is in his 22nd
season here and some of his staff have been with him almost from the start.
There are three relaxing lounges, lavishly appointed with leather
chesterfields, antiques and objets d'art, and an attractive conservatory for
soaking up the view. Such is the emphasis on peace and quiet that TVs and
telephones in the bedrooms are optional extras: classical cassettes, books and
board games are much more the order of the day. Night-time cosseting
runs to huge bath towels and luxury toiletries in the thoughtfully equipped
modern bathrooms. Reserved for the truly discerning are the balconied,
front-facing bedrooms. ★Half-board terms only. No children under 12.
Packed lunches and afternoon tea are provided. *Rooms 13. Garden. Closed
early Dec-early Mar. Access, Amex, Visa,* (**①**) 🔷*Diners Club International*

Restaurant   £90

In the absence of a formal bar, aperitifs are taken in the lounges. No-choice   ♔
dinner is served to all, simultaneously, in a modern dining room
overlooking the floodlit garden. The Tovey style is individual and   ♨
inimitable, its subtle blends and balances of flavours carefully orchestrated
to symphonic proportions. Pre-dinner canapés are always offered and might   ♉
include a lightly curried viennoise, bobotie pizza and diced vegetable
cream tartlet; warm rolls have unusual fillings – sun-dried tomato and
hazelnuts or watercress and orange. The main menu is a no-choice, five-
course affair, with flavour upon flavour at each course – baked fillet of
trout topped with nibbed almonds, grated Parmesan and herbs plus
grapefruit segments and deep-fried parsley is typical. Similarly, baked eye
of marinated lakeland lamb is accompanied by fresh plum purée, rösti
potato, port wine gravy, fried garlic and six vegetables ranging from
celeriac purée with toasted macadamia nuts to lightly curried salsify – an
amassment of flavours that might not be to everybody's taste. The selection
of desserts, though, is always likely to please: lemon syllabub with
viennoise biscuits and sugared almonds, warm Cape brandy tart, coeur à la
crème with raspberry sauce, tipsy trifle or black cherry and rum pie with
Jersey cream. There is a separate wine list of notable New World bottles,
mainly at favourable prices. No smoking. *Seats 70. Parties 35. Private
Room. D only at 8.30 (Sat at 7, Bank Holidays at 7 & 9.30). Set D £30.*

Windermere   Roger's Restaurant   £55

Tel 053 94 44954   R

4 High Street Windermere Cumbria LA23 1AF   Map 13 D5

Roger Pergl-Wilson is the sole cook and his wife Alena the most affable of   ♨
hostesses at their cosy corner of France in the heart of the English Lakes.
Local demand for lamb, duck and steaks has partially permeated the à la   ◫
carte menu, but the French provincial cookery evenings and special fish
night menus are not to be missed. Roger's quality cooking and powerful
flavour combinations are of undiminished appeal. Wickedly rich sweets,   ☕
impressive cheeses and a good, short wine list selected with flair.
Particularly good-value, 4-course table d'hote includes canapés and coffee
with petits fours. *Seats 42. Parties 26. Private Room. D only 7-9.30. Closed
Sun, 1 week Xmas. Set D £15.50. Access, Amex, Visa,* (**①**) 🔷*Diners Club International*

Windermere   Places of Interest

Tourist Information   Tel 09662 6499.
Lake District National Park Centre   Brockhole Tel 09662 6601.
Windemere Steamboat Museum   Tel 09662 5565.

Windsor	Castle Hotel	67%	£137
Tel 0753 851011 Fax 0753 830244			**H**
High Street Windsor Berkshire SL4 1LJ			Map 5 E2

Period atmosphere and modern facilities behind a Georgian facade.
Children up to the age of 16 free in parents' room; baby-sitting and
listening. Forte Heritage. *Rooms 104. Coffee shop (10am-10.30pm). Access,
Amex, Visa,* (◐) ᴰⁱⁿᵉʳˢ ᶜˡᵘᵇ

Windsor	Oakley Court	78%	£166
Tel 0628 74141 Fax 0628 37011			**HR**
Windsor Road Water Oakley Nr Windsor Berkshire SL4 5UR			Map 5 E2

Three miles west of Windsor on the A308, this grand Victorian manor
house is in 35 acres of landscaped grounds that slope gently down to the
banks of the river Thames. Over 200 films were shot here during its
uninhabited period of the 60s and 70s, including the St Trinians series, *The
Rocky Horror Show* and Hammer's *Dracula*. Nowadays, it's a comfortable
hotel with an impressive lounge decorated in pale yellow with chandeliers
and an ornate plasterwork ceiling, two fireplaces plus an abundance of
comfortable chairs and settees. Bedrooms have all recently been
refurbished; most appealing, perhaps, are the 27 rooms in a separate
building close to the main house, which are particularly spacious and boast
splendid red granite bathrooms, and the seven luxurious rooms in the
original house which have a period feel. *Rooms 92. Garden, snooker, croquet,
pitch & putt, boating, fishing. Access, Amex, Visa,* (◐) ᴰⁱⁿᵉʳˢ ᶜˡᵘᵇ

Oak Leaf Restaurant   £100

Oak panelling, beams and candle-light assist the quiet calm of the elegant
dining room, although the tables are a bit close together. Menus range
from table d'hote luncheons to an à la carte which includes traditional
favourites and a good choice of vegetarian dishes, as well as chef Murdo
MacSween's more elaborate creations such as fillet of brill with creamed
leeks, cucumber, crayfish and a Chablis sauce. Good desserts (try the warm
brioche filled with apple and blackberries and served with a Calvados
sabayon) and petits fours. Extensive fully-priced wine list. There are a few
bargains on the long, well-balanced wine list. *Seats 120. Parties 30. Private
Room. L 12.30-2 D 7.30-10. Set L £18.75 Set D £29.*

Windsor   Places of Interest

Tourist Information   Tel 0753 852010.
  Theatres and Concert Halls
Farrer Theatre   Eton College Tel 0753 866278.
Windsor Arts Centre   Tel 0753 859336.
Theatre Royal   Tel 0753 853888.
  Historic Houses, Castles and Gardens
Frogmore Gardens   Tel 0483 211535.
Frogmore House   Tel 0753 831118.
The Savill Garden Wick Lane   Englefield Green Tel 0753 860222.
Dorney Court   Tel 0628 604638.
The Valley Gardens   (Windsor Great Park) Tel 0753 860222.
Windsor Castle   Tel 0753 868286.
Royal County of Berkshire Polo Club   North Street, Winkfield Tel 0433
  886555.
Windsor Racecourse   Tel 0753 865234.
Windsor Safari Park   Tel 0753 830886.

Winkton   Fisherman's Haunt Inn   £55

Tel 0202 477283   Fax 0202 478883

Salisbury Road Winkton Christchurch Dorset BH23 7AS   **I**

          Map 4 C4

The river Avon is just across the road from this well-kept hotel, where
good housekeeping and a relaxed atmosphere are prime assets. The
building's 17th-century origins are not all that evident, but the bars, one
featuring an old well with spring water, have a certain personality as well
as real ale. Bedrooms, furnished in various styles, are spread around the
main building (largest rooms), an old coach house and a nearby cottage.
Rooms 21. Garden. Closed 25 Dec. Access, Amex, Visa, **(I)** Diners Club International

Winsford   Royal Oak Inn   £90

Tel 064 385 455   Fax 064 385 388

Winsford Somerset TA24 7JE   **I**

          Map 3 D2

At the centre of a sleepy Exmoor village resistant to street lighting and
noise, Charles Stevens' cosy inn doubles as village local and celebrated
haunt for the hunting and fishing folk who throng the place, especially in
winter. The hotel waters run through the village and additional beats can
be arranged. Residents nonetheless enjoy the privacy of cosy chintz lounges
and cottagey main-house bedrooms which nestle under thatched eaves. Five
double bedrooms and a family cottage are in a sympathetically converted
annexe around the rear courtyard. Children under 12 stay free in parents'
room. *Rooms 14. Garden, fishing, garage. Access, Amex, Visa,* **(I)** Diners Club International

Winterbourne   Grange Resort Hotel   68%   £95

Tel 0454 777333   Fax 0454 777447   **H**

Northwoods Nr Winterbourne Avon BS17 1RP   Map 4 B2

Seven miles from Bristol, but only minutes from M4 (j19); nevertheless,
you should obtain directions when booking. The much extended Victorian
building stands in mature parkland, its once elegant interior scarcely
matched by today's utilitarian furnishings. Conference facilities occupy
much of the main house with bedrooms and leisure club in attendant
modern blocks. *Rooms 52. Garden, indoor swimming pool, keep-fit equipment,
spa bath, sauna, solarium, massage room. Access, Amex, Visa,* **(I)** Diners Club International

Winteringham   Winteringham Fields   ↑   £88

Tel 0724 733096   Fax 0724 733898   **R R**

Winteringham Humberside DN15 9PF   Map 11 E1

Dating back to the 16th century and once the property of the Marquis of
Lincolnshire, the house now belongs to Annie and Germain Schwab.
Germain adds a generous splash of originality to classical skills, as evidenced
in dinner dishes such as pan-fried calf's brain with lemon noodles, skate
wings poached in cider garnished with samphire, or marinated casserole of
goat with roast pear. Evening alternatives to the carte are the four-course
menu epicurien and the six-course *menu surprise.* Fixed-price lunch menus
offer three somewhat simpler choices for each course. Vegetarian dishes
always available. *Seats 36. Parties 10. Private Room. D only 7-9.30.
Closed Sun, Bank Holidays, 2 weeks Xmas, 1 week Aug. Set D from £32.
Access, Visa.*

Rooms   £95

Seven bedrooms, including three in converted stables, are decorated with
delightful taste, and fine period furniture complements the exposed beams
and creaking floors. Top of the range is a four-poster room. No dogs.

Winteringham   Places of Interest

Scunthorpe Tourist Information   Tel 0724 282301.
Scunthorpe Civic Theatre   Tel 0724 85912.
Normanby Hall and Country Park   Normanby Tel 0724 720588.

Wishaw   Belfry Hotel   73%

Tel 0675 470301 Fax 0675 470178	£150
	H
Lichfield Road Wishaw Warwickshire B76 9PR	Map 10 C4

This large, ivy-clad hotel in the De Vere group stands amid two
international standard golf courses set in 360 acres of grounds. Golf is big
business, so too conferences, and the facilities for both are extensive. The
largest of the several bars, with a pubby feel, overlooks one of the courses
and has special spike-proof flooring. Also notable among the public areas is
a sunken amphitheatre-style lounge with a glass roof and abundant
greenery. Bedrooms in four wings, are named after famous golfers and are
both smart and stylish, with solid period furnishings. *Rooms 219. Golf shop,
floodlit driving range, putting green, gymnasium, indoor swimming pool, spa
bath, sauna, steam room, solarium, beautician, squash, tennis, children's
playground, night club. Access, Amex, Visa,* **(I)** *Diners Club International*

Witherslack   Old Vicarage   68%

Tel 0448 52381 Fax 0448 52373	£78
	H R
Church Road Witherslack Cumbria LA11 6RS	Map 13 D6

Follow signs for the parish church in this sleepy village to find the
Georgian, former vicarage set in five acres of informal gardens. Inside, the
hotel retains the charm and character of its Victorian heyday, and personal
service from the owners is friendly and caring. There's a choice of
accommodation between the up-to-date comforts and quiet seclusion of the
Orchard House and the homelier period pieces in the Vicarage. Don't miss
the Cumberland breakfast with black pudding, free-range eggs and home-
cured bacon. New telephone exchange code (05395) from Spring '93.
Rooms 14. Garden, croquet, tennis. Access, Amex, Visa, **(I)** *Diners Club International*

Restaurant   £55

Choose either three or five courses from a fixed-price set dinner that
epitomises British country house cooking. A typical menu might comprise
a rich terrine followed by soup then a traditional roast with all the
trimmings before a choice of puddings and a splendid selection of British
farmhouse cheeses, mostly from the north of England. (Winner of our
Cheeseboard of the Year Award.)
Coffee comes with Kendal mint cake and chocolates. 3-course Sunday
lunch (£15). Good wines from Bordeaux and California and a sensible
range of half bottles. No smoking. *Seats 36. Parties 12. Private Room. L Sun
only D at 7.30 for 8. Set D £19.50/£27.50*

Witney   Witney Lodge   62%

Tel 0993 779777 Fax 0993 703467	£84
	H
Ducklington Lane Witney Oxfordshire OX8 7TJ	Map 4 C2

An attractive modern hotel just outside Witney at the junction of the A40
and A415. Bright, practical accommodation, rustic-style bar-lounge, new
purpose-built leisure centre with a decent-size indoor pool. Popular for
conferences – the main function room can take up to 150. No dogs.
*Rooms 74. Gymnasium, indoor swimming pool, spa bath, sauna, solarium,
snooker. Access, Amex, Visa,* **(I)** *Diners Club International*

Wiveliscombe   Langley House   66%   £95

Tel 0984 23318   Fax 0984 24573

HR

Langley Marsh Wiveliscombe Nr Taunton Somerset TA4 2UF   Map 3 E2

Peter and Anne Wilson's pale-peach Georgian house nestles in lovely
countryside at the foot of the Brendon Hills; drive half a mile north of
Wiveliscombe on the road to Langley Marsh. It's a pretty place with
award-winning gardens, cobbled courtyard and attractive, lived-in drawing
rooms. Bedrooms are particularly appealing with well-planned colour
schemes and lots of little extras. The Wilsons' personal care and attention
are of a high order and breakfasts are super. *Rooms 8. Garden, croquet.
Closed Feb. Access, Amex, Visa.*

Restaurant   £63

The beamed, candle-lit restaurant with its silver and crystal table settings
enhances the air of well-being to which Peter's five-course dinner, changing
nightly, does full justice. Produce is first-rate, carefully cooked and
(puddings apart) presented without choice. Warm quail breast salad with
walnut oil; hot vichyssoise with chives; grilled turbot with a crust of crab
and tomato coulis; pan-fried lamb fillet with onion and cassis purée. Fresh
strawberry galette or dark and white chocolate terrine, with West Country
cheeses to follow. The wine list is strong in red Bordeaux and half bottles.
No smoking. *Seats 18. Parties 20. Private Room. L by arrangement D 7.30-
8.30 (Sat at 8.30 only). Set D from £26.50.*

Woburn   Bedford Arms   63%   £96

Tel 0525 290441   Fax 0525 290432

H

George Street Woburn Nr Milton Keynes Bedfordshire MK17 9PX   Map 5 E1

Mount Charlotte-owned former coaching inn with a long Georgian
frontage. Adequate accommodation, though the much-needed
refurbishment planned for 1991/2 had still not happened as we went to
press for 1993! Banqueting/conference facilities for 60/90. *Rooms 55.
Access, Amex, Visa,* (**D**) *Diners Club International*

Woburn   Bell Inn   57%   £65

Tel 0525 290280   Fax 0525 290017

H

21 Bedford Street Woburn Bedfordshire MK17 9QD   Map 5 E1

A privately-owned hotel with a mixture of Tudor, Georgian and Victorian
buildings standing on either side of the street. To one side are a beamed bar
and restaurant, to the other reception and a residents' lounge. A conference
room can accommodate up to 36. Bedrooms retain much of the character
of the original buildings; all but two singles have en-suite bathrooms.
Children share family rooms without charge. No dogs. *Rooms 27. Access,
Amex, Visa,* (**D**) *Diners Club International*

Woburn   Paris House   £82

Tel 0525 290692   Fax 0525 290471

R

Woburn Park Woburn Bedfordshire MK17 9QP   Map 5 E1

A long drive through deer-filled parkland off the A4102 brings you to this
stunning folly, a mock-Tudor, half-timbered house in the grounds of
Woburn Abbey. Chef/proprietor Peter Chandler's fixed-price menus retain
a French influence, though his style has expanded to take in other
fashionable areas; thus stir-fry pork and ginger and braised oxtail in red
wine sauce feature alongside jambonneau of chicken with cucumbers, and
pochouse. His cooking aptly matches the grand setting, with good desserts
like tulipe en fantaisie to finish. Tasting notes for every wine on the short
list. *Seats 40. Parties 45. Private Room. L 12-2 D 7-10. Closed D Sun, all
Mon, Feb. Set L £19.50 Set D £32. Access, Amex, Visa,* (**D**) *Diners Club International*

Woburn   Places of Interest

Woburn Abbey   Tel 0525 290666.

Wokingham   **Stakis St Anne's Manor**   68%   £135
Tel 0734 772550   Fax 0734 772526

H

London Road Wokingham Berkshire RG11 1ST

Map 5 D2

A converted and extended manor house conveniently situated close to the
end of the A329(M). Well-appointed bedrooms and comfortable public
areas. Good leisure amenities. Banqueting/conference facilities for 300/250.
*Rooms 130. Indoor swimming pool, garden, spa bath, sauna, solarium, tennis,
steam room. Access, Amex, Visa,*

Wolverhampton   **Goldthorn Hotel**   62%   £78
Tel 0902 29216   Fax 0902 710419

H

Penn Road Wolverhampton West Midlands WV3 0ER

Map 10 B4

Intricate plaster ceilings add character to the cocktail bar and lounge at a
19th-century house with modern extension, one mile south of the town
centre. Conference facilities for up to 130. *Rooms 93. Garden. Access, Amex,
Visa,*

Wolverhampton   **Mount Hotel**   60%   £95
Tel 0902 752055

H

Mount Road Tettenhall Wolverhampton West Midlands WV6 8HL

Map 10 B4

Eight miles from junction 10 of the M6 and two miles from the centre, a
solid, 1870s redbrick building with modern bedroom wings, set in
extensive gardens. Banqueting/conference facilities (for 160/200) include
the Grand Library complete with Italian rococo-style ceiling and minstrel's
gallery. Fortnightly dinner dances in winter. Jarvis Hotels. *Rooms 56.
Garden. Access, Amex, Visa,*

Wolverhampton   **Victoria Park**   67%   £96
Tel 0902 29922   Fax 0902 29923

H

Lichfield Street Wolverhampton West Midlands WV1 4DB

Map 10 B4

Next to the town's Grand Theatre, opposite the station. Extensive
restoration has created a smart, modern hotel from what was a
considerably run-down site. A marble-tiled foyer and lively bar now set a
fashionable tone to the whole building. Bright furnishings are used
throughout, trying hard to compensate for some compact single bedrooms
and generally small bathrooms. Short on amenities, the hotel aims largely
at the conference and function trade, catering for up to 200 and 150
respectively. *Rooms 118. Access, Amex, Visa,*

Wolverhampton   Places of Interest

Tourist Information   Tel 0902 312051.
Grand Theatre   Tel 0902 29212/714775.
Civic Hall   Tel 0902 312030.
Bantock House   Bantock Park, Bradmore Tel 0902 24548.
Central Art Gallery and Museum   Tel 0902 312032.
Wolverhampton Wanderers Football Ground   Molineux Stadium
   Tel 0902 712181.
Wolverhampton Racecourse   Tel 0902 24481.
   Historic Houses, Castles and Gardens
Chillington Hall   Tel 0902 850236.
Moseley Old Hall (NT)   Tel 0902 782808.
Wightwick Manor (NT)   Tel 0902 761108.

Woodbridge   Seckford Hall   68%

£90

H

Tel 0394 385678   Fax 0394 380610

Woodbridge Suffolk IP13 6NU

Map 6 D3

Look out for the hotel sign on the A12 Woodbridge by-pass (don't turn off into the town) to find this imposing Elizabethan manor house set in extensive gardens which include an ornamental fountain and lawns leading down to a willow-fringed lake. Inside, period features abound with linen-fold panelling and heavily beamed ceiling in the Great Hall (lounge), huge stone fireplaces and carved doors. Bedrooms are comfortably furnished more in private-house than hotel style, four have four-poster beds (one dates back to 1587) and some are in a courtyard complex that includes an inspired conversion of an old tithe barn into a delightful heated swimming pool. *Rooms 35. Garden, indoor swimming pool, solarium, whirlpool bath, mini-gym, clay-pigeon shooting. Closed 25 Dec. Access, Amex, Visa,* ◖ Diners Club International

Woodford Bridge   Prince Regent Hotel   63%

£65

H

Tel 081-505 9966   Fax 081-506 0807

Manor Road Woodford Bridge Essex IG8 8AE

Map 7 B4

The main house is Georgian, although now much extended to include substantial function and conference facilities for up to 300 delegates. Smart up-to-date bedrooms are in a converted Victorian abbey joined to the original building. *Rooms 51. Garden. Access, Amex, Visa,* ◖ Diners Club International

Woodhall Spa   Dower House   62%

£60

H

Tel 0526 52588

Manor Estate Woodhall Spa Lincolnshire LN10 6PY

Map 11 E2

In over two acres of grounds on a private road, an Edwardian hotel sheltered from the nearby town centre. Comfortable armchairs around a log fire in the entrance hall give winter visitors a warm welcome, while summer guests will enjoy the garden views from the lounge and bar. Traditional bedrooms (six en suite: one with bathroom down the corridor) are spacious and quiet. *Rooms 7. Garden. Access, Amex, Visa.*

Woodstock   Bear Hotel   66%

£116

HR

Tel 0993 811511   Fax 0993 813380

Park Street Woodstock Oxfordshire OX7 1SZ

Map 5 D1

Longstanding landmark of local catering, the origins of the creeper-clad coaching inn going back to the 12th century. It stands in a quiet side street before the gates to Blenheim Palace. Bedrooms come in all shapes and sizes with decorations ranging from antique to modern. There is plenty of period charm, including heavy black beams and a Cotswold stone fireplace with roaring log fire in the downstairs lounge-bar. Forte Heritage. *Rooms 45. Access, Amex, Visa,* ◖ Diners Club International

Restaurant

£60

Darkwood reproduction furniture, white napery and original oak beams make a good contrast in the dining room. Chef Ian Rhodes lifts his menus away from the ordinary with dishes like rillettes of rabbit with a beetroot and apple salad, layered vegetables with sweet pepper sauce, or rosette of salmon grilled with sorrel and an asparagus butter sauce. Desserts can be interesting (trio of chocolate desserts with griottine cherries and sugared hazelnuts) and there's always a choice of traditional British farmhouse cheeses. Far removed from the average run-of-the-mill Forte-owned restaurant. The wine list appears to have reduced in depth during the last year. *Seats 75. Parties 20. Private Room. L 12.30-2 (Sun 12.15-2.30) D 7-10 (Sun to 9.30). Set L £12.50 (Sun £16.95) Set D £19.95.*

Woodstock   Feathers Hotel   73%

£103

HR

Tel 0993 812291   Fax 0993 813158

Market Street Woodstock Oxfordshire OX7 1SX

Map 5 D1

Eight miles north of Oxford, within walking distance of Blenheim Palace.
Situated in the heart of a historic village, behind a 17th-century Cotswold-
stone frontage, the Feathers offers a comfortable range of accommodation
with bedrooms differing in price by size (suites are particularly attractive).
All have elaborately draped curtains and a useful range of extras that
includes mineral water, chocolates, fresh flowers, magazines and tea on
arrival. Some rooms have draped awnings over the beds, while the best
have four-posters. Bathrooms are luxuriously fitted in marble throughout,
with bathrobes and an abundance of toiletries provided. The upstairs
drawing room is the most comfortable of the day rooms and a cosy bar has
flagstone flooring and an open fireplace. During warm weather the
courtyard garden is a delightful spot for light meals (which are also served
in the bar). Service is courteous and efficient. Private rooms for conferences
of up to 35 delegates. *Rooms 17. Garden, mountain bikes. Access, Amex,
Visa,*

Restaurant

£75

A quiet, sophisticated air pervades the dining room with its mix of pine
bookshelves and pale yellow, drag-painted and panelled walls. Inventive,
but not gimmicky, menus start with interesting amuse-gueule. A three-
course, fixed-price dinner menu might include smoked chicken and quail's
eggs with green herb vinaigrette followed by fillet of brill with truffle and
vermouth and a vanilla-flavoured crème brulée plus coffee and truffles to
finish. The carte offers a varied selection from spinach soufflé with wild
rice and nutmeg, through black pudding with crispy bacon and green herb
mustard to chargrilled main courses (duck, salmon, tuna) and tempting
desserts (try the selection for two). Salmon is offered three ways in one dish
(marinated, tartare and smoked), as is chocolate (soufflé, terrine and
mousse).Classic main courses such as Dover sole with sweet peppers and
baby artichokes or venison steak with green peppercorns and port are
interestingly presented. Farmhouse cheeses are served with home-made
walnut, onion and herb bread. The extensive wine list offers a good choice
of half bottles and house wines (also available by the glass). *Seats 60. Parties
60. Private Room. L 12.30-2.30 D 7.30-9.45. Set L £17.50 Set D £19.95.*

Woodstock   Places of Interest

Tourist Information   Tel 0993 811038.
Blenheim Palace   Tel 0993 811325.
Oxfordshire County Museum   Tel 0993 811456.

Woody Bay   Woody Bay Hotel   59%

£82

H

Tel 059 83 264

Woody Bay Barnstaple Devon EX31 4QX

Map 3 D1

Now under the new ownership of Martin and Colette Petch. Purpose-built
100 years ago, the hotel enjoys spectacular views from its woody site
overlooking the sea. All but two of the bedrooms make the most of the
setting, and those two cost a little less than the rest. There are two four-
poster rooms and a family suite. Not suitable for children under eight.
Leave the A49 at Martinhoe Cross (or go via the Valley of Rocks coastal
toll road). *Rooms 15. Closed 6 weeks Jan/Feb. Access, Visa.*

Woolacombe   Woolacombe Bay Hotel   65%

£175*

H

Tel 0271 870388   Fax ext 437

South Street Woolacombe Devon EX34 7BN

Map 2 C1

Family summer holidays, winter breaks and conferences (for up to 350
delegates) are the main business at this imposing Edwardian hotel, whose
lawns and gardens reach down to long, sandy beaches. Public rooms are

fairly grand, bedrooms bright and roomy, with mostly modern
furnishings. There are self-catering suites, apartments and flats. No dogs.
*Half-board terms only. **Rooms 61.** *Garden, indoor & outdoor swimming
pools, tennis, pitch & putt, squash, keep-fit equipment, shortmat bowling, games
room, hairdressing, children's playroom and organiser. Closed Jan. Access, Amex,
Visa,*

Woolacombe   Places of Interest

Woolacombe and Porthminster Beaches.

Wooler   Ryecroft Hotel   59%   £62

Tel 0668 81459   **H**

Ryecroft Hotel Wooler Northumberland NE71 6AB   Map 14 B2

Pat and David McKechnie run their little redbrick hotel alongside the
A697 in friendly fashion. There's a 30s' feel to the day rooms, which
include an entrance hall/lounge, a TV room (there are none in the
bedrooms) and a real ale bar that's extended by a conservatory. Double-
glazed bedrooms have 30s' furniture; all but two have en-suite facilities and
phone. **Rooms 11.** *Garden. Closed 2 weeks Nov, 24-30 Dec. Access, Visa,*

Wootton Common   Lugleys   £60

Tel 0983 882202   **R**

Staplers Road Wootton Common Isle of Wight PO33 4RW   Map 5 D4

A tiny restaurant in an Edwardian house, where Victorian prints combine
with stylish drapes to create a certain quaint charm. Working single-
handedly in the kitchen Angela Hewitt manages to offer a choice of home-
made breads and sensibly limits her constantly-changing menu to a choice
of three dishes at each course. Spicy fish stew, roast quails with wild
mushroom sauce and meringue timbale with orange anglaise and caramel
sauce exhibit both her skill and enthusiasm plus the value of some careful
shopping; other examples might range from sauté of chicken livers with
Indian spices and croustade to Highland grouse pie with sweet and sour
cherry sauce and passsion fruit and muscat jelly with lemon cream. Angela's
enthusiasm sometimes extends to complimentary courses – perhaps an
inter-course sorbet or a light soufflé; overall the value for money cannot be
questioned. An apartment sleeps three (one twin and one single bedroom)
and is available on a B&B basis. **Seats 16.** *D only 7-9.30 (times vary in
winter). Closed Sun & Mon, 25 & 26 Dec. No credit cards.*

Wootton Common   Places of Interest

Newport Tourist Information   Tel 0983 525450.
Quay Arts Centre Newport   Tel 0983 528825.
Carisbrooke Castle   Tel 0983 522107.
Carisbrooke Castle Museum (EH)   Tel 0983 523112.
Robin Hill Adventure Park   Tel 0983 527352.

Worcester   Brown's   £75

Tel 0905 26263   **R**

24 Quay Street Worcester Hereford & Worcester WR1 2JJ   Map 4 B1

A spacious, high-ceilinged restaurant converted from a corn mill, with
large picture windows overlooking the river. Dinner is a fixed-price (fully
inclusive), three-course affair with safe, wholesome dishes like salad of
smoked chicken and prawns with orange dressing or fresh crab salad with
avocado to start, followed by roast Barbary duck with ginger and lime and
a leg confit, or grilled calf's liver with sage and avocado. Fresh fish of the
day and sometimes a vegetarian special such as fennel and flageolet bean
casserole with lemon sauce and cornmeal dumplings complete the picture
before nougatine parfait, rhubarb crumble or praline sablé enter the final
frame. Lunches are simpler but represent good value. **Seats 95.** *Parties 100.
L 12.30-1.45 D 7.30-9.45 (Sat to 10). Closed L Sat, D Sun, Bank Holidays,
1 week Xmas. Set L £15 Set D £30. Access, Amex, Visa,*

Worcester   Fownes Resort Hotel   70%   £96

Tel 0905 613151   Fax 0905 23742   **H**

City Walls Road Worcester Hereford & Worcester WR1 2AP   **Map 4 B1**

Victorian character survives in a hotel standing on the site of a famous
glove factory. It's stylish and spacious; public rooms include a large foyer, a
smart cocktail bar and an intimate library, where dark green walls and
green leather wing chairs allow both the books and the collection of Royal
Worcester china to be seen to advantage. Spacious bedrooms, all sited away
from the busy main road, are well equipped, with freestanding mahogany
furniture and quiet colour schemes. Good desk space and seating are
provided, and there's fresh milk in the minibar for tea or coffee. Children
up to 10 stay free in parents' room. The John Fownes suite can cater for
conferences of up to 120 people theatre-style. The hotel stands by an
attractive canalside walk, just a short distance from the cathedral and city
centre. **Rooms 61.** Keep-fit equipment, sauna. Access, Amex, Visa, **◑** Diners Club International

Worcester   Giffard Hotel   61%   £75

Tel 0905 726262   Fax 0905 723458   **H**

High Street Worcester Hereford & Worcester WR1 2QR   **Map 4 B1**

Decent accommodation in concrete 1960s' hotel opposite the cathedral.
Conferences and banqueting cater for up to 130. Free garage parking is one
of the hotel's major assets. Greatly reduced rates at weekends. Rather short
on heritage for a Forte Heritage hotel! **Rooms 103.** Snooker. Access, Amex,
Visa, **◑** Diners Club International

Worcester   Places of Interest

Tourist Information   Tel 0905 726311/723471.
Swan Theatre   Tel 0905 27322.
Worcester Arts Workshop   Tel 0905 21095.
The Greyfriars (NT) House & Gardens   Tel 0905 23571.
Spetchley Park Gardens   Tel 090565 224/213.
Worcester Cathedral   Tel 0905 28854.
   Museums and Art Galleries
City Museum and Art Gallery   Tel 0905 763763.
The Dyson Perrins Museum of Worcester Porcelain   Worcester Royal
   Porcelain Works Tel 0905 23221.
The Elgar Birthplace   Crown East Lane, Lower Broadheath Tel 0905
   333224.
New Road Cricket Ground   Tel 0905 787394.
Worcester Racecourse   Tel 0905 25364.

Worfield   Old Vicarage   67%   £79

Tel 074 64 497   Fax 074 64 552   **HR**

Worfield Bridgnorth Shropshire WV15 5JZ   **Map 10 B4**

Set in two acres of grounds overlooking fields and farmland, Peter and
Christine Iles's handsome Edwardian parsonage reflects the peace and quiet
of its village setting. Twin conservatories jutting out into the garden house
a relaxing lounge with wicker chairs. Individually designed bedrooms, each
named after a local village, sport reproduction furniture, pretty soft
furnishings and copious extras: the ground-floor Leighton Suite has been
specially equipped for disabled guests. Staff are particularly friendly.
Rooms 14. Garden. Access, Amex, Visa, **◑** Diners Club International

Restaurant   £72

Daily set-price lunches and dinners combine the everyday with the slightly
more adventurous. Goat's cheese fritters are served with herb mayonnaise
and glazed kumquats; rosettes of Shropshire lamb on chive butter sauce are
escorted by a turnip and thyme gateau; honey ice cream accompanies a

warm lemon sponge pudding. Don't miss the fine selection of cheeses from around Britain. Wines, listed by colour and country, are concisely described, with a particularly good New World showing. *Seats 40. Parties 20. Private Room. L 12-2 D 7-9 (Sun at 7). Set L £14.50 Set D £21.50/£27.50.*

Worksop — Forte Travelodge — £40

Tel 0909 501528 — **L**

A57 St Anne's Drive Dunkeries Mill Worksop Nottinghamshire S80 3QD — Map 11 D2

At the junction of the A57 and A60, west of Worksop. Sheffield, Doncaster and Mansfield are all within 15 miles. *Rooms 40. Access, Amex, Visa.*

Worthing — Beach Hotel — 64% — £87

Tel 0903 234001 Fax 0903 234567 — **H**

Marine Parade Worthing West Sussex BN11 3QJ — Map 5 E4

In a prime seafront position, the Beach offers modest comfort behind its long, characterless frontage. Public rooms are on a scale large enough to handle conferences of up to 200. Fifty-three of the double-glazed bedrooms are singles; most are generally light and spacious with a traditional look. Some rooms have their own balconies directly overlooking the sea. No children under eight in the restaurant. No dogs. *Rooms 82. Coffee shop (10am-10pm). Access, Amex, Visa,* Diners Club International

Worthing — Chatsworth Hotel — 57% — £77

Tel 0903 236103 Fax 0903 823726 — **H**

Steyne Worthing West Sussex BN11 3DU — Map 5 E4

A conference-orientated hotel near the sea front with fine creeper-covered Georgian facade, overlooking a garden square. Well-kept bedrooms are not luxurious, but include the extras one now expects as standard. Children under 14 accommodated free in parents' room; cots and baby-listening available. *Rooms 105. Games room. Access, Amex, Visa,* Diners Club International

Worthing — River Kwai — £50

Tel 0903 211901 — **R**

16 Ambrose Place Worthing West Sussex — Map 5 E4

Waitresses in traditional Thai dress move gracefully around this stylish restaurant, where authentic music and cushioned bamboo chairs help set the scene for some fine cooking. Careful preparation, subtle flavourings and sound cooking are evident in dishes like hot and sour soup with prawns, beef with oyster sauce and freshly-cooked noodles with prawns, crab and bean-sprouts. The restaurant is a short walk from the main shopping street. Branch also in Tangmere, near Chichester (Tel 0243 773294). *Seats 38. Parties 20. L 12-2.30 D 6-10.30. Closed Sun. Access, Visa,* Diners Club International

Worthing — Places of Interest

Tourist Information Tel 0903 210022.
Connaught Theatre Tel 0903 35333.
Pavillion Theatre Tel 0903 820500.
Highdown Gardens Goring-by-Sea Tel 0903 48067.
Worthing Museum and Art Gallery Chapel Road Tel 0903 39999 Ext 121 *Saturday 204229.*

Worthington — Kilhey Court — 65% — £85

Tel 0257 472100 Fax 0257 422401 — **H**

Chorley Road Worthington Wigan Lancashire WN1 2XN — Map 10 B1

Built by a Wigan brewer in 1884, the main building stands in ten acres of woodland alongside the A5106, near Standish. Additions such as the new conference and business centres (catering for up to 150), a leisure club with a small pool, a bedroom block and the reception area lack much of the house's original elegance. Bedrooms are provided with a work desk and mini-bar, and finished in white ash and floral fabrics – putting practicality ahead of luxury. Rural tranquillity and proximity to the M61 and M6 are major assets. *Rooms 54. Garden, night club (Fri & Sat), indoor swimming pool, sauna, solarium, keep-fit equipment, spa bath, fishing. Access, Amex, Visa,*

Wrotham Heath Forte Posthouse   67%   £67

Tel 0732 883311   Fax 0732 885850   **H**

London Road Wrotham Heath Nr Sevenoaks Kent TN15 7RS   **Map 7 B5**

Located on the A20 close to junction 2A of the M26, offering spacious, well-designed public areas and good leisure facilities. The bar and lounge areas are in an open-plan arrangement, one section of the lounge overlooking an inner courtyard with an ornamental pool. Meeting room for 60. *Rooms 118. Garden, indoor swimming pool, sauna, solarium, whirlpool bath, gymnasium, children's play area. Access, Amex, Visa,* ●

Wrotham Heath   Travel Inn   £42

Tel 0732 884214   Fax 0732 780368   **L**

London Road Wrotham Heath Nr Sevenoaks Kent TN15 7RX   **Map 7 B5**

10 minutes drive from Brands Hatch and the town centres of Sevenoaks and Maidstone. *Rooms 40. Access, Amex, Visa,* ●

Wroxton St Mary   Wroxton House   66%   £95

Tel 0295 730482   Fax 0295 730800   **H**

Wroxton St Mary Nr Banbury Oxfordshire OX15 6QB   **Map 5 D1**

On the Stratford side of Banbury (A427), three village houses make up this genuinely friendly honey-stone hotel. Reception and a sunken lounge flank the flagstoned foyer, beyond which is a period-style bar. Bedrooms are individually decorated, with original timbers preserved in many of the original rooms; the balance in a newer block use stylish darkwood furniture. Private meeting rooms for up to 45; banqueting for 70. Children under 15 free in their parents' room. *Rooms 32. Garden, croquet. Access, Amex, Visa,* ●

Wylam   Laburnum House   £60

Tel 0661 852185   **RR**

Main Street Wylam Northumberland NE41 8AJ   **Map 15 B4**

A house dating from the early 18th century is home for a pleasant little restaurant with comfortable wicker chairs at attractively laid tables. "French and modern cuisine" is Kenn Elliott and Rowan Mahon's description of their cooking. A frequently changing menu runs from sliced melon with green figs and Parma ham or venison paté with mango purée to lobster tails with garlic, ginger and spring onion and guinea fowl breasts with Cointreau. Hazelnut meringue with raspberries and fresh cherry and Armagnac tart represent standard desserts. *Seats 40. Parties 45. D only 6.30-9.30 (Sat to 10). Closed Sun, Bank Holidays (open Good Friday), 2 weeks Feb. Access, Amex, Visa,* ●

Rooms   £50

Four neat bedrooms, all doubles and all quite large, three of which have private shower rooms and one a bathroom.

Wymondham   Number Twenty Four   NEW   £40

Tel 0953 607750

R

24 Middleton Street Wymondham Norfolk

Map 6 C2

Opening just over a year ago, chef-proprietor Richard Hughes lost no time
in establishing his reputation for serious food at this former tea shop and
delicatessen. Two tiny dining rooms have been created, offering warmth
and intimacy with an air of cosy informality. Hughes's fixed-price dinner
offers commendable value for money: the style is typified by salmon and
samphire on orange butter sauce, lamb's liver with spring cabbage and
sultanas, and warm gooseberry tart on Pimms and lemon cream. Light
lunches in similar vein are chosen from the blackboard; cheeses from the
surviving deli counter; and Adnam's wines from a brief, selective list.
*Seats 35. Parties 20. Private Room. L 12-2.30 D 7.30-9.30 (Light meals
9am-4.30pm). Closed D Mon & Tue, all Sun, 25 & 26 Dec. Set L £8.95
Set D £12.95. Access, Visa,*

Yattendon   Royal Oak   £80

Tel 0635 201325   Fax 0635 201926

IR

The Square Yattendon Nr Newbury Berkshire RG16 0UF

Map 5 D2

Oliver Cromwell is said to have rested at the Oak Inn before the Battle of
Newbury in 1644, but the inn stayed loyal to Charles I and added its regal
nomenclature in honour of the tree in which the King hid from the
Roundheads. Nowadays, owner Julie Huff rules the roost at this fine old
country inn with pretty flowering tubs in front of its creeper-clad front. A
new door has recently been added to the rear of the busy and characterful
beamed bar that leads out on to a small garden with vine-clad trellises.
Comfortable couches and large floral displays grace a small reception area
that doubles up as both hotel lounge and waiting area for the dining room,
which leads off to one side. Upstairs, most of the five comfortable
bedrooms feature large beds, and both generous towelling and thoughtful
extras are provided in the en-suite bathrooms (two are across the narrow
hallway with creaking floor); some rooms overlook the garden, others the
village square. Predominantly young staff seem genuinely keen to please. A
few minutes off junction 13 of the M4. *Rooms 5. Garden. Closed 25 Dec.
Access, Amex, Visa,*

Restaurant   £94

Dominique Orizet has installed a new kitchen and moved the serving
doors in order to ease the throughput into the dining room and cater for
the first-class bar food trade. The end results have been well worth the
effort, leaving the restaurant a calmer, more homely room with parquet
floor, lemon yellow walls, smart drapes and polished antique round tables
set with neat little floral offerings and a display of fruits in a long-stemmed
glass bowl. A fixed-price business lunch menu was introduced last year, but
dinner is still à la carte. Unannounced, a small cup of vichyssoise with
lobster eggs and chives ushered in a recent meal, followed by steamed
scallops set on a julienne of vegetables accompanied by a vivid yellow sauce
with strands of saffron and a fanned baby courgette whose flower was
stuffed with strongly flavoured red mullet; a salad of quail, artichoke heart
and foie gras was equally involved, set on leaves of spinach dressed with
balsamic vinegar and accompanied by poached quail's eggs and quartered
baby tomatoes topped with fresh dill. A complimentary inter-course apple
sorbet topped with neat Calvados was curiously ineffective. Both a
perfectly cooked rack of lamb (served with a Madeira sauce plus a timbale
of courgette-edged ratatouille) and a light casserole of monkfish, red mullet
and Dover sole (served in a bowl with turned potatoes, samphire and
croutons with rouille) were accompanied by a selection of ten vegetables –
from baby carrots and Lilliputian turnips to golden beetroot and rösti. A
light almond milk and chocolate sorbet topped with fresh mint were set
around three filo money parcels each containing half a peach – a wonderful
dessert, sadly not matched, though, by an over-iced strawberry soufflé.

Unstuffy, willing service suits the mood perfectly. A delightful small private dining room seats six. Although the wine list features no half bottles, any bottle will be opened and charged as taken – a commendable policy. *Seats 25. Parties 20. Private Room. L 12-2 D 7-10. Set L £18.50.*

Yelverton   Moorland Links   65%   £60

Tel 0822 852245   Fax 0822 855004   **H**

Yelverton Nr Plymouth Devon PL20 6DA   Map 2 C3

This well-liked, low-rise hotel is signposted off the A386 between Plymouth and Tavistock, within the Dartmoor National Park. Main day rooms include a lounge, the Gun Room bar and a ballroom giving onto the lawns. Individually decorated bedrooms are spacious and comfortable, with well-equipped, carpeted bathrooms. Conference facilities for up to 120, banqueting up to 200. Forestdale Hotels. *Rooms 30. Garden, tennis, helipad. Closed 1 week Xmas. Access, Amex, Visa,* ⓘ *Diners Club International*

Yelverton   Places of Interest

Buckland Abbey   (NT and Plymouth City Council) Tel 0822 853607.

Yeovil   Little Barwick House   £55

Tel 0935 23902   Fax 0935 20908   **RR**

Barwick Village Nr Yeovil Somerset BA22 9TD   Map 4 B3

The Colleys' listed Georgian dower house faces west with delightful sloping gardens, just off the A37 two miles south of Yeovil. Veronica's four-course fixed-price menu offers plenty of choice among her straightforward presentations of top-quality produce. Avocado and chicken tikka salad or "Popeye" pancakes of spinach and cream cheese typically precede local rack of spring lamb on a mint and cucumber sauce, baked salmon with lime and dill butter, or West Bay sole fillets à la crème. Traditional English puddings and Christopher's chatty informality complete the picture. Smoking is actively discouraged in both dining room and bedrooms. *Seats 40. Parties 40. Private Room. D only 7-9 (Sat to 9.30). Closed Sun (except residents), 2 weeks Jan. Set D from £20.90. Access, Amex, Visa,* ⓘ *Diners Club International*

Rooms   £72

Six spotlessly kept bedrooms with simple decor and furnishings promise peace and quiet in an abundantly calm rural setting. Exemplary breakfasts are served in the sunlit morning room.

Yeovil   The Manor   63%   £91

Tel 0935 231161   Fax 0935 706607   **H**

Hendford Yeovil Somerset BA20 1TG   Map 4 B3

Close to the town centre, an old mansion dating from 1735 with converted stables offering modern bedroom facilities. Conferences and private dining for up to 70; attractive conservatory opening to enclosed formal garden. Forte Heritage. *Rooms 41. Garden. Access, Amex, Visa,* ⓘ *Diners Club International*

Yeovil   Places of Interest

Tourist Information   Tel 0935 71279.
Octagon Theatre   Tel 0935 22884.
Fleet Air Arm Museum and Concorde Exhibition   Yeovilton Tel 0278 75595.
Yeovil Ski Centre   Tel 0935 21702.
  Historic Houses, Castles and Gardens
Brympton d'Evercy   Tel 0935 862528.
Clapton Court Gardens and Plant Centre   Crewkerne Tel 0460 73220/72200.
Lytes Cary Manor (NT)   Somerton Tel 045822 3297.

York	**Forte Travelodge**		**£40**
Tel 0973 531823			**L**
A64 Bilbrough Nr York North Yorkshire			Map 15 C6

On the eastbound carriageway of the A64, 7 miles south-west of York and 5 miles north-east of Tadcaster. *Rooms 40. Access, Amex, Visa.*

York	**Abbey Park Resort Hotel**	57%	**£86**
Tel 0904 658301 Fax 0904 621224			**H**
The Mount York North Yorkshire YO2 2BN			Map 15 C6

One mile from the city centre, this hotel offers modern facilities behind a Georgian facade. children up to 14 stay free in parents' room. Conferences for up to 140. *Rooms 85. Access, Amex, Visa,* 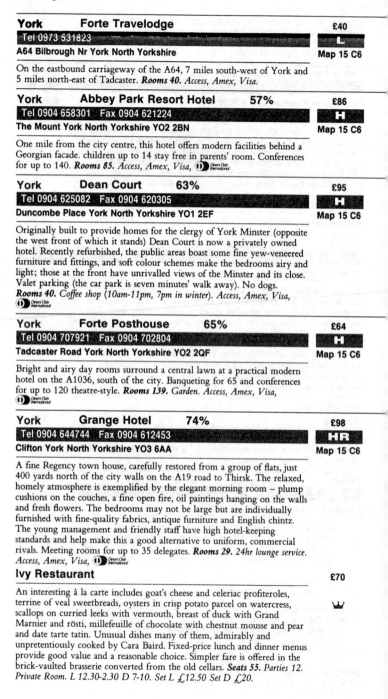 *Diners Club International*

York	**Dean Court**	63%	**£95**
Tel 0904 625082 Fax 0904 620305			**H**
Duncombe Place York North Yorkshire YO1 2EF			Map 15 C6

Originally built to provide homes for the clergy of York Minster (opposite the west front of which it stands) Dean Court is now a privately owned hotel. Recently refurbished, the public areas boast some fine yew-veneered furniture and fittings, and soft colour schemes make the bedrooms airy and light; those at the front have unrivalled views of the Minster and its close. Valet parking (the car park is seven minutes' walk away). No dogs. *Rooms 40. Coffee shop (10am-11pm, 7pm in winter). Access, Amex, Visa,* *Diners Club International*

York	**Forte Posthouse**	65%	**£64**
Tel 0904 707921 Fax 0904 702804			**H**
Tadcaster Road York North Yorkshire YO2 2QF			Map 15 C6

Bright and airy day rooms surround a central lawn at a practical modern hotel on the A1036, south of the city. Banqueting for 65 and conferences for up to 120 theatre-style. *Rooms 139. Garden. Access, Amex, Visa,* *Diners Club International*

York	**Grange Hotel**	74%	**£98**
Tel 0904 644744 Fax 0904 612453			**H R**
Clifton York North Yorkshire YO3 6AA			Map 15 C6

A fine Regency town house, carefully restored from a group of flats, just 400 yards north of the city walls on the A19 road to Thirsk. The relaxed, homely atmosphere is exemplified by the elegant morning room – plump cushions on the couches, a fine open fire, oil paintings hanging on the walls and fresh flowers. The bedrooms may not be large but are individually furnished with fine-quality fabrics, antique furniture and English chintz. The young management and friendly staff have high hotel-keeping standards and help make this a good alternative to uniform, commercial rivals. Meeting rooms for up to 35 delegates. *Rooms 29. 24hr lounge service. Access, Amex, Visa,* *Diners Club International*

Ivy Restaurant £70

An interesting à la carte includes goat's cheese and celeriac profiteroles, terrine of veal sweetbreads, oysters in crisp potato parcel on watercress, scallops on curried leeks with vermouth, breast of duck with Grand Marnier and rösti, millefeuille of chocolate with chestnut mousse and pear and date tarte tatin. Unusual dishes many of them, admirably and unpretentiously cooked by Cara Baird. Fixed-price lunch and dinner menus provide good value and a reasonable choice. Simpler fare is offered in the brick-vaulted brasserie converted from the old cellars. *Seats 55. Parties 12. Private Room. L 12.30-2.30 D 7-10. Set L £12.50 Set D £20.*

York Hill Hotel 58%

£59
H

Tel 0904 790777

60 York Road Acomb York North Yorkshire YO2 5LW

Map 15 C6

Two miles from the centre of York, this handsome Georgian house stands
in just under an acre of walled garden. Owners Peter and Debbie
Blackburn are welcoming hosts, and relaxation is easy in the comfortably
traditional lounge and little bar. Half the bedrooms are suitable for family
occupation. *Rooms 10. Garden. Closed 4 weeks Dec/Jan. Access, Amex, Visa,*
Diners Club International

York Holiday Inn 68%

£129
H

Tel 0904 648111 Fax 0904 610317

Tower Street York North Yorkshire YO1 1SB

Map 15 C6

Modern redbrick hotel whose city-centre location overlooking Clifford's
Tower is a major asset. Well-appointed bedrooms include Executive Club
rooms and suites. Conference facilities for up to 150 delegates. *Rooms 128.
Access, Amex, Visa,* Diners Club

York Judges Lodging 64%

£91
H

Tel 0904 638733 Fax 0904 679947

9 Lendal York North Yorkshire YO1 2AQ

Map 15 C6

A fine Georgian town house which was the offical residence of the Assize
Court judges from 1806. It remained such until 1977, when it was restored
and opened as a hotel. Two curved stone stairs lead you from the courtyard
to the lovely central door, beyond which is a beautifully proprotioned hall
with a small lounge area. Arched redbrick ceilings add character to the
cellar bar and the bedrooms are delightful, with antiques, fine paintings,
prints and lots of extras. *Rooms 13. Garden. Access, Amex, Visa,* Diners Club International

York Melton's

£48
R

Tel 0904 634341

7 Scarcroft Road York North Yorkshire YO2 1ND

Map 15 C6

Michael Hjort's short, seasonally-changing menu is a happy mixture of
tried and trusted combinations like roast monkfish with Noilly Prat sauce
or chocolate and orange cake, and more novel ideas such as faggot of skate
and bacon with red wine sauce and 'spaghetti' vegetables or aubergine and
coconut loaf. To ring the changes there are always daily specials with the
emphasis on seafood on Tuesdays and vegetarian dishes on Thursdays.
Desserts might include a daily special of hot apple soufflé with cider and
apple sauce or a miniature Sussex Pond pudding with custard. Both
mineral water and coffee are free to diners and prices are inclusive of
service. Short, diverse and sensibly priced wine list. *Seats 28. Private Room.
L 12.30-2 D 7-10. Closed Sun & Mon, 3 weeks Xmas/New Year, last wk
Aug. Access, Visa.*

York Middlethorpe Hall 79%

£138
HR

Tel 0904 641241 Fax 0904 620176

Bishopthorpe Road York North Yorkshire YO2 1QB

Map 15 C6

A fine example of a William and Mary house, magnificently restored by
Historic House Hotels. Middlethorpe Hall stands in well-tended grounds
close to York racecourse. Its classical exterior is complemented by a
carefully decorated and furnished interior; first impressions as you enter the
hall are flagstones, a log fire, fine paintings and a splendid carved oak
staircase. A wealth of fine-quality furniture includes some good antiques,
and the chandeliered drawing room boasts numerous beautifully
upholstered sofas and armchairs. Bedrooms are of a similarly high standard,
with plenty of extras; Edwardian-style bathrooms are graced by brass
fittings as well as high-class toiletries, generous towels and bathrobes. No
children under eight; no dogs. Smart meeting and conference facilities.
Rooms 29. Garden, croquet. Access, Amex, Visa, Diners Club International

see over

Restaurant   £100

A formal dining room with panelled walls, professional service and choice
of menus. The fixed-price lunch and dinner menus offer a good choice
with dishes that show a good understanding of classical cooking skills from
chef Kevin Francksen: chicken liver parfait with tomato chutney and
toasted brioche, sautéed kidneys turbigo in a devilled sauce, millefeuille of
pineapple and meringue with mango coulis. The carte is short but rich in
quality ingredients – goose liver, lobster, Dover sole, venison, pheasant,
partridge – with prices to match. Pudding enthusiasts can revel in a
miniature selection or in a trio of apple puddings (turnover, Calvados
sorbet, cider mousse and cinnamon custard). *Seats 60. Parties 50. Private
Room. L 12.30-2.30 D 7.30-9.45. Set L £15.90 Set D £31.*

| York | Mount Royale | 68% | £70 |

Tel 0904 628856   Fax 0904 611171 **H**

119 The Mount York North Yorkshire YO2 2DA   Map 15 C6

An individual, family-run venture that makes a pleasant alternative to the
uniformity so often found elsewhere. Two fine William IV houses are
joined to make a friendly little hotel on the edge of the city centre.
Antiques and gilt-framed oil paintings help create a welcoming atmosphere
with an air of restrained elegance. There's a homely feel throughout and
the small, oak-panelled cocktail bar is distinctly club-like. Bedrooms each
have their own individuality, although floral fabrics predominate; garden
rooms open on to the garden by way of a verandah. *Rooms 23. Garden,
outdoor swimming pool, sauna, steam room, solarium. Access, Amex, Visa,*
Diners Club International

| York | 19 Grape Lane | | £75 |

Tel 0904 636366 **R**

19 Grape Lane York North Yorkshire YO1 2HU   Map 15 C6

Contemporary English cooking takes centre stage at No. 19, located down
a narrow lane between Stonegate and Low Petergate. Light lunches, maybe
of crispy duck and bacon salad or North Sea fish terrine, are supplemented
by daily blackboard specials which offer the best value. Fixed-price dinner
(with a choice of three or four dishes per course) might include avocado
salad with Stilton dressing, crunchy baked cod with lime butter sauce and
traditional Yorkshire treacle tart. Go à la carte for smoked chicken with
tomato sorbet and beef roulade with Madeira sauce. There's usually a
Colston Bassett Stilton as an alternative to traditional hot puddings like
Yorkshire treacle tart, Eve's pudding and Bakewell tart, or a dish with "a
little of everything". *Seats 34. Parties 20. Private Room. L 12-2
D 7.30-10.30 (Sat from 7). Closed Sun & Mon, 3 days Xmas, 3 days New
Year, 2 weeks Feb, 2 weeks Sep. Set D £18.95. Access, Visa.*

| York | Novotel | 62% | £80 |

Tel 0904 611660   Fax 0904 610925 **H**

Fishergate York North Yorkshire YO1 4AD   Map 15 C6

Uniform, chain hotel, just out of city centre on the A19 Selby Road.
Conference/banqueting facilities for 200/150. *Rooms 124. Indoor swimming
pool. Access, Amex, Visa,* Diners Club International

| York | Royal York Hotel | 65% | £100 |

Tel 0904 653681   Fax 0904 623503 **H**

Station Road York North Yorkshire YO2 2AA   Map 15 C6

Part of Principal Hotels, the large Royal York hotel was built in 1878 as
one of the first great transport hotels. Its Victorian splendour has been
restored in some measure, notably in the fine central staircase and the
Birmantoft tiles in the bar. Top of the accommodation are the large

Executive rooms. The hotel is popular for conferences, with up to 180 delegates accommodated theatre-style. **Rooms 148**. *Pitch & putt. Access, Amex, Visa,*

York   Swallow Hotel   64%   £99

Tel 0904 701000   Fax 0904 702308   **H**

Tadcaster Road York North Yorkshire YO2 2QQ   Map 15 C6

A mile from the city centre on the A1036, the Swallow stands in its own grounds overlooking the historic Knavesmire racecourse. Leisure club, parking for 200+ cars, recently expanded conference facilities (for up to 150 delegates). **Rooms 113.** *Garden, croquet, indoor swimming pool, steam room, spa bath, sauna, solarium, beautician, keep-fit equipment, pitch & putt, coffee shop (11am-11pm). Access, Amex, Visa,*

York   Viking Hotel   69%   £105

Tel 0904 659822   Fax 0904 641793   **H**

North Street York North Yorkshire YO1 1JF   Map 15 C6

Tall, modern Queens Moat Houses hotel by the river between the two main bridges in the city centre. Plenty of style and comfort and a major conference venue with a choice of rooms handling up to 300 delegates. Leisure facilities include a well-equipped, supervised gymnasium. No dogs. **Rooms 188.** *Gymnasium, sauna, solarium, spa bath, golf practice net. Access, Amex, Visa,*

York   Places of Interest

Tourist Information Tel 0904 621756.
Grand Opera House Tel 0904 628877.
Theatre Royal Tel 0904 23568.
York Minster Tel 0904 623608.
York Racecourse Tel 0904 620911.
Flamingo Land Zoo and Family Fun Park Malton Tel 065 386287.
   Historic Houses, Castles and Gardens
Assembly Rooms Tel 0904 61361.
Beningbrough Hall Tel 0904 470666.
Castle Howard Tel 065 384 333.
Merchant Adventurers' Hall Tel 0904 654818.
Treasurer's House (NT) Tel 0904 624247.
Sutton Park Sutton-on-the-Forest Tel 0347 810249.
   Museums and Art Galleries
The Arc Archaeological Resource Centre Tel 0904 654324.
Fairfax House Tel 0904 655543.
Jorvik Viking Centre Tel 0904 643211.
National Railway Museum (Science Museum) Tel 0904 621261.
York Castle Museum Tel 0904 653611.
York City Art Gallery Tel 0904 623839.
York Story Tel 0904 628632.

Yoxford   Satis House   63%   £65

Tel 072 877 418   **H**

Yoxford Saxmundham Suffolk IP16 3EX   Map 6 D2

Set in three acres of parkland alongside the A12, the house dates back to 1817. Charles Dickens was a friend of the original owner and mentioned the house in *Great Expectations*. The entrance hall is paved with York stone and leads to public rooms furnished with antiques. Two of the bedrooms are older in style with large, solid wood half-tester double beds and Edwardian baths and fittings, while others are more modern. No children under 14 or dogs. Owner Chiu Blackmore conjures up Malaysian specialities in the restaurant with a Kenduri feast cooked to order. **Rooms 7.** *Garden, sauna, solarium, spa bath, keep-fit equipment, croquet. Access, Amex, Visa,*

lifetime ™

"With Lifetime - I can book rooms for a night away, while we're all still out and about."

 **cellnet**

The nearest phone.

lifetime ™

With Lifetime - I can arrange lunch with an old friend - when to see the grandchildren and still not miss a wicket."

lifetime™

'We made it - she just caught the 10.15'.

'Could you pick up some ice cream on the way home?'

'I passed Mum - I passed.'

'Sorry - we had a puncture. We'll be there just as soon as we can.'

Portable phones have for far too long been seen as the exclusive privilege of the high flying business executive.

This is now changing, thanks to Cellnet.

Because with Lifetime - our new tariff* for the lower user we intend to make the advantages of mobile communications readily available to anyone whose work, responsibilities or lifestyle, could be made easier, more enjoyable, or more secure, through being able to keep 'in touch' whenever they're out and about.

*available from mid November 1992.

The nearest phone.

For further details call Cellnet on

0800 424 323

Scotland

Aberdeen   Ardoe House   70%   £117

H

Tel 0224 867355   Fax 0224 861283

South Deeside Road Royal Deeside Grampian AB1 5YP   Map 17 D4

Though only a few minutes' drive from the centre of Aberdeen, Ardoe
House enjoys a secluded setting at the end of a winding drive. Its style is
Scottish Baronial, and day rooms retain all their best original features, with
carved oak panelling and handsome ceiling work. The drawing room and
cocktail bar are warm and inviting, and there's a choice of rooms available
for conferences and banquets (for up to 150/200). Bedrooms are
comfortable and well appointed, whether in the main building (some
reached by a fine oak staircase past a stained-glass window) or in the
sympathetically designed modern section, where the majority are located.
Children up to 12 stay free in parents' room. *Rooms 71. Garden, putting,
pétanque. Access, Amex, Visa,* ⓓ *Diners Club International*

Aberdeen   Atlantis   £62

R

Tel 0224 591403

16 Bon Accord Crescent Aberdeen Grampian AB1 2DE   Map 17 D4

Seafood is bought whenever possible from Aberdeen's renowned fish
market, and chef Mark Ronaldson favours a simple approach to preserve
the fresh flavours and textures. Orkney oysters and mussels are favourite
starters, with sole, salmon and king prawns among the most popular main
courses. If you really want to push the boat out try the cold platter with
lobster, oysters, king prawns, mussels, calamari, scallops, smoked salmon
and crab claws. Meat dishes available too, along with a vegetarian option.
*Seats 36. Parties 20. L 12-2 D 6.30-10. Closed L Sat, all Sun, Bank Holidays.
Set L £6. Access, Amex, Visa,* ⓓ *Diners Club International*

Aberdeen   Bucksburn Moat House   69%   £104

H

Tel 0224 713911   Fax 0224 714020

Oldmeldrum Road Bucksburn Aberdeen Grampian AB2 9LN   Map 17 D4

Forty-five new rooms have been added to this ultra-modern hotel between
the city and the airport. Well equipped for leisure and for conferences
(500+ theatre-style). *Rooms 144. Gymnasium, indoor swimming pool, sauna,
solarium, steam room. Access, Amex, Visa,* ⓓ *Diners Club International*

Aberdeen   Caledonian Thistle   68%   £134

H

Tel 0224 640233   Fax 0224 641627

Aberdeen Grampian AB9 1HE   Map 17 D4

City-centre hotel with Regency-style day rooms, double-glazed bedrooms
and a choice of eating places. *Rooms 80. Sauna. Access, Amex, Visa,*
ⓓ *Diners Club International*

Aberdeen   Copthorne Hotel   68%   £122

H

Tel 0224 630404   Fax 0224 640573

122 Huntly Street Aberdeen Grampian AB1 1SU   Map 17 D4

City-centre hotel behind a converted warehouse facade. Good standards of
accommodation in Classic and Connoisseur rooms and suites. 24hr room
service. Conference facilities for 200+. No dogs. *Rooms 89. Access, Amex,
Visa,* ⓓ *Diners Club International*

Aberdeen   Faraday's   NEW   £50

R

Tel 0224 869666

2 Kirk Brae Cults Aberdeen Grampian AB1 9SQ   Map 17 D4

On the A93 Aberdeen-Braemar road, Faraday's is a converted generating
station built of granite. Inside it's pure Victoriana, with bags of atmosphere
and good food prepared by chef-patron John Inches: grilled aubergine with

pesto, spicy kidney and bean soup, gratin of rock turbot with mushroom pasta, an excellent and satisfying oxtail dish. *Seats 42. Parties 32. L 12-1.30 D 7-9.30. Closed L Mon, all Sun, 2 weeks Jan. Set D £24.50. Access, Visa.*

Aberdeen	Gerard's	£67

Tel 0224 639500 **R**

50 Chapel Street Aberdeen Grampian AB1 1SN Map 17 D4

Reliable, sound cooking – French and international – is the hallmark of Gerard Flecher's city-centre restaurant, well on its way to its 20th birthday. Business and fast one-course meals are available at lunchtime, while a relaxed evening meal could start with chicken liver paté, smoked fish pancake or wild mushrooms served on a garlic bread crouton and progress to grilled halibut, a chargrilled steak or a speciality double of veal piccata in egg and cheese batter with oatmeal-coated mallard duck escalopes on a mild pepper sauce. Lastly, perhaps crepe Mont Blanc or a clafoutis with cherries and apples. *Seats 80. Parties 50. Private Room. L 12-2.30 D 6-11. Closed Sun, Local Bank Holidays, 2 days Xmas, 2 days New Year. Set L £9.45 & £13.50 Set D £18.50. Access, Amex, Visa,* **Diners Club International**

Aberdeen	Silver Darling	£64

Tel 0224 576229 **R**

Pocra Quay North Pier Aberdeen Grampian AB2 1DQ Map 17 D4

A French speciality seafood restaurant overlooking the city and old port from the farthest point of the North Quay. Most of the fish is barbecued in full view of diners through a large kitchen window. Most, equally, have accompanying sauces of individual appeal: a coulis of green peppers with the Scottish salmon; dill butter sauce with a *symphonie de brochette* of market-fresh fish and shellfish. Short, carefully annotated wine list. Booking is essential. *Seats 35. Parties 30. L 12-2 D 7-10. Closed L Sat & Sun (all Sun Dec-Easter), 2 weeks Xmas. Access, Amex, Visa,* **Diners Club International**

Aberdeen	Stakis Tree Tops	63%	£130

Tel 0224 313377   Fax 0224 312028 **H**

161 Springfield Road Aberdeen Grampian AB9 2QH Map 17 D4

In a residential area on the western edge of the city, a hotel offering singles, doubles, twins, Lady Executive rooms, family rooms and a suite, all complete with the expected up-to-date accessories. There's a well-equipped leisure club and large, comprehensive conference facilities catering for up to 620 delegates. *Rooms 112. Indoor swimming pool, gymnasium, spa bath, sauna, tennis. Access, Amex, Visa,* **Diners Club International**

Aberdeen	Travel Inn	£42

Tel 0224 821217 **L**

Murcar Bridge of Don Aberdeen Grampian AB2 8BP Map 17 D4

Rooms 40. Access, Amex, Visa, **Diners Club International**

Aberdeen	Places of Interest

Tourist Information   Tel 0224 632727.
St Andrew's Cathedral   Tel 0224 640290.
St Machar's Cathedral   Tel 0224 485988.
St Mary's R.C. Cathedral   Tel 0224 640160
Caimhill Ski Slope   Tel 0224 311781.
Alford Slope   Tel 0336 2251.
Beach Leisure Centre   Tel 0224 647647.
  Theatres and Concert Halls
Aberdeen Music Hall   Tel 0224 632080.

Aberdeen Arts Centre   Tel 0224 635208.
Capitol Theatre   Tel 0224 588345.
Haddo House Hall   Tel 06515 770 *By Tarves 10 miles.*
His Majesty's Theatre   Tel 0224 641122.
  Historic Houses, Castles and Gardens
Castle Fraser (NT)   Sauchen. Tel 033 03 463.
Cruickshank Botanic Gardens   Tel 0224 272704.
Crathes Castle Garden   Banchory. Tel 033044 525.
Drum Castle   Tel 033 08 204.
Duthie Park and Winter Gardens   Tel 0224 583155.
Kildrummy Castle Gardens   Alford Tel 09755 71264.
Seaton Park   Don Street.
Pitmedden Garden (NT)   Udny. Tel 065 13 2352.
  Museums and Art Galleries
Art Gallery/James Dun's House   Tel 0224 646333.
Peacock Artspace   Tel 0224 639539.
Maritime Museum/Provost Ross's House   Tel 0224 585788.
University Marischal Museum   Tel 0224 480241 ext 243.
Grampian Transport Museum   Alford. Tel 09755 62292.
Crombie Woolen Mill   Woodside Tel 0224 483201.

Aberdeen Airport	Aberdeen Marriott Hotel	72%	£135
Tel 0224 770011 Fax 0224 722347			H
Riverview Drive Fairburn Dyce Aberdeen Grampian AB2 0AZ			Map 17 D4

Formerly the Holiday Inn, this predominantly business hotel stands about five miles from the city centre close to the airport. Banqueting and conference facilities for up to 400. *Rooms 154. Indoor swimming pool, sauna, spa bath, solarium, keep-fit facilites, coffee shop (7am-11pm). Access, Amex, Visa,* Diners Club International.

Aberdeen Airport	Skean Dhu Hotel	65%	£96
Tel 0224 725252 Fax 0224 723745			H
Argyll Road Dyce Aberdeen Grampian AB2 0DU			Map 17 D4

Convenienlty close to the aiport terminal this Mount Charlotte hotel combines roomy, well-equipped bedrooms with a busy conference trade. *Rooms 148. Garden. Access, Amex, Visa,* Diners Club International.

Aberfeldy	Farleyer House	70%	£90
Tel 0887 820332 Fax 0887 829430			HR
Aberfeldy Tayside PH15 2JE			Map 17 C4

Hard by Castle Menzies, the 16th century mansion hidden by mature pine, beech and oak trees, is steeped in Menzies clan history. Bill and Frances Atkins make their house available to guests whose comfort and ease Bill tirelessly attends. Lounge, library and bar offer a choice of homely settings along with great comfort; their upper floor location providing fine views across the Tay valley. Bedrooms are no less appealing and exude the same air of timeless serenity. Guests have free use of the leisure facilities at the nearby Newmore Club. No dogs. *Rooms 11. Garden.*

Atkins Restaurant   ★   £90

In the restaurant (no smoking) the fixed-price dinner menu of five courses changes every day, a showcase for the talent and imagination of Frances Atkins. A typical menu in May shows her style: millefeuille of duck with mango or boudin of salmon with chive sauce; asparagus soup; saddle of lamb with a confit of shallots and artichoke mousse or poached sea trout with spinach, saffron pasta and a prawn sauce; British cheeses served with oatcakes; sorbets and fresh fruit or an assiette of chocolate or honey and whisky parfait; coffee and petits fours. The restaurant is now supplemented by a bistro open every lunchtime and evening. *Seats 34. Parties. Private Room. L by arrangement D 7.30-8.30 Meals (Bistro 10-2 & 6.30-9.30). Set D £35.00. Access, Amex, Visa,* Diners Club International.

Aberfeldy   Places of Interest

Tourist Information   Tel 0887 20276.

Aberfoyle   Braeval Old Mill   £68

| Tel 087 72 711 | **R** |

Braeval By Aberfoyle Central FK8 3UY   Map 17 B5

An old stone mill, standing on the A81 a mile south of Aberfoyle, with
exposed stone walls, pavement slab floor, black polished wood tables and
fabric wall hangings. Chef-patron Nick Nairn uses only first-rate
ingredients in dishes like saddle of roe deer with red cabbage and a game
and chocolate sauce or fillet of John Dory with scallops, mussels and a
vegetable jus. Dinner (which begins with some delicious nibbles – chopped
gravad lax on toast, mini-quiche – while one chooses from the menu) is a
four-course, fixed-price affair beginning with the day's soup and continuing
with a choice of three or so dishes at subsequent stages. Well-balanced wine
list with a good choice outside France, and an interesting house selection.
Sunday lunch (£17.50) is popular and usually features roast sirloin of beef.
*Seats 32. Parties 32. L weekdays by arrangement, Sun 12.30-1.30 D 7-9.30.
Closed D Sun & Mon, Bank Holidays, 2 weeks Nov. Set D £24.50. Access,
Visa.*

Aberfoyle   Places of Interest

Tourist information   Tel 08772 352.

Abington   Forte Travelodge   NEW   £40

| Tel 0800 850 950 | **L** |

**A74/M74 Welcome Break Service Area Abington Biggar
Strathclyde ML12 6RG**   Map 12 C2

At the junction of the A74 with the M74 at the Welcome Break Service
Area, Abington. Opens Winter '92/'93. *Access, Amex, Visa.*

Achiltibuie   Summer Isles   64%   £69

| Tel 085 482 282   Fax 085 482 251 | **HR** |

Achiltibuie by Ullapool Highland IV26 2YG   Map 16 B2

A friendly family-run hotel in a particularly beautiful area. Public areas
include a new sitting room with TV, honesty bar and games, plus a small
study with a telephone. There are no TVs or phones in the neat, light
bedrooms most of which are in Norwegian pine-log cabins a few steps
from the main building. Owners Mark and Geraldine Irvine will be happy
to give advice about fishing, bird-watching and walking. No children
under eight. *Rooms 10. Garden, coffee shop (10am-8pm in high season).
Closed mid Oct-Easter. No credit cards.*

Restaurant   £70

There are spectacular views of the Summer Isles to be had from the dining
room. Chris Firth-Bernard makes good use of top-quality produce, almost
all of which is of local provenance. The five-course dinner, served at 8
o'clock, offers no choice, but the menu is displayed at reception so
negotiation in advance is possible. A dinner in April comprised broccoli
and coriander soup with a fresh oatmeal loaf, terrine of rabbit and herbs,
halibut with steamed mussels, the sweet trolley and a selection of cheeses.
Seats 26. Parties 8. D only at 8. Set D £29.

Advie   Tulchan Lodge   77%   £320*
Tel 080 75 200   Fax 080 75 234   **H**

Advie Nr Grantown-on-Spey Highland PH26 3PW   Map 16 C3

One of the finest Edwardian shooting lodges in Scotland, Tulchan
continues to offer some of the best fishing on 8 miles of the Spey – both
banks (each beat has its own ghillie and luxurious fishing cabin where
lunch is served) – and shooting on the 25,000-acre estate (grouse, pheasant,
duck flighting and roe deer stalking). The atmosphere is much more that
of a country house weekend party than a hotel with long-serving butler
and general factotum, Joe, tending to guests' needs in immensely civilised
surrounding; antiques, important paintings, hunting trophies, an elegant
drawing room, button-back leather armchairs in the panelled library and
spacious, sumptuously decorated bedrooms with bathrooms designed to
pamper with huge bath sheets and top-quality toiletries. Dinner, for
residents only, is served butler style at a single large polished table weighed
down with silver candelabra and table decorations. The simple no-choice
menu leans heavily on Estate produce with saddle of venison or baked
salmon providing a typical main dish. *Full-board terms only. Mid-April
to September is the summer fishing season, October to January it is open
only for shooting parties and February to early April it is closed altogether.
Dogs in kennels only. *Rooms 11. Garden, game fishing, shooting, snooker,
tennis, clay-pigeon shooting. Closed Oct-Apr except by prior arrangement.*

Airth   Airth Castle   68%   £80
Tel 032 483 411   Fax 032 483 419   **H**

Airth by Falkirk Central FK2 8JF   Map 17 C5

Careful restoration has kept a sense of history at the castle, where a recent
extension programme has added more bedrooms and another two
conference rooms (up to 400 delegates can now be accommodated). Public
areas are splendid, with fine proportions, ornate ceilings and elegant
traditional furniture. Modern-day facilities are provided in bedrooms that
range from spacious Executive-style to romantic four-poster. Leisure
amenities are in the country club at the end of the drive. No dogs.
*Rooms 74. Garden, indoor swimming pool, sauna, solarium, spa bath, keep-fit
equipment, snooker, children's play areas, baby-listening. Access, Amex, Visa,*

Airth   Places of Interest

Bannockburn Museum (NT)   Tel 0780 812664 *11 miles.*

Alexandria   Cameron House   81%   £138
Tel 0389 55565   Fax 0389 59522   **HR**

Loch Lomond Alexandria Strathclyde G83 8QZ   Map 12 B1

Expensive refurbishment and a sympathetic extension have turned a
Georgian house into an elegant hotel with most impressive leisure facilities.
Just off the A82, it enjoys a splendid location by Loch Lomond on a large
estate that includes time-share lodges. Peaceful, country house-style day
rooms in the original house contrast with the more lively bar that
overlooks the leisure club. Spacious bedrooms are individually decorated
with stylish fabrics and boast comfortable armchairs; there are huge, soft
towels and bathrobes in the bathrooms. Smiling staff offer a warm
welcome and high standards of service. Families are well catered for, with a
daily crèche (normally to 5pm, but extended to 9pm on Thurs & Fri) and
baby-sitting available. No dogs. *Rooms 68. Indoor swimming pools, steam
room, sauna, solarium, spa bath, squash, badminton, snooker, gymnasium,
hairdressing, beauty salon, crèche, kiosk, 9-hole golf course, tennis, croquet,
clay-pigeon shooting, watersports centre, marina, fishing, mountain bikes. Access,
Amex, Visa,*

Georgian Room   £75

Sparkling chandeliers, rich drapes and quality silverware create a luxurious
setting for Jeff Bland's serious, sophisticated cooking; the short à la carte
menu seems to have learned something from the decor. Casserole of
langoustines with woodland mushrooms and black, ginger-flavoured
noodles and a lobster and lentil sauce; supreme of chicken with leek and
truffle ravioli, and geranium and blackcurrant parfait served with a praline
basket of fruits are indicative of the involved style. An imaginative, six-
course Celebration menu is also offered – for those wishing to become
even more involved, plus fixed-price daily menus. *Seats 60. L 12-3 D 7-10.
Set L £15.50 Set D £27.50.*

Alexandria   Place of Interest

Balloch Castle Country Park   Tel 0389 58216.

Alloa   Gean House   77%   £139
| Tel 0259 219275   Fax 0259 213827 | **HR** |
Gean Park Tullibody Road Alloa Central FK10 2HS   Map 17 C5

A stern grade A listed Lutyens-style mansion, dating from 1912, set in
mature parkland of oak and horse chestnut looking across the Ochil hills.
John Taylor consulted descendants of the original owner before embarking
on the painstaking, and much needed, restoration that has turned Gean
House into a most impressive hotel. An elegantly proportioned drawing
room, with minstrel's gallery and vast inglenook, is the centrepiece;
adjacent, the walnut-panelled dining room enjoys views down the formal
rose garden and a small library provides a cosy retreat. The barrel-vaulted
Board Room serves for private meetings or parties. Individual bedroom
decor, carefully understated, shows off some fine old workmanship to great
effect: original tiles and plumbing have been stunningly recreated in the
bathrooms. No dogs. *Rooms 10. Garden. Access, Amex, Visa,*

Restaurant   £75

Dinner is an interesting balance of serious food and private house
informality. The limited choice, fixed-price menus exhibit a further facet
of Tony Mifsud's talents (he was also involved in the interior design).
Combinations like red cabbage and juniper berry sauce with roast mallard,
and fillet of pork with a caraway and paprika sauce work well together.
Tony's special bread-and-butter pudding should be ordered in advance, but
if you forget, it is worth the 30 minutes wait. No smoking. *Seats 30.
Parties 50. Private Room. L 12-2 D 7-9.30. Set L £15 Set D £27.50.*

Altnaharra   Altnaharra Hotel   60%   £110*
| Tel &   Fax 054 981 222 | **H** |
Altnaharra By Lairg Highland IV27 4UE   Map 16 B2

Very much a place for the discerning angler, this remote 19th-century inn
keeps fishing records that go back over 100 years. Ghillies can be hired and
there's a chalet offering rod racks, deep freeze and drying facilities. Healthy
walks in lovely country are another popular option. There are no TVs or
telephones in the airy bedrooms, among which are two annexe cottages
ideal for anglers' families. *Half-board terms only. Rooms 20. Garden, game
fishing. Closed Oct-early Mar. Access, Visa.*

Alyth   Drumnacree House   £50
| Tel 082 83 2194 | **RR** |
St Ninians Road Alyth Tayside PH11 8AP   Map 17 C4

A keen amateur cook during his 20 years in the oil industry, Allan Cull is
now testing his culinary talent on paying customers. Enthusiasm and a
good deal of skill are evident in the short fixed-price dinner menu that
might include a supreme of chicken on a bed of onion confit with a grain
mustard sauce, roast gigot of lamb scented with rosemary and salmon
baked with fresh herbs; home-cured smoked salmon usually features

among the starters. In addition there are always a number of Cajun
specialities. The pink linen and candles at dinner change to green check
cloths and paper napkins for the informal à la carte lunchtime offerings.
Seats 24. *Parties 40. L 12-2 D 7-10. Closed D Sun, all Mon, 25 & 26 Dec,
1 & 2 Jan. Set L £10.25 Set D £17.50. Access, Visa.*

Rooms   £60

Five neat bedrooms offer modest comfort with duvets, TVs, tea and coffee
kit and en-suite shower rooms. **Rooms 5.** *Garden.*

Alyth   Lands of Loyal Hotel   62%   £65

| Tel 082 83 3151   Fax 082 83 3313 | **H** |

Alyth By Blairgowrie Tayside PH11 8JQ   Map 17 C4

Owned by the Howell family for three years, the hotel is a sandstone
mansion built after the Battle of Waterloo and added to over the years.
Most splendid of the day rooms is the galleried main hall with oak
panelling and a blazing fire in winter. Bedrooms offer practical
accommodation with either white melamine or older traditional-style
furniture. **Rooms 11.** *Garden. Access, Amex, Visa,* 🌐 Diners Club International

Annan   Warmanbie Hotel   59%   £61

| Tel 0461 204015 | **H** |

Annan Dumfries & Galloway DG12 5LL   Map 13 C4

Home of the Duncan family since 1953, this Georgian house by the river
Annan was converted to a hotel in 1983. There's still a homely, private
house feel about the day rooms, and a traditional look to the bedrooms,
which offer easy chairs, books, mini-bars and tea-makers. Mainly modern
bathrooms, except the four-poster room which has a Victorian tub. A
holiday cottage (Warmanbie Lodge) on the estate sleeps four people in two
bedrooms. **Rooms 7.** *Garden, game fishing, clay-pigeon shooting. Access, Amex,
Visa.*

Anstruther   Cellar   £70

| Tel 0333 310378 | **R** |

24 East Green Anstruther Fife KY10 3AA   Map 17 D5

Tucked away behind the harbour, the Cellar is full of character with
natural stone walls and, for most of the year, real fires burning in old black
grates at each end of the room – a charming setting for Peter Jukes's
cooking, which combines simplicity with sophistication. Fish from nearby
Pittenweem harbour is the mainstay of the menu and is sympathetically
handled in dishes like hot quiche of lobster, langoustines and smoked
salmon, grilled halibut with lime juice and butter, and monkfish roasted on
the bone with tomato and basil sauce by the side. The wine list is fabulous,
and the prices are fair – note the selection of Chablis, Montrachets, Alsace
and Riojas; the New World is equally well represented. **Seats 30.** *Parties
30. L 12.30-1.30 D 7.30-9. Closed L Mon-Thu, all Sun, also D Mon
Oct-May, Bank Holidays, 10 days Xmas. Set D £22.50-27.50. Access, Amex,
Visa.*

Anstruther   Places of Interest

Scottish Fisheries Museum   Tel 0333 311073.

Appin   Invercreran Hotel   67%   £82

| Tel 063 173 414   Fax 063 173 532 | **H** |

Appin Glen Creran Highland PA38 4BJ   Map 17 B4

A long, low-level, modern hotel overlooking the river and Glen
Creran. 25 acres of mature gardens and woodland surround the hotel. A
semi-circular part at the centre of the building is fronted by balconied
terracing and houses lounge and dining areas; drinks service comes from a
neat dispense bar. Downstairs are master bedrooms with spacious tiled

bathrooms, all with showers and bidets. No children under five. Dogs in kennels only. **Rooms 9.** *Garden, sauna. Closed 16 Nov-28 Feb (except 29 Dec-3 Jan). Access, Visa.*

Ardentinny   Ardentinny Hotel   59%   £78

Tel 036 981 209   Fax 036 981 345   **H**

Loch Long Ardentinny Nr Dunoon Strathclyde PA23 8TR   Map 17 B5

A former droving inn on the A880 by Loch Long, Ardentinny offers comfortable accommodation with the bonus of stunning views of the loch and surrounding mountains. There's a selection of malt whiskies to be had in the Viking and Lauder bars, where yachtsmen and fishermen take their ease. Bedrooms are good-sized, neat and bright, with white units or period furniture; some have showers only. **Rooms 11.** *Garden, croquet, fishing, hotel boat, mountain bikes. Closed Nov-mid Mar. Access, Amex, Visa,* 💳

Ardentinny   Places of Interest

Younger Botanic Garden   Benmore Tel 0369 6261 *7 miles.*

Arduaine   Loch Melfort Hotel   63%   £90

Tel 085 22 233   Fax 085 22 214   **H**

Arduaine By Oban Argyll Strathclyde PA34 4XG   Map 17 B5

Philip and Rosalind Lewis offer guests a comfortable and relaxing break at their peaceful hotel facing south across Asknish Bay. The scenery is spectacular, and there are superb views from both main-house and Cedar wing bedrooms. The latter are connected by a covered walkway; rooms have either a patio or a balcony. Day rooms include two lounges, a panelled library and the Chartroom Bar – a favourite with yachtsmen. **Rooms 27.** *Garden, mooring, kiosk. Closed Jan & Feb. Access, Visa.*

Arisaig   Arisaig House   75%   £159

Tel 068 75 622   Fax 068 75 626   **HR**

Beasdale Arisaig Highland PH39 4NR   Map 17 A4

Follow the Mallaig road alongside the spectacular West Highland railway: your rewards on arrival are grounds rich in redwood and oak, roses and rhododendrons, and vistas of Moidart and the Ardnamurchan peninsula. The house is of Victorian stone, the interior redolent of 1930s' reconstruction. Hosts Ruth and John Smither and their family perfectly match the mood and their aim is "to give guests a comfortable, relaxing and happy stay". Views from south- and west-facing bedrooms are superb, decor fresh, light and individual and housekeeping immaculate; comfort derives from large beds and easy chairs, the luxury added by bathrobes, good toiletries and bidets in the bathrooms. No children under 10. No dogs. **Rooms 15.** *Garden, croquet, snooker, helipad. Closed mid Nov-early Mar. Access, Visa,* 💳

Restaurant   £85

The nightly menus make excellent use of locally bought meat or fish, and many of the vegetables and herbs come from the hotel's gardens. Cullen skink served with hot onion bread, pan-fried scallops on a tomato and ginger confit or terrine of sweet peppers could precede Dover sole, lobster, rack of Scottish lamb or sliced loin of venison set in a nest of forest mushrooms and bacon. Desserts might include iced lemon parfait and hot chocolate soufflé served with pistachio ice cream. Fixed-price à la carte (three or four courses) and table d'hote. Nightly vegetarian menu. Lunch is a lighter affair of sandwiches, salads and omelettes. No smoking in the dining room. **Seats 36.** *Parties 8. L 12.30-2 D 7.30-8.30. Set D £29.50 & £35/£40.*

Auchterarder   Auchterarder House   75%   £130

Tel 0764 63646/7   Fax 0764 62939   **HR**

Auchterarder Tayside PH3 1DZ   Map 17 C5

A baronial-style mansion hotel popular with corporate clients and boasting
many fine features: carved oak panelling in the central hall, ribbed ceilings
and marble fireplace in the day rooms, a characterful billiard room bar,
and charming conservatory. The Brown family have added the warm
welcome and many homely touches like original paintings, an abundance
of fresh flowers and numerous objets d'art. Bedroom decor varies, but all
have extras both luxurious (like a cut-glass decanter of good sherry) and
practical (iron and ironing board). Many of the bathrooms include bidets
and separate showers. No children under 10. *Rooms 15. Garden, croquet,
pitch & putt, putting green. Access, Amex, Visa,*

Restaurant   £90

Jacket and tie are 'de rigueur' for dinner in the gracious, dado-panelled
dining room here. The short, five-course, fixed price dinner changes daily:
sautéed chicken livers with smoked salmon croutons, and langoustine
mousse may be followed by a beetroot borsht or carrot and orange soup
before a main course that might be venison pie, fillet of beef with Stilton
cream sauce or Tay salmon with hollandaise. Passion fruit bavarois and
fresh fruit savarin typify the puddings. Reservations are essential for both
lunch and dinner. No smoking. **Seats 25. Parties 60. Private Room.**
L 12-2.30 D 7-9.30. Set L £18.50 Set D £27.

Auchterarder   Gleneagles Hotel   86%   £195

Tel 0764 62231   Fax 0764 62134   **H**

Auchterarder Tayside PH3 1NF   Map 17 C5

The name is synonymous with golf but this resort hotel has almost
everything: a Champneys Health Spa in the leisure centre, Jackie Stewart's
Shooting School, the Mark Phillips Equestrian Centre and a shopping
arcade which includes such famous names as Harvey Nichols, Mappin and
Webb, Burberry's and even a branch of the Bank of Scotland. This is a
grand hotel in every sense of the word with large, high-ceilinged public
rooms featuring numerous faux-marble fluted columns and pilasters, and
decorative plaster ceilings. The cocktail bar, champagne bar and restaurant
all boast pianists and there is dancing to a live band in the drawing room
each evening. The grading of bedrooms depends largely on size and
outlook; all are individually decorated to the same high standards from the
smallest single room to the twenty full suites. With more staff than guests,
levels of service are kept high. **Rooms 236.** *Garden, indoor swimming pool,
sauna, solarium, whirlpool bath, gymnasium, hairdressing, tennis, squash, golf
courses, pitch & putt, bowling green, croquet, riding, clay-pigeon shooting, coarse
and game fishing, snooker, valeting, shopping arcade, bank, post office. Access,
Amex, Visa,* ●

Auchterarder   Places of Interest

Tourist Information   Tel 0764 63450

Auchterhouse   Old Mansion House   68%   £90

Tel 082 626 366   Fax 082 626 400   **HR**

Auchterhouse By Dundee Tayside DD3 0QN   Map 17 C5

Seven miles from Dundee on the B954, a 16th-century Scottish baronial
house has been skilfully converted by Nigel and Eva Bell to a charming
and relaxed hotel. Some nice architectural features include the vaulted
entrance hall, an open Jacobean fireplace and a splendidly ornate 17th-
century plasterwork ceiling. Pleasantly furnished bedrooms – two are
family suites with separate children's bedrooms – have good bathrooms
well stocked with toiletries. **Rooms 6.** *Garden, croquet, outdoor swimming
pool, squash, tennis. Closed Xmas, 1 week Jan. Access, Amex, Visa,* ●

Restaurant £66

Much local produce is used for the varied carte that is supplemented by a
separate vegetarian menu. No under-10s at night. No smoking. *Seats 50.
Parties 20. Private Room. L 12-2 D 7-9.30 (Sun to 9). Set L £10.95.*

Aviemore   Aviemore Highlands Hotel   61%   £70

Tel 0479 810771   Fax 0479 811473   **H**

Aviemore Centre Aviemore Highland PH22 1PJ   Map 17 C4

On the new A9 Perth to Inverness road, a modern hotel popular for both
business and pleasure, with banqueting/conference facilities for around 200,
and amenities for families. Children up to 14 can stay free in their parents'
room. *Rooms 103. Access, Amex, Visa,*

Aviemore   Stakis Aviemore Four Seasons   70%   £96

Tel 0479 810681   Fax 0479 810534   **H**

Aviemore Highland PH22 1PF   Map 17 C4

A high-rise hotel at the heart of the skiing centre, with views of the Spey
Valley and the Cairngorms. Centrally-heated bedrooms with smart
darkwood furniture range from singles to triples. Main day room is a
bright, picture-windowed lounge. Conference facilities for 120. *Rooms 89.
Garden, indoor swimming pool, sauna, spa bath, solarium, steam bath,
gymnasium, ski school, coffee shop (10am-5pm). Access, Amex, Visa,*

Aviemore   Stakis Coylumbridge Resort Hotel   61%   £99*

Tel 0479 810661   Fax 0479 810862   **H**

Aviemore Highland PH22 1QN   Map 17 C4

Skiing is the thing at Aviemore, but this sprawling modern hotel caters
admirably for all sorts of activities for both adults and children. It's also
geared up for large conferences (maximum 750 delegates). All the
bedrooms are suitable for family use, and baby-sitting, baby-listening and
(at busy times) a creche are provided. *Half-board terms only. Rooms 175.
Indoor swimming pool, spa bath, sauna, steam bath, solarium, beauty & hair
salon, tennis, archery. Access, Amex, Visa,*

Aviemore   Places of Interest

Tourist Information   Tel 0479 810363.
Strathspey Steam Railway   Tel 0479 810725.
Stakis Aviemore Centre Ice Rink   Tel 0479 810624.
Drambuie Dry Ski Slope   Aviemore Centre Tel 0479 810310.
Cairngorm Reindeer Centre   Tel 0479 861228.
Cairngorm Chairlift Company   Tel 0479 861261.

Ayr   Caledonian Hotel   64%   £110

Tel 0292 269331   Fax 0292 610722   **H**

Dalblair Road Ayr Strathclyde KA7 1UG   Map 12 B2

Town-centre hotel with 114 bedrooms, leisure facilities and a new
conference suite (for up to 200). Many bedrooms suitable for families.
Within easy reach of eight golf courses, thus popular for sporting breaks.
Jarvis. *Rooms 114. Indoor swimming pool, gymnasium, spa bath, sauna,
solarium, snooker. Access, Amex, Visa,*

Ayr   Fouters Bistro   £40

Tel 0292 261391   **R**

2a Academy Street Ayr Strathclyde KA7 1HS   Map 12 B2

Cheerful bistro in vaulted basement premises. Scottish produce is cooked in
French style with consistently enjoyable results. Good-value brasserie menu
and over twenty half bottles on the wine list. *Seats 38 Parties 14. L 12-2
D 6.30-10.30 (Sun 7-10). Closed L Sun, all Mon, 25 & 26 Dec, 1-3 Jan.
Access, Amex, Visa,*

Ayr   The Stables   £45
Tel 0292 283704   R

Queen's Court 41 Sandgate Ayr Strathclyde KA7 1BD   Map 12 B2

Part of a shopping precinct formed from a group of Georgian buildings,
The Stables has the feel of a bistro and a menu of traditional Scottish dishes.
Pies are the speciality of the house: venison, ham and haddie, the real
McCoy with beef, mussels, pickled walnuts and spices. Also roasts, steaks,
haggis and cold dishes. The coffee shop menu is available all day. *Seats 27.*
Parties 10. Meals 10-10 (Mon 10-5). Closed D Mon, all Sun, 25 & 26 Dec,
1 & 2 Jan. Access, Amex, Visa, **Diners Club International**

Ayr   Places of Interest

Tourist Information   Tel 0292 284196.
Gaiety Theatre   Tel 0292 264639.
Ayr Racecourse   Tel 0292 264179.
Ayr Ice Rink   Tel 0292 263024.
   Historic Houses, Castles and Gardens
Burns Cottage   Alloway. Tel 0292 41215.
Blairquhan Castle and Gardens   Straiton Maybole. Tel 065 57 239.
Culzean Castle Garden and Country Park (NT)   Maybole. Tel 065 56
   274.
Penkill Castle   Girvan. Tel 046 587 261.

Ballachulish   Ballachulish Hotel   60%   £69
Tel 085 52 606   Fax 085 52 629   H

Ballachulish Argyll Highland PA39 4JY   Map 17 B4

An imposing inn set below rugged mountains which sweep down to Loch
Linnhe. Impressive views are shared by restaurant, cocktail bar and
baronial residents' lounge. There's a "local" atmosphere in the Ferry Bars.
Bedrooms are called Lairds or Chieftains, the latter enjoying the best of the
light, space and views. Guests have free use of the leisure centre at the sister
hotel *The Isles of Glencoe* about two miles away. Families are well catered
for. *Rooms 30. Garden, sea fishing. Access, Visa,* **Diners Club International**

Ballachulish   Places of Interest

Tourist Information   Tel 085 52 296

Ballater   Craigendarroch Hotel   74%   £125
Tel 033 97 55858   Fax 033 97 55447   H

Braemar Road Ballater Grampian AB3 5XA   Map 17 C4

Once the Highland retreat of the Keiller family of Dundee, now a fine
hotel in Scottish baronial style combined with a wealth of sports and
leisure amenities. Fair-sized bedrooms are bright and modern, with plenty
of toiletries in the bathrooms, and views of the Dee valley to wake up to.
There are two bars (one with regular live music nights), and three
restaurants. No dogs, but excellent facilities for children. *Rooms 50.*
Garden, indoor swimming pool, gymnasium, spa bath, sauna, solarium, beauty
and hair salon, squash, tennis, dry ski slope, snooker, baby-sitting, baby-listening,
crèche (9-5.30 daily). Closed 5-10 Jan. Access, Amex, Visa, **Diners Club International**

Ballater   Tullich Lodge   71%   £160
Tel 033 97 55406   Fax 033 97 55397   HR

Ballater Grampian AB35 5SB   Map 17 C4

Hector Macdonald and Neil Bannister have been installed at their
delightful pink granite mansion (on the A93, one mile east of Ballater)
since 1968. Crenellations and towers are outward distinguishing features,
while inside antiques, pictures and handsome furnishings grace the drawing

room and chintzy little sitting room (the perfect place to retire with a book). Bedrooms are individually decorated in keeping with the rest of the place, and the Tower Room, on the third floor, provides not only exercise but a splendid Victorian bathroom; televisions are available on request only, however a wireless is in every room. This is a hotel of real character and atmosphere, and many of the guests return regularly. High tea is served to children in the kitchen. **Rooms 10.** Garden. Closed Dec-Mar. *Access, Amex, Visa,* 🔴 *Diners Club International*

Restaurant   £62

Dinner in the mahogany-panelled restaurant offers no choice, but Hector can be relied upon to provide a good, straightforward meal prepared from the best seasonal produce. A typical menu might include smoked venison with spiced lentils, spinach and bean soup, filleted cod with a white wine sauce and mussels, lemon and raspberry tart or Scottish cheeses. A lighter lunch (soup, open sandwich or grilled lamb cutlet, cheese and coffee) is served at 1 o'clock in the bar. Jacket and tie requested. No smoking in the dining room. **Seats 26.** L at 1 D 7.30-8.30. Set L in the bar £7.50 Set D £23.

Ballater   Places of Interest

Tourist Information Tel 03397 55306.
Balmoral Castle Tel 03397 42334 Open May to July. *8 miles.*
Braemar Castle Tel 03397 41219.

Banchory   Invery House   78%   £145
Tel 033 02 4782   Fax 033 02 4712   **HR**
Bridge of Feugh Banchory Royal Deeside Grampian AB31 3NJ   Map 17 D4

Owners Stewart and Sheila Spence bought the house in 1985 and have turned it into a country house hotel of great charm and character. It is a Georgian mansion set on the west bank of the river Feugh in 40 acres of grounds that include a croquet lawn and walled garden. Tasteful decor is pleasantly non-designer with fresh flowers, ormolu vases, tapestry fire screens and the like adding a homely touch to the elegantly proportioned drawing room. Antique-furnished bedrooms are named after the novels of Sir Walter Scott, a frequent visitor to the house, and offer various extras like a decanter of sherry, fresh fruit and mineral water. Smart, spacious bathrooms often find room for an old washstand or wicker chair, taking them a little out of the ordinary. Bedrooms are properly serviced at night and a room service can provide hot food 24 hours a day. Children up to 10 stay free in parents' room. **Rooms 14.** Garden, croquet, tennis, snooker, game fishing, putting, helipad. Access, Amex, Visa, 🔴 Diners Club International

Restaurant   £90

Clive Lamb's menus are refreshingly unfussy, though never lacking interest. Bavarois of smoked Dee salmon and ragout of halibut and monkfish show what he can do with fish, while on the meaty side game pie made with venison, pheasant, duck and pigeon, flavoured with Guinness and topped with flaky pastry, is a noted speciality. No smoking. **Seats 36.** Parties 10. Private Room. L 12.30-2.15 D 7.30-10 (Sun to 9). Set L £19.50 Set D £33.50.

Banchory   Raemoir House   71%   £105
Tel 033 02 4884   Fax 033 02 2171   **HR**
Raemoir Banchory Grampian AB31 4ED   Map 17 D4

Three generations of the Sabin family have built friendly hospitality into the fabric of their hotel, an 18th-century mansion set in a 3500 acre estate. Rich red brocade chairs, panelled walls and well-worn antiques enhance the traditional look of the morning room, and the bar is fashioned from a Tudor four-poster. Bedrooms are all different in size and character, but most have inviting chaises longues, day beds or armchairs. Five rooms are in the historic 16th century Ha'Hoose immediately behind the mansion.

There are some self-catering apartments converted from the original coach-house and stables. *Rooms 25. Croquet, sauna, solarium, keep-fit equipment, tennis, game fishing, 9-hole golf, shooting, helipad. Closed 1 week Jan. Access, Amex, Visa,*

Restaurant £68

Top-quality produce is cooked without undue elaboration and served in generous portions by friendly staff. Chicken and ham paté, goujons of lemon sole or golden game consommé precede Dee salmon, pan-fried brill, sautéed breast of pheasant or a Raemoir special – a tiny joint of three lamb chops served with a traditional garnish. There's a long choice for vegetarians, plus homely sweets. *Seats 64. Parties 85. Private Room. L by arrangement on Sun 12.30-2 D 7.30-9. Set L £12.75 Set D £21.50.*

Banchory   Tor-na-Coille Hotel   66%   £75
Tel 033 02 2242   Fax 033 02 4012   **H**

Inchmarlo Road Banchory Grampian AB3 4AB   Map 17 D4

Built as a private house in 1873 and a hotel since the turn of the century, Tor-Na-Coille retains much of its Victorian character. Roxanne Sloan is continuing a programme of refurbishment in the antique-furnished bedrooms, and the lounge has also been redecorated. The function room can accommodate 90 people for a banquet, 80 for a conference. The hotel copes very well with children (under-10s stay free in parents' room). *Rooms 25. Garden, croquet, squash, playground, baby-sitting, baby-listening, crèche (8-4, Mon-Fri). Closed 25 & 26 Dec. Access, Amex, Visa,*

Banchory   Places of Interest

Tourist Information   Tel 03302 2000.

Bearsden   October Restaurant   £75
Tel 041-942 7272   Fax 041-942 9650   **R**

128 Drymen Road Bearsden Glasgow Strathclyde G61 3RB   Map 12 B1

Ferrier Richardson's airy restaurant, hung with colourful modern art, self-consciously mirrors his modernistic approach to food. Influences on his cooking are truly international, while his combinations in flavouring continue to find favour among a loyal clientele. The menu, though not long, is full of interest. Salmon is a favourite medium, and on a recent carte it appears four times: warm smoked with avocado and dill vinaigrette; with tomato in a cream soup; a supreme of filo pastry with an orange and watercress butter sauce; and with monkfish and mussels in a lightly curried casserole. Lamb satay and grilled sirloin steaks are typical meat choices, while desserts could include warm lemon tart and lime sorbet, and a trio of caramel puddings. *Seats 55. Parties 55. L 12-2 D 7-10. Closed Sun, Bank Holidays,2 weeks Aug, 1 week Easter. Set L £9.95. Access, Visa.*

Bearsden   Places of Interest

Bearsden Ski Club   Tel 041 942 2933.

Beattock   Auchen Castle   65%   £68
Tel 068 33 407   Fax 068 33 667   **H**

Beattock Nr Moffat Dumfries & Galloway DG10 9SH   Map 12 C3

Signposted from the A74 a mile north of Beattock, a Scottish baronial-style mansion built in 1849, once the home of the William Younger family for 70 years. The hillside position offers views over upper Annandale and the Moffat hills and there are terraced gardens running down to a trout lake. A comfortable, traditional air pervades the public rooms, which include a chintzy lounge and a bar with unusual seating brought from Hong Kong. Best bedrooms are in the main house; these are spacious with antique furniture and easy chairs. Other rooms have fitted furniture and there are ten more functional rooms in a separate lodge. *Rooms 25. Garden, game fishing, shooting, dinner dance (winter Sat). Closed 3 wks Xmas/New Year. Access, Amex, Visa,* ⓘ Diners Club International

Beattock   Places of Interest

Dumfries Tourist Information Tel 0387 53862.
Drumlanrig Castle and Country Park Tel 0848 31682.
   Museums and Art Galleries
Dumfries Museum Tel 0387 53374.
Gracefield Arts Centre Tel 0387 62084.
Robert Burns Centre Tel 0387 64808.
Burns House Tel 0387 55297.

Blairgowrie   Kinloch House   70%   £132★

Tel 0250 884237   Fax 0250 884333   **HR**

Kinloch by Blairgowrie Tayside PH10 6SG   Map 17 C5

Highland cattle graze in the parkland that surrounds a creeper-clad 19th-century house which has been turned into a relaxing country hotel by David and Sarah Shentall. Public areas include a period drawing room but most guests prefer the convivial atmosphere of the comfortable bar or the charm of the plant-filled conservatory with its Lloyd Loom chairs and tables. In the spacious new wing the rooms are perhaps the best, traditionally furnished and boasting particularly luxurious bathrooms. Extras include books, magazines, ironing boards and bathrobes. Shooting parties and fishermen appreciate the Sportsman's room, which offers everything from a deep freeze to dog bowls. Room service is limited. ★Half-board terms only. *Rooms 21. Garden. Closed 2 weeks Dec. Access, Amex, Visa,* ⓘ Diners Club International

Restaurant   £57

A civilised dining room where a daily-changing menu brings a good choice of dishes, both simple and more elaborate. Starters might encompass smoked salmon, and chicken and sweetbread paté; main dishes, pan-fried sirloin steak, quenelles of salmon and loin of lamb roasted with herbs and served with Madeira sauce and a spinach mousse. A number of dishes carry a supplement to the set dinner price. An informal lunch menu, where dishes are individually priced, ranges from open sandwiches to ballotine of Barbary duck. No children under 7 at night. No smoking. *Seats 55. Parties 30. Private Room. L 12.30-2 D 7-9.15. Set D from £20.90.*

Blairgowrie   Places of Interest

Tourist Information Tel 0250 2960.

Bonnyrigg   Dalhousie Castle   66%   £115

Tel & Fax 0875 20153   **H**

Bonnyrigg Nr Edinburgh Lothian EH19 3JB   Map 12 C1

An impressive 15th-century, red sandstone castle overlooking a bend in the South Esk river. Public rooms retain many original features such as the fine tracery of the rib-vaulted ceiling in the entrance hall, an oak-panelled library and atmospheric dungeon restaurant. Most bedrooms feature solid oak furniture and plainly decorated, modern bathrooms. New owners have recently taken over and will, hopefully, attend to areas in poor state of repair. *Rooms 25. Garden. Access, Amex, Visa,* ⓘ Diners Club International

Bonnyrigg   Places of Interest

Tourist Information Tel 031 660 6814.

Bridge of Allan   Kipling's   £45

`Tel 0786 833617`   **R**

Mine Road Bridge of Allan Central FK9 4DT   Map 17 C5

Chef-patron Peter Bannister attracts a loyal and regular following to his
restaurant set in lawns in the middle of residential Bridge of Allan. Market-
fresh produce goes into daily-changing menus typified by sardines
provençale, grilled snapper hollandaise, pigeon breasts with pepper sauce or
noisettes of lamb with port and orange. *Seats 65. Parties 65. L 12.30-1.30
D 7-9. Closed D Sun, all Mon, Bank Holidays except Good Friday, 1 week
Xmas, 2 weeks Aug. Set L £11.50. Access, Amex, Visa,*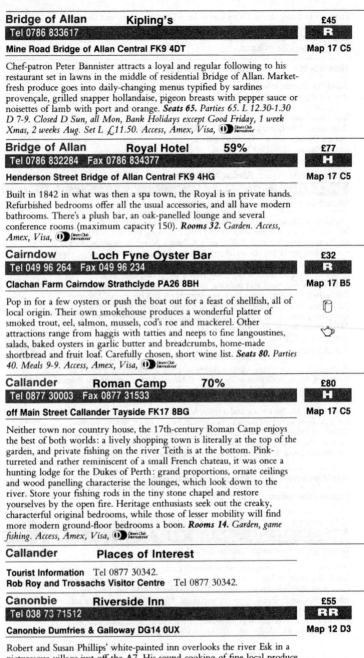

Bridge of Allan   Royal Hotel   59%   £77

`Tel 0786 832284   Fax 0786 834377`   **H**

Henderson Street Bridge of Allan Central FK9 4HG   Map 17 C5

Built in 1842 in what was then a spa town, the Royal is in private hands.
Refurbished bedrooms offer all the usual accessories, and all have modern
bathrooms. There's a plush bar, an oak-panelled lounge and several
conference rooms (maximum capacity 150). *Rooms 32. Garden. Access,
Amex, Visa,*

Cairndow   Loch Fyne Oyster Bar   £32

`Tel 049 96 264   Fax 049 96 234`   **R**

Clachan Farm Cairndow Strathclyde PA26 8BH   Map 17 B5

Pop in for a few oysters or push the boat out for a feast of shellfish, all of
local origin. Their own smokehouse produces a wonderful platter of
smoked trout, eel, salmon, mussels, cod's roe and mackerel. Other
attractions range from haggis with tatties and neeps to fine langoustines,
salads, baked oysters in garlic butter and breadcrumbs, home-made
shortbread and fruit loaf. Carefully chosen, short wine list. *Seats 80. Parties
40. Meals 9-9. Access, Amex, Visa,*

Callander   Roman Camp   70%   £80

`Tel 0877 30003   Fax 0877 31533`   **H**

off Main Street Callander Tayside FK17 8BG   Map 17 C5

Neither town nor country house, the 17th-century Roman Camp enjoys
the best of both worlds: a lively shopping town is literally at the top of the
garden, and private fishing on the river Teith is at the bottom. Pink-
turreted and rather reminiscent of a small French chateau, it was once a
hunting lodge for the Dukes of Perth: grand proportions, ornate ceilings
and wood panelling characterise the lounges, which look down to the
river. Store your fishing rods in the tiny stone chapel and restore
yourselves by the open fire. Heritage enthusiasts seek out the creaky,
characterful original bedrooms, while those of lesser mobility will find
more modern ground-floor bedrooms a boon. *Rooms 14. Garden, game
fishing. Access, Amex, Visa,*

Callander   Places of Interest

Tourist Information   Tel 0877 30342.
Rob Roy and Trossachs Visitor Centre   Tel 0877 30342.

Canonbie   Riverside Inn   £55

`Tel 038 73 71512`   **RR**

Canonbie Dumfries & Galloway DG14 0UX   Map 12 D3

Robert and Susan Phillips' white-painted inn overlooks the river Esk in a
picturesque village just off the A7. His sound cooking of fine local produce
results in an enjoyable five-course dinner: queen scallops in white wine
jelly; leek and parsnip soup; chargrilled fillet of Highland lamb with
kidney and wine sauce; Cotherstone, smoked Westmorland and

Ribblesdale cheeses; dark and sticky treacle pudding. Lunch and supper menus, written on a blackboard and changed daily, offer lighter choices in a similar vein. Concise wine list with fair prices. **Seats 28.** *Parties 28. L 12-2 D 7.30-8.30. Closed L Sun, 2 days Xmas, 2 days New Year, 2 weeks Nov, 2 weeks Feb. Set D £21. Access, Visa.*

Rooms   £62

The residents' lounge is quiet and cosy, and the lounge bar stocks a variety of specialised malt whiskies. Eight bedrooms, with matching fabrics and thoughtful extras, have a homely appeal. All but two have modern en-suite bathrooms. No dogs.

Chapel of Garioch   Pittodrie House   65%   £99

Tel 046 681 444   Fax 046 681 648   **H**

Chapel of Garioch Nr Inverurie Highland AB51 9HS   Map 16 D3

Fishing, stalking, shooting and riding are all available locally, combining with facilities on the premises to make this a fine base for sporting holidays. The house dates largely from the 17th century (rebuilt from 15th-century origins) and the reception rooms are very traditional and homely, with antiques, family portraits and log fires. The wine bar is stocked with more than ninety malt whiskies. Bedrooms are either in the main building (motley fabrics, antiques, some bathrooms not en suite) or in a 1990-built wing, with reproduction furniture and decent modern bathrooms. There are banqueting and conference facilities for up to 130. **Rooms 27.** *Garden, croquet, tennis, squash, snooker, clay-pigeon shooting. Access, Amex, Visa,* Diners Club International

---

Cleish   Nivingstone House   65%   £90

Tel 0577 850216   Fax 0577 850238   **H**

Cleish Kinross Tayside KY13 7LS   Map 17 C5

Formerly a farmhouse, stone-built Nivingstone House enjoys a tranquil setting in 12 acres of gardens at the foot of the Cleish Hills. Public rooms include a quiet drawing room and a cosy, plush wine bar warmed by a real fire. Pretty bedrooms with Laura Ashley fabrics and wallpapers are well kept, like the whole hotel, and there are neat bathrooms, a few of which have shower and WC only. **Rooms 17.** *Garden, croquet, putting green, golf driving net. Access, Amex, Visa,* Diners Club International

---

Colbost   Three Chimneys Restaurant   £60

Tel 047 081 258   **R**

Colbost By Dunvegan Isle of Skye Highland IV55 8ZT   Map 16 A3

The cooking at Eddie and Shirley Spear's charming old crofter's cottage (yes, it does have three chimneys) puts the emphasis on Skye seafood, much of it delivered from the fishing boats straight to the door. Skye langoustines served in the shell with a pot of herb and lemon mayonnaise are hard to beat, but the salmon, sole, lobsters and oysters also all have their fans. Beef steak, lamb and venison cater for meat-eaters and there's always a vegetarian main course. Super sweets (including Glendale-grown soft fruits), Scottish cheeses, home-baked breads. No smoking. The restaurant is 4 miles west of Dunvegan on the scenic B884 to Glendale. **Seats 30.** *Parties 24. L 12.30-2 D 7-9. Closed Sun (open Sun before Bank Holidays), Nov-Easter. Access, Visa.*

Colbost   Places of Interest

Dunvegan Castle   Tel 047 022 206.
Skye Silver   Colbost Tel 047 081 263.
Colbost Folk Museum   Tel 047 022 296.

Contin   Craigdarroch Lodge   56%   £70

Tel 0997 421265   **H**

Contin By Strathpeffer Highland IV14 9EH   Map 16 B3

Built as a shooting lodge in the early part of the 19th century,
Craigdarroch stands along a tree-lined drive off the A835 at the foot of the
mountains. It's a great base for touring, walking and all kinds of outdoor
activities – much of its business now revolves around special golfing
packages. The hotel's own leisure facilities are expanding (latest is the
indoor swimming pool), while for more relaxing moments the bar and
lounge offer a cosy welcome. Bedrooms are modest but well heated, with
functional contemporary furniture. *Rooms 13. Garden, tennis, indoor
swimming pool, sauna, solarium, snooker. Closed Jan & Feb.* **(I)** *Diners Club International*

Craigellachie   Craigellachie Hotel   68%   £87

Tel 0340 881204   Fax 0340 881253   **HR**

Craigellachie Grampian AB3 9SS   Map 16 C3

A hundred years old and still going strong, this solidly built hotel on the
A95 overlooks a stretch of the river Spey. Public areas include an airy
lounge with lace-draped grand piano, antique sideboard and plenty of good
armchairs and sofas, plus a small library and snug green bar. Floral chintzy
fabrics decorate the bedrooms, which have smart modern bathrooms and
either antique or contemporary traditional-style furniture. *Rooms 30.
Garden, sauna, solarium, keep-fit equipment, games room. Access, Amex, Visa,*
(I) *Diners Club International*

Restaurant   £66

The Ben Aigan restaurant puts great reliance on local produce for its four-
course dinners: asparagus in a timbale of aspic with a caper and red onion
dressing; Spey salmon fresh or smoked; honey-glazed, clove-studded lamb;
Angus beef Wellington. Cheeses served with warm herb brioche. No
smoking. *Seats 50. Parties 60. Private Room. L 12.30-1.45 D 7.30-9.30.
Set L £9.75 Set D £24.75.*

Craignure   Isle of Mull Hotel   56%   £84

Tel 068 02 351   Fax 068 02 462   **H**

Craignure Isle of Mull Argyll Strathclyde PA65 6BB   Map 17 A5

A long, low modern building where all bedrooms look out across the
Sound of Mull. Day rooms offer plenty of space to relax, and one of the
lounges has access to a patio. Children up to the age of 6 stay free in
parents' room. *Rooms 60. Garden. Closed Nov-Mar. Access, Visa.*

Craignure   Places of Interest

Tourist Information   Tel 06802 377.

Crieff   Crieff Hydro   62%   £83*

Tel 0764 2401   Fax 0764 3087   **H**

Crieff Tayside PH7 3LQ   Map 17 C5

A family hotel par excellence, with an impressive range of leisure activities
to keep everyone busy and fit. Apart from singles, most of the bedrooms
are of a decent size, furnished with either lightwood units or more
traditional or antique pieces. Table licence only, no bar. Banqueting for up
to 350 and conference facilities for up to 400 people. *Half-board terms
only. No dogs. From Jan '93 the phone number changes to 0764 65555,
the fax 0764 653087. *Rooms 199. Garden, croquet, indoor swimming pool,
whirlpool, spa bath, sauna, steam room, sunbeds, boutique, hairdressing and
beauty salon, tennis, squash, badminton, 9-hole golf course, putting, bowling
green, snooker, riding school, football pitch, cinema, playroom, playground.
Access, Amex, Visa,* **(I)** *Diners Club International*

Crieff   Places of Interest

Tourist Information Tel 0764 2578.
Visitors Centre Tel 0764 4014.
Drummond Castle Gardens Muthill. Tel 076481 321.

Crinan   Crinan Hotel   69%   £100

HR

Tel 054 683 261   Fax 054 683 292

Crinan By Lochgilphead Strathclyde PA31 8SR   Map 17 B5

At the northern end of the canal connecting Loch Fyne with the Atlantic
stands a tiny fishing village (population 58) and the Ryans' hotel which has
been constructed in such a way that every window has a view either
westwards up the Jura sound or down over the canal's 15th, and final, lock.
Interiors by Mrs Ryan (alias Frances MacDonald the well-known artist)
add colour to Italian varnished pine bedrooms of which the pick have
private balconies. *Rooms 22. Garden. Closed 3 days Xmas. Access, Visa.*

Lock 16 Restaurant   ★   £75

On the hotel's top floor, this restaurant opens *only* when the local fishing
fleet comes in (late afternoon) to unload at the quayside below. Most of the
fish is loaded straight into a waiting pantechnicon to be whisked off to
Europe, but not before Nick Ryan takes the pick of the catch – to be
served that evening at the very peak of freshness. Corryvreckan prawns,
Loch Craignish mussels, Loch Fyne queen clams and locally-smoked salmon
form the basis of the feast. Whole Stilton with oatcakes and Mount Kenya
coffee round off the meal in style. An interesting wine list is designed to
suit all tastes and pockets, written with passion and knowledge – ask for
advice. Booking essential. Gentlemen require jackets and ties. *Seats 20.
D only at 8. Closed Sun & Mon, Oct-Mar. Set D £37.50.*

Westward Room   £65

Seafood also features in Crinan's ground-floor restaurant, where the menu
changes nightly, but carnivores will usually find some Aberdeen Angus
beef, either roast or charcoal grilled, on the menu. Lemon cheesecake,
hazelnut meringue and Scottish farmhouse cheeses with oatcakes might
follow. New chef Andrew Yuill has settled in well, will his boss's (Nick
Ryan above) customers now desert him and come downstairs? *Seats 50.
Parties 70. D only 7-9. Closed 3 days Xmas. Set D £25.*

Cromarty   Thistles   £48

R

Tel 038 17 471

20 Church Street Cromarty Highland IV11 8XA   Map 16 C3

It's worth a trip across the Black Isle to find this small, friendly, family-run
restaurant. David Wilkinson's menus range from braised oxtail and good
Scottish cock-a-leekie soup to more cosmopolitan dishes like pavé of veal
loin with fresh basil, boudin of guinea fowl and pistachios, and feuilleté of
sweetbreads. Good desserts to finish: perhaps ratafia ice-cream, nougat glacé
or crèpes au whisky. No smoking. *Seats 24. Parties 30. L 12-2 (by
arrangement in winter) D 7.30-9. Closed D Sun, all Mon, 25 & 26 Dec, 1 &
2 Jan, 1 week Oct, 2 weeks Feb. Access, Visa.*

Cumbernauld   Travel Inn   £42

L

Tel 0236 725339   Fax 0236 736380

**4 South Muirhead Road Cumbernauld Nr Glasgow Strathclyde G67
1AX**   Map 17 C6

Rooms 37. Access, Amex, Visa, **Diners Club International**

Cumbernauld   Westerwood Hotel   73%   £90

Tel 0236 457171   Fax 0236 738478   **HR**

St Andrews Drive Westerwood Cumbernauld Strathclyde G68 0EW   Map 17 C6

Set on a hill above the A80, Westerwood is a new hotel and country club
with a golf course (designed by Dave Thomas and Severiano Ballesteros)
that boasts a 40ft waterfall at the 15th green and wonderful views over the
Campsie Hills. For après-golf choose between the hotel's luxurious lounge
and cocktail bar with fabric-covered walls and indoor garden or the less
formal tartan-carpeted country club. Artificial trees are a novel form of
decor in good standard bedrooms. Beds are turned down at night and staff
are friendly and helpful. No dogs. *Rooms 47. Garden, 18-hole golf course,
bowling green, pétanque, tennis, indoor swimming pool, snooker, gymnasium, spa
bath, steam room, beautician, hairdressing, coffee shop (11am-10pm). Access,
Amex, Visa,* ◐ Diners Club International

Old Masters Restaurant   £55

An unusual circular dining room with dark-green watered silk-effect walls
and tented ceiling from which hangs a large brass chandelier. Sharing the
same executive chef, Bruce Sangster, as its sister restaurant at *Murrayshall
House* in Scone, it is no surprise to find skilled, sophisticated cooking here,
too, by Malcolm Warham Gateau of baked root vegetables with cream
and Swiss cheese on a basil and parsley sauce, breast of pheasant stuffed
with a sage and apricot filling under pastry with a lemon honey sauce, and
hot bittersweet chocolate soufflé with chilled Calvados cream typify the
style. Some interesting New World wines, French bottles more predictable.
Service is as smooth and confident as the cooking. *Seats 70. Parties 20.
D only 7.30-9.45. Closed Sun. Set D £18.50.*

Cumbernauld   Places of Interest

Palacerigg Country Park   Tel 0236 720047.

Cupar   Ostlers Close   £60

Tel 0334 55574   **R**

25 Bonnygate Cupar Fife KY15 4BU   Map 17 C5

Wild mushrooms garnered from nearby forests, herbs and salad ingredients
from his own garden and other good local produce give Jimmy Graham's
careful cooking a head start at an unpretentious restaurant hidden down an
alleyway off Bonnygate. Cream of salmon soup, confit of duck on a bed of
salad leaves with hazelnut vinaigrette, fillet of Pittenween turbot topped
with asparagus on a lobster stock and roast saddle of roe venison served
with mushrooms in a game sauce show the range. Honey, Drambuie,
oatmeal and orange ice cream is a popular sweet, hot sticky toffee pudding
another. *Seats 28. Parties 20. L 12.15-2 D 7-9.30 (Sat to 10). Closed Sun &
Mon, 25 & 26 Dec, 1 & 2 Jan, 1 week Jun. Access, Visa.*

Cupar   Places of Interest

Tourist Information   Tel 0334 52874.
Scottish Deer Centre   Bow-of-Fife Tel 033 781 391.

Dalguise   Kinnaird   76%   £155

Tel 0796 482440   Fax 0796 482289   **HR**

Kinnaird Estate Dalguise By Dunkeld Tayside PH8 0LB   Map 17 C5

On the B898 to the north of Dunkeld, about four miles off the A9, the
18th-century Kinnaird House, surrounded by its 9000-acre estate, has a
splendid position overlooking the river Tay. Extensively, and expensively,
renovated over the last few years, it has now become a fine country house
hotel. Spacious bedrooms, each with gas log fire, are lavishly decorated in
great style and comfort with sybaritic bathrooms. Day rooms, furnished
almost entirely with antiques, include the red cedar-panelled drawing
room, where fresh flowers and family mementos and pictures create a

homely feel, and a clubby snooker room. Musical events are becoming a
regular feature. No children under 12. Dogs in (heated) kennels only.
*Rooms 9. Garden, tennis, croquet, game fishing, shooting, snooker. Closed Feb.
Access, Amex, Visa.*

Restaurant £88

Exquisite painted panels depicting figures in an Arcadian landscape compete
for attention with magnificent, real-life views over the Tay valley from the
high windows of this supremely elegant dining room. John Webber's
sophisticated, stylish cooking is entirely appropriate to the setting: ravioli
of rabbit and morel mushrooms, steamed salmon tartare with a tomato
butter sauce, breast of Gressingham duck with a confit of the leg and a
jasmine blossom sauce, best end of lamb with onion and coriander tartlet,
prune and brandy parfait. Good selection of wines by the half bottle. No
smoking. *Seats 45. Parties 25. Private Room. L 12.30-1.45 D 7.15-9.30.
Set L £19.50 Set D £38.*

Dirleton   Open Arms Hotel   67% £110

| Tel 0620 85241   Fax 0620 85570 | H |

Dirleton Nr North Berwick Lothian EH39 5EG Map 12 D1

A good name for a friendly, characterful hotel in a charming position
overlooking the village green and the ruins of 16th-century Dirleton
Castle. It's been in the same family for nearly half a century, and there's a
relaxed, domestic warmth to the lounge, which has comfortable armchairs
and sofas, a log fire, magazines and newspapers; the bar is tiny but full of
character. Bedrooms are mostly bright and airy, with floral curtains; each
has an easy chair and personal touches such as flowers and fruit. Banquets
for up to 80, more in the garden marquee. *Rooms 7. Garden. Closed 5 days
New Year. Access, Visa.*

Drumnadrochit   Polmaily House   63% £100

| Tel 045 62 343 | HR |

Drumnadrochit Highland IV3 6XT Map 16 B3

Uninterrupted peace and relaxation are virtues fostered by owners Alison
and Nick Parsons, whose hotel is little changed from its origins as a private
house. There's a little bar, a drawing room and a library with cards, board
games and a TV. TVs are absent from the bright, airy bedrooms (two not
en suite), though they now have telephones. Children under 18 stay free in
parents' room. No dogs. *Rooms 9. Garden, croquet, tennis, outdoor swimming
pool. Closed Nov-Mar. Access, Visa.*

Restaurant £56

Nick Parsons affably plays host while Alison, with Barbara Drury,
produces small-choice dinners based on fresh local ingredients. Typical
dishes: layered pork, bacon and parsley terrine with Cumberland sauce and
oranges, Atlantic whitefish and prawn soup, paupiettes of lemon sole filled
with crab soufflé, roast guinea fowl with shallots and green lentils, mango
ice cream with exotic fruits and walnut biscuits. No smoking. *Seats 30.
Parties 12. D only 7.30-9.30. Set D £20.*

Drybridge   Old Monastery Restaurant £55

| Tel 0542 32660 | R |

Drybridge Buckie Grampian AB56 2JB Map 16 C3

The former monastery enjoys lovely views of the sea and the mountains
beyond. Maureen Gray offers a warm welcome front of house, while
Douglas in the kitchen uses the best of the local larder with fish from the
Spey, venison and game birds. His dishes are satisfying and well presented,
and Scottish influences mingle with classic French (pigeon breast with
claret and hawthorn sauce, French onion soup using Aberdeen Angus beef
for the stock). There are plenty of half bottles on a well-priced wine list.
*Seats 45. Parties 45. L 12-1.45 D 7-9.30 (Sat to 10). Closed Sun & Mon,
Bank Holidays, 3 weeks Jan, 2 weeks Nov. Access, Amex, Visa.*

Drybridge   Places of Interest

Banff Boyndie Bay beach   Inverboyndie.
Buckle Maritime Museum   Tel 0542 32121.

Dryburgh   Dryburgh Abbey   58%   £106
| Tel 0835 22261   Fax 0835 23945 |

H

St Boswells Dryburgh Borders TD6 0RQ   **Map 12 D2**

From the A68 at St Boswells follow signs to Dryburgh's ruined abbey; this
splendid early-Victorian sandstone house stands adjacent on the banks of the
Tweed. Acquired in 1991 by the Grose family (who also own the
Thurlestone Hotel in South Devon), the hotel has undergone a complete
internal transformation since. An ideal venue for coarse fishing and
shooting parties, or simply as a base for touring, it now has additional
conference facilities accommodating up to 200. Family breaks include free
stay in parents' room for under-12s. *Rooms 30. Garden, croquet, putting,
fishing. Access, Visa,* (I) ᴰⁱⁿᵉʳˢ Cˡᵘᵇ

Dryburgh   Places of Interest

Jedburgh Tourist Information   Tel 0835 63435 *8 miles.*
Jedburgh Abbey   Tel 0835 63925.
Mary 'Queen of Scots' House   Tel 0835 63331.

Drymen   Buchanan Highland Hotel   62%   £115
| Tel 0360 60588   Fax 0360 60943 |

H

Main Street Drymen by Loch Lomond Central G63 0BQ   **Map 17 B5**

A former coaching inn whose role has gradually expanded: besides its 50
comfortably fitted bedrooms there's an excellent leisure centre (the
Buchanan Club) and a versatile range of conference and banqueting suites
(up to 200 delegates and 130 for a function). Children up to 12 stay free in
parents' room. Baby-sitting and baby-listening are available. *Rooms 50.
Garden, bowling green, 9-hole golf course, tennis, gymnasium, indoor swimming
pool, sauna, spa bath, coffee shop (10am-9pm). Access, Amex, Visa,* (I) ᴰⁱⁿᵉʳˢ Cˡᵘᵇ

Drymen   Place of Interest

Ben Lomond   Tel 041 552 8391 *11 miles.*

Dulnain Bridge   Auchendean Lodge   62%   £61
| Tel 047 985 347 |

HR

Dulnain Bridge Grantown-on-Spey Highland PH26 3LU   **Map 16 C3**

An owner-run country hotel set in spectacular scenery a mile south of
Dulnain Bridge. A range of activities – canoeing on the Spey, skiing in the
Cairngorms, shooting, fishing and hiking – is available locally. The hotel is
a converted Edwardian hunting lodge, now comfortably enough equipped
not to disappoint guests kept in by spells of inclement weather. There's
period furniture in two open-fired lounges. Individually styled bedrooms
have electric blankets, radio/alarms and TVs, but no phones. *Rooms 7.
Garden, pitch & putt. Closed 2 weeks Jan. Access, Amex, Visa,* (I) ᴰⁱⁿᵉʳˢ Cˡᵘᵇ

Restaurant   £55

Dinner is a daily-changing, four-course affair making good use of local
game, fish and garden vegetables. Typical fare might be Stilton and walnut
paté, cep and mushroom soufflé, baked haddock with chanterelle cream,
venison casserole with juniper berries and pavlova with kiwi fruit after a
plate of Scottish and French cheeses. No smoking. *Seats 18. Parties 18.
D only 7.30-9. Set D £21.50.*

Dulnain Bridge Muckrach Lodge 59%
£74
H
Tel 047 985 257   Fax 047 985 325

Dulnain Bridge Grantown-on-Spey Highland PH26 3LY
Map 16 C3

19th-century hunting lodge set in ten acres of grounds in Dulnain Valley.
Refurbishment has recently taken place, covering the little bar, the dining
room (now with a conservatory) and the simply appointed bedrooms.
Children up to five are accommodated free in parents' room; children's
menu offered. No dogs. *Rooms 12. Garden. Closed 3 weeks Nov. Access,
Amex, Visa,*

Dumbarton Forte Travelodge
£40
L
Tel 0389 65202

A82 Milton Dumbarton Strathclyde G82 2TY
Map 12 B1

On the A82 westbound, 8 miles west of Glasgow, 1 mile east of
Dumbarton centre. *Rooms 32. Access, Amex, Visa.*

Dunblane Cromlix House 82%
£125
HR
Tel 0786 822125   Fax 0786 825450

Kinbuck Dunblane Central FK15 9JT
Map 17 C5

The 5,000-acre Cromlix estate has been in the same family for 500 years
and the collection of fine furniture, paintings, porcelain, silver and
glassware acquired over many generations give the 19th-century house an
authentic air of gracious country living. The surrounding country offers all
sorts of pursuits including shooting, trout fishing in lochs, plus a stretch of
the river Allan, and the peaceful drawing room and conservatory are
marvellously restful retreats from all the outdoor activity. Individually
decorated bedrooms are largely furnished with well-chosen antiques. The
Honeymoon Suite, done out in lilac and pink, has a draped brass bed and
an Edwardian bathroom. *Rooms 14. Garden, tennis, shooting, fishing, croquet,
clay-pigeon shooting. Access, Amex, Visa,*

Restaurant
£84

In the hushed and formal restaurant, smoothly professional staff expertly
orchestrate the courses. Ian Corkhill uses local produce: asparagus soup
with chive quenelles, potted rabbit with roast apples and a walnut sauce,
loin of lamb topped with a shallot mousse on a rosemary and sultana sauce,
hot orange and marmalade soufflé. Dinner includes canapés, petits fours and
coffee. Some interesting selections on a good, worldwide wine list; bargains
to be found among occasional bin ends. *Seats 32. Parties 45. Private Room.
L 12.30-1.30 D 7.30-9.30 (Sun to 9). Closed Xmas. Set L £15 & £20
Set D £32.*

Dunblane Stakis Dunblane Hydro 61%
£111
H
Tel 0786 822551   Fax 0786 825403

Perth Road Dunblane Central FK15 0HG
Map 17 C5

Handsome Victorian building set high above the main road to Perth in 44
acres of grounds. Main attraction is the leisure facility, and it's well geared
up to family holidays. Conferences are also big business, with room for up
to 500 theatre-style. *Rooms 240. Garden, indoor swimming pool, keep-fit
equipment, sauna, solarium, beauty salon, tennis, putting, baby-sitting,
baby-listening. Access, Amex, Visa,*

Dunblane Places of Interest

Tourist Information   Tel 0786 824428.
Dunblane Cathedral   Tel 0786 824254.
Leighton Library   Tel 0786 822850.
Doune Motor Museum   Carse of Cambus. Tel 0786 841203.

Dundee   Angus Thistle   69%   £108

Tel 0382 26874   Fax 0382 22564   **H**

Marketgait Dundee Tayside DD1 1QU   **Map 17 C5**

A modern, six-storey hotel in the heart of the city offering a good standard
of bedroom accommodation (including five suites) and conference facilities
for up to 500 delegates. 24hr room service. *Rooms 58. Access, Amex, Visa,*
Diners Club International

Dundee   Invercarse Hotel   59%   £80

Tel 0382 69231   Fax 0382 644112   **H**

371 Perth Road Dundee Tayside DD2 1PG   **Map 17 C5**

Some three miles west of the city centre, the privately owned Invecarse is
an extended Victorian house set on a hill affording views across the Tay to
the Fife hills beyond. About half the bedrooms are singles with shower and
WC only, others have spacious, carpeted bathrooms and pleasant lightwood
furniture. Public rooms include a lounge bar, with Victorian windows
taking advantage of the view, and a red leather-furnished cocktail bar.
Conferences for up to 200. *Rooms 39. Garden. Access, Amex, Visa,*
Diners Club International

Dundee   Travel Inn   £42

Tel 0382 561115   **L**

Kingsway West Invergowrie Dundee Tayside DD2 5JU   **Map 17 C5**

Rooms 40. Access, Amex, Visa, Diners Club International

Dundee   Places of Interest

Tourist Information   Tel 0382 27723.
St Paul's Cathedral   Tel 0382 24486.
Camperdown Country Wildlife Park   Tel 0382 623555.
University Botanic Garden   Tel 0382 66939.
Olympia Leisure Centre   Tel 0382 203888.
Shaw's Dundee Sweet Factory   Tel 0382 610369.
Tay Road Bridge Observation Platforms.
   Theatres and Concert Halls
The Dance Factory   Tel 0382 561166.
Dundee Repertory Theatre   Tel 0382 23530.
Whitehall Theatre   Tel 0382 22684.
Dundee Film Theatre   Tel 0382 23141.
   Museums and Art Galleries
Barrack Street Museum   Tel 0382 23141.
Broughty Castle Museum   Tel 0382 76121.
McManus Galleries   Tel 0382 23141.
Mills Observatory   Tel 0382 67138.
Seagate Gallery and Printmakers Workshop   Tel 0382 26331.
H.M. Frigate Unicorn   Tel 0382 200900.
R.R.S. Discovery   Tel 0382 201175.

Dunfermline   King Malcolm Thistle   65%   £93

Tel 0383 722611   Fax 0383 730865   **H**

Queensferry Road Dunfermline Fife KY11 5DS   **Map 17 C5**

Fifteen miles from the centre of Edinburgh and a short drive from junction
2 of the M90. Modern bedrooms have all the expected amenities plus 24hr
room service. The Malcolm Suite can accommodate up to 150 delegates
theatre-style. *Rooms 48. Garden. Access, Amex, Visa,* Diners Club International

Dunfermline   Places of Interest

Tourist Information Tel 0383 720999.
Knockhill Motor Racing Circuit Tel 0383 723337.

Duror **Stewart Hotel** 59%	£80
Tel 063 174 268 Fax 063 174 328	**H**
Glen Duror Appin Duror Highland PA38 4BW	**Map 17 B4**

The hospitable Lacy family and their young staff offer a friendly welcome
at their Victorian house, which stands in five acres of terraced gardens with
beautiful views of Loch Linnhe. The oldest part was built 120 years ago in
the style of a hunting lodge. An open fire warms the simple yet pleasant
bar and upstairs there's a quiet and spacious lounge. Bedrooms are in a new
wing; they are simple and neat, with views (most), modest modern
furniture and tiny bathrooms. Children up to 12 stay free in parents' room.
Rooms 19. Garden, riding, sailing, clay-pigeon shooting. Closed mid Oct-Easter.
Access, Amex, Visa,

East Kilbride **Bruce Swallow Hotel** 59%	£72
Tel 035 52 29771 Fax 035 52 42216	**H**
Cornwall Street East Kilbride Strathclyde G74 1AF	**Map 12 B2**

Purpose-built, concrete-and-glass hotel in East Kilbride's centre aimed
primarily at the business person. *Rooms 79. Beauty and hair salon. Access,
Amex, Visa,*

East Kilbride **Stuart Hotel** 62%	£60
Tel 035 52 21161 Fax 035 52 64410	**H**
Cornwall Way East Kilbride Strathclyde G74 1JR	**Map 12 B2**

A modern hotel whose day rooms include two bars and a function suite
with an unusual brass ceiling. Biggest and best bedrooms are Executives.
Conference facilities for up to 200, banqueting for 150. *Rooms 39. Closed
25 Dec, 1 Jan. Access, Amex, Visa,*

East Kilbride   Places of Interest

The Ice Bowl Ice Rink Tel 03552 44065.

Edinburgh **Alp-Horn**	£42
Tel 031-225 4787	**R**
167 Rose Street Edinburgh Lothian EH2 4LS	**Map 12 C1**

Swiss restaurant with pine-clad columns and ceiling, alpine landscape scenes
and cowbells lending an authentic air. Cheese and beef fondues (for two or
more) are well-executed specialities, but air-dried Swiss beef and ham, veal
sausage (*kalbsbratwurst*), venison with apple and cranberry sauce and spätzli,
plus *emincé de veau zurichoise* with rösti potatoes are also faithful to their
origins. Apfel strudel is made on the premises. Lunchtimes see a sensibly-
priced 2- or 3-course menu and a shortened à la carte. Try the Swiss wines,
even though they may seem expensive alongside the rest of the wine list.
*Seats 62. Parties 18. Private Room. L 12-2 D 6.30-10. Closed Sun, 25 & 26
Dec, 1 & 2 Jan, local holidays. Set L £9.25. Access, Visa.*

Edinburgh **L'Auberge**	£75
Tel 031-556 5888	**R**
56 St Mary Street Edinburgh Lothian EH1 1SX	**Map 12 C1**

Daniel Wencker's long-established (19 years) and comfortable French
restaurant is in Edinburgh's 'old town'. The sensibly short carte might
include ravioli of salmon with fresh mussels and chervil or puff pastry

lattice of Orkney scallops with an Oriental dressing, followed by roasted supreme and thigh of Border guinea fowl with tarragon and button onions or fillet of Scottish beef with woodland mushrooms and a red wine jus. 2- and 3-course fixed-price lunches (including Sundays) and a 3-course fixed-price dinner are also offered. Lots of half bottles on an extenisve French wine list, but few bargains among the classics; better value in lesser-known names. **Seats 50**. *Parties 20. L 12.15-2 D 6.30-9.30 (Sat to 10). Closed 25 & 26 Dec, 1st 2 wks Jan. Set L £10.95 (from £11.45 Sun) Set D £19.85. Access, Amex, Visa,* ◐ Diners Club International

---

Edinburgh   The Balmoral   83%   £185

Tel 031-556 2414   Fax 031-557 3747   **HR**

Princes Street Edinburgh Lothian EH2 2EQ   Map 12 C1

An established landmark with its prominent clock tower next to Waverley Station (at the eastern end of Princes Street), the North British was one of the greatest of all the railway hotels, originally built in 1902. Following a major modernisation and refurbishment programme, much of the Victorian splendour and shape of the building remains, particularly in the public areas. A kilted doorman greets you on arrival at the renamed Balmoral and will arrange to park your car; there's a magnificent and opulent entrance foyer featuring solid marble, ornate columns, glittering chandeliers, plush carpeting and seating and delightful flower arrangements, overlooked by a balustraded gallery. The reception desk is hidden around a corner and the staff carry out their duties efficiently and with a smile. To the rear of the foyer lies the elegant Palm Court Lounge (*the* place for afternoon tea or morning coffee) and there's a discreet Lobby Bar and Perrin's Wine Bar well away from the entrance. Luxurious bedrooms with splendid decorations and furnishings throughout, including special rooms for non-smokers, disabled and female guests. Complimentary herbal tea on arrival, linen sheets, a carriage clock and professional hairdryer are pluses, but no telephones on desks or in bathrooms, nor fresh milk in otherwise well-stocked mini-bars, are minuses. Bathrooms are also all they should be, with bathrobes and quality toiletries provided, but do not provide shaving mirrors. Turn-down service at night, superb and comprehensive leisure complex (there's even a TV in the sauna!), and a business centre. Now a Forte Grand hotel. **Rooms 189**. *24hr room service, health club. Access, Amex, Visa,* ◐ Diners Club International

Grill Room   NEW   £75

Steps lead down from Princes Street to a magnificent, spacious room panelled in shiny maroon, with a large central chandelier and pictures that range from 17th-century bowls of fruit to modern watercolours. Discreet, professional staff serve from a menu that combines traditional grills and a daily roast with chef Ralph Kutzner's specialities: these could include lightly smoked sea bass on a truffle sauce, pressed duck (for two, order in advance) and medallions of venison in a white pepper sauce. The set lunch price includes wine. **Seats 50**. *Parties 10. L 12-2.15 D 7-10.30. Closed L Sat & Sun. Set L £15.50 Set D £27.50.*

Bridges Brasserie   £36

A brasserie in the Continental style, with an all-day menu of salads, sandwiches, appetisers (stuffed mushrooms, quiche, paté) and main courses (fish and chips, veal escalope, grilled rib-eye steak). Also a wide selection of cakes and pastries, coffees and teas. **Seats 95**. *Parties 12. Meals 7am-11pm. Set L £9.50.*

Edinburgh   Barnton Thistle   63%   £113

Tel 031-339 1144   Fax 031-339 5521   **H**

Queensferry Road Edinburgh Lothian EH4 6AS   Map 12 C1

On the A90, handy for airport and city centre, providing modern comfort for both leisure and business visitors. Conference/banqueting facilities for 130/100. **Rooms 50**. *Access, Amex, Visa,* ◐ Diners Club International

Edinburgh   Braid Hills Hotel   60%   £78

Tel 031-447 8888   Fax 031-452 8477   **H**

134 Braid Road Edinburgh Lothian EH10 6JD   **Map 12 C1**

Entrance through the the the sun-lounge leads to a hotel full of warmth and
character, with deep-red walls, stained-glass windows, fringed lampshades
and vintage furniture. Lofty, comfortable bedrooms combine modern and
more traditional furnishings. *Rooms 69. Garden. Access, Amex, Visa,*
Diners Club International

Edinburgh   Caledonian Hotel   79%   £192

Tel 031-225 2433   Fax 031-225 6632   **HR**

Princes Street Edinburgh Lothian EH1 2AB   **Map 12 C1**

Affectionately known as 'the Caley', the hotel stands on the site of the old
Caledonian railway station and is one mile from the current Waverley
station. The carpeted foyer leads to a grand, gracefully proportioned and
elegant lounge, furnished with plush shot-silk sofas. Carriages Bar retains
the redbrick former station entrance as an inside wall and was recently
refurbished. Bedrooms are individually styled, featuring well-chosen
furniture and luxurious drapes; 5th-floor rooms are smaller than some of
the others; the process of bedroom refurbishment is continuing. Towelling
robes are provided in all the bathrooms, which include a TV/radio
speaker; elegant antique-style fittings in Executive bathrooms. Plus factors
are the number of telephone extensions in the rooms, 24hr lounge service,
a turn-down service and chocolates at night. Families are particularly well
catered for. No dogs. Conference facilities for up to 400; banqueting for
220. Queens Moat Houses. *Rooms 240. News kiosk. Access, Amex, Visa,*
Diners Club International

Pompadour Room   £100

The Pompadour is elegant and formal; ornate plasterwork frames large
wall paintings of delicate flowers, a pianist plays soothing music and
excellent staff provide impeccable service. Chef Tony Binks features
Scottish dishes each lunchtime as *Legends of the Scottish Table* while in the
evenings the other side of the *Auld Alliance* is reflected in a modern French
menu (including a five-course *menu dégustation*). Good French and Scottish
cheeses. *Seats 50. Parties 10. L 12.30-2.30 D 7.30-10.30. Closed L Sat &
Sun, also D Sun Nov-Mar. Set L £17.95 Set D £38.50*

Carriages Restaurant   £60

The hotel's second restaurant serves familiar dishes like French onion soup,
tournedos Rossini, roast duckling and grilled Dover sole along with a few
Scottish favourites such as Musselburgh pie and haggis. Exemplary staff.
Seats 150. L 12.30-2.30 D 6.30-10. Set L £12.95.

Edinburgh   Carlton Highland   68%   £138

Tel 031-556 7277   Fax 031-556 2691   **H**

North Bridge Edinburgh Lothian EH16 6XY   **Map 12 C1**

Besides well-equipped bedrooms and comfortable day rooms the Carlton
Highland has a fine leisure centre, conference facilities for up to 350, two
restaurants and a night club with dancing and live entertainment Tuesday
to Saturday. Children up to 14 stay free in their parents' room (15 rooms
suitable for family use). *Rooms 199. Indoor swimming pool, gymnasium, spa
bath, sauna, solarium, steam room, squash, snooker, hair & beauty salon, coffee
shop (10am-6pm). Access, Amex, Visa,* Diners Club International

Edinburgh   Channings   64%   £105
Tel 031-315 2226   Fax 031-332 9631   PH
South Learmouth Gardens Edinburgh Lothian EH4 1EZ   Map 12 C1

A series of fine adjoining Georgian town houses a few minutes walk from
the city centre. Traditional features – oak panelling, high moulded ceilings,
ornate fireplaces, antique furniture and prints – remain in the peaceful
lounges, while the bedrooms (some overlooking old Edinburgh) are
individually furnished in a more contemporary manner. Staff are friendly
and there's a relaxed ambience throughout this privately owned hotel,
where children up to 14 years can stay free in their parents' rooms.
Rooms 48. *Terrace. Access, Amex, Visa,*

Edinburgh   Forte Posthouse   62%   £67
Tel 031-334 0390   Fax 031-334 9237   H
Corstorphine Road Edinburgh Lothian EH12 6UA   Map 12 C1

On the A8 halfway between airport and city centre, with both
Murrayfield (for the rugby) and the zoo nearby. Conference facilities for
up to 120 delegates. **Rooms 208.** *Access, Amex, Visa,*

Edinburgh   Forte Travelodge   £40
Tel 031-441 4296   L
A720 Dreghorn Link City bypass Edinburgh Lothian EH13 9QR   Map 12 C1

On the eastbound carriageway of the A720 Edinburgh City bypass at
Dreghorn, and 8 miles south of the city centre. **Rooms 40.**
Access, Amex, Visa.

Edinburgh   George Inter-Continental Hotel   74%   £163
Tel 031-225 1251   Fax 031-226 5644   H
19 George Street Edinburgh Lothian EH2 2PB   Map 12 C1

Very conveniently located for the shopping on Edinburgh's Princes Street.
The classical facade conceals a grand entrance lobby complete with elegant,
fluted Corinthian columns, polished marble floors and a raised seating area
behind a wooden balustrade from where one can observe the busy comings
and goings. Other public areas include a clubby Gathering of the Clans bar
sporting clan mementos and curios from the whisky trade. Luxurious
bedrooms have comfortable settees or armchairs and quality freestanding
furniture (mostly in yew wood), teletext TVs and beverage facilities neatly
hidden away in cabinets. Conference/banqueting facilities for 200/250.
Rooms 195. *News kiosk, 24hr lounge service, dinner dance (Saturdays). Access,
Amex, Visa,*

Edinburgh   Granada Lodge   £43
Tel 031-653 2427   Fax 031-653 6106   L
A1 Musselburgh Bypass Musselburgh Edinburgh Lothian EH21 8RE   Map 12 C1

Rooms 44. *Access, Amex, Visa,*

Edinburgh   Hilton National   68%   £150
Tel 031-332 2545   Fax 031-332 3805   H
69 Belford Road Edinburgh Lothian EH4 3DG   Map 12 C1

A modern hotel just a few minutes walk from Princes Street. Public areas
centre on a glitzy, split-level cocktail bar; a more pubby bar is to be found
in what was on old flour mill. **Rooms 144.** *Access, Amex, Visa,*

Edinburgh   Holiday Inn Garden Court   65%   £91

Tel 031-332 2442   Fax 031-332 3408   **H**

107 Queensferry Road Edinburgh Lothian EH4 3HL   Map 12 C1

Formerly a Crest hotel, now the only Garden Court not purpose-built.
Bedrooms are somewhat smaller than the normal Holiday Inn standard and
36 of the single rooms have shower and WC only. Meeting rooms for up
to 70. Ample free parking. *Rooms 119. Gymnasium. Access, Amex, Visa,*

Edinburgh   Howard Hotel   75%   £160

Tel 031-557 3500   Fax 031-557 6515   **H**

36 Great King Street Edinburgh Lothian EH3 6QH   Map 12 C1

A stark exterior designed by James Craig (1766) conceals a wealth of
architectural splendour. Three inter-connected town houses now make up
the Howard, employing the three domed stairwells as a unifying theme.
Service lives up to the elegant and civilised ambience given splendour by
crystal chandeliers, marble fireplaces, Scottish antiques and wallcoverings
that evoke the grandeur of the 18th century. Bedrooms have consummate
style and comfort, with individual colour schemes making best use of
irregular room shapes and available daylight; a valeting service is offered.
Bathrooms echo the period without detracting from the comforts
provided: twin basins, shower stalls, luxury lighting, toiletries and
bathrobes. Children are accommodated free of charge when sharing their
parents' room. No dogs. *Rooms 16. Garden, valeting. Access, Amex, Visa,*

Edinburgh   Indian Cavalry Club   £42

Tel 031-228 3282   **R**

3 Atholl Place Edinburgh Lothian EH3 8HP   Map 12 C1

Modern Indian cooking with an emphasis on steaming; the menu
unusually suggests side dishes as suitable accompaniments for main-course
dishes and also suggested wines to match. Stylish setting with enormous
swagged curtains. Downstairs, the Tiffin Room offers lighter snacks in a
bar setting. *Also at:* 8-10 Eyre Place (Tel 031-556 2404). *Seats 73. Parties
6. Private Room. L 12-2.30 D 5.30-11.30. Set L from £6.95 Set D from
£9.95 (vegetarian) & £15.95. Access, Amex, Visa,*

Edinburgh   Kalpna   £35

Tel 031-667 9890   **R**

2 St Patrick Square Edinburgh Lothian EH8 9EZ   Map 12 C1

Gujerati vegetarian food has few finer homes than Kalpna, a non-smoking
restaurant in the student area. Their elephant logo was designed to show
that you can be big, strong and intelligent without eating meat. Here you
will feast on bhel poori, dosa masala, wok-fried vegetables with ginger,
nuts and a sweet/sour sauce, special rice dishes like basmati with coconut,
lentils, lemon and coriander, stuffed paratha bread, carrot-based halva with
almonds and cardamom and gulab jaman. The lunchtime buffet starts at
£3.50, and there are various price options in the evening with a choice of
set thali meals. New sister restaurant, *Spices*, at 110, West Bow Street,
Grassmarket is not exclusively vegetarian. *Seats 65. Parties 30. Private
Room. L 12-2 D 5.30-10.30. Closed L Sat, all Sun, Xmas/New Year. Set L
from £3.50 Set D from £8. Access, Visa.*

Edinburgh   Kelly's   £55

Tel 031-668 3847   **R**

46 West Richmond Street Edinburgh Lothian EH8 9DZ   Map 12 C1

In a former baker's shop in a Georgian block just off the Pleasance, Jeff and
Jacquie Kelly run one of Edinburgh's better restaurants. The room is small
and L-shaped, with wall lamps, plants, tubular chairs and pink napery.

Cooking is modern British, and the short, fixed-price dinner menu is full of good things: moist, full-of-flavour galantine of duck with Cumberland sauce; a beautifully balanced turbot parcel with a seafood mousse and a leek and lemon timbale with a dill beurre blanc; lemon tart with crème anglaise. No smoking before 9 pm. *Seats 36. Parties 20. D only 6.45-9.45. Closed Sun & Mon, 1st week Jan, 1st 3 weeks Oct. Set D £18.50. Access, Amex, Visa.*

Edinburgh   King James Thistle   70%   £128

Tel 031-556 0111   Fax 031-557 5333   **H**

St James Centre 107 Leith Street Edinburgh Lothian EH1 3SW   Map 12 C1

Accommodation is first rate at this luxurious hotel in a position that's ideal for both business and tourist visitors. Double-glazing keeps traffic noise at bay, and bedrooms with chic co-ordinated soft furnishings have smart darkwood furniture, good writing areas and mini-bars. En-suite bathrooms are well equipped, with powerful showers. Twenty bedrooms are set aside for non-smokers and there are several Lady Executive rooms. Public areas are split between the ground and third floors. The street-level foyer-lounge is elegant, with marble-effect floor, chandelier and comfortable winged armchairs. The American-themed bar, brasseries and cocktail bar are reached by means of a swift and efficient lift. The hotel is linked to a shopping centre. Conference/banqueting facilities for 250. *Rooms 147. Access, Amex, Visa,* **Diners Club International**

Edinburgh   Martin's   £75

Tel 031-225 3106   **R**

70 Rose Street North Lane Edinburgh Lothian EH2 3DX   Map 12 C1

Don't be put off by the somewhat unprepossessing cobbled back lane near Princes Street where Martin's is to be found. Inside, Martin and Gay Irons nurture their customers in a restaurant where clever lighting and lots of fresh flowers create a charming atmosphere. Chef Forbes Stott produces short daily-changing menus utilising good ingredients (most of the vegetables are organically grown and Martin's father provides the herbs from his own garden) that are simply but carefully cooked in dishes like green pepper and mushroom soup, braised squid with tomato and fennel seeds, pan-fried gurnard with capers and onion, or grilled breast of chicken with rosemary. Fixed-price, two-course lunches offer a small choice. Desserts might range from apple and muscatel strudel with caramel ice cream to interesting sorbets (elderflower and mango) and hot banana and almond tartlet. Unpasteurised Scottish and Irish cheeses. No background music. No smoking. Sensibly-priced wines on a decent list. *Seats 28. Parties 8. Private Room. L 12-2 D 7-10. Closed L Sat, all Sun & Mon, 4 weeks Dec/Jan, 1 week Oct. Set L £9.95. Access, Amex, Visa,* **Diners Club International**

Edinburgh   Pierre Victoire   £40

Tel 031-226 2442   **R**

38 Grassmarket Edinburgh Lothian EH1 2JU   Map 12 C1

Food is more important than decor and the sometimes hectic service is friendly and informal at three no-frills bistros. The menus offer some interesting variations on bistro fare: baked oysters with crispy bacon and hollandaise; sole, smoked salmon and spinach roulade with lemon cream; roast chicken breast stuffed with seafood mousse and fresh mint; rare rib-eye steak with watercress and red wine. *Also at:* 10 Victoria Street Tel 031-225 1721 and 18 Union Street Tel 031-557 8451. *Seats 45. Parties 30. Private Room. L 12-3 D 6-11. Closed Sun except Aug, 25 & 26 Dec, 1 & 2 Jan. Set L £4.90. Access.*

Edinburgh	**Ristorante Raffaelli**	£40
Tel 031-225 6060		R
10 Randolph Place Edinburgh Lothian		Map 12 C1

A sophisticated setting for generally mainstream Italian cooking. Good home-made pasta in a dish like ravioli with fresh sage in a rich cream sauce and tender veal just falls off the bone in a garlicky osso buco. Rather mundane desserts on the trolley but good Italian cheeses: provolone, dolcelatte, pecorino. Snacks in the wine bar next door. *Seats 60. Parties 20. Private Room. L 12.15-2.30 D 6.30-9.30 (Sat to 10). Closed L Sat, all Sun, 25 & 26 Dec, 1 & 2 Jan. Access, Amex, Visa,*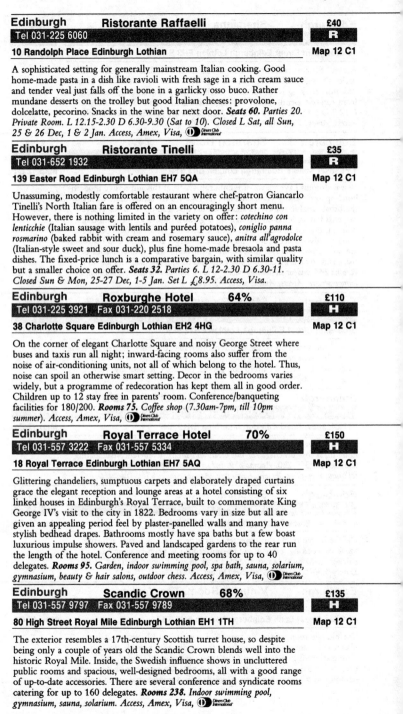

Edinburgh	**Ristorante Tinelli**	£35
Tel 031-652 1932		R
139 Easter Road Edinburgh Lothian EH7 5QA		Map 12 C1

Unassuming, modestly comfortable restaurant where chef-patron Giancarlo Tinelli's North Italian fare is offered on an encouragingly short menu. However, there is nothing limited in the variety on offer: *cotechino con lenticchie* (Italian sausage with lentils and puréed potatoes), *coniglio panna rosmarino* (baked rabbit with cream and rosemary sauce), *anitra all'agrodolce* (Italian-style sweet and sour duck), plus fine home-made bresaola and pasta dishes. The fixed-price lunch is a comparative bargain, with similar quality but a smaller choice on offer. *Seats 32. Parties 6. L 12-2.30 D 6.30-11. Closed Sun & Mon, 25-27 Dec, 1-5 Jan. Set L £8.95. Access, Visa.*

Edinburgh	**Roxburghe Hotel**	64%	£110
Tel 031-225 3921 Fax 031-220 2518			H
38 Charlotte Square Edinburgh Lothian EH2 4HG			Map 12 C1

On the corner of elegant Charlotte Square and noisy George Street where buses and taxis run all night; inward-facing rooms also suffer from the noise of air-conditioning units, not all of which belong to the hotel. Thus, noise can spoil an otherwise smart setting. Decor in the bedrooms varies widely, but a programme of redecoration has kept them all in good order. Children up to 12 stay free in parents' room. Conference/banqueting facilities for 180/200. *Rooms 75. Coffee shop (7.30am-7pm, till 10pm summer). Access, Amex, Visa,*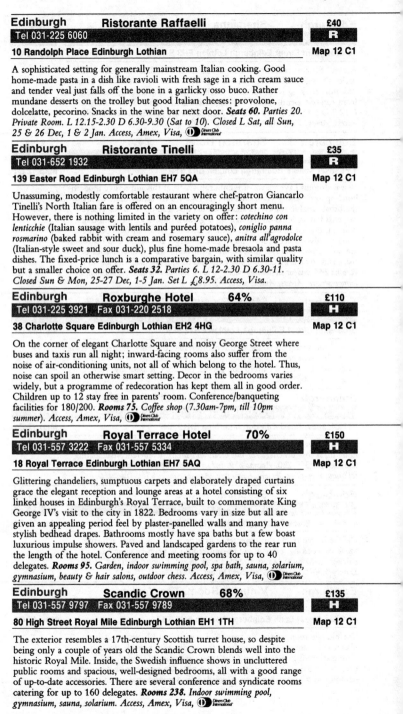

Edinburgh	**Royal Terrace Hotel**	70%	£150
Tel 031-557 3222 Fax 031-557 5334			H
18 Royal Terrace Edinburgh Lothian EH7 5AQ			Map 12 C1

Glittering chandeliers, sumptuous carpets and elaborately draped curtains grace the elegant reception and lounge areas at a hotel consisting of six linked houses in Edinburgh's Royal Terrace, built to commemorate King George IV's visit to the city in 1822. Bedrooms vary in size but all are given an appealing period feel by plaster-panelled walls and many have stylish bedhead drapes. Bathrooms mostly have spa baths but a few boast luxurious impulse showers. Paved and landscaped gardens to the rear run the length of the hotel. Conference and meeting rooms for up to 40 delegates. *Rooms 95. Garden, indoor swimming pool, spa bath, sauna, solarium, gymnasium, beauty & hair salons, outdoor chess. Access, Amex, Visa,*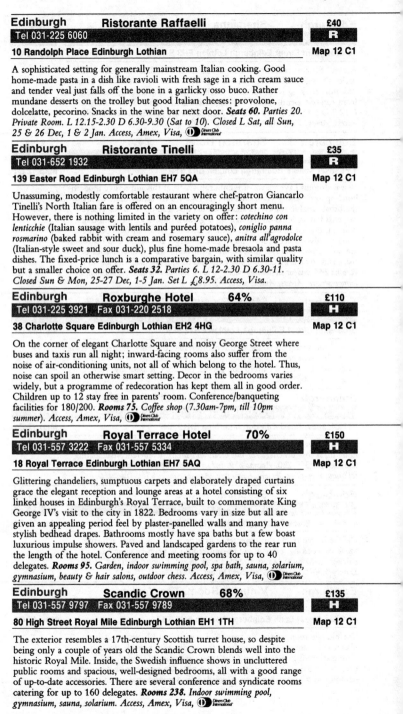

Edinburgh	**Scandic Crown**	68%	£135
Tel 031-557 9797 Fax 031-557 9789			H
80 High Street Royal Mile Edinburgh Lothian EH1 1TH			Map 12 C1

The exterior resembles a 17th-century Scottish turret house, so despite being only a couple of years old the Scandic Crown blends well into the historic Royal Mile. Inside, the Swedish influence shows in uncluttered public rooms and spacious, well-designed bedrooms, all with a good range of up-to-date accessories. There are several conference and syndicate rooms catering for up to 160 delegates. *Rooms 238. Indoor swimming pool, gymnasium, sauna, solarium. Access, Amex, Visa,*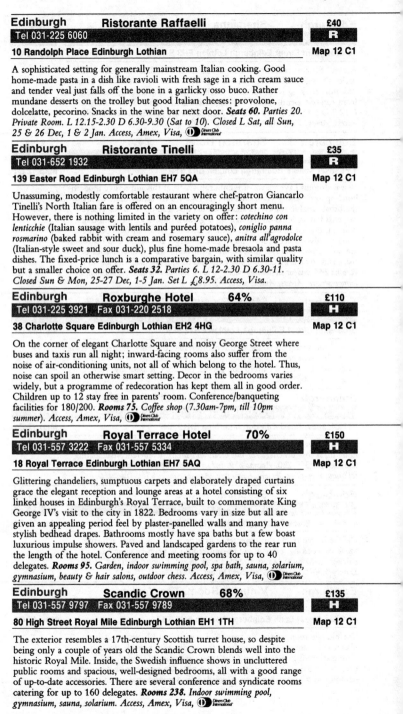

Edinburgh   Shamiana   £40

Tel 031-228 2265   **R**

14 Brougham Street Edinburgh Lothian EH3 9JH   Map 12 C1

Around the corner from the King's Theatre is an Indian restaurant with
decidedly untypical black, white and grey-tiled decor. North-West Indian
Kashmiri cooking is the speciality with subtle spicing ringing the changes
from run-of-the-mill Indian cooking. *Seats 43. Parties 6. Private Room.
L 12-2 D 6-11.30. Closed L Sat & Sun, 25 Dec, 1 Jan. Set L from £5.95.
Access, Amex, Visa,* ⓓ Diners Club International

Edinburgh   Sheraton Hotel   74%   £199

Tel 031-229 9131   Fax 031-228 4510   **H**

1 Festival Square Edinburgh Lothian EH3 9SR   Map 12 C1

Best bedrooms have views of Edinburgh Castle at this impressive modern
hotel opposite Usher Hall. Cars and luggage are efficiently dealt with and
the broad marble walkways and escalators that lead up to the extensive,
carpeted lounge areas on the first floor give an impression of spaciousness
which is carried right through to the bedrooms. Decor throughout the
hotel has always been rather bland but the large, air-conditioned bedrooms
are now more colourful than before. Bathrooms are less liberal with both
space and towelling. Large conference and banqueting facilities for 485.
*Rooms 263. Indoor swimming pool, spa bath, sauna, solarium, gymnasium, 24hr
lounge service. Access, Amex, Visa,* ⓓ Diners Club International

Edinburgh   Stakis Grosvenor Hotel   64%   £106

Tel 031-226 6001   Fax 031-220 2387   **H**

Grosvenor Street Edinburgh Lothian EH12 5EF   Map 12 C1

Behind the Victorian facade of this comfortable, centrally situated hotel are
sombrely decorated modern rooms. Banqueting facilities for 450 and
conference facilities for up to 300 people. No dogs. *Rooms 136. Access,
Amex, Visa,* ⓓ Diners Club International

Edinburgh   Swallow Royal Scot   65%   £120

Tel 031-334 9191   Fax 031-316 4507   **H**

111 Glasgow Road Edinburgh Lothian EH12 8NF   Map 12 C1

Five miles west of the city centre, two miles from the airport, a large 70s
hotel that's low on character but clean and smart. Conference/banqueting
facilities for 350/250. *Rooms 259. Indoor swimming pool, spa bath, sauna,
solarium, keep-fit equipment, hair salon. Access, Amex, Visa,* ⓓ Diners Club International

Edinburgh   Szechuan House   £25

Tel 031-229 4655   **R**

95 Gilmore Place Edinburgh Lothian EH3 9NU   Map 12 C1

Off the beaten track, this unpretentious little restaurant serves authentic
Szechuan cooking, particularly tea-smoked duck, peppery gong bao
chicken, fried mussels and shredded pork in fish flavour. *Seats 44. Parties 8.
D only 5.30-12. Closed Mon. Set D from £9.20. Access, Visa.*

Edinburgh   Vintners Room, The Vaults   £55

Tel 031-554 6767   **R**

87 Giles Street Leith Edinburgh Lothian EH6 6BZ   Map 12 C1

The old sale room of the Vintners' Guild with its 17th-century Italian
plasterwork (smoke-blackened from the candles that provide the only
illumination) is home to Tim Cumming's appealingly robust, well-
executed cooking. Wild boar, rabbit and pistachio terrine with conserves,
salmon and sole ramekin with seaweed, grilled mussels and queen scallops

with almond butter, home-made fettuccine, oxtail with grapes, sea trout
with scallops, salsify and chervil, paupiettes of veal with hazelnuts and
balsamic vinegar are all typical of his style – modern combinations using
market-fresh ingredients. Leave room for the good selection of puddings:
prune, armagnac and almond tart, chocolate parfait with coffee bean sauce,
sticky toffee pudding, pears in red wine with cinnamon cream. Informal
lunch in the Long Room offers a 2- or 3-course, fixed-price menu with a
small choice (perhaps pigeon salad, red mullet with fennel and brandy snap
baskets with coffee and walnut ice cream); the setting is more formal for
dinner. No smoking. Predominantly French wine list, keenly priced, with
an excellent selection of wies by the glass. *Seats 65. Parties 25. Private
Room. L 12-2.30 D 7-10.30. Closed Sun, 2 wks Xmas. Set L from £9.*
Access, Amex, Visa,

Edinburgh   Places of Interest

Tourist Information   Tel 031-557 1700.
Edinburgh Airport Tourist Information   Tel 031-333 2167.
British Rail, Waverley Station   Tel 031-556 2451.
Busline   Tel 031-225 3858.
St. Giles Cathedral   Tel 031-225 4363.
St Mary's R.C. Cathedral   Tel 031-225 2978.
Clan Tartan Centre   Tel 031-553 5161.
Meadowbank Sports Centre and Stadium   Tel 031-661 5351.
Hillend Ski Centre   Tel 031-445 4433.
Central Cycle Hire   Tel 031-228 6333.
Portobello Swimming Pool   Tel 031-667 7211
Royal Commonwealth Pool   Tel 031-667 7211
Murrayfield Ice Rink   Tel 031-337 6933.
Edinburgh Zoo   Tel 031-334 9171.
Ingliston Motor Racing Circuit   Tel 041-641 2553.
Camera Obscura   Tel 031-226 3709.
Edinburgh Experience   Tel 031-556 4636.
   Theatres and Concert Halls
Church Hill Theatre   Tel 031-447 7597.
Festival Fringe: Enquiries Tel 031-226 5257.
International Festival Box Office   Tel 031-225 5756.
Kings Theatre   Tel 031-229 1201.
Netherbow Arts Centre   Tel 031-556 9579.
Playhouse Theatre   Tel 031-557 2590.
Royal Lyceum Theatre   Tel 031-229 9697.
Queens Hall   Tel 031-668 2019.
Traverse Theatre   Tel 031-226 2633.
Usher Hall   Tel 031-228 1155.
   Historic Houses, Castles and Gardens
Dalkeith Country Park   Tel 031-663 5684.
Edinburgh Castle   Tel 031-225 9846.
Edinburgh Dungeon   Tel 031-225 1331.
Craigmillar Castle   Tel 031-661 4445.
Dalmeny House   South Queensferry Tel 031-331 1888.
Edinburgh Butterfly and Insect World   Lasswade Tel 031-663 4932.
Hopetoun House   South Queensferry Tel 031-331 2451.
The Georgian House   Tel 031-225 2160.
Lennoxlove   Haddington. Tel 062 082 3720.
Palace of Holyroodhouse   Tel 031-556 7371.
Royal Botanic Garden   Tel 031-552 7171.
   Museums and Art Galleries
The Fruitmarket Gallery   Tel 031-225 2383.
Edinburgh Crystal Visitor Centre   Penicuik Tel 0968 75128.
Collective Gallery   Tel 031-220 1260.
Edinburgh Gallery   Tel 031-557 5227.
Royal Scottish Academy   Tel 031-225 6671.
Edinburgh University Collection of Historical Instruments   Tel 031-447
   4791.
Huntly House Museum and Museum of Childhood   Tel 031-225 2424.

National Gallery of Scotland Tel 031-556 8921.
Scottish National Portrait Gallery Tel 031-556 8921.
Scottish National Gallery of Modern Art Tel 031-556 8921.
Royal Museum of Scotland Tel 031-225 7534.
Scottish Whisky Heritage Centre Tel 031-220 0441.

Elgin   Mansion House   67%   £95
Tel 0343 548811   Fax 0343 547916   **H**
The Haugh Moray Elgin Grampian IV30 1AN   Map 16 C3

Set in gardens next to the river Lossie, the turreted mansion built in the
mid-19th century is within a stone's throw of the town centre. The
chandeliered entrance hall makes a good first impression, and spruce day
rooms comprise the piano lounge (a favourite pre-dinner meeting place),
the Wee Bar and the still room with its whisky collection. Good-sized
bedrooms offer a lot of extras, from a welcoming glass of sherry to mini-
bars, tea-makers, hairdryers and trouser presses. A staircase connects the
bedrooms to the Country Club, whose facilities include an all-day snack
bar. Conference/banqueting for 180/200. No dogs. *Rooms 23. Garden,
sauna, spa bath, gymnasium, snooker. Access, Amex, Visa,*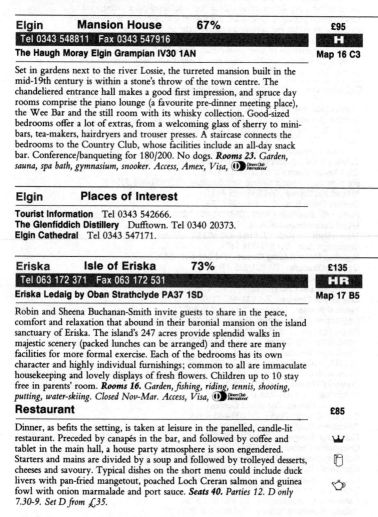

Elgin   Places of Interest
Tourist Information Tel 0343 542666.
The Glenfiddich Distillery Dufftown. Tel 0340 20373.
Elgin Cathedral Tel 0343 547171.

Eriska   Isle of Eriska   73%   £135
Tel 063 172 371   Fax 063 172 531   **HR**
Eriska Ledaig by Oban Strathclyde PA37 1SD   Map 17 B5

Robin and Sheena Buchanan-Smith invite guests to share in the peace,
comfort and relaxation that abound in their baronial mansion on the island
sanctuary of Eriska. The island's 247 acres provide splendid walks in
majestic scenery (packed lunches can be arranged) and there are many
facilities for more formal exercise. Each of the bedrooms has its own
character and highly individual furnishings; common to all are immaculate
housekeeping and lovely displays of fresh flowers. Children up to 10 stay
free in parents' room. *Rooms 16. Garden, fishing, riding, tennis, shooting,
putting, water-skiing. Closed Nov-Mar. Access, Visa,*

Restaurant   £85

Dinner, as befits the setting, is taken at leisure in the panelled, candle-lit
restaurant. Preceded by canapés in the bar, and followed by coffee and
tablet in the main hall, a house party atmosphere is soon engendered.
Starters and mains are divided by a soup and followed by trolleyed desserts,
cheeses and savoury. Typical dishes on the short menu could include duck
livers with pan-fried mangetout, poached Loch Creran salmon and guinea
fowl with onion marmalade and port sauce. *Seats 40. Parties 12. D only
7.30-9. Set D from £35.*

Erskine   Forte Posthouse   62%   £62
Tel 041-812 0123   Fax 041-812 7642   **H**
by Erskine Bridge Strathclyde PA8 6AN   Map 12 B1

Close to the M8 on the south side of Erskine Bridge. Conference facilities
for up to 600, banqueting to 450. *Rooms 166. Indoor swimming pool, keep-fit
equipment, spa bath, sauna, solarium, beautician, children's playground, pitch and
putt. Access, Amex, Visa,*

Ettrickbridge   Ettrickshaws Hotel   62%   £72
Tel 0750 52229 · **H**
Ettrickbridge Selkirk Borders TD7 5HW   Map 12 D2

A turn-of-the-century house standing in spectacular countryside 45 miles from Edinburgh. The drawing room, bar and restaurant all enjoy the views, and all the public rooms are weather-proofed by log fires. The bedrooms are of a good size, with varying decor and traditional furniture; all overlook the river and hills. No children under nine. *Rooms 6. Garden, game fishing. Closed Dec & Jan. Access, Visa,* ⓘ

Falkirk   Hotel Cladhan   60%   £82
Tel 0324 27421   Fax 0324 611436 · **H**
Kemper Avenue Falkirk Central FK1 1UF   Map 12 C1

Behind the somewhat unprepossessing modern exterior the Cladhan's interior is stylish and attractive. Public areas are open-plan and designed in a striking modern style with an art deco influence. The bedrooms are light and airy, with good-quality fitted furniture and thermostatically controlled heating. The hotel can cater for banquets and conferences for up to 250. *Rooms 37. Garden. Access, Amex, Visa,* ⓘ

Falkirk   Pierre's   £50
Tel 0324 35843 · **R**
140 Graham's Road Falkirk Central FK2 7BQ   Map 12 C1

Pierre Renjard is the chef/patron at this pleasant little corner of France. His menus stick in the main to tried and tested favourites from the French bistro repertoire: moules marinière, soupe de poissons, French onion soup, scampi provençale, steak au poivre, salade paysanne, crepes flambées. *Seats 38. Parties 25. L 12-2 D 6.45-9.30 (Sat from 7). Closed L Sat, all Sun & Mon, 1-4 Jan. Set L £6.95 Set D £10.85. Access, Amex, Visa,* ⓘ

Falkirk   Places of Interest

Tourist Information Tel 0324 20244.
  Museums and Art Galleries
Kinneil Museum and Roman Fortlet Tel 0506 824318.
Falkirk Museum Tel 0324 24911.

Forfar   Royal Hotel   57%   £63
Tel & Fax 0307 62691 · **H**
Castle Street Forfar Tayside DD8 3AE   Map 17 C4

A modest entrance conceals a thriving, compact, well-kept hotel complete with leisure centre, ballroom and roof garden. A cheerful welcome and real fire greet guests in the tiny tartan reception area with cosy bar and rattan-furnished lounge nearby. Bedrooms, apart from one four-poster room, are small but neat and practical. No dogs. Conferences for up to 220. *Rooms 19. Indoor swimming pool, spa bath, sauna, solarium, hair salon, coffee shop (10am-11pm). Access, Amex, Visa,* ⓘ

Forfar   Places of Interest

Tourist Information Tel 0307 67876.
Edzell Castle and Gardens Nr Brechin. Tel 031-244 3101 *18 miles.*
Barrie's Birthplace (NT) Kirriemuir. Tel 0575 72646 *6 miles.*

Fort William   Crannog Seafood Restaurant   £40
Tel 0397 705589 · **R**
Town Pier Fort William Highland PS33 7NG   Map 17 B4

Converted ticket office and bait store in a quayside setting with views down Loch Linnhe. Scrubbed tables and a simple, mainly fish menu (including a vegetarian dish of the day). Langoustines are a speciality and they smoke salmon, trout and mussels on the premises. Try cranachan (toasted oats with whisky, cream and raspberries), or vacherin (meringue, whipped cream, ginger and Cointreau) to finish. New branch in Glasgow. *Seats 60. Parties 20. L 12-2.30 D 6-9.30. Closed Tue & Wed in winter, all Nov. Access, Visa.*

Fort William   The Factor's House   £57

| Tel 0397 705767   Fax 0397 702953 | RR |

Torlundy Fort William Highland PH33 6SN   Map 17 B4

Dinner at this former manager's house on the Inverlochy Castle Estate is mostly for residents, but outsiders can join in. Soup is followed by, for example, roast lamb or salmon en croute. Charcoal grilled sirloin is always on the menu. *Seats 24. D only 7-9. Closed Mon, also mid Nov-mid Mar. Set D £17.50. Access, Visa,* (Ⓓ) Diners Club International

Rooms   £83

Bedrooms have views of either Ben Nevis or the surrounding hills. Guests have the use of the facilities of Inverlochy Castle. *Rooms 7. Garden*

Fort William   Inverlochy Castle   90%   £220

| Tel 0397 702177/8   Fax 0397 702953 | HR |

Torlundy Fort William Highland PH33 6SN   Map 17 B4

The solidly built stone castle, which is not grand in size (as castles go), enjoys a splendid position in 50 acres of grounds that form a tranquil enclave within the 500-acre Inverlochy Estate. Staying at Inverlochy Castle is special not just because of the grand surroundings, such as the imposing Great Hall with its chandeliers hanging from an elaborately frescoed ceiling, but also due to the high quality of personal service one receives from resident managing director Michael Leonard. (There are occasions, though, when owner Greta Hobbs' erstwhile constant presence is missed.) All day rooms are of impressive dimensions and magnificently appointed to the highest standard. Bedrooms are filled with antique furniture, restful colour schemes and sumptuous soft furnishings. Bathrooms come with huge bath sheets and generously-sized robes. Exemplary standards of housekeeping, along with splendid Scottish breakfasts, complete a memorable experience. Dogs in kennels only. *Rooms 16. Garden, croquet, tennis, game fishing, tennis, snooker. Closed mid Nov-mid Mar. Access, Amex, Visa,* (Ⓓ) Diners Club International

Restaurant   ↑   £95

Dining here is a most civilised affair; a fine room with a pair of massive, heavily-carved sideboards, immaculate table settings with silver cutlery and views across Loch Marak to the mountains beyond; service is attentive and caring. The kitchen, now in Simon Haigh's steady hands, plays its part by using only the finest ingredients to create dishes that do not lose any interest or merit for being relatively uncomplicated and described on the menu without hyperbole. The fixed-price, four-course dinner might include a salad of roasted scallops with a chive oil dressing, carrot and coriander soup, Scottish lobster with baby fennel and tarragon, pot-roasted guinea fowl with morel sauce, and best end of new season's lamb with a salad of garden leaves and herbs. To finish choose between cheese served with home-made oat biscuits and walnut bread, or sweets like redcurrant mousse with a sauce of cherries. At lunchtime they will happily serve just a bowl of soup from the à la carte menu or a full meal. Some value-for-money wines on a generally pricey list that shows all-round depth. *Seats 28. Private Room. L 12.30-1.45 D 7.15-9.30. Set L £21/£24 Set D £39.95.*

Fort William	Mercury Hotel	58%	£88

Tel 0397 703117   Fax 0397 700550

H

Achintore Road Fort William Highland PH33 6RW

Map 17 B4

Functional modern Mount Charlotte Thistle hotel on the A82. The views of Loch Linnhe are a major feature. Children up to 13 stay free in parents' room. *Rooms 86. Pool table. Access, Amex, Visa,*

Fort William	Places of Interest

Tourist Information   Tel 0397 703781.

Gairloch	Creag Mor	66%	£77

Tel 0445 2068   Fax 0445 2044

H

Charleston Gairloch Highland IV21 2AH

Map 16 B3

Larry and Betty Nieto offer year-round hospitality among the spectacular scenery of Wester Ross. The two-level Gallery Lounge enjoys marvellous views and also houses an exhibition of watercolours. In the bar there's a choice of more than 100 whiskies. Bedrooms are neat, bright and well equipped for a comfortable stay. *Rooms 17. Garden, games room, coffee shop (8am-11pm). Access, Visa.*

Gairloch	Places of Interest

Tourist Information   Tel 0445 2130
Inverewe Garden   Tel 044586 356.

Garve	Inchbae Lodge	57%	£54

Tel 099 75 269

H

Inchbae by Garve Highland IV23 2PH

Map 16 B3

Les and Charlotte Mitchell welcome many regulars among the guests at their peaceful hotel, which stands six miles west of Garve on the A835 Inverness-Ullapool road. Day rooms include a lounge and tiny bar; bedrooms are divided between the lodge itself and the Red Cedar Chalet. There are no phones or TVs in the rooms. Families are welcomed, but credit cards are not. *Rooms 12. Garden, clay-pigeon shooting, game fishing.*

Gatehouse of Fleet — Cally Palace 69% £112
Tel 0557 814341   Fax 0557 814522   **H**

Gatehouse of Fleet Dumfries & Galloway DG7 2DL   Map 13 B4

A hundred acres of grounds provide a secluded setting for an 18th-century
mansion with lofty public rooms decorated in Louis XIV style and a plush
cocktail bar. Bedrooms have pleasant decor, good bathrooms and
thoughtful extras. Conference facilities (for up to 80) are well patronised,
and the hotel is also popular for family holidays and special occasions.
*Rooms 54. Indoor swimming pool, sauna, solarium, tennis, games room, dinner
dance (Sat). Closed Jan & Feb. Access, Visa.*

Gatehouse of Fleet — Murray Arms Inn £79
Tel 0557 814207   Fax 0557 814370   **I**

Anne Street Gatehouse of Fleet Dumfries & Galloway DG7 2HY   Map 13 B4

A warm, friendly old posting inn whose hospitable day rooms include the
Burns Room, where the poet reputedly wrote *Scots Wha Hae*. There's also
a little cocktail bar. Bedrooms, all centrally heated, are by no means grand
but lack nothing to provide a good night's rest. These, and the bathrooms,
are kept in very good order. Children up to 16 free in parents' room. The
inn stands on the A75 Dumfries to Stranraer road. *Rooms 13. Garden,
croquet, coffee shop (10am-5pm). Access, Amex, Visa,* **Diners Club International**

Gatehouse of Fleet — Places of Interest

Tourist Information   Tel 0557 814212.

Giffnock — Macdonald Thistle 64% £102
Tel 041-638 2225   Fax 041-638 6231   **H**

Eastwood Toll Giffnock Nr Glasgow Strathclyde G48 6RA   Map 12 B2

Modern commercial hotel convenient for Glasgow Airport (six miles) and
the city centre (five miles). Conference facilities for up to 150, banqueting
up to 100. *Rooms 58. Keep-fit equipment, sauna, solarium. Access, Amex,
Visa,* **Diners Club International**

Glamis — Castleton House 71% £90
Tel 030 784 340   Fax 030 784 506   **HR**

Eassie By Glamis Forfar Tayside DD8 1SJ   Map 17 C5

On the A94 three miles from Glamis Castle, a Victorian hotel has been
turned by William and Maureen Little into a charming little country hotel
with the emphasis on comfort, service and good food. The six bedrooms,
all with en-suite facilities, are furnished with high-quality reproduction
pieces, and there are showers above the dark-panelled tubs. Children stay
free in parents' room. The hotel can arrange shooting and stalking. No
dogs. *Rooms 6. Garden, putting. Access, Amex, Visa.*

Restaurant £48

William uses local produce, plus fruit and vegetables from his own garden,
on a varied menu that includes both fish and meat. Some dishes are as
simple as can be: asparagus hollandaise, roast lamb, grilled Angus beef;
others a bit more out of the ordinary, like potato blinis with sautéed
chicken livers, wild mushrooms and a port and ginger jus, or blackened
cushion of zander served with tomato and gazpacho garnish. No smoking.
Seats 28. Parties 60. L 12-2.30 D 7-9.30. Set L £11.75 Set D £19.50.

Glamis   Places of Interest

Glamis Castle   Tel 030 784 242/3.
Folk Museum   Tel 030 784 288.

Glasgow   Amber

£36

R

Tel 041-339 6121

130 Byres Road Glasgow Strathclyde G12 8TD   Map 12 B1

One of Glasgow's favourite Chinese restaurants. Under colonial fans and red-tinged lights, menus, music and cutlery may appear Westernised but the cooking is authentic. Lunch choices offer remarkable value without compromising quality and the chef's specialities include fried wun tun, stuffed green peppers, Peking and aromatic duck, and a fried combination for two of duck, king prawn, meat, chicken, fish ball, squid and Chinese vegetables. *Seats 70. Parties 70. L 12-2 D 5-11.30 Meals (Sat 12-12). Closed 3 days Chinese New Year. Set L from £4.50 Set D from £12.50. Access, Amex, Visa,* ◑

Glasgow   Ashoka West End

£30

R

Tel 041-339 0936

1284 Argyle Street Glasgow Strathclyde   Map 12 B1

Punjabi restaurant on the corner of Glasgow's longest and shortest streets. Dozens of variations on lamb, chicken and prawn; thalis and set meals for 2+. *Seats 70. Parties 30. D only 5-12.30 (Fri & Sat to 1). Set D from £16.75. Access, Amex, Visa,* ◑

Glasgow   Brasserie on West Regent Street

£42

R

Tel 041-248 3801

176 West Regent Street Glasgow Strathclyde G2 8HF   Map 12 B1

Part of the *Rogano* stable, with the familiar tartan carpet and smart, white-aproned staff, the Brasserie places more contemporary reliance on fresh local and seasonal produce. Simply prepared celery and almond soup and grilled salmon béarnaise share an all-day menu with the more elaborate scampi tartlets provençale and chicken stuffed with smoked salmon. For something lighter for lunch or after the theatre, mussels marinière and ham and haddie with wholemeal bread typify the choice. Friendly wine prices to match the food. *Seats 100. Parties 75. Private Room. L Sat 12-3 D Sat 6-12 Meals Mon-Fri 12-11. Closed Sun, Bank Holidays. Set meals £15. Access, Amex, Visa,* ◑

Glasgow   Buttery

£75

R

Tel 041-221 8188

652 Argyle Street Glasgow Strathclyde G3 8UF   Map 12 B1

Dishes on an esoteric menu involve some unexpected combinations: melon filled with a minted cucumber sorbet and port sauce, mixed game kebab with a redcurrant and thyme sauce, baked cod with a grape and walnut beurre blanc, Buttery fruit platter with lavender jelly – just one of a wide choice for vegetarians. Long list of teas and tisanes. *Seats 54. Parties 12. Private Room. L 12-2.30 D 7-10.30. Closed L Sat, all Sun, Bank Holidays. Set L £14.25. Access, Amex, Visa,* ◑

Glasgow Café Gandolfi £25

Tel 041-552 6813 **R**

64 Albion Street Glasgow Strathclyde Map 12 B1

All-day eating in a bistro-style café that was once a Victorian pub. *Seats 60. Parties 20. Meals 9.30am-11.30pm. Closed Sun, Bank Holidays. No credit cards.*

Glasgow Copthorne Hotel 64% £118

Tel 041-332 6711 Fax 041-332 4264 **H**

George Square Glasgow Strathclyde G2 1DS Map 12 B1

An imposing Victorian landmark with a modern glass colonnade overlooking busy George Square; Queen Street railway station is adjacent. "Classic" and roomier "Connoisseur" bedrooms; under-16s stay free in parents' room. Conference and banqueting suites can accommodate up to 100. *Rooms 140. Access, Amex, Visa,*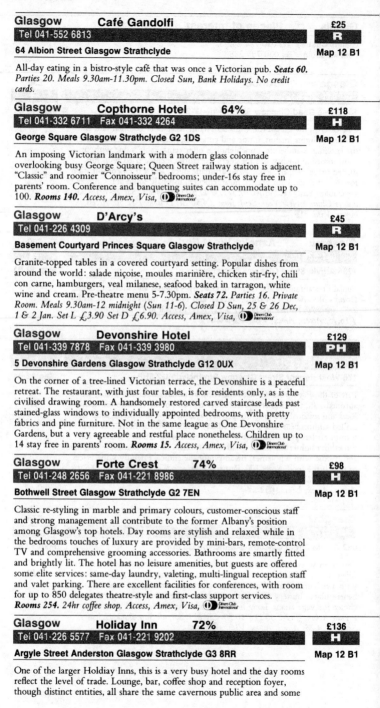

Glasgow D'Arcy's £45

Tel 041-226 4309 **R**

Basement Courtyard Princes Square Glasgow Strathclyde Map 12 B1

Granite-topped tables in a covered courtyard setting. Popular dishes from around the world: salade niçoise, moules marinière, chicken stir-fry, chili con carne, hamburgers, veal milanese, seafood baked in tarragon, white wine and cream. Pre-theatre menu 5-7.30pm. *Seats 72. Parties 16. Private Room. Meals 9.30am-12 midnight (Sun 11-6). Closed D Sun, 25 & 26 Dec, 1 & 2 Jan. Set L £3.90 Set D £6.90. Access, Amex, Visa,*

Glasgow Devonshire Hotel £129

Tel 041-339 7878 Fax 041-339 3980 **PH**

5 Devonshire Gardens Glasgow Strathclyde G12 0UX Map 12 B1

On the corner of a tree-lined Victorian terrace, the Devonshire is a peaceful retreat. The restaurant, with just four tables, is for residents only, as is the civilised drawing room. A handsomely restored carved staircase leads past stained-glass windows to individually appointed bedrooms, with pretty fabrics and pine furniture. Not in the same league as One Devonshire Gardens, but a very agreeable and restful place nonetheless. Children up to 14 stay free in parents' room. *Rooms 15. Access, Amex, Visa,*

Glasgow Forte Crest 74% £98

Tel 041-248 2656 Fax 041-221 8986 **H**

Bothwell Street Glasgow Strathclyde G2 7EN Map 12 B1

Classic re-styling in marble and primary colours, customer-conscious staff and strong management all contribute to the former Albany's position among Glasgow's top hotels. Day rooms are stylish and relaxed while in the bedrooms touches of luxury are provided by mini-bars, remote-control TV and comprehensive grooming accessories. Bathrooms are smartly fitted and brightly lit. The hotel has no leisure amenities, but guests are offered some elite services: same-day laundry, valeting, multi-lingual reception staff and valet parking. There are excellent facilities for conferences, with room for up to 850 delegates theatre-style and first-class support services. *Rooms 254. 24hr coffee shop. Access, Amex, Visa,*

Glasgow Holiday Inn 72% £136

Tel 041-226 5577 Fax 041-221 9202 **H**

Argyle Street Anderston Glasgow Strathclyde G3 8RR Map 12 B1

One of the larger Holdiay Inns, this is a very busy hotel and the day rooms reflect the level of trade. Lounge, bar, coffee shop and reception foyer, though distinct entities, all share the same cavernous public area and some overlook the indoor pool. Bedrooms designated Executive or King Leisure are the best, though few in number, but all rooms benefit from large beds and good seating. Two bedrooms are specially equipped with a variety of high-tech aids for the profoundly deaf. Free parking for residents. *Rooms 298. Indoor swimming pool, sauna, solarium, spa bath, gymnasium, hairdressing, squash, kiosk, coffee shop (10am-9pm). Access, Amex, Visa,*

| Glasgow | Hospitality Inn | 67% | £109 |

Tel 041-332 3311   Fax 041-332 4050

36 Cambridge Street Glasgow Strathclyde G3 3HN   Map 12 B1

Mount Charlotte Thistle hotel with conference suites to hold up to 1500 and a free 250-space car park for residents. Especially roomy de luxe bedrooms and efficient 24hr room service, but otherwise somewhat impersonal. *Rooms 307. Coffee shop (7am-11.30pm). Access, Amex, Visa,*

| Glasgow | Jurys Pond Hotel | 59% | £134 |

Tel 041-334 8161   Fax 041-334 3846

2 Shelly Road Great Western Road Glasgow Strathclyde G12 0XP   Map 12 B1

Overlooking the boating pond from which it takes its name, this is the first Scottish outlet for the Irish-based Jurys group (it was previously the Stakis). Good leisure and conference facilities, the latter for up to 150. Well set up for families (under-18s stay free in parents' room). The hotel stands on the Great Western Road three miles west of the city centre. *Rooms 137. Indoor swimming pool, children's pool, gymnasium, spa bath, sauna, solarium, baby-sitting, baby-listening. Access, Amex, Visa,*

| Glasgow | Kelvin Park Lorne Hotel | 63% | £79 |

Tel 041-334 4891   Fax 041-334 1659

923 Sauchiehall Street Glasgow Strathclyde G3 7TE   Map 12 B1

10 minutes from the city centre, a Queens Moat Houses hotel with a choice of accommodation, five new conference suites and the Kings Suite, which can hold up to 250 theatre-style. *Rooms 99. Coffee shop (11.30-10), dinner dance (monthly Sat). Closed 25 & 26 Dec. Access, Amex, Visa,*

| Glasgow | Loon Fung | | £45 |

Tel 041-332 1240   Fax 041-332 3705

417 Sauchiehall Street Glasgow Strathclyde G2 3JD   Map 12 B1

Colourful carvings of the dragon and phoenix (Loon Fung) decorate one end of this smart restaurant, which takes pride in its authentic Cantonese cooking. It's open all day, with a set lunch, and dim sum available until 7. Sliced abalone with oyster sauce, crunchy stuffed duck and sizzling platters of Cantonese-style fillet steak take centre stage in the evening. Vegetarian set dinner and banquets for six or more by prior arrangement. *Seats 200. Parties 200. Meals 12-11.30. Closed 3 days Chinese New Year. Set L from £5.70 Set D from £12. Access, Amex, Visa,*

| Glasgow | Mata Hari | | £35 |

Tel 041-332 9789

17 West Princes Street Glasgow Strathclyde   Map 12 B1

Malaysian cooking in a basement restaurant with a non-smoking section. Dishes to try include chicken, beef and prawn satay (also mushroom for vegetarians), *kari udang* (prawns with green pepper, coconut and spices), *rendang ayam* (chicken with spices and lemon grass), *assam manis ikan* (fish in a sweet and sour sauce) and *acar* (mixed vegetable pickle with sesame in a spiced lemon grass sauce). Very cheap set lunch menu. *Seats 62. Parties 62. L 12-2 D 6-11 (Fri & Sat to 11.30). Closed L Sat, all Sun, 25 & 26 Dec, 1 Jan. Set L from £5 Set D £15. Access, Amex, Visa,*

Glasgow   Moat House International   69%   £128
H

Tel 041-204 0733   Fax 041-221 2022

Congress Road Glasgow Strathclyde G3 8QT   Map 12 B1

Adjacent to the Scottish Exhibition Centre, with fine views across the
Clyde, the Moat House is also only moments from the M8, the motorway
that bisects the city. Historical connections with Glasgow's shipbuilding
past are recalled by the vast mural which dominates one end of the
spacious, glass-walled public areas. On ground and mezzanine floors
conference and banqueting suites will hold up to 1000, serviced by a self-
contained business centre. The chief recreation area is the Waterside health
and leisure club. Roomy bedrooms are identically equipped with maple-
effect fitted furniture and marble-finish bathrooms; state-of-the-art TV
includes a breakfast order facility, bill check and automatic payment
service. *Rooms 300. Indoor swimming pool, gymnasium, spa bath, sauna,
solarium, coffee shop (7am-11pm), baby-sitting, baby-listening. Access, Amex,
Visa,* ●

Glasgow   October Café   £35
R

Tel 041-221 0303

The Rooftop Princes Square Glasgow Strathclyde G1 3JN   Map 12 B1

City-centre restaurant at the top of the Princes Square shopping precinct.
The menu takes its influences from near and far: Perthshire game terrine
with beetroot and tarragon dressing; salmon with vegetable spaghetti,
ginger and white wine butter sauce; lamb and mixed pepper satay; teriyaki
beef with wasabi. Crème brulée is a speciality dessert. A bar menu is also
available (try the marinated squid with chili or Orkney Cheddar – or
both). *Seats 50. Parties 120. L 12-2.30 D 6-11. Closed Sun. Access, Visa.*

Glasgow   One Devonshire Gardens   82%   £155
HR

Tel 041-339 2001   Fax 041-337 1663

1 Devonshire Gardens Glasgow Strathclyde G12 0UX   Map 12 B1

Ten minutes from the city centre in a tree-lined Victorian terrace, three
town houses have been made into a hotel of distinction. Bedrooms are
sumptuous, with French mahogany furniture and rich fabrics that extend
to bedhead drapes and scatter cushions on the sofas and settees. Colour
schemes are very masculine in the main with dark reds and blues, though
some lighter rooms are in grey or beige. Thoughtful touches include fresh
flowers, books, magazines, and wonderful marble bathrooms have
generously sized hooded bath robes. Friendly staff offer a high level of
service to complement the luxurious surroundings. Besides the restaurant
there's a residents' dining room and a bar. Banquets for up to 32 and
conferences up to 50. In 1988 Leonard Bernstein found a stay here to be
"friendly and pure theatre – truly inspirational"; we would concur.
Rooms 27. Access, Amex, Visa, ●

Restaurant   £80

In stylish surroundings – dark drapes, elegant china and glassware –
pinafored waitresses serve dishes from a menu that changes with the
markets and the seasons. A good wine list, albeit at stiffish prices, with
several lesser-known wines among the clarets. *Seats 40. Parties 20. Private
Room. L 12.30-2 D 7-10. Closed L Sat. Set L £19 Set D £32.*

Glasgow   La Parmigiana   £50
R

Tel 041-334 0686

447 Great Western Road Glasgow Strathclyde G12 8HH   Map 12 B1

An unpretentious family-run trattoria, rather smarter than most. The menu
is fairly standard Italian, with good pasta and fish sections. Among the
starters is *vitello tonnato*, an Italian classic no longer seen on many menus.

Popular budget lunch; booking advisable. *Seats 50. Parties 60. L 12-2.30
D 6-11. Closed Sun, L Bank Holidays. Set L £6.50. Access, Amex, Visa,*
(i) *Diners Club International*

Glasgow	**Ristorante Caprese**	£35
Tel 041-332 3070		**R**
217 Buchanan Street Glasgow Strathclyde		Map 12 B1

Don't be put off by the unprepossessing entrance to this cheerful,
inexpensive and atmospheric Italian restaurant close to Glasgow's new
Royal Concert Hall. Red check cloths adorn the tables and the walls are
covered with photos and postcards from their many regular customers.
The menu holds few surprises but cooking is enjoyably robust and homely.
House specialities include veal cordon bleu, steak pizzaiola and chicken
Kiev. *Seats 60. Parties 70. Private Room. L 12-2.30 D 5.30-11. Closed L Sat,
all Sun, Bank Holidays. Set L from £5.50. Access, Amex, Visa,* (i) *Diners Club International*

Glasgow	**Rogano**	£75
Tel 041-248 4055		**R**
11 Exchange Place Glasgow Strathclyde G1 3AN		Map 12 B1

Popular as ever among tourists, business people and the citizens of Glasgow
spending their own money, and as firmly traditional as its setting of ocean-
liner decor and white-aproned waiters, this Glasgow institution never strays
far from familiar waters. Oysters and strong fish soup still occupy the
masthead of the menu. Salmon, langoustines, scallops and monkfish follow
with a wake of meunières, thermidors and papillotes. Triple chocolate
marquise, tarte tatin with crème fraiche and Cornish Yarg or Dunsyre Blue
could herald a good port. Good value 'theatre dinner' served 5-6.30pm and
after 10pm in the café. *Seats 50. Parties 50. Private Room. L 12-2.30 D 7-11
(Sun to 10) (café 12-11, Fri & Sat 12-12). Closed L Sun, all Bank Holidays.
Access, Amex, Visa,* (i) *Diners Club International*

Glasgow	**Stakis Grosvenor** 66%	£111
Tel 041-339 8811 Fax 041-334 0710		**H**
Grosvenor Terrace Glasgow Strathclyde G12 0TA		Map 12 B1

At the west end of the city, just opposite the Botanical Gardens, a Victorian
frontage conceals much refurbishment. Conference/banqueting for up to
400, an all-day coffee shop, 50% non-smoking bedrooms and 14 spacious
family rooms (under-12s stay free) are among the facilities. *Rooms 95.
Coffee shop (7.30am-10pm), dinner dance (Sat), baby-sitting, baby-listening.
Access, Amex, Visa,* (i) *Diners Club International*

Glasgow	**Swallow Hotel** 61%	£88
Tel 041-427 3146 Fax 041-427 4059		**H**
517 Paisley Road West Glasgow Strathclyde G51 1RW		Map 12 B1

A mile west of the city centre at junction 23 of the M8, near Ibrox Park, a
busy modern hotel with conference facilities for up to 300, a leisure club
and handy, secure car parking. *Rooms 119. Indoor swimming pool,
gymnasium, spa bath, sauna, steam room, baby-sitting, baby-listening. Access,
Amex, Visa,* (i) *Diners Club International*

Glasgow	**Tinto Firs Hotel** 62%	£98
Tel 041-637 2353 Fax 041-633 1340		**H**
470 Kilmarnock Road Glasgow Strathclyde G43 2BB		Map 12 B1

A modern, if modest, hotel in the suburbs (three miles from the city
centre) with club class bedrooms and two suites. Banqueting for 130,
conferences up to 200. Friendly staff create a relaxed atmosphere. Mount
Charlotte Thistle. *Rooms 30. Garden. Access, Amex, Visa,* (i) *Diners Club International*

Glasgow   Town House   69%   £102

Tel 041-332 3320   Fax 041-332 9756   **H**

54 West George Street Glasgow Strathclyde G2 1NG   **Map 12 B1**

Converted from a town house that used to be home to the Royal Scottish
Academy of Music and Drama, some fine architectural features have been
retained including a vaulted entrance hall and bas-reliefs (honouring
famous composers) that grace the cantilevered staircase. The individually
decorated bedrooms are its main strength; sufficiently roomy to
accommodate a large quilt-covered bed, armchairs or a sofa around a coffee
table, a breakfast table and desk. All have remote-control TVs, mini-bar
and three telephone points. The cooking in the dining room fails to live up
to the grandeur of the decor. Parking is virtually impossible without a 5 to
10 minute walk – a serious drawback. *Rooms 34. Closed 25 & 26 Dec.
Access, Amex, Visa,* ⓘ *Diners Club International*

Glasgow   Two Fat Ladies   £55

Tel 041-339 1944   **R**

88 Dumbarton Road Glasgow Strathclyde G11 6NX   **Map 12 B1**

Generous portions of market-fresh fish are the big attraction at this relaxed
restaurant near the City Art Gallery. The kitchen is in the window.
*Seats 28. Parties 28. D only 6.30-10.30. Closed Sun & Mon, 2 weeks
Xmas/New Year. Access, Visa,* ⓘ *Diners Club International*

Glasgow   Ubiquitous Chip   £65

Tel 041-334 5007   **R**

12 Ashton Lane Glasgow Strathclyde G12 8SJ   **Map 12 B1**

Downstairs in a leafy, covered courtyard is the restaurant, which specialises
in Scottish dishes. "Upstairs at the Chip" has a snackier menu of similar
provenance and is open all day. Scottish regional winner of our 1993 Wine
Cellar of the Year award – see comments on Regional Winners; single
malt whiskies are also outstanding. *Seats 135. Parties 30. L 12-2.30
D 5.30-11. Closed Xmas/New Year. Set meals from £23.50. Access, Amex,
Visa,* ⓘ *Diners Club International*

Glasgow   Places of Interest

Tourist Information   Tel 041-204 4400.
Caledonian MacBrayne Ferries   Tel 0475 33755.
City Tours   Tel 041-226 4826.
ScotRail   Tel 041-204 2844.
Glasgow Airport   Tel 041-848 4440.
Glasgow Cathedral   Tel 041-552 3205.
St Mary the Virgin Cathedral   Tel 041-339 4956.
Glasgow Ski Centre Club   Tel 041-427 4991.
Hamilton Park Racecourse   Tel 0698 283806.
Kelvin Hall Int. Sports Arena   Tel 041-357 2525.
Celtic F.C.   Celtic Park Tel 041-556 2611.
Rangers F.C.   Ibrox Stadium Tel 041-427 8811.
Calderpark Zoo   Tel 041-771 1185.
   Theatres and Concert Halls
Citizens Theatre   Tel 041-429 0022.
Glasgow Royal Concert Hall   Tel 041-332 6633.
Cumbernauld Theatre   Kildrum Tel 0236 737235.
Glasgow Film Theatre   Tel 041-332 6535.
Greenock Arts Guild Theatre   Tel 0475 23038.
Royal Scottish Academy of Music   Tel 041-332 5057.
Scottish Exhibition and Conference Centre   Tel 041-248 3000.
The Tramway   Tel 041-227 5511.
City Halls   Tel 041-227 5511 .
Kings Theatre   Tel 041-227 5511.
Mitchell Theatre   Tel 041-227 5511.

Pavilion Theatre   Tel 041-332 1846.
SNO Henry Wood Hall   Tel 041-226 3868.
Theatre Royal   Tel 041-332 4000.
Third Eye Centre   Tel 041-332 7521.
Tron Theatre   Tel 041-552 4267.
  Historic Houses, Castles and Gardens
Greenbank Garden   Tel 041-639 3281.
Botanic Gardens   Tel 041-334 2422.
The Hill House   Helensburgh. Tel 0436 3900.
Hutcheson's Hall   Tel 041-552 8391.
Pollock House & Park   (Burrell Collection in Pollock Park) Tel 041-632
  0274.
Provands Lordship   Tel 041-552 8819.
The Tenement House   Tel 041-333 0183.
  Museums and Art Galleries
Art Gallery and Museum   Tel 041-357 3929.
Burrell Collection   Tel 041-649 7151.
Dome of Discovery   Tel 041-427 1792.
Hunterian Art Gallery   Tel 041-330 5431.
Hunterian Museum   Tel 041-330 4221.
McLean Museum and Art Gallery   Greenock Tel. 0475 23741.
McLellan Galleries   Tel 041-351 1854.
Museum of Tranport   Tel 041-357 3929.
Peoples's Palace   Tel 041-554 0223.
Paisley Museum and Art Galleries   Paisley. Tel 041-889 3151.
Police Museum   Tel 041-204 2626.

Glasgow Airport	**Forte Crest**	67%	£88
Tel 041-887 1212 Fax 041-887 3738			**H**
Abbotsinch Nr Paisley Strathclyde PA3 2TR			Map 12 B1

The only hotel located directly beside Glasgow airport. All the bedrooms
are sound-proofed, double-glazed and air-conditioned. Formerly the
Excelsior. Banqueting/conference facilities for 300/500. *Rooms 300. Access,
Amex, Visa,* 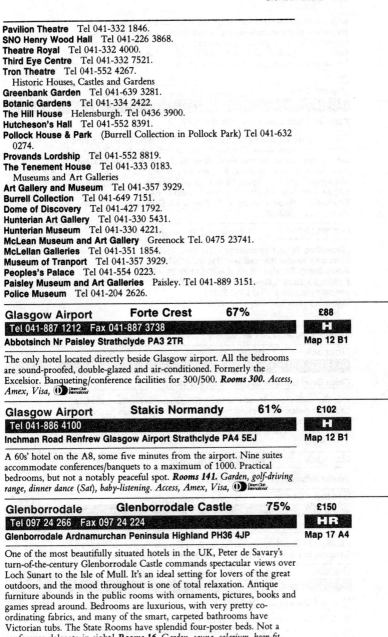 *Diners Club International*

Glasgow Airport	**Stakis Normandy**	61%	£102
Tel 041-886 4100			**H**
Inchman Road Renfrew Glasgow Airport Strathclyde PA4 5EJ			Map 12 B1

A 60s' hotel on the A8, some five minutes from the airport. Nine suites
accommodate conferences/banquets to a maximum of 1000. Practical
bedrooms, but not a notably peaceful spot. *Rooms 141. Garden, golf-driving
range, dinner dance (Sat), baby-listening. Access, Amex, Visa,* Diners Club International

---

Glenborrodale	**Glenborrodale Castle**	75%	£150
Tel 097 24 266 Fax 097 24 224			**HR**
Glenborrodale Ardnamurchan Peninsula Highland PH36 4JP			Map 17 A4

One of the most beautifully situated hotels in the UK, Peter de Savary's
turn-of-the-century Glenborrodale Castle commands spectacular views over
Loch Sunart to the Isle of Mull. It's an ideal setting for lovers of the great
outdoors, and the mood throughout is one of total relaxation. Antique
furniture abounds in the public rooms with ornaments, pictures, books and
games spread around. Bedrooms are luxurious, with very pretty co-
ordinating fabrics, and many of the smart, carpeted bathrooms have
Victorian tubs. The State Rooms have splendid four-poster beds. Not a
conference delegate in sight! *Rooms 16. Garden, sauna, solarium, keep-fit
equipment, beauty salon, tennis, putting, croquet, riding, clay-pigeon shooting,
fishing, mooring, hotel boat, snooker. Closed Nov-Easter. Access, Amex, Visa.*

Restaurant   £75

The dining room is elegant, with a beamed ceiling, panelled walls and
heavy drapes. Cooking is usually traditional Scottish, but changes each year

with a new chef who is encouraged to bring his own ideas. A high proportion of the ingredients used come from the hotel's own land – vegetables from the garden, and poultry, eggs and game birds from the hotel farm – while Loch Sunart provides fish and shellfish. No smoking. Booking is suggested. *Seats 32. Private Room. L 12-2 D 7-9. Set D from £27.50.*

Glenrothes   Balgeddie House   65%   £87
Tel 0592 742511   Fax 0592 621702   H

Balgeddie Way Glenrothes Fife KY6 3ET   Map 17 C5

Until recently surrounded by farmland, the hotel is now part of a suburb of Glenrothes new town. The whole place is well kept, from lounge and oak-panelled bar to the bedrooms; those on the first floor are spacious, with fine modern bathrooms, those on the top floor more compact, with sloping ceilings. Two separate bars with juke box, fruit machine and pool tables set the tone. Children stay free in parents' room. Functions/conferences for up to 70. *Rooms 18. Garden, croquet. Access, Amex, Visa,*

Glenrothes   Places of Interest

Glenrothes Tourist Information   Tel 0592 754954.
Kirkcaldy Tourist Information   Tel 0592 267775.
Adam Smith Theatre   Kirkcaldy Tel 0592 260498.
Falkland Palace & Garden (NT)   Tel 0337 57397.
Kirkcaldy Ice Rink   Tel 0592 52151.
Crystals Arena Ice Rink   Tel 0592 773774.
  Museums and Art Galleries
Burntisland Edwardian Fair   Tel 0592 260732.
Kirkcaldy Museum and Art Gallery   Tel 0592 260732.

Gourock   Stakis Gantock Hotel   64%   £96
Tel 0475 34671   Fax 0475 32490   H

Cloch Road Gourock Strathclyde PA15 1AR   Map 12 A1

Friendly staff, smart day rooms and well-equipped bedrooms including Executive suites. Fine views across the Clyde. Extensive banqueting and conference facilities. *Rooms 101. Indoor swimming pool, keep-fit equipment, floodlit tennis, spa bath, sauna, solarium, children's playground. Access, Amex, Visa,*

Gourock   Places of Interest

Tourist Information   Tel 0475 39467.

Gretna Green   Forte Travelodge   £40
Tel 0461 37566   L

A74 Trunk Road Gretna Green Dumfries & Galloway CA6 5HQ   Map 13 C4

On the A74 northbound, 8 miles north of Carlisle on the main route to Glasgow, just 2 miles north of Gretna. *Rooms 41. Access, Amex, Visa.*

Gullane   Greywalls Hotel   76%   £145
Tel 0620 842144   Fax 0620 842241   HR

Muirfield Gullane Lothian EH31 2EG   Map 12 D1

Built in 1901, Greywalls is one of the few examples of Lutyens' architecture north of the Border. In a lovely position next to Muirfield Golf Course, the house has a perfect unity of design. The Library is a very fine room with lightwood panelling, grand piano, 'His Master's Voice' gramophone and an open fire; to the north you glimpse the Firth of Forth, to the south Gertrude Jekyll's rose garden. There's a clubby bar and a delightful sun room. Bedrooms are generally of fine proportions and full of light; little personal touches like books and portable radios make the hotel a home from home. Enchanting cottage-style rooms in the lodge. Good breakfast, friendly service. **Rooms 23.** *Garden, tennis, croquet. Closed Nov-Mar. Access, Amex, Visa,*

Restaurant £80

Careful cooking and neat presentation are hallmarks of Paul Baron's cooking in a delightful dining room. Everything from bread to petits fours is made in house. Breast of wood pigeon or fillet of hare with red cabbage and Malmsey Madeira sauce, home-cured bresaola, celery and apple salad with walnut oil dressing, sorbet or home-made courgette and mint soup, roast best end of lamb with whole, sweet garlic, roast quail with grapes, seafood casserole, tangy lemon tart and poached pear with caramel sauce are typical dishes from the fixed-price, four-course menu that changes daily. Booking is essential for dinner. Exceptional list of clarets, sound Burgundies and some good values outside France, though champagnes are steeply priced. **Seats 50.** *Parties 16. Private Room. L 12.30-2 D 7.30-9.30. Set L £15 Set D £32.50.*

Gullane La Potinière ★ £65

Tel 0620 843214	**R**
Main Street Gullane Lothian EH31 2AA	**Map 12 D1**

Inside the cottage setting the flowers hit you centre stage, their colour and perfume filling the beamed dining room. David Brown is the most attentive of hosts and Hilary goes from strength to strength in the kitchen, her French-inspired cooking taking on board a lightness and sophistication. Tomato and mint soup, sole meunière with basil, breast of Barbary duck with a red wine reduction sauce, apricot parfait typify the style. A constantly evolving wine list, one of the very best in the land and past winner of our Cellar of the Year award, offers remarkable value. Note the French country wines, and make return trips, because there's a lot in the cellar that's biding its time! No credit cards. No smoking till coffee time. Plan your visit well in advance as the single sitting for dinner is booked months ahead. **Seats 30.** *Parties 10. L at 1 D at 8. Closed L Fri & Sat, D Sun-Tue, all Wed, 25 & 26 Dec, 1 & 2 Jan, 1 week Jun, Oct. Set L £15.75 Set D £24.50. No credit cards.*

Harray Loch Merkister Hotel 57% £59

Tel 085 677 366	**H**
Harray Loch Orkney KW17 2LF	**Map 16 C1**

First and last a fishing hotel, with great sport on Loch Harray and three other lochs. The brown trout fishing is among the best in the world, and boats, outboards and ghillies can be arranged. Deep-freezing facilities are available, and smoking of the fish can be organized. Owner Angus MacDonald is a keen fisherman himself, and is always willing to give guidance, and his wife Elma runs the hotel with great charm. Centre of affairs is the bar, and after swapping fishy tales guests settle down for a comfortable night in the modest, well-kept bedrooms. Birdwatchers are also attracted here, and the hotel has a bird hide in the grounds. **Rooms 15.** *Garden, tennis, game fishing. Closed Oct-Mar. Access, Amex, Visa.*

Helmsdale Navidale House 60% £101*

Tel 043 12 258	**H**
Helmsdale Highland KW8 6JS	**Map 16 C2**

Beautifully situated in six acres of woods and gardens running down to the foreshore, this friendly former hunting lodge is a popular sporting hotel. The bar is small and cosy; the lounge rather old-fashioned. Bedrooms in the main house are pleasantly furnished, with period pieces and functional tiled bathrooms. All rooms now en suite. A lodge and two garden chalets (for parties of four or six) provide additional accommodation. Children stay free in parents' room. *Half-board terms only. **Rooms 14.** *Garden, game fishing. Closed Nov-New Year. Access, Visa.*

Helmsdale   Places of Interest

Tourist Information   Tel 04312 640.
Dunrobin Castle   Golspie Tel 04083 3177.

Ingliston   Norton House   66%   £95
Tel 031-333 1275   Fax 031-333 5305   H

Ingliston Nr Edinburgh Lothian EH28 8LX   **Map 12 C1**

Standing peacefully in extensive grounds, Victorian Norton House is
nonetheless close to the airport and only 15 minutes from central
Edinburgh. The foyer features marble columns, an oak staircase, a carved
oak fireplace and a gallery and there's an appealing pub called the Norton
Tavern in the old stables complete with barbecue area, walled garden and
children's play area. Best of the well-equipped bedrooms are the 30 newest,
designated Executive, with decent oak furniture. Conference rooms for up
to 300. Recent investment in refurbishment throughout is a reflection of
the hotel's ownership by Richard Branson's Voyager Hotels. *Rooms 47.
Garden. Access, Amex, Visa,* ◍ *Diners Club International*

Inverness   Bunchrew House   70%   £115
Tel 0463 234917   Fax 0463 710620   H

Bunchrew Inverness Highland IV3 6TA   **Map 16 C3**

From Inverness follow the signs to Beauly/Drywall on the A862. A mile
from the outskirts of Inverness you'll find the entrance to 16th-century
Bunchrew House, which stands in 15 acres of landscaped gardens and
woodland on the shores of Beauly Firth. Alan and Patsy Wilson opened
Bunchrew as a hotel in 1987, and summer 1991 saw the conversion of a
second wing, adding a further five luxury bedrooms. It remains very much
their home with a convivial, rather masculine bar and a muted lounge
graced by a log fire and much reading matter. The new chef prepares local
produce in a traditional style. Staff are friendly and courteous. *Rooms 11.
Garden, fishing. Access, Amex, Visa,* ◍ *Diners Club International*

Inverness   Caledonian Hotel   69%   £111
Tel 0463 235181   Fax 0463 711206   H

33 Church Street Inverness Highland IV1 1DX   **Map 16 C3**

Alongside the river Ness, a smart city-centre hotel with good conference
(for up to 300 delegates) and leisure facilities plus modern public rooms.
Ample parking. Children free up to the age of 14 in parents' room. Jarvis
Hotels. *Rooms 100. Indoor swimming pool, gymnasium, spa bath, sauna,
solarium. Access, Amex, Visa,* ◍ *Diners Club International*

Inverness   Culloden House   73%   £135
Tel 0463 790461   Fax 0463 792181   HR

Culloden Inverness Highland IV1 2NZ   **Map 16 C3**

An Adam-style Georgian mansion set in 40 acres of parkland. History
abounds, both in the house (Bonny Prince Charlie once seized it) and in
the surrounding countryside. The traditional feel is preserved within the
chandeliered hall, and in the grandly proportioned lounge and dining room
with their ornate plasterwork, friezes and carved fireplace surrounds. Some
bedrooms are grand, while those in the wings tend to be much smaller.
Some rooms have spa baths and antique four-posters, with pretty crown
canopies and co-ordinated fabrics all adding to the style. Four new suites
are in the Garden Pavilion 200 yards from the main building. No children
under ten. *Rooms 23. Garden, tennis, snooker, sauna, solarium. Access, Amex,
Visa,* ◍ *Diners Club International*

Restaurant   £73

Lunch in the Adam Room is à la carte and dinner an inclusive affair of five
courses. Michael Simpson applies classical French skills to the best of local

produce in dishes like lentil and tomato broth, paté of sole and scallops in pastry, pan-fried sirloin of beef or loin of venison with a honey and sherry sauce and a pastry parcel of wild rice, apple and raisins. A vegetarian main course is always available. **Seats 40. Parties 50. Private Room. L 12.30-2 D 7-9. Set D £27.50.**

Inverness	**Dunain Park**	69%	£110

Tel 0463 230512 Fax 0463 224532

HR

Inverness Highland IV3 6JN

Map 16 C3

Ann and Edward Nicoll's handsome former hunting lodge stands in six acres of garden and woodland a mile from Inverness on the A82 road to Loch Ness. Various styles of accommodation are available, top of the range being six suites in the main building with spacious sitting rooms and Italian marble bathrooms. Two rooms are in cottages in the grounds. **Rooms 14. Garden, croquet, indoor swimming pool, sauna. Closed 2 weeks Feb.** Access, Amex, Visa, 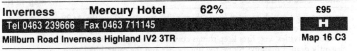 Diners Club International

Restaurant

£62

The dining room overlooks extensive gardens, where many of the vegetables, fruit and herbs are grown for the kitchen. Ann Nicoll's cooking is Scottish with French influences, based on seasonal local produce: game terrine with a confit of onions; lemon sole encircling a soufflé of smoked haddock and whiting with a Barsac sauce; loin of lamb in pastry; breast of duck with a tarragon sauce. Always available is a separate menu of fillet and sirloin Highland beef steaks served plain or with a variety of sauces and crisp mushrooms, onions and other vegetables. Sweets from the buffet. No smoking in the dining room. **Seats 36. Parties 12. Private Room. D only 7-9.**

Inverness	**Kingsmills Hotel**	67%	£105

Tel 0463 237166 Fax 0463 225208

H

Culcabock Road Inverness Highland IV2 3LP

Map 16 C3

18th-century house modernised and extended. Conference facilities for up to 70, banqueting up to 40. Swallow Hotels. **Rooms 84. Keep-fit equipment, spa bath, sauna, solarium, beauty & hair salon, pitch & putt.** Access, Amex, Visa, Diners Club International

---

Inverness	**Mercury Hotel**	62%	£95

Tel 0463 239666 Fax 0463 711145

H

Millburn Road Inverness Highland IV2 3TR

Map 16 C3

At the foot of the Kessoch Bridge, which connects Inverness with the Black Isle. Can cater for conferences of up to 300 delegates, although other facilities are limited. Mount Charlotte Thistle. **Rooms 118.** Access, Amex, Visa, Diners Club International

---

Inverness   Places of Interest

Tourist Information Tel 0463 234353.
Eden Court Theatre Tel 0463 221718.
Cawdor Castle Tel 066 77 615.
Culloden Battlefield and Museum Tel 0463 790607 *7 miles.*
St Andrew's Cathedral Tel 0463 233535.
Inverness Museum and Art Gallery Tel 0463 237114.
Inverness Ice Centre Tel 0463 235711.
Clan Tartan Centre Holm Woolen Mills Tel 0463 223311.

Irvine   Hospitality Inn   68%

£101

H

Tel 0294 74272   Fax 0294 77287

46 Annick Road Irvine Strathclyde KA11 4LD

Map 12 B2

A Moorish theme pervades the central concourse, lounge and bar. Superior bedrooms are round the atrium and the pool. Mount Charlotte Thistle. Conference facilities for up to 300, banqueting to 200. *Rooms 128. Indoor swimming pool, spa bath, putting. Access, Amex, Visa,* ⓘ International

Irvine   Places of Interest

The Galleon Ice Rink   Kilmarnock. Tel 0563 24014 10 miles.

Isle of Raasay   Isle of Raasay Hotel   57%

£60

H

Tel 047 862 222

Isle of Raasay by Kyle of Lochalsh Highland IV40 8PB

Map 16 A3

The Isle of Raasay is a 15-minute trip by ferry from Skye and its only hotel is this Victorian house with a modern accommodation block. The whole place is light and neat, from the lounge with its lovely views and the pine-ceilinged bar to the bedrooms, which have traditional furnishings, tweedy fabrics and carpeted bathrooms. Motorists should note that there's no petrol on Raasay. *Rooms 12. Garden, courtesy transport. Closed Oct-Mar. No credit cards.*

Kelso   Ednam House   64%

£72

H

Tel 0573 224168   Fax 0573 226319

Bridge Street Kelso Borders TD5 7HT

Map 12 D2

A town-centre Georgian house with lawns reaching down to the River Tweed. It's a fishing hotel, and outside high season the large majority of guests are salmon fishers (Feb/Mar & Oct/Nov). The bars (where lunches are served Monday to Saturday) are convivial and the lounges are quietly traditional. Well-kept bedrooms match modern comforts with old-fashioned courtesies. *Rooms 32. Garden, croquet, fishing. Closed 24 Dec-12 Jan. Access, Visa.*

Kelso   Sunlaws House   72%

£123

H

Tel 057 35 331   Fax 057 35 611

Heiton Kelso Borders TD5 8JZ

Map 12 D2

An imposing Scottish country house three miles from Kelso on the A698, at the south end of Heiton village, offering peace, quiet and plenty of sporting activities. Log fires keep things cosy in the entrance hall, the elegantly draped drawing room, and the central hall with its ornate carved wooded fireplace. The two best bedrooms also have log fires, along with antique furnishings. Other main-house rooms use good-quality darkwood pieces, while those in the converted stable block tend to have fitted units. Bathrooms are decorated to match their individually styled bedrooms where beds are turned down at night. Falconry, hawking, horse trail riding and archery can be arranged for guests. *Rooms 22. Garden, tennis, croquet, putting, game fishing, clay-pigeon shooting. Access, Amex, Visa,* ⓘ International

Kelso   Places of Interest

Tourist Information   Tel 0573 23464.
Tait Concert Hall   Tel 0450 75991.
Kelso Museum   Tel 0573 25470.
   Historic Houses, Castles and Gardens
Floors Castle   Tel 0573 23333.
Mellerstain   Gordon. Tel 057 381 225.

Kenmore   Kenmore Hotel   62%   £101

Tel 0887 830205   Fax 0887 830262   **H**

Kenmore By Aberfeldy Tayside PH15 2NU   **Map 17 C5**

Reputedly Scotland's oldest inn (1572) the Kenmore attracts both
fishermen (they have 2 miles of fishing on the Tay, which flows past the
inn) and golfers to this pretty village. The various cosy public rooms, now
called the Poets Parlour to commemorate a visit by Robert Burns, are
made even more inviting by real fires. Bedrooms, 14 in a Victorian
gatehouse opposite, vary considerably in decor and furnishings with
everything from melamine to antiques. Guests have free use of the
swimming pool and leisure facilities at the nearby Kenmore Club.
Rooms 38. 18-hole golf course, game fishing, tennis. Access, Amex, Visa.

Kentallen of Appin   Ardsheal House   67%   £160★

Tel 063 174 227   Fax 063 174 342   **HR**

Kentallen of Appin Highland PA38 4BX   **Map 17 B4**

A private drive bordering Loch Linnhe yields stunning views on the
approach to Robert and Jane Taylor's stone and granite hotel. The views
remain glorious from the hotel itself, which is set in 900 acres of hills,
woods, garden and shorefront. With leather sofas, parquet floor, scatter
rugs and Victorian snooker room, the house has a faintly masculine look
but the atmosphere is very much that of a country house party. Bedrooms,
all with antiques and each with an individual charm and character, have
direct-dial phones but no TVs. Spotless bathrooms have fluffy towels and
good toiletries. Excellent breakfasts. ★Half-board terms only. *Rooms 13.
Closed early Nov-week before Easter. Access, Amex, Visa.*

Restaurant   £80

The conservatory dining room enables the garden (which contributes
vegetables and herbs to the kitchen) to be enjoyed along with George
Kelso's sound cooking. Dinner could include tartlet of queen scallops and
monkfish with creamed leeks and prawn bisque sauce or game terrine to
start, then a choice of two soups, meat and fish main courses, a mixed salad
and a couple of desserts, maybe apricot pancakes and bread-and-butter
pudding. Lunches on the lawn. A pleasant wine list with some good bottles
under £20. No smoking in the dining room. *Seats 40. Parties 40. L 12-2
D at 8.15. Set L £17.50 Set D £32.50.*

Kentallen of Appin   Holly Tree   65%   £122

Tel 063 174 292   Fax 063 174 345   **H**

Kentallen of Appin Argyll Highland PA38 4BY   **Map 17 B4**

An old railway station which has been cleverly converted into a civilised
hotel, the Holly Tree stands on the edge of Loch Linnhe, three miles south
of Ballachulish Bridge. The little bar was once the station tea room, and
there's a delightful lounge with a central fireplace and comfortable seating.
Bedrooms are equally appealing, with floral fabrics and pine furniture;
bathrooms are up-to-date and attractively tiled. The restaurant is non-
smoking. The hotel has its own fishing boat and creels. Children under 5
stay free in parents' room; families are well catered for. *Rooms 11. Garden,
fishing. Access, Amex, Visa,* **D** Diners Club International

Kilchrenan   Ardanaiseig   76%   £150★

Tel 086 63 333   Fax 086 63 222   **HR**

Kilchrenan By Taynuilt Strathclyde PA35 1JG   **Map 17 B5**

The backdrop of mighty Ben Cruachan and vistas of moody Loch Awe
together create a stunning location; celebrated gardens of rhododendron
and azalea surrounding an elegant, if severe, baronial house establish
Ardanaiseig as a special hotel. Experienced hoteliers from Jackson's Hole,

Wyoming, Tom and Carmen Robbins bring their own brand of hospitality to the Highlands, admirably supported by manager Mrs Sercombe and staff. With no two bedrooms alike in dimensions and outlook, each is imbued with its own character, using quality fabrics and fine antiques. Pride of place, nonetheless, belongs to the palatial lounge and panelled library bar, whose views rank among the serenest in the land. *Half-board terms only. No children under 8. No dogs. *Rooms 14. Garden, tennis, fishing, hotel boat, snooker, helipad. Closed Nov-Easter. Access, Amex, Visa,* **(I)** Diners Club International

Restaurant   £80

Chef Graeme Cockburn has alighted from his previous job cooking in the prestigious Royal Scot train to take over the kitchens here where the scenery isn't constantly on the move; there are, however, splendid views over Loch Awe from the red dining room. Not all dishes are equally successful, although the goat's cheese soufflé is outstanding and lemon tart first-rate. The set-price menu changes daily with about four choices at each stage; fillet of salmon with Oban mussels and fennel, and roast wood pigeon with baby onion and *sauce diable* are typical main dishes, and there's a regular list of plainer alternatives like smoked salmon, steak and best end of local lamb. Lunchtime brings a short à la carte. *Seats 30. Parties 28. L 12-2 D 7.30-9. Set D £33.50.*

Kilchrenan   Taychreggan Hotel   66%   £72

Tel 086 63 211   Fax 086 63 244   **H**

Kilchrenan By Taynuilt Strathclyde PA35 1HQ   Map 17 B5

Still between owners as we went to press, Taychreggan was fortunate in having manageress Jenny McIntyre to hold the fort with charm and equanimity during a difficult period. The building is in 25 acres of private grounds right on the shore of Loch Awe (the longest freshwater loch in Scotland) and is an ancient drover's inn built from stone, modestly extended in the 1970s to enclose a delightful cobbled courtyard. The largest of several lounges has low-backed modern settees and a wood-burning stove. Bedrooms (some with lovely views) vary considerably from those in the new wing with white melamine furniture to the best rooms which feature antique pieces. No room TVs (there is one in the lounge), but extras include fruit, flowers and mineral water. *Rooms 15. Garden, croquet, boating, coarse and game fishing. Closed Nov-Feb. Access, Amex, Visa,* **(I)** Diners Club International

Restaurant   £55

White-painted brick walls and a pink colour scheme feature in the dining room, which offers a set four-course dinner. This might comprise a smoked venison starter before a langoustine consommé and the likes of pan-fried salmon or apricot-stuffed loin of pork as the main dish. Although officially there's no choice, alternatives can always be found if required. Substantial bar lunches. *Seats 40. L 12.15-2.15 D 7.30-8.45. Set D £24*

Kildrummy   Kildrummy Castle   70%   £96

Tel 097 55 71288   Fax 097 55 71345   **H**

Kildrummy Alford Grampian AB3 8RA   Map 17 C4

Built in 1900 as a rather grandiose castellated country house, the hotel has a lovely setting overlooking the ruins of a 13th-century castle, and gardens which feature specimen trees, Alpine plants and rare shrubs. (Grampian has more than 70 castles, many just a short drive from the hotel.) The baronial entrance hall contrasts with the Adam elegance of the sunny drawing room. Two carved lions act as sentries on a splendidly ornate staircase which leads to the bedrooms. These are less grand than the day rooms but are comfortable, spacious and warm. Charming attic rooms have sloping ceilings. Children stay free in parents' room. Long-serving owner Thomas Hanna strongly motivates his staff, who are outgoing and friendly. Trout and salmon fishing are available on a 3½-mile stretch of the river Don, and

local centres organise shooting, stalking, riding and pony trekking.
Rooms 16. *Garden, snooker, clay-pigeon shooting. Closed 3 weeks Jan.*
Access, Amex, Visa.

Kilfinan   Kilfinan Hotel

£68

Tel 070 082 201   Fax 070 082 205

Kilfinan By Tighnabruaich Strathclyde PA21 2AP   Map 17 B5

The white-painted old coaching inn set amid magnificent scenery attracts a
sporting clientele who enjoy fishing, deerstalking and rough shooting.
Good walking country begins right outside and there's boating on Kilfinan
Bay. Two bars make up for the lack of a lounge. Bedrooms are furnished
with a mix of modern units and antiques; some overlook St Finnan's
graveyard, surprisingly a very pleasant view. Families are well catered for,
with baby-sitting and children's food available. **Rooms 11.** *Garden, game
fishing. Access, Amex, Visa,*

Restaurant

£55

Crisp table linen, cutlery and glassware gleaming in the candle-light, and a
glowing log fire make the twin dining rooms particularly appealing. A
capable kitchen produces 4-course, fixed-price dinners with such dishes as
jumbo prawns and garlic mayonnaise, cream of onion soup, supreme of
salmon with saffron sauce or sirloin steak with green peppercorn sauce, and
chocolate profiteroles or a selection of cheese. Good coffee, served with
petits fours. Outdoor eating in good weather. **Seats 22.** *Private Room.*
L 12-2 D 7.30-9.30. Set L £15 Set D £21.

Killiecrankie   Killiecrankie Hotel   64%

£84

Tel 0796 473220   Fax 0796 472451

Killiecrankie By Pitlochry Tayside PH16 5LG   Map 17 C4

Four acres of landscaped gardens overlook the river Garry and the Pass of
Killiecrankie. There's something of the feeling of an inn about the little
hotel, which was built as a manse in 1840. The reception hall and small
panelled bar (which has a sun trap extension) have displays of stuffed
animals and an upstairs lounge offers various board games plus a few books
as distractions. A bar has a conservatory-style extension. Pine-furnished
bedrooms are fresh and bright. All now have remote control TV, direct-
dial phones and smart modern bathrooms. **Rooms 11.** *Garden, croquet,
putting. Closed Jan & Feb. Access, Amex, Visa.*

Killiecrankie Place of Interest

Blair Castle   Tel 079-681 207.

Kilmelford   Cuilfail Hotel   52%

£50

Tel 085 22 274   Fax 085 22 264

H

Kilmelford Strathclyde PA34 4XA   Map 17 B5

A creeper-covered, stone-built roadside inn 15 miles south of Oban. In the
mellow hall antiques and stag's heads give a traditional feel which is echoed
in the two lounges, one of which has pine panelling and dark green velour
chesterfields. Good-sized bedrooms (all recently redecorated) use a variety
of period furnishings. **Rooms 12.** *Garden, keep-fit equipment, sauna, solarium.*
Access, Visa.

Kilmore   Glenfeochan House   70%

£118

Tel 063 177 273   Fax 063 177 624

Kilmore Oban Strathclyde PA34 4QR   Map 17 B5

Built in 1875 (though some parts are probably much older), the house
stands at the head of Loch Feochan, five miles south of Oban, on a 350-acre
estate of hills, lochs, rivers and farmland. The six-acre garden is a source of
great pride and is open to the public; there's also a Victorian walled
garden. Inside, all is spick and span, from the entrance hall and stairway

featuring pitch pine to the drawing room with a fine moulded ceiling and complementary antiques. Bedrooms have plain walls, floral curtains and more antiques. TVs and radios are provided, but no phones. The Tulip Room has an en-suite round bathroom in the turret. Self-catering accommodation is available in the farmhouse. No children under ten. No dogs. *Rooms 3. Garden, croquet, fishing. Closed Nov-early Mar. No credit cards.*

Restaurant £68

Guests gather for dinner at 8 and non-residents can join them by prior arrangement. Patricia Baber is an excellent cook and her short dinner menus (discussed at breakfast time) make as much use as possible of produce from the estate or local sources: fresh or home-smoked salmon or trout, Jura venison with rowan jelly, squat lobster, roast guinea fowl with damson and gin sauce. *Seats 10. D only at 8. Set D £27.*

Kilwinning   Montgreenan Mansion   70%   £84
Tel 0294 57733   Fax 0294 85397   H
Montgreenan Estate Nr Kilwinning Strathclyde KA13 7QZ   Map 12 A2

18th-century features, including marble and brass fireplaces and decorative plasterwork, have been retained at this impressive Georgian-style mansion, which stands in 45 acres of gardens and grounds four miles north of Irvine on the A736. Day rooms are of quite grand proportions, the lounge-library being particularly appealing. There are several conference rooms (maximum capacity 100). Bedrooms, furnished with reproduction pieces or antiques, range from standard singles to suites. Children up to 16 stay free in parents' room. *Rooms 21. Garden, croquet, putting, 5 practice golf holes, tennis, snooker. Access, Amex, Visa,* **Diners Club International.**

Kilwinning   Places of Interest
Brodick Castle, Garden and Country Park   Isle of Arran. Tel 0770 2202 *via ferry from Ardrossan.*

Kinclaven by Stanley   Ballathie House   74%   £105
Tel 0250 883268   Fax 0250 883396   HR
Kinclaven by Stanley Tayside PH1 4QN   Map 17 C5

A large, turreted, greystone mid-Victorian mansion with a splendid location overlooking the river Tay. Fresh flowers and a sprinkling of antiques enhance the day rooms, which include a snug, dado-panelled bar with blue leather seating and a sunny drawing room. Bedrooms in the house and lodge are individually decorated in fine style, with four-posters, half testers or canopied beds in the Master rooms (no dogs in these rooms). Standard rooms are more cottagey but equally appealing. Children up to 11 stay free in parents' room. *Rooms 27. Garden, tennis, fishing, croquet, putting. Closed 25 & 26 Dec, 3 weeks Feb. Access, Amex, Visa,* **Diners Club International.**

Restaurant £65

Dishes served in the restrained elegance of the dining room may be simple or elaborate. Chicken liver paté and sirloin steak exemplify the former, while more esoteric offerings could include baked Brie wrapped in spinach leaves served over a rhubarb yoghurt dressing, or gateau of salmon with a dill mousse and Savoy cabbage set on a mussel cream sauce. Good choice of vegetarian dishes. No smoking. *Seats 80. Parties 12. Private Room. L 12.15-1.45 D 6.45-8.30. Set L £14.50 Set D £25.*

Kingussie   The Cross   £68
Tel 0540 661166   RR
25 High Street Kingussie Highland PH21 1HX   Map 17 C4

March 1993 is now the date for the move of the Cross to a spacious riverside setting – The Old Tweed Mill on Ardbroilach Road – just seconds from their previous High Street address. Things will be much as before, including the phone number, although there will be more space in the dining area and, eventually, nine letting rooms above (half-board terms only). The emphasis will remain on food, which will be available lunch and dinner every day except Tuesday. Ruth Hadley will doubtless continue to make fine use of local ingredients in dishes like poached Lochinver turbot on a spicy peanut sauce, mousse of pike with a creamy prawn sauce and her famous venison Francatelli – fillet of local wild deer, lightly sautéed with a port wine and redcurrant sauce. The magnificent wine list (last year's winning Cellar of the Year) has great depth throughout. Lovers of pudding wines are particularly spoilt for choice. *Seats 18. Parties 18. D only 6.30-9 (Sat to 9.30). Closed Sun & Mon, 3 weeks May/Jun, 6 weeks Nov/Dec. Set D from £25. Access, Visa.*

Kingussie   Places of Interest

Tourist Information   Tel 0540 661297.
Kincraig Highland Wildlife Park   Tel 054 04 270.
Waltzing Waters   Newtonmore Tel 05403 752.

Kinlochbervie   Kinlochbervie Hotel   64%   £80

Tel 0971 521275   Fax 0971 521438   H

Kinlochbervie by Lairg Highland IV27 4RP   Map 16 B2

The promontory at Kinlochbervie (almost at the northernmost tip of mainland Scotland) forms two harbours, one facing the Atlantic, the other within Loch Clash. Picture windows on two sides of the hotel lounge and dining room overlook both from high up on a hill. Best bedrooms (and a first-floor residents' lounge crammed with literature for walkers and fishermen) enjoy these views to the full. A rear-facing room, however, rather invalidates one's special trip, so insist on a view. A convivial bar and bistro adjacent are popular with locals. 47 miles from Lairg. *Rooms 14. Fishing. Closed Xmas/New Year, Jan & Feb. Access, Amex, Visa,* ⊕ *Diners Club International*

Kinross   Granada Lodge   £43

Tel 0577 64646   Fax 0577 64108   L

M90 Junction 6 Kinross Tayside KY13 7NQ   Map 17 C5

Rooms 35. Access, Amex, Visa, ⊕ *Diners Club International*

Kinross   Windlestrae Hotel   62%   £75

Tel 0577 63217   Fax 0577 64733   H

The Muirs Kinross Tayside KY13 7AS   Map 17 C5

There were just four bedrooms here when the Doyles arrived ten years ago; the latest extension brings that number up to 45 and a new leisure centre, with good-sized swimming pool, was nearing completion in the summer of '92 as we went to press. Spacious bedrooms are well kept and comfortable with Parker Knoll easy chairs and mostly lightwood unit furniture. Smart bathrooms all have thermostatically controlled showers over the tubs and generous towelling. Staff are friendly and helpful (getting a shirt laundered overnight presented no problem) and there's a pretty garden. *Rooms 45. Garden, swimming pool, sauna, steam room, spa bath, solarium, keep-fit equipment. Access, Amex, Visa,* ⊕ *Diners Club International*

Kirkmichael   Log Cabin Hotel   59%   £46

Tel 0250 881288   Fax 0250 881402   H

Kirkmichael Tayside PH10 7NB   Map 17 C4

Built of Norwegian pine logs, the hotel stands on the A924 high in Glen Derby. There is a snug bar serving an impressive number of malt whiskies, but this is essentially an out-of-doors place, with fishing, shooting and walking heading the list of activities. There are no telephones or TVs in the simply appointed bedrooms, though TVs can be supplied on request. *Rooms 13. Garden, games room, game fishing, shooting, clay-pigeon shooting. Closed 25 & 26 Dec. Access, Amex, Visa,* ⊕ *Diners Club International*

Kirknewton   Dalmahoy Hotel   78%   £120
Tel 031-333 1845   Fax 031-335 3203   **HR**

Kirknewton Lothian EH27 8EB   Map 17 C6

Surrounded by two mature golf courses and with a well-equipped leisure centre, Dalmahoy offers plenty of diversions. The original Georgian mansion contains the reception area with separate concierge desk, two smart lounge-like bars with quality settees and armchairs, and eight high-ceilinged period bedrooms. Standardised rooms and a further informal bar-restaurant are in a new extension; these are good-sized rooms with oak furniture, matching fabrics and all the usual modern comforts. Conference/banqueting facilities for 220/160. Children up to the age of 16 accommodated free in parents' room. *Rooms 115. Garden, 18-hole golf courses, putting, tennis, indoor swimming pool, squash, sauna, solarium, snooker, gymnasium, spa bath, beautician, coffee shop (9am-10pm). Access, Amex, Visa,* Diners Club International

Restaurant   £70

A fairly ambitious à la carte menu and generally competent cooking in a stylish setting with views over the golf course. Table d'hote menu available only on request at dinner. *Seats 100. Parties 24. Private Room. L 12-2 D 7-10. Closed L Sat. Set L £12.50 Set D £20.*

Kirknewton   Places of Interest

Epsom Polo Club   Dalmahoy Estate Office. Tel 031-333 1331.

Kyle of Lochalsh   Lochalsh Hotel   63%   £97
Tel 0599 4202   Fax 0599 4881   **H**

Ferry Road Kyle of Lochalsh Highland IV40 8AF   Map 16 B3

A simple, sturdy, white-painted building opposite the ferry terminal and looking over the sea to Skye. Beauty spots abound locally, and a day's sightseeing can conclude agreeably with a dram or two in the cocktail bar. Bedrooms are fresh, bright and comfortable. *Rooms 40. Garden. Access, Amex, Visa,* Diners Club International

Kyle of Lochalsh   Places of Interest

Tourist Information   Tel 0599 4276.
Eilean Donan Castle   Wester Ross. Tel 059 985 202.
Lochalsh Woodland Garden   Tel 059981 219.

Langbank   Gleddoch House   68%   £130
Tel 047 554 711   Fax 047 554 201   **H**

Langbank Strathclyde PA14 6YE   Map 12 B1

The large windows of Gleddoch House look out on to beautiful countryside, and inside there's plenty to please the eye too. In the main lounge area there are leather easy chairs in which to relax, and dado panelling and more leather chairs give a period feel to the baize-lined bar, which offers a hundred different brands of whisky. The rooms are all named after Scottish birds, each engraved on the door-plate. Children under 12 stay free in parents' room. *Rooms 33. Garden, sauna, squash, 18-hole golf course, riding. Access, Amex, Visa,* Diners Club International

Lerwick   Shetland Hotel   61%   £70
Tel 0595 5515   Fax 0595 5828   **H**

Holmsgarth Road Lerwick Shetland ZE1 0PW   Map 16 D2

Close to the town centre and overlooking the harbour, the Shetland is a skilfully designed modern hotel that caters well for both the summer tourist and the year-round oil business. Bedrooms are uniformly light and spacious, practical rather than stylish, but with private bathrooms throughout. There is a bright, comfortable bar, a long-hours coffee shop and impressive function hall. Banqueting facilities available for up to 200 and conferences for 350 delegates. Children up to 11 stay free in parents' room. **Rooms 66.** *Garden, indoor swimming pool, sauna, solarium, coffee shop (11am-9.30pm) Access, Amex, Visa,* (1) *DinersClub International*

Lerwick   Places of Interest

Tourist Information Tel 0595 3434.

Letham   Fernie Castle   60%   £68

Tel 033 781 381   Fax 033 781 422   **H**

Letham By Cupar Fife KY7 7RU   Map 17 C5

The castle was first recorded in the mid 14th century, and later additions have not spoilt its charm. Best of the public rooms is the first-floor drawing room in a Georgian extension and the most atmospheric the medieval Keep Bar with its rough-stone vaulted ceiling. Bedrooms vary from a very small single without desk or dressing table to a few spacious rooms with reproduction antique furniture; most fall somewhere between the two. Children under 12 stay free in parents' room. No dogs. Banqueting facilities for 140, conferences for 160. **Rooms 16.** *Access, Amex, Visa,* (1) *DinersClub International*

Linlithgow   Champany Inn   ★   £110

Tel 050 683 4532   **R**

Champany Linlithgow Lothian EH49 7LU   Map 12 C1

To buy the best and cook it simply but skilfully is the secret of Clive and Anne Davidson's success at the collection of old buildings that comprises the Champany Inn. Aberdeen Angus beef, their speciality, comes from the charcoal grill as rib eye, porterhouse, sirloin, carpet bagger (fillet stuffed with a fresh oyster) and chateaubriand amongst others having been cut to order by butcher, Nigel Best, in full view of the customer. Seafood is another strength, with lobster and crayfish coming from the sea-water pool that is also a decorative feature of the restaurant. Scottish lamb features in season and their own smokehouse provides smoked salmon and beef. The sweet trolley includes fresh fruits and a selection of home-made ice creams. Past winner of our Cellar of the Year award, the biblical wine list here is extraordinary – 10 own-label house wines, burgundies by the bucketful, an enormous South African selection and a good worldwide choice at fair prices. No children under eight. **Seats 50.** *Parties 14. L 12.30-2 D 7-10. Closed L Sat, all Sun, 2 weeks Xmas. Set L £13.75. Access, Amex, Visa,* (1) *DinersClub International*

Linlithgow   Champany Inn Chop & Ale House   £40

Tel 050 683 4532   **R**

Champany Linlithgow Lothian EH49 7LU   Map 12 C1

The same outstanding Aberdeen Angus steaks (though less expensive and cut a bit smaller) as at its sister restaurant, together with various burgers, deep-fried Scottish prawn tails, char-grilled grain-fed chicken and a cold buffet with help-yourself salad bar, are amongst the offerings at this much less formal eaterie. For afters go for the home-made, hot malted waffles or Champany's own cheesecake served with apricot purée. **Seats 32.** *Parties 6. L 12-2.30 (Sat to 2.15, Sun from 12.30) D 6.30-10. Closed 2 weeks Xmas. Access, Amex, Visa,* (1) *DinersClub International*

Linlithgow   Places of Interest

Tourist Information Tel 0506 844600.
Linlithgow Palace Tel 0506 842896.

Lochinver   Inver Lodge Hotel   70%   £114

Tel 057 14 496   Fax 057 14 395   **H**

Lochinver Highland IV27 4LU   Map 16 B2

Built at the beginning of 1988, the hotel is set high above the village in a
scene of exceptional peace and beauty. It's an ideal base for fishing (10 rods
on local rivers, 10 more with boats on the lochs), bird-watching and hill
walking, and after the day's activity the lounge and cocktail bar offer
comfort and conviviality. Generously sized bedrooms – each named after a
nearby mountain or loch – feature bold earth tones and colourful fabrics.
Two rooms, Suilven and Canisp, have dining tables and sofas. *Rooms 20.
Sauna, solarium, fishing, snooker. Closed Nov-Mar. Access, Amex, Visa,*

Lochinver   Places of Interest

Tourist Information   Tel 05714 330.

Markinch   Balbirnie House   74%   £125

Tel 0592 610066   Fax 0592 610529   **H**

16 Rothesay Mews Markinch By Glenrothes Fife KY7 6NE   Map 17 C5

A fine example of the 18th-century classical period of architecture,
Balbirnie House sits in the middle of a very pretty 400-acre park
overlooking a golf course. It opened as a hotel in late 1989. The splendid
public rooms include a gallery with vaulted ceiling, "spider's web"
windows and cherubic murals, a book-lined library bar and a well-
proportioned drawing room with a marble fireplace, beautiful fabrics,
luxurious seating and oil paintings. The Gamekeeper's inn was converted
from an 1815 kitchen. Function rooms can accommodate up to 120 for
banquets, 150 for conferences. Bedrooms progress in size to very spacious
de luxe rooms and suites; all have individual, stylish fabrics and the best
boast antiques. *Rooms 30. Garden, keep-fit equipment, snooker. Access, Amex,
Visa,*

Maryculter   Maryculter House   66%   £90

Tel 0224 732124   Fax 0224 733510   **H**

South Deeside Road Maryculter Grampian AB1 0BB   Map 17 D4

Eight miles from Aberdeen city centre, the house enjoys a beautiful
location on the banks of the river Dee. Most appealing public room is the
16th-century bar, whose stone walls extend through three floors up to the
pitched roof. There is also a roomy bar/lounge and a patio for dining or
drinking al fresco. Twelve new bedrooms and a conference room for up to
200 were due to come on line after went to press. *Rooms 11. Garden.
Access, Amex, Visa,*

Melrose   Burts Hotel   £64

Tel 089 682 2285   Fax 089 682 2870   **I**

Market Square Melrose Borders TD6 9PN   Map 12 D2

Graham and Anne Henderson have been the owners for more than 20
years of this 18th-century inn set on the historic town square. It's a friendly
place, and the little lounge bar is a popular local meeting place. Bedrooms
have pleasant matching bedcovers and curtains, padded headboards and
good-quality furniture. Bathrooms, five of which have just shower/WC,
feature large fluffy bath sheets. Shooting, fishing and other outdoor pursuits
can be arranged. *Rooms 21. Garden, snooker. Closed 26 Dec. Access, Amex,
Visa,*

Melrose   George & Abbotsford Hotel   56%   £75

Tel 089 682 2308   Fax 089 682 3363   **H**

High Street Melrose Borders TD6 9PD   **Map 12 D2**

A Victorian look has been restored to this town-centre former coaching
inn, once a haunt of Sir Walter Scott. Glass-shaded brass chandeliers, red
plush upholstery and dado panelling set the tone in the day rooms; separate
conference rooms accommodate up to 160. Bedrooms, while not quite so
appealing, are neatly kept and range from standards with shower/WC only
to the four-poster rooms which have whirlpool baths. Children up to 15
stay free in parents' room. *Rooms 31. Garden, game fishing. Access, Amex,
Visa,*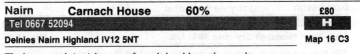

Melrose   Places of Interest

Tourist Information   Tel 089 682 2555.
Teddy Melrose Teddy Bear Museaum   Tel 089 682 2464.
  Historic Houses, Castles and Gardens
Abbotsford House   Tel 0896 2043 *Home of Sir Walter Scott.*
Mertoun Gardens   St Boswells. Tel 0835 23236.
Priorwood Garden   Tel 089682 2555.
Thirlestane Castle   Lauder Tel 05782 430.

Milngavie   Black Bull Thistle   59%   £87

Tel 041-956 2291   Fax 041-956 1896   **H**

Main Street Milngavie Strathclyde G62 6BH   **Map 12 B1**

A useful stopover six miles from the centre of Glasgow. Mount Charlotte
Thistle. *Rooms 27. Access, Amex, Visa,*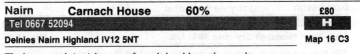

Muir-of-Ord   Dower House   £64

Tel &   Fax 0463 870090   **RR**

Highfield Muir-of-Ord Highland IV6 7XN   **Map 16 B3**

Personally run by Robyn and Mena Aitchison, the house stands a mile
from Muir of Ord on the A862 Dingwall road, in three acres of mature
grounds. Dinner in the ornate dining room (no smoking) comprises five
courses prepared by Robyn. Smoked salmon omelette, scallops with basil
butter sauce, breast of wood pigeon in a mustard coat, fillet of beef with
fennel and Madeira, and marmalade tart with whisky cream show the
style. No smoking. *Seats 18. Parties 26. L by arrangement D 7.30-8.30.
Closed 1 week Oct, 2 weeks Feb, Xmas. Set D £25. Access, Amex, Visa.*

Rooms   £90

The five bedrooms are comfortable and cottagey, and all have Victorian-
style bathrooms with cast-iron baths and brass fittings. One has its own
sitting room. No dogs.

Nairn   Carnach House   60%   £80

Tel 0667 52094   **H**

Delnies Nairn Highland IV12 5NT   **Map 16 C3**

The house stands in eight acres of wooded and lawned grounds
overlooking the Moray Firth. It's 14 miles from Inverness, 2 miles from
Nairn and close to the A96. Built in 1914, it remained a private residence
until 1980, and the family owners (Graham and Andrea Stubbs) have kept
much of the original decor. Accommodation includes the Princess Alice
suite with a four-poster. *Rooms 14. Garden, riding. Access, Amex, Visa.*

Nairn   Clifton Hotel   70%   £96

Tel 0667 53119   Fax 0667 52836   **HR**

Viewfield Street Nairn Highland IV12 4HW   Map 16 C3

A truly civilised town house overlooking the Moray Firth; the beach is a
very short walk away, and the Nairn Pottery studio is next door.
J. Gordon Macintyre, hotelier and patron of the arts, has been at the helm
for many years and has filled the house with hand-chosen antiques. Public
areas include a long red hallway hung with framed prints, the yellow
sitting room, the green room (no smoking) and a drawing room full of
fresh and dried flowers and fragrant with pot-pourri. There are antiques,
too, in the bedrooms, where TVs and telephones do not intrude. *Rooms 16.
Garden. Closed Nov-Mar. Access, Amex, Visa,* 🔘

Green Room   £60

A brief, hand-written menu is presented in French, but the owner is on
hand to translate and explain. Some typical dishes are *artichaut vinaigrette,
salade tiède de gésier, langoustines provençale, salmon beurre blanc, cote de porc
flamande.* The pudding menu goes British with the likes of caramel custard,
sherry trifle and chocolate chestnut cake. *Seats 40. Parties 24.
L by arrangement D 7-9.30.*

Nairn   Golf View Hotel   64%   £125

Tel 0667 52301   Fax 0667 55267   **H**

Seabank Road Nairn Highland IV12 4HD   Map 16 C3

Built at the very end of the last century, the hotel stands on the shores of
the Moray Firth, overlooking Black Isle. It's a great place for family
holidays, with a games room, pool, a children's play area and weekend
evening entertainment. Nearly half the bedrooms are suitable for family
occupation (accommodation and food for under-4s are free). Baby listening
and baby sitting can be arranged. *Rooms 48. Garden, outdoor swimming pool,
tennis, putting, sauna, hairdressing, games room. Access, Amex, Visa,* 🔘

Nairn   Newton Hotel   65%   £85

Tel 0667 53144   Fax 0667 54026   **H**

Inverness Road Nairn Highland IV12 4RX   Map 16 C3

At the bottom of a winding, tree-lined private road, this imposing building
is set in 27 acres with sweeping views overlooking the Nairn golf course
and the Moray Firth beyond. The high-ceilinged rooms within the main
house are more interesting than the newer, more contemporary ones in the
adjacent Newton Court, a converted granary and stables. The peaceful
setting, well-chosen antiques and velvet upholstery recall the gracious
Victorian era. Families welcome. *Rooms 44. Garden, sauna, solarium, tennis,
games room. Access, Amex, Visa,* 🔘

Nairn   Places of Interest

Tourist Information   Tel 0667 52753.
Cawdor Castle   Cawdor Tel 06677 615 *6 miles.*

Newburgh   Udny Arms Hotel   60%   £73

Tel 035 86 89444   Fax 035 86 89012   **H**

Main Street Newburgh Grampian AB41 0BL   Map 16 D3

The Victorian facade is on the main street but at the back there are pleasant
views over a golf course and the Ythan estuary. Day rooms vary: perhaps
the most appealing is the mellow cocktail bar with its pine-board
banquettes, scrubbed pine tables and Windsor chairs. Catering outlets
comprise a dining room, bistro and café-bar. Bedrooms are furnished
mainly in traditional style and are all en suite; the best rooms overlook the
picturesque estuary. Children stay free in parents' room. Theatre-style
conferences for up to 125. Parking for 100 cars. *Rooms 26. Garden. Access,
Amex, Visa.*

Newburgh　　Places of Interest

Dundee and Perth Polo Club　Newhill Auchtermuchty. Tel 031-557 3313.

Newhouse　　Travel Inn　　£42

`Tel 0698 860277　Fax 0698 861353`　　**L**

Glasgow Road Newhouse Nr Motherwell Strathclyde ML1 5SY　　Map 12 B2

Rooms 40. Access, Amex, Visa, 🌐 *Diners Club International*

Newmill-on-Teviot　　Old Forge Restaurant　　£40

`Tel 0450 85298`　　**R**

Newmill-on-Teviot Nr Hawick Borders TD9 0JU　　Map 12 D3

Both the size and the success of Bill and Margaret Irving's tiny restaurant (on the A7 four miles south of Hawick) make advance booking essential for Margaret's four-course restricted-choice dinners. Bread, jellies and chutneys are all made on the premises; seasonal herbs and salad vegetables are also home-grown. Eyemouth crab on a crisp croissant, apple and pea soup with hazelnuts, and caramelised pork roast with braised cabbage rely on fine local produce. To finish, first-rate Scottish farmhouse cheeses are a commendable alternative to the likes of dark chocolate torte or pavlova. Fair prices on a good all-round wine list that spans the world. *Seats 24. Parties 28. D only 7-9.30. Closed Sun & Mon, Bank Holidays, 2 weeks May/Jun, 2 weeks Nov. Set D £12.95 (3-courses mid-week)/£15.95. Access, Visa.*

Newton Stewart　　Kirroughtree Hotel　　75%　　£100

`Tel 0671 2141　Fax 0671 2425`　　**HR**

Newton Stewart Dumfries & Galloway DG8 6AN　　Map 13 B4

Standing in a high position amid eight acres of landscaped gardens, Kirroughtree dates from 1719. Main day room is an oak-panelled lounge with rococo furnishings and French doors that open on to the terrace and croquet lawn. Bedrooms are decorated in individual style, ornately furnished and very spacious. The vast and splendid Regal Suite has a sitting room with lovely views of Wigtown Bay in the mid-distance. Smartly tiled and carpeted bathrooms boast many extras. Raymond Dilks and his staff take excellent care of their guests. No children under ten in hotel or restaurant. *Rooms 22. Garden, tennis, badminton, lawn bowling, putting, croquet. Closed 2 Jan-early Feb. Access, Amex, Visa,* 🌐 *Diners Club International*

Restaurant　　£65

Roux-trained Ian Bennett cooks in fine style, and guests can choose a smoking or non-smoking room (both are plush and comfortable). Four-course dinner menus offer such dishes as cassolette of Dublin Bay prawns with fresh noodles and basil followed by cream of leek and potato soup, canon of lamb with sorrel and mint or roast Gressingham duck with apples and cider. Justifiably praised desserts might include strawberry sablé with mango purée, profiteroles or mocha parfait with coffee bean sauce. A la carte lunches range from grilled goat's cheese with truffles or moules marinière to poussin with port and grapes or smoked salmon salad, plus similarly good desserts. Gentlemen should wear jackets and ties. There are some great names on a generally overpriced wine list. *Seats 70. Parties 60. Private Room. L 12.30-1.30 D 7-9.30. Set D £27.*

Newton Stewart　　Places of Interest

Tourist Information　Tel 0671 2431.

Newtonmore　　Ard-na-Coille Hotel　　67%　　£110*

`Tel 0540 673214　Fax 0540 673453`　　**HR**

Kingussie Road Newtonmore Highland PH20 1AY　　Map 17 C4

High in the forest, amongst its two acres of pine woodland, Nancy Ferrier and Barry Cottam's former shooting lodge is today a tranquil and intimate

country hotel. Edwardian-style public rooms and sunny terrace have an
open outlook towards the Cairngorm mountains. Most of the guest
bedrooms have a southerly aspect and all enjoy uninterrupted views of the
Spey Valley. Each is different in decor and period furniture; all are
immaculately kept. *Half-board terms only. **Rooms 7.** *Garden. Closed
6 weeks Nov/Dec, 1 week Apr, 1 week Sep. Access, Visa.*

Restaurant   £65

Five-course set dinner, prepared by the proprietors, is served at 7.45pm
after much care with cooking and presentation and equal emphasis on local
produce. Chargrilled Loch Linnhe scallops, a carrot, ginger and coriander
soup, and roast Ayrshire guinea fowl with shallot and tarragon sauce typify
the balance of ingredients and flavours. Farmhouse cheeses could then
precede an iced orange soufflé with orange and Grand Marnier salad. A
super wine list with tremendous depth and great value – lots of quality
wines at very kind prices. **Seats 18.** *Parties 12. L by arrangement D at 7.45.
Set D £25.*

Newtown St Boswells	Le Provençale	£40
Tel 0835 23284		**R**
Monksford Road Newtown St Boswells Borders TD6 0SB		**Map 12 D2**

Frenchman René Duzelier in the kitchen and his Scottish wife Elizabeth at
front of house make a fine team in their spotless little restaurant just off the
A68. The daily-changing menu is handwritten with English descriptions in
a distinctive French script. Straightforward cooking of dishes like snails in
garlic butter, marinated sweet herring, ham and cheese omelette, braised
pork chop in a creamy tarragon sauce, Grand Marnier pancakes. Keenly
priced all-French wine list. **Seats 40.** *Parties 40. Private Room. L 12-2.30
D 6.30-10. Closed Sun & Mon, 2 weeks Jul, 1 week Nov. No credit cards.*

North Berwick	Marine Hotel	62%	£100
Tel 0620 2406 Fax 0620 4480			**H**
Cromwell Road North Berwick Lothian EH39 4LZ			**Map 12 D1**

Fine coastal views of the Firth of Forth are enjoyed from this imposing
Victorian hotel with a long golfing tradition (it overlooks the 16th green
of the North Berwick Championship Westlinks Course). Bedrooms are
more practical than luxurious, save for those in the turret. Banqueting for
250; conferences up to 350. Forte Heritage. **Rooms 84.** *Access, Amex, Visa,*

North Berwick   Places of Interest

Tourist Information   Tel 0620 2197.
Malleny Garden (NT)   Balerno Tel 031449 2283.

North Middleton	Borthwick Castle	66%	£95
Tel 0875 20514 Fax 0875 21702			**H**
North Middleton Nr Gorebridge Lothian EH23 4QY			**Map 12 D2**

Hardly altered since being built in 1430 (although Cromwell's cannon left
their mark), historic Borthwick Castle once held Mary Queen of Scots as a
prisoner. She escaped from a window of the vast stone-vaulted main hall
which now serves as the dining room, bar and lounge with leather sofas
around the huge fireplace. Spiral staircases within the massive stone walls
lead to bedrooms offering more atmosphere than luxury. Most bathrooms
have shower and WC only. Probably the most genuinely atmospheric
medieval castle hotel in the country. **Rooms 10.** *Garden. Access, Amex, Visa,*
Diners Club International

North Queensferry   Queensferry Lodge   63%   £68

Tel 0383 410000   Fax 0383 419708   **H**

**St Margaret's Head North Queensferry Nr Inverkeithing
Lothian KY11 1HP**   Map 17 C5

A modern family-run hotel at the north end of the Forth road bridge.
Bedrooms are quite generous on space and accessories, and sparkling
bathrooms have good showers over the tubs and ample towelling. A
tourist information office is manned from 10 to 6 throughout the year, and
in a Scottish crafts shop you can find out all about the Firth of Forth and
its famous bridges. Conference and banqueting facilities for 200. Children
up to 10 free in parents' room. *Rooms 32. Coffee shop (10.30am-10pm).
Access, Amex, Visa.*

Oban   Alexandra Hotel   57%   £84

Tel 0631 62381   Fax 0631 64497   **H**

Corran Esplanade Oban Strathclyde PA54 5AA   Map 17 B5

Built in the late 1860s, the hotel stands on the esplanade a short stroll from
the town centre. Adequate bedrooms, two lounges and a cocktail bar. Trips
can be arranged on the hotel's motor cruiser, the *Ocean Ranger. Rooms 61.
Garden. Access, Amex, Visa.*

Oban   Columba Hotel   60%   £75

Tel 0631 62183   Fax 0631 64683   **H**

North Pier Esplanade Oban Strathclyde PA34 5QD   Map 17 B5

An Edwardian sandstone building on the North Pier, with views across the
bay to the Western Isles. Three bars offer a choice for a relaxing drink, and
conference suites can cater for up to 400 delegates. Children stay free when
sharing parents' room. Some rooms have shower/WC only. *Rooms 49.
Closed early Jan-early Mar. Access, Visa,* ⓓ Diners Club International

Oban   Knipoch Hotel   72%   £118

Tel 085 26 251   Fax 085 26 249   **HR**

by Oban Strathclyde PA34 4QT   Map 17 B5

The Craig family's elegant Georgian hotel stands on the A816 halfway
along the shore of Loch Feochan, an arm of the sea stretching four miles
inland. Lounges and bars are filled with family heirlooms, and there are
plenty of magazines to read in the leathery comfort of fireside armchairs.
Well-proportioned bedrooms have period furniture and particularly well-
appointed bathrooms. A purpose-built bedroom extension blends well with
the original. Good housekeeping. *Rooms 17. Garden. Closed mid Nov-mid
Feb. Access, Amex, Visa,* ⓓ Diners Club International

Restaurant   £92

Dinner is set five courses featuring excellent produce from garden, loch and
the hotel's own smokery; their salmon is cured, marinated in juniper,
rowan, Barbados sugar, herbs and whisky then smoked over oak for three
days. Soup and home-baked bread precede a fish course, followed by the
centrepiece – often a prime cut of Aberdeen Angus beef. Next comes
cheese, then dessert (fruit in a basket, chocolate terrine) and coffee with
petits fours. *Seats 40. Private Room. L by arrangement D 7.30-9. Set D £36.*

Oban   Places of Interest

Tourist Information   Tel 0631 63122.
Highland Theatre   Tel 0631 62444.
Gateway Leisure Centre   Tel 0631 62345.
Easdale Island Folk Museum   Tel 08523 370.
Oban Distillery   Tel 0631 64262.
Highland Salmon Centre   Kilninver Tel 08562 202.
Sealife Centre   Barcaldine Tel 063172 386.

Onich   Allt-nan-Ros Hotel   63%   £95

HR

Tel 085 53 250   Fax 085 53 462

Onich by Fort William Highland PH33 6RY   Map 17 B4

The name means 'Burn of the Roses', a reference to the stream which runs
through the garden of this Victorian former shooting lodge and into Lochs
Leven and Linnhe. There are exceptional views across the hotel's gardens
and mountain scenery beyond from all the public rooms and bedrooms.
Superior rooms have large bay windows and two country cottage-style
bedrooms are in converted stables. *Rooms 21. Garden, putting. Closed early
Nov–Mar. Access, Amex, Visa,* ① *Diners Club International*

Restaurant   £55

Four-course dinners offer a triple choice of starter, main course and sweet,
plus a soup. Typical dishes run from spinach and mushroom strudel and
grilled scallops in a lemon, caviar and butter sauce, to steamed monkfish in
a wild mushroom fish sauce and sirloin of beef in a mixed peppercorn
sauce. To finish, perhaps sticky toffee pudding or poached rhubarb with
vanilla ice cream. Coffee is served with petits fours. A smaller lunchtime
menu is available. Straightforward wine list with useful notes. *Seats 50.
Parties 12. L 12.30-2 D 7-8.30. Set D £19.50.*

Onich   Lodge on the Loch   63%   £135*

H

Tel 085 53 237   Fax 085 53 463

Creag Dhu Onich Nr Fort William Highland PH33 6RY   Map 17 B4

Loch and mountain views are a spectacular feature at this friendly little
hotel, which stands just off the A82 (five miles north of Glencoe, ten miles
south of Fort William). Plump-cushioned sofas make for easy relaxation in
the lounge, and there's a modern bar. Best bedrooms are the Chieftains
with loch views. *Half-board terms only. Rooms 18. Garden. Closed mid
Nov–mid Dec, early Jan–early Feb. Access, Visa,* ① *Diners Club International*

Onich   Onich Hotel   61%   £70

H

Tel 085 53 214   Fax 085 53 484

Onich Nr Fort William Highland PH33 6RY   Map 17 B4

Fine views of Loch Linnhe, well-maintained gardens and multifarious
activities for all ages make the Onich hotel a popular year-round choice.
Iain Young has put his personal stamp on the place for over 30 years,
developing an atmosphere of friendly informality where guests and locals
chat together in the bars. It lies on the A82 ten miles south of Fort
William, making it a splendid base from which to explore the West
Highlands and Islands. The best front bedrooms are balconied; all rooms
have neat bathrooms and many sport new curtains and bedspreads. None is
denied a fair share of the view, but some suffer slightly from proximity to
the road. *Rooms 27. Watersports centre, ski hire shop, garden, solarium, spa
bath, pool table, coffee shop (8am-9pm). Access, Amex, Visa,* ① *Diners Club International*

Peat Inn   Peat Inn   ★   £78

RR

Tel 033 484 206   Fax 033 484 530

Peat Inn By Cupar Fife KY15 5LH   Map 17 C5

The village which takes its name from this former coaching inn is not
much more than a crossroads, but David and Patricia Wilson have really
put it on the map. The dining room has the feel of an upmarket French
country restaurant, with carved sideboard, high-backed tapestry chairs, red
and gold curtains and rough white plaster walls. David's modern cooking
makes use of local supplies where possible and in the evening there's a
choice of four-course set menu, six- or seven-course tasting menu and à la
carte. Many favourites stay on the list – fish soup, lobster, spring lamb in
its season – and some creatures appear in more than one guise: pigeon

breast in a beef broth with pulses as a starter; with mushrooms in a red wine sauce as a main course; venison liver with an onion confit to start, noisettes of venison saddle with red wine and port as a main. Caramelised apple pastry with caramel sauce is a favourite sweet; others include a trio of caramel desserts and a little pot of chocolate and rosemary. A typical fixed-price, four-course, no-choice lunch might start with smoked haddock with a cheese and herb crust, followed by a pastry case filled with mixed fish in vermouth and cream sauce and then roast loin and leg of spring lamb in its juices with braised shoulder; dark and white chocolate parfait with a coffee bean sauce and coffee with petits fours to finish. An imbiber's bible of fine wines is well laid out with helpful tasting notes and a few unusual listings by grape variety. *Seats 48. Parties 24. Private Room. L at 1 D 7-9.30. Closed Sun & Mon. Set L £18.50 Set D £28 & £38. Access, Amex, Visa,*

Rooms   £125

The Residence, built in 1987, offers eight luxurious suites, each with high-quality fabrics and period French furniture chosen by design graduate Patricia. Italian marble bathrooms.

Peebles   Cringletie House   65%   £80
Tel 072 13 233   Fax 072 13 244   HR
Peebles Lothian EH45 8PL   Map 12 C2

Set well back from the A703, three miles north of Peebles, this Scottish baronial-style mansion offers peace and quiet and enjoys views of the distant Meldon and Moorfoot Hills. Open fires, fresh flowers from the gardens and antiques enhance the traditional decor. Most impressive of the day rooms is the panelled drawing room with fine painted ceiling. Well-kept bedrooms offer considerable comfort and excellent bathrooms boast big soft towels. *Rooms 13. Garden, putting, croquet. Closed Jan-mid Mar. Access, Visa.*

Restaurant   £60

A two-acre walled kitchen garden provides much of the fresh produce served in the lofty twin dining rooms. Cooking is soundly based, with dishes such as mousseline of ham with asparagus cream, Turkish stuffed aubergine with cinnamon and walnuts, baked monkfish with saffron and orange sauce, and pork fillet with wild mushrooms on the daily-changing menu. Good wine list includes some excellent burgundies. *Seats 56. Parties 12. Private Room. L 1-1.45 D 7.30-8.30. Set L £13.50 Set D £22.50.*

Peebles   Park Hotel   62%   £84
Tel 0721 20451   H
Innerleithen Road Peebles Borders EH45 8BA   Map 12 C2

A handsome, whitewashed building on the A72. Views of gardens and hills are enjoyed by many of the bedrooms, which include one with a four-poster. Guests may use the extensive leisure facilities of the Peebles Hydro, a sister hotel under the same ownership. *Rooms 24. Garden, putting. Access, Amex, Visa,*

Peebles   Peebles Hotel Hydro   70%   £97
Tel 0721 20602   Fax 0721 22999   H
Innerleithen Road Peebles Borders EH45 8LX   Map 12 C2

There seem to be few facilities not provided by the energetic Pieter van Dijk, manager for over 20 years at this fine holiday hotel overlooking the Tweed valley. Formally a hydropathic hotel, its extensive sports facilities in the 30 acres of grounds are a major attraction, keeping even the most active guests fully occupied. Public rooms of grand proportions are both attractive and comfortable; in the bar there's a good selection of malt whiskies. A sun room overlooks the valley, as do some of the good-size bedrooms, which are charmingly furnished and well kept. Families are well catered for with the likes of children's high tea, baby-sitting and baby-changing facilities in Bubbles leisure centre. The hotel also offers adaptable conference and function facilities for up to 400 delegates. *Rooms 137. Garden, indoor swimming pool, sauna, solarium, spa bath, gymnasium, beautician, hairdressing, tennis, squash, badminton, pitch & putt, putting, croquet, riding, games room, snooker, coffee shop (10am-11pm), kiosk, children's playground & playroom, dinner dance (Fri & Sat). Access, Amex, Visa,*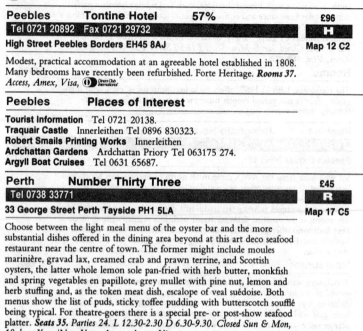

Peebles   Tontine Hotel   57%   £96

Tel 0721 20892   Fax 0721 29732   **H**

High Street Peebles Borders EH45 8AJ   Map 12 C2

Modest, practical accommodation at an agreeable hotel established in 1808. Many bedrooms have recently been refurbished. Forte Heritage. *Rooms 37. Access, Amex, Visa,*

Peebles   Places of Interest

Tourist Information   Tel 0721 20138.
Traquair Castle   Innerleithen Tel 0896 830323.
Robert Smails Printing Works   Innerleithen
Ardchattan Gardens   Ardchattan Priory Tel 063175 274.
Argyll Boat Cruises   Tel 0631 65687.

Perth   Number Thirty Three   £45

Tel 0738 33771   **R**

33 George Street Perth Tayside PH1 5LA   Map 17 C5

Choose between the light meal menu of the oyster bar and the more substantial dishes offered in the dining area beyond at this art deco seafood restaurant near the centre of town. The former might include moules marinière, gravad lax, creamed crab and prawn terrine, and Scottish oysters, the latter whole lemon sole pan-fried with herb butter, monkfish and spring vegetables en papillote, grey mullet with pine nut, lemon and herb stuffing and, as the token meat dish, escalope of veal suédoise. Both menus show the list of puds, sticky toffee pudding with butterscotch soufflé being typical. For theatre-goers there is a special pre- or post-show seafood platter. *Seats 35. Parties 24. L 12.30-2.30 D 6.30-9.30. Closed Sun & Mon, 10 days Xmas/New Year. Access, Amex, Visa.*

Perth   Royal George Hotel   62%   £91

Tel 0738 24455   Fax 0738 30345   **H**

Tay Street Perth Tayside PH1 5LD   Map 17 C5

A Georgian jumble of a hotel close to the city centre with some rooms facing the river Tay. Refurbished day rooms are quite extensive and offer many quiet, comfortable seating areas. Some bedrooms are old-fashioned, while the more recently updated are most appealing, with floral fabrics, easy chairs, darkwood furniture and up-to-date bathrooms. A limited room service is offered. *Rooms 42. Garden. Access, Amex, Visa,*

Perth   Stakis City Mills Hotel   59%   £86

Tel 0738 28281   Fax 0738 43423   **H**

West Mill Street Perth Tayside PH1 5QP   Map 17 C5

Right in the heart of Perth, the Stakis is based on a watermill dating back to the 15th century. Single, double and twin rooms, plus a couple of family rooms. Banquet facilities for 130, conferences 120. *Rooms 76. Access, Amex, Visa,*

Perth   Places of Interest

Tourist Information   Tel 0738 38353.
Perth Theatre   Tel 0738 21031.

St Ninian's Cathedral   Tel 0738 21373.
Perth Museum and Art Gallery   Tel 0738 32488.
Dewars Ice Rinks   Tel 0738 37810.
Perth Showgrounds   Tel 0738 23780.
Perth Hunt Racecourse   Tel 0738 51597.
Caithness Glass Visitor Centre   Inveralmond Tel 0783 37373.
   Historic Houses, Castles and Gardens
Branklyn Garden (NT)   Tel 0738 25535.
Megginch Castle Gardens   Errol. Tel 08212 222.

Peterhead	Waterside Inn	67%	£69
Tel 0779 71121 Fax 0779 70670			**H**
Fraserburgh Road Peterhead Grampian AB42 7BN			Map 16 D3

A modern hotel which is comfortable and efficiently run. There's a series
of bars to suit every taste, and several conference rooms (maximum
capacity 250). 40 studio bedrooms in a separate block are compact and
functional, while those in the main building are more spacious and
luxurious; children up to 13 stay free in parents' room. Greatly reduced
rates at weekends. *Rooms 110. Garden, croquet, indoor swimming pool, keep-fit
equipment, spa bath, sauna, solarium, snooker, coffee shop (7am-10pm). Access,
Amex, Visa,*

Peterhead	Places of Interest

Tourist Information   Tel 0779 71904.
Arbuthnot Museum   Tel 0779 77778.

Pitlochry	Green Park Hotel	58%	£74
Tel 0796 473248 Fax 0796 473520			**H**
Cluny Bridge Road Pitlochry Tayside PH16 5JY			Map 17 C4

From manicured lawns to neat carpeted bathrooms, this Victorian lochside
hotel is very well kept. Fresh flowers and an original tapestry frieze adorn
the panelled entrance hall but it is the splendid view across the loch from
the lounge which is the major attraction. Bedrooms feature good Japanese
elm furniture and pretty matching bedcovers and curtains. *Rooms 37.
Garden, putting, game fishing, games room. Closed Nov-Mar. Access, Visa.*

Pitlochry	Pitlochry Hydro	64%	£93
Tel 0796 472666 Fax 0796 472238			**H**
Knockard Road Pitlochry Tayside PH16 5JH			Map 17 C4

Set high above Pitlochry, the Hydro is a well-run, well-maintained and
sturdily built late-Victorian hotel. Its simple attractions are supplemented
by good leisure facilities, mostly housed in the Hydro Club. Bedrooms,
including a couple of suites, have modern tiled bathrooms. Children up to
14 stay free in parents' room. No dogs. *Rooms 62. Garden, croquet, indoor
swimming pool, gymnasium, spa bath, sauna, solarium, snooker, putting. Closed
Jan & Feb. Access, Amex, Visa,* ①

Pitlochry	Places of Interest

Tourist Information   Tel 0796 2215.
Pitlochry Theatre Festival   Tel 0796 2680 *May-Oct.*
Blair Castle   Blair Atholl. Tel 079 681 207.

Port Appin	Airds Hotel	76%	£212*
Tel 063 173 236 Fax 063 173 535			**HR**
Port Appin Appin Strathclyde PA38 4DF			Map 17 B5

Once a ferry inn for "those in passage" to the island of Lismore, the Allen
family's hotel enjoys a fine setting in two acres of gardens with splendid
views of Loch Linnhe (albeit across a busy road). Day rooms are ideal for
relaxation, with inviting chairs and sofas, coal fires and plenty of reading

material. Bedrooms are not large but make good use of high-quality fabrics and have well-kept modern bathrooms. No dogs. *Half-board terms only. **Rooms 13.** *Garden. Closed early Jan-early Mar. No credit cards.*

Restaurant   £78

The best local produce goes into Betty and Graeme Allen's kitchen and sympathetic, essentially simple treatment results in very enjoyable daily-changing four-course dinners. Mousseline of scallops with a Barsac cream sauce, parfait of chicken livers or braised leg of duckling with salad and a potato cake can start the meal, followed by soup and a trio of main courses such as fillet of turbot with white wine and chive sauce or roast rack of lamb with onion marmalade and crab apple and mint jelly. Desserts are a strong point and it could be difficult to choose between, for example, poached pear shortcake with a caramel and lime sauce and date pudding with butterscotch. There's a vast and far-ranging wine list. Front tables get the loch views. No smoking. **Seats 36.** *L 12.30-1.30 D 8-8.30. Set D £33.*

Port William   Corsemalzie House   61%   £75
Tel 098 886 254   **H**
Port William By Newton Stewart Dumfries & Galloway DG8 9RL   Map 13 B4

Forty wooded acres make a secluded setting for a 19th-century stone mansion which nowadays is a popular and unpretentious hotel with many sporting attractions. Fishing is a major activity (rights on stretches of the rivers Bladnoch and Tarff, plus nearby lochs) and there's good rough shooting and arrangements with local golf courses. The lounge and bar provide easy relaxation, and bedrooms are generally of a decent size; all have private bath or shower. Children under 13 in parents' room are charged at £3 a night. **Rooms 14.** *Garden, putting, croquet, game fishing, shooting. Closed 25 & 26 Dec, 14 Jan-mid Mar. Access, Visa.*

Portpatrick   Knockinaam Lodge   73%   £96
Tel 077 681 471   Fax 077 681 435   **H R**
Portpatrick Nr Stranraer Dumfries & Galloway DG9 9AD   Map 13 A4

Marcel and Corinna Frichot are in their eighth year at this Victorian lodge, which stands at the foot of a wooded glen looking out to sea. It's a place of timeless tranquillity and scenic splendour, and the gardens reach down to a private beach. Day rooms are light, stylish and comfortable, with open fires in cool weather; the drawing room features some fine watercolours, while a stag's head takes the eye in the wood-panelled bar. Most bedrooms are of a generous size and several command sea views. Children sharing parents' rooms stay free, with breakfast charged as taken. **Rooms 10.** *Garden, croquet, sea fishing. Closed Jan-mid Mar. Access, Amex, Visa,*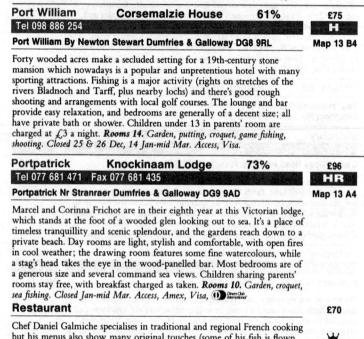

Restaurant   £70

Chef Daniel Galmiche specialises in traditional and regional French cooking but his menus also show many original touches (some of his fish is flown in from the Seychelles). The table d'hote, written in French only, could include assiette de langoustine et bar en papillote aux pommes peau à l'ail; noisette de lotte à la réglisse (licorice) sa nage à la cardamome; pièce de boeuf poelée à la moelle (bone marrow) et au vin de Bordeaux; and soufflé chaud au chocolat mi-amer sa tuile à l'orange. Excellent French farmhouse cheeses. No smoking. No children under 10 in dining room (but high tea can be provided). Gentlemen should wear jackets and ties. **Seats 26.** *Parties 32. L 12-2 D 7.30-9. Set L £19 Set D £30.*

Portree   Rosedale Hotel   53%   £68
Tel 0478 3131   Fax 0478 2531   **H**
Beaumont Crescent Portree Isle of Skye Highland IV51 9DB   Map 16 A3

The only hotel on the Portree waterfront enjoys splendid views across the harbour towards Ben Tianavaig and the Isle of Raasay. It was built from a row of fishermen's cottages dating from the reign of William IV, and it's a

veritable warren of passages and stairs. Day rooms comprise two lounges with simple easy chairs, and two bars. Bedrooms, some very small, are practically equipped, with fitted units and colourful fabrics. Seven rooms have shower/WC only. Four rooms are in a separate cottage (Beaumont House) along the quay. **Rooms 23.** *Garden. Closed Oct-mid May. Access, Visa.*

Portree   Places of Interest

Tourist Information   Tel 0478 2137.
An Tuireann Arts Centre   Tel 0478 3306.
Old Skye Crofter's House Folk Museum   Luib Tel 0471 822427.
Skye Woolen Mill   Tel 0478 2889.
The Museum of the Isles   Isle of Skye. Tel 04714 305.
Talisker Distillery   Carbost Tel 047842 203 *20 miles.*

Quothquan   Shieldhill   75%   £98

Tel 0899 20035   Fax 0899 21092   **HR**

Quothquan Biggar Strathclyde ML12 6NA   Map 17 C6

Shieldhill exudes the warmth of continuous habitation since 1199: crested carpeting laid throughout the public areas owes its origins to the Chancellor family, residents for seven centuries. With open fires and deep sofas, the atmosphere is one of a Scottish baronial mansion, while the laid-back welcome is more firmly rooted in contemporary California (Jack Greenwald and Christine Dunstan also own Santa Barbara's *Cheshire Cat*). Bedrooms are individually styled in restful tones of Laura Ashley prints, to which fresh flowers, fruit bowl and sherry decanter add an apposite welcome. Several baths are jacuzzis; and all the beds supremely comfortable. Substantial Scottish breakfasts and attentive service overall; no smoking in the bedrooms and restaurant. Stronger on humanities than unabashed luxury. No dogs. **Rooms 11.** *Garden, croquet, fishing. Access, Amex, Visa,* (D)Diners Club

Restaurant   £65

A civilised restaurant where Jack Greenwald presides with an informal urbanity while chef David Clunis confidently prepares dishes that are full of interest without being gimmicky. The style is modern – salad of pigeon breast with mixed berries and raspberry dressing, tournedos of beef on lentils with sherry vinegar jus – and Scottish produce is well represented with the likes of Oban mussels in white wine and parsley cream or Perthshire venison with caramelised shallots. Good puds include an excellent, tangy lemon tart. There is now a no-choice set menu in addition to the sensibly short à la carte. No smoking. **Seats 38.** *Parties 35. Private Room. L 12-2 D 7-9 (Sat to 9.30). Set D £22.50.*

Quothquan Place of Interest

New Lanark Conservation Village   Tel 0555 61345 *8 miles.*

Rockcliffe   Baron's Craig   65%   £103

Tel 055 663 225   **H**

Rockcliffe By Dalbeattie Dumfries & Galloway DG5 4QF   Map 13 C4

An 1880 granite house set in 12 acres of woods, lawns and gardens from which there are fine views of the Solway Firth. Walkers and golfers love it (the latter have six courses within close reach), and enjoy returning to lounges stocked with books and newspapers. Many sea-borne activities can also be arranged. Bedrooms are warm and comfortable. **Rooms 27.** *Garden, golf practice net, putting, sailing, windsurfing, waterskiing. Closed Nov-Easter. Access, Visa.*

Rockcliffe   Places of Interest

Kircudbright Tourist Information   Tel 0557 30494.
Threave Garden   nr Castle Douglas Tel 0556 2575 *12 miles.*

Rothes   Rothes Glen Hotel   65%   £98

Tel 034 03 254   Fax 034 03 566   **H**

Rothes Nr Elgin Grampian AB38 7AH   Map 16 C3

Forty acres of grounds at the head of the Glen of Rothes provide rural peace at a baronial house designed by the architect of Balmoral Castle. Inside, there's an elegant lounge with ribbed ceiling and white marble fireplace, plus a bar and TV room. Antique furniture graces most of the variously-sized bedrooms, all of which have good private bathrooms (three are not en suite). *Rooms 16. Garden, putting. Closed Xmas-Jan. Access, Amex, Visa,* 🔵 *Diners Club International*

St Andrews   Rufflets Hotel   65%   £120

Tel 0334 72594   Fax 0334 78703   **H**

Strathkinness Low Road St Andrews Fife KY16 9TX   Map 17 D5

They are justly proud of their ten acres of award-winning gardens at this 1920s-built hotel on the B939 to the south of town. Inside, the hotel is as well kept as the gardens, with pretty floral fabrics and wallpapers and mostly traditional darkwood furniture. Three particularly attractive rooms are in a rose-covered cottage in the grounds. Children up to 10 stay free in parents' room. Public areas include an appealing entrance hall, lounge and formal drawing room. *Rooms 20. Garden, putting. Access, Amex, Visa,* 🔵 *Diners Club International*

St Andrews   Rusack's Hotel   74%   £134

Tel 0334 74321   Fax 0334 77896   **H**

Pilmour Links St Andrews Fife KY16 9JQ   Map 17 D5

Public rooms at this grand Victorian hotel are sumptuous, with trompe l'oeil marble columns and crystal chandeliers in the foyer lounge plus high-quality furnishings throughout. The spacious sun lounge affords panoramic views of the Old Course and the golf-themed Champions Bar is a good place to re-live the triumphs and disasters of the day's golf. Traditionally furnished bedrooms, the best of which have some antique pieces, feature a variety of stylish fabrics and easy chairs. Smart bathrooms have generous towelling bathrobes. Well-turned-out staff provide a high level of service that includes valet parking, automatic luggage porterage and proper bedroom service in the evenings. Forte. *Rooms 50. Sauna, solarium. Access, Amex, Visa,* *Diners Club International*

St Andrews   St Andrews Old Course Hotel   82%   £194

Tel 0334 74371   Fax 0334 77668   **H**

St Andrews Fife KY16 9SP   Map 17 D5

Alongside the 17th hole of the famous Old Course, the hotel also commands views of the city, St Andrews Bay and the Highlands beyond from the glorious day rooms. Exemplary service from smart, friendly staff combines with the baronial feel of the building to produce real luxury. The slate-floored foyer with stone-effect walls leads through to a spacious reception area with darkwood panelling, stencilled ceiling and silk Oriental rugs on the parquet floor. The book-lined library, sunny conservatory and convivial Road Hole bar with its two fireplaces all offer top-class comfort. Attention to detail in the bedrooms is equally meticulous, with traditional wooden furniture, TVs hidden away in cabinets and footstools with the comfortable armchairs. High-class toiletries and generously-sized bathrobes add to the exuberance in the marble bathrooms. The Spa is an extensively equipped health and leisure centre with facilities that range from beauty treatments to a 50' pool under a glass roof. The hotel also provides fine facilities for banqueting and conferences (up to 300 people). Children up to 12 stay free in parents' room. *Rooms 125. Garden, indoor swimming pool, spa bath, steam room, solarium, gymnasium, golf shop. Access, Amex, Visa,* 🔵 *Diners Club International*

St Andrews   Places of Interest

Tourist Information   Tel 0334 72021.
East Sands Leisure Centre   Tel 0334 76506.

St Fillans   Four Seasons Hotel   60%   £72

Tel & Fax 076 485 333   **H**

St Fillans Nr Crieff Tayside PH26 2NF   Map 17 C5

The setting, in four acres of grounds, is one of outstanding natural beauty, with Lock Earn in the foreground and the mountains beyond. Simple but comfortable public rooms take advantage of the location: there are several small lounges, a bar, restaurant and coffee shop. Bedrooms are also unfussy in their appointments and include six chalets on a wooded hillside behind the main building. Children up to 11 stay free in parents' room. *Rooms 18. Garden, water-skiing. Closed mid Nov-mid Feb. Access, Amex, Visa.*

Scarista   Scarista House   67%   £82

Tel 085 985 238   Fax 085 985 277   **HR**

Scarista Isle of Harris Highland PA85 3HX   Map 16 A2

The Callaghans' former manse on the Atlantic coast of Harris must be one of the most remote hotels in Britain. Ruggedly beautiful countryside and endless deserted beaches are a magnet for walkers, bird watchers and fishermen, who also appreciate the warm welcome and homely comforts of Scarista House. One of the two lounges is lined with books and there is a record collection available for guests' use. Bedrooms in the annexe are larger and more modern than those in the main house, which have a touch more character. No children under 8. *Rooms 7. Garden. Closed mid Oct-Mar. No credit cards.*

Restaurant   £54

Jane Callaghan's simple, hearty dinners are based on good local produce using only free-range eggs and meat, and avoiding farmed seafood. Bread, cakes and preserves are all home-made. *Seats 20. Parties 8. Private Room. D only at 8. Set D £22.*

Scone   Murrayshall House   72%   £105

Tel 0738 51171   Fax 0738 52595   **HR**

Scone Tayside PH2 7PH   Map 17 C5

Golf is a major attraction at this turn-of-the-century stone mansion, with a professional on hand to give tuition, a golf shop and a clubhouse with bar. Fabric-covered walls feature in the stylish day rooms, dark blue damask to match the soft furnishings in the quiet lounge and a bold floral pattern in the lounge bar. Best bedrooms are those in the original part of the house, those in the newer wing being somewhat smaller, but all offer many extras like fresh flowers, fruit, magazines and mineral water. Rooms are properly serviced in the evenings as are the bathrooms which boast robes and large bath sheets but also, alas, cheap plastic tubs. Children up to 10 stay free in parents' room. *Rooms 19. Garden, croquet, bowling, tennis, golf. Access, Amex, Visa,*

Old Masters Restaurant   £70

A harpist or pianist plays in a quietly luxurious room whose walls are hung with Dutch oil paintings. Local produce is put to excellent use in a menu which mixes Scottish and French influences: seafood stew scented with fennel and Sauternes, salmon fillet baked in pastry with a vermouth and dill sauce, medallion of venison crowned with a mousse of maize-fed chicken and wild mushrooms served with a burgundy, tomato and tarragon sauce. Among the choice to finish is a trio of the pastry chef's favourite puddings. *Seats 60. Parties 80. Private Room. L Sun only 12-2 D 7-9.30. Set D £20.*

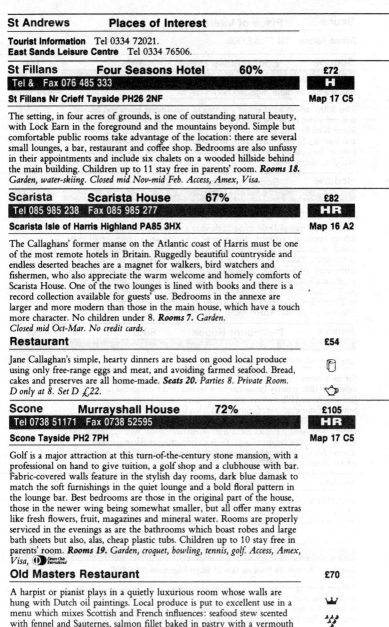

Scone   Place of Interest

Scone Palace Tel 0738 52300.

Scourie   Eddrachilles Hotel   60%   £68

Tel 0971 502080   Fax 0971 502477   **H**

Badcall Bay Scourie Highland IV27 4TH   Map 16 B2

This 200-year-old hotel enjoys a setting of outstanding peace and beauty,
and the views from the lounge are really spectacular. It's close to Handa
Island Bird Sanctuary, and it's a great base for walking, climbing, fishing
and boating. Seven of the neatly kept bedrooms have shower/WC only.
No children under three. No dogs. *Rooms 11. Garden, boat hire. Closed
Nov-Feb. Access, Visa.*

Scourie   Scourie Hotel   60%   £66

Tel 0971 2396   Fax 0971 2423   **H**

Scourie by Lairg Highland IV27 4SX   Map 16 B2

Built by the second Duke of Sutherland as a coaching inn, this is now a
fishing hotel *par excellence*. Brown trout, sea trout and salmon are all to be
found in the 25,000 acres of grounds, and boats can be supplied for many
of the beats. Tales swapped in the lounges and cocktail bar are naturally
fairly fishy. Bedrooms are modern and well kept, with fitted furniture and
good-sized bathrooms (two rooms are without en-suite facilities). There are
no TVs, but the views from the windows are very watchable. Children up
to 12 stay free in parents' room. *Rooms 21. Garden, game fishing.
Closed mid Oct-Mar. Access, Amex, Visa,*

Selkirk   Philipburn House   60%   £99

Tel 0750 20747   Fax 0750 21690   **H**

Linglie Road Selkirk Borders TD7 5LS   Map 12 D2

Set back from the A707/A708 junction, a mile from the town centre, this
extended 18th-century house has been turned into a delightful family hotel.
Jim and Anne Hill, owners since 1971, cater for all kinds of visitors –
business, fishing, tourist, family – and friendly hospitality is their
watchword. Bedrooms – in the house, by the pool or in the 'log cabin' –
feature pine, pretty fabrics and a host of extras. Parents will appreciate the
privacy provided by many separate but connecting children's rooms.
*Rooms 16. Garden, outdoor swimming pool, games room, children's playground,
crèche. Access, Visa,*

Selkirk   Places of Interest

Tourist Information Tel 0750 20054.
Bowhill Tel 0750 20732.
Halliwell's House Museum Tel 0750 20096.

Skeabost Bridge   Skeabost House   60%   £82

Tel 047 032 202   Fax 047 032 454   **H**

Skeabost Bridge By Portree Isle of Skye Highland IV51 9NP   Map 16 A3

Twelve acres of woodland and gardens surround a former hunting lodge
on Loch Snizort. It's a comfortable place, with family owners, and
relaxation is easy in the lounges, the flagstoned sun lounge, the cosy bar
and the billiard room. Pretty bedrooms include one with a four-poster and
a few in the nearby Garden House. The hotel owns eight miles of the river
Snizort, which runs through the grounds, and has a boat on a nearby loch.
*Rooms 26. Garden, 9-hole golf course, fishing, snooker. Closed mid Oct-mid
Apr. Access, Visa.*

Skeabost Bridge Place of Interest

Edinbane Pottery Tel 047082 234.

Skelmorlie Manor Park 61% £75

Tel 0475 520832 Fax 0475 520832 **H**

Skelmorlie Nr Largs Strathclyde PA17 5HE Map 12 A1

Built in 1840 and modernised with some care, the hotel stands on a hill above the coast road between Largs and Wemyss Bay. The gardens are a source of great pride with 15 acres of lawns, shrubberies, water gardens, rhododendron walks and woodland. The main talking point inside is the bar, notable for its vast stock of whiskies and a unique map of the Clyde carved in walnut and sycamore. Seven bedrooms are in the main building, the rest in the recently refurbished nearby stable block. No dogs.
Rooms 23. Garden. Access, Amex, Visa, ◐ *Diners Club International*

Sleat Kinloch Lodge 67% £160

Tel 047 13 214 Fax 047 13 277 **HR**

Sleat Isle of Skye Highland IV43 8QY Map 17 A4

Kinloch Lodge is a white stone building at the head of Loch Na Dal in the south of the island. Built in 1680, it is now the home of Lord and Lady Macdonald, and guests are made to feel like family friends. Its isolated position makes it a haven of peace and the views are truly outstanding. Two stylish drawing rooms adorned with ancestral portraits, fine antiques, porcelain pieces and each with a roaring fire provide the perfect spot for afternoon tea or a pre-dinner drink. Bedrooms, mostly rather small, are comfortable and quiet, with no phones or TVs to disturb the peace. Furniture is a mixture of antique and modern pieces and the two rooms not en suite have bathrooms across the corridor. *Rooms 10. Garden, shooting, fishing. Closed Dec-mid Mar. Access, Visa.*

Dining Room £82

Good home cooking by Lady Macdonald and three others. Local ingredients, hearty portions, friendly staff. Some typical dishes from the five-course, small-choice menu: celery, Stilton and pear soup, smoked mackerel and walnut paté, mixed seafood in saffron and white wine sauce served with mousseline potatoes, stir-fried vegetables and cauliflower italienne, roast duck with orange. No smoking in the dining rooms. Coffee and fudge is served in the drawing rooms. *Seats 28. Parties 12. D only 7.30-8.30. Set D £35.*

Sleat Places of Interest

Clan Donald Centre Armadale Castle Tel 04714 305.
Kylerhea Otter Haven.

South Queensferry Forth Bridges Moat House 61% £114

Tel 031-331 1199 Fax 031-319 1733 **H**

South Queensferry Lothian EH30 9SF Map 12 C1

60s' hotel with spectacular views of both Forth bridges and good leisure facilities. 5 miles from Edinburgh airport. Conference/banqueting facilities for 250/200. *Rooms 108. Garden, croquet, indoor swimming pool, gymnasium, snooker, spa bath, sauna, solarium, squash, beauty & hair salon. Access, Amex, Visa,* ◐ *Diners Club International*

South Queensferry Places of Interest

Dalmeny House Tel 031-331 1888.
Hopetoun House Tel 031-331 2451.

Spean Bridge   Letterfinlay Lodge   55%   £63

Tel 039 781 622   **H**

Spean Bridge Highland PH34 4DZ   Map 17 B4

Here since 1963, the Forsyth family have created a comfortable and very
Scottish atmosphere in a ruggedly beautiful setting on the banks of Loch
Lochy. The public rooms include a cosy little bar, a homely TV lounge
and a sun lounge with glorious views. Bedrooms furnished in various styles
are named by colour and decorated accordingly; all have private
bathrooms, three not en suite. Five rooms are considered suitable for family
use. *Rooms 13. Closed Nov–mid Mar. Access, Amex, Visa,* ① Diners Club International

Stewarton   Chapeltoun House   71%   £90

Tel 0560 82696   Fax 0560 85100   **H**

Stewarton-Irvine Road Stewarton Strathclyde KA3 3ED   Map 17 B6

A turn-of-the-century mansion set in private gardens off the B769 Irvine
road two miles out of Stewarton. Its bedrooms, ranging in size from
medium to spacious, all boast antique furniture and a range of extras such
as fruit, sweets, iced water, sherry, flowers and sewing kits; the bathrooms
are similarly well equipped with toiletries, bathrobes and good towels. Of
the public rooms, the hall/lounge is the best, with panelled walls and a
pargeted frieze below the coffered ceiling; the drawing room has
reproduction coffee tables and green draylon seating. No children
under 12. *Rooms 8. Garden, game fishing. Closed 1 wk Jan. Access, Amex,
Visa,* ① Diners Club International

Stirling   Places of Interest

Tourist Information   Tel 0786 75019.
MacRobert Arts Centre   Tel 0786 61081.
Stirling Castle   Tel 0786 50000.
Smith Art Gallery and Museum   Tel 0786 71917.
Regimental Museum of Argyll and Sutherland Highlanders   Tel 0786
   75165.

Stornoway   Cabarfeidh Hotel   64%   £79

Tel 0851 702604   Fax 0851 705572   **H**

Manor Park Stornoway Isle of Lewis Highland PA87 2EU   Map 16 A2

An early-70s hotel with a rather faceless exterior (belying the inviting
interior) on the edge of town, a brisk walk from the Ullapool ferry
terminal. The Viking Bar (with a longship for a counter), a cocktail bar
and a restaurant divided into three differently styled areas comprise the
public rooms. Cheerful bedrooms, all en suite. Open all year round.
Rooms 46. Garden. Access, Amex, Visa, ① Diners Club International

Stornoway   Places of Interest

Tourist Information   Tel 0851 703088,

Strachur   Creggans Inn   61%   £98

Tel 036 986 279   Fax 036 986 637   **H**

Strachur Strathclyde PA27 8BX   Map 17 B5

Sir Fitzroy and Lady Maclean's white-painted inn stands by Loch Fyne on
the road to the Isles. It's a great part of the world for fishing, walking and
touring, after which a glass of the hotel's own Old MacPhunn ten-year-old
vatted malt goes down well in the bar. There's a peaceful sitting room and
a large garden lounge, both with delightful views. Decor varies in the
small but charming bedrooms, almost all of which have bathrooms en
suite. *Rooms 21. Garden, fishing. Access, Amex, Visa,* ① Diners Club International

Strachur   Places of Interest

Crarae Glen Garden Minard. Tel 0546 86614.
Inveraray Castle Tel 0499 2203 *20 miles*.
Argyll Wildlife Park Inveraray Tel 0499 2264.
European Sheep and Wool Centre Lochgoiliead Tel 03013 247.

Stranraer   North West Castle   68%   £70

Tel 0776 4413   Fax 0776 2646   **H**

Cairnryan Road Stranraer Dumfries & Galloway DG9 8EH   Map 13 A4

Much extended since being built in 1820, the hotel stands opposite the
ferry port. It was once the house of explorer Sir John Ross, whose name is
commemorated in the panelled bar. Bedrooms include six suites, and 12
rooms are considered suitable for family occupation. Conference and
banqueting facilities for 180 delegates. Sister establishment to the Cally
Palace Hotel in Gatehouse of Fleet. *Rooms 74. Indoor swimming pool, curling
rink, sauna, solarium, spa bath, gymnasium, snooker, coffee shop (10am-9.30pm),
dinner dance (Sat, October-April). No credit cards.*

Stranraer   Places of Interest

Tourist Information Tel 0776 2595.
  Historic Houses, Castles and Gardens
Castle Kennedy and Lochinch Gardens Tel 0776 2024.
Logan House and Botanic Garden Tel 077686 231.
Glenwhan Gardens Dunragit Tel 05814 222.

Strathblane   Kirkhouse Inn   £72

Tel 0360 70621   Fax 0360 70896   **I**

Glasgow Road Strathblane Central G63 9AA   Map 12 B1

On the A81 Stirling to Aberfoyle road, ten miles north of Glasgow, this
roadside inn is at the foot of the Campsie Fells and thus popular with
walkers. An ideal touring centre as Loch Lomond, the Trossachs, Glasgow
and Stirling are all within 30 minutes by car. Sprucely kept public areas
include a busy public bar and quieter lounge and restaurant. Pastel colours
are used in the bedrooms, which include a honeymoon suite with a sunken
bath. Children up to 12 stay free in parents' room. Adventure weekends
are a new attraction. *Rooms 15. Garden, pool table. Access, Amex, Visa,*
① Diners Club International

Strathtummel   Port-an-Eilean Hotel   65%   £56

Tel 0882 634233   **H**

Strathtummel By Pitlochry Tayside PH16 5RU   Map 17 C4

The Hallewells are in their 19th year at this Victorian hunting lodge
beautifully situated on the shore of Loch Tummel. Large traditionally
furnished bedrooms are well supplied with books and have no TVs or
telephones to disturb the peace. Lounges and the cosy cocktail bar enjoy
splendid views of mountain and loch. On the B8019. *Rooms 8. Garden,
coarse & game fishing. Closed Nov-Apr. No credit cards.*

Talladale   Loch Maree Hotel   £66

Tel 044 584 288   Fax 044 584 241   **I**

Achnasheen Talladale Highland IV2 2HC   Map 16 B3

A purpose-built fishing hotel beautifully situated on the banks of the loch
between Gairloch and Kinlochewe. The glorious outdoors is certainly a
major attraction, and inside things have changed dramatically from the
former time-warp Victorian cosiness. The hotel owns eight boats (complete
with mandatory ghillies) for sea trout and salmon fishing on the loch.
Rooms 18. Garden, fishing, boating, games room. Access, Visa.

Tarbert   Stonefield Castle   58%   £122

Tel 0880 820836   Fax 0880 820929   **H**

Loch Fyne Tarbert Strathclyde PA29 6YJ   Map 12 A1

Sixty acres of grounds surround the 19th-century chateau-style building,
and many of the rooms command spectacular views over Loch Fyne. Day
rooms are in comfortable, traditional style, so too the bedrooms in the
main house. Wing rooms are more ordinary but certainly adequate.
*Rooms 33. Garden, outdoor swimming pool (Easter to October), sauna, solarium,
snooker, mooring. Access, Amex, Visa,* (D) *Diners Club International*

Tarbert   Places of Interest

Tourist Information   Tel 0880 820429.

Tiroran   Tiroran House   70%   £195*

Tel & Fax 068 15 232   **HR**

Tiroran Isle of Mull Strathclyde PA69 6ES   Map 17 A5

More family home than traditional hotel, Tiroran owes its uniqueness to
the hospitality of Wing Commander and Mrs Blockley, who converted
their sporting lodge for guests' use in 1977. Many return annually to enjoy,
among other things, the spectacular views of Loch Scridain across some 15
acres of gardens and woodland. The house, furnished with antiques and
family silver, contains six bedrooms of individual decor and charm; the
rest are in adjacent pine cottages looking down the garden. Biscuits, cheese
and a half bottle of wine are typical of the thoughtful touches that await
arriving guests; breakfast, too, is exemplary. No phones, no TVs, no
children under ten. *Half-board terms only. **Rooms 9.** Garden, croquet,
games room. Closed early Oct-mid May. No credit cards.*

Restaurant   £70

Non-residents, welcomed if space allows, will encounter a dinner party
atmosphere. The table d'hote main course may be duckling breast in gin
and juniper with wild rice and caramelised apples or pan-fried Mull
scallops with Barsac sauce. Starters and puddings look to the garden for
salad crops, herbs, soft fruits and chicken and duck eggs. The excellent
daily-baked bread and fine Scottish cheeses are fitting additions. Lunch, for
residents only, is served on the verandah. *Seats 20. D only at 7.45. Closed
L except residents. Set D £28.50.*

Tiroran   Places of Interest

Iona   Tel 06817 407
Fingal's Cave   Staffa Tel 041-552 8391.

Tobermory — Tobermory Hotel — 57% — £58

Tel 0688 2091 Fax 0688 2140 — **H**

53 Main Street Tobermory Isle of Mull Strathclyde PA75 6NT — **Map 17 A4**

Ring the bell to gain access to this small, carefully maintained hotel on the waterfront of Tobermory Bay. The owners Martin and Kay Sutton put hospitality top of their list, and two cosy lounges furnished with floral sofas and easy chairs, well-chosen ornaments and pictures offer welcoming touches like magazines and fresh flowers. Compact bedrooms have cheerful decor and functional furniture. The bathrooms (just five of which are en suite) are well kept. ***Rooms 15.*** *Access, Visa.*

Tobermory — Places of Interest

Tourist Information Tel 0688 2182

Troon — Marine Highland Hotel — 67% — £132

Tel 0292 314444 Fax 0292 316922 — **H**

Crosbie Road Troon Strathclyde KA10 6HE — **Map 12 B2**

Not far from Prestwick and Glasgow, and with good conference facilities (for up to 220), this handsome Victorian sandstone structure overlooks the 18th fairway of Royal Troon championship golf course. Accommodation options are standard, deluxe or top-of-the-range Ambassador suites. Families welcome, with an occasional supervised crèche, baby sitting and baby listening offered. ***Rooms 72.*** *Indoor swimming pool, sauna, solarium, whirlpool bath, steam room, gymnasium, beauty salon, squash, putting, snooker. Access, Amex, Visa,* Diners Club International

Troon — Piersland House — 64% — £85

Tel 0292 314747 Fax 0292 315613 — **H**

15 Craigend Road Troon Strathclyde KA10 6HD — **Map 12 B2**

A sandstone and timbered building dating from 1890 and originally owned by the grandson of whisky man Johnnie Walker. From the reception, stairs lead up to a galleried landing with exposed roof timbers. Further pleasing architectural features are to be found in the bar/lounge, which boasts stone-mullioned windows, an embroidered frieze and a ribbed ceiling. Bedrooms are individually and prettily appointed. Meeting/conference facilities for up to 80. ***Rooms 19.*** *Garden, putting, croquet. Access, Amex, Visa,* Diners Club International

Troon — Places of Interest

Tourist Information Tel 0292 317696.

Turnberry — Turnberry Hotel — 84% — £170

Tel 0655 31000 Fax 0655 31706 — **HR**

Turnberry Strathclyde KA26 9LT — **Map 12 A3**

When Turnberry opened in 1906 it became the world's first hotel and golf resort, and the country club and spa keep it today in the forefront of sporting hotels. It is also established as a top-flight conference and banqueting venue (up to 150 delegates in the self-contained Turnberry Suite). The hotel overlooks the famous links of Ailsa and Arran, to the islands of that name and towards the Mull of Kintyre beyond. Day rooms combine comfort and splendour at a high level, and bedrooms, too, are notably stylish, with luxuriously equipped bathrooms. Children up to 12 stay free in parents' room. ***Rooms 132.*** *Garden, indoor swimming pool, gymnasium, spa bath, sauna, solarium, beauty & hair salon, 2 18-hole golf courses, 12-hole pitch & putt, health spa, tennis, riding, snooker, helipad, grill (8am-8pm). Access, Amex, Visa,* Diners Club International

See over

Restaurant   £90

The main restaurant offers a luxurious menu of classics and modernised
variants, while the restaurant at the Spa, called The Bay at Turnberry, is
open for lunch and dinner seven days a week providing a healthy menu
that eschews red meat and rich sauces. Comprehensive wine list includes,
unusually, several good Swiss wines. *Seats 200. Parties 8. Private Room.
L 1-2.30 D 7.30-10. Closed L Mon-Sat. Set L £17.50 Set D £31.50.*

Tweedsmuir   Crook Inn   59%   £52

Tel 089 97 272   Fax 089 97 294   **H**

Tweedsmuir Nr Biggar Borders ML12 6QN   Map 12 C2

Standing on the A701 and set in the ruggedly beautiful Tweed valley, the
Crook is a good base for walking, climbing and touring holidays. Burns
wrote *Willie Wastle's Wife* in what is now the bar, and locally-born John
Buchan set many of his novels in the area. Neat bedrooms are simple in
their appointments, with no TVs or telephones. There are a few Art Deco
features in the lounge and some of the bathrooms. A craft centre has
recently been created from the old stable block. *Rooms 8. Garden, fishing.*
Access, Amex, Visa,

Uig   Uig Hotel   59%   £82

Tel 047 042 205   Fax 047 042 308   **H**

Uig Isle of Skye Highland IV51 9YE   Map 16 A3

On a hillside at the north end of the island, the former coaching inn is
handy for the ferry to Uist and Harris. It was established as a hotel in 1946
by Grace Graham, who still plays an active role. You come here to enjoy
the peace and solitude, the wonderful scenery, the walks and the wildlife.
Day rooms are neat and homely, and there are sea views from the glass-
fronted sun lounge, which features fine water colours and etchings of
distinction. Comfortable bedrooms with smart co-ordinated colour schemes
include six in Sobhraig House, a converted steading next to the hotel.
No children under 12. *Rooms 17. Garden, pony trekking. Closed mid
Oct-mid Apr. Access, Amex, Visa,*

Ullapool   Altnaharrie Inn   ★★   £130

Tel 085 483 230   **R R**

Ullapool Highland IV26 2SS   Map 16 B2

Altnaharrie lies on the southern shores of Loch Broom opposite the fishing
village of Ullapool, from which guests should phone to announce their
arrival. Cars are left in one of Ullapool's hotel car parks and guests make
the 10-minute crossing in the hotel launch to the beautifully restored inn,
built originally as a stop-over point for drovers. Walking and watching the
wildlife are favourite occupations, but with Gunn Eriksen in the kitchen
eating is alone certainly worth the visit. She is the backbone of this
extraordinary restaurant with rooms, yet guests will be lucky to catch even
the faintest glimpse of this immensely talented chef, for she remains
ensconced in the kitchen not bothering with curtain calls, venturing
outside her domain and into the public's gaze only when she deems it safe
to do so, when satiated guests are about to return whence they came, on
the morning's return boat trip. Gunn's style of cooking is hard to pin
down, but the epithet 'artist' can justly be applied to her; there appears to
be a tremendous intensity within her and an iron will to make things
work. She offers no choice (apart from puddings) on the 5-course set menu,
so there's no chance for her to get anything wrong; you place your trust in
her talent and sit back and enjoy. Fred Brown unobtrusively runs the front
of the house, ably assisted by two staff; guests gather in two comfortable
lounges with open fire places for pre-dinner drinks, having been given the
chance at an earlier opportunity to take in the day's dinner offerings. The
atmosphere invites cross-talk and, at the appropriate moment, diners move
en masse into the lovely, sparkling dining room with its whitewashed walls
and polished wood tables. Place setting are immaculate, with shining

Norwegian silverware and glassware. All the tables enjoy views of the loch, where, if you are lucky, you might catch sight of porpoises playing in the water. Many of the ingredients come from the idyllic surroundings. Flavours are given their head, and colours and textures delight the eye. Dishes are nothing short of sensational, as shown in a summer menu: a basket of pastry with asparagus on a lemon sauce with mussels and bitter cress sauce, a clear soup of lobster with herbs and ginger, layers of breast of Scottish wood pigeon, foie gras and squab on a bed of cabbage and green juniper berries, in a cave of strudel with a sauce of pigeon juices and wild mushrooms; a selection of 20 or more cheeses from the British Isles, Norway and France; hazelnut and almond cake with coffee ice cream and cherries in champagne. To accompany this marvellous food there is a sound wine list with lots of half bottles; mainly French but the rest of the world gets a look-in. *Seats 16. Parties 16. D only at 8. Closed L except residents, early Nov-Easter. Set D from £45. Amex.*

Rooms   £240*

Good taste and restraint have created eight peaceful, comfortable en-suite bedrooms, kept in spotless condition. Fresh colours, duvets on the beds and a torch for when the generator is switched off at night. Immaculate bathrooms, some with reproduction Edwardian tubs and brass fittings. No young children. *Half-board terms only.

Ullapool	Ceilidh Place	£86
Tel 0854 612103 Fax 0854 612886		▮
14 West Argyle Street Ullapool Highland IV26 2TY		Map 16 B2

Literally meaning 'Meeting Place', Ceilidh Place is much more: bookshop, arts centre, coffee shop and venue for theatre, music and poetry all housed in a cosy collection of welcoming rooms. Such is the extent of the live entertainment that the single little TV is more than adequate. The pretty bedrooms are comfortable and spotless; the eight rooms that are en suite also have phones. Eleven additional rooms in a separate building across the street offer more spartan, budget accommodation with shared facilities. Families are well catered for. *Rooms 13. Coffee shop (10am-8.30pm) Closed 2 weeks Jan. Access, Amex, Visa,* ⑴ Diners Club International

Ullapool	Places of Interest

Tourist Information   Tel 0854 2135.

Uphall	Houstoun House	68%	£110
Tel 0506 853831 Fax 0506 854220			H
Uphall Lothian EH52 6JS			Map 12 C1

Three buildings, the main one distinctively gabled, and set in 20 acres of fine gardens; close to Uphall golf course, two minutes from the M8 and close enough to Edinburgh for city visits. Apart from its convenience, it also offers comfortable and roomy accommodation in bedrooms that are either contemporary in style or more traditional, some with four-posters. Day rooms also vary in age and character; there's a pleasantly modern lounge overlooking the tree-lined drive and three panelled dining rooms. Under new ownership. *Rooms 30. Garden. Access, Amex, Visa,* ⑴ Diners Club International

Whitebridge	Knockie Lodge	67%	£150*
Tel 045 63 276 Fax 045 63 389			H
Whitebridge Highland IV1 2UP			Map 17 B4

Tak' the high road (B862) from Fort Augustus past Loch Tarff and into the hills; a two-mile drive onward and downward through verdant forests is rewarded by stunning vistas over Loch Nan Lann. Within, an air of spaciousness pervades the lodge, for ten years the home of the Milward family, for whom personal service is a watchword. Accommodation comprises three doubles, five twin-bedded rooms and two singles. No children under ten. *Half-board terms only. Rooms 10. Garden, fishing, sailing, snooker. Closed Nov-Apr. Access, Amex, Visa,* ⑴ Diners Club International

Abercynon   Llechwen Hall   £60
Tel 0443 742050   Fax 0443 742189   **I**

Abercynon Nr Llanfabon Mid-Glamorgan CF37 4HP   Map 9 C6

Literally at the head of the valley (above A4054), Llechwen Hall is a 17th-
century farmhouse, converted to a gentlemen's residence in Victorian times,
whence to country inn five years ago. Victorian character is retained in
bedroom extensions whose accoutrements are nevertheless up-to-date, with
neat bathrooms en suite. A lively local trade adds welcoming warmth to
the bars and restaurant and there are banqueting and conference facilities
(for up to 90) in the Nelson suite. Under-3s stay free in parents' room.
Rooms 11. Garden. Access, Amex, Visa, Diners Club International

Aberdovey   Plas Penhelig   62%   £76
Tel 0654 767676   Fax 0654 767783   **H**

Aberdovey Gwynedd LL35 0NA   Map 8 C3

A wooded driveway leads from the A493 to the house, whose seven acres
of award-winning grounds include a walled kitchen garden. Inside, the feel
is Edwardian in the oak-panelled hall and in the south-facing lounge, while
bedrooms are more modern in aspect. The largest rooms have a table and
two chairs. The terrace is an agreeable spot for an alfresco drink. *Rooms 11.
Garden, croquet, putting, tennis. Closed Jan-Mar. Access, Visa.*

Aberdovey   Trefeddian Hotel   58%   £100*
Tel 0654 767213   Fax 0654 767777   **H**

Aberdovey Gwynedd LL35 0SB   Map 8 C3

Three generations of the Cave family have run the Trefeddian, which
stands a mile outside Aberdovey with fine views across Cardigan Bay. Day
rooms, which include lounge, reading room and bar, offer a choice of
peace and quiet or conviviality. Neat, practical bedrooms include several
with balconies. *Half board terms only in the hotel. Self-catering
accommodation is also available. *Rooms 46. Garden, indoor swimming pool,
tennis, putting, snooker. Closed 2 Jan-20 Mar. Access, Visa.*

Abergavenny   Walnut Tree Inn   ★★   £77
Tel 0873 852797   Fax 0873 859764   **R**

Llandewi Skirrid Abergavenny Gwent NP7 8AW   Map 9 D5

The look is of a country pub, the whitewashed building bedecked with
baskets of flowers. Inside, an informal bar leads through to the main dining
area, a long, narrow room with tables set along the walls. But this is no
ordinary pub, as Franco and Anna Taruschio have been demonstrating for
almost 30 years. Franco's cooking has found fame literally worldwide;
based on a Mediterranean theme, but taking in many other influences, his
dishes range from homely lasagne bolognese to a sophisticated fricassée of
John Dory, scallops, saffron and ginger. Crispy crab pancake and home-
cured bresaola are great favourites among the starters and the Thai pork
appetiser has proved a great hit. Local ingredients feature in many dishes,
including asparagus (au gratin or hollandaise), Llanover salt duck with
gooseberries and damsons, and salmon with rhubarb and ginger. A recent
feature is an 18th-century recipe of pasta with porcini, truffles and Parma
ham. The sweet menu has always been a highlight, and there are first-rate
Italian and British cheeses. Italian wines are naturally to the fore on a well-
balanced list; one niggle, however: £5 for a glass of standard Muscat de
Beaumes de Venise is a bit steep! *Seats 44. Parties 44. L 12-3 D 7.15-10.
Closed Sun & Mon, Xmas, 2 weeks Feb. No credit cards.*

Abergavenny   Places of Interest

Tourist Information   Tel 0873 77588.
Abergavenny Showground   Tel 0873 3152.

Aberkenfig   New Garden   £35

| Tel 0656 724361 | **R** |

40 Pandy Road Aberkenfig Nr Bridgend Mid Glamorgan   **Map 9 D4**

Hardly impressive from the outside, yet modern and stylish decor inside
with an extensive, predominantly Cantonese menu on offer and on-the-ball
service to complement it. Proprietor Kin Hing Chan started the business in
1979 with himself as chef, so he obviously keeps a strict control over
quality – as is evident in stuffed crab claws with sweet and sour sauce,
Malayan satay pork, crispy aromatic duck and steamed sea bass and black
bean sauce. Hot pot dishes are good and satisfyingly filling. Reasonable
prices and generous portions all round. Unusually diverse wine list and
regular live music indicate that this venue is popular for more than just
good Chinese cooking. *Seats 160. Parties 100. L 12-2 D 5.30-12. Closed
L Sun, 3 days Xmas. Set meals from £12. Access, Amex, Visa,*

Abersoch   Porth Tocyn Hotel   69%   £88

| Tel 0758 713303   Fax 0758 713538 | **HR** |

Bwlchtocyn Abersoch Gwynedd LL53 7BU   **Map 8 B3**

Check directions to find Porth Tocyn, once a row of lead-miners' cottages,
high above Cardigan Bay. The Fletcher-Brewer family have guarded their
reputation for attentive hospitality for more than 40 years, and the chintzy
lounges, with their bright floral decor, fresh flowers and family antiques,
contribute just the right degree of homeliness. Bedrooms, though generally
small, are individually furnished in a similar style, many with restful sea
views, all with private bathrooms and showers. Families with children are
well catered for. *Rooms 17. Garden, outdoor swimming pool, tennis.
Closed Nov-week before Easter. Access.*

Restaurant   £60

The focal point of Louise Fletcher-Brewer's culinary output is her short-
choice two- or five-course dinner menu, changed daily. Lobster and mango
salad and almond roulade with avocado filling to start; pan-fried turbot
with pepper butter or roast Welsh lamb with rosemary sauce are flanked
by interesting herby soups and homely crumbles, syllabub or cheesecake.
Lunch is casual, maybe alfresco by the pool, with a hot and cold buffet on
Sundays. Improving, diverse wine list. *Seats 50. Parties 8. L 12.30-2
D 7.30-9.30. Set L (Sun) £14 Set D £17.50/£23.*

Abersoch   Riverside Hotel   59%   £80

| Tel 075 881 2419 | **H** |

Abersoch Gwynedd LL53 7HW   **Map 8 B3**

Messing about on the river is a favourite pastime at the Bakewell family's
cheerful hotel, the river in question being the Soch (canoe and rowing boat
available). At the front is a harbour, overlooked by the little lounge.
Bedrooms are neat, modern and functional. Reduced rates for children. No
dogs. *Rooms 12. Garden, indoor swimming pool. Closed mid Nov-end Feb.
Access, Amex, Visa,*

Aberystwyth   Conrah Country Hotel   63%   £85

| Tel 0970 617941   Fax 0970 624546 | **H** |

Chancery Aberystwyth Dyfed SY23 4DF   **Map 9 B4**

Tucked away at the end of a long drive, three miles south of Aberystwyth,
set in 22 acres of grounds and woods, the Conrah puts peace, friendliness
and fine views high on the agenda, and the three drawing rooms provide
them in abundance. 11 of the bedrooms are in the main house, the rest
around a courtyard. All are comfortable and cheerful; bathrooms are
private, only two not en suite. *Rooms 20. Garden, croquet, indoor swimming
pool, sauna. Closed 1 week Xmas. Access, Amex, Visa,*

Aberystwyth   Places of Interest

Tourist Information   Tel 0970 612125.
Aberystwyth Arts Centre   Tel 0970 622882.
Aberystwyth Arts Centre   (Exhibitions) Tel 0970 622887.
Llywernog Silver-Lead Mine Museum   Ponterwyd Tel 097085 620.
Strata Florida Abbey   Tel 09745 261 *10 miles.*
Vale of Rheidol Railway   Tel Brecon Mountain Railway 0685 4854.

Barry   Bunbury's   £50

Tel 0446 732075	R

14 High Street Barry South Glamorgan CF6 8EA   Map 9 C6

30s' sounds and setting behind the Barry Hotel. The main menu covers a
good range of dishes, from aubergine and walnut caviar to poached salmon
with a vermouth and watercress sauce, chicory-stuffed chicken and venison
in red wine. There's also a lunchtime blackboard menu with dishes like
cottage pie or spicy peanut chicken priced at around £4. *Seats 32. Parties
36.* L *10.30-2.30* D *7.30-10 (Sat to 10.30). Closed Sun & Mon, Bank
Holidays.* Access, Visa, ⦿ *Diners Club International.*

Barry   Mount Sorrel Hotel   59%   £85

Tel 0446 740069 Fax 0446 746600	H

Porthkerry Road Barry South Glamorgan CF6 8AY   Map 9 C6

Converted from two Victorian houses 30 years ago, with more recent
additions for extra accommodation, meeting rooms and leisure facilities.
Comfortable day rooms, very acceptable bedrooms (children up to 12 stay
free when sharing with parents). *Rooms 50. Indoor swimming pool, keep-fit
equipment, sauna, coffee shop (7am-8pm), dinner dance (monthly).*
Access, Amex, Visa, ⦿ Diners Club International.

Barry   Places of Interest

Knap Swimming Pool   Tel 0446 735 175.
Barry Island Pleasure Park   Tel 0446 741250.

Beaumaris   Bulkeley Arms   59%   £70

Tel 0248 810415 Fax 0248 810146	H

Castle Street Beaumaris Anglesey Gwynedd LL58 8AW   Map 8 B1

A sturdy Georgian building with splendid views across the Menai Straits to
Snowdonia. Families and individual guests are equally well catered for, and
children up to 12 stay free in parents' rooms. Bedrooms are delightfully
old-fashioned, with light oak furniture, writing desks and armchairs. There
are two bars, a sunny residents' lounge and a function room holding up to
160. *Rooms 43. Garden, beauty salon, massage, chiropodist, snooker.* Access,
Amex, Visa, ⦿ *Diners Club International.*

Beaumaris   Places of Interest

Bangor Information Centre   Tel 0248 352786.
Theatr Gwynedd   Bangor Tel 0248 351708 *7 miles.*
Cathedral Church of St. Deiniol   Bangor Tel 0248 351693.
                            Historic Houses, Castles and Gardens
Beaumaris Castle   Tel 0248 810361.
Beaumaris Gaol Museum   Tel 0248 810921.
Penrhyn Castle (NT)   Nr Bangor Tel 0248 353084.
Pencarreg Glyn Garth   Nr Beaumaris Tel 0248 713545.

| Beddgelert | **Royal Goat Hotel** | **60%** | **£68** |

Tel 076 686 224   Fax 076 686 422

Beddgelert Gwynedd LL55 4YE Map 8 B2

The Roberts family play host to the regulars who come for Snowdonia's fishing, walking and climbing. Beyond the white-painted facade an entrance hall/reception has heavily carved furniture and brass ornaments, more of which feature in the comfortable residents-only bar; there's plenty of lounge space and two dining rooms. Children up to 11 stay free in parents' room. Function facilities for up to 150. *Rooms 34. Garden, games room, fishing. Access, Amex, Visa,*

Beddgelert   Places of Interest

National Trust Information Point   Tel 076 686 293.
Sygun Copper Mine   Tel 076 686 595.

| Betws-y-Coed | **Royal Oak** | **59%** | **£70** |

Tel 0690 710219   Fax 0690 710603

Holyhead Road Betws-y-Coed Gwynedd LL24 0AY Map 8 C2

A solid stone edifice on the river Llugwy where there's a traditional and welcoming air in both the reception and bar with studded brown leather and antique oak furniture. Bedrooms have restful autumnal decor, simple modern furniture and two armchairs; six annexe rooms have glossy laminated furniture with eye-catching mirrored bedheads. No dogs. *Rooms 27. Garden, coffee shop (7.30am-9pm). Closed 25 & 26 Dec. Access, Amex, Visa,*

Betws-y-Coed   Places of Interest

Plas-y-Brenin National Centre for Mountain Activities   Capel Curig
   Tel 06904 214.
Swallow Falls   Tel 0690 710796.

| Bontddu | **Bontddu Hall** | **62%** | **£80** |

Tel 0341 49661   Fax 0341 49284

Bontddu Nr Dolgellau Gwynedd LL40 2SU Map 8 C3

Michael and Margaretta Ball's Victorian country mansion stands high above the Mawddach estuary in 14 acres of gardens. The views are outstanding, particularly from the day rooms and the sun terrace. There's a strong period feel, with features like marble columns, a colourful skylight above the main staircase and Victorian church benches in the bar. Bedrooms, the majority also offering fine views, include a four-poster room and one with a spa bath. Children up to 16 stay free in parents' room. *Rooms 20. Garden. Closed Nov-Easter. Access, Amex, Visa,*

| Brechfa | **Ty Mawr** | **60%** | **£64** |

Tel 0267 202332   Fax 0267 202437

Brechfa Nr Carmarthen Dyfed SA32 7RA Map 9 B5

Three stone-built cottages dating from the 15th century make up Beryl and Dick Tudhope's tiny hotel, which stands by the bridge over the river Marlais (the middle name of Dylan Thomas). Relaxation is the name of the game, whether it's over a book in the lounge or a drink in the bar, and peace is guaranteed by the absence of phones and TVs in the cottagey, pine-furnished bedrooms. *Rooms 5. Garden. Closed 2 weeks Jan. Access, Amex, Visa.*

Bridgend   Forte Travelodge   £40
Tel 0656 659218   L

M4 Junction 36 Service Area Sarn Park Nr Bridgend
Mid Glamorgan CF32 9RW   Map 9 C6

Located on the M4 at junction 36 at the Welcome Break Service Area.
Situated midway between Cardiff and Swansea, 2 miles from Bridgend.
Rooms 40. Access, Amex, Visa.

Cardiff   Angel Hotel   66%   £124
Tel 0222 232633   Fax 0222 396212   H

Castle Street Cardiff South Glamorgan CF1 2QZ   Map 9 B6

Between the Castle and Arms Park rugby stadium, the distinctive Angel
has kept its individual character for over 100 years, although with varying
consistency of standards over the years. Liveried doormen show guests into
the foyer, where chandeliers, pillars and a mural of clouds and cherubs try
to make a good impression. Bedrooms are generally roomy, with what was
once chic decor. There are several function rooms and the galleried Dragon
Suite can cater for 300+. Ask for their helpful parking leaflet. Queens
Moat Houses. *Rooms 91. Gymnasium, sauna, solarium, snooker.*
Access, Amex, Visa, ①

Cardiff   Armless Dragon   £50
Tel 0222 382357   R

97 Wyeverne Road Cathays Cardiff South Glamorgan CF2 4BG Map 9 B6

Ostensibly courting the 'adventurous end of a staid market', this bustling
bistro is handily placed for the Sherman Theatre and University College.
Skate, sole, sewin and shark show the piscine bias of the daily board;
Barbados, bonne femme and *orientale* the eclectic nature of its presentation.
Crispy chicken winglets with Chinese five-spice, crab soup with lemon
grass and laverball-and-mushroom starters are long-standing favourites.
Sweets are not a strong point. *Seats 45. L 12.30-2.15 D 7.30-10.30 (Sat to
11). Closed L Sat, all Sun & Mon, Bank Holidays except Good Friday, 24
Dec-1 Jan. Access, Amex, Visa,* ①

Cardiff   Campanile Hotel   £36
Tel 0222 549044   Fax 0222 549000   L

Caxton Place Pentwyn Cardiff South Glamorgan CF2 7HA   Map 9 B6

Closest M4 junction is J29; off the Pentwyn interchange of the A48.
Rooms 50. Access, Amex, Visa, ①

Cardiff   Cardiff International   67%   £107
Tel 0222 341441   Fax 0222 223742   H

Mary Ann Street Cardiff South Glamorgan CF1 2EQ   Map 9 B6

Modern hotel connected to the new Cardiff World Trade Centre, with a
mix of Victorian brick and cast-iron and an arcade-style interior echoing
the architecture of Cardiff's markets. Smallish bedrooms and bathrooms
and inward-facing rooms are short on daylight. Valet parking in a
neighbouring NCP car park is a bonus. Smart and keen staff. Children up
to 12 accommodated free in their parents' room. Banqueting/conference
facilities for 120/40. *Rooms 143. Coffee shop (11am-11pm).*
Access, Amex, Visa, ①

Cardiff   Cardiff Marriott Hotel   69%   £125
Tel 0222 399944   Fax 0222 395578   H

Mill Lane Cardiff South Glamorgan CF1 1EZ   Map 9 B6

Formerly the Holiday Inn, handy for the station and Arms Park. Bright
public areas, decent leisure centre. Conference and banqueting facilities for
300. *Rooms 182. Gymnasium, indoor swimming pool, spa bath, sauna,
solarium, squash. Access, Amex, Visa,* ①

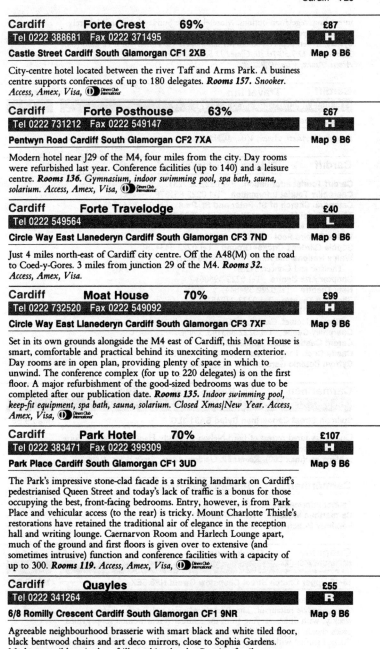

Cardiff	**Forte Crest**	69%	**£87**

Tel 0222 388681   Fax 0222 371495   **H**

Castle Street Cardiff South Glamorgan CF1 2XB   Map 9 B6

City-centre hotel located between the river Taff and Arms Park. A business centre supports conferences of up to 180 delegates. *Rooms 157. Snooker. Access, Amex, Visa,* Diners Club International

Cardiff	**Forte Posthouse**	63%	**£67**

Tel 0222 731212   Fax 0222 549147   **H**

Pentwyn Road Cardiff South Glamorgan CF2 7XA   Map 9 B6

Modern hotel near J29 of the M4, four miles from the city. Day rooms were refurbished last year. Conference facilities (up to 140) and a leisure centre. *Rooms 136. Gymnasium, indoor swimming pool, spa bath, sauna, solarium. Access, Amex, Visa,* Diners Club International

Cardiff	**Forte Travelodge**		**£40**

Tel 0222 549564   **L**

Circle Way East Llanederyn Cardiff South Glamorgan CF3 7ND   Map 9 B6

Just 4 miles north-east of Cardiff city centre. Off the A48(M) on the road to Coed-y-Gores. 3 miles from junction 29 of the M4. *Rooms 32. Access, Amex, Visa.*

Cardiff	**Moat House**	70%	**£99**

Tel 0222 732520   Fax 0222 549092   **H**

Circle Way East Llanederyn Cardiff South Glamorgan CF3 7XF   Map 9 B6

Set in its own grounds alongside the M4 east of Cardiff, this Moat House is smart, comfortable and practical behind its unexciting modern exterior. Day rooms are in open plan, providing plenty of space in which to unwind. The conference complex (for up to 220 delegates) is on the first floor. A major refurbishment of the good-sized bedrooms was due to be completed after our publication date. *Rooms 135. Indoor swimming pool, keep-fit equipment, spa bath, sauna, solarium. Closed Xmas/New Year. Access, Amex, Visa,* Diners Club International

Cardiff	**Park Hotel**	70%	**£107**

Tel 0222 383471   Fax 0222 399309   **H**

Park Place Cardiff South Glamorgan CF1 3UD   Map 9 B6

The Park's impressive stone-clad facade is a striking landmark on Cardiff's pedestrianised Queen Street and today's lack of traffic is a bonus for those occupying the best, front-facing bedrooms. Entry, however, is from Park Place and vehicular access (to the rear) is tricky. Mount Charlotte Thistle's restorations have retained the traditional air of elegance in the reception hall and writing lounge. Caernarvon Room and Harlech Lounge apart, much of the ground and first floors is given over to extensive (and sometimes intrusive) function and conference facilities with a capacity of up to 300. *Rooms 119. Access, Amex, Visa,* Diners Club International

Cardiff	**Quayles**		**£55**

Tel 0222 341264   **R**

6/8 Romilly Crescent Cardiff South Glamorgan CF1 9NR   Map 9 B6

Agreeable neighbourhood brasserie with smart black and white tiled floor, black bentwood chairs and art deco mirrors, close to Sophia Gardens. Modern, sensibly-priced no-frills cooking by the Canning family ranges from smoked sewin with red onion salad or chicken and green peppercorn paté with onion confiture to steaks, pasta dishes and calf's liver with beetroot sauce and mashed potatoes. Fixed-price, 3-course lunch menu and

interesting vegetarian options. More elaborate Sunday lunch and leisurely
brunch (kippers, fishcakes, devilled kidneys, haddock Monte Carlo, prairie
oysters, frozen pepper vodka *inter alia*). **Seats 46.** *Parties 46. L 12-2.30 (Sun
11.30-4.30) D 7.30-10.30. Closed D Sun, Bank Holidays. Set L £10.95.
Access, Amex, Visa,*

Cardiff   Travel Inn   £42

Tel 0633 680070   Fax 0633 681143   L

Newport Road Castleton Nr Cardiff South Glamorgan CF3 8UQ   Map 9 B6

Rooms 49. Access, Amex, Visa,

Cardiff   Places of Interest

Cardiff Tourist Information Tel 0222 227281.
Caerphilly Tourist Information Tel 0222 851378.
Cathedral Church of St. Peter and St. Paul Tel 0222 561545.
The National Museum of Wales Tel 0222 397951.
Welsh Folk Museum St. Fagans Tel 0222 569441.
Wales Empire Pool Tel 0222 382296.
Sophia Gardens Cricket Ground Tel 0222 343478.
Wales National Ice Rink Tel 0222 383451.
  Theatres and Concert Halls
Chapter Arts Centre Tel 0222 396061.
New Theatre Tel 0222 394844.
Sherman Theatre Tel 0222 230451.
St. David's Hall Tel 0222 371236.
  Historic Houses, Castles and Gardens
Caerphilly Castle Tel 0222 883143 *5 miles.*
Cardiff Castle Tel 0222 822083.
Castle Coch Tongwynlais Tel 0222 810101.
Dyffryn Botanic Garden Tel 0222 593328.

Carmarthen   Ivy Bush Royal   59%   £86

Tel 0267 235111   Fax 0267 234914   H

Spilman Street Carmarthen Dyfed SA31 1LG   Map 9 B5

Once a favoured retreat of Lord Nelson and Lady Hamilton, today a Forte
Heritage hotel on the West Wales heritage trail. Coach tours and
conferences (max 200). **Rooms 80.** *Garden. Access, Amex, Visa,*

Carmarthen   Places of Interest

Tourist Information Tel 0267 231557.
Carmarthen Museum Tel 0267 231691.
Pembrey Beach *20 miles.*

Chepstow   Beckfords   £62

Tel 0291 626547   R

15-16 Upper Church Street Chepstow Gwent NP6 5EX   Map 9 D6

Jeremy Hector provides relaxed three-course dinners in his elegant
Georgian-style restaurant. The short, fixed-price only menu changes
weekly, with dishes varying from the familiar (French onion soup, grilled
goat's cheese, pepper steak) to just a little bit different – like supreme of
chicken stuffed with Welsh cheese and wrapped in smoked bacon, or duck
served on a bed of rice noodles with a ginger, mushroom, soy and red
wine sauce. A blackboard lunch menu is similar, although dishes are a bit
simpler in style. Always a roast at Sunday lunchtime. **Seats 38.** *Parties 35.
Private Room. L 12.30-1.45 (Sun to 2.30) D 7.30-10. Closed L Mon, D Sun,
Bank Holidays. Set L (Sun) £12.95 Set D £22. Access, Visa.*

Chepstow   Castle View Hotel   £60

Tel 0291 620349   Fax 0291 627397   **I**

16 Bridge Street Chepstow Gwent NP6 5EZ   Map 9 D6

This friendly little hotel was built in the 17th century as a private
residence, perhaps with stones from neighbouring Chepstow Castle, which
was by then already in ruins. Original walls and timbers may still be seen,
both in the public area and in some bedrooms (where furnishings are
largely 60s' utilitarian; the noisy plumbing belongs to a previous era as
well). One room, with its own lounge, is in a small cottage next door.
There's a secluded walled garden. Families are well catered for. Good
variety of snacks in the bar. *Rooms 11. Garden. Access, Visa.*

Chepstow   Leadon's Brasserie   NEW   £42

Tel 0291 627402   **R**

Beaufort Square Chepstow Gwent NP6 5XJ   Map 9 D6

A bustling basement with lively atmosphere, lined with blackboard menus
under a stone barrel-vaulted ceiling. Wide-ranging dishes, updated daily
according to shopping, score highly for value and skilful cooking: seafood
au gratin and rack of lamb alongside more adventurous chicken tikka in
filo with mint raita, and pork fillet over leeks and Stilton in a pastry case
glazed with creamy hollandaise. Vegetarian options, fruity desserts, good-
value wines and cheerful service. *Seats 46. Parties 12. L 12-2 D 7-10. Closed
Sun. Set D £11.95. Access, Visa.*

Chepstow   St Pierre Hotel   66%   £95

Tel 0291 625261   Fax 0291 629975   **H**

St Pierre Park Chepstow Gwent NP6 6YA   Map 9 D6

The heart of the hotel is a 14th-century mansion standing in 400 acres
complete with a large lake. An extensive leisure club, two golf courses and
a conference area (up to 220 delegates theatre-style) make it a fine base for
work or leisure. Among the day rooms are spacious lounges, three
restaurants and a poolside bar. Bedrooms, many with splendid views,
include 30 of Executive standard and 43 in the Lakeside village. Children
up to 16 stay free in parents' room. No dogs. Country Club Hotels.
*Rooms 147. Garden, croquet, tennis, bowling, badminton, indoor swimming
pool, sauna, spa bath, solarium, beauty salon, squash, clay-pigeon shooting, coffee
shop (10am-10). Access, Amex, Visa,*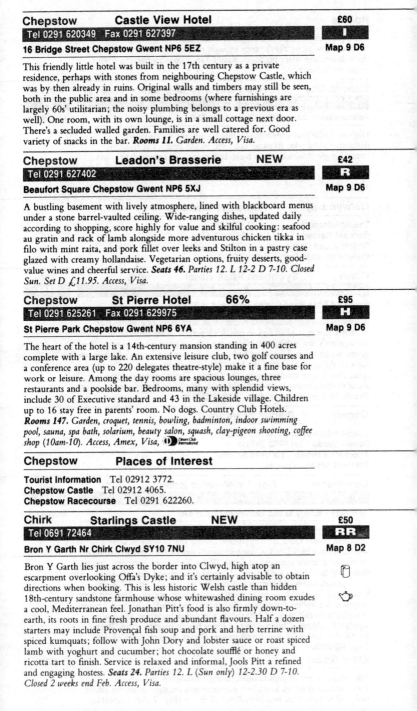

Chepstow   Places of Interest

Tourist Information   Tel 02912 3772.
Chepstow Castle   Tel 02912 4065.
Chepstow Racecourse   Tel 0291 622260.

Chirk   Starlings Castle   NEW   £50

Tel 0691 72464   **RR**

Bron Y Garth Nr Chirk Clwyd SY10 7NU   Map 8 D2

Bron Y Garth lies just across the border into Clwyd, high atop an
escarpment overlooking Offa's Dyke; and it's certainly advisable to obtain
directions when booking. This is less historic Welsh castle than hidden
18th-century sandstone farmhouse whose whitewashed dining room exudes
a cool, Mediterranean feel. Jonathan Pitt's food is also firmly down-to-
earth, its roots in fine fresh produce and abundant flavours. Half a dozen
starters may include Provençal fish soup and pork and herb terrine with
spiced kumquats; follow with John Dory and lobster sauce or roast spiced
lamb with yoghurt and cucumber; hot chocolate soufflé or honey and
ricotta tart to finish. Service is relaxed and informal, Jools Pitt a refined
and engaging hostess. *Seats 24. Parties 12. L (Sun only) 12-2.30 D 7-10.
Closed 2 weeks end Feb. Access, Visa.*

Rooms   £44

The eight bedrooms share a couple of bathrooms along a single landing.
Set under low eaves, they're cosy enough, with truly comfortable beds,
thick duvets and water bottles in winter. Great country breakfasts with
home-made preserves.

Colwyn Bay	Hotel Seventy Degrees	61%	£77
Tel 0492 516555 Fax 0492 515565			**H**
Penmeanhead Colwyn Bay Clwyd LL29 9LD			Map 8 C1

High on a cliff that affords panoramic sea and mountain views, this
distinctive hotel takes its name not from its 70s origin but from the
unusual angle at which it was built. Day rooms are light and airy, and
bedrooms are given a touch of character by Impressionist posters. Children
up to 12 stay free in parents' room. *Rooms 43. Access, Amex, Visa,*
Diners Club International

Colwyn Bay   Places of Interest

Tourist Information   Tel 0492 530478.
Bodnant Garden   Tal-y-Cafn Tel 0492 650460.
Bodelwyddan Castle   Bodelwyddan Tel 0745 583539 *10 miles.*
Welsh Mountain Zoo   Tel 0492 532938.

Conwy	Sychnant Pass Hotel	60%	£56
Tel 0492 596868 Fax 0492 870009			**HR**
Sychnant Pass Road Conwy Gwynedd LL32 8BJ			Map 8 C1

A substantial white-pebbledash house set in three acres of grounds that
include a stream, a pond and woods. It's lovely walking country but when
the weather's not so kind the lounge and bar are good places to relax. Fine
views can be enjoyed from the bedrooms, the best and largest of which are
those in the original part of the house where furnishings are traditional;
other rooms have modern units. The Conwy Tunnel considerably eases
access to this pleasant location. Children up to 12 stay free in parents' room.
Rooms 14. Garden. Access, Amex, Visa, *Diners Club International*

Conwy   Places of Interest

Tourist Information   Tel 0492 592248.
Conwy Castle   Tel 0492 592358.
Aberconwy House   Tel 0492 592246
Smallest House   Quayside

Coychurch	Coed-y-Mwstwr Hotel	70%	£80
Tel 0656 860621 Fax 0656 863122			**HR**
Coychurch Bridgend Mid Glamorgan CF35 6AF			Map 9 C6

High above the Vale of Glamorgan, the "whispering trees" of this
Victorian hotel's name are easily heard among the 17 acres of ancient
woodland in which Coed-y-Mwstwr stands, one of the most attractively
positioned country mansions in South Wales. True to its Victorian origins,
decor and furnishings are a blend of homely charm and elegant period
style: private suites and function rooms (for conferences up to 220 and
banqueting for 150) have high ceilings, chandeliers, oak panelling and huge
fireplaces. Bedrooms throughout are spacious and comfortable with crown-
canopied beds and carpeted bathrooms containing bathrobes and a good
supply of toiletries. Children up to 14 stay free in parents' room. *Rooms*
24. Outdoor swimming pool, tennis, garden, croquet, snooker. Access, Amex,
Visa, *Diners Club International*

Elliot Room   £75

The setting is one of high-beamed ceiling, chandeliers and wood-panelled
walls, and fixed-priced lunch and dinner menus are equally serious affairs,
designed to reflect the best ingredients of the locality. Welsh specialities
(such as smoked salmon, Cardigan Bay oysters or pork fillet with chicken

mousseline and a laverbread and orange sauce) feature on the à la carte: healthy options weigh in with the likes of marinated tofu and Oriental stir-fry vegetables. Careful attention is paid to both the cheeseboard and well-stocked cellar. *Seats 50. Parties 150. Private Room. L 12-2.30 D 7.30-10.15 (Sat to 10.30, Sun to 9.30). Set L £12.50/£16 Set D £24.*

Criccieth	Bron Eifion Hotel	58%	£76

Tel 0766 522385   Fax 0766 522003   **H**

Criccieth Gwynedd LL52 0SA   **Map 8 B2**

Built in the 1870s, the house stands in well-kept grounds half a mile west of Criccieth on the A497. The period feel remains strong, both in the main hall with stone pillars, wall panelling and minstrel's gallery, and in the bedrooms, some of which have been elevated to de luxe standard in the hotel's recent refurbishment. *Rooms 19. Garden, croquet, putting.* Access, Visa.

Criccieth   Places of Interest

Criccieth Castle   Tel 0766 522227.
Lloyd George Memorial Museum   Llanystumdwy Tel 0286 672255.
Dwyfor Ranch Rabbit Farm   Llanystumdwy Tel 0766 523136.

Crickhowell	Bear Hotel	£48

Tel 0873 810408   Fax 0873 811696   **I**

High Street Crickhowell Powys NP8 1BW   **Map 9 D5**

Once a stopping-off point on the London-West Wales coaching route, the Bear continues its tradition of hospitality as the focal point of the market town. The bar, with its low black beams, sturdy old furniture and open fires, is a good place for a drink and a chat with owners and locals, and upstairs there's a quiet residents' lounge. Bedrooms, some grouped round a courtyard, have good-quality furniture and warm, well-chosen fabrics. Top of the range is a four-poster room with a spa bath. *Rooms 24. Garden.* Access, Amex, Visa.

Crickhowell	Gliffaes Country House Hotel	63%	£59

Tel 0874 730371   Fax 0874 730463   **H**

Crickhowell Powys NP8 1RH   **Map 9 D5**

Fishing is the favourite pastime at this distinctive late-Victorian house (spot the campanile), which overlooks a mile of water on the left bank of the Usk. Many other outdoor activities have a following here, while the sitting room and drawing room are splendid places for doing nothing. Bedrooms are spacious and attractively furnished with old or antique pieces. No dogs. *Rooms 22. Garden, croquet, tennis, putting, golf practice net, snooker. Closed Jan & Feb. Access, Amex, Visa,* Diners Club International

Crickhowell   Places of Interest

Tretower Court & Castle   Tel 0874 730279.

Cross Hands	Forte Travelodge	£40

Tel 0269 845700   **L**

A48 Cross Hands Nr Llanelli Dyfed SA14 6NW   **Map 9 B5**

On the A48 eastbound, just 11 miles east of Carmarthen. *Rooms 32. Access, Amex, Visa.*

East Aberthaw	Blue Anchor Inn	£50

Tel 0446 750329   **R**

East Aberthaw Nr Barry South Glamorgan CF6 9DD   **Map 9 C6**

Andrew Lawrence is the go-ahead young chef in a quaint old thatched inn owned for 40 years by the Coleman family. Lunchtime brings an extensive bar menu, while typical evening choices run from leek, cheese and lentil quenelles or salad of herring and smoked scallops to grilled monkfish, herb-crusted rack of lamb and breast of pheasant with a chestnut purée stuffing. Children welcome before 8pm. *Seats 60. Private Room. L 12-2.45 D 7-9.30 (Sat to 9.45). Closed D Sun, 26 Dec, 1 Jan. Access, Visa.*

Eglwysfach   Ynyshir Hall   69%   £80

Tel 0654 781209   Fax 0654 781366   **H**

Eglwysfach Machynlleth Powys SY20 8TA   **Map 8 C3**

Once Queen Victoria's shooting lodge, the house stands in 12 acres of beautifully landscaped gardens next to an RSPB reserve. Joan and Rob Reen have totally transformed the mainly Georgian house, and their interest in interior design is evident throughout the stylish day rooms; Rob is an accomplished artist and his works grace the walls. Both the comfortable drawing room, furnished with cushion-bedecked sofas and rugs, and the bar with its picture window overlooking a rock garden, are delightful. Individually-named bedrooms really catch the eye with their use of contrasting colours and fabrics complemented by carefully chosen antiques. With their charming and courteous manner, the Reens have created an impressive and civilised small hotel. No facilities for children under 9. *Rooms 9. Garden, pitch & putt. Access, Amex, Visa,* **(D)** Diners Club International

Ewloe   St David's Park Hotel   69%   £99

Tel 0244 520800   Fax 0244 520930   **H**

St David's Park Ewloe Clwyd CH5 3YB   **Map 8 D2**

Purpose-built on Georgian inspiration, this fine example of modern hotel construction stands by the junction of the A55 and A494. Its interior continues the Georgian theme, with the period's decorative style used throughout. The business and conference markets are well catered for (250+ delegates can be seated theatre-style) and there's a well-equipped leisure club. Bedrooms, furnished in light oak, include suites and studio rooms, ladies' executive rooms, family rooms and some designed for disabled guests. Children up to 16 stay free in parents' room. *Rooms 121. Indoor swimming pool, gymnasium, spa bath, steam room, sauna, solarium, beautician, games room, children's playroom, snooker. Access, Amex, Visa,* **(D)** Diners Club International

Fishguard   Fishguard Bay Hotel   59%   £55

Tel 0348 873571   Fax 0348 873030   **H**

Quay Road Goodwick Fishguard Dyfed SA64 0BT   **Map 9 A5**

Ten acres of woodland stand at the back while Cardigan Bay is straight ahead and the ferry service to Rosslare is only minutes away. A popular venue for functions, with conferences accommodating up to 200, banqueting up to 300. Best bedrooms have bay-facing balconies: several others still lack en-suite facilities. Children up to 14 stay free in their parents' room. *Rooms 62. Garden. Access, Amex, Visa,* **(D)** Diners Club International

Gowerton   Cefn Goleu Park   69%   £80

Tel 0792 873099   **HR**

Cefn Stylle Road Gowerton West Glamorgan SA4 3QS   **Map 9 B6**

Bought by Emma and Claude Rossi in 1987, the house has been lovingly restored. A stunning vaulted central hall contains unique showcases of china dolls, and is ringed by a minstrel's gallery leading to four master bedrooms with Victorian elegance recreated. Further similarly appointed accommodation is available in the adjoining coach house. No dogs. *Rooms 6. Garden. Closed Jan. Access, Visa.*

Restaurant   £60

Claude and Bernard Rossi deal in substantial portions and robust flavours on a menu with British, French and Italian influences. *Seats 40. Parties 20. Private Room. L (Sun only) 12.30-2 D 7.30-9.30. Closed D Sun, all Mon. Set L £11.50.*   ♛

Gwbert-on-Sea   Cliff Hotel   60%   £79   H

Tel 0239 613241   Fax 0239 615391

Gwbert-on-Sea Cardigan Dyfed SA43 1PP   Map 9 B4

Dramatically located on 30 acres of headland overlooking Cardigan Island, a privately owned hotel whose convivial atmosphere is augmented by friendly staff and high-profile management. There's a wealth of recreational facilities, both on and off-site, for all the family (under-12s free in parents' room); conference and banqueting (max 200). Self-catering apartments offering full use of the hotel facilities are also available. *Rooms 73. Garden, 9-hole golf course, outdoor swimming pool, sauna, solarium, gymnasium, squash, snooker. Access, Amex, Visa,*

Halkyn   Forte Travelodge   £40   L

Tel 0352 780952

A55 Halkyn Clwyd CH8 8RF   Map 8 D1

On the A55 westbound 13 miles west of Chester, 5 miles south of Holywell and 15 miles north-west of Wrexham. *Rooms 31. Access, Amex, Visa.*

Harlech   The Cemlyn   £55   RR

Tel 0766 780425

High Street Harlech Gwynedd LL46 2YA   Map 8 B2

A large picture window provides wonderful views from Ken Goody's unpretentious little restaurant, but his nightly menus provide the greatest draw, with two or three courses offered at fixed prices. Local produce (with interesting combinations of natural flavours) and the best local seafood are the highlights: cream of smoked haddock soup, braised lamb's tongue with mustard and capers, spicy king prawns with ginger, coriander, chili, tomato and coconut, free-range Lleyn pork cooked in yoghurt and honey with cardamon and orange; Linzertorte and thick Anglesey cream or unpasteurised Welsh cheeses to finish. Sensibly-priced wine list with a good choice. *Seats 52. Parties 10. Private Room. D only 7-9 (Sat to 9.30). Closed Nov-mid Mar. Set D £14.95/£17.95. Access, Visa.*

Room   £40

There is one twin-bedded room with comfortable armchairs, hundreds of books and the same great view as the restaurant. Don't miss the marvellous breakfast. No children under 8. No dogs.

Harlech   Places of Interest

Tourist Information   Tel 0766 780658.
Theatr Ardudwy   Tel 0766 780667.
Harlech Castle   Tel 0766 780552.

Lake Vyrnwy   Lake Vyrnwy Hotel   64%   £70   H

Tel 069 173 692   Fax 069 173 289

Lake Vyrnwy (via Oswestry) Llanwyddyn Powys SY10 0LY   Map 8 C3

25,000 acres of shooting rights and fly fishing on the lake make this tranquil retreat a popular sporting hotel. There are miles of splendid walks, while inside the 100-year-old house there's tea by the fireside, a convivial drink in the bar or an hour or two with a board game. Bedrooms are brightly decorated in unfussy style with a mixture of antique and period furniture. Banqueting and conference facilities for up to 120. *Rooms 30. Garden, tennis, shooting, fishing, sailing. Access, Amex, Visa,*

Lake Vyrnwy   Places of Interest

Powysland Museum & Montgomery Canal Centre   The Canal Wharf, Welshpool Tel 0938 554656.
Montgomeryshire Showground   Welshpool Tel 0938 554818.
Powis Castle (NT)   Welshpool Tel 0938 554336.
Glebe House Garden   Welshpool Tel 0938 553602.

Lamphey   Court Hotel   59%   £87

	H
Tel 0646 672273 Fax 0646 672480	

Lamphey Pembroke Dyfed SA71 5NT   Map 9 A5

A hotel since 1978, the Court is peacefully situated in extensive grounds
just a mile from the south Pembrokeshire coast. The reception hall, with its
handsome staircase, and the day rooms have a charm and elegance that
echoes their Georgian origins; main-house bedrooms enjoy fine views,
good facilities and large, newly retiled bathrooms. The Westminster
annexe houses purpose-designed studios with sitting rooms and sofa beds.
Children under 16 are accommodated free in their parents' room.
Conference suite (for up to 90), and leisure centre with sun terrace.
Rooms 31. Garden, indoor swimming pool, keep-fit equipment, sauna, solarium.
Access, Amex, Visa, (1) *Diners Club International*

Lamphey   Places of Interest

Pembroke Tourist Information   Tel 0646 682148.
Tenby Tourist Information   Tel 0834 2402.
Colby Woodland Garden (NT)   Amroth, Tenby Tel 0558 822800/0834
   811725 *13 miles.*
National Museum of Gypsy Caravans Romany Crafts and
   Lore   Pembroke Tel 0646 681308.
Manor House Wildlife and Leisure Park   Tenby Tel 0646 651201.
Tenby Museum and Picture Gallery   Tel 0834 2809.
Tenby Beach
Torch Theatre   Milford Haven Tel 06462 5267 *15 miles.*

Llanarmon Dyffryn Ceiriog   Hand Hotel   £58

	I
Tel 069 176 666 Fax 069 176 262	

Llanarmon Dyffryn Ceiriog Nr Llangollen Clwyd LL20 7LD   Map 8 D2

Originally a 16th-century farmhouse, the hotel stands in beautiful
countryside in a picturesque village at the head of the Ceiriog Valley. An
old black range in reception, antiques in lounge and bar plus a log fire all
add up to a cosy, traditional atmosphere. Bedrooms are neat and simple,
with plain walls and white fitted furniture. *Rooms 13. Garden, tennis.*
Access, Amex, Visa, (1) *Diners Club International*

Llanarmon Dyffryn Ceiriog   West Arms Hotel   £78

	I
Tel 069 176 665 Fax 069 176 622	

Llanarmon Dyffryn Ceiriog Nr Llangollen Clwyd LL20 7LD   Map 8 D2

Nestling in the lovely Ceiriog valley, this 400-year-old country inn has lost
none of his charm through recent restoration. Slate-flagged floors, vast
inglenooks and beams offset by period furnishings preserve the atmosphere
of a bygone age. Though six of the bedrooms are now fairly modern, the
rest retain exposed beams, brass bedsteads and antique furniture, to which
neatly added bathrooms provide the requisite modern comforts. A private
garden suite accommodates meetings and dinner parties for up to 70 guests.
Rooms 14. Garden, game fishing. Access, Amex, Visa, (1) *Diners Club International*

Llanberis   Y Bistro   £50

	R
Tel 0286 871278	

43-45 High Street Llanberis Gwynedd LL55 4EU   Map 8 B2

Danny and Nerys Roberts's friendly and informal restaurant remains as
popular and as good value as ever: fixed-priced meals, from two to four
courses, include canapés, side salad and home-baked bread plus coffee with
chocolate florentines. Welsh farm produce and seafood take centre stage, as
in the home-cured herrings in sweet dill, lamb's kidneys Turbigo, pan-fried
pork loin with apples, sage, onion and dry cider, and garlic-studded roast

leg of lamb with rosemary cream. Nerys's varied vegetarian selections, tangy lemon cheesecake and well-kept Welsh farmhouse cheeses are equally commendable. *Seats 50. Parties 40. Private Room. D only 7.30-9.30 (Sat to 9.45). Closed Sun & Mon in winter, Bank Holidays. Set D £17-22.50. Access, Visa.*

Llanberis   Places of Interest

Museum of the North, Power of Wales Tel 0286 870636.
Snowdon Mountain Railway   Tel 0286 870223.
Welsh Slate Museum   Tel 0286 870630.

Llandderfel   Palé Hall   71%

Tel 067 83 285	£80 H
Llandderfel Nr Bala Gwynedd LL23 7PS	Map 8 C2

Owners Tim and Jain Ovens offer rest, relaxation and country house hospitality in their imposing Victorian mansion. The quiet Dee Valley setting and lovely views make a good start, continued in the public areas: the drawing room with its gilded plaster ceiling and crystal chandelier, the blue lounge, the bar-cum-library and the lofty Great Hall with galleried oak staircase. Individually decorated bedrooms, some with open fireplaces, have splendid bathrooms, most with bidets, some with spa baths. Kennels available. *Rooms 17. Garden, sauna, solarium, coarse fishing. Access, Visa,* Diners Club International.

Llandeilo   Cawdor Arms   65%

Tel 0558 823500	£59 H
Llandeilo Dyfed SA19 6EN	Map 9 C5

Formerly The Bear, whence the mail departed daily for London (202 miles), this former seat of the Cawdor family is now owned by Miss Audrey Tibbs. While missing out on 1990s' splendour, it remains an elegant period piece of some gentility, echoed in its four-poster Victorian suite, plushly draped French Room and Howard's Room, where a certain Mr Hughes rested following a forced landing during a harrowing transatlantic flight in 1927. Well-proportioned, pillared Georgian day rooms possess a slightly faded elegance and charm. *Rooms 17. Access, Amex, Visa,* Diners Club International.

Llandrillo   Tyddyn Llan   65%

Tel & Fax 049 084 264	£74 HR
Llandrillo Nr Corwen Clwyd LL21 0ST	Map 8 C2

Peter and Bridget Kindred run a delightful country hotel surrounded by lawns midway between Bala and Corwen on the B4401. Outdoor pursuits include four miles of fishing (for grayling, trout and some salmon) on the River Dee, with a gillie provided if required; further local lake and reservoir fishing. Fine paintings, prints and ornaments take the eye in the lounge, and there are antiques in the bedrooms. *Rooms 10. Garden, croquet, fishing. Access, Visa.*

Restaurant   £60

The dining room is in Georgian style and it provides a splendid setting for getting away from it all for a quiet meal at your own pace. The 3- or 4-course, fixed-price menu offers a good range – from roast pigeon with braised lentils, Welsh goat's cheese in filo pastry with spicy damson chutney or Welsh mussels to start, followed by the likes of top-quality Welsh lamb and beef (a feature of Sunday lunches) or steamed monkfish with stir-fried vegetables and lemon. Rich pickings among the desserts – icky sticky toffee pudding, walnut and treacle tart with maple syrup ice cream – are nicely balanced by lighter items – soufflé surprise or dark chocolate mousse quenelles, both served with fresh fruit. Farmhouse cheeses are served with biscuits, celery and nuts. Decently priced wine list with plenty under £15 per bottle and a house champagne around £20 – other restaurants please note! *Seats 45. Parties 45. Private Room. L 12.30-2 D 7.30-9.30. Closed 1 week Feb. Set L £11 Set D £19.50.*

Llandudno	Bodysgallen Hall	75%	£140

Tel 0492 584466   Fax 0492 582519

HR

Llandudno Gwynedd LL30 1RS

Map 8 C1

Although close to the A470, Bodysgallen enjoys a wonderful situation in
200 acres of mature parkland which includes seven acres of award-winning
formal gardens. The imposing house dates back to the 13th century, but
the majority is 17th; its interior lavishly furnished in quiet, elegant style
and exuding character through its choice antiques, polished floorboards,
fine oil paintings and wood panelling. Of the diverse main-house
bedrooms, one features a stylishly draped four-poster, and most have fine
views. Nine self-contained cottage suites are bright and roomy: dogs are
permitted only in these rooms. Richard Carr and his fine young team of
staff keep Bodysgallen at the forefront of the newer breed of country house
hotel. No children under 8. Historic House Hotels. *Rooms 28.*
Garden, croquet, tennis. Access, Amex, Visa,

Restaurant

£80

Relying on little-changing tastes, and standards that are tested and well-
liked, new chef Mair Lewis's fixed-price "Bill of Fare" offers the classic stuff
of modern British cooking: fillet of smoked trout on orange and
horseradish sauce; fillet steak with oyster mushrooms and Madeira; hot
lime tart with thick Jersey cream and, much to be applauded, a daily
savoury – glazed Welsh rarebit being an appropriate choice. There is
always a good selection of Welsh and English cheeses. The wide-ranging
wine list is strongest in fine clarets and the Cellarman's Choice offers
interesting wines at good prices. *Seats 60. Parties 40. Private Room.*
L 12.30-2 D 7.30-9.45. Set L £13.90/£15.90 Set D £31.

Llandudno	Empire Hotel	69%	£60

Tel 0492 860555   Fax 0492 860791

H

Church Walks Llandudno Gwynedd LL30 2HE

Map 8 C1

Courtesy and care are the watchwords of owners Len and Elizabeth
Maddocks, here since 1960, and their reward is a very high level of repeat
business. Russell Flint prints add distinction to the homely lounge, and
there's a choice of bars. Bedrooms vary considerably in size and price; 12
of the smaller rooms have recently been turned into suites. Eight de luxe
rooms in the Victorian house next to the main building feature antiques,
silk drapes and marble-floored bathrooms with whirlpool baths. Multi-
channel TV in all except budget rooms. Dogs in budget rooms only.
*Rooms 51. Indoor & outdoor swimming pools, spa bath, sauna, steam room, roof
garden and sun terrace, dancing (Sat). Closed 10 days Xmas/New Year.*
Access, Amex, Visa,

Llandudno	St George's Hotel	61%	£92

Tel 0492 877544   Fax 0492 878477

H

St George's Place Llandudno Gwynedd LL30 2LG

Map 8 C1

Llandudno's oldest hotel, recently restored to its former glory, houses
conferences and banqueting for up to 250. The new Shape Club offers top-
to-toe health, hair and cosmetic care. Many bedrooms afford views of the
sea and Great Orme, and the best have balconies. Under-12s stay free in
their parents' room. *Rooms 87. Spa baths, sauna, solarium, beauty salon, hair
salon, keep-fit equipment. Closed 10 days Jan. Access, Amex, Visa,*

Llandudno   St Tudno Hotel   69%   £90

HR

Tel 0492 874411   Fax 0492 860407

The Promenade Llandudno Gwynedd LL30 2LP   Map 8 C1

Effusive and attentive owners Martin and Janette Bland unexpectedly
reveal a wealth of Edwardian charm behind the terraced facade of their
delightful seafront hotel. Guests are made truly welcome in the stylish
bar/lounge and in a reading room reserved for non-smokers. Bedrooms,
though modestly sized, achieve a feeling of space through sympathetic use
of bright fabrics and natural daylight. Bathrooms are thoughtfully kitted
out with top-class towelling and toiletries. Private boardroom for up to 10;
dinner parties for 50. No dogs. *Rooms 24. Indoor swimming pool, patio.
Access, Amex, Visa.*

Garden Room   £65

While conservatory-style furniture, potted plants and painted trelliswork
and trees on the walls create the garden-room illusion, David Harding's
modern British menus are altogether more authentic. At fixed prices, lunch
and dinner start with the likes of grilled goat's cheese with leaf salad and
bacon, and crab tart with butter sauce. Following a soup or sorbet come
salmon, venison, free-range chicken, Welsh lamb and a daily vegetarian
main dish. Lavish desserts, savoury and organically produced Welsh cheeses
all follow. Lighter lunches are served in the coffee lounge. Fair prices on
the thoughtfully-put-together and helpfully descriptive wine list. No
smoking. *Seats 60. L 12.30-2 D 6.45-9.30. Set L £11.50 Set D £23.50.*

Llandudno   Places of Interest

Tourist Information   Tel 0492 876413.
Mostyn Art Gallery   Tel 0492 874151.
Llandudno Dry Ski Slope   Tel 0492 874707.
Alice in Wonderland Visitor Centre   Tel 0492 860082.

Llangammarch Wells Lake Country House Hotel 68%   £90

HR

Tel 059 12 202   Fax 059 12 457

Llangammarch Wells Powys LD4 4BS   Map 9 C4

Standing in 50 acres of parkland and enjoying genuine tranquillity, a
mainly Edwardian building run along personable lines by Jean-Pierre and
Jan Mifsud. Grandly proportioned day rooms include a handsome parlour
lounge that retains much of the period character by using traditional
furnishings and fabrics. Bedrooms have river views and are individually
styled with a combination of antiques and restful colour schemes. Smart,
efficient staff mirror the owners' enthusiasm. Popular with fishermen as the
river Irfon runs through the grounds. *Rooms 19. Garden, pitch & putt,
tennis, fishing, clay-pigeon shooting, snooker. Closed Jan. Access, Amex, Visa.*

Restaurant   £65

Fixed-price, four-course dinners are typified by cream of winter vegetable
soup with hazelnut dumplings, timbale of salmon, smoked salmon and crab
with a cucumber and mint yoghurt sauce, followed by fillet of Welsh
venison with mustard and horseradish sauces and finishing with a langue de
chat basket of plum and almond mousse with plum and orange sauce.
Table d'hote lunches are served in the restaurant or lighter lunches in the
lounge. No children under 12 in the dining room. Plenty of choice on the
varied wine list. *Seats 50. Parties 8. L 1-2 (non-residents by arrangement only)
D 7-8.45. Set L £14.50 Set D £24.50.*

Llangefni   Tre-Ysgawen Hall   79%   £107

Tel 0248 750750   Fax 0248 750035   **HR**

Capel Coch Nr Llangefni Anglesey Gwynedd LL77 7UR   **Map 8 B1**

A tree-lined drive leads from the B5111 to this fine Victorian mansion
with friendly owners and staff. Handsome public rooms leading off a grand
entrance include a bar and a traditionally styled lounge that looks
southward over the gardens. Bedrooms are of a very good size and
appointed to a high degree of comfort and elegance, with beautiful fabrics
complementing hand-picked, mainly antique furniture. Bathrooms, too, are
excellent, particularly two with corner whirlpool baths. 3000 acres of
private shooting. Banqueting/conference facilities for up to 120. *Rooms 19.
Garden, helipad, croquet, shooting, clay-pigeon shooting, kennels.Access, Amex,
Visa,* (D) Diners Club International

Restaurant   £70

Housed in a large conservatory-style extension, the restaurant is both
elegant and formal, much in keeping with the house's atmosphere. Steven
Morris, formerly sous-chef, is now in charge of the kitchen. *Seats 60.
Parties 120. Private Room. L 12-2.30 (Sat from 12.30) D 7.30-9.30.
Set L £14 Set D £18.*

Llangefni   Places of Interest

Holyhead Tourist Information   Tel 0407 762622.
Wylfa Nuclear Power Station   Tel 0407 710471 *10 miles.*

Llangollen   Hand Hotel   55%   £65

Tel 0978 860303   Fax 0978 861277   **H**

Bridge Street Llangollen Clwyd LL20 8PL   **Map 8 D2**

Country hotel with gardens reaching down to the river Dee. Simple,
attractive rooms. Banqueting and conference facilities for up to 80.
Rooms 57. Garden, fishing. Access, Amex, Visa, (D) Diners Club International

Llangollen   Royal Hotel   59%   £81

Tel 0978 860202   Fax 0978 861824   **H**

Bridge Street Llangollen Clwyd LL20 8PG   **Map 8 D2**

Looking just a little like a fairy-tale castle, the Royal overlooks a 14th-
century stone bridge on the banks of the Dee. Simple bedrooms, two bars
and a comfortable lounge. Forte Heritage. *Rooms 33. Access, Amex, Visa,*
(D) Diners Club International

Llangollen   Places of Interest

Tourist Information   Tel 0978 860828.
European Centre for Traditional and Regional Cultures   Tel 0978
861292.
Llangollen Railway   Tel 0978 860951.
Valle Crucis Abbey   Tel 0978 860326 *2 miles.*
Chirk Castle   Tel 0691 777701 *6 miles.*

Llangybi   Cwrt Bleddyn Hotel   71%   £95

Tel 0633 49521   Fax 0633 49220   **H**

Tredunnock Nr Usk Gwent NP5 1PG   **Map 9 D6**

A large house standing in 17 acres of countryside three miles from
Caerleon, between Llangybi and Tredunnock. Some original features date
back to the 17th century but the interior is modernised to a great extent,
including spacious bedrooms with separate seating areas. The lounge and
private meeting rooms feature carved panelling and fireplaces. Extensive
leisure amenities. Conference facilities for up to 200. No dogs. *Rooms 36.
Garden, indoor swimming pool, sauna, solarium, spa bath, hair salon, games
room, clay-pigeon shooting, tennis, squash. Access, Amex, Visa,* (D) Diners Club International

Llanrug   Seiont Manor   71%   £100

Tel 0286 673366   Fax 0286 2840   **H**

Llanrug Caernarfon Gwynedd LL55 2AQ   Map 8 B2

Eighty acres of parkland provide pleasant walks, and Snowdonia National
Park and the Isle of Anglesey are both a short drive away. Fishing is
available on the river Seiont, and guests have complimentary access to a
nearby golf course. Public rooms, including a traditional oak-panelled bar,
a lounge and a very comfortable library, are also furnished in a manner
that befits the ancient character of the building. Bedrooms are in two
purpose-built blocks which extend from the original stone building and are
in a style sympathetic to it. Rooms have either little balconies or patio
doors, are of a good size and all boast antique or good-quality period
furniture, plus modern accessories like remote-control TVs and wall safes.
Children up to 14 stay free in parents' room. Conference facilities for up to
100 delegates. **Rooms 28.** *Garden, indoor swimming pool, spa bath, sauna,*
solarium, fishing. Access, Amex, Visa,  *Diners Club International*

Llanrug   Places of Interest

Caernarfon Tourist Information   Tel 0286 672232.
Caernarfon Castle   Tel 0286 77617 *World Heritage Listed Site.*
Segontium Roman Fort Museum   Caernarfon Tel 0286 5625.

Llanrwst   Meadowsweet   63%   £45

Tel 0492 640732   **HR**

Station Road Llanrwst Gwynedd LL26 0DS   Map 8 C2

Overlooking the Conwy Valley towards Snowdonia, Meadowsweet's
attractions include nearby fishing and riding in addition to the home
comforts and fine food provided by John and Joy Evans. Their steady
improvements over the last decade have produced an intimate hotel of true
quality. Individually designed bedrooms feature antique pine furniture and
this year have new beds and armchairs; all have en-suite shower rooms,
though there's also a separate bathroom on each floor. Under-10s
accommodated free in parents' room. **Rooms 10.** *Access, Visa.*

Restaurant   £60

John Evans is a self-taught cook whose dedication to fresh ingredients and
innovative combinations becomes an integral part of the Meadowsweet
philosophy. The five-course fixed-price dinner might comprise hot spiced
wild mushrooms, home-cured gravad lax with soured cream sauce, boned
quail on chicken liver risotto with wine and olive sauce, fine Welsh
farmhouse cheeses and chocolate marquise with orange custard. A spendid,
classic wine list runs to 600 bins of true depth with an honest eye for
quality and value. No smoking. **Seats 36.** *Parties 12. L 12-1.30 D 6.30-9.30*
(Sun to 9). Closed L in winter. Set L £8.95. Set D £26

Llansanffraid Glan Conwy   Old Rectory   73%   £79

Tel 0492 580611   Fax 0492 584555   **HR**

Llanrwst Road Llansanffraid Glan Conwy Gwynedd LL28 5LF   Map 8 C1

Michael and Wendy Vaughan's attractive Georgian house stands on a
hillside just off the A470, affording it excellent views over the Conwy
estuary and Snowdonia. On the ground floor there is a fine sitting room
with pine panelling, groups of comfortable armchairs and sofas, and a cosy
morning room offering a quiet and peaceful atmosphere: ornaments,
paintings and prints make the rooms traditional and homely throughout.
The bedrooms contain armchairs, antique furniture and quality fabrics;
bathrooms are excellent. Two new coach-house rooms allow smoking and
entertain pets – both of which are otherwise actively discouraged. No
children under 12. **Rooms 6.** *Garden. Closed 7 Dec-20 Feb.*
Access, Amex, Visa.

Restaurant £70

Guests are seated at 8pm around the communal table, though a separate
table or personal dietary requirement may be arranged in advance. Wendy
uses only Welsh Black beef and Welsh mountain lamb, while other market
produce is almost entirely local. A herb broth of fish and seafood, and beef
fillet with leek pancakes are typical of the no-choice first and main courses.
Goat's cheese soufflé may be offered as an alternative to the farmhouse
cheeses; Vale of Clwyd milk and cream are used exclusively in the home-
made ice creams. Four courses and coffee are included in the fixed-price
dinner. Good choice of half bottles on the wine list. No smoking. *Seats 16.
Parties 14. Private Room. D only at 8. Set D £26.*

Llanvihangel Gobion   Llansantffraed Court   66% £88
Tel 0873 840678   Fax 0873 840674 **H**
Llanvihangel Gobion Abergavenny Gwent NP7 9BA Map 9 D5

The owners describe the house as neo-classical Lutyens with strong
Georgian influences. It stands on the B4598 Abergavenny road, in
extensive parkland on the fringe of the Usk valley with the Black
Mountains as a backdrop. Most characterful of the bedrooms are on the
top floor, with oak beams and dormer windows. Children up to 12 stay
free in parents' room. The lounge and bar provide ample space for a
relaxing chat or drink. *Rooms 21. Garden. Access, Amex, Visa,* (D) *Diners Club International*

Llanwnda   Stables Hotel   57% £56
Tel 0286 830711   Fax 0286 830413 **H**
Llanwnda Nr Caernarfon Gwynedd LL54 5SD Map 8 B2

Three miles south-west of Caernarvon on the A499, this is a modest single-
storey hotel set around original Victorian stables which now house a bar
and restaurant. Conference facilities for up to 100. Children up to 12 stay
free in parents' room. *Rooms 14. Garden, outdoor swimming pool, helipad.
Closed Xmas/New Year. Access, Amex, Visa.*

Llyswen   Llangoed Hall   80% £115
Tel 0874 754525   Fax 0874 754545 **HR**
Llyswen Brecon Powys LD3 0YP Map 9 D5

Distinguished buildings have occupied this site for many centuries, but the
present magnificent hall (the work of Sir Clough Williams-Ellis of
Portmeirion fame) dates only from 1912; the south wing alone survives
from the 1632 Jacobean mansion. Sir Bernard Ashley has made a
marvellous job of restoring the hall, whose day rooms feature paintings
from his private collection, antiques, chintzes and large sofas. Laura Ashley
fabrics make an elegant contribution to the bedrooms, whose individual
decor is complemented by all sorts of thoughtful extras. Wood-floored
bathrooms epitomise the quality. Service works well under general
manager Tom Ward. Children under eight at the management's discretion.
Dogs are not allowed in the hotel, but heated kennels are available.
*Rooms 23. Garden, croquet, tennis, fishing, snooker, helipad. Access, Amex,
Visa,* (D) *Diners Club International*

Restaurant £100

The dining room, graciously done out in yellow and cornflower blue, is a
splendid setting for enjoying the talents of Mark Salter. His cooking is
modern classical, with many innovative touches and an emphasis on
lightness. Many of the ingredients are grown in the kitchen garden, while
others are supplied locally where possible. Chargrilled calf's liver salad with
a citrus fruit dressing, thyme-roasted monkfish on a bed of niçoise
vegetables, roast breasts of partridge on a chestnut terrine and fillet of beef
with boulangère potatoes and an oxtail sauce typify his style. To round
things off try an irresistible hot plum soufflé with ginger ice cream,
caramelised apple tart or baked goat's cheese served with home-made
chutney and toasted walnut and sultana bread. An excellent wine list

including plenty of half bottles; subjective notes precede each section; only first growth clarets are denoted. *Seats 46. Parties 40. Private Room. L 12.15-2.30 D 7.15-9.30. Set L £14.75 Set D £35.50.*

Llyswen   Places of Interest

Brecon Tourist Information   Tel 0874 4437.
Cathedral Church of St. John the Evangelist   Brecon Tel 0874 4876.
Builth Wells Tourist Information   Tel 0982 553307.
Wyeside Arts Centre   Builth Wells   Tel 0982 552555.
Royal Welsh Showground   Llanelwedd   Tel 0982 553683.

Machynlleth   Wynnstay Arms   57%   £53

Tel 0654 702941   Fax 0654 703884   H

Maengwyn Street Machynlleth Powys SY20 8AE   Map 8 C3

Main-street hotel with a neo-Georgian facade. Convivial bar, choice of lounges (including non-smoking). Children up to 16 stay free in parents' room. *Rooms 20. Access, Amex, Visa,*

Machynlleth   Places of Interest

Centre for Alternative Technology   Llwyngwern Quarry Tel 0654 702400 *2½ miles.*

Merthyr Tydfil   Baverstock Hotel   57%   £62

Tel 0685 6221   Fax 0685 723670   H

Heads of the Valley Road Merthyr Tydfil Mid Glamorgan CF44 0LX   Map 9 C5

Low-rise modern hotel in an elevated position on the A465. Modest facilities and adequate bedrooms. A good deal of business comes from conferences and meetings in a variety of rooms (50 residential, 400 daytime). Reduced rates at weekends when businessmen are thin on the ground. *Rooms 53. Garden. Access, Amex, Visa,*

Merthyr Tydfil   Places of Interest

Ynysfach Engine House   Tel 0685 721858/83704.
Cyfarthfa Castle Museum and Art Gallery   Tel 0685 723112.

Miskin   Miskin Manor   70%   £107

Tel 0443 224204   Fax 0443 237606   H

Penddylan Road Pontyclun Miskin Mid-Glamorgan CF7 8ND   Map 9 C6

A handsome stone mansion in 20 acres of garden and woodland, Miskin Manor was built in 1858. Day rooms are very comfortable and deep sofas in floral fabrics invite guests to relax and gaze out over the gardens. The bedrooms are vast – even singles have sofas – and are luxurious without being ostentatious. Some have four-posters and there are two suites. There's a sports and leisure complex and conference facilities for up to 180 delegates. Hidden Hotels. *Rooms 32. Garden, indoor swimming pool, gymnasium, spa bath, steam room, sauna, solarium, beauty salon, badminton, coffee shop (10am-11pm), crèche (9am-3pm Mon-Fri). Access, Amex, Visa,*

Monmouth   King's Head   64%   £70

Tel 0600 712177   Fax 0600 713545   H

Agincourt Square Monmouth Gwent NP5 3DY   Map 9 D5

Returned once more to family ownership, this timber-fronted former coaching inn retains its links with a notable past; Kings Henry V and Charles I, Lord Nelson and the Hon CS Rolls all having played their part in the King's Head's history. Bedrooms are full of character with their blackened beams and antique furniture; four are suitable for family use, with under-5s staying free. Separate conference and banqueting rooms accommodate up to 200. *Rooms 29. Access, Amex, Visa,*

Monmouth   Places of Interest

Tourist Information   Tel 0600 3899.
Nelson Collection and Local History Centre   Tel 0600 3519.

Mumbles	Norton House	65%	£70

Tel 0792 404891   Fax 0792 403210   **HR**

17 Norton Road Mumbles Swansea West Glamorgan SA3 5TQ   **Map 9 C6**

A pretty white-painted Georgian house with wisteria round the door,
personally run in friendly fashion by Jan and John Powers. The main day
room is the bar with an unusual umbrella-vaulted ceiling, and there is a
small lounge on the first floor, but it's only just big enough for a single
three-piece suite. Bedrooms vary from three rooms with four-posters and
one with rough stone walls and timbered ceiling, to the majority of smaller
rooms in a newer wing. Decor mostly features attractive, matching floral
fabrics which compensate for less good carpeting; nevertheless, all have
homely touches like fresh flowers, mineral water and a welcoming
decanter of sherry. Many of the bathrooms have very small wash basins
and three have shower and WC only, but all have good towelling.
Excellent breakfasts begin with a huge glass of freshly squeezed orange
juice. No children under 8. No dogs. *Rooms 15. Garden. Closed 25 & 26
Dec. Access, Amex, Visa,* ⓘ ⬛

Restaurant   **£60**

Although dishes have Welsh names, with clear English explanations, the
cooking is not native to the principality. Pigeon breast in filo pastry with
orange duxelles and port dressing, pork fillet with apple and onion sauce,
and warm pear frangipane tart with butterscotch sauce demonstrate the
style. *Seats 36. Parties 8. Private Room.
L by arrangement D 7.15-9.30 (Sun 7-9).*

Mumbles	PA's Winebar	£45

Tel 0792 367723   **R**

95 Newton Road Mumbles West Glamorgan SA3 4BN   **Map 9 C6**

Wine bar/brasserie fare ranges from creamy garlic mushrooms through
olive toasts to veal casserole, pan-fried Dover sole, spicy prawns and
lasagne. Overlooks Oystermouth Castle. Tables outside in summer.
*Seats 32. L 12-2.30 D 6-9.30. Closed Sun, 3 weeks Oct, 2 days Xmas.
Access, Visa.*

Mumbles   Places of Interest

Caswell Bay Beach

Newport	Celtic Manor	75%	£118

Tel 0633 413000   Fax 0633 412910   **H**

Coldra Woods Newport Gwent NP6 2YA   **Map 9 D6**

One minute from junction 24 of the M4, but barely visible from the
motorway (as it is set in 300 acres of woodland), this major function and
conference venue (8 suites, for up to 350 delegates) has been converted
from an 18-bedroom hotel to one with 75 and many flexible business
facilities. The extended frontage houses two bars, one in pub style, an
elegant drawing room and a large patio conservatory (used for breakfast).
Bedrooms are of a good size and feature triple glazing, freestanding
darkwood furniture with work space for the businessman, attractive
window seating and smartly tiled, well-lit bathrooms. The original manor
bedrooms are larger and furnished to a similar standard. *Rooms 75. Garden,
indoor swimming pool, sauna, solarium, gymnasium, helipad. Access, Amex,
Visa,* ⓘ ⬛

Newport — Country Court Hotel 69% £107

Tel 0633 413733   Fax 0633 413713   H

Chepstowe Road Newport Gwent NP6 2LX   Map 9 D6

Stakis hotel built round a courtyard garden. Roomy overnight accommodation, leisure centre, self-contained facilities for business meetings. *Rooms 141. Gymnasium, indoor swimming pool, spa bath, sauna, solarium. Access, Amex, Visa,*

Newport — Hilton National 61% £112

Tel 0633 412777   Fax 0633 413087   H

The Coldra Newport Gwent NP6 2YG   Map 9 D6

Practical modern hotel at junction 24 of the M4, with leisure and business centres. Conference/banqueting facilities for 500/400. *Rooms 119. Indoor swimming pool, keep-fit equipment, sauna, steam room. Access, Amex, Visa,*

Newport — Kings Hotel 62% £64

Tel 0633 842020   Fax 0633 244667   H

7 High Street Newport Gwent NP9 1QU   Map 9 D6

Victorian town-centre hotel opposite the railway station (and just off the M4 at junction 26). Boardroom suites for 20-80 people and ballroom catering for up to 220. Roomy bedrooms (under 12s accommodated free in parents' room), large traditional lounge and a cheerful bar. *Rooms 47. Access, Amex, Visa,*

Newport — Places of Interest

Tourist Information   Tel 0633 842962.
Dolman Theatre   Tel 0633 263670.
Newport Centre   Tel 0633 259676.
Tredegar House   Tel 0633 815880.
Cathedral Church of St. Woolos   Tel 0633 63338.
Museum and Art Gallery   Tel 0633 840064.
Roman Legionary Museum   Caerleon Tel 0633 423.

Northop — Hall Forte Travelodge £40

Tel 0244 816473   L

A55 Northop Hall Mold Clwyd CH7 6HB   Map 8 D2

Located on the A55 eastbound, 3 miles north east of Mold. Approximately 10 miles west of Chester. *Rooms 40. Access, Amex, Visa.*

Northop — Soughton Hall 79% £99

Tel 0352 86811   Fax 0352 86382   HR

Northop Nr Mold Clwyd CH7 6AB   Map 8 D2

Set in 10 acres of gardens on its own 150-acre estate, grand Soughton Hall retains much of the charm and character derived from its origins as a bishop's palace, built in 1714. On the ground floor there's a cosy library and bar; on an upper floor the baronial-style drawing room has a carved stone fireplace, tapestries, drapes and Oriental carpets. Period furniture, co-ordinated decor and plenty of extras, from the pair of armchairs, fruit and mineral water to the generous toiletries and towels in well-equipped bathrooms, make these arguably the best hotel bedrooms in North Wales. Breakfast is taken in the original Servants' Hall where a black-leaded range still features. Welcoming and attentive staff, directed by the resident Rodenhurst family, contribute greatly to the feeling of relaxation and well-being. Private meeting rooms for 40; dining for up to 90 guests. No children under 12. No dogs. *Rooms 12. Garden, snooker, archery, chauffeur service. Closed 2 weeks Jan. Access, Amex, Visa.*

See over

Restaurant £70

The splendid State Dining Room, with its polished tables, crystal glass and
fine china, is on the first floor overlooking the garden. Fixed-price dinner
menus incorporate old classics and traditional dishes, with care taken to
reflect the current interest in lighter eating. Nightly specialities; notable
sweets and cheeses; extensive wine list. Smoking is not encouraged.
Seats 40. Parties 22. Private Room. L Sun 12-2, Mon-Sat by arrangement
D 7-9.30 (Sat to 10, Sun to 7.30). Set D £23.50.

Northop   Places of Interest

Mold Tourist Information Tel 0352 59331.
Clwyd Theatre Mold Tel 0352 55114 4 miles.

Pantmawr   Glansevern Arms £55

Tel 055 15 240   **I**

Pantmawr Nr Llangurig Powys SY18 6SY   Map 9 C4

Personally owned and managed for 25 years by Mr Edwards and family,
the Glansevern Arms commands a magnificent position overlooking the
upper reaches of the Wye, on the A44, four miles west of Llangurig. An
intimate bar and lounge soak in the glorious hill scenery by day and glow
with warmth from log fires at night. Residents equally enjoy the peace and
quiet afforded by bedrooms with private sitting areas, uninterrupted by
any phones, where the views should provide a greater attraction than
television. **Rooms 7.** *Closed 1 week Xmas. No credit cards.*

Pantmawr   Places of Interest

Newtown Tourist Information Tel 0686 625580.
Gregynog House and Gardens Newtown Tel 0686 650224 *28 miles.*
Robert Owen Memorial Museum Newtown Tel 0686 626345.
W H Smith Museum Newtown Tel 0686 626280.

Penally   Penally Abbey   65% £76

Tel 0834 3033   **HR**

Penally Nr Tenby Dyfed   Map 9 B5

In a tranquil hillside setting overlooking sand dunes and Carmarthen Bay,
Penally Abbey is a gothic-style stone-built mansion with an adjoining
coach house. There's a tiny bar, a vine-shaded conservatory and a homely
lounge where guests can play various musical instruments. Some bedrooms
have four-posters, pine wardrobes and period wash-stands. Cheerful staff
and welcoming hosts. No dogs. **Rooms 11.** *Garden, croquet, indoor swimming*
pool, games room. Access, Visa.

Restaurant £50

Elleen Warren puts prime ingredients to good use on her fixed-price
dinner menus. Typical dishes could include leek and lamb soup, crab
thermidor, breast of duck with cranberry, port and orange sauce, and fillet
of beef with a mild Roquefort sauce. No children under seven. No
smoking. *Seats 30. Parties 20. Private Room. L by arrangement D 7.30-9.30.*
Set D £18.95.

Penmaenpool   George III Hotel £85

Tel 0341 422525   Fax 0341 423565   **I**

Penmaenpool Nr Dolgellau Gwynedd LL40 1YD   Map 8 C3

The George III is a 17th-century inn boasting a superb situation at the head
of the Mawddach estuary. Friendly staff and attractive decor give an air of
hospitality to the bar, with its antique oak tables, brasses and paintings;
there's also a very cosy residents' lounge. Bedrooms are of a decent size,
with quality furniture. **Rooms 12.** *Garden, fishing. Closed 25 Dec.*
Access, Amex, Visa.

Porth   G & T's Village Bistro   £48

Tel 0443 685775   Fax 0443 687614   **RR**

64 Pontypridd Road Porth Mid Glamorgan CF39 9NL   Map 9 C6

Chef Martin Glass continues to strive for the appreciation of classical
French cooking in an unfashionable quarter of the Rhondda. *Crepe fourée
au poulet fumé et champignons* and *magret de canard au miel et au citron* typify
his efforts, and the results are reliable. **Seats 45.** *Parties 12. L 12.15-2.15
D 7.30-9.30 (Sat to 10). Closed D Sun. Access, Amex, Visa,* ❶ Diners Club International

Rooms   £34

Seven modestly-priced bedrooms share a couple of bathrooms on the
restaurant's upper floor, perched beside the cascading River Taff.

Porthkerry   Egerton Grey   73%   £85

Tel 0446 711666   Fax 0446 711690   **H**

Porthkerry Nr Cardiff South Glamorgan CF6 9BZ   Map 9 C6

A delightful 17th-century house, once a rectory, tucked away in a lovely
little valley ten miles from Cardiff and three from Barry. Anthony and
Magda Pitkin generate an air of peaceful informality which is evident as
soon as you enter the parquet-floored foyer, and personal attention is the
order of the day. Rugs, plump-cushioned seating, period decor and a piano
grace the lounge, and the library is charming. Bedrooms vary in size, shape
and design but all boast pretty, well-chosen fabrics, light, restful colour
schemes and antique or period furniture. The carpeted bathrooms are first
rate, many of them offering wonderful old baths with huge shower heads.
There are two suites. No dogs. **Rooms 10.** *Garden, croquet, tennis.
Access, Amex, Visa.*

Portmeirion   Hotel Portmeirion   74%   £84

Tel 0766 770228   Fax 0766 771331   **H**

Portmeirion Gwynedd LL48 6ER   Map 8 B2

Portmeirion was created (between 1925 and 1972) by Sir Clough
Williams-Ellis on a secluded peninsula on the Traeth Bach estuary. It's a
fairytale village comprising 50 buildings arranged round a central piazza.
The hotel is based on an early-Victorian villa near the shore and contains
some stunning public rooms: among others the black and white marble-
floored hall and the Indian-themed Jaipur Bar particularly take the eye.
Guests stay either in the main hotel building with the pick of the sea views
or in the surrounding suites and cottages that make up the village. The
latter are newly refurbished to the high standard of the others and are
within very comfortable walking distance of the hotel. Five de luxe suites
in the Anchor and Fountain building overlook the swimming pool and
estuary and are the latest rooms to have been revamped. Children under
four stay free in parents' room. No dogs. Conference/banqueting facliities
for up to 100. **Rooms 34.** *Garden, croquet, 18-hole golf course, outdoor
swimming pool, sea fishing, tennis, coffee shop (10am-5pm), village shops (closed
Jan-Mar). Closed 3 weeks Jan. Access, Amex, Visa,* ❶ Diners Club International

Portmeirion   Places of Interest

Portmeirion Village   Tel 0766 770228.
Gloddfa Slate Mine and Llechwedd Slate Caverns   Blaenau Ffestiniog
     Tel 0766 830664.
Ffestiniog Railway   Porthmadog Tel 0766 831654.
Llechwedd Slate Caverns   Tel 0766 830306.

Presteigne   Radnorshire Arms   61%   £86

Tel 0544 267406   Fax 0544 260418   **H**

High Street Presteigne Powys LD8 2BE   **Map 9 D4**

A small country inn that's a fine example of Elizabethan magpie
architecture. Good-sized, well-furnished bedrooms, plus a characterful bar
with oak beams and high-back settles. Forte Heritage. *Rooms 16. Garden.
Access, Amex, Visa,* Diners Club International

Pwllheli   Plas Bodegroes   £70

Tel 0758 612363   Fax 0758 701247   **RR**

Nefyn Road Pwllheli Gwynedd LL53 5TH   **Map 8 B2**

Chris and Gunna Chown pride themselves on finding the finest ingredients
virtually on their doorstep, in an area renowned for succulent seafood,
Welsh lamb and beef, free-range chicken and ducks and their eggs. Many
herbs and vegetables come straight from the restaurant's gardens. Chris's
five-course, fixed-price dinners offer plenty of choice and great value:
typical examples from recent menus might include crab and asparagus salad
with pineapple vinaigrette, pan-fried lamb's liver with sage and ratatouille,
roast rabbit with cabbage, bacon and a liver raviolo, strudel of Welsh
cheeses with celery and walnut salad, and hot chocolate tart with exotic
fruits and lime syrup. The enterprising wine list wins (for the second year
running) our Cellar of the Year award for Wales; it helpfully rates wines
according to sweetness and prices venerable claret vintages reasonably; see
further comment under Cellar of the Year section. No smoking. *Seats 35.
Parties 45. Private Room. D only 7-9.30 (Sun to 9). Closed Mon, Jan-Feb.
Set D £25. Access, Visa.*

Rooms   £70

Recently increased to eight, the en-suite bedrooms echo the delightful
Georgian house's inherent charm, their co-ordinated colours and fabrics
combining with either antique or modern pine furniture. Smoking is
actively discouraged.

Reynoldston   Fairyhill   64%   £75

Tel 0792 390139   Fax 0792 391358   **HR**

Reynoldston Gower Swansea West Glamorgan SA3 1BS   **Map 9 B6**

Rescued from dereliction by its current owners, Fairyhill today offers a
tranquil retreat in 24 acres of park and woodland containing a meandering
trout stream. Signs of its 18th-century origins are evident in irregular oak
doorways and uneven landings; antique Welsh dressers are in keeping.
Superior main-house bedrooms have full-sized baths en suite, the remainder
shower/WC only, and a two-bedroomed converted stable with a walled
garden is offered as a 'super de luxe' suite; two rooms in the coach house
are suitable as a family suite. Banquets/conferences up to 40. *Rooms 15.
Garden, fishing. Closed Xmas/New Year. Access, Visa.*

Restaurant   £64

French with Welsh overtones describes the weekly-changing menu
prepared by the two Julies – Bishop and Winchester. Crisply-fried cockles
for bar nibbles, chicken and mushroom velouté with puff pastry and
Welsh lamb roast with a minty Provençal garnish epitomise the balance. A
central buffet groans with a range of home-made desserts alongside a
display of Welsh cheeses. Short wine list assembled by grape variety.
*Seats 70. Parties 40. Private Room. L (Sun only) 12.30-1.15 D 7.30-9. Set L
(Sun) £12.95.*

Rossett   Llyndir Hall   71%

£117

Tel 0244 571648   Fax 0244 571258

Llyndir Lane Rossett Nr Wrexham Clwyd LL12 0AY

Map 8 D2

Ten minutes drive from the centre of Chester, this 'Strawberry Gothic' hall is surrounded by beautiful parkland. Bedrooms are well sized and furnished with antique pieces, the effect being both tasteful and elegant without being ostentatious. Most of the rooms are in a sympathetic new building. A gracious and sunny drawing room looks out over the lush lawns. Children up to 14 stay free in parents' room. Banquet and conference facilities for up to 120. *Rooms 38. Garden, croquet, indoor swimming pool, spa bath, steam room, solarium, coffee shop (7am-11pm, till 10 weekends). Access, Amex, Visa,*

Rossett   Places of Interest

Wrexham Tourist Information   Tel 0978 357845.
Bersham Industrial Heritage Museum Centre   Bersham
  Tel 0978 261529 *8 miles.*
Chirk Castle (NT)   Tel 0691 777701.
Erddig (NT)   Tel 0978 355314.
Bangor-on-Dee Racecourse   Tel 0978 780323 *10 miles.*

Ruthin   Ruthin Castle   62%

£75

Tel 082 42 2664   Fax 082 42 5978

Corwen Road Ruthin Nr Wrexham Clwyd LL15 2NU

Map 8 C2

30 acres of grounds surround ancient Ruthin Castle, where relics of the past include a drowning pool, whipping post and dungeons. More civilised diversions today centre around the cocktail bar, splendid lounge, or comfortable bedrooms appointed in traditional style. The Great Hall is the scene of regular medieval banquets. No dogs. *Rooms 58. Garden, snooker, fishing. Access, Amex, Visa,*

Ruthin   Places of Interest

Ruthin Tourist Information and Craft Centre   Tel 08242
  4774/5675/3992.
Cathedral Church of St. Asaph   Tel 0745 583597 *16 miles.*

St David's   St Non's Hotel   56%

£73

Tel 0437 720239   Fax 0437 721839

St David's Dyfed SA62 6RJ

Map 9 A5

A friendly family hotel just outside the town which offers some of the best children's terms around: under-6s sharing parents' room both stay and eat free. Other bonuses include five ground-floor bedrooms for the less mobile, and free golf at the picturesque St David's 9-hole course. *Rooms 24. Garden. Access, Amex, Visa,*

St David's   Warpool Court   62%

£108

Tel 0437 720300   Fax 0437 720676

St David's Dyfed SA62 6BN

Map 9 A5

Bordering National Trust parkland, Warpool Court enjoys spectacular scenery and panoramic views over St Brides Bay to the offshore islands beyond. Equally eye-catching within is the Ada Williams collection of unique armorial and ornamental hand-painted tiles which bedeck the public areas and many of the bedrooms. Private rooms for functions and conferences accommodate up to 70 people. Children under 14 stay free in parents' room. Free golf at the St David's course. *Rooms 25. Garden, tennis, indoor swimming pool, keep-fit equipment, sauna, games room, children's play area. Access, Amex, Visa,*

St. David's — Places of Interest

Haverfordwest Tourist Information   Tel 0437 763110.
County Showground   Haverfordwest Tel 0437 764331.
St. David's Bishop's Palace   Tel 0437 720517.
Cathedral Church of St. David and St. Andrew   Tel 0437 720202.
  Museums and Art Galleries
Scolton Manor Museum   Spittal Tel 0437 731328.
Graham Sutherland Gallery   Haverfordwest Tel 0437 751297.

Swansea	**Forte Crest** 69%	£87
Tel 0792 651074 Fax 0792 456044		**H**
39 The Kingsway Swansea West Glamorgan SA1 5LS		Map 9 C6

High-riser in the city centre, updated from its 60s' look. Leisure and
business centres (conference facilities for 200+). *Rooms 99. Indoor
swimming pool, gymnasium, sauna, solarium. Access, Amex, Visa,* Diners Club International

---

Swansea	**Hilton National** 65%	£83
Tel 0792 310330 Fax 0792 797535		**H**
Phoenix Way Enterprise Park Llansamlet Swansea West Glamorgan SA7 9EG		Map 9 C6

Two-storey hotel three miles from the city centre and two from the M4
(J45). Conference facilities for up to 200. *Rooms 120. Keep-fit equipment,
sauna. Access, Amex, Visa,* Diners Club International

Swansea	**Keenan's & Brayley's Bistro**	£45
Tel 0792 644111		**R**
82 St Helen's Road Swansea West Glamorgan SA4 1BQ		Map 9 C6

Owned and run by chef Chris Keenan, the restaurant sports overhead fans,
pine panelling and wrought-iron behind its ordinary exterior. In a relaxed
atmosphere Chris produces excellent food, typified by salmon mousse,
spiced chicken stir-fry and veal escalopes with asparagus. The same menu is
served in *Brayley's Bistro* which has a separate entrance. *Seats 24. Parties 30.
Private Room. L 12.30-2.30 D 7-11. Closed L Sat & Mon, all Sun.
Access, Amex, Visa.*

[CLOSED overprinted diagonally across the entry]

Swansea	**Langland Court Hotel**	£75
Tel 0792 361545 Fax 0792 362302		**I**
31 Langland Court Road Langland Swansea West Glamorgan SA3 4TD		Map 9 C6

Take the coastal road from Swansea to Mumbles (five miles) and follow
signs to Langland Bay to find this comfortable clifftop inn. Public areas
take the form of a Tudor-style residence, to which *Polly Garters*, the Dylan
Thomas-themed pub bar, adds much character. Period-style main-house
bedrooms mostly have fine views of the Bristol Channel, while further
rooms occupy the adjacent former stables. Conference/banqueting for up to
160. No dogs. *Rooms 21. Garden, hair salon. Access, Amex, Visa,* Diners Club International

---

Swansea	**Number One**	£52
Tel 0792 456996		**R**
1 Wind Street Swansea West Glamorgan SA1 1DE		Map 9 C6

The atmosphere at Kate Taylor's bistro is convivial and the seating strictly
limited, so booking is advised. There's nothing pretentious about either the
surroundings or Kate's no-nonsense cooking. Fish and shellfish are popular
choices – hot oysters with laverbread and Stilton, salmon beurre blanc,
local sea bass – while meat dishes might include rillettes of pork, braised
quail with polenta, steak en croute and venison pie. Separate menus for
desserts and cheese, with Welsh varieties heading the latter. Good-value 2-
and 3-course lunches with a small choice. *Seats 28. Parties 45. Private Room.*

L 12-2.30 D 7-9. Closed D Mon & Tue, all Sun, 25-30 Dec. Set L
£7.95/£9.95. Access, Amex, Visa.

Swansea	**Swansea Marriott**	**67%**	**£122**
Tel 0792 642020 Fax 0792 650345			**H**

Maritime Quarter Swansea West Glamorgan SA1 3SS   **Map 9 C6**

Modern, four-storey redbrick hotel in a bayside location. Good-size
bedrooms look out over either the bay or the marina. Sparse public areas.
Rooms 118. Indoor swimming pool, keep-fit equipment, spa bath, sauna. Access,
Amex, Visa, Diners Club International

Swansea   Places of Interest

Tourist Information   Tel 0792 468321.
Clyne Gardens   Tel 0792 401737.
Caswell Bay Beach.
Pembrey Motor Racing Circuit   Tel 0554 891042.
Pembrey Sands Beach.
Afan Lido Swimming Pools   Port Talbot Tel 0639 884141 *12 miles.*
St. Helen's Cricket Ground   Tel 0792 466321.
Singleton Park Showground   Tel 0792 302429.
   Theatres and Concert Halls
Brangwyn Hall   Tel 0792 470002.
Dylan Thomas Theatre   Tel 0792 473238.
Grand Theatre   Tel 0792 462028.
Taliesin Arts Centre   Tel 0792 295438.
   Museums and Art Galleries
Cery Richards Gallery   Tel 0792 295438.
Glynn Vivian Art Gallery   Tel 0792 655006/651738.
Maritime and Industrial Museum   Tel 0792 470371/650351.
Parc Howard Museum and Art Gallery   Llanelli Tel 0554 773538
   16 miles.

Talsarnau	**Maes-y-Neaudd**	**70%**	**£97**
Tel 0766 780200 Fax 0766 780211			**HR**

Talsarnau Nr Harlech Gwynedd LL47 6YA   **Map 8 C2**

A gracious, historic manor house (built of Welsh granite and slate) where
successive developments from its 14th-century origins have culminated in
conversion to a stylish hotel by the present owners. The Slatters and
Horsfalls run a smart place with extremely courteous and friendly staff.
Day rooms include a chintzy lounge, an oak-beamed bar with a fine
inglenook fireplace and a relaxing, sunlit conservatory. Imaginatively
designed and furnished, the bedrooms (four in an adjoining coach house)
vary from beamed dormers to well-proportioned Georgian rooms
containing a wealth of antique and reproduction furniture, many enjoying
fine views of Tremadoc Bay or Snowdonia National Park. A boardroom
has been created to accommodate up to 20, with banqueting for 50.
Under-5s stay free in parents' room, but at the management's discretion!
Rooms 16. Garden, croquet. Access, Amex, Visa, Diners Club International

Restaurant   £70

A five-course menu is changed daily, offering a sparse choice of starters
(smoked trout sushi with cucumber dressing or timbale of foie gras with
smoked mussels) and main dishes (beef Wellington with carrot and celeriac
purée or supreme of roast guinea fowl stuffed with pine nuts and herbs)
interspersed with soup (leek and potato) and fish (steamed pockets of sole
stuffed with parsley and chive mousse). The setting provides fabulous views
not matched by any great magic in the cooking. Diverse wine list. No
smoking. *Seats 40. Parties 14. Private Room. L 12-2 (Mon-Sat by*
arrangement) D 7-9. Set L £13.50 Set D £26.

Talyllyn   Tynycornel Hotel   59%   £80

Tel 0654 782282   Fax 0654 782679   **H**

Talyllyn Tywyn Gwynedd LL36 9AJ   Map 8 C3

Fishing is the main attraction here, but the marvellous setting on Talyllyn
Lake in Snowdonia National Park makes it a popular base for hikers and
lovers of the great outdoors. Rough shooting can also be organised. The
atmosphere is cosy and relaxed in the lounge and bar, and bedrooms have a
neat, simple appeal. Children stay free in parents' room. *Rooms 15. Garden,
outdoor swimming pool, sauna, solarium, fishing. Access, Amex, Visa,*
Diners Club International

Talyllyn Place of Interest

Talyllyn Railway and Narrow-gauge Railway Museum   Tel 0654
710472.

Tintern   Beaufort Hotel   60%   £92

Tel 0291 689777   Fax 0291 689727   **H**

Tintern Abbey Chepstow Gwent NP6 6SF   Map 9 D5

Stone-built hotel whose front rooms look out on to the ruins of 800-year-
old Tintern Abbey. Jarvis Hotels. *Rooms 24. Garden, games room. Access,
Amex, Visa,* Diners Club International

Tintern Abbey   Royal George   59%   £64

Tel 0291 689205   Fax 0291 689448   **H**

Tintern Abbey Nr Chepstow Gwent NP6 6SF   Map 9 D5

Tony and Maureen Pearce offer a warm welcome at their friendly hotel set
at the foot of a lovely wooded hillside. A trout stream runs alongside, and
the ruins of Tintern Abbey are just a short walk away. There's ample bar
and lounge space (one lounge is stocked with board games) and a function
room that can accommodate 120 for banquets or 80 for conferences. Some
of the bedrooms have balconies overlooking the gardens. One child under
14 free when sharing with two adults; each additional child £6. Ten
rooms are suitable for family occupation. *Rooms 19. Garden, fishing.
Access, Amex, Visa,* Diners Club International

Tintern   Places of Interest

Tourist Information   Tel 0291 689431.
Tintern Abbey   Tel 0291 624647.

Trellech   Village Green   £64

Tel 0600 860119   **RR**

Trellech Nr Monmouth Gwent NP5 4PA   Map 9 D5

Jane and Bob Evans work hard to create warmth and atmosphere while
housing two types of diner in a single setting. The bistro-esque blackboard
menu offers a long choice with cut-price quality in the brasserie:
fisherman's pie, fritto misto, Brie and broccoli pithiviers are typical of up
to eighteen main courses on offer. The à la carte menu in the restaurant
might include crab and courgette strudel with pimento sauce, rum and
orange-flavoured duck and pork terrine or carrot mousse with coriander
butter sauce to start, followed by roulade of salmon and sole, duck breast
Montmorency, tournedos en croute or pork tenderloin with a creamy
curry sauce and soft fruits. Very short wine list. *Seats 70. Parties 24. Private
Room. L 12-1.45 D 7-9.45 (Sat to 10). Closed D Sun, all Mon (open D Bank
Holidays), 10 days Jan. Access, Visa.*

Rooms   £45

An adjacent stable conversion houses two basic, en-suite cottagey bedrooms
(in phone-free privacy); one double, one twin. Bed and breakfast or self-
catering terms.

Welsh Hook   Stone Hall

£52

RR

Tel 0348 840212   Fax 0348 840815

Welsh Hook Wolfscastle Nr Haverfordwest Dyfed SA62 5NS

Map 9 A5

Check directions carefully to seek out this charming 14th-century manor house hidden down lanes near Wolfscastle. Owner Martine Watson oversees while new chef Remi Faubel cooks an imaginative French carte, though plainer dishes may be requested from a shorter table d'hote. *Coquilles St Jacques à la bretonne, grenadin de veau aux princes des montagnes* and *gratinée de fruits rouges* are indicative of the former. English translations and recommendations from a French-dominated wine list are impeccably handled by host Dr Alan Watson. *Seats 34. Parties 45. Private Room. D only 7.30-9.30. Closed Mon Dec-Mar, 2 weeks Dec. Set D £13.50. Access, Amex, Visa.*

Rooms

£53

Three double and two single bedrooms, all with neat bathrooms, are simply furnished and softly decorated. Residents have a private lounge for post-prandial relaxation.

Channel Islands
& Isle of Man

Alderney

St Anne	Inchalla Hotel	63%	£70

Tel 0481 823220   Fax 0481 823551

HR

The Val St Anne Alderney

Map 3 F4

Valerie Wills and her young staff run this small, modern hotel with care and enthusiasm, and all is kept spotlessly clean. Public areas include a homely lounge with patio doors opening on to the lawn, and one of the east-facing bedrooms also has patio doors and a little paved area with seating. All the rooms are bright and cheerful, with simple wood-effect laminate units. No dogs. *Rooms 11. Garden, sauna, solarium, spa bath. Closed 1 week Xmas/New Year. Access, Amex, Visa.*

Restaurant

£38

Seafood is always of a good quality – from oven-baked crab claws and seafood soup to Dover sole, skate, plaice, catch of the day and crab and lobster salads – but meat dishes are also well executed. Vegetarian options and desserts served from a trolley. Traditional Sunday roast lunches. *Seats 35. Parties 22. L (Sun only) 1-2 D 7-8.45. Closed D Sun. Set L £10.90 Set D £12.*

Guernsey

Pleinmont	Imperial Hotel	£54

Tel 0481 64044

I

Pleinmont Torteval Guernsey

Map 3 E4

Rocquaine Bay is only 60 yards away, and the gardens, bar and restaurant face the sea. Day rooms make the most of the setting, so, too, most of the bright, simple bedrooms, some of which have balconies and all of which are now en suite and have direct-dial telephones. The Portelet Bar is a popular local meeting place. Terms can be quoted inclusive of car hire. No dogs. "Children welcome if well behaved." *Rooms 17. Access, Visa.*

St Martin	St Margaret's Lodge	63%	£80

Tel 0481 35757   Fax 0481 37594

H

Forest Road St Martin Guernsey

Map 3 E4

Midway between the airport and St. Peter Port, the lodge is close to the south coast with its beaches and cliff paths. The modern interior includes a comfortable lounge and lounge bar. Bedrooms, all with en-suite facilities, include three suites. Guests can take a twice-daily courtesy coach for shopping in town. Conference/banqueting for 120. *Rooms 47. Garden, outdoor swimming pool, sauna, solarium. Access, Amex, Visa.*

St Martin	La Trelade Hotel	61%	£70

Tel 0481 35454   Fax 0481 37855

H

Forest Road St Martin Guernsey

Map 3 E4

A holiday hotel in its own grounds off the main airport road. Two split-level lounge areas have modern brown leather-look seating, and the bar has smart and comfortable salmon-pink upholstery. Bedrooms are decent-sized and are equipped with simple white built-in units and clean bathrooms, some with shower and bath, others with shower only. Friendly staff. Families are well catered for with a children's play area and both baby-sitting and baby-listening available. *Rooms 45. Garden, outdoor swimming pool, putting, croquet, gamesroom, dinner dance (Friday). Access, Amex, Visa,*

St Peter Port   Absolute End

Tel 0481 723822

£50

R

St George's Esplanade St Peter Port Guernsey

Map 3 E4

On the seafront about a mile from the town centre, this is a pretty,
cottagey restaurant specialising in fish and shellfish. The choice runs from
home-smoked brill, salmon and trout to prawn pancakes, salmon en croute
and Dover sole grilled or meunière. Some meat dishes, too, and a decent
choice for vegetarians. Good-value table d'hote lunch. Garden terrace for
summer eating. *Seats 60. Parties 50. Private Room. L 12-2 D 7-10. Closed
Sun, Jan. Set L £10. Access, Amex, Visa,*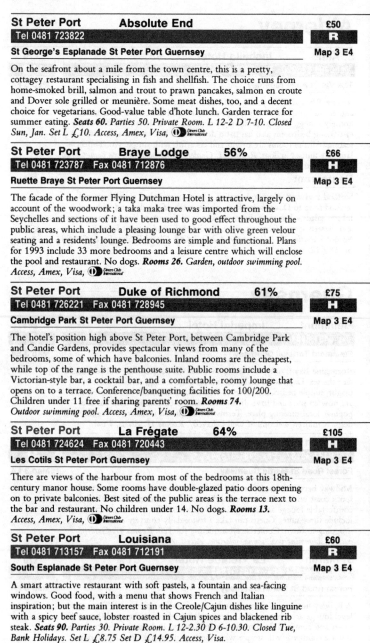

St Peter Port   Braye Lodge   56%

Tel 0481 723787   Fax 0481 712876

£66

H

Ruette Braye St Peter Port Guernsey

Map 3 E4

The facade of the former Flying Dutchman Hotel is attractive, largely on
account of the woodwork; a taka maka tree was imported from the
Seychelles and sections of it have been used to good effect throughout the
public areas, which include a pleasing lounge bar with olive green velour
seating and a residents' lounge. Bedrooms are simple and functional. Plans
for 1993 include 33 more bedrooms and a leisure centre which will enclose
the pool and restaurant. No dogs. *Rooms 26. Garden, outdoor swimming pool.
Access, Amex, Visa,*

St Peter Port   Duke of Richmond   61%

Tel 0481 726221   Fax 0481 728945

£75

H

Cambridge Park St Peter Port Guernsey

Map 3 E4

The hotel's position high above St Peter Port, between Cambridge Park
and Candie Gardens, provides spectacular views from many of the
bedrooms, some of which have balconies. Inland rooms are the cheapest,
while top of the range is the penthouse suite. Public rooms include a
Victorian-style bar, a cocktail bar, and a comfortable, roomy lounge that
opens on to a terrace. Conference/banqueting facilities for 100/200.
Children under 11 free if sharing parents' room. *Rooms 74.
Outdoor swimming pool. Access, Amex, Visa,*

St Peter Port   La Frégate   64%

Tel 0481 724624   Fax 0481 720443

£105

H

Les Cotils St Peter Port Guernsey

Map 3 E4

There are views of the harbour from most of the bedrooms at this 18th-
century manor house. Some rooms have double-glazed patio doors opening
on to private balconies. Best sited of the public areas is the terrace next to
the bar and restaurant. No children under 14. No dogs. *Rooms 13.
Access, Amex, Visa,*

St Peter Port   Louisiana

Tel 0481 713157   Fax 0481 712191

£60

R

South Esplanade St Peter Port Guernsey

Map 3 E4

A smart attractive restaurant with soft pastels, a fountain and sea-facing
windows. Good food, with a menu that shows French and Italian
inspiration; but the main interest is in the Creole/Cajun dishes like linguine
with a spicy beef sauce, lobster roasted in Cajun spices and blackened rib
steak. *Seats 90. Parties 30. Private Room. L 12-2.30 D 6-10.30. Closed Tue,
Bank Holidays. Set L £8.75 Set D £14.95. Access, Visa.*

St Peter Port	Le Nautique		£50
Tel 0481 721714			**R**
The Quay Steps St Peter Port Guernsey			Map 3 E4

Long-established French restaurant standing on the seafront, overlooking
the harbour. Fish is the pick of the menu, as you might expect, with
turbot, monkfish, skate, cod, Dover sole and sea bass either simply grilled
or with a selection of classic sauces (dugléré, meunière, hollandaise).
Guernsey lobster is offered grilled and flambéed with whisky, Thermidor,
or cold with mayonnaise and salad. Duck, lamb, and steaks are also popular
and there's a selection of three vegetarian dishes. Service is polished and
efficient, booking essential. Smart dress is preferred. Short wine list with
many bottles also offered in halves. *Seats 68. Parties 30. Private Room.
L 12-2 D 7-10. Closed Sun, 1st 2 wks Jan. Access, Amex, Visa,*

St Peter Port	Old Government House	68%	£110
Tel 0481 724921 Fax 0481 724429			**H**
Ann's Place St Peter Port Guernsey			Map 3 E4

Traditional standards of decor and service are to be found at this hillside
hotel, where the classically elegant entrance hall is a reminder of the days
when it actually was the Governor's residence. The Governor's Bar is cosy
and intimate with its military memorabilia and the Centenary Bar, opened
in 1958 to mark 100 years of the hotel's existence, features dancing to the
hotel band Monday to Saturday in summer and weekends in winter. Best
bedrooms are in a modern wing. Conference/banqueting facilities for 150.
Rooms 72. Garden, outdoor swimming pool, solarium. Access, Amex, Visa,

St Peter Port	St Pierre Park	70%	£125
Tel 0481 728282 Fax 0481 712041			**H**
Rohais St Peter Port Guernsey			Map 3 E4

A short drive from St Peter Port, set in 45 acres of parkland that include a
9-hole golf course designed by Tony Jacklin and extensive leisure facilities
with three tennis courts. Bedrooms, most of them with balconies, are
furnished with built-in units and offer plenty of writing space and up-to-
date accessories. Bright day rooms running off the foyer include a terrace
lounge/bar that overlooks a large ornamental lake. Families are well catered
for with a children's playground, a children's menu served in Café Renoir
up to 7pm and both baby-sitting and baby-listening available.
Conference/banqueting facilities for up to 200. *Rooms 135. Garden, indoor
swimming pool, spa bath, sauna, solarium, beauty & hair salons, snooker,
gymnasium, tennis, 9-hole golf course, coffee shop (10am-10pm), dinner dance
(Saturday in summer). Access, Amex, Visa,*

Herm

Herm	White House	64%	£110*
Tel 0481 722159 Fax 0481 710066			**H**
Herm			Map 3 E4

A few steps from the beach, the only hotel on car-less Herm island has
recently added a conservatory to the restaurant and six further bedrooms,
all of which have sea views. Quiet, comfortable accommodation and
beautiful views are on offer, along with two welcoming lounges with open
fires, chesterfields, ornaments and magazines. The bar is made from a
German ammunition hut. Self-catering cottages and flats also available.
Children under 6 stay free in low season only. * Half-board terms only.
No dogs. *Rooms 38. Garden, outdoor swimming pool, tennis. Closed 11 Oct-15
Mar. Access, Visa.*

Jersey

Bouley Bay	**Water's Edge Hotel**	**68%**	**£110**

Tel 0534 862777   Fax 0534 63645

H

The Slipway Bouley Bay Trinity Jersey JE3 5AS

Map 3 F4

A large terrace, picture windows in the bar/lounge and balconies on eight
bedrooms take full advantage of the view over a picturesque harbour. You
enter via a splendid marble-floored foyer which gives on to the
characterful Black Dog Bar with a popular snack menu. Bedrooms are
good-sized, with pretty decor. Families are well catered for with children's
meals offered, baby-sitting and wonderful gardens in which children can
let off steam. 15 minutes from St Helier by car. *Rooms 51. Garden, outdoor
swimming pool, sauna, solarium, coffee shop (10am-5.30pm). Closed Nov-Apr.
Access, Amex, Visa,* 🔵 *Diners Club International*

Gorey	**Jersey Pottery**	↑	**£57**

Tel 0534 51119

R

Gorey Jersey

Map 3 F4

🫖

Not far from Gorey village, this remarkable pottery-cum-restaurant tourist
complex continues to show others how it should be done. Clever
landscaping and building design provide cool, leafy gardens and terraces to
enjoy excellent quality produce, whether from the self-service café or from
the more pampering restaurant. The reputation is built on the freshest of
seafood served generously and stylishly with, perhaps, steamed mussels with
a surprisingly complementary cider-based sauce, or melon halves heaped
with prawns and picked crab to start; lobster salad or the huge seafood
platters of extraordinary diversity to follow. A tempting display of home-
made tarts, cakes and pastries to finish. Well-thought-out wine list, slick
friendly service. A walk around the pottery factory and gift shop may aid
digestion but not the wallet. Note early closing time. *Seats 300. Parties
300. Meals 9-5.30. Closed Sat & Sun, Bank Holidays, 10 days Xmas.
Access, Amex, Visa,* 🔵 *Diners Club International*

Gorey	**Moorings Hotel**	**62%**	**£90**

Tel 0534 53633   Fax 0534 56660

H

Gorey Pier Gorey Jersey JE3 6EW

Map 3 F4

A small, friendly waterfront hotel between Mont Orgueil Castle and
Gorey Harbour. It's also just a short distance from Grouville Bay beach.
Two bars provide a choice for relaxing over a drink, and there's a lounge
and roof garden. Bedrooms are furnished in simple style, and three are
suitable for family occupation. Baby-listening available. Free use of
swimming pool and night club in sister hotel one mile away. No dogs.
Rooms 16. Access, Amex, Visa.

Gorey	**Old Court House**	**64%**	**£90**

Tel 0534 54444   Fax 0534 53587

H

Gorey Jersey JE3 9EX

Map 3 F4

On the edge of Gorey, and handy for Royal Bay beach, the Old Court
House is a popular place for family holidays. Public areas include a beamed
restaurant dating in part from the 15th century. New-wing bedrooms have
balconies, while the pleasant older rooms are more spacious. No dogs.
*Rooms 58. Garden, outdoor swimming pool, sauna. Closed Nov-Feb.
Access, Amex, Visa,* 🔵 *Diners Club International*

Havre des Pas   Ommaroo Hotel   58%   £70

Tel 0534 23493   Fax 0534 59912   **H**

Havre des Pas St Helier Jersey JE2 4UQ   Map 3 F4

Traditional seaside hotel whose best rooms (available at a supplement) have
sea-facing balconies. Bedrooms recently redecorated. Emphasis on
friendliness and service. Children free up to the age of two, thereafter 50%;
baby-sitting and baby-listening services available. *Rooms 85. Garden.
Closed Nov-Feb. Access, Amex, Visa,*

Havre des Pas   Hotel de la Plage   66%   £100

Tel 0534 23474   Fax 0534 68642   **H**

Havre des Pas St Helier Jersey JE2 4UQ   Map 3 F4

A well-run modern hotel on the seafront, with picture windows to
enhance the views. Day rooms are in various styles: subdued and modern
in the split-level lounge-bar, tropical in the Caribbean bar, bamboo in the
sun lounge. Sea-facing bedrooms have balconies; inland-view rooms are
cheaper. Baby-sitting by arrangement. No dogs. *Rooms 78. Keep-fit
facilities, solarium, games room. Closed end Oct-early Apr. Access, Amex, Visa,*

Portelet Bay   Portelet Hotel   66%   £100

Tel 0534 41204   Fax 0534 46625   **H**

Portelet Bay St Brelade Jersey   Map 3 F4

A modern, straightforward, but comfortable hotel where everything is
well kept. Most popular of the public rooms is the sun lounge overlooking
the pool to St Brelade's Bay beyond. Elsewhere there's a quiet residents'
lounge and a 70s-style cocktail bar. Many bedrooms have balconies and all
are welcoming with flowers and fruit. Free early-morning tea or coffee and
paper, mini-bus to town. No dogs. *Rooms 86. Garden, outdoor swimming
pool, putting, games room. Closed Oct-Apr. Access, Amex, Visa,*

Rozel Bay   Château la Chaire   74%   £105

Tel 0534 863354   Fax 0534 865137   **HR**

Rozel Valley Rozel Jersey   Map 3 F4

Chateau La Chaire stands in seven acres of wooded grounds just minutes
from the picturesque harbour of Rozel Bay. In the splendid panelled
entrance hall a wide oak staircase takes the eye and the drawing room is
grand, with chandelier, hand-painted pewter moulding, pillars and
traditional futniture. Next door is Raymond's Bar, which has yet more
panelling and chandeliers, and dark bamboo-style furniture. The elegant
ambience continues in the bedrooms, which have classically styled
furniture, well-co-ordinated colour schemes, fresh flowers and ornaments;
the carpeted bathrooms have brass fittings and quality toiletries and some
boast jacuzzis. *Rooms 14. Garden. Access, Amex, Visa,*

Restaurant   £76

The dining room is elegant, with oak-panelled walls and a pretty, non-
smoking conservatory. There's also a terrace for alfresco eating. David
Tilbury and his team produce a very varied modern menu typified by
terrine of freshwater fish set on a pool of watercress sauce, cream of
asparagus and mussel soup and pavé of veal loin with sautéed spinach and
peppered lemon grass sauce. Summer pudding (with of course Jersey
cream) is a popular seasonal dessert. *Seats 70. Parties 32. Private Room.
L 12.15-2 (Sun to 2.15) D 7-10 (Sun & Bank Holidays to 9.30).
Set L £10.25 Set D £21.50.*

Rozel Bay   Granite Corner   ★   £82

Tel 0534 863590   Fax 0534 864362   **R**

Rozel Harbour Trinity Jersey   **Map 3 F4**

Though still the most serious authentically French cooking on the Island,
inconsistencies and imperfections can sometimes appear in Jean-Luc Robin's
otherwise exemplary operation. A pleasing cottagey room stands right on
the picturesque little harbour (parking is difficult in season). The fixed-
price four-course menu offers exceptional value. The carte tends toward
more classical elements: scallops simply handled with a faultless beurre
blanc, a delicate salmon terrine slightly masked by a vigorous herb cream,
richly flavoured mushroom soup. Main courses are equally rich: noisettes
of lamb (tender and pink) with a herb crust and roast shallots, large fillet of
beef Rossini (both topped with a tranche of foie gras). A good choice of
cheese, but it was clumsily served and in poor condition on a recent visit.
Louise Robin looks after front of house. *Seats 25. Parties 8.* L 12.30-1.30
(Sun to 2) D 7.30-9 *(Sat to 9.30). Closed L Mon, D Sun. Set L £12.
Access, Visa.*

St Aubin   La Haule Manor   60%   £62

Tel 0534 41426   **H**

La Haule St Aubin Jersey   **Map 3 F4**

An 18th-century manor house only a few yards from the beach. First
registered as a hotel in 1952, it's a pleasant spot and a good base for
touring. Fresh flowers add a splash of colour to the bedrooms, many of
which enjoy sea views. Children up to seven stay free in parents' room.
There's a large function facility catering for up to 160 for a banquet, 200
for a conference. *Rooms 20. Garden. Access, Amex, Visa,* ●)

St Aubin   Old Court House Inn   £80

Tel 0534 46433   Fax 0534 45103   **I**

St Aubin Jersey   **Map 3 F4**

Modern comforts and old-world charm in a tall, handsome house dating
back to 1450 and overlooking the harbour. It's a family-run
hotel/restaurant/inn with a young outlook and a popular alfresco eating
trade. The beamed cellar bars and upstairs Mizzen Bar (well-known to
Bergerac fans as the *Royal Barge* pub) are favourite rendezvous. Bedrooms,
the best with harbour views, are furnished with old pine. No dogs.
Rooms 9. Closed 25 & 26 Dec. Access, Visa.

St Brelade   Atlantic Hotel   70%   £120

Tel 0534 44101   Fax 0534 44102   **H**

La Moye St Brelade Jersey JE3 8HE   **Map 3 F4**

A functional 70s' block high above St Ouen's Bay, the Atlantic Hotel is
surrounded by three acres of grounds. All rooms have balconies to take
advantage of the views (of either La Moye golf course or the bay and sea)
and are furnished to a very high standard, with top-quality mahogany
furniture, fine floral fabrics and Chinese-style china; some of the larger
rooms have sofa beds and the Garden studios and two luxury suites have
their own terraces. In the spacious entrance hall, glazed terracotta flooring,
brown leather armchairs and a pool with waterfall please the eye; another
major feature is the Palm Club, a well-equipped health and leisure centre.
Children up to 14 stay free in parents' room. No dogs. *Rooms 50. Garden,
indoor & outdoor swimming pools, sauna, solarium, spa bath, keep-fit equipment,
tennis. Closed Jan & Feb. Access, Amex, Visa,* ●)

St Brelade   Hotel Chateau Valeuse   64%   £76

Tel 0534 46281   Fax 0534 47110   **H**

Rue de la Valeuse St Brelade Jersey JE3 8EE   **Map 3 F4**

A friendly, relaxed hotel (now under new ownership) in the sweep of St
Brelade's Bay. The gardens are quite a feature, and in sunny weather drinks
and snacks are served alfresco. Inside are two lounges and the Tudor Bar.
Many of the bedrooms have south-facing balconies, some overlooking the
garden and pool. No children under five. No dogs. *Rooms 33. Outdoor
swimming pool. Closed Nov-Mar. Access, Visa.*

St Brelade   La Place Hotel   67%   £110

Tel 0534 44261   Fax 0534 45164   **H**

Route du Coin La Haule St Brelade Jersey JE3 8BF   **Map 3 F4**

Once a farmhouse but now much enlarged by modern extensions, La Place
is for those who like rural surroundings. The main public rooms are part
of the original, 400-year-old building. There's a delightful open-air seating
area in a south-facing courtyard, a bright bar with green bamboo furniture
and two lounges, one of which has a black-beamed ceiling, a pink granite
fireplace, antique furniture and polished brass ornaments. Many of the
bedrooms have been recently refurbished, including seven around the pool.
Children up to seven stay free in parents' room; children's high tea is
offered. *Rooms 40. Outdoor swimming pool, sauna. Access, Amex, Visa,*
Diners Club International

St Brelade   Sea Crest   62%   £79

Tel 0534 46353   Fax 0534 47316   **HR**

Petit Port St Brelade Jersey JE3 8HH   **Map 3 F4**

Julian and Martha Bernstein are personally in charge of their relaxing
white-painted hotel, which overlooks a rocky bay at the south-west end of
the island. Day rooms, which feature modern artwork, include a cocktail
bar opening on to a sun lounge and terrace. Best of the bedrooms are five
with balconies. Children under five stay free in parents' room. No dogs.
*Rooms 7. Garden, outdoor swimming pool. Closed mid Jan-mid Feb.
Access, Amex, Visa.*

Restaurant   £68

Local seafood appears regularly on a traditional menu which includes dishes
prepared at the table. Book a table by the window for the best views.
*Seats 60. Parties 20. L 12.30-2 (Sun to 3) D 7.30-10. Closed all Mon, also
D Sun in winter. Set L £10 Set D £16.*

St Brelade's Bay   Hotel L'Horizon   72%   £90

Tel 0534 43101   Fax 0534 46269   **H**

St Brelade's Bay Jersey   **Map 3 F4**

Leisure facilities shine at this Clipper hotel, which overlooks a sandy beach
in the heart of St Brelade's Bay. Club L'Horizon is a well-equipped centre
for relaxing or keeping fit, and a 40ft motor yacht is available for day
charter. Public areas include a bar with picture windows and beach views,
a drawing room, a library and three restaurants. Good-sized bedrooms have
decent-quality furniture and well-equipped bathrooms. At certain times
(out of season) children can stay free in their parents' room; baby-sitting
can be arranged. Banqueting/conference facilities for 200+. No dogs.
*Rooms 104. Garden, indoor swimming pool, sauna, solarium, spa bath, keep-fit
equipment, hairdressing, coffee shop (10am-midnight). Access, Visa.*

St Brelade's Bay   St Brelade's Bay Hotel   70%

£134

H

Tel 0534 46141   Fax 0534 47278

St Brelade's Bay Jersey

Map 3 F4

This smartly whitewashed, low-level hotel bears evidence of the long-term care and pride heaped upon it by the Colley family. Behind it is a lovely garden set with sun-loungers where parents can relax while a lifeguard teaches their children to swim; inside, an airy, spacious foyer leads you to the elegant and comfortable lounge, with antiques, chesterfields, parquet floors and beautiful rugs. There's live music in the cocktail bar, and a club room and games room for younger guests. First- and second-floor rooms are traditional, while those on the third floor are more modern; all are attractively and tastefully decorated and furnished. Families are well catered for. *Rooms 82. Garden, croquet, outdoor swimming pool, sauna, solarium, games room, tennis, putting. Closed 12 Oct-29 Apr. Access, Visa.*

St Clement's Bay   Hotel Ambassadeur   63%

£70

H

Tel 0534 24455   Fax 0534 23185

St Clement's Bay Jersey

Map 3 F4

Modern hotel with simple decor and new owners. There's a spacious, sunny lounge and a cocktail bar. Best rooms overloook the bay and have large patio windows and wrought-iron balustrades. *Rooms 69. Outdoor swimming pool, games room. Closed 3 Jan-15 Feb. Access, Amex, Visa.*

St Helier   Apollo Hotel   63%

£84

H

Tel 0534 25441   Fax 0534 22120

9 St Saviour's Road St Helier Jersey JE2 4LA

Map 3 F4

A modern two-storey hotel built round a courtyard. Public areas provide plenty of space to relax: there are two bars (one in pub style), a coffee shop serving snacks throughout the day, an indoor leisure centre and a sun-trap terrace. Bedrooms, some with balconies, include many suitable for family occupation. *Rooms 85. Indoor swimming pool, spa bath, sauna, solarium, gymnasium, coffee shop (10am-9pm). Access, Amex, Visa,* **D** Diners Club International

St Helier   Beaufort Hotel   60%

£90

H

Tel 0534 32471   Fax 0534 20371

Green Street St Helier Jersey

Map 3 F4

A few minutes' walk from the beach and the town centre, this friendly modern hotel offers comfortable accommodation, free car parking and leisure facilities. A pianist plays nightly in the bar, and the large terrace is fun when the sun shines. Bedrooms each have two armchairs. Suites and four-poster rooms available. No dogs. *Rooms 54. Indoor swimming pool, spa bath, sauna, solarium, games room (summer). Access, Amex, Visa,* **D** Diners Club International

St Helier   La Capannina

£60

R

Tel 0534 34602   Fax 0534 77626

65 Halkett Place St Helier Jersey

Map 3 F4

Popular and cheerful Italian restaurant whose standard menu is supplemented by daily specials – usually seafood, such as lobster bisque, stuffed clams, red mullet or brill meunière. 10% service and "£2 cover charge when applicable." *Seats 130. Parties 40. Private Room. L 12-2 D 7-10. Closed Sun, Bank Holidays, 1 week Xmas. Access, Visa,* **D** Diners Club International

St Helier   Grand Hotel   68%

£117

HR

Tel 0534 22301   Fax 0534 37815

The Esplanade St Helier Jersey JE4 8WD

Map 3 F4

The long, gabled frontage of the Grand is a distinctive feature on the seafront and the entrance is appropriately impressive, with ornate, coloured pillars and a marble floor. The smart period-style bar and lounge have fine

views and so do balconied front bedrooms, which attract a hefty surcharge.
It's a busy hotel catering for both holiday and business visitors
(conference/banqueting facilities for 180/250). Families are well catered for
with free accommodation for under-14s in their parents' room, plus baby-
sitting and special children's meals also available. De Vere Hotels.
*Rooms 115. Indoor swimming pool, sauna, solarium, spa bath, keep-fit
equipment, beauty salon, hairdressing, snooker, news kiosk, garage.*
Access, Amex, Visa, (i) Diners Club International

Victoria's   £70

Polished service, elegant appointments, and a traditional French/British à la
carte menu (plus a limited choice, fixed-price menu) that features fresh fish   ♕
and shellfish – typically, moules marseillaise, paupiette of sole, prawn
consommé, crab soup with seaweed and daily specials. Vegetarian main
dishes are available, often featuring mushrooms as a favoured ingredient.
Dancing to live music every evening; gentlemen should wear jackets and
ties. Breakfast and dinner are also served in the Regency restaurant. 10%
service is automatically added to the fixed-price menus. *Seats 250.*
L 12.15-2.15 D 7-10 (Sun to 9.30). Set L £14 Set D £19.50.

St Helier   Pomme d'Or Hotel   65%   £85

Tel 0534 78644   Fax 0534 37781   **H**
The Esplanade St Helier Jersey JE2 3NF   Map 3 F4

A convenient harbourside location in the town centre helps make this
large, white-painted and green-tiled hotel popular with tourists. Air-
conditioned public rooms include Le Pommier coffee shop and The Wharf
pub. Pleasant, well-designed bedrooms and spotless bathrooms are equipped
with everything needed for a comfortable stay. Conference/banqueting
facilities for 300. No dogs. *Rooms 150. Coffee shop (7am-11pm).*
Access, Amex, Visa, (i) Diners Club International

St Lawrence   Little Grove   73%   £132

Tel 0534 25321   Fax 0534 25325   **HR**
Rue du Haut St Lawrence Jersey JE3 1JQ   Map 3 F4

Built of local pink granite in the 18th-century, Little Grove provides a
pleasant mix of traditional charm and modern comfort. A welcoming
reception area leads you to an intimate library with bottle-green leather
armchairs and sage-green wing chairs, a bar with plum-striped sofas and
more green leather chairs, plus a lounge with a fine granite fireplace. The
bedrooms are good-sized and boast period-style furniture in light woods.
Well-co-ordinated chintzy fabrics and antique pieces, bathrooms have
ceramic tile floors, shower risers or cubicles, quality brass fittings, good
toiletries and bathrobes. No children under 12. No dogs. *Rooms 13.*
Garden, croquet, outdoor swimming pool. Access, Amex, Visa, (i) Diners Club International

Old Masters Restaurant   £65

Sunny summer days find lunch served under parasols on the warm south-
facing terrace, but eating inside is equally pleasurable with 16th and 17th-   ♕
century Dutch paintings on the walls. The menus are short and imaginative   ♟
offering modern dishes which are artistically presented. Local fish and
shellfish are featured and some vegetables, herbs, eggs and honey are home-   🍶
produced. Some typical dishes: mussels in a saffron-infused sauce with
croutons and rouille, terrine wrapped in herb pancakes dressed with a
hazelnut vinaigrette, kidneys roasted in their own fat served with wild rice   🫖
and a shallot and madeira sauce, Scottish salmon stuffed with lobster
mousse set on a basil-flavoured butter sauce. *Seats 38. Parties 20.*
Private Room. L 12.30-1.45 D 7.30-9.30. Set L £12.50 Set D £17.50.

St Peter	**Mermaid Hotel**	64%	£90

Tel 0534 41255   Fax 0534 45826   **H**

Airport Road St Peter Jersey JE3 7BN   Map 3 F4

Guests, once drawn to the peace afforded by the 18 acres of grounds and
gardens featuring a small ornamental lake, are now also attracted to the
indoor leisure complex with the hotel almost built around the indoor
swimming pool. A new outdoor pool has also recently been added.
Bedrooms are standard in decor, pleasant and bright, with carpeted,
compact bathrooms. The pubby Tavern bar is heavily beamed and has a
sun-trap terrace. A child up to 12 can stay free in parents' room. No dogs.
*Rooms 68. Garden, indoor swimming pool, spa bath, sauna, tennis, keep-fit
equipment, putting. Access, Amex, Visa,*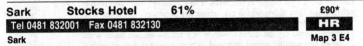

Sark

Sark	**Aval Du Creux**	57%	£63

Tel 0481 832036   Fax 0481 832368   **HR**

Sark   Map 3 E4

Peter and Cheryl Tonks's friendly little hotel started life as a farmhouse.
Public rooms consist of two simply furnished lounges with a homely
appeal and a small bar hung with local pictures. There are six bedrooms in
the main house, six smaller ones in the annexe. Four are suitable for family
use. Modest shower rooms are clean and tidy. *Rooms 12. Garden, outdoor
swimming pool, children's splash pool, boules. Closed Oct-Apr. Access, Visa.*

Restaurant   £52

Seafood plays the leading role here, with local crab served hot in a shell
with cheese glaze, plus oysters, lobster (surf'n'turf) and monkfish. Fresh
asparagus from Guernsey (in season) and pan-fried pigeon breast with
gingerbread sauce, and guinea fowl in filo pastry with sweet red peppers
show that care is taken not only in preparation but also in attaining quality
ingredients. *Seats 40. Parties 32. Private Room. L 12-2 D 7-8. Set D £15.95.*

Sark	**Hotel Petit Champ**	61%	£66

Tel 0481 832046   **H**

Sark   Map 3 E4

Splendid sea views are a feature at this small hotel, now under new
ownership. There's a tiny bar, leafy sun lounges and a quiet, homely
lounge. Bedrooms are best described as cosy and undisturbed by TVs or
telephones; some rooms have sliding patio doors. No children under seven.
No dogs. *Rooms 16. Garden, outdoor swimming pool, putting, horse & carriage
hire, sea fishing, yacht charters. Closed Oct-Easter. Access, Amex, Visa,*
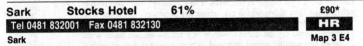

Sark	**Stocks Hotel**	61%	£90*

Tel 0481 832001   Fax 0481 832130   **HR**

Sark   Map 3 E4

Following four years of uncertainty, the Armorgie family have now
purchased the hotel and restaurants outright, demonstrating their long-term
commitment to their business. Peace and relaxation come without too
much trouble, with a homely atmosphere in the lounge, and comfortable,
unfussy bedrooms decorated with darkwood furniture and floral fabrics.
No TVs in the rooms. * Half-board terms only. *Rooms 25. Garden, outdoor
swimming pool, coffee shop (10am-10pm). Closed mid Oct-Easter. Access, Visa,*
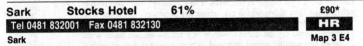

Cider Press Restaurant   £50

Both table d'hote and à la carte menus are offered, with local fish and
shellfish always featuring on both. Moules marinière, mackerel, oysters,
Sark rabbit, lobster and crab, plus regular pasta dishes are all typical
offerings. Traditional roast lunch every Sunday; "all-weather barbecue
lunch" served on the front lawn or inside. Coffee, lunch, cream teas and
light evening meals served in the *Courtyard Bistro*, with alfresco tables in
summer adjacent to the swimming pool; children's supper menu served
here from 5.30-7pm. **Seats 60.** *Parties 12. Private Room. L 12-2.30 D 7.30-9
(Sun to 9). Set L £9.50 Set D £16.50.*

Isle of Man

Ballasalla   La Rosette   £72
Tel 0624 822940   R

Main Road Ballasalla   Map 13 B6

Local seafood, including crab and queenies (little scallops), and
straightforward meat dishes get simple classic treatment in a French-style
restaurant with several alcoves and private rooms. Fixed-price lunches offer
three courses with a good choice, except for "the dessert of the day".
*Seats 45. Parties 18. Private Room. L 12-3 D 7-10. Closed Sun, 1st 2 weeks
Jan. Set L £12.50. Access, Visa.*

Douglas   Palace Hotel   65%   £85
Tel 0624 662662   Fax 0624 625535   H

Central Promenade Douglas   Map 13 B6

The excellent leisure complex, with its own bar/café, the cinemas, the
night club and the public casino provide plenty of entertainment for guests
at the modern Palace, one of the focal points of the island's night life. Other
day rooms are smart and spacious, and bedrooms, though not large, are
quite well equipped. There are four suites. Banqueting and conference
facilities for 300+. Pleasant, helpful staff. No dogs. *Rooms 135. Indoor
swimming pool, sauna, solarium, spa bath, beauty & hair salon, casino, night
club, coffee shop (7am-10pm). Access, Amex, Visa,* (D) *Diners Club International*

Douglas   Sefton Hotel   63%   £65
Tel 0624 626011   Fax 0624 676004   H

Harris Promenade Douglas   Map 13 B6

A turn-of-the-century seafront hotel with smart rooms behind its grand
white frontage. The spacious interior is modern with just a hint of days
gone by. An art deco carvery restaurant, neatly decorated coffee shop and
swish cocktail bar all add to the comfortable feel. There are good sea views
from both the lounge and the balconies of the best bedrooms. Popular for
weekend and special breaks (golf, rambling, bird-watching etc). Conference
and banqueting facilities for 100. *Rooms 80. Indoor swimming pool, spa bath,
sauna, solarium, steam rooms, keep-fit equipment, beauty salon, coffee shop
(9.45am-11pm). Access, Amex, Visa,* (D) *Diners Club International*

Ramsey   Grand Island Hotel   67%   £80
Tel 0624 812455   Fax 0624 815291   H

Bride Road Ramsey   Map 13 B5

On the coast a mile from Ramsey, the handsome white-painted hotel looks
down past terraced lawns to Ramsey Bay. Originally a Georgian manor
house, it has a traditional look and feel, and there are a few antiques among
the furnishings. Bedrooms are done out prettily, with pinks and blues
predominating. There are extensive conference facilities (for up to 500
delegates). *Rooms 54. Garden, croquet, putting, indoor swimming pool, spa
bath, sauna, steam room, beauty and hair salon, snooker, coarse fishing.
Access, Amex, Visa,* (D) *Diners Club International*

Ramsey   Harbour Bistro   £45

Tel 0624 814182   R

5 East Street Ramsey   Map 13 B5

Fish and shellfish, much of it landed on the nearby quay, is the chief
attraction of this friendly, informal bistro. Available as starter or main
course, the choice ranges from queenies (succulent little scallops, a Manx
speciality) to crisp-fried fillets of plaice, a sauté of giant prawns and the
ever-popular fisherman's pie. Plenty of meat options, too, and some
naughty desserts ("To hell with the calorie count – let's enjoy ourselves"
says the menu). **Seats 46.** Parties 20. L 12.15-2.30 D 6.30-10.30. Closed
Xmas, Good Friday, 2 weeks Oct. Set L £9.95. Access, Visa.

Northern Ireland

Annalong   Glassdrumman House   69%   £85

Tel 039 67 68451   Fax 039 67 67041   **HR**

85 Mill Road Annalong Co Down BT34 4QN   **Map 18 B2**

Just off the A2 coast road, this former farmhouse stands between the
mountains of Mourne and the sea, with fine views of both. Service is high
on the list of priorities, with James the butler on hand serving drinks in the
library or drawing room. Spacious bedrooms boast a variety of bright
sunny fabrics, plus flowers, fruit and fresh water. 24 hour room service is
unusual for a small hotel. *Rooms 9. Garden, tennis. Access, Amex, Visa,*

Restaurant   £60

Memories is a French style restaurant whose fixed-price dinner menus
make good use of natural fresh foods – beef cattle reared on the mountain
slopes, fish and shellfish from the local ports, trout from the hotel farm and
organically grown vegetables. *Seats 60. Parties 16. Private Room.
L 12.30-2.30 D 7-9.30. Set D from £19.50.*

Belfast   Bengal Brasserie   £30

Tel 0232 640099   **R**

339 Ormeau Road Belfast Co Antrim BT7 3GL   **Map 18 D2**

In a modern shopping arcade about a mile south of the city centre, this
Indian restaurant houses enough plastic greenery for a small forest. Bengali
cooking here is above average, and besides a wide choice of lamb, chicken
and prawn dishes there's lobster, crayfish and a blackboard offering
interesting specials such as scampi masala, tandoori duck, deer bhuna and
Indian river fish. Service is notably attentive and helpful. *Seats 46. Parties
60, Private Room. L 12-2 D 5.30-11.15 (Sun to 10.15). Closed L Sun, 25
Dec, 1 Jan. Set L from £3.95. Access, Visa,*

Belfast   Dukes Hotel   67%   £92

Tel 0232 236666   Fax 0232 237177   **H**

65 University Street Belfast Co Antrim BT7 1HL   **Map 18 D2**

In a residential district near Queen's University and the Botanical Gardens,
the Victorian facade of this recently converted, Chinese-owned hotel belies
its modern interior, epitomised by the black leather and chrome seating in
the foyer. Bedrooms are spacious and uncluttered, and each features the
work of a different impressionist painter. Huge, soft bath sheets add luxury
to otherwise stark bathrooms. There are two bars, a function complex
(capacity 130 theatre-style) and a health club. Children up to 16 stay free in
parents' room. Greatly reduced weekend rates. No dogs. *Rooms 21. Keep-fit
equipment, sauna. Access, Amex, Visa,*

Belfast   Manor House   £40

Tel 0232 238755   **R**

47 Donegall Pass Belfast Co Antrim BT7 1DQ   **Map 18 D2**

Sound Cantonese cooking on a long menu that also includes advice on how
to use chopsticks and a short history of the cuisine of the Guangzhou area
of Canton. Most of what's on offer is very familiar, but the more
adventurous could try braised fish head with bean curd or duck's web with
fish lips. *Seats 120. Parties 50. Private Room. Meals 12-12. Closed 25 & 26
Dec. Set L from £5.50 Set D from £13.50. Access, Visa,*

Belfast   Nick's Warehouse   £45

Tel 0232 439690   **R**

35-39 Hill Street Belfast Co Antrim BT1 2LB   **Map 18 D2**

The main menu at this converted warehouse is served in the first-floor
restaurant (popular with business people at lunchtime) and in the ground
floor wine bar at night. Uncomplicated yet interesting dishes can include

warm salad of smoked chicken and eel, fillet of salmon with a basil beurre
blanc, breast of pheasant with lemon grass and ginger sauce, puff parcels
with a savoury chickpea stuffing. Less formal but equally interesting menu
in the wine bar. *Seats 50. L 12-3 D 6-9. Closed Sat & Sun, Bank Holidays.
Access, Visa,*

Belfast	Plaza Hotel	64%	£82
Tel 0232 333555 Fax 0232 232999			**H**
15 Brunswick Street Belfast Co Antrim BT2 7GE			Map 18 D2

Very modern city-centre business hotel with well-equipped bedrooms.
Children up to 14 stay free in parents' room. The two conference rooms
can handle up to 100 delegates theatre-style. No dogs. *Rooms 83. Access,
Amex, Visa,*

Belfast	Roscoff	★	£74
Tel 0232 331532			**R**
Lesley House Shaftesbury Square Belfast Co Antrim			Map 18 D2

Not only the best but also the only modern minimalist restaurant in town,
Roscoff is a team effort between chef/patron Paul Rankin and his wife
Jennie, who heads front of house and the dessert department. Inspiration for
Paul's cooking is classical French, with modern adaptations and a strong
hint of California. The result is considerable sophistication through menus
that run from warm salad of grilled vegetables with shaved Parmesan and
balsamic vinegar to corn-fed chicken with Puy lentils, salt chili turbot and
chargrilled fillet of beef on wild mushroom crostini with a rosemary
vinaigrette. A concise and carefully compiled wine list with prices that will
not deter diners who appreciate quality; plenty of half bottles and ten
house wines available by the glass. *Seats 70. L 12.15-2.15 D 6.30-10.30.
Closed L Sat, all Sun, 11 & 12 Jul, 26 Dec, 1 Jan. Set L £11.95
Set D £17.50. Access, Amex, Visa,*

Belfast	Strand Restaurant		£35
Tel 0232 682266			**R**
12 Stranmillis Road Belfast Co Antrim BT9 5AA			Map 18 D2

Anne Turkington is a charming hostess and her welcoming restaurant and
wine bar has a great following. Curtains on brass rails break up the dining
areas, and upstairs there's an attractive conservatory bar. Menus change
regularly and offer generous portions of well-cooked food which is served
throughout the day, and you can eat as many or as few courses as you like.
Make a quick lunch with a couple of starters such as curried chicken
pancakes, oyster fritters or leek tart, or extend to a full spread with plaice
florentine, liver and bacon or chili con carne (a Strand speciality). *Seats 80.
Parties 25. Private Room. L Sun 12-3 D Sun 5-10 Meals Mon-Sat 12-12.
Closed 25 & 26 Dec, 12 & 13 July. Access, Amex, Visa,*

Belfast	Welcome Restaurant		£40
Tel 0232 381359			**R**
22 Stranmillis Road Belfast Co Antrim BT9 5AA			Map 18 D2

Beyond the pagoda roof at the entrance are lanterns, dragons, screens and
Chinese ornaments. The menu is as long as the usual Chinese, varied but
with few surprises. Table settings are Western. *Seats 80. Parties 28. L 12-2
D 5-11.30 (Sun to 10.30). Closed L Sat & Sun, 24-26 Dec. Set L from
£12.50. Access, Visa,*

Belfast   Wellington Park   59%   £90
Tel 0232 381111   Fax 0232 665410   H
21 Malone Road Belfast Co Antrim BT9 6RU   Map 18 D2

A thriving conference trade (maximum capacity 150 theatre-style) creates a
bustle, but three of the numerous bars are kept for residents and their
guests. Bedrooms are fairly basic, half having exposed brick walls and half
white plaster. Children up to 12 stay free in parents' room. No dogs.
Rooms 56. Access, Amex, Visa,

Belfast   Places of Interest

Tourist Information   Tel 0232 246609.
Mount Stewart House and Gardens (NT)   Greyabbey Tel 024774 387 *17
miles.*
Northern Ireland Aquarium   Portaferry Tel 02477 28062 *25 miles.*
Ulster Museum and Botanic Gardens   Tel 0232 381251.
Belfast Zoo   Tel 0232 776277 *5 miles North.*
Malone House Art Gallery and Gardens   Upper Malone Rd Tel 0232
681246.
Dixon Park   Upper Malone Rd Tel 0232 320202.
Transport Museum   Tel 0232 451519.
  Theatres and Concert Halls
Grand Opera House   Great Victoria St Tel 0232 241919.
Lyric Theatre   Ridgeway St Tel 0232 381081.
Ulster Hall   Bedford St Tel 0232 323900.
Group Theatre   Bradford St Tel 0232 229685.

Bushmills   Bushmills Inn   £68
Tel 026 57 32339   Fax 026 57 32048   I
25 Main Street Bushmills Co Antrim BT57 8QA   Map 18 C1

Bushmills, which lies two miles from the Giant's Causeway, is the home of
the world's oldest distillery. The hotel, originally a 19th-century inn,
derives a fresh, modern look from stripped pine and fashionable pastel in
some of the day rooms, though the bar is delightfully original. Bedrooms
are furnished in sturdy pine. Conferences are held in an oak-beamed loft.
Rooms 11. Garden. Access, Visa.

Bushmills   Places of Interest

Giant's Causeway Tourist Information   Tel 02657 31855/31582.

Comber   La Mon House   59%   £73
Tel 0232 448631   Fax 0232 448026   H
The Mills 41 Gransha Road Comber Co Down BT23 5RF   Map 18 D2

A low-rise modern hotel set in farmland. Best public area is the bar, which
has copper-topped tables; there's a small residents' lounge but it's often in
private use. The new fun bar includes a disco and karaoke. Bedrooms are
practical, with simple fitted furniture and striped wallpaper; nine are
larger, with balconies and deckchairs and there are eight small singles with
showers only. Banqueting facilities for 450, conferences up to 600 theatre-
style. No dogs. *Rooms 46. Garden, indoor swimming pool, sauna, solarium,
gymnasium, whirlpool bath, riding, live band and disco (Sat). Access, Amex,
Visa,*

Comber   Places of Interest

Wildfowl and Wetlands Centre   Castle Espie Tel 0242 874146 *3 miles.*

Crawfordsburn Old Inn £77

Tel 0247 853255 Fax 0247 852775 **I**

15 Main Street Crawfordsburn Co Down BT19 1JH Map 18 D2

The oldest hotel in continuous use in all Ireland, the 16th-century inn today plays host to many business people (there are conference facilities for up to 100 delegates). Belfast and its City Airport are easy distances away, yet the pretty village setting is among Northern Ireland's finest. Inside, oak beams, antiques and gas lighting provide a fitting atmosphere. Bedrooms are individual in style and charm; some have antiques, some four-posters; a few boast private sitting rooms. Children up to 10 stay free in parents' room. No dogs. *Rooms 33. Garden. Access, Amex, Visa.*

Dunadry Dunadry Inn 64% £98

Tel 084 94 32474 Fax 084 94 33389 **H**

2 Islandreagh Drive Dunadry Co Antrim BT41 2HA Map 18 D2

Proximity to Belfast Airport makes this riverside converted linen mill set in 10 acres a busy place, and it also has a thriving function trade with a maximum conference capacity of 300 theatre-style. Day rooms include the Copper Bar, scene of a popular lunchtime buffet, a conservatory and a leisure complex. Ground-floor bedrooms are the most modern and have the bonus of access to the garden; they have a rather masculine decor, darkwood furniture and neat bathrooms. Children up to 12 stay free in parents' room. No dogs. *Rooms 67. Garden, croquet, indoor swimming pool, keep-fit equipment, spa bath, sauna, solarium, crazy golf. Closed 24-27 Dec. Access, Amex, Visa,* Diners Club International

Dunmurry Forte Crest Belfast 67% £85

Tel 0232 612101 Fax 0232 626546 **H**

300 Kingsway Dunmurry Co Antrim BT17 9ES Map 18 D2

Ten minutes drive from Belfast city centre, set in 14 acres of gardens. Conference/meeting capacity of 450. Ample car parking. *Rooms 82. Keep-fit equipment, squash. Access, Amex, Visa,* Diners Club International

Garvagh Blackheath House & MacDuff's Restaurant £55

Tel 0265 868433 **R R**

112 Killeague Road Blackhill Garvagh Co Londonderry BT51 4HH Map 18 C1

Joseph and Margaret Erwin offer a friendly welcome at their listed former rectory, built in 1791 for the Parish of Aghadowey. Margaret is a skilled exponent of country house cooking, making fine use of local produce, with seasonal game a speciality. Note also puffs for starters, carrageen moss pudding to finish. *Seats 34. Parties 34. Private Room. D only 7-9.30. Closed Sun & Mon, 25 & 26 Dec, 12 Jul. Access, Visa,* Diners Club International

Rooms £55

The five spacious, well-kept bedrooms are summery, and have flowers, fruit, books, and good bathrooms; there's also a delightful, grandish residents' lounge.

Holywood Culloden Hotel 72% £140

Tel 023 17 5223 Fax 023 17 6777 **H R**

142 Bangor Road Craigavad Holywood Co Down BT18 0EX Map 18 D2

An example of Victorian Gothic architecture overlooking Belfast Lough, the Culloden stands in 12 acres of mature gardens. Splendid features such as pointed arches, ribbed ceilings and stained-glass windows remain in most of the public areas, although the red-plush bar is a modern interpretation of the Gothic theme. Most bedrooms are in an extension; furniture varies in style but all rooms are good-sized and of a high standard. Four function suites can accommodate up to 500 people. The Elysium health and fitness club is a great attraction. No dogs. *Rooms 91. Garden, croquet, indoor swimming pool, keep-fit equipment, sauna, spa bath, solarium, squash, tennis, snooker. Closed 24-25 Dec. Access, Amex, Visa,*

Restaurant £65

Pink decor, views over the garden and upholstered reproduction chairs make the restaurant a comfortable and agreeable place and there are plenty of staff on hand to provide swift and friendly service. The menu is strong on grills. *Seats 150. Parties 120. Private Room. L 12.30-2.30 D 7-9.45 (Sun to 8.30). Closed L Sat. Set D £16.*

Holywood   Places of Interest

Ulster Folk and Transport Museum   Cultra Tel 0232 428428.

Larne   Magheramorne House   63%   £72

Tel 0574 279444 Fax 0574 260138	H
Magheramorne Larne Co Antrim BT40 3HW	Map 18 D1

Set in 40 acres of woodland overlooking Larne Lough, the house dates from the 1880s. The entrance hall is in conservatory style, the lounge has a peaceful, traditional feel and there's a conference facility handling up to 200. No dogs. *Rooms 22. Garden, indoor swimming pool. Access, Amex, Visa,*

Londonderry   Everglades Hotel   59%   £65

Tel 0504 46722 Fax 0504 49200	H
Prehen Road Londonderry Co Londonderry BT47 2PA	Map 18 C1

Modern low-rise hotel south of town on the A5. Bright, fresh bedrooms, where children up to 12 can stay free with their parents. Conferences for up to 400. *Rooms 52. Garden. Access, Amex, Visa,*

Londonderry   Places of Interest

Tourist Information   Tel 0504 267284.
Derry's Walls.
St. Columb's Cathedral   off London St Tel 0504 262746.
O'Doherty's Tower   Magazine St Tel 0504 265238.
Display Centre   Butcher St Tel 0504 362016.
Ulster-American Folk Park   Omagh Tel 0662 243292.
Brachmore Stone Circus   Nr Cookstown.

Newtownards   Strangford Arms   58%   £86

Tel 0247 814141 Fax 0247 818846	H
92 Church Street Newtownards Co Down BT23 4AL	Map 18 D2

Local meeting place and businessman's hotel, the Strangford Arms is a well-run, friendly establishment that was once the Headquarters of the North Down Militia. The Horseshoe bar is a smart, convivial spot for relaxation, and the bedrooms all have desk space. No dogs. *Rooms 40. Garden. Closed 25 Dec, 12 Jul. Access, Amex, Visa,*

Portballintrae   **Bayview Hotel**   58%   £60

Tel 026 57 31453   Fax 026 57 32360   **H**

Bayhead Road Portballintrae Nr Bushmills Co Antrim BT57 8RZ   Map 18 C1

The long pebbledash building stands on the North Antrim coastal road, overlooking the tiny harbour and the bay. Conferences (for up to 150), functions and wedding receptions are big business, but private guests can relax in their own lounge or enjoy a drink in the cheerful Porthole Bar. Bedrooms, one with a little lounge area, have generally modern bathrooms. No dogs. *Rooms 16. Indoor swimming pool, sauna, solarium, snooker. Access, Amex, Visa,*

Portrush   **Ramore**   ★   £72

Tel 0265 822448   **R**

The Harbour Portrush Co Antrim BT56 8VM   Map 18 C1

Set behind huge picture windows overlooking the harbour, the restaurant is a roomy, comfortable venue for enjoying the talents of George McAlpin. The menu is deceptively simple, with the expected slight emphasis on seafood. Prawn terrine is served with baby quenelles of smoked salmon and avocado; seafood antipasto is marinated in olive oil and Noilly Prat and served with salad leaves and a coriander and lime dressing. Fillet or sirloin steak is topped with an onion and mushroom glaze and served on a raw tomato butter sauce. Desserts are a speciality with soufflés always on the list. *Seats 60. D only 7-10, lunchtime wine bar downstairs. Closed Sun & Mon, 2 weeks Feb, Xmas/New Year. Access, Visa.*

Portrush   **Places of Interest**

Dunluce Castle *3 miles.*

Templepatrick   **Templeton Hotel**   66%   £100

Tel 084 94 32984   Fax 084 94 33406   **H**

882 Antrim Road Templepatrick Ballyclare Co Antrim   Map 18 D2

Near Belfast International Airport, this ultra-modern hotel has a distinctive profile with a steeply pitched roof reaching to the ground. Public areas vary in style from the sophisticated black-and-gold cocktail bar to Sam's Bar with flagstone floor, peat fire and mosaic-topped tables. Good-sized bedrooms have lightwood fitted furniture with decent work space and cheerful green and coral colour schemes. Friendly, helpful staff. 24hr room service. Extensive conference facilities (up to 400). Parking is easy and free. *Rooms 20. Garden. Access, Amex, Visa,*

Republic of Ireland

Adare — Adare Manor — 79% — £201 — HR
Tel 061 396566   Fax 061 396124

Adare Co Limerick   Map 19

The neo-Gothic mansion, former home of the Earls of Dunraven, is set in 900 acres on the banks of the river Maigue. Its splendid, chandeliered drawing room and the glazed cloister of the dining room look down geometrical box-patterned gardens towards the new Robert Trent Jones golf course. The gallery, modelled after the Palace of Versailles, contains unique 15th-century Flemish choirstalls and fine stained-glass windows; banqueting for up to 220. Over fifty, individually carved fireplaces enhance the ambience of spacious bedrooms which boast locally-made mahogany furniture, cut-glass table lamps and marble bathrooms with strong showers over huge bathtubs. Children under 12 are accommodated free in their parents' room. *Rooms 64. Garden, indoor swimming pool, gymnasium, sauna, riding, fishing, clay-pigeon shooting, golf. Access, Amex, Visa,* ◐

Restaurant   £95

There have been changes in style, though fewer in content, since the departure of Ian McAndrew. Local produce, including vegetables and herbs from the estate's own gardens, take pride of place on the French-style à la carte, and a gourmet menu is presented to highlight the skills of the kitchen brigade. French-biased wine list is strong in Bordeaux, with a less than inspired choice from the New World. *Seats 65. Parties 65. Private Room. L 12.30-2.30 (Sun to 3) D 7.30-10. Set L £15 Set D £35.*

Adare — Dunraven Arms — 65% — £90 — H
Tel 061 396209   Fax 061 396541

Adare Co Limerick   Map 19

A base for abundant sporting activity, the Dunraven Arms stands at the heart of the prettiest of Irish villages. Golf and fishing are nearby and guests may ride to hounds alongside manager Bryan Murphy. Hence the most recent bedrooms, in an adjoining block, provide plenty of space for riding tack. As the hotel is also a popular function venue (maximum 400 in recently extended facilities), main-house bedrooms can be rather less relaxing. Under-12s stay free in parents' room. *Rooms 47. Garden, news kiosk, shop. Access, Amex, Visa,* ◐

Adare — Mustard Seed — £55 — R
Tel 061 396451

Main Street Adare Co Limerick   Map 19

Several cottagey rooms in a village house are the setting for cooking that's based on classical French, with overtones of modern Irish. Prime local produce finds it way into the kitchen, the basis of original dishes like feuilleté of pheasant, mallard and pigeon with a game essence, or 'pot on the stove' – oxtail, beef and tongue with winter vegetables. Equally imaginative are pumpkin and coconut soup, and a paste of venison livers with japonica jelly. Tempting sweets: baked pear with Cashel blue cheese. *Seats 46. Parties 18. Private Room. D only 7-10. Closed Sun & Mon, 25 & 26 Dec, Feb. Access, Amex, Visa,* ◐

Ahakista — Shiro — ★ — £70 — R
Tel 027 67030

Ahakista Nr Bantry Co Cork   Map 19

In a remote priest's house overlooking Dunmanus Bay, Kei and Werner Pilz run a Japanese restaurant of exquisite charm and quality. Guests sit at polished tables adorned with little Bonsai trees, the room filled with Kei's watercolours and calligraphy. She also does the cooking – solely Japanese – which is a model of delicate texture and subtle flavour. The five-course dinner changes daily, using fresh, locally-sourced ingredients. Flower-

decked *zensai* appetisers, *moriawase* – a delicate snack of egg dishes and
sushi, plus *suimono* soup precede a choice of main courses, perhaps steamed
salmon with spicy sauce (*sake-mushi*), a selection of deep-fried *tempura*
dishes or chicken, beef, pork cutlets, liver and vegetables grilled on the spit
and served with a traditional sweet sauce. Masu-yaki is a speciality from
Sapporo in the north of Japan: grilled wild sea-trout in boiled ginger,
garlic mayonnaise and lemon. Home-made ice cream rounds off a unique
experience. 5% supplement for paying by credit card. Bookings only.
Seats 12. *Parties 12. Private Room. D only 7-9. Set D £30. Access, Amex,
Visa,*

Athy   Tonlegee House   £55
Tel & Fax 0507 31473   R
Athy Co Kildare   Map 19 C4

Comfort and style combine at Mark and Molly Molloy's Georgian
restaurant with rooms on the outskirts of Athy. While Molly looks after
the diners with an easy charm Mark exercises his talents in the kitchen on
such dishes as ravioli of crab and cockles with fennel sauce, brill with garlic
potatoes and lobster sauce, and rack of lamb with tarragon, lemon tart and
fresh raspberries and cream vie with a good selection of Irish farmhouse
cheeses to provide the afters. Main dish price includes starter, soup course,
between-course sorbet, dessert (cheese is extra) and coffee with petits fours.
Seats 40. *Parties 50. L Sun 12.30-3 (Mon-Sat by arrangement) D 7-10.30.
Closed D Sun, 25 & 26 Dec, Good Friday. Set D from £18. Access, Visa.*

Rooms   £55

Five recently refurbished bedrooms offer an attractive alternative to the
local hotels. No dogs. Garden.

Ballina   Downhill Hotel   65%   £92
Tel 096 21033   Fax 096 21338   H
Downhill Road Ballina Co Mayo   Map 18 B3

Landscaped gardens overlooking the river Brosna provide a peaceful setting
for this popular hotel with extensive leisure and conference facilities.
Hospitality rooms and purpose-built conference centre accommodate from
10 to 400. An oval 50ft pool is the focal point of the leisure club; the
adjacent Frog's Pavilion piano bar provides nightly entertainment.
Particularly good facilities for children in high summer. **Rooms 52.** *Garden,
indoor swimming pool, spa bath, sauna, solarium, keep-fit equipment, squash,
tennis, games room, snooker. Closed 4 days Xmas. Access, Amex, Visa,*

Ballina   Mount Falcon Castle   60%   £80
Tel & Fax 096 21172   HR
Ballina Co Mayo   Map 18 B3

The redoubtable Constance Aldridge has presided over her Victorian
mansion for well over half a century and guests love the 'home from
home' atmosphere. The 100-acre estate provides peaceful walks and the
lived-in drawing room with its deep sofas and roaring fire is a good place
to make friends, with a bit of luck someone might play the piano in the
panelled entrance hall. Bedrooms are clean and simple, with antique
furniture. **Rooms 10.** *Garden, tennis, game fishing. Closed Xmas, Feb & Mar.
Access, Amex, Visa,*

Restaurant   £50

Country house cooking, with the emphasis on fresh ingredients. You can
have a separate table, but most people are drawn to the long candlelit
dinner table where Mrs Aldridge holds court. Gravad lax is a speciality of
the house, and there's always a flavoursome soup from a large silver tureen.
For main course there's usually a roast and perhaps some salmon.
Vegetables come from the garden, and butter and cream are provided by   *See over*

774 Republic of Ireland

two Jersey cows. There's a wide selection of Irish cheeses. *Seats 22. Parties 22. D only at 8. Set D £16.50.*

Ballyconnell   Slieve Russell Hotel   66%   NEW   £60

| Tel 049 26444   Fax 049 26511 | **H** |

Ballyconnell Co Cavan   Map 18C3

Named after a nearby mountain and situated in a lovely fishing area just south of the pretty border town of Ballyconnell '(famous for its canal, which is currently under reconstruction and will shortly link the Shannon and Lough Erne) this large modern hotel has recently been completed to international standards. Not at all what might be expected in the quiet Cavan countryside, the foyer boasts a marble colonnade and central staircase which sets the tone for all the public areas. Bedrooms are roomy with extra large beds and big marble bathrooms. Good leisure facilities at the adjoining Country Club include a large pool. *Rooms 150. Indoor swimming pool, sauna, steam room, spa bath, gymnasium, squash, tennis, 18-hole golf course. Access, Amex, Visa,* **D** *Diners Club International*

Ballyhack   Neptune Restaurant   NEW   £50

| Tel 051 89284 | **R** |

Ballyhack Harbour Ballyhack Co Wexford   Map 19 C5

Don't miss this smashing little bistro/restaurant – it's just on the Wexford side of the Passage East-Ballyhack car ferry but the main Wexford road off the ferry swings away to the right and it's easy to overlook. Once discovered, settle into one of the informal, comfortable little rooms, or the coveted conservatory, soak up Valerie McAuliffe's wonderful sunny colours – Mediterranean summer blues, soft yellows and white – and order up some of Pierce's huge hand-picked Wexford mussels in garlic butter or, perhaps, their famous hot crab Brehat, zinging with Cork Dry Gin. Their chocolate ice cream is the darkest, creamiest ever – and a magic partner for warm, ripe Wexford strawberries. *Seats 35. Parties 30. Private Room. L 12.30-3 D 6.30-10 (Sat to 10.30). Closed Mon, Xmas-17 Mar. Set D £11.50. Access, Amex, Visa,* **D** *Diners Club International*

Ballylickey   Ballylickey Manor House   67%   £94

| Tel 027 50071   Fax 027 50124 | **H** |

Ballylickey Bantry Bay Co Cork   Map 19 B6

For four generations the home of the Franco/Irish Graves family, their 300-year-old former shooting lodge has lost none of its lived-in appeal: family antiques, furniture and ornaments pack the lounges and private dining room. Within the lodge are five spacious suites; seven further well-appointed bedrooms are housed in wooden cottages set around the swimming pool in extensive gardens. The views of Bantry Bay are fabulous. *Rooms 12. Closed Nov-Mar. Access, Visa.*

Ballylickey   Sea View House   69%   £60

| Tel 027 50462   Fax 027 51555 | **HR** |

Ballylickey Bantry Co Cork   Map 19 B6

Resplendent and secluded in private grounds just by Ballylickey bridge, Miss Kathleen O'Sullivan's intimate hotel commands fine views of Bantry Bay and the mountains beyond. A large lounge, library and TV room and the bright, new cocktail bar are all stylishly furnished. In a new elevated bedroom extension bay windows make the most of the view, and ground floor accommodation is provided for disabled guests. Immaculate housekeeping. No dogs. *Rooms 17. Garden. Closed Nov-Mar. Access, Amex, Visa.*

Restaurant   £50

Colourfully attired local girls provide the service in two adjoining dining rooms replete with fresh flowers and antiques. The five-course, set price dinner menu changes nightly, offering a commendably varied choice with plenty of local seafood. No smoking. "10% service is added in lieu of gratuities." **Seats 50.** *Parties 30. L 12.45-2 D 7-9.30. Closed L Mon-Sat. Set D £21.*

| **Ballynahinch** | **Ballynahinch Castle** | **71%** | **£112** |

Tel 095 31006   Fax 095 31085

H

Recess Ballynahinch Co Galway   **Map 18 A3**

Standing in 350 acres of land overlooking a bend in the Ballynahinch river, this crenellated mansion dating from the 18th century probably has one of the best locations in Connemara. Fishing for 61 rods on the river attracts anglers and those who simply enjoy the atmosphere in the fishermen's bar, where the catches are measured, weighed and entered in the fishing log. A fire burns year-round in the mellow entrance hall and in the public rooms in chilly weather; antiques add to the traditional feel. All the bedrooms have mahogany furniture in traditional style; the eight newest are the best, with views of the river. **Rooms 28.** *Garden, croquet, tennis, shooting, fishing, bicycles. Access, Amex, Visa,* **◑** Diners Club International

---

| **Ballyvaughan** | **Gregans Castle** | **71%** | **£88** |

Tel 065 77005   Fax 065 77111

H R

Ballyvaughan Co Clare   **Map 19 B4**

Views of Galway Bay and the limestone hills of the Burren are the natural attractions of Gregans Castle, once the home of the Princes of Burren, and they are complemented by impressive architectural features and delightful decor. The Hadens have aimed for peace and quiet, and there is a deliberate absence of TVs and radios; rooms vary in size and shape, but each is decorated in the best of taste. Day rooms include a comfortable lounge and a library with leather-bound classics as well as the latest magazines; to the other side of the marble-floored foyer is the lively Corkscrew Bar where snacks are served all day. The hotel lies on the N67, 3 miles south of Ballyvaughan. No dogs. Children up to 10 stay free in parents' room. **Rooms 22.** *Garden. Closed Nov-Mar. Access, Visa.*

Restaurant   £75

Order your meal from 7pm onwards as you relax in the bar before filtering through to the restaurant with its pastoral decor, floral-patterned crockery, cut glassware and smart silver. Peter Haden's menus offer four carefully balanced courses (plus sorbet) served in sensibly sized portions. Local seafood, plus lamb from Ireland and France, are favoured raw materials. Typical dishes could include king scallop and mussel broth, pheasant and lentil terrine, coulibiac of wild salmon, breast of duck with orange and sultana sauce, and noisettes of Burren spring lamb with ratatouille and a cream of garlic sauce. **Seats 60.** *Parties 40. Private Room. L 12-3 (in bar) D 7-8.30. Set D £24.*

Ballyvaughan   Places of Interest

Tourist Information   Tel 065 81171.
Cliffs of Moher.
The Burren.

| **Beaufort** | **Dunloe Castle** | **71%** | **£90** |

Tel 064 44111   Fax 064 44583

H

Beaufort Nr Killarney Co Kerry   **Map 19 A5**

The original castle was built at the start of the 13th-century, and all that now remains is the empty shell of the keep. The hotel is modern; the tiled foyer has rugs, a seating area and marble-effect painting around the doorways to give a good first impression. A spacious main lounge is on the first floor, affording splendid views of the Gap of Dunloe (the lovely parkland setting is one of the hotel's chief attractions). Luxurious yellow carpeting, good easy chairs and well-chosen antiques make it attractive and comfortable. Bedrooms have plain white walls, solid pine furniture and long beds. Sister hotel to Hotel Europe (Killarney) and Ard-na-Sidhe (Caragh Lake). Banqueting/conference facilities for 400/800. *Rooms 140. Garden, indoor swimming pool, sauna, tennis, riding, cycling, game fishing, putting. Closed Oct-Apr. Access, Amex, Visa,* ⓓ ⬛

Blackrock   Ayumi-Ya

| | £40 |
| Tel 01 2831767 | R |

Newpark Centre Newtownpark Avenue Blackrock Co Dublin   Map 19 D4

Situated in a small shopping centre, the Ayumi-Ya was Dublin's first Japanese restaurant and still offers the widest range of authentic dishes. Diners are offered the choice of western or Japanese-style seating when booking – also the time to opt for a teppanyaki table if you want food cooked in front of you. In addition to teppanyaki and an à la carte menu for old hands, set menus ranging from vegetarian, through the Ayumi-Ya dinner course to a special seasonal dinner make the choices easier. Staff are helpful and may wisely advise a series of starters to maximise on the Japanese eating experience – tempura (deep-fried food in light batter), yakitori (skewered poultry), osashimi (assorted raw fish) and miso soup might all be tried together for example, with sake or green tea. *Seats 60. Parties 12. L Sun only 12.30-2.30 D 6-10. Closed 24-26 Dec, Good Friday. Set L from £10 Set D from £12.75. Access, Amex, Visa,* ⓓ ⬛

Blackrock   Clarets

| | £65 |
| Tel 01 2882008   Fax 01 2833273 | R |

63 Main Street Blackrock Co Dublin   Map 19 D4

An unpretentiously comfortable restaurant where you can expect enjoyable cooking at realistic prices. Chef-patron Alan O'Reilly uses seasonal produce in his progressive Irish cooking. Appealing dishes come in generous portions, and there's plenty of innovation: twice-baked Swiss cheese and shiitake mushroom soufflé, or pan-fried fillets of brill with scallop mousse, angel hair pasta and beurre blanc. *Seats 50. Parties 15. L 12.30-2.30 D 7-10. Closed L Sat, all Sun & Mon, Bank Holidays. Set L £11.95 Set D £21.95. Access, Amex, Visa.*

Blessington   Downshire House   57%

| | £63 |
| Tel 045 65199   Fax 045 65335 | H |

Blessington Co Wicklow   Map 19 D4

A comfortable village hotel (19 miles from Dublin) which has seen careful modification and improvements over the last 30 years. Owners Rhoda Byrne and her long-serving staff extend an informal, friendly welcome. Public rooms consist of a pair of tiny residents' lounges and a decent bar. Bedrooms are plain and practical, reached by an old-fashioned teak staircase. Conference rooms accommodate up to 100. *Rooms 25. Garden, croquet, tennis. Closed mid Dec-6 Jan. Access, Visa.*

Boyle   Cromleach Lodge   NEW

| | £75 |
| Tel 071 65155   Fax 071 65455 | R |

Ballindoon Castlebaldwin Nr Boyle Co Sligo   Map 19 B

The views from every table are almost heartbreakingly lovely, the service thoughtful and discreet and Moira Tighe's skilfully cooked food outstanding. Start, perhaps, with a chicken and crab 'sausage' on a carrot and Sauternes sauce (light, delicately flavoured sausage with a crispy crust, set in a pool of rich, aromatic orange – the Sauternes suiting perfectly the natural sweetness of the carrot) or tartlet of organic leek and smoked bacon (a dainty little tart of very light, crisp pastry filled with finely sliced, juicy leeks and bacon). Soups are intensely flavoured, salads vibrant. A dish such as wild Lough Gill salmon on a bed of organic spinach may have a wonderful white wine sauce with a hint of saffron and stuffed fillet of pork one flavoured with Madeira. Vegetables are organic, desserts such as florentina cone filled with tropical fruits (a crunchy cone, with luscious fruits spilling out like a treasure chest) are beautiful and imaginative, matching the quality of the Rosenthal china they are served on. There are ten rooms for guests wishing to stay the night. *Seats 50. Parties 20. Private Room. L by arrangement D 7-9 (Sun 6.30-8). Closed 3 days Xmas, 3 weeks Jan. Set L £15 Set D £26.50. Access, Amex, Visa.*

Bray **Tree of Idleness**	**£65**
Tel 01 286 3498	**R**
Seafront Bray Co Wicklow	**Map 19 D4**

A seafront restaurant opened in 1979 by Akis Courtellas, who sadly died last year. Though strongly rooted in Akis's Greek-Cypriot background the menu covers much else besides: ravioli of chicken mousse and wild mushrooms with carrot sauce, pigeon breasts with garlic in a thyme and honey caramel, Dublin Bay prawns, fillet steak in a red wine and truffle sauce. The sweet trolley is loaded down with an abundance of exotic fruits – some of them fresh, some in wine or as compotes – displayed in cut glass bowls. An exceptional wine list is strong in Bordeaux with all the best vintages back to '61 and beyond. *Seats 50. Parties 20. D only 7.30-11 (Sun to 10). Closed Mon, Bank Holidays, 1 week Xmas, 2 weeks Sep. Set D from £15.50. Access, Visa,* **Diners Club** *International*

Bunratty Fitzpatricks Shannon Shamrock 60%	**£109**
Tel 061 361177 Fax 061 471252	**H**
Bunratty Co Clare	**Map 19 B4**

Hard by Bunratty Castle (only 4 miles from Shannon airport), a touring and activity base central to County Clare. Leisure centre with indoor pool; conference/banqueting for up to 200. Children under 12 accommodated free in parents' room. Guests of the low-rise hotel share facilities with time-share homes in the grounds. *Rooms 115. Indoor swimming pool, sauna, steam room. Closed 25 Dec. Access, Amex, Visa,* **Diners Club** *International*

Bunratty **MacCloskey's**	**£65**
Tel 061 364082	**R**
Bunratty House Mews Bunratty Co Clare	**Map 19 B4**

MacCloskey's is situated in the cellars of 17th-century Bunratty House, and the intimate atmosphere is enhanced by wrought-iron candle brackets with red candles and an abundance of fresh flowers. The five-course, fixed-price menu offers a wide choice of straightforward dishes such as chicken liver paté with a redcurrant glaze, escalope of salmon with lemon and chive sauce or roast fillet of pork with tarragon. Finish, maybe, with lemon mousse or home-made ice cream. *Seats 60. Parties 25. Private Room. D only 7-10. Closed Sun & Mon, 22 Dec-24 Jan, Good Friday. Set D £26. Access, Amex, Visa,* **Diners Club** *International*

Caragh Lake **Hotel Ard-na-Sidhe** 70%	**£90**
Tel 066 69105 Fax 066 69282	**H**
Caragh Lake Nr Killorglin Co Kerry	**Map 19 A5**

Built in 1880 and restored in 1915, this handsome redstone mansion enjoys a setting of considerable peace and beauty in wooded gardens and grassed terraces on the edge of the lake. The two lounges are both comfortable, with settees, chairs upholstered in French reproduction style and summery curtains. Good-sized bedrooms furnished with antiques have long beds and crisp cotton sheets. Eight rooms with private patios are in the garden house. Same owners as Hotel Europe (Killarney) and Dunloe Castle (Beaufort). *Rooms 20. Garden, game fishing. D 7-9.30. Closed Oct-Apr. Access, Amex, Visa,* **Diners Club** *International*

Caragh Lake   Caragh Lodge   65%   £72

Tel 066 69115   Fax 066 69316   **H**

Caragh Lake Nr Killorglin Co Kerry   **Map 19 A5**

Personally supervised by owner Mary Gaunt, the lodge is a Victorian
house set in seven acres of secluded gardens running down to the shore of
Caragh Lake (boating, fishing, swimming). Peace and quiet are in plentiful
supply, in the grounds, in the attractive antique-furnished day rooms and in
the bedrooms, some of which are in cottages. No phones or TVs intrude.
Children under 6 stay free in parents' room. No dogs. *Rooms 10. Garden,
sauna, tennis, game fishing, rowing boat, bicycles. Closed mid Oct-Easter.
Access, Amex, Visa.*

Carrickmacross   Nuremore Hotel   62%   £95

Tel 042 61438   Fax 042 61853   **H**

Carrickmacross Co Monaghan   **Map 18 C3**

A modern low-rise hotel set in 100 acres of woods and parkland on the N2
south of town. Major refurbishment over the last two years has seen the
bright, airy bedrooms upgraded and the addition of a new leisure club.
Many rooms overlook the trout-filled lake. Conference/banqueting
facilities for 200/400. No dogs. *Rooms 69. Garden, indoor swimming pool,
sauna, solarium, spa bath, gymnasium, squash, tennis, games room, 18-hole golf
course. Access, Amex, Visa,* ⓓ *Diners Club International*

Cashel   Cashel House   76%   £115

Tel 095 31001   Fax 095 31077   **HR**

Cashel Co Galway   **Map 18 A3**

Friendliness and professionalism combine at this enchanting and ever-
improving hotel set in 50 acres of prize-winning woodland gardens
between the mountains and the sea; they even have their own private
beach. The numerous day rooms are filled with antiques, objets d'art, fresh
flowers and pictures, with several log fires burning throughout the year.
Antiques also find their way into many of the bedrooms, which have been
individually decorated with considerable style by Kay McEvilly. The
Garden Suite rooms are particularly spacious, with separate seating areas.
Beds are turned down at night and everything from black pudding to
marmalade and soda bread is home-made for the excellent breakfasts.
*Rooms 32. Garden, tennis, sea & game fishing, boating, horse riding (inc
dressage). Access, Amex, Visa.*

Restaurant   £70

Pretty Royal Tara china (made in Galway) features in the sunny, split-level
restaurant with its large conservatory extension. Fixed-price, four-course
dinners always include an inter-course sorbet and make good use of local
produce, striking a good balance between simplicity and sophistication.
Cleggan Bay flat oysters or cream of artichoke and asparagus soup might
sit happily alongside baked fillet of brill with a Provençal sauce or escalope
of veal with a cream and mushroom sauce. Fish always features, as do
lobsters from their own tank. A fresh fruit tart (perhaps apple, rhubarb or
yellow plum) and home-made ice creams are regulars among the desserts.
*Seats 70. Parties 10. Private Room. L 1-2 D 7.30-8.30 (Sun 7.30-9).
Closed 10-31 Jan. Set D from £25.50.*

Cashel   Zetland House   65%   £99

Tel 095 31111   Fax 095 31117   **H**

Cashel Co Galway   **Map 18 A3**

On the edge of Cashel Bay in an area of great natural beauty, the Zetland
was built as a sporting lodge in the early 1800s. It remains a favoured base
for outdoor pursuits, including fishing of all kinds and rough shooting for
snipe and woodcock. Sitting rooms are invitingly cosy, and most of the
bedrooms and suites offer spectacular sea views. *Rooms 20. Garden, croquet,
fishing, tennis, snooker. Closed Nov-Easter. Access, Amex, Visa,* ⓓ *Diners Club International*

Cashel Cashel Palace 70% £120

Tel 062 61411 Fax 062 61521

H

Main Street Cashel Co Tipperary Map 19 C5

A handsome redbrick and stone mansion set back from the main street,
Cashel Palace was built in 1730 and was until 1960 a bishop's palace. The
reception lounge is grand, with a high ceiling, fluted Corinthian columns
and a large chandelier. Pine panelling in the hall and staircase are typical
early Georgian features. In the vaulted basement, both bar and coffee shop
have flagstoned floors and the former has tartan upholstery. First-floor
rooms boast high ceilings, marble fireplaces and antiques; second-floor
rooms are cottagey, with pretty matching fabrics. A further corridor offers
small bedrooms with simple fitted furniture. No dogs. *Rooms 20. Garden,
coarse fishing, coffee shop (10am-10pm 7 days Apr-Oct, Tues-Sat Nov-Mar).
Closed 25 & 26 Dec. Access, Amex, Visa,*

Cashel Chez Hans £65

Tel 062 61177

R

Rockside Cashel Co Tipperary Map 19 C5

A panelled bar with roaring log fire provides the welcome at this former
Wesleyan chapel where Hans-Peter Matthia's formula of serving the best-
quality seafood and meat in formidably-sized portions continues to please.
Quenelles of brill and turbot with butter sauce, Kinsale lobster bisque, rack
of spring lamb with herb crust and tarragon sauce, and half a farm fresh
duckling with honey and thyme sauce indicate the style. *Seats 60. Parties
60. D only 6.30-10. Closed Sun & Mon, Bank Holidays, 3 weeks Jan.
Access, Visa.*

Castledermot Doyle's School House Country Inn £49

Tel 0503 44282

R

Main Street Castledermot Co Kildare Map 19 C4

The surroundings don't match up to John Doyle's strong inexpensive
country cooking. His patés, especially game in season, are well-known and
specialities such as local free-range pork or old-fashioned beef and oyster pie
are worth looking out for. Desserts, such as profiteroles with Bailey's, are
light, while Irish farmhouse cheeses with crunchy home-made oat biscuits
are an interesting alternative. Dinners are considerably more sophisticated
than lunches. *Seats 35. Parties 25. Private Room. L 12.30-2 or by arrangement
D Nov-Mar 7.30-10.30, Apr-Oct 6.30-10.30. Closed L Tue-Sat, D Sun, all
Mon, mid Jan-mid Feb. Set L £10.50 Set D £17.50. Access, Amex, Visa,*

Castledermot Kilkea Castle £123

Tel 0503 45156 Fax 0503 45187

HR

Kilkea Castledermot Co Kildare Map 19 C4

Kilkea Castle dates from the twelfth century, is the oldest inhabited castle
in Ireland and has been run as a hotel under the present ownership since
1988. Although not on a huge scale, the castle has an elegance and
grandeur that many larger castles lack and it has been renovated and
converted to its present use with skill and sensitivity. Rooms, many with
wonderful views over the formal gardens and surrounding countryside, are
splendidly furnished to incorporate modern comforts in a manner
appropriate to their age and style. By contrast, the Health and Fitness Club,
although architecturally discreet, is totally modern and includes indoor
heated swimming pool, saunas, jacuzzi, steam room, fully equipped
exercise-room and sunbed. Outdoor sports include clay-pigeon shooting,
archery, tennis and fishing on the nearby River Griese. *Rooms 45. Access,
Amex, Visa,*

De Lacy's   £70

De Lacy's Restaurant is named after Hugh de Lacy who built Kilkea Castle
in 1180. The first floor restaurant is suitably grand, with bright, airy
atmosphere and magnificent views. Scottish chef George Smith has a light
touch and, despite the somewhat flowery language on the menu, produces
colourful, interesting food with clear flavours and plenty of contrast in
flavour and texture. Local seasonal produce features, much of it taken from
the gardens below, where guests can wander around after dining, to see the
old fruit trees, vegetables and herbs. Not suprisingly, salads and vegetables
are a special strength. Desserts are sophisticated and beautiful, to match
their surroundings. *Seats 45. Parties 14. L 12.30-2.30 D 7-9.30. Closed 25
Dec. Set L £13.95 Set D £23.50.*

Clifden   Abbeyglen Castle   60%   £90
Tel 095 21201   Fax 095 21797   **H**

Sky Road Clifden Co Galway   Map 18 A3

Crenellations, towers and pointed-arch windows give an individual air to
the hotel's exterior, and its garden setting plays host to the pool and
multifarious outdoor activities. Owner/manager Paul Hughes, incumbent
since 1970, welcomes his many guests who return year after year. Public
areas include a smart residents' lounge and a pubby bar with a peat fire.
Bedrooms are good-sized; the best have matching fabrics and reproduction
furniture. No longer any restrictions on children. Conferences for up to
200 delegates. *Rooms 40. Outdoor swimming pool, sauna, solarium, snooker,
tennis, pitch & putt. Closed 10 Jan-1 Feb. Access, Amex, Visa,* ◑ Diners Club International

---

Clifden   Ardagh Hotel   60%   £66
Tel 095 21384   Fax 095 21314   **HR**

Ballyconneely Road Clifden Co Galway   Map 18 A3

With a splendid location overlooking Connemara's Ardbear Bay, about
two miles south of Clifden, the modern Ardagh offers extensive public
areas, from a bar filled with supremely comfortable settees and armchairs
to a delightful little plant-filled sun lounge on the top floor. Good-sized
bedrooms have a variety of pretty floral wallpapers. A nearby golf club
welcomes visitors. No dogs. *Rooms 21. Garden, solarium. Access, Amex,
Visa,* ◑ Diners Club International

Restaurant   £55

There is much to savour in the first-floor dining rooms: glorious views
through picture windows and Monique Berings Bauvet's interesting way
with local produce. Lighter lunches in the bar. *Seats 55. Parties 30. D only
7.15-9.30. Closed Nov-Mar. Set D from £19.80.*

Clifden   Rock Glen Manor   61%   £84
Tel 095 21035   Fax 095 21737   **H**

Roundstowe Road Clifden Co Galway   Map 18 A3

Lying just a mile and a half from Clifden on the Roundstone road, a
delightfully converted 18th-century shooting lodge is the home of John
and Evangeline Roche. Its location is magnificent and the sun lounge and
drawing room make ideal spots for soaking in the views. There's a cosy
bar, too, lined with colourful prints and cartoons. The less active enjoy the
use of fourteen ground floor bedrooms, while breakfast lovers will
appreciate the hotel's nationally acclaimed Irish country breakfasts. The
tennis court is all-weather and floodlit. *Rooms 29. Garden, tennis, snooker,
fishing. Closed Oct-mid Mar. Access, Amex, Visa,* ◑ Diners Club International

Clonmel   Clonmel Arms   61%

Tel 052 21233   Fax 052 21526

Sarsfield Street Clonmel Co Tipperary

£65

H

Map 19 C5

In the heart of Clonmel, with parking along the quayside, the hotel has popular conference and function facilities for up to 450. Bedrooms mostly have pastel and primrose colour schemes; four bathrooms have shower/WC only. A few rooms are suitable for family use, and there are two family suites. The Gate Buttery transforms into a 'fun bar' with music at night. **Rooms 35.** *Coffee shop (10am-7pm). Access, Amex, Visa,* (1) *Diners Club International*

Cong   Ashford Castle   86%

Tel 092 46003   Fax 092 46260

Cong Co Mayo

£199

HR

Map 18 B3

Set amid 350 acres of parkland, with origins dating back to the early 13th century, Ashford Castle stands proudly overlooking the lakes of Western Ireland, its tranquillity epitomised by fragrant formal gardens, its exclusivity symbolised by the great cut stone bridge that marks the entrance. Inside is a succession of grand public rooms decked out with wood panelling, oil paintings, carved balustrades, suits of armour and magnificent fireplaces. Discreet but spacious, separate conference and banqueting rooms accommodate up to 140. Immaculately kept bedrooms and luxury suites contain elegant furniture and period pieces; bathrooms are vast, luxurious and truly pampering, equally reflecting the Castle's unique ambience. Children under 12 stay free in their parents' room. No dogs. **Rooms 83.** *Garden, croquet, 9-hole golf course, riding, fishing, tennis, coarse & game fishing, lake cruising, bicycles, boutique, coffee shop (10am-4.30pm). Access, Amex, Visa,* (1) *Diners Club International*

Restaurant

£95

The room itself is large, with handsome panelling, chandeliers and vast windows looking out to the grounds, its spaciousness scarcely conducive to intimacy. Service, however, is as discreet and professional as ever, and daily menus present a wide choice: from "A Taste of Ireland" come potato and garlic grass soup and traditional Irish stew. On the table d'hote Clew Bay scallops, Connemara hill lamb and local farmhouse cheeses reassert reliance on the finest of Irish produce. Predictable wine list with high prices. **Seats 130.** *Parties 135. Private Room. L 12.45-2 D 7-9.30. Set L £19 Set D £32.*

Connaught Room

£95

Part of the original Georgian house built in 1715, the Connaught Room is opulent and exclusive, with chandeliers, sparkling crystal and immaculate table settings. Denis Lenihan is in charge of the cooking in both restaurants and the menus are fairly similar. **Seats 40.** *Private Room. L 1-2.30 D 7-9.30.*

Cork   Forte Travelodge

Tel 021 310722

Jct South Ring Road/Kinsale Road Cork Airport Blackash Nr Cork Co Cork

£40

L

Map 19 B6

$1\frac{1}{2}$ miles south of Cork city centre on the main airport road. *Access, Amex, Visa.*

Cork   Arbutus Lodge   65%

Tel 021 501237   Fax 021 502893

Montenotte Cork Co Cork

£72

HR

Map 19 B6

The former home of a Lord Mayor of Cork stands high above rare trees with fine views of the city, the river Lee and surrounding hills. The house is full of fine furniture and its walls are studded with paintings, many by modern Irish artists. Careful modernisation has given a classy look to the best, superior bedrooms, which have stylish fabrics, antique furniture and fine bathrooms, with robes provided. There are also some smaller standard and single rooms. Staff are friendly and helpful, and there's always a welcome to arriving guests from one of the Ryan family. **Rooms 19.** *Garden, croquet, tennis. Access, Amex, Visa,*

Restaurant   £74

Declan and Michael Ryan were among the pioneers of good eating in Ireland, with many of their protégés receiving honourable mentions in these pages. Menus offer a balance of Irish and French-inspired dishes with a bias towards the latter, as in foie gras en terrine and fillet of turbot with sauce poivron. Alongside are Cork crubeens (pig's trotters), garden lovage soup and Arbutus-style bacon and cabbage. A marvellous choice of Irish cheeses follows, and an excellent sweet trolley. The wine list remains superb, with some inexpensive bargains and wonderful old clarets and burgundies. *Seats 50. Parties 30. Private Room. L 1-2 D 7-9.30. Closed Sun, 1 week Xmas. Set L £12.50 Set D £21.*

Cork	Bully's	£25
Tel 021 273555		**R**
40 Paul Street Cork Co Cork		**Map 19 B6**

Chef-patron Eugene Buckley cooks first-rate pizzas with exceptionally light, crisp bases in a special wood-burning oven. Fresh pasta and light, yeasty white bread are both made daily. Also fresh fish, omelettes and grills. *Seats 40. Parties 20. Meals 12-11.30. Closed 25 & 26 Dec, Good Friday. No credit cards.*

Cork	Clifford's	£70
Tel 021 275333		**R**
18 Dyke Parade Cork Co Cork		**Map 19 B6**

There's a stylish ambience to this smart town house restaurant, once a library, adorned with the Cliffords' collection of contemporary Irish art. Menus, changing monthly to incorporate the best seasonal produce, are equally classy: Michael's cooking is confident and Dierdre's service exemplary. For the good-value lunch, a rabbit and pigeon hamburger in mustard sauce, casserole of spring lamb with baby vegetables, perhaps, and a butterscotch-sauced warm banana crepe. Dinner is a more involved affair with specialities such as gateau of Clonakilty black pudding with smoked Kassler, ravioli of Dublin Bay prawns in light bisque and Clifford's marquise of two chocolates. Farmhouse cheeses served from a trolley. *Seats 45. Parties 50. Private Room. L 12.30-2.30 D 7.30-10.30. Closed L Sat & Mon, all Sun, Bank Holidays, 2 weeks Aug. Set L £12 Set D £25.50. Access, Amex, Visa,*

Cork	Crawford Gallery Café	£45
Tel 021 274415		**R**
Emmet Place Cork Co Cork		**Map 19 B6**

The Crawford Gallery, a fine building dating from 1724, stands next to the Opera House. Lunch is served six days a week, dinner on Wednesday, Thursday and Friday, and quality is assured by the close ties with Ballymaloe House at Shanagarry. The catch from Ballycotton heads the bill, and other choices run from lunchtime open sandwiches and chicken pie to cheese fondue, guinea fowl with bread and redcurrant sauces, and fried escalopes of baby beef with grain mustard sauce. *Seats 70. Parties 200. Private Room. L 12-2.30 D 6.30-9.30. Closed D Mon, Tue & Sat, all Sun, Bank Holidays, 2 weeks Xmas. Access, Visa.*

Cork	Fitzpatrick Silver Springs	64%	£105

Tel 021 507533   Fax 021 507641

H

Tivoli Cork Co Cork   **Map 19 B6**

A modern tower-block hotel overlooking the river Lee, some five minutes drive from the city centre, with eye-catching external glass skylift and spacious superior bedrooms worth paying extra for. Self-contained conference suites accommodate up to 800; activity centre includes a 25-metre pool and indoor tennis. Children under five stay free in their parents' room. *Rooms 110. Garden, indoor swimming pool, spa bath, sauna, steam room, solarium, gymnasium, beautician, indoor & outdoor tennis, 9-hole golf, bowling. Access, Amex, Visa,* **①** Diners Club International

Cork	Huguenot	£20

Tel 021 273357

R

French Church Street Cork Co Cork   **Map 19 B6**

Bistro food and good value provided by Michael Callaghan and family. West Cork black pudding with peppered pears, Provençal chicken breast and osso buco are among the classy offerings on a seasonally-changing menu. *Seats 70. L 10.30-2.30 D 6-10.30 (Sun Jun-Aug 6-10), Sat Jun-Aug 12.30-11. Closed L Sun (all Sun in winter), 25 & 26 Dec. Set D £6.95. Access, Visa.*

Cork	Imperial Hotel	69%	£110

Tel 021 274040   Fax ext 2507

H

South Mall Cork Co Cork   **Map 19 B6**

Conferences, banqueting (up to 350) and a lively atmosphere housed behind neo-classical facade in the heart of Cork. Modern bedrooms have a mix of furniture from fitted units to antiques. *Rooms 101. Closed 1 week Xmas. Access, Amex, Visa,* **①** Diners Club International

Cork	Isaacs	NEW	£35

Tel 021 503805

R

48 MacCurtain Street Cork Co Cork   **Map 19 B6**

The Ryan family of Arbutus Lodge have got together with chef Canice Sharkey to create this refreshingly relaxed middle-market restaurant in a converted 18th-century warehouse. Softly aged brickwork, terracotta paintwork and vibrant modern paintings provide a clue to what to expect of the menu: an eclectic mixture of styles and influences, all brought together in cheerful harmony under Sharkey's watchful eye. Quality and value are the aim: try the fish soup served with a gutsy rouille and garlic croutons, or a few slices of char grilled monkfish with a punchy niçoise sauce followed, perhaps, by a luscious summer fruit compote, a shimmering palette of barely-warmed soft fruit, with home-made vanilla ice cream. *Seats 90. Parties 60. Private Room. L 12-2.30 D 6.30-10.30 (Sun to 9). Closed L Sun, 3 days Xmas. Access, Visa.*

Cork	Jacques	£55

Tel 021 277387

R

9 Phoenix Street Cork Co Cork   **Map 19 B6**

Conveniently situated just behind the Imperial Hotel, a cosy, informal restaurant that transforms from an inexpensive day-time outlet into one with more serious intentions from early evening onwards. Jacqueline and Eithne Barry offer a menu that ranges from modern starters like grilled polenta and Parmesan with goat's cheese, tomato and black olive or braised onion and thyme toppings or Eastern-style marinated quail to more classic main courses of bacon-wrapped guinea fowl, pork Dijon, Barbary duck and escalope of veal, although the addition of Chinese noodles, bruschetta and deep-fried leeks keep the theme up-to-date. *Seats 55. Parties 16. L 12-4 D 6-10.30. Closed D Mon, all Sun, Bank Holidays, 10 days Xmas. Set D from £7.90 (6-7pm) Access, Amex, Visa,* **①** Diners Club International

Cork   Jurys Hotel   66%   £126

Tel 021 276622   Fax 021 274477   **H**

Western Road Cork Co Cork   **Map 19 B6**

Low rise modern hotel in a riverside setting a short walk from the city
centre. Renovation is improving the bedrooms, which will have fax lines
and larger bathrooms, plus double and single beds. Children up to 12 stay
free in parents' room. Banqueting/conferences for 500/600. No dogs.
*Rooms 185. Garden, indoor & outdoor swimming pools, spa bath, sauna,
masseuse, gymnasium, squash, tennis. Closed 24-26 Dec. Access, Amex, Visa,*
Diners Club International

Cork   Lovetts   £72

Tel 021 294909   **R**

Churchyard Lane off Well Road Douglas Cork Co Cork   **Map 19 B6**

Anonymous portraits by a 19th-century Cork artist gaze down at diners in
a comfortable restaurant to the south of town. Excellent fresh seafood and
specially smoked products are the main features: smoked Killaloe eel and
Galway Bay oysters preceding poached brill, Bere Island scallops and roast
monkfish – all capably cooked in a straightforward manner. Shorter, fixed-
price lunch and dinner menus offer the likes of bean and pickled pork
salad, seafood pasta, chicken peperonata and Mr Lovett's celebrated gateaux.
Worldwide wine list, with even China represented. *Seats 45. Parties 50.
Private Room. L 12.30-2 D 7-10. Closed L Sat, all Sun, Bank Holidays. Set L
£13.50 Set D £22. Access, Amex, Visa,* Diners Club International

Cork   Morrisons Island Hotel   69% NEW   £109

Tel 021 275858   Fax 021 275833   **H**

Morrisons Quay Cork Co Cork   **Map 19 B6**

Designed and run on the same lines as Stephen's Hall in Dublin, Cork's first
all-suites hotel is very central and right on the river bank so you can watch
the fish from your window. Well-equipped suites include a lobby and
kitchenette in addition to the usual accommodation and this compact,
thoughtfully designed hotel has style, especially in the foyer with its
Oriental rugs and rich colours and the restaurant, which features locally
made hand-painted furniture. *Rooms 40. Closed (possibly) 1 wk Xmas.
Access, Amex, Visa,* Diners Club International

Cork   O'Keeffe's   £65

Tel 021 275645   **R**

23 Washington Street West Cork Co Cork   **Map 19 B6**

Marie and Tony O'Keeffe took over Cliffords' old premises against all
advice in 1990 and their brave move has proved a success. The menu is
based squarely on fresh seasonal ingredients but is unusually flexible as
Marie cooks everything to order including vegetarian dishes on request.
Typical choices are colourful and quite robust, like bavarois of salmon with
sesame toast, or pheasant with savoury rice on a cranberry coulis. *Seats 33.
Parties 33. L by arrangement D 6.30-10.30. Closed Sun, Bank Holidays,
1 week Xmas. Access, Amex, Visa,* Diners Club International

Cork   Rochestown Park Hotel   67%   £60

Tel 021 892233   Fax 021 892178   **H**

Rochestown Road Cork Co Cork   **Map 19 B6**

The hotel stands in lovely gardens and is convenient for the airport. The
original part of this hotel is a former home of the Lord Mayors of Cork
and features well-proportioned, gracious public rooms. Modern bedrooms
are functional and comfortable with full amenities. *Rooms 39. Garden.
Access, Amex, Visa,* Diners Club International

Cork   Places of Interest

Tourist Information Tel 021 273251.
Triskell Arts Centre off South Main Street Tel 021 272022.
Crawford School of Art and Gallery Emmett Place Tel 021 966777.
G.A.A. Athletic Grounds Pairc Chaoimh Tel 021 963311.
St. Anne's Shandon Street. **Bells of Shandon**.
St. Finbarre's Crawford Street.
St. Colman's Cathedral Cobh. *25 miles.*
Everyman Palace MacCurtain Street Tel 021 501673.
Opera House Emmett Place Tel 021 270022.
   Historic Houses, Castles and Gardens
Blarney Castle House and Gardens Tel 021 385252.
Fota Wildlife Park Carrigtwohill, Nr Cobh Tel 021 812678.

Crossmolina   Enniscoe House   63%   £88
Tel 096 31112 Fax 096 31773

Castlehill Nr Crossmolina Ballina Co Mayo   Map 18 B3

Generations of Kelletts have been here since the 1660s. Now, under Susan Kellett, the current owner, guests also have the opportunity to experience real Irish country house life. Family portraits and antiques adorn the lived-in day rooms and bedrooms, some with canopied or four-poster beds, still cling to the elegance of a time gone by. The grounds, which run down to the shore of Loch Conn, include wooded parkland and a working farm. Some self-catering accommodation has been created in the old stable yard at the rear of the main house. **Rooms 6.** *Garden, game fishing. Closed mid Oct-end Mar. Access, Amex, Visa.*

Dalkey   Il Ristorante   £60
Tel 01 284 0800

108 Coliemore Road Dalkey Co Dublin   Map 19 D4

An intimate restaurant above a pub, the latter quite smart enough for pre-dinner drinks, with just six candle-lit tables in a pretty room with rag-painted walls. Celine Pons provides the warm Irish welcome while Italian husband Roberto exercises his skills in the kitchen. The northern Italian cooking is classical in style but the presentation is modern, with good eye appeal. Penne with sun-dried tomatoes, Ligurian fish soup, scampi risotto, liver veneziana, saltimbocca alla romana. An exclusively Italian wine list is full of interest. **Seats 26.** *Parties 22. D only 7.30-10.30. Closed Mon, Bank Holidays except Good Friday, 1 week Xmas, end Jan-mid Feb. Access, Amex, Visa.*

Delgany   Glenview Hotel   61%   £73
Tel 01 287 3399 Fax 01 287 7511

Glen of the Downs Delgany Co Wicklow   Map 19 D4

Living up to its name, the hotel enjoys panoramic views of the Glen O'the Downs, a renowned beauty spot, yet it is only 15 miles south of Dublin. Bedrooms in the newest part of the long, low building are the largest and have picture windows. Conferences for up to 150 delegates. **Rooms 26.** *Garden. Access, Visa.*

Dingle   Doyle's Seafood Bar & Townhouse   £50
Tel 066 51174 Fax 066 51816

4 John Street Dingle Co Kerry   Map 19 A5

Popular family-run restaurant with flagstoned floors and lots of pine.
Generous portions of excellent local fish landed by Dingle boats are on offer, and cooking is straightforward, letting the freshness come through. Seafood chowder, oysters, hot trout smokies, home-smoked salmon, sweet and sour marinated herrings and salmon tartare with horseradish cream

feature among the starters, while fish also dominates the choice of main courses: lobster, prawns, black sole fillets with orange beurre blanc, mussels and more... Strawberry shortcake, chocolate biscuit cake and meringue with raspberry purée are typical desserts. Lunchtime brings a choice of lighter and snackier items. Unusual wine list features some good wines from France, Germany, Spain and Australia – particularly strong on whites. **Seats 50.** *Parties 12. D only 6.30-9. Closed Sun, also mid Nov-mid Mar. Access, Visa,* ◑

Rooms   £55

Excellent bedrooms put many hotels to shame, with antiques, stylish fabrics and luxurious bathrooms featuring good over-tub showers. There's also a civilised lounge. **Rooms 8.**

Dublin	**Al Fresco**	**NEW**	£65
Tel 01 771883			**R**
27 Lower Stephen Street Dublin 2 Co Dublin			**Map 19 D4**

The late-lamented *Shay Beano* has been replaced by a sister restaurant to *Il Primo* with its own new brand of Italian chic. Try *carpaccio al pesce*, marinated wild Irish salmon served with an onion and garlic marmalade followed perhaps by *tagliatelle con frutta di mare*, pasta and mixed seafood (squid, mussels, salmon) in a white wine and cream sauce, and *verdure misto*, a mixed salad of leaves in season. Finish with an excellent cheese plate – pecorino, parmigiano and gorgonzola – or tiramisu and strong black coffee. Any wine under £40 can be sampled by the glass and de Braams mineral water is free. **Seats 30.** *Parties 16. Meals 12-12. Closed Sun, Bank Holidays. Access, Visa,* ◑

Dublin	**Ayumi-Ya Japanese Steakhouse**	**NEW**	£40
Tel 01 622233			**R**
132 Lower Baggot Street Dublin Co Dublin			**Map 19 D4**

This informal basement restaurant, an offshoot of the Ayumi-Ya Restaurant in Blackrock, serves simple tasty dishes inexpensively and is clearly signed from the street. Crisp, colourful specialities include kushi-yaki (food cooked on skewers), teriyaki (food marinated then grilled over charcoal) and teppanyaki steaks (cooked on a hot iron plate). Try ebifari (big prawns, deep fried in breadcrumbs) or mushroom panko age (mushrooms stuffed with salted plums, breadcrumbed and deep-fried), both served with a green salad with wakame (seaweed) and bean curd and soy sauce. Main courses include beef teriyaki and salmon teriyaki, both presented sizzling on board-mounted iron dishes. **Seats 40.** *Parties 20. Private Room. L 12.30-2.30 D 6.30-12.30. Closed L Sat, all Sun. Set L from £6.95. Access, Visa.*

Dublin	**Berkeley Court**	**76%**	£173
Tel 01 601711 Fax 01 617238			**H**
Lansdowne Road Dublin Co Dublin			**Map 19 D4**

At the luxury end of the Dublin market, set in grounds once occupied by the University College Botanical Gardens, Berkeley Court is the flagship of the Doyle group. A split-level lobby-lounge sets the tone with mirrored columns, brass-potted parlour palms and a mish-mash of modern, Chinese and French reproduction furniture. More sedate are the Gothic panelled bar, elegant Berkeley Room and bright conservatory. Ballroom, boardroom and several suites hold functions for up to 275 people. Seventeen executive suites, generously proportioned and complemented by classic furnishings, are easily the pick of the bedroom accommodation (though at a high premium), and more of the standard doubles are in the process of similar upgrading. Guests have use of the well-equipped Riverview racquet and fitness centre, 5 minutes away. **Rooms 207.** *Indoor swimming pool, sauna, solarium, hair salon, Grill room 7.30am-11.30pm, news kiosk, boutique. Access, Amex, Visa,* ◑

Dublin	Blooms Hotel	60%	£140

Tel 01 715622   Fax 01 715997

H

Anglesea Street Dublin Co Dublin

Map 19 D4

Modern city-centre hotel named after Dublin's most famous fictional son.
The public bar is popular with locals. Other public areas are rather limited.
Standardised bedrooms with telephone extensions in the bathrooms.
Rooms 86. Closed 25 & 26 Dec. Access, Amex, Visa,

Dublin	Burlington Hotel	70%	£122

Tel 01 605222   Fax 01 608496

H

Upper Leeson Street Dublin Co Dublin

Map 19 D4

With 500 bedrooms, the Burlington is Ireland's largest hotel. Built in the
70s and only a short walk from the main shopping streets. Public rooms
are on a grand scale: several large crystal chandeliers light the bustling
lobby/lounge and the two bars are in the Joycean style of old Dublin; the
large Presidents' Bar in particular is genuinely atmospheric. Bedrooms have
solid brass-bound oak furniture, coordinating fabrics and wallpaper, good
work and sitting space, and decent tiled bathrooms with generous shelf
space and bathrobes. There is an Irish cabaret with large cast six nights a
week from May to October but it's also open to non-residents, so booking
is advisable. Conferences for up to 1000 delegates. No dogs. **Rooms 500.**
Hairdressing, kiosk, boutique. Access, Amex, Visa,

Dublin	Chapter One	NEW	£70

Tel 01 732266

R

18/19 Pannell Square Dublin Co Dublin

Map 19 D4

Underneath the Dublin Writers Museum this characterful vaulted cellar
restaurant serves good, stylish food. Try meltingly tender calf's liver, served
warm with strips of bacon on a bed of tossed salad, or delicate, pretty
quenelles of fish poached in white wine with cream and dill and fresh
tomato sauce. Juicy slices of pork fillet are served on a delicious little potato
cake to soak up the meat juices and wine sauce. There's a good farmhouse
cheese selection and desserts are pretty and tempting. **Seats 100.** Parties 50.
Private Room. L 12-2.30 (Sun from 12.30) D 6-11. Closed L Sat, D Sun-Thu,
Bank Holidays, 1 week Xmas, 1 week St Patrick's Day. Set D £18.50. Access,
Amex, Visa,

Dublin	Hotel Conrad	73%	£193

Tel 01 765555   Fax 01 765424

H

Earlsfort Terrace Dublin 8 Co Dublin

Map 19 D4

A very modern international hotel whose few concessions to its location
are some paintings by Irish artists and Alfie Byrne's pubby bar in the
basement. Situated in the heart of Dublin off St Stephen's Green, the
Conrad is five minutes' walk from business, shopping and cultural centres.
Containing its own business centre, it's a popular banqueting and
conference venue seating up to 270. Other public areas include an open-
plan foyer, lobby lounge and cocktail bar with pale wood panelling, and an
all-day brasserie. Roomy bedrooms and marble-floored bathrooms score
highly for comfort and convenience, with coffee tables, work space and
well-lit vanitory units. Children under 10 stay free in their parents' room.
Rooms 190. News kiosk, brasserie (7am-11.30pm). Access, Amex, Visa,

Dublin	Le Coq Hardi		£100

Tel 01 689070

R

35 Pembroke Road Ballsbridge Dublin 4 Co Dublin

Map 19 D4

Their fifteen years here have not dimmed the enthusiasm of John and
Catherine Howard, who run this restaurant in an end-of-terrace Georgian
house in calm, club-like style. High ceilings, ornate plasterwork and

immaculate napery and glassware make a fine setting for classical French
cuisine, its modern influences confined mostly to patriotic reliance on local
suppliers and Irish cottage industries. Seasonal suggestions might include
roast fillet of mackerel with warm potato salad preceding braised oxtail or
roast rack of spring lamb with ratatouille. Classical dishes are epitomised
by *la terrine de foie gras avec les brioches* and *le homard à la vapeur servi avec
beurre à l'estragon*. A seven-course tasting menu covers a range from rabbit
terrine to wild Irish salmon and cote de boeuf with beef marrow and
Beaujolais sauce. A connoisseur's wine list (for those with long pockets)
features exceptional Bordeaux; burgundy drinkers will not be
disappointed, and the choice of vintage armagnacs is bound to impress; the
collection of Mouton Rothschilds dates back to 1945, but only some are
for sale. 12½% service charge is added to all prices. **Seats 50.** Parties 50.
*Private Room. L 12-2.30 D 7-11. Closed L Sat, all Sun, Bank Holidays,
1 week Xmas, 2 weeks Aug. Set L £16 Set D £28. Access, Amex, Visa,*

Dublin   Ernie's   £80
Tel 01 269 3260   **R**

Mulberry Gardens Donnybrook Dublin 4 Co Dublin   Map 19 D4

The walls are crammed with original pictures, mostly of Irish subjects, in
an elegant restaurant set around three sides of a pretty courtyard garden,
resplendent with floodlit fountain. The menu majors on good Irish produce
either simply cooked, as in roast rack of Wicklow lamb with turmeric and
herb crumble and grilled cockles and mussels wrapped in bacon, or more
adventurously so in dishes like ravioli of veal with rhubarb butter sauce or
sea trout en croute with Pernod-scented jus. **Seats 60.** Parties 75.
*L 12.30-2.30 D 7.15-10.15. Closed L Sat, all Sun & Mon, Bank Holidays,
1 week Xmas. Set L £13.95 Set D £19.95. Access, Amex, Visa,*

Dublin   La Fiesta   £45
Tel 01 753109   **R**

41 Lower Camden Street Dublin Co Dublin   Map 19 D4

Eamonn O'Catháin cooks his favourite dishes from around the world at
this unpretentiously cheerful restaurant. Couscous is the speciality, and
other dishes might include brandade de morue (a favourite from Eamonn's
days at *Shay Beano*), calalou (West Indian soup), spaghettini tapénade and
grilled shark. **Seats 60.** Parties 20. L 12.30-4pm D 7-11.30. Closed L Sat,
D Mon-Wed, all Sun, Bank Holidays, 1 week Xmas. Set L £4.25. Access,
Visa.

Dublin   Les Frères Jacques   £80
Tel 01 679 4555   **R**

74 Dame Street Dublin Co Dublin   Map 19 D4

Evocative prints, French-speaking staff and a theatreland location (next
door to the Olympia) imbue Les Frères with its distinctively Parisian
atmosphere, to which *le patron* adds his infectious Gallic charm. Essentially
French cuisine is on daily-changing, fixed-price menus: live lobsters from
the tank, native rock oysters and Atlantic turbot and sea bass in light,
colourful sauces reflect a fishy bias. A la carte, *confit de canard* with
Périgord-style potatoes and *tournedos de veau* with pistou sauce redress the
balance at night. 12½% service charge is added to all prices. **Seats 60.** Parties
40. *Private Room. L 12.30-2.30 D 7.30-10.30 (Fri & Sat to 11). Closed L Sat,
all Sun, Bank Holidays, 1 week Xmas. Set L £13 Set D £20. Access, Amex,
Visa.*

Dublin George's Bistro & Piano Bar £60

Tel 01 679 7000   Fax 01 679 7560   R

29 South Frederick Street Dublin 2 Co Dublin   Map 19 D4

The menu is distinctly old-fashioned, the ingredients top-quality, which
suits the mostly middle-aged, well-heeled after-theatre crowd who frequent
this popular bistro in a side street near Trinity College and the Dail. Steaks,
rack of lamb and Dover sole are favourite main courses, with something
like garlic mushrooms or avocado with crab to start. The other attraction
is live music (piano with female vocal) which tends to inhibit conversation,
but fuels the late-night buzz. Lunch is served on the ground floor, dinner
in the basement. *Seats 90. Parties 60. Private Room. L 12-3.30 D 7-12.30.
Closed Sun & Mon, Bank Holidays, 1 week Xmas. Set L £8 Set D £22.
Access, Amex, Visa,*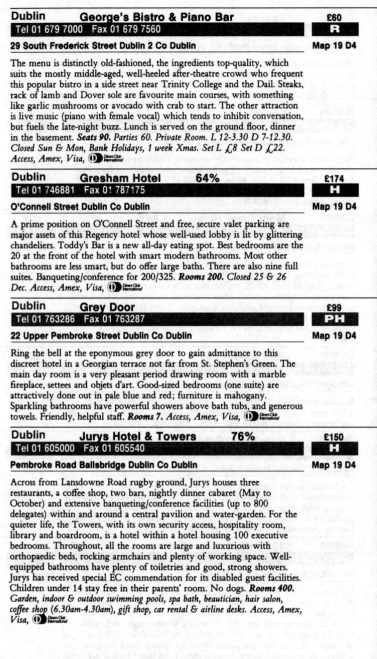

Dublin Gresham Hotel 64% £174

Tel 01 746881   Fax 01 787175   H

O'Connell Street Dublin Co Dublin   Map 19 D4

A prime position on O'Connell Street and free, secure valet parking are
major assets of this Regency hotel whose well-used lobby is lit by glittering
chandeliers. Toddy's Bar is a new all-day eating spot. Best bedrooms are the
20 at the front of the hotel with smart modern bathrooms. Most other
bathrooms are less smart, but do offer large baths. There are also nine full
suites. Banqueting/conference for 200/325. *Rooms 200. Closed 25 & 26
Dec. Access, Amex, Visa,*

Dublin Grey Door £99

Tel 01 763286   Fax 01 763287   PH

22 Upper Pembroke Street Dublin Co Dublin   Map 19 D4

Ring the bell at the eponymous grey door to gain admittance to this
discreet hotel in a Georgian terrace not far from St. Stephen's Green. The
main day room is a very pleasant period drawing room with a marble
fireplace, settees and objets d'art. Good-sized bedrooms (one suite) are
attractively done out in pale blue and red; furniture is mahogany.
Sparkling bathrooms have powerful showers above bath tubs, and generous
towels. Friendly, helpful staff. *Rooms 7. Access, Amex, Visa,*

Dublin Jurys Hotel & Towers 76% £150

Tel 01 605000   Fax 01 605540   H

Pembroke Road Ballsbridge Dublin Co Dublin   Map 19 D4

Across from Lansdowne Road rugby ground, Jurys houses three
restaurants, a coffee shop, two bars, nightly dinner cabaret (May to
October) and extensive banqueting/conference facilities (up to 800
delegates) within and around a central pavilion and water-garden. For the
quieter life, the Towers, with its own security access, hospitality room,
library and boardroom, is a hotel within a hotel housing 100 executive
bedrooms. Throughout, all the rooms are large and luxurious with
orthopaedic beds, rocking armchairs and plenty of working space. Well-
equipped bathrooms have plenty of toiletries and good, strong showers.
Jurys has received special EC commendation for its disabled guest facilities.
Children under 14 stay free in their parents' room. No dogs. *Rooms 400.
Garden, indoor & outdoor swimming pools, spa bath, beautician, hair salon,
coffee shop (6.30am-4.30am), gift shop, car rental & airline desks. Access, Amex,
Visa,*

Dublin **Kapriol** **£64**

Tel 01 751235 **R**

45 Lower Camden Street Dublin Co Dublin 2 **Map 19 D4**

Unprepossessing from the outside but neat as a new pin within. Family room with a menu of traditional Italian favourites. ***Seats 30.*** *Parties 32. D only 7.30-12. Closed Sun, Bank Holidays, 3 weeks Aug. Access, Amex, Visa,* Diners Club International

Dublin **Locks** **£82**

Tel 01 543391 **R**

1 Windsor Terrace Portobello Dublin 8 Co Dublin **Map 19 D4**

Portions are generous at a canal-side restaurant whose menu includes specials from the day's catch. Charcoal-grilled steak is another favourite. ***Seats 47.*** *Parties 30. Private Room. L 12.30-2 D 7.15-11. Closed L Sat, all Sun, Bank Holidays, 1 week Xmas. Set L from £12.95 Set D from £18.95. Access, Amex, Visa,* Diners Club International

Dublin **Mont Clare Hotel** **64%** **£135**

Tel 01 616799 Fax 01 615663 **H**

Merrion Square Dublin Co Dublin **Map 19 D4**

Virtually rebuilt and extended in 1990, the Mont Clare now clearly aims at the corporate business market. Only the large Dublinesque bar, full of stained glass and dark wood, and popular with the surrounding business community, has been retained. Most bedrooms are not large but polished wood furniture provides plenty of workspace. There are phones handily placed on the desks as well as by the bed and smart, if smallish, marble bathrooms. No dogs. ***Rooms 74.*** *Valet parking. Access, Amex, Visa,* Diners Club International

Dublin **Montrose Hotel** **63%** **£98**

Tel 01 269 3311 Fax 01 269 1164 **H**

Stillorgan Road Dublin Co Dublin **Map 19 D4**

South of town, near the campus of University College, offering good public areas and practical, often spacious, bedrooms. Children under 10 stay free in parents' room. ***Rooms 180.*** *Access, Amex, Visa,* Diners Club International

Dublin **New Royal Dublin Hotel** **63%** **£96**

Tel 01 733666 Fax 01 733120 **H**

40 Upper O'Connell Street Dublin 1 Co Dublin **Map 19 D4**

On Dublin's most celebrated street, a privately-owned, recently refurbished, modern hotel with identical bedrooms and a new all-day bar and brasserie. Striking conference venue in O'Connell Hall (capacity 250). Limited amount of secure parking in a basement garage. ***Rooms 117.*** *News kiosk, brasserie (7am-midnight). Access, Amex, Visa,* Diners Club International

Dublin **101 Talbot** **NEW** **£32**

Tel 01 745011 **R**

101 Talbot Street Dublin 1 Co Dublin **Map 19 D4**

Upstairs in a busy shopping street, a stone's throw from O'Connell Street and just around the corner from the Abbey and Peacock Theatres, this bright, airy restaurant has a rather arty cheap and cheerful atmosphere which harmonises well with the wholesome Mediterranean-influenced food. Leanings towards wholefoods and vegetarian dishes – yellow split pea and vegetable soup, for example, or broccoli and blue cheese filo parcels are balanced by interesting meals for carnivores, good home baking and some very moreish desserts – and, for once, the cheap and cheerful description carries through to the bill. ***Seats 80.*** *Parties 50. L 12-3 D 6.30-11 (light meals 10am-11pm). Closed D Mon, all Sun, Bank Holidays. Access, Visa.*

| Dublin | Oisins | £72 |

Tel & Fax 01 753433 **R**

31 Upper Camden Street Dublin Co Dublin Map 19 D4

Original Irish Specialities In Nostalgic Surroundings. Oisins doesn't actually mean that, but it could, with a menu that includes crubeens (pig's trotters), pigeon breast with Guinness and mustard sauce, black sole with mushrooms, and Irish stew with dumplings. Nettle soup is a popular starter, carrageen moss (blancmange made with West Coast seaweed) a favourite dessert. Very friendly service, regular live music. *Seats 40. Parties 40. D only 6.30-10.30. Closed Sun & Mon, Bank Holidays. Set D £25. Access, Amex, Visa,*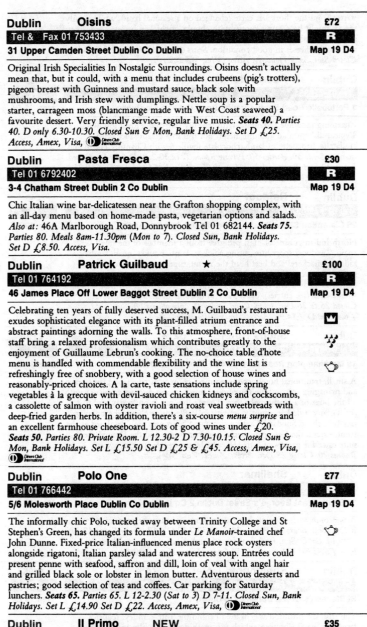

| Dublin | Pasta Fresca | £30 |

Tel 01 6792402 **R**

3-4 Chatham Street Dublin 2 Co Dublin Map 19 D4

Chic Italian wine bar-delicatessen near the Grafton shopping complex, with an all-day menu based on home-made pasta, vegetarian options and salads. *Also at: 46A Marlborough Road, Donnybrook Tel 01 682144. Seats 75. Parties 80. Meals 8am-11.30pm (Mon to 7). Closed Sun, Bank Holidays. Set D £8.50. Access, Visa.*

| Dublin | Patrick Guilbaud ★ | £100 |

Tel 01 764192 **R**

46 James Place Off Lower Baggot Street Dublin 2 Co Dublin Map 19 D4

Celebrating ten years of fully deserved success, M. Guilbaud's restaurant exudes sophisticated elegance with its plant-filled atrium entrance and abstract paintings adorning the walls. To this atmosphere, front-of-house staff bring a relaxed professionalism which contributes greatly to the enjoyment of Guillaume Lebrun's cooking. The no-choice table d'hote menu is handled with commendable flexibility and the wine list is refreshingly free of snobbery, with a good selection of house wines and reasonably-priced choices. A la carte, taste sensations include spring vegetables à la grecque with devil-sauced chicken kidneys and cockscombs, a cassolette of salmon with oyster ravioli and roast veal sweetbreads with deep-fried garden herbs. In addition, there's a six-course *menu surprise* and an excellent farmhouse cheeseboard. Lots of good wines under £20. *Seats 50. Parties 80. Private Room. L 12.30-2 D 7.30-10.15. Closed Sun & Mon, Bank Holidays. Set L £15.50 Set D £25 & £45. Access, Amex, Visa,*

| Dublin | Polo One | £77 |

Tel 01 766442 **R**

5/6 Molesworth Place Dublin Co Dublin Map 19 D4

The informally chic Polo, tucked away between Trinity College and St Stephen's Green, has changed its formula under *Le Manoir*-trained chef John Dunne. Fixed-price Italian-influenced menus place rock oysters alongside rigatoni, Italian parsley salad and watercress soup. Entrées could present penne with seafood, saffron and dill, loin of veal with angel hair and grilled black sole or lobster in lemon butter. Adventurous desserts and pastries; good selection of teas and coffees. Car parking for Saturday lunchers. *Seats 65. Parties 65. L 12-2.30 (Sat to 3) D 7-11. Closed Sun, Bank Holidays. Set L £14.90 Set D £22. Access, Amex, Visa,*

| Dublin | Il Primo NEW | £35 |

Tel 01 783373 **R**

16 Montague Street Dublin Co Dublin 2 Map 19 D4

A small Italian restaurant, unpretentious almost to the point of austerity, but the cooking is imaginative, well-cooked and good value. Warm spinach salad with new potatoes, shallots and balsamic vinegar is a typical starter from the short à la carte (changed on a seasonal basis), while a daily special might be creamy risotto with chunks of chicken breast, a few livers and wild mushrooms. Home-made pasta is excellent, portions are generous and Italian cheeses in good condition. *Seats 44. Parties 18. L 12-3 D 6-11. Closed Sun, Bank Holidays. Access, Visa,*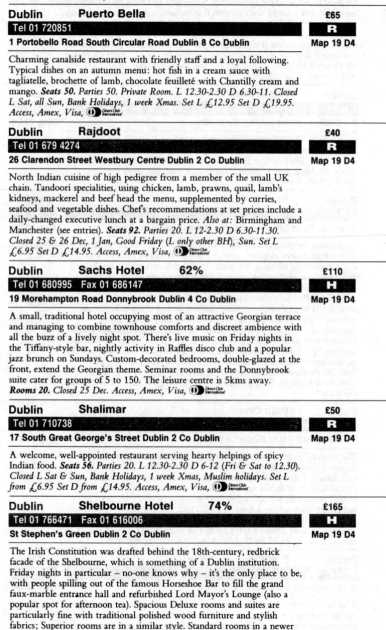

Dublin	Puerto Bella	£65

Tel 01 720851   **R**

1 Portobello Road South Circular Road Dublin 8 Co Dublin   **Map 19 D4**

Charming canalside restaurant with friendly staff and a loyal following. Typical dishes on an autumn menu: hot fish in a cream sauce with tagliatelle, brochette of lamb, chocolate feuilleté with Chantilly cream and mango. *Seats 50. Parties 50. Private Room. L 12.30-2.30 D 6.30-11. Closed L Sat, all Sun, Bank Holidays, 1 week Xmas. Set L £12.95 Set D £19.95. Access, Amex, Visa,*

Dublin	Rajdoot	£40

Tel 01 679 4274   **R**

26 Clarendon Street Westbury Centre Dublin 2 Co Dublin   **Map 19 D4**

North Indian cuisine of high pedigree from a member of the small UK chain. Tandoori specialities, using chicken, lamb, prawns, quail, lamb's kidneys, mackerel and beef head the menu, supplemented by curries, seafood and vegetable dishes. Chef's recommendations at set prices include a daily-changed executive lunch at a bargain price. *Also at:* Birmingham and Manchester (see entries). *Seats 92. Parties 20. L 12-2.30 D 6.30-11.30. Closed 25 & 26 Dec, 1 Jan, Good Friday (L only other BH), Sun. Set L £6.95 Set D £14.95. Access, Amex, Visa,*

Dublin	Sachs Hotel	62%	£110

Tel 01 680995   Fax 01 686147   **H**

19 Morehampton Road Donnybrook Dublin 4 Co Dublin   **Map 19 D4**

A small, traditional hotel occupying most of an attractive Georgian terrace and managing to combine townhouse comforts and discreet ambience with all the buzz of a lively night spot. There's live music on Friday nights in the Tiffany-style bar, nightly activity in Raffles disco club and a popular jazz brunch on Sundays. Custom-decorated bedrooms, double-glazed at the front, extend the Georgian theme. Seminar rooms and the Donnybrook suite cater for groups of 5 to 150. The leisure centre is 5kms away. *Rooms 20. Closed 25 Dec. Access, Amex, Visa,*

Dublin	Shalimar	£50

Tel 01 710738   **R**

17 South Great George's Street Dublin 2 Co Dublin   **Map 19 D4**

A welcome, well-appointed restaurant serving hearty helpings of spicy Indian food. *Seats 56. Parties 20. L 12.30-2.30 D 6-12 (Fri & Sat to 12.30). Closed L Sat & Sun, Bank Holidays, 1 week Xmas, Muslim holidays. Set L from £6.95 Set D from £14.95. Access, Amex, Visa,*

Dublin	Shelbourne Hotel	74%	£165

Tel 01 766471   Fax 01 616006   **H**

St Stephen's Green Dublin 2 Co Dublin   **Map 19 D4**

The Irish Constitution was drafted behind the 18th-century, redbrick facade of the Shelbourne, which is something of a Dublin institution. Friday nights in particular – no-one knows why – it's the only place to be, with people spilling out of the famous Horseshoe Bar to fill the grand faux-marble entrance hall and refurbished Lord Mayor's Lounge (also a popular spot for afternoon tea). Spacious Deluxe rooms and suites are particularly fine with traditional polished wood furniture and stylish fabrics; Superior rooms are in a similar style. Standard rooms in a newer wing are smaller and those on lower floors suffer somewhat from external noise. Bathrobes, mini-bars and three telephones are provided in all rooms. Room service can become a bit overstretched at busy times. Valet parking, but no leisure facilities within the hotel. Forte. *Rooms 164. News kiosk. Access, Amex, Visa,* (D) Diners Club International

Dublin   Ta Se Mohogani Gaspipes   NEW   £45

Tel 01 679 8138   **R**

17 Manor Street Stoneybatter Dublin Co Dublin 7   **Map 19 D4**

A first for Dublin, this stylish little American restaurant has opened up a new area, both geographically and in food terms. From an eclectic, short à la carte menu (changed when it seems appropriate and augmented by daily specials) chargrills are a speciality and home-made garlic sausages with red peppers and onions not to be missed. Portions are generous, accompaniments such as stuffed baked potato, pitta bread and fresh vegetables are all included and it is possible for the disciplined to eat very cheaply. Desserts, however, may disappoint. *Seats 40. Parties 16. L 12-3 D 6-11.30. Closed Sun & Mon, Bank Holidays. Access, Visa.*

Dublin   The Westbury   79%   £173

Tel 01 679 1122   Fax 01 679 7078   **HR**

Off Grafton Street Dublin 2 Co Dublin   **Map 19 D4**

Nestled in the heart of Grafton Street, with its own integral shopping mall, the Westbury exudes the warmth of a home-from-home, albeit a very grand one. Mannequins meandering among the tables constitutes a typical tea-time diversion; there's slick table service in the Terrace Bar and Dublin's Joycean traditions are echoed in the lively Sandbank Seafood Bar with its stained-glass and rosewood panelling. Pinks and blues are key colours in the bedrooms, which offer a high standard of comfort and accessories; they range from newly modernised singles to luxury penthouse suites. Business gatherings and banquets (to a maximum of 200) are accommodated in elegantly furnished boardrooms and function suites. Here, as elsewhere, the Westbury has the atmosphere of a top-class hotel with legions of staff providing a good level of service. *Rooms 205. Beautician, hair salon, gymnasium, news kiosk, coffee shop (10am-10pm, Sun 8pm). Access, Amex, Visa,* (D) Diners Club International

Russell Room   £85

The traditional French menu holds few surprises, though the cooking is sound and both service and surroundings suitably stylish. Praiseworthy Irish salmon and seafoods make a strong showing, and flambéed crepes Suzette a completely apposite dessert for the setting. A three-course table d'hote lunch (four courses at dinner) offers a choice of five or so dishes at each course. Easy-to-use, but unspectacular wine list. 15% service charge is added to all menu prices. *Seats 100. Parties 40. Private Room. L 12.30-2.30 D 6.30-10.30 (Sun to 9.30). Set L £14.50 Set D £18.50.*

Dublin Airport   Forte Crest   57%   £110

Tel 01 379211   Fax 01 425874   **H**

Collinstown Dublin Airport Co Dublin   **Map 18 D3**

The former Dublin International Hotel provides modern, carefully soundproofed accommodation close to the airport, and courtesy coaches to the terminal. Conference and exhibition suites for up to 150; leisure facilities nearby. Choice of restaurants includes *Sampans* Chinese. *Rooms 192. Access, Amex, Visa,* (D) Diners Club International

Dublin   Places of Interest

Tourist Information   Tel 01 747733.
Dublin Airport   Tel 01 376387/375533.
Bank of Ireland   College Green Tel 01 776801.
Trinity College (Book of Kells) and Dublin Experience

Dublin Zoo   Phoenix Park Tel 01 771425.
Fairyhouse Racecourse   Ratoath Tel 01 256167.
Leopardstown Foxtrot   Tel 01 893607.
The Curragh   Co Kildare Tel 045 41205.
Gaelic Athletic Association (GAA)   Tel 01 363222.
Croke Park Football Ground   Hurling and Gaelic Football.
Rugby Union of Ireland   Tel 01 684601.
Landsdowne Road Rugby Ground   Baub Bridge.
   Theatres and Concert Halls
Abbey and Peacock Theatres   Lower Abbey Street Tel 01 787222.
Andrew's Lane Theatre   Exchequer Street Tel 01 6795720.
Eblana Theatre   Store Street Tel 01 6798404.
Gaiety Theatre   South King Street Tel 01 771177.
Gate Theatre   Cavendish Row Tel 01 744045.
Olympia Theatre   Dame Street Tel 01 777744.
Tivoli Theatre   Francis Street Tel 01 544472.
National Concert Hall   Earlsfoot Terrace Tel 01 711888.
Point Depot (Exhibitions and Concerts)   North Wall Quay Tel 01 363633.
Irish Film Centre   Eustace Street Tel 01 778788.
   Museums and Art Galleries
Chester Beatty Library and Gallery of Oriental Art   Shrewsbury Road Tel 01 692386.
Civic Museum   South William Street Tel 01 6794260.
Dublin Writer's Museum   Parnell Square North Tel 01 722077.
Fry Model Railway Museum   Malahide Castle Tel 01 452758.
Irish Museum of Modern Art/Royal Hospital   Kilmainham Tel 01 718666.
Guinness Brewery   James's Gate Tel 01 536700 *ext. 5155.*
Hugh Lane Municipal Gallery   Parnell Square Tel 01 741903.
National Gallery of Ireland   Merrion Square West Tel 01 615133.
National Museum of Ireland   Kildare Street Tel 01 618811.
National Wax Museum   Granby Row, Parnell Square Tel 01 726340.
Natural History Museum   Merrion Street Tel 01 618811.
   Historic Houses, Castles and Gardens
Dublin Castle   Dame Street Tel 01 6793713.
Joyce Tower   Sandycove Tel 01 2809265.
Kilmainham Gaol   Kilmainham Tel 01 535984.
Malahide Castle   Malahide Tel 01 452655.
Marsh's Library   St. Patrick Close Tel 01 543511.
National Botanic Gardens   Glasnevin Tel 01 377596.
Newbridge House   Donabate Tel 01 436534.
Newman House   St. Stephen's Green Tel 01 757255.
Number Twenty Nine   Lower Fitzwilliam Street Tel 01 765831.
Christ Church Cathedral   Christ Church Place Tel 01 778099.
St. Patrick's Cathedral   Patrick's Close Tel 01 754817.
Whitefriar Street Carmelite Church   Aungier Street Tel 01 758821.

Dun Laoghaire	Digby's	£74
Tel 01 280 4600		**R**
5 Windsor Terrace Dun Laoghaire Co Dublin		Map 19 D4

A colourful first-floor restaurant in a Victorian terrace overlooking the sea, run by husband-and-wife team Jane and Paul Cathcart. The varied menu changes frequently to reflect Paul's visits to the markets but fish features strongly in summer and wild game in winter. Well-tried combinations include pork steak Normandy style (with apple stuffing and a cream and Calvados sauce) and fillets of plaice stuffed with crab. Excellent desserts: tangy tarte au citron and smooth, light chocolate truffle cake. Wine bar and light meals on the ground floor. No-smoking area. *Seats 52. Parties 52. L (Sun only) 12.30-3 D 7-11 (Sun to 10). Closed D Tue, Bank Holidays. Set L £10.50 Set D £16.50. Access, Amex, Visa,* Diners Club International

Dun Laoghaire	Restaurant Na Mara	£75
Tel 01 280 0509 Fax 01 284 4649		R
1 Harbour Road Dun Laoghaire Co Dublin		Map 19 D4

Railway buffs will find this restaurant overlooking the harbour fascinating, for it is sited in the old Kingstown terminal building and owned by Irish Rail Catering Services. The interior is classical, the menus a mixture of traditional and modern, with the main emphasis on fish: roulade of crab and spinach with a lime yoghurt dressing, paupiette of sole filled with prawns, scallops flamed with brandy and butter sauce, lobster Newburg or Thermidor. Also meat and vegetarian dishes. Good cooking and capable service. 15% service charge is added to the bill. *Seats 80. Parties 75. Private Room. L 12.30-2.30 D 7-10.30. Closed Sun, 1 week Xmas. Set L £12.75 Set D £22. Access, Amex, Visa,*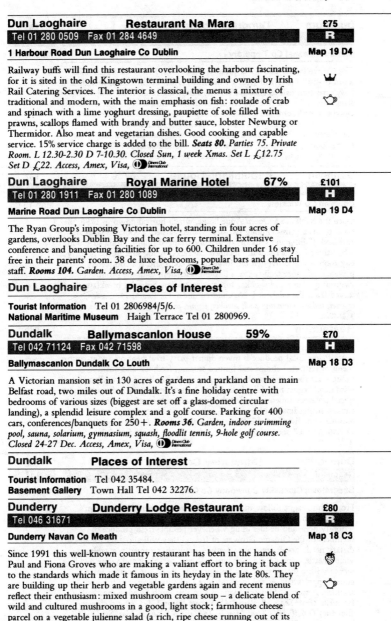

Dun Laoghaire	Royal Marine Hotel	67%	£101
Tel 01 280 1911 Fax 01 280 1089			H
Marine Road Dun Laoghaire Co Dublin			Map 19 D4

The Ryan Group's imposing Victorian hotel, standing in four acres of gardens, overlooks Dublin Bay and the car ferry terminal. Extensive conference and banqueting facilities for up to 600. Children under 16 stay free in their parents' room. 38 de luxe bedrooms, popular bars and cheerful staff. *Rooms 104. Garden. Access, Amex, Visa,*

Dun Laoghaire	Places of Interest

Tourist Information   Tel 01 2806984/5/6.
National Maritime Museum   Haigh Terrace Tel 01 2800969.

Dundalk	Ballymascanlon House	59%	£70
Tel 042 71124 Fax 042 71598			H
Ballymascanlon Dundalk Co Louth			Map 18 D3

A Victorian mansion set in 130 acres of gardens and parkland on the main Belfast road, two miles out of Dundalk. It's a fine holiday centre with bedrooms of various sizes (biggest are set off a glass-domed circular landing), a splendid leisure complex and a golf course. Parking for 400 cars, conferences/banquets for 250+. *Rooms 36. Garden, indoor swimming pool, sauna, solarium, gymnasium, squash, floodlit tennis, 9-hole golf course. Closed 24-27 Dec. Access, Amex, Visa,*

Dundalk	Places of Interest

Tourist Information   Tel 042 35484.
Basement Gallery   Town Hall Tel 042 32276.

Dunderry	Dunderry Lodge Restaurant	£80
Tel 046 31671		R
Dunderry Navan Co Meath		Map 18 C3

Since 1991 this well-known country restaurant has been in the hands of Paul and Fiona Groves who are making a valiant effort to bring it back up to the standards which made it famous in its heyday in the late 80s. They are building up their herb and vegetable gardens again and recent menus reflect their enthusiasm: mixed mushroom cream soup – a delicate blend of wild and cultured mushrooms in a good, light stock; farmhouse cheese parcel on a vegetable julienne salad (a rich, ripe cheese running out of its crisp filo case); tender porchetta redolent with herbs and garlic; supreme of pheasant with celeriac and apple purée. Sauces are excellent and the dessert trolley should not be missed. Sunday lunch is exceptional value. The wine list is constantly expanding and compiled with thought. *Seats 40. Parties 12. L Sun 1-2 (other days by arrangement, open L Sat May-Aug) D 7-9.30. Closed D Sun, all Mon, Bank Holidays. Set L £13 Set D £21.50. Access, Amex, Visa,*

Dundrum   Dundrum House   66%   £86

Tel 062 71116   Fax 062 71366   **H**

Dundrum Cashel Co Tipperary   Map 19 B5

The Crowe family take great pride in their hotel, a large Georgian house
set in beautiful parkland with a trout-filled river. Public rooms include a
lofty reception hall in cheerful yellow, a drawing room filled with wing
armchairs and a bar (the old chapel) with live music every night in season.
Good-size bedrooms are furnished with antiques but are otherwise fairly
plain. A new 18-hole golf course has recently been laid out. Plans to be
completed by 1993 include a leisure centre with indoor swimming pool,
plunge pool, gymnasium, sauna and steam room. *Rooms 55. Garden,
18-hole golf course, snooker, fishing. Access, Amex, Visa,* (I) *Diners Club International*

Dunlavin   Rathsallagh House   67%   £92

Tel 045 53112   Fax 045 53343   **HR**

Dunlavin Co Wicklow   Map 19 C4

Once the stables to a Queen Anne house, which burned down in 1798, the
hotel boasts a prize-winning two-acre walled garden, a 530-acre farm and
parkland. Fishing and stalking are readily arranged (plus hunting in season),
while those less energetically inclined can relax by log fires in the homely
day rooms. The converted old forge in the courtyard is a completely
private conference facility (for up to 50 delegates), with the promise of
swimming, sauna and snooker for later recreation. Splendid breakfasts
served from the sideboard. No children under 12. *Rooms 14. Garden,
croquet, indoor swimming pool, snooker, tennis, practice golf. Access, Visa,*
(I) *Diners Club International*

Restaurant   £62

There's an easy-going atmosphere, and Joe and Kay O'Flynn are charming   🍵
hosts. Prime local produce is given dinner-party treatment on a four-course
menu of restricted choice and limited saucing; freshness and quality,
though, are the watchwords: oxtail soup, grilled scallops or woodland salad
with quails' eggs; brill fillet baked with hollandaise or smoked bacon and
spiced potatoes. Luscious trolleyed sweets and Irish farmhouse cheeses create
equally fitting finales. New World wines are well represented on the
sensible wine list. *Seats 50. Parties 50. Private Room. L (Sun only) 1-2
D 7.30-8.30. Closed D Sun, all Mon, 3 days Xmas, 1 week from 2 Jan. Set D
£25.*

Dunworley   Dunworley Cottage   £50

Tel 023 40314   **R**

Butlerstown Clonakilty Dunworley Co Cork   Map 19 B6

From Timoleague follow the signs to Dunworley, then the restaurant's   🍵
own signs, to find this remote old stone cottage. They take their food very
seriously here, and besides using whenever possible fresh produce of
members of the Organic Growers of Ireland they will also cater for special
dietary needs. Soups are quite a feature – mussels, creamed vegetables,
young nettle – and a local speciality is West Cork black and white pudding
served with a sherry sauce and lingonberries. Steaks are popular main
courses, plus whatever the local catch provides in the way of fish and
shellfish. A special children's menu is available, with Swedish meatballs a
favourite treat. *Seats 50. Parties 45. Private Room. L 1-3 (by arrangement
Jun-Aug) D 6.30-10. Closed Mon & Tue, also 6 Jan-early Mar. Set D £17.
Access, Amex, Visa,* *Diners Club International*

Durrus   Blairs Cove House Restaurant   £60
Tel 027 61127   R

Blairs Cove Durrus Nr Bantry Co Cork   Map 19 A6

Exposed stone walls and a lofty timbered ceiling make a most attractive
setting, while fine views of Bantry Bay explain the fishy emphasis of
Sabine de Mey's dinner menus. Following prodigious buffet starters, feast
on wild salmon with horseradish crust and beurre blanc, John Dory with
orange sauce, or steaks and spring lamb masterfully cooked over a wood-
fired grill. Numerous fine desserts are laid out on the grand piano, and
coffee follows in a Turkish copper pot. Accommodation in comfortable
self-catering apartments nearby can be arranged by ringing 027 61041.
*Seats 70. Parties 70. D only 7.30-9.30. Closed Sun (also Mon Sep-Jun),
Nov-Feb. Set D £22. Access, Amex, Visa,*

Ennis   Auburn Lodge   61%   £65
Tel 065 21247   Fax 065 21202   H

Galway Road Ennis Co Clare   Map 19 B4

Well-equipped bedrooms and friendly, helpful staff at a modern, sprawling
hotel north of town on the N18, close to both Lake Ballyalla and the Cliffs
of Moher. Conference and banqueting suites accommodate up to 500. 25
new rooms have recently been added. *Rooms 100. Garden, Access, Amex,
Visa,*

Ennis   Old Ground Hotel   66%   £95
Tel 065 28127   Fax 065 28112   H

Ennis Co Clare   Map 19 B4

Traditional ivy-clad hotel, next to Ennis Cathedral; convenient for
Shannon airport. Banqueting for 180; conferences for up to 250. Ground-
floor bedrooms are suitable for the disabled. Children under 16 stay free in
their parents' room. Forte Heritage. *Rooms 58. Access, Amex, Visa,*

Ennis   West County Inn   59%   £78
Tel 065 28421   Fax 065 28801   H

Clare Road Ennis Co Clare   Map 19 B4

Modern hotel on the tourist route with garden conservatory and *Ebonys*
night club featuring a summer season "Taste of Irish" cabaret. Bedrooms
for the disabled. Children under 12 stay free in their parents' room. The
cavernous Pyramid suite accommodates 550 for banquets and 800 for
theatre-style conferences. *Rooms 100. Keep-fit equipment, snooker. Access,
Amex, Visa,*

Ennis   Places of Interest

Tourist Information Tel 065 28366.

Enniskerry   Curtlestown House   NEW   £50
Tel 01 282 5083   R

Curtlestown Enniskerry Co Wicklow   Map 19 D4

Although so near to Dublin this cosy little farmhouse is very much a
country restaurant and the menu is quite simple. Typical offerings might
include home-made soup of the day (possibly cream of vegetable) or
smoked fillets of trout raifort (well-smoked fillets with an attractive and
tasty salad of mixed leaves and horseradish sauce) all served with freshly
baked bread and butter followed at lunchtime, perhaps, by a home-cooked
roast served with a communal dish of small potatoes steamed in their
jackets, chunky carrot batons and lightly cooked broccoli spears – simple
and delicious. Home-made apple crumble is served with real egg custard.

Seats 40. Parties 20. Private Room. L (Sun only) 12.30-2.30 D 8-10.
Closed Mon. Set L £9.50 Set D from £15. Access, Visa

Enniskerry   Enniscree Lodge Inn   £60

Tel 01 286 3542   Fax 01 286 6037   **RR**

Cloon Enniskerry Co Wicklow   Map 19 D4

Just half an hour outside Dublin (turn off the N11 at Bray) this friendly
old inn has a cosy bar for winter, a terrace for sunny weather and good all-
day bar food. The terrace restaurant offers imaginative seasonal menus in a
spectacular environment overlooking the Glencree valley and Sugarloaf
mountains. Crab and fennel bisque, Wicklow lamb and Gaelic steaks;
Baileys and brown bread ice cream reflect the chef's interest in updated
traditional Irish food. *Seats 40. Parties 12. Private Room. L 12.30-2.30*
D 7.30-9.30 (Sat to 10, Sun to 9). Closed Mon & Tue in winter, 3 Jan-14
Feb. Set D £18.50. Access, Amex, Visa, **(D)** Diners Club International

Rooms   £67

Ten decent-sized bedrooms, many of which have breathtaking views, are
well equipped and modestly furnished, with adequate en-suite bathrooms.
Under-12s stay free in their parents' room. No dogs.

Ferrycarrig Bridge   Ferrycarrig Hotel   61%   £90

Tel 053 22999   Fax 053 41982   **H**

Ferrycarrig Bridge Nr Wexford Co Wexford   Map 19 D5

Set in landscaped gardens stretching down to the water's edge and a path
leads to Ferrycarrig Castle. All bedrooms look out over the Slaney estuary
at a friendly, well-run modern hotel on the N11 not far from Wexford.
Day rooms are smart and comfortable, and the best accommodation – on
the 2nd and 4th floors – has stylish grey-stained units, herringbone-
patterned walls, extra-long beds and tiled bathrooms with ample shelf
space. New leisure centre and first-floor conference centre (handling up to
400 delegates) this year. *Rooms 40. Garden, gymnasium, steam bath. Access,*
Amex, Visa, **(D)** Diners Club International

Galway   Ardilaun House   66%   £94

Tel 091 21433   Fax 091 21546   **H**

Taylors Hill Galway Co Galway   Map 19 B4

A much-extended Georgian building in attractive gardens. Ardilaun House
specialises in business conferences, seminars and wedding receptions. The
main lounges, which boast fine moulded plaster friezes, are sometimes
taken up for meetings, but private guests can still find space in the plush
blue bar. Bedrooms are good-sized with nice traditional furniture. Good
housekeeping and maintenance throughout. No dogs. *Rooms 90. Garden,*
gymnasium, sauna, solarium, snooker. Closed 6 days Xmas. Access, Amex, Visa,
(D) Diners Club International

Galway   Corrib Great Southern Hotel   66%   £96

Tel 091 55281   Fax 091 51390   **H**

Dublin Road Galway Co Galway   Map 19 B4

In the heart of town, overlooking Eyre Square, an imposing building
catering for up to 1,000 conference delegates. 65 new bedrooms and a
leisure centre have been added since last year's Guide, and the rooftop
swimming pool overlooks the city. O'Flahertys pub is a convivial meeting
place. *Rooms 185. Access, Amex, Visa,* **(D)** Diners Club International

| Galway | Great Southern | 68% | £122 |

Galway   Great Southern   68%   £122

Tel 091 64041   Fax 091 66704   **H**
Eyre Square Galway Co Galway   **Map 19 B4**

Facing Eyre Square, with railway and bus stations to the rear, the Great
Southern is an imposing Victorian building with a certain grandeur
retained in remodelled public rooms, and a popular Irish bar in the
basement. Separate banqueting for 350 and conference suites (max 450).
Generally spacious bedrooms have darkwood fruniture and brass light
fittings. *Rooms 116. Indoor swimming pool, sauna, hair salon, steam room.*
Access, Amex, Visa, **Diners Club International**

Galway   Malt House Restaurant   £50

Tel 091 67866   **R**
Old Malt Mall off High Street Galway Co Galway   **Map 19 B4**

The chef relies heavily on the local fish markets for daily fare at his
cavernous, black-beamed bar and restaurant. The lunchtime table d'hote
offers especially good value: baked mussels and seafood chowder, seafood
vol-au-vent and deep-fried plaice fillets, and a traditional apple sponge with
custard. Duckling with peaches perhaps, veal steak béarnaise and rack of
lamb with rosemary redress the balance by night, alongside top-class
lobster, scallops and prawns. *Seats 68. Parties 75. L 12.30-2.30 D 7-10.*
Closed Sun, Bank Holidays, 4 days Xmas. Set L £9.90 Set D £20.85. Access,
Amex, Visa, **Diners Club International**

Galway   Places of Interest

Tourist Information   Tel 091 63081.
Ballybrit Racecourse   Tel 091 53870.

Glen of Aherlow   Aherlow House   63%   £54

Tel 062 56153   Fax 061 355405   **H**
Glen of Aherlow Nr Tipperary Co Tipperary   **Map 19 B5**

Originally a hunting lodge, the Tudor-inspired building stands in a clearing
within a 14-acre coniferous forest enwrapped by the famed Galtee
mountains. A large terrace outside the lounge bar presents wonderful views
over the Glen of Aherlow. Bedrooms are individually decorated in
appealing fashion with good-quality fabrics. Three rooms are suitable for
families. Facilities for disabled guests. Under-10s stay free in parents' room.
A separate function room caters for up to 220. No dogs. *Rooms 10. Closed*
Mon-Thurs Nov-mid-Dec & mid-Jan to early March. Access, Amex, Visa,
Diners Club International

Gorey   Marlfield House   81%   £146

Tel 055 21124   Fax 055 21572   **HR**
Gorey Co Wexford   **Map 19 D5**

Beautiful, mature gardens surround this 18th-century mansion. The
sumptuous interior, which includes a large oval foyer with fluted Doric
pilasters, a white marble floor, bust and palms, is impressive and there's a
very stylish bar with ruched drapes and pale blue and yellow damask
upholstery. Owner Mary Bowe's passion is for interior design and in six
fabulous rooms she has excelled herself; all are individually decorated with
elaborately draped fabrics, well-chosen prints and pictures, noteworthy
antiques and luxurious bathrooms. Older rooms are smaller and more
ordinary, but all have good extras and lovely cotton bedding with *broderie*
anglaise trimming; some have four-poster beds. No dogs. *Rooms 19.*
Gardens, sauna, croquet, grass tennis, helipad. Closed Dec & Jan. Access, Amex,
Visa.

Restaurant   **£90**

A verdant restaurant, almost an extension of the garden, with jungle-like
murals and a plant-filled conservatory extension. Young chef Rose
Brannock produces fixed-price menus that offer a good choice and are both

interesting and gimmick-free. Terrine of salmon and sweetbread with Noilly Prat sauce followed by pan-fried lamb kidneys with potato cake and orange liqueur sauce plus white chocolate mousse with a raspberry sauce might comprise a lunch, while dinner sees a few more involved dishes: Bannow Bay oysters in filo pastry parcels with hollandaise and vegetable butter sauce; terrine of pheasant and pigeon with pear purée and blackcurrant sauce; pan-fried fillet of beef with a bone marrow and herb crust and peppercorn sauce; fillets of sole grilled with fresh asparagus and a tomato and chive sauce. The wine list is not over-long, but is well chosen and includes some classic clarets from good years. No children under seven in the evening. *Seats 60. Parties 30. Private Room. L 12.30-2 D 7-9.30. Set L £15.50 Set D £26.50.*

Greystones   The Hungry Monk   £55

Tel 01 2875759   **R**

Greystones Co Wicklow   Map 19 D4

A collection of monk-related pictures and bric-a-brac sets the informal tone of this unpretentious first-floor restaurant of uncompromising quality at affordable prices. Table d'hote menus and Sunday lunch offer lamb's kidneys dijonnaise, moules normande and vegetarian samosas; salmon with watercress sauce, seafood vermicelli and rack of Wicklow lamb. Daily specials from the blackboard are predominantly fish and game, alongside bargain wine offers from owner and wine buff Pat Keown. His connoisseur's list has great depth and there are several house wines under £10 as well as a good choice of half bottles. *Seats 40. Parties 36. L 12.30-3 D 7-11. Closed L Tue-Fri, all Mon. Set L £10.95 Set D £13.95. Access, Visa.*

Howth   Adrian's   NEW   £60

Tel 01 391696   **R**

3 Abbey Street Howth Dublin Co Dublin   Map 19 D4

Crudités and a herby dip welcome you to this little family-run restaurant, quickly followed by yeasty rolls, garlic bread with sesame seeds and olive bread, still warm from the oven. Service may then slow down but Catriona Holden's imaginative, carefully cooked food is worth waiting for. Although carnivores and vegetarians are well catered for, the bias is towards fresh fish from the harbour. Try the Howth bisque followed, perhaps, by poached selection of fish – salmon, brill, fresh prawns and a couple of huge mussels in the half-shell, served on a very delicate mustard sauce. Pretty, sophisticated desserts are available separately, or as a trio of, for example, hazelnut biscuit glacé, Amaretto cheesecake and chocolate mousse, with nutty wafers and raspberry coulis. *Seats 32. Parties 25. Private Room. Meals 12-9.30 (Sun 12-7). Set L £14 Set D £16. Access, Amex, Visa.*

Howth   King Sitric   £70

Tel 01 326729   Fax 01 392442   **R**

East Pier Harbour Road Howth Co Dublin   Map 19 D4

Local seafood, much of it both caught and landed within sight of the King Sitric, is very much the speciality at this well-established fish restaurant on the harbourfront in Howth. Owner-chef Aidan MacManus gives a token nod to carnivores with dishes such as chicken Kiev or rack of lamb with redcurrant sauce, but it is with the great, simple fish dishes like sole on the bone or lobster with butter sauce that he excels. In addition to dinner, there is now an upstairs seafood bar open for lunch where less expensive dishes ranging from crab bisque with the famous King Sitric brown bread, through fisherman's platters and Balscadden Bay lobster mayonnaise to meringue Sitric or farmhouse cheeses can be enjoyed at tables overlooking Balscadden Bay and Howth Harbour. The champagnes and the grand cru

Chablis are as good as you can get if price is no consideration. *Seats 60.
Parties 75. Private Room.L (seafood bar) 12.30-3 D 6.30-11. Closed Sun, Bank
Holidays, 10 days Xmas & Easter. Set D £22. Access, Amex, Visa,* 🄳 Diners Club International

Howth   Places of Interest

Howth Castle Gardens   Tel 01 322624.

Kanturk	Assolas Country House	66%	£100
Tel 029 50015 Fax 029 50795			**HR**
Kanturk Co Cork			Map 19 B5

A quietly situated 17th-century manor house run by Joe Bourke and his
family since 1965. It's very much their home, and guests appreciate the air
of informality. The day room, with its log fire, is immediately welcoming,
and antique furniture creates a traditional look in the spotlessly kept
bedrooms. Good breakfasts. No dogs. *Rooms 9. Garden, croquet, tennis, game
and coarse fishing, boating. Closed Nov-Mar. Access, Visa,* 🄳 Diners Club International

Restaurant   £65

Dark red walls, well-polished old sideboards and airy drapes make the
dining room a charming spot. The daily-changing menu usually features
fish as a main course. Hazel Bourke is an excellent cook with fresh herbs
enhancing the best local produce in dishes like grilled black sole on the
bone or roast loin of lamb. Locally smoked salmon comes with blinis and
sour cream, desserts occupy a trolley, there's a selection of Munster
farmhouse cheeses, and coffee is served in the dining room. *Seats 30. Parties
34. Private Room. D only 7-8.30 (Sun to 8). Set D £25.*

Kenmare	Park Hotel	85%	£200*
Tel 064 41200 Fax 064 41402			**HR**
Kenmare Co Kerry			Map 19 A6

A substantial Victorian hotel offering lovely rural views down the
Kenmare estuary to the mountains beyond. The entrance hall is lit up by
fresh flowers and a fire in the marble fireplace and there's also a fine lounge
with gilt-framed oil paintings. 37 of the bedrooms are very spacious and
luxurious, with separate seating areas, good sofas or armchairs and antiques:
bathrooms have telephones, hooded bathrobes, huge towels and good soap.
Seven of the smaller rooms have shower/WC only. Most rooms have
individual heat control. Service is warm and friendly and the whole place
is run with superb professionalism. ★ Half-board terms only. No dogs.
*Rooms 50. Garden, croquet, 9-hole golf course, tennis, games room. Closed mid
Nov-Xmas, 4 Jan-Easter. Access, Visa.*

Restaurant   £85

Efficient staff provide first-rate service, as befits the pleasing ambience of
the restaurant with its pristine white linen and beautiful views. The menu
highlights local produce, notably lobsters and scallops direct from Kenmare
Bay. Starters could include quail salad or terrine of turbot and trout; also
good meat main courses. A quite splendid wine list, though champagnes,
clarets and burgundies especially are steeply priced; Californian wines are
exceptionally well represented. Irish regional winner of our Wine Cellar of
the Year award – see comments on Regional Winners. *Seats 80. Parties 30.
Private Room. L 1-1.45 D 7-8.45. Set L £16.50 Set D £33.*

Kenmare	Sheen Falls Lodge	86%	£220
Tel 064 41600 Fax 064 41386			**HR**
Kenmare Co Kerry			Map 19 A6

One kilometre out of Kenmare, across the Lansdowne suspension bridge,
an impressive new hotel in an idyllic setting, sitting on the high ground of
a promontory. It's painted a distinctive shade of yellow and floodlit at
night, contrasting memorably with the turbulent waters of Sheen Falls and
rapids on one side and the broad expanse of Kenmare Bay on the other. A

delightful walk is laid out around the 300 acres of lawns, semi-tropical gardens and lush woodland that surround the house and boast many colours of rhododendrons and azaleas. Views from the lodge take in the beautiful distant mountains and woodlands of south-west Kerry. Inside, a spacious lobby features marbled columns and one of many real log fires that create a warm atmosphere in the public rooms, which include a mahogany-panelled library with over 1,000 volumes (both classics and more up-to-date reads), a bar with red leather seating and a sunny yellow lounge that retains the stone fireplace and oak floor of the original hunting lodge.

Large, uncluttered bedrooms all have exceptional views, their own lobby and huge beds with real linen bedding. Huge, soft-pile towels, bathrobes and twin hand basins enhance the luxury of the marble bathrooms, which feature gold-plated fittings. An iron and board, personal safe, video recorder and shaving mirrors are also provided in every room for use by guests. Nine of the 40 rooms are suites and include a disabled persons' suite, an extra- spacious, well-equipped business suite and a self-contained apartment with versatile accommodation. The impressive conference suite, named after William Petty (the polymath physician-general to Oliver Cromwell's army and original owner of the land), is state-of-the-art and caters for up to 150 delegates, theatre-style.

A real taste of timeless Ireland at its most serene – the waters of the Holy Well beside the boathouse on the foreshore are reputed to have healing properties and the stone-arched bridge over the falls dates back to 1777. Nevertheless, almost every modern hotel amenity is provided and true luxury is at hand; guests will probably be either too relaxed or too busy to notice the lack of a swimming pool. *Rooms 40. Garden, croquet, clay-pigeon shooting, spa bath, sauna, solarium, steam room, billiard room, gymnasium, riding, tennis, games room, coarse & game fishing, valeting, library, boutique, helipad. Closed Jan-mid Mar. Access, Amex, Visa,* ⓘ 🏷

La Cascade Restaurant   £90

Views of the falls, floodlit at night, are an attraction here, but the sophisticated menu is always full of interest, too. Both a daily table d'hote and an extravagant à la carte are offered and should please even the most discerning diner. Thai-spiced cream of sweetcorn soup with cucumber and raita, terrine of foie gras with beetroot purée and toasted brioche, warm quail salad with fresh truffle and fried quail's eggs, plus tortellini of lobster, caviar and butter sauce exemplify the style of the starters; main courses continue the theme using expensive ingredients, with fresh truffle alongside pan-fried wood pigeon breasts served with deep-fried yams and caviar accompanying fillets of black sole on a red wine butter sauce. Local wild Atlantic salmon is cured and smoked on the premises. Excellent service to match the setting. Weekday lunch is served in the lounge (oysters, open sandwiches, fish casserole, stir-fried chicken, tasting plate of desserts), followed by afternoon tea (£7.50 3-5pm). *Seats 120. Parties 8. Private Room. L Sun only 1-2 D 7.30-9.30. Set D from £30.*

Kilcoran	Kilcoran Lodge	58%	£66
Tel 052 41288 Fax 052 41994			**H**
Kilcoran Cahir Co Tipperary			Map 19 C5

Bedrooms vary in size at a former hunting lodge overlooking the Suir Valley, set in 20 acres. Conference/banqueting facilities for 300/220. *Rooms 23. Indoor swimming pool, spa bath, sauna, solarium, keep-fit equipment, riding, coarse & game fishing. Access, Amex, Visa,* ⓘ 🏷

Kilkenny	Newpark Hotel	58%	£87
Tel 056 22122 Fax 056 61111			**H**
Castlecomer Road Kilkenny Co Kilkenny			Map 19 C5

60s' hotel on the N77. Basic bedrooms and a good leisure centre. Conference/banqueting facilities for 500/400. Children up to 4 free in parents' room. *Rooms 60. Indoor swimming pool, children's pool, plunge pool, team room, spa bath, sauna, solarium, keep-fit equipment, tennis, dinner dance (monthly). Access, Amex, Visa,* Diners Club International

Kilkenny Places of Interest

Tourist Information Tel 056 21755.
Irish National Design Centre Tel 056 22118

Killarney Aghadoe Heights Hotel 70% £130

Tel 064 31766 Fax 064 31345 **H**

Aghadoe Killarney Co Kerry **Map 19 A5**

A low-rise modern hotel refurbished in glitzy style inside but tempered by beautiful views over the mountains and islands around Lake Killarney outside. A library-style lounge is on the ground floor and the leisure facilities have recently been expanded. Bedrooms and bathrooms are neatly appointed but not spacious. Conference/banqueting facilities for 50/70. Sister hotel to *Fredrick's* in Maidenhead, England. ***Rooms 61.*** *Garden, indoor swimming pool, sauna, spa bath, solarium, steam room, gymnasium, beauty salon, tennis, fishing, boutique, helipad. Access, Amex, Visa,* Diners Club International

Killarney Cahernane Hotel 66% £106

Tel 064 31895 Fax 064 34340 **HR**

Muckross Road Killarney Co Kerry **Map 19 A5**

True picture-postcard material, the former home of the Earls of Pembroke, with its cleverly contrived modern extension, enjoys unspoilt views across meadowland and lake to the mountains beyond. Choice of accommodation is between the manor bedrooms, predominantly furnished with antiques, and the spacious (if rather plainer) rooms with good bathrooms in the new wing. Good porterage, housekeeping and a warm, friendly atmosphere contribute to comfort of a high order. ***Rooms 52.*** *Garden, croquet, game fishing, tennis, pitch & putt, hair salon, boutique. Closed 4 Jan-Easter. Access, Amex, Visa,* Diners Club International

Restaurant £65

There is a diverse choice on two five-course set menus or a short carte that is mainly French with a few Italian influences. Fettuccine with smoked salmon and carpaccio with lemon pepper rub shoulders with cod boulangère, venison rosettes in juniper berry sauce and Gaelic steak flambé. Crepes Suzette, perhaps, to follow, plus Irish farmhouse cheeses and hand-made chocolates. The sound list of world-wide wines is listed by country, with noteworthy Australian and Californian selections. ***Seats 90.*** *Parties 30. Private Room. D only 7-9.30. Set D £25.*

Killarney Hotel Europe 72% £84

Tel 064 31900 Fax 064 32118 **H**

Killorglin Road Fossa Killarney Co Kerry **Map 19 A5**

Views of lake and mountains are enjoyed from this large, modern hotel and most of the bedrooms have balconies to make the most of the setting. Pine-furnished bedrooms offer a generous amount of space and there is a luxurious penthouse floor. In the same group as Dunloe Castle and Ard-na-Sidhe, the hotel caters equally well for private guests and conference (up to 500 delegates theatre-style) and there is an excellent health and fitness centre. No dogs. ***Rooms 210.*** *Garden, indoor swimming pool, spa bath, sauna, hair salon, gymnasium, indoor tennis, riding. Closed Nov-Mar. Access, Amex, Visa,* Diners Club International

Killarney — Gaby's Seafood Restaurant £50

Tel 064 32519   Fax 064 32747   **R**

27 High Street Killarney Co Kerry   Map 19 A

Geert Maes, chef-patron since 1976, takes fresh local fish, cooks it simply
and accurately, and serves it with a smile. Specialities listed on the menu
are grilled salmon, black sole in cream, seafood mosaic and lobster with
cognac, wine, cream and spices. For non-seafood lovers there's sirloin or
fillet steak. Simple sweets include apple pie, chocolate mousse and home-
made ice cream. Good wines, especially white burgundies. *Seats 60. Parties
50. L 12.30-2.30 D 6-10. Closed L Sun & Mon (also D Sun Oct-Apr), Feb.
Access, Amex, Visa,*

Killarney — Great Southern   69%   £108

Tel 064 31262   Fax 064 31642   **H**

Killarney Co Kerry   Map 19 A

A substantial Victorian building near the town centre. The gardens are
extensive, and the interior boasts a grand central hall with Ionic columns,
chandeliers and plenty of seats. Bedrooms in various styles have breakfast
tables and easy chairs. The hotel is well equipped for conferences, with
facilities for up to 1,000 delegates theatre-style. *Rooms 183. Garden, indoor
swimming pool, sauna, solarium, spa bath, gymnasium, snooker, tennis,
hairdressing, baby-sitting. Closed 6 weeks Jan/Feb. Access, Amex, Visa,*

Killarney — Torc Great Southern   63%   £81

Tel 064 31611   Fax 064 31824   **H**

Park Road Killarney Co Kerry   Map 19 A

Well-run holiday hotel half a mile from the centre, on the Cork road. It's
modern and low-rise, with fine views of the Kerry mountains. *Rooms 96.
Garden, indoor swimming pool, sauna, tennis. Closed Oct-Mar. Access, Amex,
Visa,*

Killarney — Places of Interest

Tourist Information   Tel 064 31633.
Ross Castle.

Killiney — Court Hotel   68%   £87

Tel 01 285 1622   Fax 01 285 2085   **H**

Killiney Bay Killiney Co Dublin   Map 19 D

Twenty minutes' drive, or by Dart, from central Dublin, an extended
Victorian mansion looking across landscaped gardens to Killiney Bay.
International conference centre seats up to 300 theatre style. Mostly sea-
facing bedrooms are spacious and well appointed with darkwood furniture
and pleasant matching fabrics. Under-12s stay free in parents' room. No
dogs. *Rooms 86. Garden. Access, Amex, Visa,*

Killiney — Fitzpatrick's Castle   68%   £129

Tel 01 285 1533   Fax 01 285 0207   **H**

Killiney Co Dublin   Map 19 D

The Dublin area's only castle hotel, nine miles from the city; Fitzpatrick's
was built in 1741 and converted by the present owners to the hotel in
1974. It's to their credit that the house has a lived-in appeal throughout its
spacious lounges, bars and two restaurants – even the dungeons have latter-
day appeal as a disco. Darkwood furniture and draped curtains are a
common theme of the roomy bedrooms, some of which are mini-suites.
Conference facilities for up to 270; banqueting for 400. *Rooms 85. Garden,*

indoor swimming pool, sauna, gymnasium, steam room, squash, tennis, beautician, hair salon. Access, Amex, Visa, (I) Diners Club International

Killiney   Places of Interest

Ayesha Castle   Tel 01 2852323.

Killorglin   Nick's Restaurant   £65

| Tel 066 61219 | **R** |

Lower Bridge Street Killorglin Co Kerry   **Map 19 A5**

Nick and Anne Foley's steak and seafood restaurant depends entirely on daily catches and landings for its specialities and on local suppliers for the lamb, beef and organically grown vegetables which balance the menu. Nick's cooking is mainly French traditional: moules marinière, scallops mornay and tournedos chasseur; portions are generous. A lively atmosphere's engendered by a pianist in the bar area. Interesting wine list, although short on red half bottles. **Seats 80.** Parties 35. Private Room. *D only 6-10. Closed Mon Nov-Easter, 25 & 26 Dec. Access, Amex, Visa,* (I) Diners Club International

Kinsale   Actons Hotel   60%   £86

| Tel 021 772135 . Fax 021 772231 | **H** |

Pier Road Kinsale Co Cork   **Map 19 B6**

Quayside hotel created from several period houses; views over the harbour. Conferences for up to 400 delegates. Forte Heritage. **Rooms 57.** *Garden, indoor swimming pool, sauna, solarium, gymnasium. Access, Amex, Visa,* (I) Diners Club International

Kinsale   Blue Haven Hotel   £84

| Tel 021 772209   Fax 021 774268 | **I** |

3 Pearse Street Kinsale Co Cork   **Map 19 B6**

Bedrooms at this small blue-and-white hotel near the quay vary from quite small to reasonably large. Smart white furniture is used, and the works of local artists adorn the walls. Only one room has a bath, six others have showers and the rest share a bathroom. The bar is very appealing with wood panelling, natural stone and a log fire, and has lots of cosy corners, opening on to a cane-furnished conservatory which, in turn, leads to a patio. No dogs. **Rooms 10.** *Sea fishing, coffee shop (10.30am-11.30pm). Closed 25 Dec. Access, Amex, Visa,* (I) Diners Club International

Kinsale   Max's Wine Bar   £40

| Tel 021 772443 | **R** |

Main Street Kinsale Co Cork   **Map 19 B6**

Named after a dog long since departed who used to lie across the doorway, this delightful little restaurant has charmed visitors to Kinsale for 17 years and, despite improvements including a conservatory, remains reassuringly unchanged. Plants and fresh flowers are reflected in the highly varnished table tops and the light, creative menus are always tempting, with an emphasis on starters and salads such as hot baked crab and asparagus, served attractively on a shell-shaped dish, or just-melting warm baked goat's cheese scattered with toasted almonds on a bed of lettuce. Fresh fish is handled simply and with confidence and home-made bread is irresistible. **Seats 40.** *Parties 12. L 1-3 D 7-10.30. Closed Nov-Feb. Set D £12. Access, Visa.*

Kinsale   Old Presbytery   £36

| Tel 021 772027 | **R R** |

Cork Street Kinsale Co Cork   **Map 19 B6**

In the middle of a historic fishing village, the Old Presbytery offers peace and comfort in abundance. Coal fires warm the public areas and Victorian antiques reinforce the homely, traditional feel. The old kitchen has been converted into a dining room, where dinner is served Mon-Sat. The menu changes daily, with patés and the day's fish specials among the favourites. **Seats 14.** *Parties 14. Private Room. D only 7.30-8.30. Closed Sun, 1 week Xmas. Set D £13. No Credit Cards.*

Rooms   £32

Six rooms with big, comfortable beds and good fresh linen. No children under 14. No dogs.

Kinsale   Places of Interest

Charles Fort   Tel 021 772263.

Knocklofty   Knocklofty House   66%   £99

| Tel 052 38222   Fax 052 38289 | **H** |

Knocklofty Nr Clonmel Co Tipperary   Map 19 C5

The 17th-century galleried library, at the heart of this largely Georgian hotel, enjoys fine views of the river Suir as it flows through the 100-acre estate. There is often a cocktail pianist at the grand piano and board games are provided if you want to make your own entertainment. Spacious bedrooms have pleasant matching fabrics and are mostly furnished with antiques. Carpeted bathrooms, two with shower and WC only, are smartly tiled. **Rooms 13.** *Garden, croquet, indoor swimming pool, solarium, whirlpool bath, keep-fit equipment, tennis, squash, clay-pigeon shooting, game fishing, games room, riding. Closed 2 weeks Jan. Access, Visa.*

Leighlinbridge   The Lord Bagenal Inn   £45

| Tel 0503 21668 | **R** |

Leighlinbridge Co Carlow   Map 19 C4

Over the last decade this famous old inn has built up a formidable reputation for good food, interesting wines and hospitality. Whether you need to break a journey for a snack or a quick meal, take Sunday lunch with the family or have a special evening out, this very traditional inn can provide something appropriate, ranging from excellent home-made paté, to prime local steaks, seafood from the nearby Wexford coast and wild Slaney salmon. Owner James Kehoe's interest in wine is reflected in a wide-ranging and user-friendly list. **Seats 90.** *Parties 25. Private Room. L 12.30-2.30 D 6-10.30 (bar food 12.30-10.30). Closed 25 Dec, Good Friday. Set L £8 Set D £16.50. Access, Visa,* 🔵 Diners Club International

Letterfrack   Rosleague Manor   72%   £90

| Tel 095 41101   Fax 095 41168 | **HR** |

Letterfrack Connemara Co Galway   Map 18 A3

Siblings Patrick and Anne Foyle have tremendous flair for interior design and the five vast, newest rooms are fabulous – decorated with great style and enhanced by quality antiques. A delightful soft Irish charm pervades this delightful, pink pebbledash house standing in 30 acres of landscaped gardens overlooking Bernadeg Bay. An open fire burns in one of the two pleasant lounges and a conservatory bar has a black and white-tiled floor, Lloyd Loom chairs and greenery abounding. All but four of the bedrooms are large with separate seating areas or full suites. **Rooms 20.** *Garden, croquet, sauna, tennis, billiards, sea & coarse fishing. Closed Nov-Easter. Access, Visa.*

Restaurant   £58

A most elegant and civilised dining room with antique round tables under a pair of glittering chandeliers. Patrick Foyle's fixed-price, four-course menus are short and well balanced with starters like baked devilled crab, smoked trout mousse with smoked salmon or grilled grapefruit followed by a choice of soups – perhaps cream of celery and herbs or gazpacho. Medallions of monkfish with garlic and pine nuts, poached wild salmon and rack of Connemara lamb are typical main courses. Good Irish cheeses,

"real ices", whiskey trifle, peach and brandy brulée plus charming service
put the icing on the cake. *Seats 60. Parties 8. L 1-2.30 D 8-9.30 (Sun to 9).
Set D from £22.*

Limerick	Greenhills Hotel	57%	£90

Tel 061 53033   Fax 061 53307

H

Ennis Road Limerick Co Limerick

Map 19 B5

On the main road from Limerick to Shannon Airport, Greenhills is a
family-run hotel that caters for tourists and the business community
(conferences up to 300). The health and leisure centre is a major new
attraction. *Rooms 60. Garden, indoor swimming pool, children's pool, steam
room, spa bath, sauna, solarium, beauty salon, massage, gym, tennis, Closed 25
Dec. Access, Amex, Visa,* (D) Diners Club

Limerick	Jurys Hotel	66%	£103

Tel 061 327777   Fax 061 326400

H

Ennis Road Limerick Co Limerick

Map 19 B5

1960s' low-rise hotel, recently refurbished throughout, in a 5-acre garden
on the banks of the Shannon. Extensive conference/banqueting (for up to
180) and up-to-date leisure centre that includes a children's pool; under-12s
stay free in their parents' room. *Rooms 96. Garden, indoor swimming pool,
plunge pool, steam room, spa bath, sauna, gymnasium, tennis, coffee shop.
Closed 25 Dec. Access, Amex, Visa,* (D) Diners Club

Limerick	Limerick Inn	66%	£105

Tel 061 51544   Fax 061 326281

H

Ennis Road Limerick Co Limerick

Map 19 B5

Three or four miles out of town on the main road between Limerick and
Shannon Airport, this sprawling but not unattractive modern hotel owned
by the Ryan family offers excellent conference facilities and also boasts a
popular health and leisure centre. Children up to 12 stay free in parents'
room. *Rooms 153. Garden, indoor swimming pool, sauna, solarium, whirlpool
bath, gymnasium, keep-fit equipment, tennis, putting, snooker, coffee shop
(7.30am -11pm). Closed 25 Dec. Access, Amex, Visa,* (D) Diners Club

Limerick	Two Mile Inn	60%	£76

Tel 061 53122   Fax 061 53783

H

Ennis Road Limerick Co Limerick

Map 19 B5

A purpose-built modern hotel just outside Limerick beside the N19 to
Shannon Airport. It's quite a walk from reception to the farthest rear block
of the long single-storey complex. The hotel bar is plainly furnished, while
the central concourse has a striking pyramid roof. A big entertainment
complex features cabaret artists and bands, and there's a popular
discotheque. Bedroom wings surround a neat garden. No dogs. *Rooms 125.
Garden. Closed 24-26 Dec. Access, Amex, Visa,* (D) Diners Club

Limerick	Places of Interest

Tourist Information   Tel 061 317522.
City Gallery of Art.

Malahide	Bon Appétit		£80

Tel 01 845 0314

R

9 St James Terrace Malahide Dublin Co Dublin

Map 18 D3

Now only 15 minutes from Dublin airport, the Bon Appétit has
established a new following since moving from the city centre to this
elegant Georgian terrace in 1989 and is very much a leading northside
restaurant. Aperitifs are served in the ground-floor drawing room/bar
which overlooks the estuary and is notable for some pleasing local
watercolours, while the intimate restaurant, decorated in warm tones of red

and dark green, is in the basement. Here, chef/patron Patsy McGuirk serves classical French food based on top-quality local ingredients, especially luxury seafood in dishes such as Wexford crab claws in butter sauce or Dover sole (McGuirk's own creation, a whole boned sole stuffed with turbot, prawns and mushrooms in a white wine sauce, baked in the oven). *Seats 55. Parties 60. Private Room. L 12.30-2 D 7-11. Closed L Sat, all Sun, Bank Holidays, 1 week Xmas. Set L £10 Set D £20. Access, Amex, Visa,* ⓓ Diners Club International

Malahide   Roches Bistro   £55

Tel 01 845 2777   **R**

12 New Street Malahide Co Dublin   Map 18 D3

Francophile sisters Orla Roche and Niamh Boylan run the nearest to a French family restaurant to be found in Co Dublin. Set in Malahide's attractive main street, it's intimate, with blue and white check linen and an open fire in winter. The wide-ranging set menus change daily and feature both French country cooking and seafood dishes like warm terrine of salmon and sole, or fillet of brill with cucumber and vermouth. Apple and frangipane tart is a speciality dessert and there's a good selection of farmhouse cheeses. *Seats 35. Parties 30. L 12-2.30 D 7-10.30. Closed D Mon-Wed, all Sun, Bank Holidays, 2 weeks Jan. Set L £10.95 Set D £18.95. Access, Amex, Visa,* ⓓ Diners Club International

Mallow   Longueville House   72%   £114

Tel 022 47156   Fax 022 47459   **HR**

Mallow Co Cork   Map 19 B5

The Callaghan family have put the stamp of friendly informality on their ancestral home, a handsome Georgian hall on an estate that includes cattle and sheep farming. Lofty day rooms feature gilt-framed family portraits and mirrors, colourful moulded ceilings and log fires. Antique furniture and stylish fabrics take the eye in the bedrooms, which generally have smart modern bathrooms. No dogs. *Rooms 16. Game & coarse fishing, games room, snooker. Closed 20 Dec-28 Feb. Access, Amex, Visa,* ⓓ Diners Club International

Presidents' Restaurant   £63

The dining room is graced with portraits of Irish presidents, a chandelier and an Adam mantelpiece in Italian marble. William Callaghan makes good use of the produce from the family farm and garden, which supplies a large proportion of the menu. The wine list includes something for everyone. No smoking in the dining room, but tables in the library are available to puffers. *Seats 40. Parties 20. Private Room. L 12.30-2 D 7-9. Set L £12 Set D £22.*   ♕

Maynooth   Moyglare Manor   77%   £110

Tel 01 628 6351   Fax 01 628 5405   **HR**

Moyglare Maynooth Co Kildare   Map 19 C4

A white pebbledash Georgian house standing in lush green stud-farm country west of Dublin. Many period features survive and ample public rooms, if not exactly cluttered, are comfortably filled in traditional style, with good-quality armchairs and settees, and lots of antiques, paintings, mirrors and flowers. The bar has a peat fire burning in its marble fireplace, heavy oak furniture is a feature of the lounge and there's prettily decorated sun lounge with ruffled Dutch blinds and rattan furniture. Antiques also feature in the bedrooms, where fine rugs cover fitted carpets and the beds are antique (many four-posters or half-testers). Modern comforts, good bathrooms. No children under 12. No dogs. *Rooms 17. Garden, tennis. Closed 3 days Xmas. Access, Amex, Visa,* ⓓ Diners Club International

Restaurant   £68

Traditional surroundings for enjoying simple dishes like potato and leek soup, salmon hollandaise, quail with burgundy sauce, steaks and apple pie.   ♕ 🐚

xcellent clarets. *Seats 80. Parties 50. Private Room. L 12.30-2.30*
7.30-9.30 (Sun to 8.30). Closed L Sat. Set L £9.95 Set D £18.50.

Monkstown	**Mr Hung's**	£50

Tel 01 284 3982
R

a The Crescent Monkstown Co Dublin
Map 19 D4

although William Hung's Chinese restaurant claims to specialise in
Cantonese and Szechuan cuisine, its chef, Mr Lai, is from Hong Kong,
therefore he is far more at home with rather old-fashioned, standard
Cantonese dishes. For starters, try spare ribs, pancake roll, or stuffed crab
laws; chicken, beef and seafood dishes, sizzling or otherwise, can be good
oo. Also customers are encouraged to ask for dishes which are not
included on the menu. Relaxed atmosphere, very friendly and attentive
service. Considering the proximity to Dublin Bay it is a pity that only
frozen prawns are used. *Seats 80. Parties 20. L 12.30-2.30 D 6-12.30. Closed
Mon-Thu, all Sun, Good Friday, 25 & 26 Dec. Set D from £15.50. Access,
Amex, Visa,* **Diners Club International**

Mountrath	**Roundwood House**	58%	**NEW**	£58

Tel 0502 32120
HR

Mountrath Co Laois
Map 19 C4

f staying in a delightful Palladian villa from the early Georgian period,
secluded in mature woods of lime, beech and chestnut, appeals then
Roundwood House is for you. Do not expect 'every modern convenience'
and you will not be disappointed – instead, enjoy staying in an unspoilt,
characterful old house with shutters on the windows of the old-fashioned
bedrooms and hot-water bottles laid out ready in your bathroom. *Rooms 6.
Garden, croquet. Access, Amex, Visa,* **Diners Club International**

Restaurant	£60

Rosemarie Kennan's food suits the house perfectly – good, interesting
country house cooking without unnecessary frills. Sunday lunch is
especially good value. *Seats 26. Parties 16. L Sun only at 1.30 D at 8.30.*

Moycullen	**Drimcong House Restaurant**	★	£50

Tel 091 85115
R

Moycullen Co Galway
Map 19 B4

A mile west of Moycullen on the main Galway/Clifden road, the lakeland
home of Gerry and Marie Galvin is also a very fine restaurant. Diners can
enjoy a drink in the lounge before settling down to dinner served at
polished oak tables. Gerry puts a modern accent on classical skills, and both
the 5-course table d'hote and à la carte menus change regularly according
to what's available locally. Fish and shellfish are a speciality, with such
dishes as oyster broth, pan-fried scallops in smoked salmon sauce and grilled
trout with a wild garlic sauce. Ballotine of game and chicken in orange
sauce, loin of lamb with sweetbread mousse and grilled fillet of beef with
shallots and garlic typify the choice for meat-eaters. Sweets include splendid
ice creams and sorbets. There are separate menus for vegetarians (5-course
£15.50) and children (3-course £8.50). The wine list has a particularly
good page of half bottles. *Seats 50. Parties 12. Private Room. D only
7-10.30. Closed Sun, Mon, Bank Hols, Jan & Feb. Set D £17.95. Access,
Amex, Visa,* **Diners Club International**

Mullingar	**Crookedwood House**	£70

Tel 044 72165
R

Crookedwood Mullingar Co Meath
Map 19 C3

This attractive, well-established Midlands restaurant has some very
tempting menus – try as much as you can from dishes such as grilled breast
of wood pigeon with juniper berry and gin sauce, warm salad of scallops
and smoked salmon served with the most irresistibly moist nutty brown

bread. Local meats and free-range poultry feature and game, especially venison, in season – try the venison goulash with spätzle. The vegetable selection is particularly good and simple desserts include home-made ices and apple pies. *Seats 35. Parties 40. Private Room. L (Sun only) 12.30-2 D 7-10. Closed D Sun & Mon, Bank Holidays, 2 weeks Oct. Set L £12 Set D £17. Access, Amex, Visa,* ⓘ *Diners Club International*

Navan   Ardboyne Hotel   60%   £68

Tel 046 23119   Fax 046 22355   **HR**

Dublin Road Navan Co Meath   Map 18 C5

A modern hotel with a thriving conference and function trade, the Ardboyne stands in its own grounds on the outskirts of town. Dark timbers, deep red banquette seating, an open fire and dim lighting make the bar cosy and convivial, while fresh flowers and soft lamplight give a pleasing impression in the lounge. Bedrooms have fitted wooden furniture, an armchair, good desk/dressing table space and compact, functional, tiled bathrooms. Conference/ banqueting facilities for 700/400. No dogs. *Rooms 27. Garden, coffee shop (7am-10pm), disco (Fri & Sat). Closed 24-27 Dec. Access, Amex, Visa,* ⓘ *Diners Club International*

Terrace Restaurant   £55

This attractive, busy restaurant serves simple, unpretentious food and does it well. The carvery is their speciality and serves quality local meats to any degree of 'doneness', but don't overlook dishes like steak and Guinness casserole. Good desserts from the buffet. *Seats 97. Parties 40. Private Room. L 12.30-2.30 D 5.30-10. Closed 24-26 Dec. Set L £10.95 Set D from £11.95.*

Newbawn   Cedar Lodge   62%   £68

Tel 051 28386   Fax 051 28222   **H**

Carrigbyrne Newbawn Co Wexford   Map 19 C5

Standing in lush countryside beneath the slopes of Carrigbyrne Forest, Cedar Lodge is 14 miles from Wexford on the main Rosslare to Waterford road. Open fires burn in the brick-lined lounge bar and restaurant, adorned with paintings and frescoes by local artists. Practical, neatly appointed bedrooms and conference/function suite for up to 100 are in adjoining low-rise wings. *Rooms 18. Garden. Closed 25 & 26 Dec, Jan. Access, Visa.*

Newbridge   Hotel Keadeen   68%   £80

Tel 045 31666   Fax 045 34402   **H**

Ballymany Newbridge Co Kildare   Map 19 C4

Particularly fine landscaped gardens surround the hotel, which stands well back from the N7 just south of the town and not far from the Curragh racecourse. Best of the public areas is the main bar, which is in red plush/rustic style with lots of nice quiet corners. Bedrooms are good-sized, with furniture ranging from white fitted melamine units to Louis XIV reproduction; some rooms have stylish fabrics and wall coverings. There are extensive function facilities. *Rooms 37. Garden. Closed 25-27 Dec. Access, Amex, Visa,* ⓘ *Diners Club International*

Newmarket-on-Fergus   Clare Inn   64%   £99

Tel 061 368161   Fax 061 368622   **H**

Dromoland Newmarket-on-Fergus Co Clare   Map 19 B4

A modern hotel on a hilltop, with Dromoland Castle's golf course in its grounds. The whole place is kept in good order, and public areas include a well-equipped leisure centre and conference suites which can accommodate 400 delegates. Sea angling can be arranged from the hotel's boat *Lady Christeen*. Bedrooms have functional laminated units and a wide variety of matching fabrics. Children up to 14 stay free in parents' room. *Rooms 121.*

...arden, indoor swimming pool, sauna, solarium, spa bath, gymnasium, pitch & ...tt, games room, coffee shop (2.30pm-10pm). *Access, Amex, Visa,*

...ewmarket-on-Fergus   Dromoland Castle   78%   £205   HR

...el 061 368144   Fax 061 363355

...ewmarket-on-Fergus Co Clare   Map 19 B4

...n a 375-acre estate that includes a golf course this is a real castle complete ...ith towers and crenellations. Public rooms are suitably grand, with a ...rge collection of family portraits, log fires in marble fireplaces and ornate ...othic-style cornices detailed in gold. The drawing room is the scene of ...aceful afternoon tea. All the spacious, stylishly decorated bedrooms offer ...enty of thoughtful little extras. The Conference Centre includes the Brian ...oru Hall with seating for 450 theatre-style. Children up to 8 stay free in ...arents' room. No dogs. *Rooms 73. Garden, golf, riding, fishing, tennis, ...ooker. Access, Amex, Visa,*

...estaurant   £100

...he setting is sumptuous, with glittering chandeliers suspended from high ...ilings, elegant blue-rimmed Coalport china and cut glass; a harpist ...aying in the background adds to the luxurious atmosphere. The main ...enu is a sophisticated French carte with well-conceived dishes such as ...dine of pigeon laced with foie gras served with a parsley vinaigrette, or ...ot-roasted fillet of veal with a ragout of mushrooms and buttons of salsify ...rved on a sage-flavoured jus. Market specialities and a table d'hote add to ...e choice, and there's a luxurious six-course Taste of Ireland menu. A ...ecial symbol denotes dishes with a particularly low fat content. 15% ...rvice charge is added to all bills "in lieu of gratuities". Stiff prices on the ...und wine list. *Seats 90. Parties 10. Private Room. L 12.30-2 D 7.30-10. ...t L £18 Set D £32.*

...ewport   Newport House   67%   £116   HR

...el 098 41222   Fax 098 41613

...ewport Co Mayo   Map 18 A3

...creeper-clad Georgian mansion with lawns reaching down the estuary. ...ewport House boasts a splendid central hall with a sweeping staircase and ...alleried landing. The day rooms are quiet and civilised, with antiques, ...ather armchairs and open fires. Most bedrooms feature antique pieces, ...me of massive proportions. A hotel offering traditional hospitality. ...ooms 20. Garden, sea & game fishing, snooker. Closed 7 Oct-18 Mar. Access, ...mex, Visa,*

...estaurant   £60

...glass chandelier, damask curtains, a marble fireplace and good quality ...ble settings offer elegance which is matched by excellent, unfussy ...oking. Home-smoked salmon makes an excellent starter (sometimes ...rved "with its own mousse"), then maybe half-a-dozen oysters, soup, and ...eef stroganoff or pan-fried duck breast with apple and an orange and ...amson sauce. Vegetables come from the walled garden, which diners are ...vited to visit. *Seats 39. Parties 16. D only 7.30-9.30. Set D £26.*

...ughterard   Connemara Gateway Hotel   65%   £90   H

...el 091 82328   Fax 091 82332

...ughterard Co Galway   Map 18 B3

...modern low-rise exterior conceals surprisingly characterful public areas, ...articularly the foyer with its old pine boarding and the bar, which ...atures a variety of rural artefacts and traditional three-legged chairs. Fresh ...d dried flower arrangements abound as does the work of local artists and ...ulptors. Bedrooms vary somewhat in quality, the best having matching ...oral fabrics or locally woven bedcovers and smart bathrooms. Good ...ildren's facilities and golf courses nearby. Conference/banqueting facilities for 300/200. *Rooms 62.* Garden, croquet, indoor swimming pool, sauna, solarium, snooker, tennis. Closed Jan (usually). Access, Amex, Visa.

Oughterard   Currarevagh House   65%   £74

Tel 091 82313   Fax 091 82731

HR

Oughterard Connemara Co Galway   Map 18

The Hodgson family house is an early-Victorian manor house set in parkland, woods and gardens by Lough Corrib. The current owners (fifth generation, here since 1966) run it along the lines of a private house, with the emphasis on old-fashioned hospitality and service. Day rooms have a warm, homely appeal, and the drawing room is the scene of traditional afternoon tea. The accent is firmly on peace in the bedrooms, with no phones or TVs to intrude. The hotel has sporting rights over 5000 acres and fishing facilities that include boats and ghillies. *Rooms 15.* Garden, croquet, tennis, fishing, mooring, swimming, hotel boat. Closed Nov-Mar. No credit cards.

Restaurant   £50

June Hodgson bases her cooking on fresh local produce, and simplicity is the keynote of her no-choice five-course dinner menu: mussel chowder, paté maison, poached salmon, John Dory with cucumber sauce, confit of duck, roast beef with horseradish sauce. No smoking. Snack lunches. Fair prices on the concise wine list; check out the bin ends. *Seats 28.* D only at 8. Set D £16.80.

Oughterard   Sweeny's Oughterard House   59%   £98

Tel 091 82207   Fax 091 82161

H

Oughterard Co Galway   Map 18

Successive generations of the Higgins family have cemented a reputation for hospitality at their 200-year-old house in a lovely sheltered setting on the wooded banks of the Oughterard River. Scenic drives, healthy walks, tea on the lawn, and above all, fishing, are favourite outdoor activities while the bar and antique-furnished lounges are good places to relax indoors. Bedrooms vary both in size and furniture. Four-poster and king-size doubles available. *Rooms 20.* Garden, patio. Closed 4 weeks Dec/Jan. Access, Amex, Visa, Diners Club International.

Oysterhaven   The Oystercatcher   £65

Tel 021 770821

R

Oysterhaven Co Cork   Map 18

Down beside a creek just outside Kinsale, a flower-clad cottage has been converted and filled with pictures and antiques to make this olde-worlde restaurant. But the extensive set menu is modern and owner-chef Bill Patterson presents fashionable dishes such as wild mushrooms in a brioche or pressed duck confit with morels and port, followed by braised pig's trotter stuffed with sweetbreads or steamed breast of guinea fowl with green grapes. Prettily presented desserts include a good crème brulée. *Seats 30.* Parties 20. Private Room. L by arrangement for parties of 7 or more D 7.30-9.30 (bookings only in winter). Closed Jan. Set D £20.95. Access, Visa.

Parknasilla   Great Southern   72%   £147

Tel 064 45122   Fax 064 45323

H

Parknasilla Sneem Co Kerry   Map 19

Palm trees mingle with rhododendrons in the 200 acres of lovely shoreside woodland in which this imposing late-Victorian building stands. The tone is set by the entrance hall, where fresh flowers stand on an antique table. Bedrooms are decorated in a variety of restful colour schemes. The bar and sun lounge have been extended recently and the pool complex refurbished, making the leisure facilities even more attractive. Meeting rooms for up to

80. **Rooms 84.** *Garden, indoor swimming pool, sauna, spa bath, steam room, keep-fit equipment, tennis, riding, games room, snooker, sea-fishing, 9-hole golf course, water sports. Closed Jan-Mar. Access, Amex, Visa,* Diners Club International

Rathmullan   Rathmullan House   62%   £71
Tel 074 58188   Fax 074 58200   H
Rathmullan Nr Letterkenny Co Donegal   Map 18 C1

Several members of the Wheeler family work in their extended Georgian house set amid beautiful parkland overlooking Lough Swilly. Public areas include a period drawing room, a library and a cellar bar. Accommodation ranges from well-appointed master suites to budget rooms without bathrooms. The Egyptian Baths include an ionised indoor saltwater pool and steam room. The setting is very peaceful, with a garden that leads down through trees to the deserted sandy beach; a splendid base for touring Donegal. **Rooms 23.** *Garden, tennis, croquet, indoor swimming pool, sauna, steam room. Closed Nov-mid Mar. Access, Amex, Visa,* Diners Club International

Rathnew   Hunter's Hotel   £50
Tel 0404 40106   Fax 0404 40338   R
Newrath Bridge Rathnew Co Wicklow   Map 19 D4

Several steps back in time, one of Ireland's oldest coaching inns whose owners' slight eccentricity renders it all the more interesting. Set in an attractive rambling building, the restaurant overlooks award-winning gardens and everything about it, including the service, is refreshingly old-fashioned. Go for Wexford mussels with garlic butter, Wicklow lamb roast with fresh herbs, and nursery puddings such as rhubarb tart or lemon meringue pie from the daily-changing 3- and 4-course tables d'hote. 17 delightfully old-fashioned bedrooms (7 not en-suite) **Seats 54.** *Parties 14. L 12.30-2.30 (Sat & Sun to 3) D 7.30-9. Set L £12 Set D £18.50. Access, Amex, Visa,* Diners Club International

Rathnew   Tinakilly House   70%   £130
Tel 0404 69274   Fax 0404 67806   HR
Rathnew Wicklow Co Wicklow   Map 19 D4

Tinakilly is a substantial mid-19th-century mansion set in large well-stocked gardens and overlooking the mud-flats near Wicklow Harbour, much loved by wild-fowlers. The interior has been restored to a high standard and furnished with antiques and bric-a-brac appropriate to the period. A new east wing has added fifteen bedrooms, relocated the restaurant, and now accommodates conferences and banqueting for up to 150. There remains a pleasing blend of old world charm and modern comfort assured by the Power family and their attentive staff. Very good breakfasts. No children under 7. No dogs. **Rooms 29.** *Garden, tennis. Access, Amex, Visa,* Diners Club International

Restaurant   £75

Bee Power's famous brown bread and spicy soups – fresh nettle and Irish whiskey, for instance – feature daily at dinnertime. Menus are based on home-grown fruit and vegetables and fine local produce, especially seafood. Start, perhaps, with crispy confit of duck with a garden salad, cassis and lemon zest, then soup, a sorbet, the day's fish choice and pan-fried mignons of veal with Noilly Prat and pink grapefruit. Desserts might feature a tangy lemon tart or choux swans filled with syllabub. Good wines, featuring some of the best French growers. **Seats 70.** *Parties 65. Private Room. L 12.30-2 D 7.30-9 (Sun till 8). Set L £16.50 Set D £25.*

Renvyle   Renvyle House   64%   £82

Tel 095 43511   Fax 095 43515   **H**

Renvyle Co Galway   Map 18 A3

Standing at the edge of the Atlantic Ocean, hedged in by some 200 acres of
farm, walking lands and private lake, the hotel offers a wealth of leisure
pursuits, conferences (max 70) and banqueting for 160. Bedrooms vary
from family-size with balconies to attic rooms with dormer windows,
though the newer wing has rather less character than the original.
*Rooms 74. Garden, croquet, sauna, solarium, 9-hole golf course, putting, bowling
green, riding, fishing, tennis, snooker. Closed 1 Jan-17 Mar. Access, Amex,
Visa,* **(D)** Diners Club International

Riverstown   Coopershill House   68%   £80

Tel 071 65108   Fax 071 65466   **HR**

Coopershill Riverstown Co Sligo   Map 18 B2

Peace and tranquillity abound at this Georgian family mansion at the
centre of a 500-acre sheep farm and woodland estate, home to the O'Hara
family since being built in 1774. A visit here is more like being a house
guest, enjoying the owners' quiet hospitality than staying in a hotel.
Antiques and pictures accumulated over seven generations furnish the
restful day rooms and spacious bedrooms. No TVs or radios, but homely
touches with books, fresh flowers and mineral water. *Rooms 7. Garden,
croquet, coarse and game fishing, boating, clay-pigeon shooting. Closed mid
Nov-mid Mar. Access, Amex, Visa,* **(D)** Diners Club International

Restaurant   £50

Dinner is an elegant affair with a log fire in the marble fireplace and
antique polished tables set with silver candelabra. Lindy O'Hara's satisfying
home cooking covers five courses (no choice) with dishes like cheese
parcels, mulligatawny soup, roast duck with cranberry sauce, Irish cheeses,
pears in red wine and lemon mousse (a menu from the spring). No
smoking. *Seats 14. D only 8-8.45. Set D £20.*

Rosslare   Great Southern   62%   £76

Tel 053 33233   Fax 053 33543   **H**

Rosslare Co Wexford   Map 19 D5

Its position overlooking Rosslare harbour makes this modern hotel a useful
stopover for ferry users and there's plenty to keep children happy with a
crèche and playground. Public rooms are light and spacious, with ample
seating; many of the simply-furnished bedrooms are suitable for family
occupation. Up to 150 conference delegates can be accommodated theatre-
style. *Rooms 99. Garden, indoor swimming pool, keep-fit equipment, tennis,
sauna, steam room, snooker, hairdressing, children's play area. Closed Jan-Mar.
Access, Amex, Visa,* **(D)** Diners Club International

Rosslare   Kelly's Strand Hotel   71%   £82

Tel 053 32114   Fax 053 32222   **H**

Rosslare Co Wexford   Map 19 D5

Over the years, the Kelly family have developed what started out as a tea
room for Sunday beachgoers into a holiday hotel par excellence offering a
'cruise liner experience'. Personal service is high on their list of priorities.
The leisure complex (including a 15 metre exercise pool, counter
swimming jet, Canadian hot tub, Turkish bath) is a big draw; beauty
treatments include aromatherapy and hydrotherapy. There's live
entertainment every night. Bedrooms are light, modern and practical. No
dogs. *Rooms 99. Garden, croquet, bowls, indoor swimming pools, sauna,
solarium, spa bath, gymnasium, beauty salon, hairdressing, tennis, squash,*

badminton, bicycles, games rooms, snooker, crèche, children's play area, crazy golf, giant chess and draughts. Closed early Dec-late Feb. Access, Visa.

Rosslare   Places of Interest

Ferry Terminal Tourist Information   Tel 053 33622.

Rossnowlagh   Sand House   68%   £88

Tel 072 51777   Fax 072 52100

H

Rossnowlagh Co Donegal   Map 18 B2

Sitting right by a large sandy beach overlooking Donegal Bay, the crenellated Sand House hotel has a new Atlantic conservatory lounge to take advantage of views that are also enjoyed by many of the bedrooms. The Britton family and their staff extend a warm welcome which is reinforced by a fire in the Victorian-style lobby. Bedrooms, immaculate like the rest of the hotel, are individually decorated with expensive, stylish fabrics; furniture varies from antiques to fairly modest fitted units, and superior rooms have chaises longues. A delightful, peaceful hotel, as the many regular guests will testify. *Rooms 40. Garden, tennis, croquet, surfing, canoeing, sea, game & coarse fishing, games room. Closed mid Oct-Easter. Access, Amex, Visa,* **(D)** *Diners Club International*

Roundwood   Roundwood Inn   £60

Tel 01 281 8107

R

Roundwood Co Wicklow   Map 19 D4

In the highest village of the Wicklow Hills, the Schwalms' 17th-century inn soaks in the spectacular scenery. The proprietors' German origins are amply evident in the pickled herrings, smoked Westphalian ham, wiener schnitzel, and splendid gateaux on an à la carte menu which scarcely strays from the traditional (veal cordon bleu, roast Wicklow lamb, grilled salmon, broiled peppersteak). A good-value, fixed-price lunch offers a good choice – from smoked salmon terrine or seafood chowder to venison ragout and chilled oranges with Grand Marnier. Throughout the day excellent bar food includes substantial snacks and specialities like Galway oysters, smoked Wicklow trout and Irish stew, served at sturdy tables set around the fire. *Seats 45. Parties 35. Private Room. L 1-2.30 D 7.30-9.30 (Sat to 10). Closed D Sun, all Mon, 25 Dec, Good Friday. Set L £13.95. Access, Visa.*

Scotshouse   Hilton Park   62%   £84

Tel 047 56007   Fax 047 56033

H

Scotshouse Nr Clones Co Monaghan   Map 18 C3

Johnny and Lucy are the eighth generation of Maddens to own this secluded country mansion, and they run it very much as a family home which takes in guests. The house is full of interest (heirlooms, portraits, four-poster beds) and there are fine views from all the rooms. The estate extends to 600 acres and includes three lakes. No dogs. *Rooms 5. Garden, croquet, 9-hole golf course, shooting, coarse & game fishing, boating. Closed Oct-Easter. Access, Amex, Visa,.*

Shanagarry   Ballymaloe House   63%   £104

Tel 021 652531   Fax 021 652021

H R

Shanagarry Co Cork   Map 19 C6

400 acres of land surround Ballymaloe House, a half Jacobean, half Georgian country house. Furnishings are a mixture of antique and modern, and decor very much reflects the taste of the Allens, with a large collection of modern pictures and paintings. Bedrooms in the main house are homely and traditional, those in converted outhouses bright, cottagey and roomy. *Rooms 30. Garden, outdoor swimming pool, tennis. Closed 24-26 Dec. Access, Amex, Visa,* **(D)** *Diners Club International*

see over

Restaurant   £80

Local produce takes top billing in the restaurant, whose three rooms feature
a great collection of Irish art. Preparation and presentation are notably
straightforward, with nothing to mask the freshness and flavours. Fish is
caught off Ballycotton, with weekly deliveries of shellfish from Kenmare.
Meat comes from nearby farms and their own kitchen garden provides
fruit, vegetables and herbs. Typical dishes on constantly changing menus
includes excellent patés and terrines, turbot with sea kale and hollandaise,
warm smoked salmon with cucumber and fennel, roast spring lamb and
escalopes of beef with peppers and chilis. *Seats 90. Parties 30. Private Room.
L (Sun) at 1 D 7-9.30 (Sun buffet only at 7.30). Set L £15 Set D £30.*

Shannon	Great Southern	64%	£106

Tel 061 61122   Fax 061 61982

H

Shannon Airport Shannon Co Clare   Map 19 B4

Airport hotel directly opposite the main terminal building, totally
refurbished two years ago. Soundproofed bedrooms include 11 Executive
rooms and 3 suites. Conference facilities for up to 170 in the Burren room.
Rooms 115. Garden, coffee shop. Closed 25 Dec. Access, Amex, Visa,
Diners Club International

Shannon	Places of Interest

Airport Tourist Information   Tel 061 61664/61565.

Skerries	Red Bank Restaurant	NEW	£75

Tel 01 849 1005

R

7 Church Street Skerries Co Dublin   Map 18 D3

A converted bank is the unexpected location for one of north Dublin's
best-known seafood restaurants, where owner-chef Terry McCoy creates
imaginative, generous dishes based on the day's catch. Enjoy a drink in the
comfortable reception area, then tuck into specialities such as baked crab
Loughshinney, a light, creamy starter with sherry, followed perhaps by
seafood selection 'Paddy Attley', an intriguing mixed fish dish with three
sauces named after a local fisherman. Menus change with the seasons and
favour organic produce, carnivores are not forgotten – and an old-
fashioned dessert list offers such temptations as baked chocolate cheesecake,
apple meringue pie and home-made ices. *Seats 45. Parties 14. Private Room.
D only 6.15-10. Closed Sun & Mon, 4 days Xmas, 2 weeks Nov. Set D £21.*
Access, Amex, Visa, Diners Club International

Sligo	Sligo Park	58%	£79

Tel 071 60291   Fax 071 69556

H

Pearse Road Sligo Co Sligo   Map 18 B2

A modern hotel in seven acres of parkland just south of town. New leisure
centre, recently refurbished public areas with a coffee shop and
conference/banqueting facilities for up to 450. Children under six
accommodated free in their parents' room. *Rooms 89. Indoor swimming
pool, steam room, plunge pool, children's pool, spa bath, sauna, solarium,
gymnasium, snooker, tennis, coffee shop (10am-7pm).* Access, Amex, Visa,
Diners Club International

Sligo	Places of Interest

Tourist Information   Tel 071 61201.

Spiddal	Boluisce Seafood Bar	£45

Tel 091 83286   Fax 091 83285

R

Spiddal Village Connemara Co Galway   Map 19 B4

The Glanville family's menu extends from the simplest snacks, seafood
chowder, fish and vegetarian salads in the downstairs bar to an impressive
array of piscine specialities in their convivial, first-floor restaurant. A fine

place for mussels in cream sauce, crab claws with garlic butter, monkfish, prawns and scallops, through to an excellent lobster Thermidor; for meat eaters there's lasagne and stir-fried chicken. Home-baked brown bread and apple pie are other winners, not to mention the Irish cheeses. *Seats 60. Parties 10. Meals 12-10 (Sun 4-10). Closed L Sun, 24-26 Dec. Access, Visa.*

Spiddal	**Bridge House Inn**	£65

Tel 091 83118	**I**
Spiddal Co Galway	**Map 19 B4**

A family-owned inn by Galway Bay immaculately kept and managed by the long-serving Esther Feeney. The neat and tidy pine-clad bar has French windows opening to the garden, and the Stirrup Room opens conveniently from breakfast to suppertime. Modest bedrooms are decorated with pretty matching bedcovers and curtains; some have shower/WC only. No children under 4. No dogs. *Rooms 14. Garden. Closed Xmas-mid Feb. Access, Amex, Visa,*

Stillorgan	**China-Sichuan Restaurant**	£50

Tel 01 288 4817	**R**
4 Lower Kilmacud Road Stillorgan Co Dublin	**Map 19 D4**

Five miles south of Dublin city centre is the only Chinese state-owned restaurant in the British Isles, with its chef and special spices supposedly supplied direct from Sichuan (Szechuan) province. China-Sichuan serves authentic Sichuan dishes not to be found elsewhere in the Republic of Ireland. Although the menu is limited, there are enough exciting dishes from which to choose, with the spicy and chili-hot dishes marked as such. Try the Sichuan speciality of smoked duckling – juicy, succulent meat with a delicate and subtle smoky flavour; try also Ma-Po tofu (braised beancurd cooked with minced pork in a wonderful hot and spicy sauce). Steamed black sole with ginger sauce is another must, not to mention spiced beef, fried lamb and chicken with cashew nuts. Also recommended are the seafood dishes; only fresh Dublin Bay prawns are used here – they are more tender and delicate both in texture and flavour than the frozen king prawns commonly used by many other establishments. Excellent value for money, even if prices are higher than you might find in London, but service is average. The wine list is extensive, covering wines from all over the world. Smart decor and intimate atmosphere. *Seats 50. Parties 24. L 12.30-2.30 (Sat, Sun & Bank Holidays 1-2.30) D 6-11.30 (Sun & Bank Holidays 6-11). Closed 25-27 Dec. Set L from £7 Set D £16.50. Access, Amex, Visa.*

Stillorgan	**Mr Hung's Sawadee Thai Restaurant** NEW	£50

Tel 01 288 8727	**R**
3 Lower Kilmacud Road Stillorgan Co Dublin	**Map 19 D4**

A cool and ultra-smart Thai restaurant offering a short and authentic menu. To start, try the crispy spring rolls, beef or chicken satay, or deep-fried prawns wrapped in ham and served in sweet and sour sauce. There is quite a wide range for the main course among the various curries, stir-fries, seafood and vegetables; prices are high, but service is excellent and the wine list suitable. *Seats 140. Parties 60. L 12.30-2.30 D 6-12.30 (Sun Apr-Dec 1-12). Closed Good Friday, 25 & 26 Dec. Set L £7.95 Set D £18. Access, Amex, Visa,*

Straffan	**Kildare Hotel**	86%	£244

Tel 01 6273333 Fax 01 6273312	**HR**
Straffan Co Kildare	**Map 19 C4**

Set in lush countryside and overlooking its own 18-hole Arnold Palmer-designed golf course, this hotel (formerly Straffan House) holds a unique position of unrivalled opulence and a sense of other-worldliness which is heightened by a distinctly French atmosphere, a legacy from the Barton wine family who lived here in the 19th century. The interior is magnificent in concept, with superb furnishings and a wonderful collection of original paintings by well-known artists, including William Orpen and Jack B Yeats, who has a room devoted to his work. All rooms and bathrooms are individually designed in the grand style, with great attention to detail. Country Club golf and fishing facilities charged at half the rate charged to non-residents. Conference/banqueting for 60/40 in the main house, but up to 600 in the sports centre. 17 miles from Dublin, 24 miles from the airport. *Rooms 45. Garden, croquet, indoor swimming pool, sauna, solarium, hair & beauty salon, gymnasium, 18-hole golf course, squash, tennis, snooker, coarse and game fishing. Access, Amex, Visa,*

The Byerley Turk   £120

Although the restaurant is in a new wing, the impressively draped tall windows, marble columns and rich decor in tones of deep terracotta, cream and green harmonise perfectly with the style of the original house and it takes a sharp eye to detect the differences. The room is cleverly shaped to create semi-private areas and make the most of window tables, laid with crested china, monogrammed white linen, gleaming modern crystal and silver. Chef Michel Flamme's leanings towards classical French cuisine are tempered by traditional Irish influences in dishes such as champ potatoes served with grilled black and white pudding and apple sauce or roast tail of monkfish with a smoked bacon and red peppercorn sauce. Presentation is refreshingly simple and especially appropriate for the likes of Dublin coddle – a rich stew of Irish sausages and rashers with herb dumplings, cannelloni filled with Dublin Bay prawns and mousse, estoufade of wild Irish salmon with a warm vinaigrette of olive oil and fresh basil, and ravioli of lentils, sun-dried tomatoes and wild mushrooms; thickly-sliced veal kidney, veal steak, chargrilled wing rib of beef and tournedos Rossini complete the picture. Desserts include a millefeuille of caramelised apples scented with cinnamon and Alexandra's chocolate delight – guaranteed to please chocoholics. Good Irish and French cheeses. *Seats 80. Parties 30. L 12.30-2 D 7-10. Set L £22 Set D £29.*

Swords   Le Chateau   £55

Tel 01 406353   **R**

River Mall Main Street Swords Dublin Co Dublin   Map 18 D3

In a shopping mall near Dublin airport, John Dowd's cooking easily outclasses the surroundings. The menu is mainly classic French with a few more original offerings (such as pasta Tara – a well balanced dish of home-made pasta with garlic, cream, bacon and baby mushrooms) added for good measure. Lunch is particularly good value. *Seats 60. Parties 20. Private Room. L 12.15-2.30 D 7-11. Closed Mon, Bank Holidays, 1 week Xmas/New Year. Set L £10.50 Set D £19.75. Access, Amex, Visa,*

Swords   Forte Travelodge   NEW   £40

Tel 01 800 709 709 (in Ireland) 0800 850 950 (from England)   **L**

N1 Dublin/Belfast Road Swords Bypass Nr Dublin Co Dublin   Map 18 D3

On the southbound carriageway of the Swords bypass at Swords roundabout, 1½ miles north of Dublin airport, 16 miles north of Dublin city centre. Opens winter '92/'93. *Access, Amex, Visa.*

Thomastown   Mount Juliet Hotel   81%   £220

Tel 056 24455   Fax 056 24522   **HR**

Mount Juliet Thomastown Co Kilkenny   Map 19 C5

The imposing 18th-century Mount Juliet Hotel stands in 1500 acres of parkland and formal gardens through which flow the rivers Kings and Nore; a traditional stone bridge crosses the latter for access to the hotel. Its exquisite interior is no less striking: public rooms feature wonderful moulded plasterwork and the Parlour boasts a colourful marble fireplace. The bedrooms and generously proportioned suites are individually styled,

with soft floral fabrics, solid oak furniture and deep-cushioned sofas; most
have fine Adam fireplaces. Bathrooms are equally luxurious with many
extras. Three suites are in Ballylinch House on the estate. Recreational
facilities include a Jack Nicklaus-designed golf course, and a brand new
leisure centre abutting the clubhouse. Children under 14 stay free in their
parents' room. Kennelling for dogs. Meeting rooms for up to 50,
banqueting for 140. *Rooms 32. Garden, croquet, snooker, game fishing, golf,
clay-pigeon shooting, archery, tennis, riding, helipad. Access, Amex, Visa,*

Lady Helen McCalmont Restaurant   £75

Dining in this elegant, airy dining room, with its delicate pastel
plasterwork and sweeping views over the gentle greens of the grounds and
rolling countryside, is first of all a feast for the eyes – something which
must influence Chris Farrell when he uses the finest ingredients to create
colourful, flavoursome dishes, many of them garnished with fresh seasonal
fruit and flowers. Local beef is a speciality, as in lightly char grilled
medallions of beef fillet served on a fresh herb jus. Wild salmon from the
River Nore often features too – poached in a citrus bouillon, perhaps, and
served with saffron sauce. *Seats 55. Parties 20. Private Room. Closed 2 weeks
after New Year. L 12.30-2.30 D 7-9.30. Set L £16 Set D £29.*

Waterford	Dwyer's Restaurant	NEW	£55
Tel 051 77478			**R**
8 Mary Street Waterford Co Waterford			Map 19 C5

Owner-chef Martin Dwyer creates memorable culinary combinations in
his soothing backstreet restaurant. Here, in a converted barracks, restrained
pastels, comfortable, functional seating and gentle classical music prepare
diners for a disciplined approach – totally without showmanship, one
delicious course follows another; start, perhaps, with fresh prawns in garlic
butter – freshly caught local prawns and all the better for that but the
stroke of originality is to set them in a rösti nest, to absorb all the buttery
juices. This attention to detail, and to contrasts of flavour and texture, is
typical – it surfaces again in almond-coated roast breast of guinea fowl, set
in a pool of chive sauce and served with a mixed lettuce salad with
croutons and scallions and a deliciously piquant wholegrain mustard
dressing. Local fish usually steals the show, though, and desserts are a
delight. *Seats 30. Parties 10. D only 6-10 (set dinner 6-7.30). Closed Sun,
Xmas, Easter, 2 weeks Jul. Set D £12. Access, Amex, Visa,*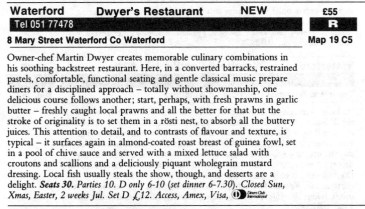

Waterford	Granville Hotel	69%	£76
Tel 051 55111 Fax 051 70307			**H**
Waterford Co Waterford			Map 19 C5

Well kept inside and out, the Cusacks' hotel stands right on the quayside.
Paintings, antiques, a grandfather clock and a marble fireplace take the eye
in the central hall, while bedrooms of various sizes lack nothing in style.
All have good-sized bathrooms. No dogs. Lots of nice touches throughout,
including ruffled Dutch blinds at bedroom corridor windows. Children up
to 12 stay free in parents' room; baby-sitting and cots available. Conference
facilities for up to 300. *Rooms 74. Access, Amex, Visa,*

Waterford	Jurys Waterford Hotel	60%	£89
Tel 051 32111 Fax 051 32863			**H**
Ferrybank Waterford Co Waterford			Map 19 C5

From a position high on the banks of the river Suir, all the bedrooms enjoy
good views of Waterford City and are comfortably furnished with
darkwood furniture. The leisure centre has a good-sized pool and is a
popular attraction. Children up to 14 stay free in parents' soom; special
activities for children during the summer. Conference/banqueting facilities
for up to 600. *Rooms 99. Indoor swimming pool, plunge pool, sauna, spa bath,
steam room, gymnasium, tennis. Access, Amex, Visa,*

Waterford   Prendiville's Restaurant   NEW   £60

Tel 051 78851

Cork Road Waterford Co Waterford

R

Map 19 C5

Chef Paula Prendiville and her husband Peter only moved into this
converted gatelodge in 1990 but they have already built up an enviable
reputation for imaginative food, professionalism and reasonable prices –
something to bear in mind if you are travelling to Ireland via Rosslare, as
traffic off the ferry hits Waterford in the early evening just in time for
dinner. Menus based firmly on the best of local ingredients favour organic
produce and transform it into creative dishes with an original twist, such as
rillettes of smoked and wild salmon on wholemeal toast or sautéed lamb
cutlets with a compote of onions in honey and red wine. Elegant desserts
are irresistible. *Seats 50. Parties 16. Private Room. L 12.30-2.15
D 6.30-10.30. Closed Sun, 24-26 Dec. Set L £9.95. Access, Visa.*

Waterford   Tower Hotel   57%   £100

Tel 051 75801   Fax 051 70129

The Mall Waterford Co Waterford

H

Map 19 C5

Near Reginald's Tower, alongside the River Suir, practical accommodation
in a city-centre hotel with a new leisure centre. Conference/banqueting
facilities for 600/500. Children up to 3 free in parents' room. *Rooms 125.
Indoor swimming pool, sauna, spa bath, gymnasium. Closed 25 & 26 Dec.
Access, Amex, Visa,* 🔵 *Diners Club International*

Waterford   Waterford Castle   80%   £193

Tel 051 78203   Fax 051 79316

The Island Ballinakill Waterford Co Waterford

HR

Map 19 C5

It's hard to imagine a more perfect setting for this 18th-century castle than
the 310-acre private island reached by ferry. Stone arches and walls above
old panelling, a fine ribbon plaster ceiling, a real fire burning in a huge
stone fireplace and antique leather chairs make the entrance hall impressive,
and the drawing room is sumptuous indeed. Bedrooms are individually
decorated in fine style, and boast splendid bathrooms with Victorian baths.
Dogs in kennels only. An 18-hole golf course is currently under
construction. *Rooms 19. Garden, indoor swimming pool, gymnasium, croquet,
tennis, riding, clay-pigeon shooting, bicycles, snooker, games room. Access, Amex,
Visa,* 🔵 *Diners Club International*

Restaurant   £80

Mellow oak panelling beneath an intricate Elizabethan-style plaster ceiling,
oil paintings, comfortable Regency-striped chairs, fine table settings and a
pianist add up to a splendid setting in which to enjoy Paul McCluskey's
accomplished cooking. Lunch might comprise sautéed sweetbreads with
shiitake mushrooms or leek and potato soup followed by fillets of plaice
meunière or noisettes of pork with apple and Calvados. Dinner is along
similar lines, generally avoiding over-elaboration but maintaining the
emphasis on natural flavours: escalopes of monkfish with grapefruit
sabayon, Rossmore oysters (on ice or with cucumber and tomato julienne
and lime butter sauce), steamed turbot with wild mushrooms and soy
butter sauce, sirloin steak with bone marrow and red wine sauce. Even the
vegetarian dishes sound interesting – carrot mousse with an oatmeal filling
and island vegetables in puff pastry with white butter sauce. Short à la carte
and fixed-price menus for both lunch and dinner. Good all-round wine list.
*Seats 60. Parties 60. Private Room. L 12.30-2 (Sun from 11.30) D 7-10 (Sun
to 9). Set L £15.50 Set D £28.50.*

Waterford   Places of Interest

Tourist Information   Tel 051 75788.
Waterford Cathedral   Tel 051 74757.

Waterford Crystal Glass Factory   Kilbarry Tel 051 73311.

Wexford	**White's Hotel**	**60%**	**£66**

Tel 053 22311 Fax 053 45000	**H**
George Street Wexford Co Wexford	**Map 19 D5**

An 18th-century building which has metamorphosed from a lodging for
militiamen (founded by John White) to the home of Oscar Wilde's mother
Speranza, to a coaching inn and finally to a hotel, White's is labyrinthine in
character. Public areas include a large red plush bar/lounge and a reception
with easy chairs, a marble fireplace and a real fire. Most bedrooms are in
an extension; all are practical, with modest fitted units and neat, fully tiled
bathrooms. There are extensive conference/function facilities for up to 600.
No dogs. *Rooms 82. Coffee shop (8am-9.30pm). Access, Amex, Visa,*
Diners Club International

Wexford	**Places of Interest**

Tourist Information   Tel 053 23111.
Johnstown Castle Demesne and Agricultural Museum.
Water Skiing Centre.

Wicklow	**Old Rectory**	**59%**	**£78**

Tel 0404 67048 Fax 0404 69181	**HR**
Wicklow Co Wicklow	**Map 19 D4**

Owners since 1977, Paul and Linda Saunders are welcoming hosts at their
pink-washed Victorian rectory on the edge of town. The lounge features a
white marble fireplace and corniced ceiling, while individually appointed
bedrooms offer various homely extras. Breakfast brings a choice of Irish,
Scottish or Swiss menus. *Rooms 6. Garden Closed Nov-Easter. Access, Amex,*
Visa, *Diners Club International*

Restaurant	**£60**

Dinner in the tiny dining room is a gastronomic treat prepared with an
artist's eye by Linda. Flowers play an important part in garnishing (and for
eating) and one of the menus is a vegetarian floral selection. Main courses
are served with a selection of vegetables and speciality salad garnished with
organic leaves and edible flowers. Spanish bottles to the fore on a helpful
wine list. No smoking. *Seats 12. Parties 4. D only at 8. Set D £23.*

Wicklow	**Places of Interest**

Tourist Information   Tel 0404 69117.
Mount Usher Gardens.

Youghal	**Aherne's Seafood Restaurant**	**£60**

Tel 024 92424	**RR**
163 North Main Street Youghal Co Cork	**Map 19 C6**

A warm welcome and efficient service in the cocktail bar get guests off to
a good start in the Fitzgibbon family's renowned seafood restaurant in an
expanded pub. Menus, changed daily and attractively presented against a
watercolour background, offer a wide choice of local seafood in dishes such
as hot potato and smoked salmon gratin, seafood chowder and pan-fried
monkfish with pernod and fennel. Look out for speciality shellfish dishes
such as mussels, clams, oysters, crab and prawns cooked in olive oil and
their own juices, all served with a superb moist, malty bread. Sample
desserts include a fine medley of home-made ice creams. *Seats 50. Parties*
60. Private Room. L 12.30-2 (Sun to 1.45) D 6.30-9.30. Closed 4 days Xmas.
Set L £11.30 Set D £18.50. Access, Visa.

Rooms	**£75**

Aherne's has recently added accommodation in the shape of ten en-suite
bedrooms.

Quick Reference Lists: Outside London

Hotels under £65 for 2

England

Acle Forte Travelodge
Aldeburgh Uplands
All Stretton Stretton Hall Hotel
Alton Forte Travelodge
Alton Grange Hotel
Altrincham George & Dragon
Alveston Forte Posthouse
Amesbury Forte Travelodge
Arundel Norfolk Arms
Ashford Forte Posthouse
Ashford Travel Inn
Axbridge Oak House
Baldock Forte Travelodge
Bamburgh Lord Crewe Arms
Barnard Castle Jersey Farm Hotel
Barnsley Forte Travelodge
Barton Mills Forte Travelodge
Barton Stacey Forte Travelodge
Barton-under-Needwood Forte
   Travelodge
Basildon Campanile Hotel
Basildon Travel Inn
Basingstoke Forte Travelodge
Basingstoke Forte Posthouse
Basingstoke Travel Inn
Bebington Forte Travelodge
Beccles Waveney House
Billingshurst Forte Travelodge
Birmingham Campanile Hotel
Birmingham Forte Posthouse
Birmingham Granada Lodge
Birmingham Airport Forte Posthouse
Blyth Forte Travelodge
Blyth Granada Lodge
Bolton Forte Posthouse
Boreham Street White Friars Hotel
Boroughbridge The Crown
Bournemouth Forte Posthouse
Bourton-on-the-Water Dial House
Braithwaite Ivy House
Branscombe Masons Arms
Brentwood Forte Posthouse
Brentwood Forte Travelodge
Burnley Forte Travelodge
Burtonwood Forte Travelodge
Cambridge Arundel House
Cannock Travel Inn
Canterbury Canterbury Hotel
Canterbury Ebury Hotel
Carcroft Forte Travelodge
Carlisle Granada Lodge
Castle Cary Bond's
Castle Combe Castle Inn
Cheltenham On The Park

Cheltenham Travel Inn
Chessington Travel Inn
Chester Forte Posthouse
Chesterfield Forte Travelodge
Chiddingfold Crown Inn
Chippenham Granada Lodge
Christchurch Travel Inn
Clayton-le-Woods Pines Hotel
Corsham Methuen Arms
Colsterworth Forte Travelodge
Coventry Campanile Hotel
Coventry Campanile Hotel
Coventry Forte Posthouse
Crewe Forte Travelodge
Crick Forte Posthouse
   Northampton/Rugby
Croydon Forte Posthouse
Croydon Travel Inn
Darlington White Horse
Derby Forte Posthouse
Derby International Hotel
Desborough Forte Travelodge
Dinnington Dinnington Hall
Doncaster Campanile Hotel
Dorking Forte Travelodge
Dover Forte Posthouse
Dover Travel Inn
Droitwich Forte Travelodge
Dudley Forte Travelodge
Dulverton Carnarvon Arms
Dunchurch Dun Cow
Dunchurch Forte Travelodge
Dunstable Forte Travelodge
East Dereham King's Head
Eastleigh Forte Travelodge
Eccleshall St George Hotel
Ely Forte Travelodge
Epping Forte Posthouse
Fairford Bull Hotel
Fairy Cross Portledge Hotel
Farnham Trevena House
Faugh String of Horses
Fenstanton Forte Travelodge
Ferrybridge Granada Lodge
Fleet Forte Travelodge
Fontwell Forte Travelodge
Fossebridge Fossebridge Inn
Gateshead Forte Travelodge
Gatwick Airport Forte Posthouse
Gayton Travel Inn
Gloucester Travel Inn
Goathland Mallyan Spout
Gordano Forte Travelodge
Goudhurst Star & Eagle Inn
Grantham Forte Travelodge
Grantham Granada Lodge

Grimsthorpe Black Horse Inn
Grizedale Grizedale Lodge
Hagley Travel Inn
Hailsham Forte Travelodge
Hartlebury Forte Travelodge
Hartlepool Grand Hotel
Hartshead Moor Forte Travelodge
Hatherleigh George Hotel
Havant Forte Posthouse
Haydock Forte Travelodge
Haydock Forte Posthouse
Hayes Travel Inn
Heathrow Airport Forte Posthouse Ariel Hotel
Heathrow Airport Granada Lodge
Helland Bridge Tredethy Country Hotel
Hereford Travel Inn
High Wycombe Forte Posthouse
Horsham Travel Inn
Hull Campanile Hotel
Hull Forte Posthouse
Ilminster Forte Travelodge
Ipswich Forte Posthouse
Kendal Woolpack Hotel
Kenton Travel Inn
Kings Lynn Forte Travelodge
Kintbury Dundas Arms
Knapton Knapton Hall
Knutsford Forte Travelodge
Lancaster Forte Posthouse
Langho Northcote Manor
Leicester Forte Posthouse
Leicester Granada Lodge
Letchworth Broadway Toby Hotel
Lincoln D'Isney Place
Liverpool Campanile Hotel
Lolworth Forte Travelodge
Long Melford Black Lion
Lower Swell Old Farmhouse
Ludlow Forte Travelodge
Luton Forte Posthouse
Luton Hotel Ibis
Luton Leaside Hotel
Lympsham Batch Farm
Lyndhurst Lyndhurst Park
Manchester Forte Posthouse
Manchester Granada Lodge
Market Drayton Corbet Arms
Marston Forte Travelodge
Melksham King's Arms
Melton Mowbray George Hotel
Mere Old Ship Hotel
Mickleton Three Ways Hotel
Middleton Stoney Jersey Arms
Middleton-in-Teesdale Teesdale Hotel
Montacute King's Arms Inn
Morden Forte Travelodge
Moreton-in-Marsh Redesdale Arms
Moretonhampstead White Hart Inn
Needham Market Pipps Ford
Newark Forte Travelodge
Newark-on-Trent Grange Hotel
Newcastle-under-Lyme Forte Posthouse
Newcastle-upon-Tyne Campanile Hotel
Newmarket White Hart
North Petherton Walnut Tree Inn
Northampton Forte Travelodge
Northampton Travel Inn

Norwich Forte Posthouse
Nottingham Forte Posthouse
Nuneaton Forte Travelodge
Nuneaton Travel Inn
Okehampton Forte Travelodge
Old Harlow Travel Inn
Oldbury Forte Travelodge
Ormesby St Margaret Ormesby Lodge
Oswestry Forte Travelodge
Oxford Forte Travelodge
Penrith Forte Travelodge
Peterborough Forte Travelodge
Plymouth Campanile Hotel
Pocklington Feathers Hotel
Podimore Forte Travelodge
Preston Novotel
Preston Travel Inn
Ravenstonedale Black Swan Inn
Reading Forte Travelodge
Reading Forte Posthouse
Redditch Campanile Hotel
Reeth Burgoyne Hotel
Retford Forte Travelodge
Rotherham Campanile Hotel
Rotherham Travel Inn
Ruckhall Ancient Camp Inn
Rugeley Forte Travelodge
Runcorn Campanile Hotel
Rushden Forte Travelodge
St Austell White Hart
St Margaret's Wallett's Court
St Mawes Rising Sun
Saltash Granada Lodge
Scole Scole Inn
Scotch Corner Forte Travelodge
Seahouses Olde Ship Hotel
Sedgemoor Forte Travelodge
Sedlescombe Brickwall Hotel
Sherborne Forte Posthouse
Shipdham Shipdham Place
Skipton Forte Travelodge
Slaidburn Hark to Bounty Inn
Sleaford Forte Travelodge
Solihull Travel Inn
Somerton Lynch Country House Hotel
South Cave/Hull Forte Travelodge
South Milford Forte Posthouse Leeds/Selby
South Mimms Forte Posthouse
South Mimms Forte Travelodge
South Witham Forte Travelodge
Southampton Forte Posthouse
Southampton Southampton Park Hotel
Southport New Bold Hotel
Southwold The Crown
Stilton Bell Inn
Stockport Forte Travelodge
Stockport Travel Inn
Stoke Mandeville Belmore Hotel
Stokesley Chapters
Stowmarket Forte Travelodge
Stratford-upon-Avon Forte Posthouse
Street Bear Hotel
Stretton Ram Jam Inn
Sutton Coldfield Forte Travelodge
Sutton Scotney North Forte Travelodge
Sutton Scotney South Forte Travelodge
Swavesey Forte Travelodge

Swindon Forte Posthouse
Tamworth Granada Lodge
Taunton Forte Posthouse
Taunton Travel Inn
Teignmouth Thomas Luny House
Telford Forte Travelodge
Thornaby-on-Tees Forte Posthouse
Thrapston Forte Travelodge
Thrussington Forte Travelodge
Thurrock Granada Lodge
Tiverton Forte Travelodge
Toddington Granada Lodge
Towcester Forte Travelodge
Tring Travel Inn
Tutbury Ye Olde Dog & Partridge Inn
Umberleigh Rising Sun Inn
Uppingham Forte Travelodge
Uttoxeter Forte Travelodge
Uttoxeter White Hart
Wakefield Campanile Hotel
Wakefield Forte Posthouse
Wakefield Granada Lodge
Wallingford Shillingford Bridge Hotel
Walsall Forte Posthouse
Walsall Wood Baron's Court
Warminster Granada Lodge
Warrington Travel Inn
Washington Forte Posthouse
Washington Granada Lodge
Weedon Crossroads Hotel
Wentbridge Forte Travelodge
Whitewell Inn at Whitewell
Wilmington Home Farm
Winkton Fisherman's Haunt Inn
Woodhall Spa Dower House
Wooler Ryecroft Hotel
Worksop Forte Travelodge
Wrotham Heath Forte Posthouse
Maidstone/Sevenoaks
Wrotham Heath Travel Inn
Yelverton Moorland Links
York Forte Posthouse
York Hill Hotel
Yoxford Satis House

Scotland

Aberdeen Travel Inn
Abington Forte Travelodge
Annan Warmanbie Hotel
Cumbernauld Travel Inn
Dulnain Bridge Auchendean Lodge
Dumbarton Forte Travelodge
Dundee Travel Inn
East Kilbride Stuart Hotel
Edinburgh Forte Travelodge
Edinburgh Forte Posthouse
Edinburgh Granada Lodge
Erskine Forte Posthouse
Forfar Royal Hotel
Garve Inchbae Lodge
Gretna Green Forte Travelodge
Harray Loch Merkister Hotel
Isle of Raasay Isle of Raasay Hotel
Kilmelford Cuilfail Hotel

Kinross Granada Lodge
Kirkmichael Log Cabin Hotel
Melrose Burts Hotel
Newhouse Travel Inn
Spean Bridge Letterfinlay Lodge
Stirling Granada Lodge
Strathtummel Port-an-Eilean Hotel
Tobermory Tobermory Hotel
Tweedsmuir Crook Inn

Wales

Abercynon Llechwen Hall
Brechfa Ty Mawr
Bridgend Forte Travelodge
Cardiff Campanile Hotel
Cardiff Campanile Hotel
Cardiff Forte Travelodge
Cardiff Forte Posthouse
Cardiff Travel Inn
Chepstow Castle View Hotel
Conwy Sychnant Pass Hotel
Crickhowell Bear Hotel
Crickhowell Gliffaes Country House Hotel
Cross Hands Forte Travelodge
Fishguard Fishguard Bay Hotel
Halkyn Forte Travelodge
Llanarmon Dyffryn Ceiriog Hand Hotel
Llandeilo Cawdor Arms
Llandudno Empire Hotel
Llanrwst Meadowsweet
Llanwnda Stables Hotel
Machynlleth Wynnstay Arms
Merthyr Tydfil Baverstock Hotel
Newport Kings Hotel
Northop Hall Forte Travelodge
Pantmawr Glansevern Arms
Pencoed Forte Travelodge
Port Talbot Travel Inn
Tintern Abbey Royal George
Wrexham Forte Travelodge

Channel Islands

St Aubin La Haule Manor
Sark Aval Du Creux

Northern Ireland

Portballintrae Bayview Hotel

Republic of Ireland

Ballylickey Sea View House
Blessington Downshire House
Cork Blackash Forte Travelodge
Delgany Glenview Hotel
Glen of Aherlow Aherlow House
Swords Forte Travelodge

15 Minutes Off Motorway

Eating in the motorway service areas may cut out extra travelling time, but it also cuts out any possibility of pleasing the discerning palate.
Yet throughout the land outstanding eating is available just a short drive from the motorway network, and the list that follows pinpoints STARRED RESTAURANTS that need no more than a 15-minute detour. And if you're looking for somewhere to spend the night in style, we also feature DE LUXE AND GRADE 1 HOTELS within a similar range.
So even when time is important, you don't have to leave out the good things - just leave the motorway! For further details of these establishments, see individual entries in the main section of the Guide.

England

M1

J12	**Flitwick** Flitwick Manor
J13	**Aspley Guise** Moore Place Hotel
J16	**Northampton** Swallow Hotel
J22	**Leicester** Holiday Inn
J23	**Quorn** Quorn Country Hotel
J24	**Castle Donington** Donington Thistle Hotel
J25	**Nottingham** Forte Crest
	Nottingham Royal Moat House International Hotel
	Nottingham Rutland Square Hotel
J33	**Sheffield** Moat House
J47	**Leeds** Haley's Hotel

M3

J2	**Egham** Runnymede Hotel
J3	**Ascot** Royal Berkshire Hotel
	Bagshot Pennyhill Park Hotel
J6	**Basingstoke** Audleys Wood Thistle Hotel
J8	**Winchester** Lainston House

M4

J4	**Heathrow Airport** Edwardian Hotel
	Heathrow Airport (West Drayton) Excelsior Hotel
	Heathrow Airport Heathrow Hilton
	Heathrow Airport (West Drayton) Holiday Inn
	Heathrow Airport Sheraton-Heathrow
	Heathrow Airport (Hayes) Sheraton Skyline
J6	**Slough** Holiday Inn
	Slough Copthorne Hotel
	Windsor Oakley Court Hotel
J8/9	**Bray-on-Thames** Waterside Inn
	Maidenhead Fredrick's Hotel
	Taplow Cliveden
J10	**Sindlesham** Reading Moat House

J11	**Reading** Caversham Hotel
	Reading Ramada Hotel
	Shinfield L'Ortolan
J13	**Newbury** Foley Lodge Hotel
	Newbury Regency Park Hotel
J15	**Swindon** Blunsdon House Hotel
	Swindon Holiday Inn
J16	**Purton** Pear Tree
J17	**Beanacre** Beechfield House
	Castle Combe Manor House
	Easton Grey Whatley Manor Hotel
J18	**Bath** Bath Spa Hotel
	Bath Combe Grove Hotel
	Bath Francis Hotel
	Bath Priory Hotel
	Bath Queensberry Hotel
	Bath Royal Crescent Hotel
	Colerne Lucknam Park Hotel
J19	**Bristol** Hilton International
	Bristol Moat House

M5

J4	**Bromsgrove** Country Court Hotel
	Bromsgrove Grafton Manor
	Chaddesley Corbett Brockencote Hall
J5	**Abberley** Elms Hotel
	Droitwich Spa Chateau Impney Hotel
J7	**Worcester** Fownes Hotel
J8	**Malvern** Croque-en-Bouche
J9	**Corse Lawn** Corse Lawn House
J11	**Cheltenham** The Epicurean
	Cheltenham The Greenway
	Cheltenham Redmond's
	Gloucester Hatton Court
J13	**Painswick** Painswick Hotel
	Stroud Oakes
J14	**Thornbury** Thornbury Castle
J25	**Hatch Beauchamp** Farthings Country House Hotel
	Taunton Castle Hotel
J29	**Whimple** Woodhayes
J31	**Exeter** Royal Clarence

M6

| J2/3 | **Ansty** Ansty Hall |
| | **Coventry** De Vere Hotel |

J6   **Birmingham** Copthorne Hotel
     Birmingham Holiday Inn
     Birmingham Hyatt Regency
     Birmingham
     Birmingham Norton Place Hotel
     Birmingham Plough & Harrow
     Hotel
     Birmingham Swallow Hotel
     Sutton Coldfield New Hall

J15   **Hanchurch** Hanchurch Manor
J17   **Nantwich** Rookery Hall
J19   **Alderley Edge** Alderley Edge
     Hotel
J32   **Longridge** Heathcote's
J40   **Penrith** North Lakes Gateway
     Hotel
     Ullswater Leeming House Hotel
     Ullswater Sharrow Bay Hotel &
     Restaurant
J42   **Wetheral** Crown Hotel
J43   **Brampton** Farlam Hall Hotel

M11

J8   **Broxted** Whitehall Hotel
J8   **Hatfield Heath** Down Hall Hotel
J12   **Cambridge** Midsummer House
     Restaurant

M20

J3   **Wrotham Heath** Forte Posthouse
J8   **Lenham** Chilston Park
J9   **Ashford** Eastwell Manor
     Ashford International Hotel
J11   **Hythe** Hythe Imperial Hotel

M23

J9   **Horley** Langshott Manor
J10   **East Grinstead** Gravetye Manor &
     Restaurant
     Gatwick Airport Gatwick Hilton
     International
     Gatwick Airport (Horley) Gatwick
     Penta Hotel
     Gatwick Airport Forte Crest
     Gatwick
     Gatwick Airport Copthorne
     Effingham Park
     Turners Hill Alexander House
J11   **Cuckfield** Ockenden Manor Hotel
     Lower Beeding South Lodge

M25

J9   **Sutton** Holiday Inn
J10   **Guildford** The Angel
J14   **Heathrow Airport** Heathrow
     Hilton

M27

J9   **Fareham** Solent Hotel
J12   **Portsmouth** Holiday Inn

M40

J4   **Marlow** Compleat Angler Hotel
     Medmenham Danesfield House
J7   **Great Milton** Le Manoir aux
     Quat'Saisons & Restaurant
J9   **Oxford** Old Parsonage
J15   **Leamington Spa** Mallory Court &
     Restaurant
     Stratford-upon-Avon Billesley
     Manor
     Stratford-upon-Avon Ettington
     Park
     Stratford-upon-Avon Moat House
     International
     Stratford-upon-Avon Welcombe
     Hotel

M42

J4   **Hockley Heath** Nuthurst Grange
J6   **Birmingham** Birmingham
     Metropole
     Meriden Forest of Arden Hotel
J9   **Wishaw** Belfry Hotel

M50

J1   **Puckrup** Puckrup Hall
J2   **Ledbury** Hope End Country
     House

M53

J5   **Puddington** Craxton Wood Hotel
J12   **Chester** Chester Grosvenor
     Chester Crabwall Manor

M54

J4   **Shifnal** Park House Hotel

M56

J5   **Manchester Airport** Hilton
     International
J6   **Handforth** Belfry Hotel
     Wilmslow Stanneylands Hotel

M62

J26   **Bradford** Restaurant Nineteen

M63

J9   **Manchester** Charterhouse Hotel
     Manchester Copthorne Hotel
     Manchester Holiday Inn Crowne
     Plaza
     Manchester Hotel Piccadilly
     Manchester Ramada
     Renaissance
     Manchester Yang Sing

A1(M)

JN **Newcastle-upon-Tyne** Swallow Gosforth Park Hotel
Newcastle-upon-Tyne Holiday Inn
Newcastle-upon-Tyne 21 Queen Street

Scotland

M8

J2 **Edinburgh** The Balmoral
Edinburgh Caledonian Hotel
Edinburgh Edinburgh Sheraton
Edinburgh George Inter-Continental Hotel
Edinburgh Howard Hotel
Edinburgh King James Thistle Hotel
Edinburgh Royal Terrace Hotel
Edinburgh Sheraton Hotel
J17 **Glasgow** One Devonshire Gardens
J17/18 **Glasgow** Forte Crest
Glasgow Town House
J18 **Glasgow** Holiday Inn
Glasgow Moat House International

M9

J3 **Linlithgow** Champany Inn Restaurant
J9 **Dunblane** Cromlix House
J10/11 **Alloa** Gean House

M80

J4 **Cumbernauld** Westerwood Hotel

Wales

M4

J24 **Newport** Celtic Manor Hotel
J25 **Llangybi** Cwrt Bleddyn Hotel
J32 **Cardiff** Park Hotel
Cardiff Moat House
J34 **Miskin** Miskin Manor

Restaurants With Rooms

England

Barnstaple Lynwood House
Baslow Fischer's Baslow Hall
Birdlip Kingshead House
Blandford Forum La Belle Alliance
Bradford Restaurant 19
Brampton Tarn End
Brimfield Poppies Restaurant
Campsea Ashe Old Rectory
Cartmel Uplands
Cawston Grey Gables
Cheltenham Redmond's
Clun Old Post Office
Cowan Bridge Cobwebs
Dorchester Yalbury Cottage
Dorrington Country Friends
East Buckland Lower Pitt
Erpingham Ark
Glastonbury No. 3 Restaurant & Hotel
Great Dunmow The Starr
Gulworthy Horn of Plenty
Harwich Pier at Harwich
Haworth Weavers
Hayfield Bridge End Restaurant
Helford Riverside
Horndon on the Hill Hill House

Kington Penrhos Court
Knutsford La Belle Epoque
Lavenham Great House
Lympstone River House
Manchester Airport Moss Nook
New Alresford Hunters
Northwich Wincham Hall
Oxford Bath Place Hotel & Restaurant
Padstow Seafood Restaurant
Paulerspury Vine House
Pool-in-Wharfedale Pool Court
Powerstock Three Horseshoes Inn
Ross-on-Wye Pheasants
Stonor Stonor Arms
Storrington Manley's
Sturminster Newton Plumber Manor
Ulverston Bay Horse Inn & Bistro
Uppingham The Lake Isle
Waterhouses Old Beams
Wath-in-Nidderdale Sportsman's Arms
Watlington Well House
Williton White House
Winteringham Winteringham Fields
Wylam Laburnum House
Yeovil Little Barwick House

Scotland

Alyth Drumnacree House
Canonbie Riverside Inn
Fort William The Factor's House
Muir of Ord Dower House
Peat Inn Peat Inn
Ullapool Altnaharrie Inn

Wales

Chirk Starlings Castle
Harlech The Cemlyn
Porth G & T's Village Bistro
Pwllheli Plas Bodegroes
Trellech Village Green
Welsh Hook Stone Hall

Northern Ireland

Garvagh Blackheath House & MacDuff's

Republic of Ireland

Athy Tonlegee House
Castledermot Doyle's School House
    Country Inn
Dingle Doyle's Seafood Bar & Townhouse
Enniskerry Enniscree Lodge Inn
Kinsale Old Presbytery
Youghal Aherne's Seafood Restaurant

Inns

England

Alcester Arrow Mill
Andover White Hart Inn
Ashington Mill House Inn
Axbridge Oak House
Bainbridge Rose & Crown Inn
Buckler's Hard Master Builder's House
Burton-on-Trent Riverside Inn
Canterbury Falstaff Hotel
Castle Combe Castle Inn
Charlbury Bell Hotel
Charlbury The Bull at Charlbury
Chiddingfold Crown Inn
Chipping Norton Crown & Cushion
Clanfield The Plough at Clanfield
Corsham Methuen Arms
Dartmouth Royal Castle Hotel
Dorchester-on-Thames George Hotel
Driffield Bell Hotel
Dunchurch Dun Cow
East Dereham King's Head
Eccleshall St George Hotel
Eton Christopher Hotel
Faugh String of Horses Inn
Frilford
Heath Dog House Hotel
Godalming Inn on the Lake
Goudhurst Star & Eagle Inn
Greta Bridge Morritt Arms
Grimsthorpe Black Horse Inn
Grindleford Maynard Arms
Hatherleigh George Hotel
Kintbury Dundas Arms
Lacock At The Sign of The Angel
Ledbury The Feathers
Lower Swell Old Farmhouse
Lynmouth Rising Sun Inn
Macclesfield Sutton Hall
Market Drayton Corbet Arms
Melksham King's Arms
Mellor Millstone Hotel

Mere Old Ship Hotel
Middleton Stoney Jersey Arms
Minster Lovell Old Swan
Montacute King's Arms Inn
Moreton-in-Marsh Redesdale Arms
Moretonhampstead White Hart Inn
Odiham George Hotel
Pocklington Feathers Hotel
Ravenstonedale Black Swan Inn
Ruckhall Ancient Camp Inn
Rugby Periquito Hotel
St Austell White Hart
Scole Scole Inn
Seahouses Olde Ship Hotel
Shepperton Warren Lodge
Slaidburn Hark to Bounty Inn
Southwold The Crown
Stilton Bell Inn
Stratfield Turgis Wellington Arms
Thornton-le-Fylde River House
Troutbeck Mortal Man Inn
Tutbury Ye Olde Dog & Partridge Inn
Umberleigh Rising Sun Inn
Uttoxeter White Hart
Whitewell Inn at Whitewell
Winchester Wykeham Arms
Winkton Fisherman's Haunt Inn
Winsford Royal Oak Inn
Yattendon Royal Oak

Scotland

Gatehouse of Fleet Murray Arms Inn
Kilfinan Kilfinan Hotel
Melrose Burts Hotel
Strathblane Kirkhouse Inn
Talladale Loch Maree Hotel
Ullapool Ceilidh Place

Wales

Abercynon Llechwen Hall
Chepstow Castle View Hotel
Crickhowell Bear Hotel
Llanarmon Dyffryn Ceiriog Hand Hotel
Llanarmon Dyffryn Ceiriog West Arms
  Hotel
Pantmawr Glansevern Arms
Penmaenpool George III Hotel
Swansea Langland Court Hotel

Channel Islands

Pleinmont Imperial Hotel
St Aubin Old Court House Inn

Northern Ireland

Bushmills Bushmills Inn
Crawfordsburn Old Inn

Republic of Ireland

Kinsale Blue Haven Hotel
Rathnew Hunter's Hotel
Spiddal Bridge House Inn

Town House Hotels

This exclusive category highlights a small number of hotels of distinctive personality. Most are conversions of town residences which retain not only their period façades but also interior character and, to some extent, the feel of a private house. None of them has more than 50 bedrooms, and very few are owned by groups.
Excellent personal service is another attribute.

England

Bedford Woodlands Manor
Brighton Topps Hotel
Bury St Edmunds Angel Hotel
Cheltenham On The Park
Chipping Camden Cotswold House
Poole Mansion House
Sherborne Eastbury Hotel
Tetbury The Close
Wareham Priory Hotel
York Grange Hotel
York Mount Royale

Scotland

Edinburgh Howard Hotel
Elgin Mansion House
Glasgow One Devonshire Gardens
Nairn Clifton Hotel

Wales

Llandudno St Tudno Hotel

Republic of Ireland

Cashel Cashel Palace
Cork Arbutus Lodge

Private House Hotels

Private House hotels are de luxe 'bed and breakfast' establishments. This handful of hotels offers guests comfortable, often luxurious accommodation and personal service, but they do not have restaurants or public rooms, though some may have a drawing room. With the usual percentage rating, they would have suffered by not having normal hotel facilities and are therefore not graded.

England

Bath Fountain House
Chartham Thruxted Oast
Leeds 42 The Calls
Lincoln D'Isney Place
Teignmouth Thomas Luny House

Scotland

Edinburgh Channings
Glasgow Devonshire Hotel

Republic of Ireland

Dublin Grey Door

Country House Hotels

This is a select category of small hotels offering civilised comfort, good service and fine food in an attractive and peaceful rural setting. Most of them are imposing country mansions, converted and run with loving care by dedicated owners, often a husband-and-wife team. They have no more than 35 bedrooms; all have recommended in-house restaurants, many of star standard.

England

Amberley Amberley Castle
Bath Combe Grove Manor
Battle Netherfield Place
Bilbrough Bilbrough Manor
Bowness-on-Windermere Linthwaite House
Bradford-on-Avon Woolley Grange
Buckland Buckland Manor
Burley Burley Manor
Chagford Gidleigh Park
Charingworth Charingworth Manor
Chedington Chedington Court
Cheltenham Greenway
East Grinstead Gravetye Manor
Freshford Homewood Park
Grasmere Michael's Nook
Great Milton Le Manoir aux Quat'Saisons
Grimston Congham Hall
Horley Langshott Manor
Leamington Spa Mallory Court
Lewdown Lewtrenchard Manor
Maiden Newton Maiden Newton House
Morston Morston Hall
Nidd Nidd Hall

Oakham Hambleton Hall
Puckrup Puckrup Hall
South Molton Whitechapel Manor
Ston Easton Ston Easton Park
Storrington Abingworth Hall
Storrington Little Thakeham
Taplow Cliveden
Thornbury Thornbury Castle
Uckfield Horsted Place
Ullswater Sharrow Bay
Walkington Manor House

Scotland

Alloa Gean House
Alexandria Cameron House
Arisaig Arisaig House
Ballater Tullich Lodge
Banchory Invery House
Dunblane Cromlix House
Eriska Isle of Eriska
Fort William Inverlochy Castle

Wales

Llandudno Bodysgallen Hall
Llangefni Tre-Ysgawen Hall
Llyswen Llangoed Hall
Northop Soughton Hall

Republic of Ireland

Gorey Marlfield House
Letterfrack Rosleague Manor
Riverstown Coopershill House

Beautifully Situated Hotels

England

Abberley Elms Hotel
Alcester Arrow Mill
Alston Lovelady Shield
Amberley Amberley Castle
Amberley Amberley Inn
Ambleside Rothay Manor
Applethwaite Underscar Manor
Ashbourne Callow Hall
Ashford Eastwell Manor
Aylesbury Hartwell House
Bagshot Pennyhill Park
Bakewell Hassop Hall
Baslow Cavendish Hotel
Bassenthwaite Armathwaite Hall
Battle Netherfield Place
Beanacre Beechfield House
Bilbrough Bilbrough Manor
Borrowdale Borrowdale Hotel
Borrowdale Stakis Lodore Swiss Hotel
Boughton Monchelsea Tanyard Hotel
Bradford-on-Avon Woolley Grange
Brampton Farlam Hall
Bromsgrove Grafton Manor
Broxted Whitehall
Buckland Buckland Manor
Burley Burley Manor
Calstock Danescombe Valley Hotel
Canterbury Howfield Manor
Carlyon Bay Carlyon Bay Hotel
Carlyon Bay Porth Avallen Hotel
Cartmel Aynsome Manor
Castle Combe Manor House
Chaddesley Corbett Brockencote Hall
Chadlington The Manor
Chagford Gidleigh Park
Chagford Great Tree Hotel
Chagford Mill End
Charingworth Charingworth Manor
Chedington Chedington Court
Cheltenham Greenway
Chittlehamholt Highbullen
Churt Frensham Pond Hotel
Climping Bailiffscourt
Colerne Lucknam Park
Cornhill-on-Tweed Tillmouth Park
Corse Lawn Corse Lawn House
Cranbrook Kennel Holt Hotel
Crathorne Crathorne Hall
Crosby-on-Eden Crosby Lodge
Dovedale Izaak Walton Hotel
Dulverton Ashwick House

Easington Grinkle Park
East Grinstead Gravetye Manor
Easton Grey Whatley Manor
Elcot Elcot Park Resort Hotel
Evershot Summer Lodge
Fairy Cross Portledge Hotel
Flitwick Flitwick Manor
Freshford Homewood Park
Freshwater Farringford Hotel
Gillingham Stock Hill House
Gittisham Combe House
Golant Cormorant Hotel
Grasmere Michael's Nook
Grasmere Wordsworth Hotel
Great Snoring Old Rectory
Grizedale Grizedale Lodge
Hackness Hackness Grange
Haslemere Lythe Hill Hotel
Hatfield Heath Down Hall
Hawkshead Tarn Hows
Haytor Bel Alp House
Hintlesham Hintlesham Hall
Hockley Heath Nuthurst Grange
Holbeton Alston Hall
Hope Cove Cottage Hotel
Hope Cove Lantern Lodge
Horton-cum-Studley Studley Priory
Hunstrete Hunstrete House
Huntsham Huntsham Court
Hurstbourne Tarrant Esseborne Manor
Jervaulx Jervaulx Hall
Kilve Meadow House
Lamorna Cove Lamorna Cove Hotel
Land's End State House
Langley-on-Tyne Langley Castle
Leamington Spa Mallory Court
Ledbury Hope End
Lenham Chilston Park
Lewdown Lewtrenchard Manor
Linton Wood Hall
Liskeard Well House
Longhorsley Linden Hall
Looe Talland Bay Hotel
Lower Beeding South Lodge
Lower Slaughter Lower Slaughter Manor
Malvern Cottage in the Wood
Markington Hob Green
Marlow Compleat Angler Hotel
Matlock Riber Hall
Mawnan Smith Budock Vean Hotel
Mawnan Smith Meudon Hotel
Mawnan Smith Nansidwell
Middlecombe Periton Park
Mullion Polurrian Hotel

Nantwich Rookery Hall
New Milton Chewton Glen
North Huish Brookdale House
North Stoke Springs Hotel
Oakham Hambleton Hall
Otley Chevin Lodge
Poole Haven Hotel
Porlock Oaks Hotel
Portloe Lugger Hotel
Puddington Craxton Wood
Purton Pear Tree
Rotherwick Tylney Hall
Rothley Rothley Court
Ruckhall Ancient Camp Inn
St Martin's St Martin's Hotel
St Mawes Hotel Tresanton
Salcombe Marine Hotel
Salcombe Soar Mill Cove
Sandiway Nunsmere Hall
Saunton Saunton Sands
Scalby Wrea Head
South Molton Whitechapel Manor
Stapleford Stapleford Park
Ston Easton Ston Easton Park
Storrington Abingworth Hall
Storrington Little Thakeham
Stow-on-the-Wold Wyck Hill House
Stratford-upon-Avon Billesley Manor
Stratford-upon-Avon Ettington Park
Stratford-upon-Avon Welcombe Hotel
Studland Bay Knoll House
Sutton Coldfield New Hall
Swinfen Swinfen Hall
Taplow Cliveden
Teffont Evias Howard's House
Tetbury Calcot Manor
Thornbury Thornbury Castle
Thornton-le-Fylde River House
Thurlestone Thurlestone Hotel
Torquay Osborne Hotel
Tresco Island Hotel
Turners Hill Alexander House
Ullswater Leeming House
Ullswater Old Church Hotel
Ullswater Rampsbeck Country House
  Hotel
Ullswater Sharrow Bay
Upper Slaughter Lords of the Manor
Veryan Nare Hotel
Walkington Manor House
Warminster Bishopstrow House
West Bexington Manor Hotel
Whimple Woodhayes Hotel
Whitewell Inn at Whitewell
Whitwell-on-the-Hill Whitwell Hall
Winchester Lainston House
Windsor Oakley Court
Winsford Royal Oak Inn
Woody Bay Woody Bay Hotel
York Middlethorpe Hall

Scotland

Aberfeldy Farleyer House
Achiltibuie Summer Isles
Advie Tulchan Lodge

Airth Airth Castle
Alloa Gean House
Altnaharra Altnaharra Hotel
Arduaine Loch Melfort Hotel
Arisaig Arisaig House
Auchterarder Auchterarder House
Auchterarder Gleneagles Hotel
Ballater Tullich Lodge
Banchory Invery House
Banchory Raemoir House
Beattock Auchen Castle
Chapel of Garioch Pittodrie House
Crinan Crinan Hotel
Dalguise Kinnaird
Drumnadrochit Polmaily House
Dryburgh Dryburgh Abbey
Dulnain Bridge Auchendean Lodge
Dunblane Cromlix House
Duror Stewart Hotel
Eriska Isle of Eriska
Ettrickbridge Ettrickshaws Hotel
Fort William Inverlochy Castle
Fort William Mercury Hotel
Garve Inchbae Lodge
Gatehouse of Fleet Cally Palace
Glenborrodale Glenborrodale Castle
Gullane Greywalls Hotel
Harray Loch Merkister Hotel
Helmsdale Navidale House
Inverness Bunchrew House
Inverness Culloden House
Inverness Dunain Park
Isle of Raasay Isle of Raasay Hotel
Kelso Ednam House
Kelso Sunlaws House
Kentallen of Appin Ardsheal House
Kentallen of Appin Holly Tree
Kilchrenan Ardanaiseig
Kilchrenan Taychreggan Hotel
Kildrummy Kildrummy Castle
Killiecrankie Killiecrankie Hotel
Kilmore Glenfeochan House
Kilwinning Montgreenan Mansion
Kinclaven by Stanley Ballathie House
Langbank Gleddoch House
Maryculter Maryculter House
Newton Stewart Kirroughtree Hotel
North Berwick Marine Hotel
North Middleton Borthwick Castle
Oban Knipoch Hotel
Onich Allt-nan-Ros Hotel
Onich Lodge on the Loch
Onich Onich Hotel
Peebles Cringletie House
Peebles Peebles Hotel Hydro
Pitlochry Green Park Hotel
Port Appin Airds Hotel
Port William Corsemalzie House
Portpatrick Knockinaam Lodge
Rockcliffe Baron's Craig
St Fillans Four Seasons Hotel
Scarista Scarista House
Scourie Eddrachilles Hotel
Skelmorlie Manor Park
Sleat Kinloch Lodge
Spean Bridge Letterfinlay Lodge
Strachur Creggans Inn
Strathtummel Port-an-Eilean Hotel

Talladale Loch Maree Hotel
Tarbert Stonefield Castle
Tiroran Tiroran House
Turnberry Turnberry Hotel
Whitebridge Knockie Lodge

Wales

Aberdovey Plas Penhelig
Abersoch Porth Tocyn Hotel
Aberystwyth Conrah Country Hotel
Beaumaris Bulkeley Arms
Beddgelert Royal Goat Hotel
Bontddu Bontddu Hall
Conwy Sychnant Pass Hotel
Crickhowell Gliffaes Country House Hotel
Eglwysfach Ynyshir Hall
Gwbert-on-Sea Cliff Hotel
Lake Vyrnwy Lake Vyrnwy Hotel
Llanarmon Dyffryn Ceiriog Hand Hotel
Llanarmon Dyffryn Ceiriog West Arms
  Hotel
Llandderfel Pale Hall
Llandudno Bodysgallen Hall
Llangammarch Wells Lake Country
  House Hotel
Llansanffraid Glan Conwy Old Rectory
Llyswen Llangoed Hall
Northop Soughton Hall
Pantmawr Glansevern Arms
Penmaenpool George III Hotel
Porthkerry Egerton Grey
Portmeirion Hotel Portmeirion
Reynoldston Fairyhill
Rossett Llyndir Hall
St David's Warpool Court
Talsarnau Maes-y-Neaudd

Channel Islands

Rozel Bay Chateau la Chaire
St Brelade's Bay Hotel L'Horizon
St Saviour Longueville Manor
Sark Hotel Petit Champ
Sark Stocks Hotel

Republic of Ireland

Adare Adare Manor
Ballylickey Ballylickey Manor House
Ballylickey Sea View House
Ballynahinch Ballynahinch Castle
Ballyvaughan Gregans Castle
Beaufort Dunloe Castle
Caragh Lake Hotel Ard-na-Sidhe
Caragh Lake Caragh Lodge
Cashel Cashel House
Clifden Abbeyglen Castle
Clifden Ardagh Hotel
Clifden Rock Glen Manor
Delgany Glenview Hotel
Dundrum Dundrum House
Dunlavin Rathsallagh House
Ferrycarrig Bridge Ferrycarrig Hotel
Glen of Aherlow Aherlow House
Gorey Marlfield House
Kanturk Assolas Country House
Kenmare Sheen Falls Lodge
Killarney Aghadoe Heights Hotel
Killarney Cahernane Hotel
Killarney Hotel Europe
Knocklofty Knocklofty House
Letterfrack Rosleague Manor
Mallow Longueville House
Maynooth Moyglare Manor
Newmarket-on-Fergus Dromoland
  Castle
Oughterard Currarevagh House
Parknasilla Great Southern
Rathmullan Rathmullan House
Rathnew Hunter's Hotel
Renvyle Renvyle House
Riverstown Coopershill House
Shanagarry Ballymaloe House
Straffan Kildare Hotel
Thomastown Mount Juliet Hotel
Waterford Waterford Castle
Wicklow Old Rectory

Hotels with Sporting Facilities

Fishing

England

Abingdon Upper Reaches
Alcester Arrow Mill
Allendale Bishop Field
Ambleside Nanny Brow
Appleby-in-Westmorland Tufton Arms
Aylesbury Hartwell House
Bagshot Pennyhill Park
Bainbridge Rose & Crown Inn

Baslow Cavendish Hotel
Bassenthwaite Armathwaite Hall
Beccles Waveney House
Belton Belton Woods Hotel
Bibury The Swan
Bigbury-on-Sea Burgh Island Hotel
Bodymoor Heath Marston Farm
Bolton Abbey Devonshire Arms
Bowness-on-Windermere Linthwaite
  House

Burton-on-Trent Riverside Inn
Calbourne Swainston Manor
Castle Combe Manor House
Chagford Mill End
Chittlehamholt Highbullen
Clearwell Clearwell Castle
Cornhill-on-Tweed Tillmouth Park
Dovedale Izaak Walton Hotel
Dulverton Carnarvon Arms
Easington Grinkle Park
East Grinstead Gravetye Manor
Easton Grey Whatley Manor
Egham Runnymede Hotel
Fairford Bull Hotel
Falmouth Greenbank Hotel
Fossebridge Fossebridge Inn
Gittisham Combe House
Grasmere White Moss House
Hanchurch Hanchurch Manor
Harvington The Mill
Hintlesham Hintlesham Hall
Hollingbourne Great Danes
Huntsham Huntsham Court
Kingham Mill House
Lenham Chilston Park
Lewdown Lewtrenchard Manor
Lifton Arundell Arms
Linton Wood Hall
Longham Bridge House
Lower Slaughter Lower Slaughter Manor
Lympsham Batch Farm
Lyndhurst Parkhill Hotel
Maiden Newton Maiden Newton House
Marlow Compleat Angler Hotel
Mawnan Smith Meudon Hotel
Meriden Forest of Arden Hotel
Mullion Polurrian Hotel
Needham Market Pipps Ford
Newbury Millwaters
Newby Bridge The Swan
Otley Chevin Lodge
Puckrup Puckrup Hall
Quorn The Quorn
Ravenstonedale Black Swan Inn
Ross-on-Wye Pengethley Manor
Rotherwick Tylney Hall
Rowsley Peacock Hotel
Ruckhall Ancient Camp Inn
Salcombe Marine Hotel
Samlesbury Tickled Trout
Seaview Seaview Hotel
Stanstead Abbots Briggens House
Stapleford Stapleford Park
Stonehouse Stonehouse Court
Stratfield Turgis Wellington Arms
Stratford-upon-Avon Ettington Park
Sudbury Mill Hotel
Sutton Coldfield Penns Hall
Taplow Cliveden
Tresco Island Hotel
Ullswater Old Church Hotel
Ullswater Rampsbeck Country House
    Hotel
Umberleigh Rising Sun Inn
Upper Slaughter Lords of the Manor
Wallingford Shillingford Bridge Hotel
Wansford-in-England Haycock Hotel
Wareham Priory Hotel

Warminster Bishopstrow House
Weston-under-Penyard Wharton Lodge
Whitewell Inn at Whitewell
Winchester Lainston House
Windsor Oakley Court
Winsford Royal Oak Inn
Woodbridge Seckford Hall
Worthington Kilhey Court

Scotland

Achiltibuie Summer Isles
Advie Tulchan Lodge
Alexandria Cameron House
Altnaharra Altnaharra Hotel
Annan Warmanbie Hotel
Auchterarder Gleneagles Hotel
Ballachulish Ballachulish Hotel
Banchory Invery House
Banchory Raemoir House
Beattock Auchen Castle
Bonnyrigg Dalhousie Castle
Callander Roman Camp
Dalguise Kinnaird
Dryburgh Dryburgh Abbey
Dulnain Bridge Muckrach Lodge
Dunblane Cromlix House
Eriska Isle of Eriska
Ettrickbridge Ettrickshaws Hotel
Fort William Inverlochy Castle
Garve Inchbae Lodge
Gatehouse of Fleet Cally Palace
Glenborrodale Glenborrodale Castle
Harray Loch Merkister Hotel
Helmsdale Navidale House
Inverness Bunchrew House
Kelso Ednam House
Kelso Sunlaws House
Kenmore Kenmore Hotel
Kentallen of Appin Holly Tree
Kilchrenan Ardanaiseig
Kilchrenan Taychreggan Hotel
Kilfinan Kilfinan Hotel
Kilmore Glenfeochan House
Kinclaven by Stanley Ballathie House
Kinlochbervie Kinlochbervie Hotel
Kirkmichael Log Cabin Hotel
Lochinver Inver Lodge Hotel
Melrose George & Abbotsford Hotel
Pitlochry Green Park Hotel
Port William Corsemalzie House
Portpatrick Knockinaam Lodge
Scourie Scourie Hotel
Skeabost Bridge Skeabost House
Sleat Kinloch Lodge
Stewarton Chapeltoun House
Strachur Creggans Inn
Strathtummel Port-an-Eilean Hotel
Talladale Loch Maree Hotel
Tobermory Tobermory Hotel
Tweedsmuir Crook Inn
Whitebridge Knockie Lodge

Wales

Beddgelert Royal Goat Hotel
Crickhowell Gliffaes Country House Hotel
Lake Vyrnwy Lake Vyrnwy Hotel
Llanarmon Dyffryn Ceiriog Hand Hotel
Llanarmon Dyffryn Ceiriog West Arms Hotel
Llandderfel Palé Hall
Llandrillo Tyddyn Llan
Llangammarch Wells Lake Country House Hotel
Llangollen Hand Hotel
Llangollen Royal Hotel
Llanrug Seiont Manor
Llyswen Llangoed Hall
Penmaenpool George III Hotel
Reynoldston Fairyhill
Ruthin Ruthin Castle
Talyllyn Tynycornel Hotel

Isle of Man

Ramsey Grand Island Hotel

Northern Ireland

Dunadry Dunadry Inn

Golf

England

Barnham Broom Barnham Broom Hotel
Bearsted Tudor Park
Belton Belton Woods Hotel
Cambridge Cambridgeshire Moat House
Carlyon Bay Carlyon Bay Hotel
Croydon Selsdon Park
Goodwood Goodwood Park
Hintlesham Hintlesham Hall
Huntingdon Old Bridge Hotel
Hythe Hythe Imperial
Hythe Stade Court
Meriden Forest of Arden Hotel
Morley Breadsall Priory
Mottram St Andrew Mottram Hall
Sawbridgeworth Manor of Groves
Stratford-upon-Avon Welcombe Hotel
Telford Telford Hotel
Tewkesbury Tewkesbury Park
Thundridge Hanbury Manor
Uckfield Horsted Place
Washington Moat House

Republic of Ireland

Adare Adare Manor
Ballina Mount Falcon Castle
Ballylickey Ballylickey Manor House
Ballynahinch Ballynahinch Castle
Caragh Lake Hotel Ard-na-Sidhe
Caragh Lake Caragh Lodge
Cashel Cashel House
Cashel Cashel Palace
Cashel Zetland House
Clifden Ardagh Hotel
Cong Ashford Castle
Crossmolina Enniscoe House
Dundrum Dundrum House
Ennis Auburn Lodge
Kanturk Assolas Country House
Kenmare Sheen Falls Lodge
Kilcoran Kilcoran Lodge
Killarney Aghadoe Heights Hotel
Killarney Cahernane Hotel
Killiney Court Hotel
Kinsale Blue Haven Hotel
Knocklofty Knocklofty House
Letterfrack Rosleague Manor
Mallow Longueville House
Newmarket-on-Fergus Dromoland Castle
Newport Newport House
Oughterard Currarevagh House
Parknasilla Great Southern
Rathnew Hunter's Hotel
Renvyle Renvyle House
Riverstown Coopershill House
Rossnowlagh Sand House
Straffan Kildare Hotel
Thomastown Mount Juliet Hotel

Weston-under-Redcastle Hawkstone Park
Wishaw Belfry Hotel

Scotland

Auchterarder Gleneagles Hotel
Cumbernauld Westerwood Hotel
Kenmore Kenmore Hotel
Kirknewton Dalmahoy Hotel
Langbank Gleddoch House
Melrose Burts Hotel
Scone Murrayshall House
Turnberry Turnberry Hotel

Wales

Chepstow St Pierre Hotel
Portmeirion Hotel Portmeirion

Republic of Ireland

Carrickmacross Nuremore Hotel
Dundrum Dundrum House
Newmarket-on-Fergus Clare Inn
Newmarket-on-Fergus Dromoland
   Castle
Straffan Kildare Hotel
Thomastown Mount Juliet Hotel
Waterford Waterford Castle

Indoor Swimming

England

Alsager Manor House
Appleby-in-Westmorland Appleby
   Manor
Ascot Royal Berkshire
Ashford Ashford International
Aylesbury Forte Crest
Aylesbury Hartwell House
Barford Glebe Hotel
Barnham Broom Barnham Broom Hotel
Basingstoke Hilton Lodge
Bassenthwaite Armathwaite Hall
Bath Bath Spa Hotel
Bath Combe Grove Manor
Bath Hilton National
Beaconsfield Bellhouse Hotel
Bearsted Tudor Park
Belton Belton Woods Hotel
Birmingham Copthorne Hotel
Birmingham Forte Crest
Birmingham Forte Posthouse
Birmingham Holiday Inn
Birmingham Hyatt Regency
Birmingham Swallow Hotel
Blackpool Imperial Hotel
Blackpool Pembroke Hotel
Blakeney Blakeney Hotel
Bolton Last Drop Village Hotel
Borrowdale Stakis Lodore Swiss Hotel
Bournemouth Norfolk Royale
Bournemouth Palace Court
Bournemouth Royal Bath Hotel
Bowness-on-Windermere Belsfield
   Hotel
Bramhope Forte Crest
Bramhope Parkway Hotel
Brands Hatch Brands Hatch Thistle
Brentwood Forte Posthouse
Brighouse Forte Crest
Brighton Brighton Metropole
Brighton Grand Hotel
Brighton Hospitality Inn
Bristol Aztec Hotel
Bristol Bristol Marriott Hotel
Bristol Forte Crest
Bristol Hilton Hotel
Bristol Redwood Lodge
Bristol Stakis Bristol Hotel
Bristol Swallow Royal Hotel

Broadway Lygon Arms
Brockenhurst Balmer Lawn Hotel
Brockenhurst Careys Manor
Bromsgrove Country Court
Broughton Broughton Park
Burnham Burnham Beeches Moat House
Burton-on-Trent Dovecliffe Hall
Calbourne Swainston Manor
Cambridge Cambridgeshire Moat House
Cambridge Forte Posthouse
Cambridge Holiday Inn
Canterbury Ebury Hotel
Carlisle Swallow Hilltop
Carlyon Bay Carlyon Bay Hotel
Castle Donington Donington Thistle
Cheltenham Cheltenham Park
Cheltenham Golden Valley Thistle
Chester Abbots Well
Chester Forte Posthouse
Chester Mollington Banastre
Chester Rowton Hall
Chesterfield Chesterfield Hotel
Chipping Norton Crown & Cushion
Chiseldon Chiseldon House
Chittlehamholt Highbullen
Chollerford George Hotel
Churt Frensham Pond Hotel
Cobham Hilton National
Colerne Lucknam Park
Constantine Bay Treglos Hotel
Cooden Cooden Resort Hotel
Copdock Ipswich Moat House
Coventry Forte Crest
Crick Forte Posthouse
   Northampton/Rugby
Croydon Croydon Park
Croydon Selsdon Park
Dartmouth Stoke Lodge
Doncaster Moat House
Dover Moat House
Driffield Bell Hotel
Durham Royal County Hotel
Eastbourne Grand Hotel
Egham Runnymede Hotel
Elcot Elcot Park Resort Hotel
Evesham Evesham Hotel
Exeter Forte Crest
Falmouth Falmouth Hotel
Falmouth St Michael's Hotel
Fareham Solent Hotel
Farnborough Forte Crest

Fawkham Brandshatch Place
Ferndown Dormy Hotel
Garforth Hilton National
Gateshead Swallow Hotel
Gatwick Airport Copthorne Effingham
Park
Gatwick Airport Europa Gatwick
Gatwick Airport Forte Crest Gatwick
Gatwick Airport Gatwick Penta Hotel
Gatwick Airport Gatwick Hilton
International
Gatwick Airport Holiday Inn Gatwick
Gloucester Forte Crest
Golant Cormorant Hotel
Goodwood Goodwood Park
Grasmere Wordsworth Hotel
Great Baddow Pontlands Park
Guildford Forte Crest
Hackness Hackness Grange
Harrogate Majestic Hotel
Harrogate Hotel St George
Hatfield Heath Down Hall
Havant Forte Posthouse
Haydock Forte Posthouse
Haydock Haydock Thistle
Heathrow Airport Edwardian International
Heathrow Airport Excelsior Hotel
Heathrow Airport Heathrow Hilton Hotel
Heathrow Airport Heathrow Penta Hotel
Heathrow Airport Holiday Inn Heathrow
Heathrow Airport Sheraton Heathrow
Hotel
Heathrow Airport Sheraton Skyline
Hethersett Park Farm
Hinckley Hinckley Island Hotel
Hintlesham Hintlesham Hall
Hinton Hinton Grange
Holbeton Alston Hall
Hollingbourne Great Danes
Hope Cove Lantern Lodge
Huddersfield Pennine Hilton National
Hull Forte Crest
Huntingdon Old Bridge Hotel
Hythe Hythe Imperial
Hythe Stade Court
Kings Lynn Knights Hill Hotel
Knapton Knapton Hall
Knaresborough Dower House
Knutsford Cottons Hotel
Lancaster Forte Posthouse
Langdale Langdale Hotel
Leeds Leeds Marriott Hotel
Leicester Stakis Country Court
Leicester Holiday Inn
Linton Wood Hall
Liverpool Britannia Adelphi Hotel
Liverpool Moat House
Lockington Hilton National E Midlands
Airport
Lower Beeding Cisswood House
Lower Slaughter Lower Slaughter Manor
Lymington Passford House
Maidenhead Holiday Inn
Maidstone Stakis Country Court
Manchester Britannia Hotel
Manchester Copthorne Hotel
Manchester Holiday Inn Crowne Plaza
Manchester Hotel Piccadilly

Manchester Portland Thistle
Manchester Sachas Hotel
Manchester Airport Forte Crest
Manchester Airport Hilton International
Matlock New Bath Hotel
Mawnan Smith Budock Vean Hotel
Meriden Forest of Arden Hotel
Milton Keynes Forte Crest
Moreton-in-Marsh Manor House
Morley Breadsall Priory
Mottram St Andrew Mottram Hall
Mullion Polurrian Hotel
New Milton Chewton Glen
Newbury Foley Lodge
Newbury Hilton National
Newbury Stakis Newbury Hotel
Newcastle-under-Lyme Forte Posthouse
Newcastle-upon-Tyne Holiday Inn
Newcastle-upon-Tyne Moat House
Newcastle-upon-Tyne Novotel
Newcastle-upon-Tyne Swallow Gosforth
Park
Newquay Hotel Bristol
Newton Abbot Passage House
Nidd Nidd Hall
Northampton Stakis Country Court
Northampton Swallow Hotel
Norwich Airport Ambassador Hotel
Norwich Forte Posthouse
Norwich Friendly Hotel
Norwich Hotel Norwich
Norwich Norwich Sport Village Hotel
Norwich Sprowston Manor
Nutfield Nutfield Priory
Oxford Moat House
Penrith North Lakes Gateway Hotel
Peterborough Forte Posthouse
Peterborough Moat House
Peterborough Swallow Hotel
Plymouth Boringdon Hall
Plymouth Copthorne Hotel
Plymouth Moat House
Poole Haven Hotel
Poole Sandbanks Hotel
Portsmouth Forte Crest
Portsmouth Portsmouth Marriott Hotel
Reading Caversham Hotel
Reading Forte Posthouse
Reading Ramada Hotel
Rochester Forte Crest
Rotherwick Tylney Hall
Runcorn Forte Crest
St Albans Sopwell House
St Ives Garrack Hotel
St Martin's St Martin's Hotel
Salcombe Marine Hotel
Salcombe Soar Mill Cove
Salcombe South Sands
Salcombe Tides Reach
Samlesbury Swallow Trafalgar
Samlesbury Tickled Trout
Saunton Saunton Sands
Seale Hog's Back Hotel
Shaftesbury Royal Chase Hotel
Shanklin Cliff Tops Hotel
Sheffield Forte Crest
Sheffield Moat House
Sheffield St George Swallow Hotel

Shifnal Park House
Sidmouth Fortfield Hotel
Sidmouth Victoria Hotel
Skipton Randell's Hotel
Slough Copthorne Hotel
Slough Heathrow/Slough Marriott Hotel
Solihull Moat House
Solihull St John's Swallow Hotel
South Milford Forte Posthouse
    Leeds/Selby
South Mimms Forte Posthouse
South Normanton Swallow Hotel
Southampton Forte Posthouse
Southampton Southampton Park Hotel ✓
Stafford Tillington Hall
Standish Almond Brook Moat House
Stockton-on-Tees Swallow Hotel
Stoke-on-Trent Stakis Grand Hotel
Stoke-on-Trent Stoke-on-Trent Moat
    House
Stratford-upon-Avon Billesley Manor
Stratford-upon-Avon Ettington Park
Stratford-upon-Avon Moat House
    International
Stratford-upon-Avon Windmill Park
Sunderland Swallow Hotel
Sutton Holiday Inn
Sutton Coldfield Moor Hall
Swindon Blunsdon House
Swindon De Vere Hotel
Swindon Forte Posthouse
Swindon Swindon Marriott Hotel
Taplow Cliveden
Telford Holiday Inn
Telford Moat House
Telford Telford Hotel
Tewkesbury Tewkesbury Park
Thundridge Hanbury Manor
Thurlestone Thurlestone Hotel
Torquay Grand Hotel
Torquay Imperial Hotel
Torquay Osborne Hotel
Torquay Palace Hotel
Tunbridge Wells Spa Hotel
Uckfield Horsted Place
Walberton Avisford Park
Walsall Wood Baron's Court
Warminster Bishopstrow House
Warrington Lord Daresbury Hotel
Warwick Hilton National
Washington Moat House
Watford Hilton National
West Runton The Links
Wetheral The Crown
Whitwell-on-the-Hill Whitwell Hall
Willerby Grange Park
Wilmslow Moat House
Winterbourne Grange Resort Hotel
Wishaw Belfry Hotel
Witney Witney Lodge
Wokingham Stakis St Anne's Manor
Woodbridge Seckford Hall
Woolacombe Woolacombe Bay Hotel
Worthington Kilhey Court
Wrotham Heath Forte Posthouse
    Maidstone Sevenoaks
York Novotel
York Swallow Hotel

Scotland

Aberdeen Bucksburn Moat House
Aberdeen Stakis Tree Tops
Aberdeen Airport Aberdeen Marriott
    Hotel
Airth Airth Castle
Alexandria Cameron House
Auchterarder Gleneagles Hotel
Aviemore Stakis Aviemore Four Seasons
Aviemore Stakis Coylumbridge Resort
    Hotel
Ayr Caledonian Hotel
Ballater Craigendarroch Hotel
Contin Craigdarroch Lodge
Crieff Crieff Hydro
Cumbernauld Westerwood Hotel
Drymen Buchanan Highland Hotel
Dunblane Stakis Dunblane Hydro
Edinburgh The Balmoral
Edinburgh Carlton Highland
Edinburgh Royal Terrace Hotel
Edinburgh Scandic Crown
Edinburgh Sheraton Hotel
Edinburgh Swallow Royal Scot
Elgin Mansion House
Erskine Forte Posthouse
Forfar Royal Hotel
Gatehouse of Fleet Cally Palace
Glasgow Glasgow Marriott Hotel
Glasgow Jurys Pond Hotel
Glasgow Moat House International
Glasgow Swallow Hotel
Gourock Stakis Gantock Hotel
Inverness Caledonian Hotel
Inverness Dunain Park
Inverness Kingsmills Hotel
Irvine Hospitality Inn
Kinross Windlestrae Hotel
Kirknewton Dalmahoy Hotel
Lerwick Shetland Hotel
Peebles Peebles Hotel Hydro
Peterhead Waterside Inn
Pitlochry Pitlochry Hydro
St Andrews St Andrews Old Course Hotel
South Queensferry Forth Bridges Moat
    House
Stranraer North West Castle
Troon Marine Highland Hotel
Turnberry Turnberry Hotel

Wales

Aberdovey Trefeddian Hotel
Abersoch Riverside Hotel
Aberystwyth Conrah Country Hotel
Barry Mount Sorrel Hotel
Cardiff Cardiff Marriott Hotel
Cardiff Forte Posthouse
Cardiff Moat House
Chepstow St Pierre Hotel
Ewloe St David's Park Hotel
Lamphey Court Hotel
Llandudno Empire Hotel
Llandudno St Tudno Hotel
Llangybi Cwrt Bleddyn Hotel

Llanrug Seiont Manor
Miskin Miskin Manor
Newport Celtic Manor
Newport Stakis Country Court
Newport Hilton National
Penally Penally Abbey
Rossett Llyndir Hall
St David's Warpool Court
Swansea Forte Crest
Swansea Hilton National
Swansea Swansea Marriott Hotel

Isle of Man

Douglas Palace Hotel
Douglas Sefton Hotel
Ramsey Grand Island Hotel

Channel Islands

St Brelade Atlantic Hotel
St Brelade's Bay Hotel L'Horizon
St Helier Apollo Hotel
St Helier Beaufort Hotel
St Helier Grand Hotel
St Peter Mermaid Hotel
St Peter Port St Pierre Park

Northern Ireland

Comber La Mon House
Dunadry Dunadry Inn
Holywood Culloden Hotel
Portballintrae Bayview Hotel

Republic of Ireland

Adare Adare Manor
Ballina Downhill Hotel
Ballyconnell Slieve Russell Hotel
Beaufort Dunloe Castle
Bunratty Fitzpatricks Shannon Shamrock
Carrickmacross Nuremore Hotel
Castledermot Kilkea Castle
Cork Fitzpatrick Silver Springs
Cork Jurys Hotel
Cork Rochestown Park Hotel
Dublin Berkeley Court
Dublin Jurys Hotel
Dublin Airport Forte Crest
Dundalk Ballymascanlon House
Dundrum Dundrum House
Dunlavin Rathsallagh House
Galway Corrib Great Southern Hotel
Galway Great Southern
Kilcoran Kilcoran Lodge
Kilkenny Newpark Hotel
Killarney Aghadoe Heights Hotel
Killarney Hotel Europe
Killarney Great Southern
Killarney Torc Great Southern
Killiney Fitzpatrick's Castle
Kinsale Actons Hotel
Kinsale Blue Haven Hotel
Knocklofty Knocklofty House
Limerick Greenhills Hotel
Limerick Jurys Hotel
Limerick Limerick Inn
Newmarket-on-Fergus Clare Inn
Newmarket-on-Fergus Dromoland Castle
Oughterard Connemara Gateway Hotel
Parknasilla Great Southern
Rathmullan Rathmullan House
Rosslare Great Southern
Rosslare Kelly's Strand Hotel
Sligo Sligo Park
Straffan Kildare Hotel
Waterford Jurys Waterford Hotel
Waterford Tower Hotel
Waterford Waterford Castle

Outdoor Swimming

England

Alveston Forte Posthouse
Ascot Berystede Hotel
Bagshot Pennyhill Park
Bath Combe Grove Manor
Bath Priory Hotel
Beanacre Beechfield House
Birmingham Forte Posthouse
Bognor Regis Royal Norfolk
Bonchurch Winterbourne Hotel
Borrowdale Stakis Lodore Swiss Hotel
Bournemouth Carlton Hotel
Bournemouth Swallow Highcliff Hotel

Bowness-on-Windermere Old England Hotel
Bradford Novotel
Bradford-on-Avon Woolley Grange
Bristol Redwood Lodge
Broadway Collin House
Brockenhurst Balmer Lawn Hotel
Broxted Whitehall
Buckland Buckland Manor
Burley Burley Manor
Carlyon Bay Carlyon Bay Hotel
Castle Combe Manor House
Charlecote Charlecote Pheasant
Cheltenham Hotel de la Bere
Chittlehamholt Highbullen

Climping Bailiffscourt
Coatham Mundeville Hall Garth
Cooden Cooden Resort Hotel
Corse Lawn Corse Lawn House
Coventry Novotel
Croydon Selsdon Park
Dartmouth Stoke Lodge
Dorking White Horse
Dulverton Carnarvon Arms
Eastbourne Grand Hotel
Easton Grey Whatley Manor
Egham Great Fosters
Evershot Summer Lodge
Exmouth Imperial Hotel
Fairy Cross Portledge Hotel
Falmouth Falmouth Hotel
Farnham Trevena House
Faugh String of Horses Inn
Freshwater Farringford Hotel
Gatwick Airport Chequers Thistle
Gatwick Airport Forte Posthouse
Gloucester Hatton Court
Great Baddow Pontlands Park
Great Milton Le Manoir aux Quat'Saisons
Grimston Congham Hall
Harvington The Mill
Hatherleigh George Hotel
Helland Bridge Tredethy Country Hotel
Helmsley Feversham Arms
Holbeton Alston Hall
Hunstrete Hunstrete House
Ipswich Forte Posthouse
Kidderminster Stone Manor
Lamorna Cove Lamorna Cove Hotel
Leamington Spa Mallory Court
Liskeard Well House
Looe Talland Bay Hotel
Lymington Passford House
Lyndhurst Lyndhurst Park
Lyndhurst Parkhill Hotel
Manchester Novotel
Market Drayton Goldstone Hall
Matlock New Bath Hotel
Medmenham Danesfield House
Meriden Manor Hotel
Mudeford Avonmouth Hotel
Mullion Polurrian Hotel
Needham Market Pipps Ford
New Milton Chewton Glen
Newlyn Higher Faugan Country House Hotel
Newquay Hotel Riviera
North Stoke Springs Hotel
Nottingham Novotel
Oakham Hambleton Hall
Paignton Palace Hotel
Paignton Redcliffe Hotel
Plymouth Forte Crest
Plymouth Novotel
Poole Haven Hotel
Preston Novotel
Ross-on-Wye Pengethley Manor
Rotherwick Tylney Hall
Rusper Ghyll Manor
St Austell Boscundle Manor
Salcombe Soar Mill Cove
Sawbridgeworth Manor of Groves
Sedlescombe Brickwall Hotel

Sidmouth Victoria Hotel
Silchester Romans Hotel
Stanstead Abbots Briggens House
Stevenage Novotel
Stoke Mandeville Belmore Hotel
Storrington Abingworth Hall
Storrington Little Thakeham
Stourport-on-Severn Moat House
Studland Bay Knoll House
Taplow Cliveden
Tetbury Calcot Manor
Thurlestone Thurlestone Hotel
Torquay Grand Hotel
Torquay Imperial Hotel
Torquay Livermead Cliff Hotel
Torquay Livermead House
Torquay Osborne Hotel
Torquay Palace Hotel
Tresco Island Hotel
Ventnor Royal Hotel
Veryan Nare Hotel
Walberton Avisford Park
Wallingford Shillingford Bridge Hotel
Wareham Springfield Country Hotel
Warminster Bishopstrow House
Weedon Crossroads Hotel
Weston-on-the-Green Weston Manor
Weston-super-Mare Grand Atlantic
Weston-under-Redcastle Hawkstone Park
Woolacombe Woolacombe Bay Hotel
York Mount Royale

Scotland

Aberdeen Airport Skean Dhu Hotel
Auchterhouse Old Mansion House
Drumnadrochit Polmaily House
Nairn Golf View Hotel
North Berwick Marine Hotel
Selkirk Philipburn House
Tarbert Stonefield Castle

Wales

Abersoch Porth Tocyn Hotel
Coychurch Coed-y-Mwstwr Hotel
Gwbert-on-Sea Cliff Hotel
Llandudno Empire Hotel
Llanwnda Stables Hotel
Portmeirion Hotel Portmeirion
Talyllyn Tynycornel Hotel

Channel Islands

Bouley Bay Water's Edge Hotel
Herm White House
Portelet Bay Portelet Hotel
St Aubin Old Court House Inn
St Brelade Atlantic Hotel
St Brelade Hotel Chateau Valeuse
St Brelade La Place Hotel
St Brelade Sea Crest
St Brelade's Bay St Brelade's Bay Hotel

St Clement's Bay Hotel Ambassadeur
St Lawrence Little Grove
St Martin St Margaret's Lodge
St Martin La Trelade Hotel
St Peter Mermaid Hotel
St Peter Port Braye Lodge
St Peter Port Duke of Richmond
St Peter Port Old Government House
St Saviour Longueville Manor
Sark Aval Du Creux
Sark Hotel Petit Champ
Sark Stocks Hotel

Republic of Ireland

Ballylickey Ballylickey Manor House
Clifden Abbeyglen Castle
Cork Jurys Hotel
Dublin Jurys Hotel
Renvyle Renvyle House
Rosslare Kelly's Strand Hotel
Shanagarry Ballymaloe House

Leisure Centres

England

Ashford Ashford International
Barford Glebe Hotel
Bassenthwaite Armathwaite Hall
Bath Bath Spa Hotel
Bath Combe Grove Manor
Bath Hilton National
Beaconsfield Bellhouse Hotel
Bearsted Tudor Park
Belton Belton Woods Hotel
Birmingham Copthorne Hotel
Birmingham Forte Posthouse
Birmingham Holiday Inn
Birmingham Hyatt Regency
Blackpool Imperial Hotel
Bolton Last Drop Village Hotel
Borrowdale Stakis Lodore Swiss Hotel
Bournemouth Royal Bath Hotel
Bowness-on-Windermere Belsfield
Hotel
Bramhope Forte Crest
Brighouse Forte Crest
Brighton Brighton Metropole
Brighton Grand Hotel
Bristol Aztec Hotel
Bristol Forte Crest
Bristol Hilton Hotel
Bristol Redwood Lodge
Bristol Stakis Bristol Hotel
Bristol Swallow Royal Hotel
Brockenhurst Careys Manor
Bromsgrove Country Court
Cambridge Forte Posthouse
Carlisle Swallow Hilltop
Charingworth Charingworth Manor
Cheltenham Hotel de la Bere
Cheltenham Cheltenham Park
Chester Abbots Well
Chester Forte Posthouse
Chester Mollington Banastre
Chester Rowton Hall
Chesterfield Chesterfield Hotel
**Chipping
Norton** Crown & Cushion
Churt Frensham Pond Hotel
Colerne Lucknam Park
Cooden Cooden Resort Hotel
Copdock Ipswich Moat House

Coventry Forte Crest
Crick Forte Posthouse Northampton
Rugby
Croydon Croydon Park
Croydon Selsdon Park
Dartmouth Stoke Lodge
Doncaster Moat House
Dover Moat House
Durham Royal County Hotel
Eastbourne Grand Hotel
Elcot Elcot Park Resort Hotel
Falmouth Falmouth Hotel
Fareham Solent Hotel
Farnborough Forte Crest
Fawkham Brandshatch Place
Ferndown Dormy Hotel
Garforth Hilton National
Gateshead Swallow Hotel
Gatwick Airport Copthorne Effingham
Park
Gatwick Airport Forte Crest Gatwick
Gatwick Airport Gatwick Hilton
International
Gatwick Airport Gatwick Penta Hotel
Gatwick Airport Holiday Inn Gatwick
Gloucester Forte Crest
Grasmere Wordsworth Hotel
Great Baddow Pontlands Park
Harrogate Majestic Hotel
Harrogate Hotel St George
Havant Forte Posthouse
Haydock Forte Posthouse
Haydock Haydock Thistle
Heathrow Airport Edwardian International
Heathrow Airport Excelsior Hotel
Heathrow Airport Heathrow Hilton Hotel
Hinckley Hinckley Island Hotel
Holbeton Alston Hall
Hollingbourne Great Danes
Huddersfield Pennine Hilton National
Hythe Hythe Imperial
Kings Lynn Knights Hill Hotel
Knutsford Cottons Hotel
Lancaster Forte Posthouse
Langdale Langdale Hotel
Leeds Leeds Marriott Hotel
Leicester Country Court
Leicester Holiday Inn
Liverpool Britannia Adelphi Hotel

Liverpool Moat House
Lockington Hilton National E Midlands
  Airport
Lymington Passford House
Maidstone Stakis Country Court Hotel
Manchester Copthorne Hotel
Manchester Holiday Inn Crowne Plaza
Manchester Portland Thistle
Manchester Sachas Hotel
Manchester Airport Forte Crest
Manchester Airport Hilton International
Meriden Forest of Arden Hotel
Milton Keynes Forte Crest
Morley Breadsall Priory
Mullion Polurrian Hotel
New Milton Chewton Glen
Newbury Hilton National
Newbury Stakis Newbury Hotel
Newcastle-under-Lyme Forte Posthouse
Newcastle-upon-Tyne Holiday Inn
Newcastle-upon-Tyne Moat House
Newton Abbot Passage House
Northampton Swallow Hotel
Norwich Forte Posthouse
Norwich Hotel Norwich
Norwich Norwich Sport Village Hotel
Norwich Sprowston Manor
Nutfield Nutfield Priory
Oxford Moat House
Penrith North Lakes Gateway Hotel
Peterborough Moat House
Peterborough Swallow Hotel
Portsmouth Portsmouth Marriott Hotel
Reading Forte Posthouse
Reading Ramada Hotel
St Albans Sopwell House
Salcombe Marine Hotel
Salcombe Tides Reach
Samlesbury Swallow Trafalgar
Seale Hog's Back Hotel
Shanklin Cliff Tops Hotel
Sheffield Forte Crest
Sheffield Moat House
Sidmouth Victoria Hotel
Slough Copthorne Hotel
Slough Heathrow/Slough Marriott Hotel
Solihull Moat House
Solihull St John's Swallow Hotel
South Mimms Forte Posthouse
South Normanton Swallow Hotel
Southampton Forte Posthouse
Southampton Southampton Park Hotel
Stafford Tillington Hall
Stoke-on-Trent Stakis Grand Hotel
Stoke-on-Trent Stoke-on-Trent Moat
  House
Stratford-upon-Avon Moat House
  International
Stratford-upon-Avon Windmill Park
Sunderland Swallow Hotel
Sutton Holiday Inn
Sutton
Coldfield Penns Hall
Swindon Blunsdon House
Swindon De Vere Hotel
Swindon Forte Posthouse
Swindon Swindon Marriott Hotel
Taplow Cliveden

Telford Moat House
Telford Telford Hotel
Tewkesbury Tewkesbury Park
Thundridge Hanbury Manor
Thurlestone Thurlestone Hotel
Torquay Grand Hotel
Torquay Imperial Hotel
Tunbridge Wells Spa Hotel
Walberton Avisford Park
Walsall Wood Baron's Court
Warrington Lord Daresbury Hotel
Watford Hilton National
Wetheral The Crown
Willerby Grange Park
Wilmslow Moat House
Wishaw Belfry Hotel
Woolacombe Woolacombe Bay Hotel
Wrotham Heath Forte Posthouse
  Maidstone Sevenoaks
York Swallow Hotel

Scotland

Aberdeen Burecksburn Moat House
Aberdeen Stakis Tree Tops
Aberdeen Airport Aberdeen Marriott
  Hotel
Alexandria Cameron House
Auchterarder Gleneagles Hotel
Aviemore Stakis Aviemore Four Seasons
Aviemore Stakis Coylumbridge Resort
  Hotel
Ayr Caledonian Hotel
Crieff Crieff Hydro
Dunblane Stakis Dunblane Hydro
Edinburgh The Balmoral
Edinburgh Carlton Highland
Edinburgh Royal Terrace Hotel
Edinburgh Sheraton Hotel
Edinburgh Swallow Royal Scot
Elgin Mansion House
Erskine Forte Posthouse
Forfar Royal Hotel
Glasgow Glasgow Marriott Hotel
Glasgow Jurys Pond Hotel
Glasgow Moat House International
Glasgow Swallow Hotel
Gourock Stakis Gantock Hotel
Inverness Caledonian Hotel
Inverness Kingsmills Hotel
Kinross Windlestrae Hotel
Kirknewton Dalmahoy Hotel
Peebles Peebles Hotel Hydro
Peterhead Waterside Inn
St Andrews St Andrews Old Course Hotel
Stranraer North West Castle
Troon Marine Highland Hotel
Turnberry Turnberry Hotel

Wales

Cardiff Cardiff Marriott Hotel
Cardiff Forte Posthouse
Cardiff Moat House
Chepstow St Pierre Hotel
Ewloe St David's Park Hotel

Llangybi Cwrt Bleddyn Hotel
Miskin Miskin Manor
Newport Country Court Hotel
Newport Hilton National
Rossett Llyndir Hall
Swansea Forte Crest
Swansea Swansea Marriott Hotel

Isle of Man

Douglas Palace Hotel
Douglas Sefton Hotel
Ramsey Grand Island Hotel

Channel Islands

St Brelade Atlantic Hotel
St Helier Grand Hotel
St Peter Port St Pierre Park

Northern Ireland

Comber La Mon House
Dunadry Dunadry Inn

Republic of Ireland

Ballina Downhill Hotel
Bunratty Fitzpatricks Shannon Shamrock
Carrickmacross Nuremore Hotel
Cork Fitzpatrick Silver Springs
Cork Jurys Hotel
Dundalk Ballymascanlon House
Dundrum Dundrum House
Ferrycarrig Bridge Ferrycarrig Hotel
Kilcoran Kilcoran Lodge
Kilkenny Newpark Hotel
Killarney Aghadoe Heights Hotel
Killarney Great Southern
Killiney Fitzpatrick's Castle
Kinsale Actons Hotel
Limerick Greenhills Hotel
Limerick Jurys Hotel
Limerick Limerick Inn
Parknasilla Great Southern
Rosslare Great Southern
Sligo Sligo Park
Straffan Kildare Hotel
Waterford Tower Hotel

Riding

England

Aspley Guise Moore Place
Bagshot Pennyhill Park
Bassenthwaite Armathwaite Hall
Bromsgrove Grafton Manor
Broughton Broughton Park
Hintlesham Hintlesham Hall
Hunstrete Hunstrete House
Huntingdon Old Bridge Hotel
Middlecombe Periton Park
Porlock Oaks Hotel
Pulborough Chequers Hotel
Stow-on-the-Wold Wyck Hill House
Stratford-upon-Avon Ettington Park
Taplow Cliveden
Thundridge Hanbury Manor
Thurlestone Thurlestone Hotel
Weston-under-Penyard Wharton Lodge
Woolacombe Woolacombe Bay Hotel

Scotland

Auchterarder Gleneagles Hotel
Banchory Invery House

Crieff Crieff Hydro
Duror Stewart Hotel
Eriska Isle of Eriska
Kenmore Kenmore Hotel
Peebles Peebles Hotel Hydro
Turnberry Turnberry Hotel

Northern Ireland

Comber La Mon House

Republic of Ireland

Adare Adare Manor
Beaufort Dunloe Castle
Cong Ashford Castle
Glen of Aherlow Aherlow House
Killarney Hotel Europe
Knocklofty Knocklofty House
Newmarket-on-Fergus Dromoland
Castle
Parknasilla Great Southern
Renvyle Renvyle House
Thomastown Mount Juliet Hotel

Squash

England

Ascot Royal Berkshire
Barnham Broom Barnham Broom Hotel
Bath Combe Grove Manor
Beaconsfield Bellhouse Hotel
Bearsted Tudor Park
Belton Belton Woods Hotel
Birmingham Birmingham Metropole
Birmingham Forte Crest
Bolton Last Drop Village Hotel
Borrowdale Stakis Lodore Swiss Hotel
Brandon Brandon Hall
Bristol Aztec Hotel
Bristol Redwood Lodge
Brockenhurst Balmer Lawn Hotel
Broughton Broughton Park
Cambridge Cambridgeshire Moat House
Cheltenham Hotel de la Bere
Cheltenham Golden Valley Thistle
Chester Mollington Banastre
Chester Rowton Hall
Chipping Norton Crown & Cushion
Chittlehamholt Highbullen
Churt Frensham Pond Hotel
Clayton-le-Woods Pines Hotel
Cobham Hilton National
Cooden Cooden Resort Hotel
Crooklands Crooklands Hotel
Croydon Croydon Park
Croydon Selsdon Park
Driffield Bell Hotel
Fareham Solent Hotel
Fawkham Brandshatch Place
Ferndown Dormy Hotel
Gatwick Airport Copthorne London
  Gatwick
Gatwick Airport Europa Gatwick
Gatwick Airport Gatwick Penta Hotel
Goodwood Goodwood Park
Harrogate Majestic Hotel
Huntingdon Old Bridge Hotel
Hythe Hythe Imperial
Hythe Stade Court
Land's End State House
Leamington Spa Mallory Court
Ledbury The Feathers
Liverpool Britannia Adelphi Hotel
Maidenhead Holiday Inn
Manchester Holiday Inn Crowne Plaza
Meriden Forest of Arden Hotel
Morley Breadsall Priory
Mottram St Andrew Mottram Hall
Mullion Polurrian Hotel
Neasham Newbus Arms
Newcastle-upon-Tyne Swallow Gosforth
  Park
Newquay Hotel Riviera
Nidd Nidd Hall
Norwich Norwich Sport Village Hotel
Nottingham Royal Moat House
Nutfield Nutfield Priory
Oxford Moat House
Penrith North Lakes Gateway Hotel

Portsmouth Portsmouth Marriott Hotel
Richmond Richmond Gate Hotel
Salcombe Tides Reach
Samlesbury Swallow Trafalgar
Saunton Saunton Sands
Sidmouth Victoria Hotel
Skipton Randell's Hotel
Stourport-on-Severn Moat House
Swindon Blunsdon House
Swindon Swindon Marriott Hotel
Taplow Cliveden
Telford Telford Hotel
Tewkesbury Tewkesbury Park
Thundridge Hanbury Manor
Thurlestone Thurlestone Hotel
Torquay Imperial Hotel
Torquay Livermead House
Torquay Palace Hotel
Walberton Avisford Park
Wallingford Shillingford Bridge Hotel
Warrington Lord Daresbury Hotel
Washington Moat House
Weston-on-the-Green Weston Manor
Westonbirt Hare & Hounds
Wilmslow Moat House
Wishaw Belfry Hotel
Woolacombe Woolacombe Bay Hotel

Scotland

Alexandria Cameron House
Auchterarder Gleneagles Hotel
Auchterhouse Old Mansion House
Aviemore Stakis Coylumbridge Resort
  Hotel
Ballater Craigendarroch Hotel
Banchory Tor-na-Coille Hotel
Chapel of Garioch Pittodrie House
Crieff Crieff Hydro
Drymen Buchanan Highland Hotel
Edinburgh Carlton Highland
Glasgow Glasgow Marriott Hotel
Kirknewton Dalmahoy Hotel
Langbank Gleddoch House
Peebles Peebles Hotel Hydro
South Queensferry Forth Bridges
  Moat House
Troon Marine Highland Hotel
Turnberry Turnberry Hotel

Wales

Cardiff Cardiff Marriott Hotel
Chepstow St Pierre Hotel
Gwbert-on-Sea Cliff Hotel
Lamphey Court Hotel
Llangybi Cwrt Bleddyn Hotel
Llanrug Seiont Manor
Miskin Miskin Manor
Talyllyn Tynycornel Hotel

Northern Ireland

Dunmurry Forte Crest Belfast
Holywood Culloden Hotel

Republic of Ireland

Ballina Downhill Hotel
Carrickmacross Nuremore Hotel
Cork Fitzpatrick Silver Springs
Cork Jurys Hotel
Dundalk Ballymascanlon House
Killiney Fitzpatrick's Castle
Knocklofty Knocklofty House
Rosslare Kelly's Strand Hotel
Straffan Kildare Hotel

Tennis

England

Abberley Elms Hotel
Abbot's Salford Salford Hall
Alston Lovelady Shield
Ambleside Nanny Brow
Ascot Royal Berkshire
Ashford Eastwell Manor
Aylesbury Hartwell House
Bagshot Pennyhill Park
Bakewell Hassop Hall
Barnham Broom Barnham Broom Hotel
Bassenthwaite Armathwaite Hall
Bath Bath Spa Hotel
Bath Combe Grove Manor
Battle Netherfield Place
Beanacre Beechfield House
Bearsted Tudor Park
Belton Belton Woods Hotel
Bigbury-on-Sea Burgh Island Hotel
Bodymoor Heath Marston Farm
Bognor Regis Royal Norfolk
Borrowdale Stakis Lodore Swiss Hotel
Bournemouth Swallow Highcliff Hotel
Bowness-on-Windermere Belsfield
  Hotel
Bradford-on-Avon Woolley Grange
Bramhope Parkway Hotel
Bramley Bramley Grange
Bristol Redwood Lodge
Broadway Lygon Arms
Brockenhurst Balmer Lawn Hotel
Broxted Whitehall
Buckland Buckland Manor
Burnham Burnham Beeches Moat House
Cambridge Cambridgeshire Moat House
Carlyon Bay Carlyon Bay Hotel
Castle Combe Manor House
Chagford Gidleigh Park
Charlecote Charlecote Pheasant
Cheltenham Hotel de la Bere
Cheltenham Golden Valley Thistle
Chittlehamholt Highbullen
Climping Bailiffscourt
Coatham Mundeville Hall Garth
Cobham Hilton National
Cobham Woodlands Park
Colerne Lucknam Park

Corse Lawn Corse Lawn House
Crooklands Crooklands Hotel
Croydon Selsdon Park
Dane End Green End Park
Dartmouth Stoke Lodge
Dovedale Peveril of the Peak
Droitwich Spa Chateau Impney
Dulverton Carnarvon Arms
Easington Grinkle Park
East Dereham King's Head
Easton Grey Whatley Manor
Egham Great Fosters
Egham Runnymede Hotel
Elcot Elcot Park Resort Hotel
Evershot Summer Lodge
Evesham Evesham Hotel
Exmouth Imperial Hotel
Fairy Cross Portledge Hotel
Farnham Trevena House
Fawkham Brandshatch Place
Ferndown Dormy Hotel
Flitwick Flitwick Manor
Freshford Homewood Park
Freshwater Farringford Hotel
Gillingham Stock Hill House
Goodwood Goodwood Park
Great Ayton Ayton Hall
Great Milton Le Manoir aux Quat'Saisons
Grimston Congham Hall
Hackness Hackness Grange
Harrogate Majestic Hotel
Harvington The Mill
Haslemere Lythe Hill Hotel
Hatfield Heath Down Hall
Hawkhurst Tudor Court
Hawkshead Tarn Hows
Helmsley Feversham Arms
Hethersett Park Farm
Hintlesham Hintlesham Hall
Hinton Hinton Grange
Holbeton Alston Hall
Hollingbourne Great Danes
Horton-cum-Studley Studley Priory
Hunstrete Hunstrete House
Huntsham Huntsham Court
Hurstbourne Tarrant Esseborne Manor
Hythe Hythe Imperial
Hythe Stade Court
Kidderminster Stone Manor
Kings Lynn Knights Hill Hotel

Knutsford Cottons Hotel
Leamington Spa Mallory Court
Lenham Chilston Park
Liskeard Well House
Longhorsley Linden Hall
Lower Beeding South Lodge
Lower Slaughter Lower Slaughter Manor
Lymington Passford House
Lyndhurst Lyndhurst Park
Marlow Compleat Angler Hotel
Matlock Riber Hall
Matlock New Bath Hotel
Mawnan Smith Budock Vean Hotel
Mawnan Smith Nansidwell
Medmenham Danesfield House
Meriden Forest of Arden Hotel
Minster
Lovell Old Swan
Morley Breadsall Priory
Mottram St Andrew Mottram Hall
Much Birch Pilgrim Hotel
Mullion Polurrian Hotel
Nantwich Rookery Hall
Needham Market Pipps Ford
New Milton Chewton Glen
Newcastle-upon-Tyne Swallow Gosforth Park
Newlyn Higher Faugan Country House Hotel
Nidd Nidd Hall
North
Stifford Moat House
North Stoke Springs Hotel
Northampton Westone Moat House
Norwich Norwich Sport Village Hotel
Oakham Hambleton Hall
Paignton Palace Hotel
Plymouth Boringdon Hall
Ravenstonedale Black Swan Inn
Rotherwick Tylney Hall
Rusper Ghyll Manor
St Margaret's Wallett's Court
Salcombe Soar Mill Cove
Saunton Saunton Sands
Sawbridgeworth Manor of Groves
Sevenoaks Royal Oak
Sidmouth Victoria Hotel
Silchester Romans Hotel
Six Mile Bottom Swynford Paddocks
Slough Heathrow/Slough Marriott Hotel
South Milford Forte Posthouse Leeds/Selby
Stafford Tillington Hall
Stanstead Abbots Briggens House
Stapleford Stapleford Park
Ston Easton Ston Easton Park
Storrington Abingworth Hall
Storrington Little Thakeham
Stourport-on-Severn Moat House
Stratford-upon-Avon Billesley Manor
Stratford-upon-Avon Ettington Park
Stratford-upon-Avon Welcombe Hotel
Stratford-upon-Avon Windmill Park
Studland Bay Knoll House
Swindon Blunsdon House
Swindon Swindon Marriott Hotel
Taplow Cliveden
Tewkesbury Tewkesbury Park

Thundridge Hanbury Manor
Thurlestone Thurlestone Hotel
Torquay Grand Hotel
Torquay Imperial Hotel
Torquay Livermead House
Torquay Osborne Hotel
Torquay Palace Hotel
Tresco Island Hotel
Tunbridge Wells Spa Hotel
Turners Hill Alexander House
Uckfield Horsted Place
Veryan Nare Hotel
Walberton Avisford Park
Wareham Springfield Country Hotel
Warminster Bishopstrow House
Weedon Crossroads Hotel
West Runton The Links
Weston-super-Mare Grand Atlantic
Weston-under-Redcastle Hawkstone Park
Westonbirt Hare & Hounds
Weybridge Oatlands Park
Whimple Woodhayes Hotel
Whitwell-on-the-Hill Whitwell Hall
Winchester Lainston House
Wishaw Belfry Hotel
Witherslack Old Vicarage
Wokingham Stakis St Anne's Manor
Woolacombe Woolacombe Bay Hotel
Yelverton Moorland Links

Scotland

Aberdeen Stakis Tree Tops
Advie Tulchan Lodge
Alexandria Cameron House
Auchterarder Gleneagles Hotel
Auchterhouse Old Mansion House
Aviemore Stakis Coylumbridge Resort Hotel
Ballater Craigendarroch Hotel
Banchory Invery House
Banchory Raemoir House
Chapel of Garioch Pittodrie House
Contin Craigdarroch Lodge
Crieff Crieff Hydro
Cumbernauld Westerwood Hotel
Dalguise Kinnaird
Drumnadrochit Polmaily House
Drymen Buchanan Highland Hotel
Dunblane Cromlix House
Dunblane Stakis Dunblane Hydro
Eriska Isle of Eriska
Fort William Inverlochy Castle
Gatehouse of Fleet Cally Palace
Glenborrodale Glenborrodale Castle
Gourock Stakis Gantock Hotel
Gullane Greywalls Hotel
Inverness Culloden House
Kelso Sunlaws House
Kenmore Kenmore Hotel
Kentallen of Appin Ardsheal House
Kilchrenan Ardanaiseig
Kilwinning Montgreenan Mansion
Kinclaven by Stanley Ballathie House
Kirknewton Dalmahoy Hotel
Nairn Golf View Hotel

Nairn Newton Hotel
Newton Stewart Kirroughtree Hotel
North Berwick Marine Hotel
Peebles Cringletie House
Peebles Peebles Hotel Hydro
Pitlochry Pitlochry Hydro
Scone Murrayshall House
Turnberry Turnberry Hotel

Wales

Aberdovey Plas Penhelig
Aberdovey Trefeddian Hotel
Abersoch Porth Tocyn Hotel
Chepstow St Pierre Hotel
Coychurch Coed-y-Mwstwr Hotel
Crickhowell Gliffaes Country House Hotel
Lake Vyrnwy Lake Vyrnwy Hotel
Llanarmon Dyffryn Ceiriog Hand Hotel
Llanarmon Dyffryn Ceiriog West Arms Hotel
Llandudno Bodysgallen Hall
Llangammarch Wells Lake Country House Hotel
Llangybi Cwrt Bleddyn Hotel
Llyswen Llangoed Hall
Northop Soughton Hall
Porthkerry Egerton Grey
Portmeirion Hotel Portmeirion
St David's Warpool Court

Channel Islands

Herm White House
St Brelade Atlantic Hotel
St Brelade's Bay St Brelade's Bay Hotel
St Peter Mermaid Hotel
St Peter Port St Pierre Park
St Saviour Longueville Manor

Northern Ireland

Annalong Glassdrumman House
Holywood Culloden Hotel

Republic of Ireland

Ballina Downhill Hotel
Ballina Mount Falcon Castle
Ballyconnell Slieve Russell Hotel
Ballynahinch Ballynahinch Castle
Beaufort Dunloe Castle
Blessington Downshire House
Caragh Lake Caragh Lodge
Cashel Cashel House
Cashel Zetland House
Castledermot Kilkea Castle
Clifden Abbeyglen Castle
Clifden Rock Glen Manor
Cong Ashford Castle
Cork Fitzpatrick Silver Springs
Cork Jurys Hotel
Dundalk Ballymascanlon House
Dundrum Dundrum House
Dunlavin Rathsallagh House
Ennis Auburn Lodge
Gorey Marlfield House
Kanturk Assolas Country House
Kenmare Park Hotel
Kenmare Sheen Falls Lodge
Kilkenny Newpark Hotel
Killarney Aghadoe Heights Hotel
Killarney Cahernane Hotel
Killarney Hotel Europe
Killarney Great Southern
Killarney Torc Great Southern
Killiney Fitzpatrick's Castle
Knocklofty Knocklofty House
Letterfrack Rosleague Manor
Limerick Jurys Hotel
Limerick Limerick Inn
Maynooth Moyglare Manor
Newmarket-on-Fergus Clare Inn
Newmarket-on-Fergus Dromoland Castle
Oughterard Connemara Gateway Hotel
Oughterard Currarevagh House
Parknasilla Great Southern
Rathmullan Rathmullan House
Rathnew Tinakilly House
Renvyle Renvyle House
Rosslare Great Southern
Rosslare Kelly's Strand Hotel
Rossnowlagh Sand House
Shanagarry Ballymaloe House
Sligo Sligo Park
Straffan Kildare Hotel
Thomastown Mount Juliet Hotel
Waterford Jurys Waterford Hotel
Waterford Waterford Castle

Hotels with Wheelchair Facilities

Compiled in association with the Holiday Care Service 0293 774535

England

Ambleside Rothay Manor
Ashford Eastwell Manor

Ashford Forte Posthouse
Bolton Abbey Devonshire Arms
Bristol Holiday Inn
Cambridge Holiday Inn
Cambridge University Arms

Coventry Novotel
Durham Royal County Hotel
Elcot Elcot Park
Gatwick Airport Gatwick Hilton International
Gatwick Airport Copthorne London Gatwick
Hawkshead Tarn Hows Hotel
Heathrow Airport Excelsior Hotel
Manchester Copthorne Hotel
Newbury Millwaters
Newbury Regency Park Hotel
Norwich Hotel Nelson
Norwich Hotel Norwich
Peterborough Swallow Hotel
Plymouth Copthorne Hotel
Slough Copthorne Hotel
Standish Almond Brook Moat House
Stoke-on-Trent North Stafford Hotel
Swindon Forte Crest
Worfield Old Vicarage

Scotland

Edinburgh Caledonian Hotel
Edinburgh Sheraton Hotel
Edinburgh Stakis Grosvenor Hotel
Glasgow Holiday Inn
Onich Lodge on the Loch

Wales

Cardiff Holiday Inn

Fishguard Fishguard Bay Hotel
Llangammarch Wells Lake Country House Hotel
Llangefni Tre-Ysgawen Hall
Llangollen Hand Hotel
Swansea Holiday Inn

Channel Islands

St Peter Port St Pierre Park

Northern Ireland

Larne Magheramorne House

Republic of Ireland

Ballyvaughan Gregans Castle
Cork Jurys Hotel
Dublin Jurys Hotel
Dublin Montrose Hotel
Dublin Airport Forte Crest
Dundrum Dundrum House
Ennis West Country Inn
Galway Corrib Great Southern Hotel
Kenmare Sheen Falls Lodge
Limerick Limerick Inn
Limerick Two Mile Inn

Restaurants with a non-smoking area

The following is a list of establishments where smoking is not allowed in the restaurant (or in some cases, anywhere). In addition, many hotels have bedrooms designated non-smoking, or a non-smoking lounge, and some restaurants have a non-smoking section or room. Ask what they've got to offer when you book — and remember that puffing companions can usually retire to bar, lounge, garden etc.

England

Amberley Amberley Castle
Ambleside Rothay Manor
Ambleside Wateredge Hotel
Appleby-in-Westmorland Appleby Manor
Applethwaite Underscar Manor
Aston Clinton Bell Inn
Barnstaple Lynwood House
Baslow Fischer's Baslow Hall
Bath Bath Spa Hotel
Bath Newbridge House
Beckingham Black Swan
Berwick-upon-Tweed Funnywayt'mekalivin
Bilbrough Bilbrough Manor
Birmingham Hyatt Regency

Birmingham Norton Place
Birmingham Rajdoot
Birmingham Sloans
Birmingham Swallow Hotel
Blandford Forum La Belle Alliance
Bournemouth Henry's
Bowness-on-Windermere Gilpin Lodge
Bowness-on-Windermere Linthwaite House
Braunton Otters Restaurant
Brighton Browns
Brighton La Marinade
Brimfield Poppies Restaurant
Bristol Howard's
Broadway Dormy House
Brockenhurst Le Poussin
Buckland Buckland Manor

Calstock Danescombe Valley Hotel
Cambridge Browns
Campsea Ashe Old Rectory
Cartmel Uplands
Cawston Grey Gables
Chadlington The Manor
Chagford Gidleigh Park
Chapeltown Greenhead House
Cheltenham Staithes
Chester Crabwall Manor
Chinnor Sir Charles Napier Inn
Chipping Camden Cotswold House
Chiseldon Chiseldon House
Chobham Quails Restaurant
Clanfield The Plough at Clanfield
Cockermouth Quince & Medlar
Corse Lawn Corse Lawn House
Cowan Bridge Cobwebs
Crosby-on-Eden Crosby Lodge
Dedham Fountain House & Dedham Hall
Diss Weavers
Dorking Partners West Street
Dorrington Country Friends
Dulverton Ashwick House
East Grinstead Gravetye Manor
Easton Clarke's
Ely Old Fire Engine House
Erpingham Ark
Eyton Marsh Country Hotel
Falmouth Pandora Inn
Felsted Rumbles Cottage
Flitwick Flitwick Manor
Freshford Homewood Park
Gillingham Stock Hill House
Glastonbury No. 3 Restaurant & Hotel
Grasmere Michael's Nook
Grasmere White Moss House
Great Dunmow The Starr
Great Gonerby Harry's Place
Great Milton Le Manoir aux Quat'Saisons
Grimsthorpe Black Horse Inn
Grimston Congham Hall
Grizedale Grizedale Lodge
Guist Tollbridge
Harrogate Cafe Fleur
Haslemere Morel's
Hawkshead Tarn Hows
Haworth Weavers
Hayfield Bridge End Restaurant
Herstmonceux Sundial Restaurant
Hintlesham Hintlesham Hall
Hockley Heath Nuthurst Grange
Horley Langshott Manor
Hunstrete Hunstrete House
Ixworth Theobalds
Jevington Hungry Monk Restaurant
Kendal Moon
Kendal Posh Nosh
Kintbury Dundas Arms
Lavenham The Swan
Leamington Spa Regent Hotel
Ledbury Hope End
Leeds Bhavani Junction
Leeds Brasserie Forty Four
Leeds Bryan's of Headingley
Leeds Corner Café
Leeds Low Hall
Lewdown Lewtrenchard Manor

Linton Wood Hall
Longridge Heathcote's
Lower Beeding South Lodge
Lymington Gordleton Mill
Madingley Three Horseshoes
Maiden Newton Le Petit Canard
Malvern Cottage in the Wood
Malvern Croque-en-Bouche
Manchester Gaylord
Manchester Quan Ju De
Manchester That Café
Marlow Compleat Angler Hotel
Melmerby Village Bakery
Morston Morston Hall
Nantwich Rookery Hall
Newcastle-upon-Tyne Fisherman's
  Lodge
North Huish Brookdale House
Northleach Wickens
Northwich Wincham Hall
Norwich Marco's
Old Burghclere Dew Pond
Oxford Bath Place Hotel & Restaurant
Oxford Browns
Oxford Munchy Munchy
Painswick Painswick Hotel
Paulerspury Vine House
Porlock Oaks Hotel
Powburn Breamish House
Powerstock Three Horseshoes Inn
Puckrup Puckrup Hall
Pulborough Stane Street Hollow
Ramsbottom Village Restaurant
Ridgeway Old Vicarage
Rotherwick Tylney Hall
Saffron Walden Saffron Hotel
St Martin's St Martin's Hotel
St Mawes Idle Rocks Hotel
Salcombe Soar Mill Cove
Sandiway Nunsmere Hall
Sheffield Bay Tree
Shipley Aagrah
Sissinghurst Rankins
Skipton Aagrah
South Godstone La Bonne Auberge
South Molton Whitechapel Manor
Southall Asian Tandoori Centre
Southampton Browns Brasserie
Southwold The Crown
Southwold The Swan
Spark Bridge Bridgefield House
Stapleford Stapleford Park
Stonham Mr Underhill's
Storrington Abingworth Hall
Stow-on-the-Wold Wyck Hill House
Stretton Ram Jam Inn
Sutton Coldfield New Hall
Taplow Cliveden: Waldo's Restaurant
Taunton Porters
Teignmouth Thomas Luny House
Telford Madeley Court
Tetbury Calcot Manor
Tiverton Lowman Restaurant
Tresco Island Hotel
Tunbridge Wells Spa Hotel
Turners Hill Alexander House
Uckfield Horsted Place
Ullswater Leeming House

Ullswater Old Church Hotel
Ullswater Sharrow Bay
Ulverston Bay Horse Inn & Bistro
Waterhouses Old Beams
Williton White House
Wimborne Les Bouviers
Winchester Wykeham Arms
Windermere Holbeck Ghyll
Windermere Miller Howe
Winteringham Winteringham Fields
Witherslack Old Vicarage
Wiveliscombe Langley House
Woodstock Bear Hotel
Worfield Old Vicarage
Yeovil Little Barwick House
York 19 Grape Lane

Scotland

Aberdeen Faraday's
Aberfeldy Farleyer House
Achiltibuie Summer Isles
Alexandria Cameron House
Alloa Gean House
Anstruther Cellar
Arisaig Arisaig House
Auchterarder Auchterarder House
Auchterhouse Old Mansion House
Ayr The Stables
Ballater Tullich Lodge
Blairgowrie Kinloch House
Cairndow Loch Fyne Oyster Bar
Canonbie Riverside Inn
Colbost Three Chimneys Restaurant
Craigellachie Craigellachie Hotel
Cromarty Thistles
Dalguise Kinnaird
Drumnadrochit Polmaily House
Drybridge Old Monastery Restaurant
Dulnain Bridge Auchendean Lodge
Dunblane Cromlix House
Edinburgh Alp-Horn
Edinburgh The Balmoral
Edinburgh Caledonian Hotel
Edinburgh Indian Cavalry Club
Edinburgh Kalpna
Edinburgh Kelly's
Edinburgh Martin's
Edinburgh Vintners Room, The Vaults
Fort William Crannog Seafood Restaurant
Fort William Inverlochy Castle
Glamis Castleton House
Glasgow D'Arcy's
Glasgow Mata Hari
Glasgow October Café
Glenborrodale Glenborrodale Castle
Gullane La Potinière
Kentallen of Appin Ardsheal House

Kilchrenan Ardanaiseig
Kilfinan Kilfinan Hotel
Kilmore Glenfeochan House
Kinclaven by Stanley Ballathie House
Kingussie The Cross
Muir-of-Ord Dower House
Nairn Clifton Hotel
Newton Stewart Kirroughtree Hotel
Newtonmore Ard-na-Coille Hotel
Newtown St Boswells Le Provençale
Onich Allt-nan-Ros Hotel
Peat Inn Peat Inn
Port Appin Airds Hotel
Portpatrick Knockinaam Lodge
Quothquan Shieldhill
Scarista Scarista House
Sleat Kinloch Lodge
Tiroran Tiroran House
Ullapool Altnaharrie Inn

Wales

Cardiff Quayles
Coychurch Coed-y-Mwstwr Hotel
Harlech The Cemlyn
Llanberis Y Bistro
Llandudno St Tudno Hotel
Llangammarch Wells Lake Country House Hotel
Llanrwst Meadowsweet
Llansanffraid Glan Conwy Old Rectory
Llyswen Llangoed Hall
Penally Penally Abbey
Pwllheli Plas Bodegroes
Talsarnau Maes-y-Neaudd

Channel Islands

Gorey Jersey Pottery
Rozel Bay Chateau la Chaire
St Helier Grand Hotel
St Peter Port Louisiana
St Saviour Longueville Manor
Sark Stocks Hotel

Northern Ireland

Belfast Roscoff
Holywood Culloden Hotel

Republic of Ireland

By law, all restaurants in the Republic of Ireland must have a non-smoking area.

Sunday Eating

England

(L) Lunch only   (D) Dinner only

Alderley Edge Alderley Edge Hotel
Altrincham Francs
Amberley Amberley Castle
Ambleside Rothay Manor
Ambleside Wateredge Hotel
Applethwaite Underscar Manor
Ascot Hyn's
Ascot Royal Berkshire
Ashford Eastwell Manor
Ashington The Willows (L)
Aston Clinton Bell Inn
Aylesbury Hartwell House
Basingstoke Audleys Wood
Basingstoke Hee's (D)
Baslow Fischer's Baslow Hall (L)
Bath Bath Spa Hotel
Bath Garlands
Bath Newbridge House (D)
Bath Priory Hotel
Bath Queensberry Hotel
Bath Royal Crescent Hotel
Battle Netherfield Place
Bilbrough Bilbrough Manor
Birdlip Kingshead House (L)
Birmingham Chung Ying
Birmingham Chung Ying Garden
Birmingham New Happy Gathering
Birmingham Norton Place
Birmingham Purple Rooms
Birmingham Rajdoot (D)
Birmingham Swallow Hotel
Blackwater Long's (L)
Botley Cobbett's (L)
Bournemouth Elysée Restaurant
Bournemouth Ocean Palace
Bowness-on-Windermere Gilpin Lodge
Bowness-on-Windermere Linthwaite House
Bradford Aagrah
Bradford Bharat (D)
Bradford Bombay Brasserie
Bradford K2
Bradford Nawaab
Bradford PLS Gujrati Pure Vegetarian (D)
Bradford-on-Avon Woolley Grange
Brampton Farlam Hall (D)
Brampton Tarn End (D)
Bray-on-Thames The Waterside Inn
Bridport Riverside Restaurant (L)
Brightling Jack Fuller's (L)
Brighton Black Chapati (L)
Brighton Browns
Brighton China Garden
Brighton La Marinade (L)
Bristol Jameson's Restaurant (L)
Bristol Palm Court Restaurant (D)
Bristol Swallow Royal Hotel
Broadway Collin House
Broadway Dormy House
Broadway Hunters Lodge (L)

Broadway Lygon Arms
Brockenhurst Le Poussin (L)
Bromsgrove Grafton Manor
Broughton Broughton Park
Broxted Whitehall
Buckland Buckland Manor
Calstock Danescombe Valley Hotel (D)
Camberley Tithas
Cambridge Browns
Cambridge Charlie Chan
Canterbury County Hotel
Canterbury River Kwai
Cartmel Uplands
Castle Cary Bond's (D)
Castle Combe Manor House
Cavendish Alfonso's (L)
Cawston Grey Gables (D)
Chadlington The Manor (L)
Chagford Gidleigh Park
Chapel Amble Maltsters Arms
Charingworth Charingworth Manor
Chedington Chedington Court (D)
Cheltenham Epicurean (L)
Cheltenham Greenway
Cheltenham Redmond's (L)
Chelwood Chelwood House
Chester Crabwall Manor
Chester Franc's
Chichester Comme Ca (L)
Chilgrove White Horse Inn (L)
Chinnor Sir Charles Napier Inn (L)
Chipping Camden Cotswold House
Chiseldon Chiseldon House
Cirencester Tatyan's (D)
Clanfield The Plough at Clanfield
Clun Old Post Office
Cockermouth Quince & Medlar (D)
Coggeshall White Hart (L)
Colerne Lucknam Park
Corse Lawn Corse Lawn House
Cranleigh Restaurant Bonnet (L)
Crosby-on-Eden Crosby Lodge
Dartmouth Carved Angel (L)
Dedham Fountain House & Dedham Hall (L)
Dedham Le Talbooth
Dorchester Yalbury Cottage (D)
Dorking Partners West Street (L)
Dulverton Ashwick House
Dunbridge Mill Arms Inn
East Boldon Forsters (L)
East Grinstead Gravetye Manor
Easton Clarke's (L)
Edenbridge Honours Mill Restaurant (L)
Egham La Bonne Franquette (L)
Ely Old Fire Engine House (L)
Erpingham Ark (L)
Esher Good Earth
Evershot Summer Lodge
Eversley New Mill Restaurant
Evesham Riverside Hotel (L)
Eyton Marsh Country Hotel (D)
Falmouth Pandora Inn (D)

Farnley Tyas Golden Cock **(L)**
Felsted Rumbles Cottage **(L)**
Flitwick Flitwick Manor
Folkestone Paul's
Freshford Homewood Park
Fressingfield Fox and Goose
Gillingham Stock Hill House **(L)**
Glemsford Barrett's Restaurant **(L)**
Gloucester Hatton Court
Goring-on-Thames The Leatherne Bottel
Grasmere Michael's Nook
Grasmere Wordsworth Hotel
Great Dunmow The Starr **(L)**
Great Milton Le Manoir aux Quat'Saisons
Grimston Congham Hall
Grizedale Grizedale Lodge
Guildford Mandarin **(D)**
Guiseley Prachee
Guist Tollbridge **(L)**
Gulworthy Horn of Plenty
Handforth Belfry Hotel
Handforth Handforth Chinese Restaurant
  (D)
Harrogate Café Fleur **(D)**
Harvington The Mill
Harwich Pier at Harwich
Haworth Weavers **(L)**
Helford Riverside **(D)**
Herne Bay L'Escargot
Hersham The Dining Room **(L)**
Herstmonceux Sundial Restaurant **(L)**
Hintlesham Hintlesham Hall
Hinton Hinton Grange **(D)**
Hockley Heath Nuthurst Grange
Horley Langshott Manor **(D)**
Hunstrete Hunstrete House
Huntingdon Old Bridge Hotel
Huntsham Huntsham Court **(D)**
Hurstbourne Tarrant Esseborne Manor
Ixworth Theobalds **(L)**
Jevington Hungry Monk Restaurant
Kendal Moon **(D)**
Keyston Pheasant Inn
Kington Penrhos Court
Knutsford David's Place **(L)**
Lacock At The Sign of The Angel **(L)**
Langho Northcote Manor
Lavenham Great House **(L)**
Lavenham The Swan
Leamington Spa Mallory Court
Ledbury Hope End **(D)**
Leeds Bhavani Junction **(D)**
Leeds Bryan's of Headingley
Leeds Corner Cafe
Leeds Haley's Hotel **(L)**
Leeds Maxi's Chinese Restaurant
Leeds New Asia
Leeds Sang Sang
Leeds Thai Siam **(D)**
Leicester Man Ho
Leicester Rise of the Raj
Lewdown Lewtrenchard Manor
Linton Wood Hall
Liskeard Well House
Long Melford Chimneys **(L)**
Longridge Heathcote's

Lower Beeding Cisswood House
Lower Beeding South Lodge
Lower Slaughter Lower Slaughter Manor
Lymington Gordleton Mill **(L)**
Lympstone River House **(L)**
Madingley Three Horseshoes
Maiden Newton Maiden Newton House
  (D)
Maidenhead Fredrick's
Maidstone Mandarin Chef
Malvern Anupam
Malvern Cottage in the Wood
Manchester Gaylord
Manchester Little Yang Sing
Manchester Penang Village
Manchester Quan Ju De
Manchester Rajdoot **(D)**
Manchester Siam Orchid **(D)**
Manchester Sonarga
Manchester That Café **(L)**
Manchester Yang Sing
Manchester Airport Etrop Grange
Marlow Compleat Angler Hotel
Matlock Riber Hall
Mawnan Smith Nansidwell
Medmenham Danesfield House
Melbourn Pink Geranium **(L)**
Melmerby Village Bakery **(L)**
Milford-on-Sea Rocher's
Moreton-in-Marsh Annie's **(L)**
Moreton-in-Marsh Marsh Goose **(L)**
Morston Morston Hall
Moulsford-on-Thames Beetle & Wedge
Nantwich Rookery Hall
New Alresford Hunters **(L)**
New Barnet Mims Restaurant
New Milton Chewton Glen
Newcastle-upon-Tyne King Neptune
North Huish Brookdale House **(D)**
Nottingham Higoi **(D)**
Nottingham Noble House
Nottingham Ocean City
Nottingham Rutland Square Hotel
Oakham Hambleton Hall
Oxford Al-Shami
Oxford Bath Place Hotel & Restaurant **(L)**
Oxford Browns
Oxford Cherwell Boathouse **(L)**
Oxford Restaurant Elizabeth
Oxford 15 North Parade **(L)**
Painswick Painswick Hotel
Pangbourne Copper Inn Restaurant
Paulerspury Vine House **(L)**
Penkridge William Harding's House **(L)**
Penzance Abbey Hotel **(D)**
Penzance Harris's **(D)**
Pitton Silver Plough **(L)**
Polperro Kitchen at Polperro **(D)**
Poole Mansion House
Porlock Oaks Hotel **(D)**
Powerstock Three Horseshoes Inn
Puckrup Puckrup Hall
Purton Pear Tree
Quorn Quorn Grange
Richmond Petersham Hotel
Ridgeway Old Vicarage **(L)**
Ripley Michel's **(L)**
Roade Roadhouse **(D)**

Romsey Old Manor House **(L)**
Rotherwick Tylney Hall
Saffron Walden Saffron Hotel **(L)**
St Martin's St Martin's Hotel **(D)**
St Mawes Idle Rocks Hotel
Salcombe Soar Mill Cove
Salcombe Spinnakers **(L)**
Sandiway Nunsmere Hall
Sawbridgeworth Manor of Groves **(L)**
Seaview Seaview Hotel **(L)**
Sevenoaks Royal Oak
Shanklin Old Village The Cottage **(L)**
Sheffield Nirmal's **(D)**
Shinfield L'Ortolan **(L)**
Shipley Aagrah **(D)**
Sissinghurst Rankins **(L)**
Skipton Aagrah **(D)**
Sourton Collaven Manor
South Godstone La Bonne Auberge **(L)**
South Molton Whitechapel Manor
Southall Asian Tandoori Centre
Southampton Kuti's
Southwold The Crown
Southwold The Swan
Spark Bridge Bridgefield House **(D)**
Staddle Bridge McCoy's **(D)**
Stamford The George of Stamford
Stapleford Stapleford Park
Stilton Bell Inn **(D)**
Ston Easton Ston Easton Park
Stonor Stonor Arms **(L)**
Storrington Abingworth Hall
Storrington Little Thakeham **(L)**
Storrington Manley's **(L)**
Storrington Old Forge **(L)**
Stow-on-the-Wold Wyck Hill House
Stratford-upon-Avon Billesley Manor
Streatley-on-Thames Swan Diplomat
Stretton Ram Jam Inn
Stroud Oakes **(L)**
Sturminster Newton Plumber Manor **(D)**
Sutton Partners Brasserie **(L)**
Sutton Coldfield New Hall
Taplow Cliveden
Taunton Castle Hotel
Teffont Evias Howard's House
Teignmouth Thomas Luny House **(D)**
Telford Madeley Court **(L)**
Tetbury Calcot Manor **(L)**
Tetbury The Close
Thornbury Thornbury Castle
Thundridge Hanbury Manor **(L)**
Tiverton Lowman Restaurant **(L)**
Torquay Table Restaurant **(D)**
Tresco Island Hotel
Tuckenhay Maltsters Arms
Tunbridge Wells Spa Hotel
Turners Hill Alexander House
Twickenham Hamiltons **(L)**
Uckfield Horsted Place
Ullswater Leeming House
Ullswater Old Church Hotel
Ullswater Rampsbeck Country House Hotel
Ullswater Sharrow Bay
Upper Slaughter Lords of the Manor
Uppingham The Lake Isle
Veryan Nare Hotel

Wadhurst Spindlewood
Wansford-in-England Haycock Hotel
Warminster Bishopstrow House
Waterhouses Old Beams **(L)**
Wath-in-Nidderdale Sportsman's Arms **(L)**
Watlington Well House **(L)**
Weston-under-Penyard Wharton Lodge
Wetherby Sheba **(D)**
Weybourne Gasche's **(L)**
Weybridge Casa Romana
Whimple Woodhayes Hotel **(D)**
Williton White House **(D)**
Wilmslow Harry's **(D)**
Wilmslow Stanneylands **(L)**
Windermere Miller Howe **(D)**
Windsor Oakley Court
Witherslack Old Vicarage **(D)**
Wiveliscombe Langley House **(D)**
Woburn Paris House **(L)**
Woodstock Bear Hotel
Woodstock Feathers Hotel
Worcester Brown's **(L)**
Worfield Old Vicarage
Yattendon Royal Oak
York Grange Hotel
York Middlethorpe Hall

Scotland

Aberdeen Silver Darling **(D)**
Aberfeldy Farleyer House **(D)**
Aberfoyle Braeval Old Mill **(L)**
Achiltibuie Summer Isles **(D)**
Alexandria Cameron House
Alloa Gean House
Alyth Drumnacree House **(L)**
Arisaig Arisaig House
Auchterarder Auchterarder House
Auchterhouse Old Mansion House
Ayr Fouters Bistro **(D)**
Ballater Tullich Lodge
Banchory Invery House
Banchory Raemoir House
Blairgowrie Kinloch House
Bridge of Allan Kipling's **(L)**
Cairndow Loch Fyne Oyster Bar
Canonbie Riverside Inn **(D)**
Craigellachie Craigellachie Hotel
Crinan Crinan Hotel: Westward Room **(D)**
Crinan Crinan Hotel **(D)**
Cromarty Thistles **(L)**
Dalguise Kinnaird
Drumnadrochit Polmaily House **(D)**
Dulnain Bridge Auchendean Lodge **(D)**
Dunblane Cromlix House
Edinburgh L'Auberge
Edinburgh The Balmoral
Edinburgh The Balmoral: Grill Room **(D)**
Edinburgh Caledonian: Carriages Restaurant
Edinburgh Caledonian Hotel **(D)**
Edinburgh Indian Cavalry Club
Edinburgh Shamiana **(D)**
Edinburgh Szechuan House **(D)**
Eriska Isle of Eriska **(D)**
Fort William Crannog Seafood Restaurant

Fort William The Factor's House **(D)**
Fort William Inverlochy Castle
Glamis Castleton House
Glasgow Amber
Glasgow Ashoka West End **(D)**
Glasgow D'Arcy's **(L)**
Glasgow Loon Fung
Glasgow One Devonshire Gardens
Glasgow Rogano **(D)**
Glasgow Ubiquitous Chip
Glenborrodale Glenborrodale Castle
Gullane Greywalls Hotel
Gullane La Potinière **(L)**
Inverness Culloden House
Inverness Dunain Park **(D)**
Kentallen of Appin Ardsheal House
Kilchrenan Ardanaiseig
Kilfinan Kilfinan Hotel
Kilmore Glenfeochan House **(D)**
Kinclaven by Stanley Ballathie House
Kirknewton Dalmahoy Hotel
Linlithgow Champany Inn Chop & Ale House
Muir-of-Ord Dower House **(D)**
Nairn Clifton Hotel **(D)**
Newton Stewart Kirroughtree Hotel
Newtonmore Ard-na-Coille Hotel **(D)**
Oban Knipoch Hotel **(D)**
Onich Allt-nan-Ros Hotel
Peebles Cringletie House
Port Appin Airds Hotel
Portpatrick Knockinaam Lodge
Quothquan Shieldhill
Scarista Scarista House **(D)**
Scone Murrayshall House
Sleat Kinloch Lodge **(D)**
Tiroran Tiroran House **(D)**
Turnberry Turnberry Hotel
Ullapool Altnaharrie Inn **(D)**

Wales

Aberkenfig New Garden **(D)**
Abersoch Porth Tocyn Hotel
Cardiff Quayles **(L)**
Cardiff Tandoor Ghar **(L)**
Chepstow Beckfords **(L)**
Chirk Starlings Castle
Conwy Sychnant Pass Hotel
Coychurch Coed-y-Mwstwr Hotel
East Aberthaw Blue Anchor Inn **(L)**
Gowerton Cefn Goleu Park **(L)**
Harlech The Cemlyn **(D)**
Llanberis Y Bistro **(D)**
Llandrillo Tyddyn Llan
Llandudno Bodysgallen Hall
Llandudno St Tudno Hotel
Llangammarch Wells Lake Country House Hotel **(D)**
Llangefni Tre-Ysgawen Hall
Llanrwst Meadowsweet
Llansanffraid Glan Conwy Old Rectory **(D)**
Llyswen Llangoed Hall
Northop Soughton Hall
Penally Penally Abbey **(D)**
Porth G & T's Village Bistro **(L)**
Pwllheli Plas Bodegroes **(D)**

Reynoldston Fairyhill
Swansea Norton House **(D)**
Talsarnau Maes-y-Neaudd
Trellech Village Green **(L)**
Welsh Hook Stone Hall **(D)**

Isle of Man

Ramsey Harbour Bistro

Channel Islands

Rozel Bay Chateau la Chaire
Rozel Bay Granite Corner **(L)**
St Anne Inchalla Hotel **(L)**
St Brelade Sea Crest
St Helier Grand Hotel
St Lawrence Little Grove
St Peter Port Louisiana
St Saviour Longueville Manor
Sark Aval Du Creux
Sark Stocks Hotel

Northern Ireland

Annalong Glassdrumman House
Belfast Bengal Brasserie **(D)**
Belfast Manor House
Belfast Strand Restaurant
Belfast Welcome Restaurant **(D)**
Holywood Culloden Hotel

Republic of Ireland

Adare Adare Manor
Ahakista Shiro **(D)**
Athy Tonlegee House **(L)**
Ballina Mount Falcon Castle **(D)**
Ballylickey Sea View House
Ballyvaughan Gregans Castle
Bray Tree of Idleness **(D)**
Cashel Cashel House
Castledermot Doyle's School House Country Inn **(L)**
Clifden Ardagh Hotel **(D)**
Cong Ashford Castle & Connaught Room
Cork Bully's
Cork Huguenot **(D)**
Cork Isaacs **(D)**
Dalkey Il Ristorante **(D)**
Dublin Shalimar **(D)**
Dublin The Westbury
Dun Laoghaire De Selby's
Dun Laoghaire Digby's
Dunderry Dunderry Lodge Restaurant **(L)**
Dunlavin Rathsallagh House **(L)**
Dunworley Dunworley Cottage
Enniskerry Enniscree Lodge Inn
Gorey Marlfield House
Greystones The Hungry Monk
Kanturk Assolas Country House **(D)**
Kenmare Park Hotel

Kenmare Sheen Falls Lodge
Killarney Cahernane Hotel **(D)**
Killorglin Nick's Restaurant **(D)**
Kinsale Max's Wine Bar
Letterfrack Rosleague Manor
Mallow Longueville House
Maynooth Moyglare Manor
Newmarket-on-Fergus Dromoland
  Castle
Newport Newport House **(D)**
Oughterard Currarevagh House **(D)**
Oysterhaven The Oystercatcher
Rathnew Hunter's Hotel

Rathnew Tinakilly House
Riverstown Coopershill House **(D)**
Roundwood Roundwood Inn **(L)**
Shanagarry Ballymaloe House
Spiddal Boluisce Seafood Bar **(D)**
Stillorgan China-Sichuan Restaurant
Stillorgan Mr Hung's Sawadee Thai
  Restaurant
Straffan Kildare Hotel
Swords Le Chateau
Waterford Waterford Castle
Wicklow Old Rectory **(D)**
Youghal Aherne's Seafood Restaurant

Seafood Restaurants

England

Barnstaple Lynwood House
Bridport Riverside Restaurant
Burnham-on-Crouch Contented Sole
Dartmouth Carved Angel
Falmouth Seafood Bar
Great Yarmouth Seafood Restaurant
Harrogate Drum & Monkey
Harwich Pier at Harwich
Helford Riverside
Hull Ceruttis
Lympstone River House
Newcastle-upon-Tyne Fisherman's
  Lodge
Norwich Greens Seafood Restaurant
Nottingham Loch Fyne Oyster Bar
Padstow Seafood Restaurant
Salcombe Spinnakers
Tuckenhay Maltsters Arms

Scotland

Aberdeen Atlantis
Aberdeen Silver Darling
Anstruther Cellar
Cairndow Loch Fyne Oyster Bar
Colbost Three Chimneys Restaurant
Crinan Crinan Hotel
Fort William Crannog Seafood Restaurant
Glasgow Rogano
Linlithgow Champany Inn

Channel Islands

St Peter Port Absolute End
St Peter Port Le Nautique
Sark Aval Du Creux

Northern Ireland

Portrush Ramore

Republic of Ireland

Cashel Cashel House
Cashel Chez Hans
Clifden Ardagh Hotel
Cork Lovetts
Dingle Doyle's Seafood Bar & Townhouse
Dun Laoghaire Restaurant Na Mara
Howth King Sitric
Killarney Gaby's Seafood Restaurant
Oysterhaven The Oystercatcher
Spiddal Boluisce Seafood Bar
Youghal Aherne's Seafood Restaurant

Outstanding Desserts

England

Alderley Edge Alderley Edge Hotel
Applethwaite Underscar Manor
Aston Clinton Bell
Baslow Fischer's Baslow Hall
Bath Bath Spa Hotel
Bath Priory Hotel

Battle Netherfield Place
Birmingham Norton Place
Birmingham Sloans
Birmingham Swallow Hotel
Bishop's Tawton Halmpstone Manor
Bowness-on-Windermere Gilpin Lodge
Blackwater Long's
Bradford Restaurant 19
Braunton Otters Restaurant

Bray-on-Thames The Waterside Inn
Brighton Hospitality Inn
Brighton Langan's Bistro
Broadway Lygon Arms
Broxted Whitehall
Bury Normandie
Calstock Danescombe Valley Hotel
Cambridge Midsummer House
Chadlington The Manor
Chagford Gidleigh Park
Cheltenham Le Champignon Sauvage
Chester Chester Grosvenor Hotel
Chinnor Sir Charles Napier
Corse Lawn Corse Lawn House
Dartmouth Carved Angel
Dedham Le Talbooth
East Grinstead Gravetye Manor
Eastbourne Grand Hotel
Farnley Tyas Golden Cock
Felsted Rumbles Cottage
Freshford Homewood Park
Gillingham Stock Hill House
Great Milton Le Manoir aux Quat'Saisons
Gulworthy Horn of Plenty
Harrogate Old Swan Hotel
Harvington The Mill
Haslemere Morel's
Hawkshead Tarn Hows
Kendal Moon
Longridge Heathcote's
Lymington Gordleton Mill
Malvern Croque-en-Bouche
Minster Lovell Old Swan
Morston Morston Hall
Moulsford-on-Thames Beetle & Wedge
North Huish Brookdale House
Oakham Hambleton Hall
Padstow Seafood Restaurant
Plymouth Chez Nous
Pool-in-Wharfedale Pool Court
Richmond Petersham Hotel
Shanklin Old Village The Cottage
Shinfield L'Ortolan
South Molton Whitechapel Manor
Staddle Bridge McCoy's
Ston Easton Ston Easton Park
Stonham Mr Underhill's
Storrington Manley's
Stratford-upon-Avon Billesley Manor
Sutton Coldfield New Hall
Taplow Cliveden

Taunton Castle Hotel
Thornbury Thornbury Castle
Thornton-le-Fylde River House
Tunbridge Wells Thackeray's House
Uckfield Horsted Place
Ullswater Leeming House
Ullswater Rampsbeck Country House Hotel
Ullswater Sharrow Bay
Warminster Bishopstrow House
Windsor Oakley Court
Witherslack Old Vicarage
Wootton Common Lugleys
York Melton's
York Middlethorpe Hall

Scotland

Aberfeldy Farleyer House
Arisaig Arisaig House
Cumbernauld Westerwood Hotel
Cupar Ostlers Close
Dunblane Cromlix House
Edinburgh Martin's
Edinburgh Vintners Rooms, The Vaults
Gullane Greywalls Hotel
Newton Stewart Kirroughtree Hotel
Scone Murrayshah House
Ullapool Altnaharrie Inn

Wales

Abergavenny Walnut Tree Inn
Llandudno St Tudno Hotel
Reynoldston Fairyhill

Channel Islands

Rozel Bay Granite Corner

Northern Ireland

Belfast Roscoff
Portrush Ramore

Republic of Ireland

Dun Laoghaire Digby's
Dunderry Dunderry Lodge

Restaurants offering a good cheeseboard

England

Alderley Edge Alderley Edge Hotel
Amberley Amberley Castle
Ambleside Rothay Manor
Ambleside Wateredge Hotel
Applethwaite Underscar Manor
Ascot Royal Berkshire
Ashford Eastwell Manor
Aston Clinton Bell

Aylesbury Hartwell House
Barnsley Armstrong's
Barnsley Restaurant Peano
Basingstoke Audleys Wood
Baslow Fischer's Baslow Hall
Bath Bath Spa Hotel
Bath Circus Restaurant
Bath Queensberry Hotel
Battle Netherfield Place
Beckingham Black Swan

Berwick-upon-Tweed
Funnywayt'mekalivin
Bilbrough Bilbrough Manor
Birmingham Norton Place
Birmingham Sloans
Birmingham Swallow Hotel
Bishop's Tawton Halmpstone Manor
Botley Cobbett's
Bournemouth Elysée Restaurant
Bowness-on-Windermere Gilpin Lodge
Bowness-on-Windermere Linthwaite
House
Bradford Restaurant 19
Bradford-on-Avon Woolley Grange
Brampton Farlam Hall
Brampton Tarn End
Bray-on-Thames The Waterside Inn
Brighton Langan's Bistro
Brimfield Poppies Restaurant
Bristol Hunt's
Bristol Lettonie
Bristol Markwick's
Bristol Palm Court Restaurant
Bristol Swallow Royal Hotel
Broadway Collin House
Broadway Dormy House
Broadway Lygon Arms
Brockenhurst Le Poussin
Broxted Whitehall
Buckland Buckland Manor
Bury Normandie Hotel & Restaurant
Calstock Danescombe Valley Hotel
Cambridge Midsummer House
Campsea Ashe Old Rectory
Canterbury County Hotel
Cartmel Uplands
Castle
Cary Bond's
Castle Combe Manor House
Cavendish Alfonso's
Cawston Grey Gables
Chadlington The Manor
Chagford Gidleigh Park
Chapel Amble Maltsters Arms
Chapeltown Greenhead House
Charingworth Charingworth Manor
Chedington Chedington Court
Cheltenham Le Champignon Sauvage
Cheltenham Epicurean
Cheltenham Greenway
Cheltenham Redmond's
Cheltenham Staithes
Chester Chester Grosvenor
Chester Crabwall Manor
Chichester Thompson's
Chilgrove White Horse Inn
Chinnor Sir Charles Napier Inn
Chiseldon Chiseldon House
Claygate Les Alouettes
Clun Old Post Office
Cockermouth Quince & Medlar
Colerne Lucknam Park
Corse Lawn Corse Lawn House
Cowan Bridge Cobwebs
Crosby-on-Eden Crosby Lodge
Darlington Victor's Restaurant
Dartmouth Carved Angel
Dedham Le Talbooth

Diss Salisbury House
Diss Weavers
Dorking Partners West Street
Dorrington Country Friends
Dulverton Ashwick House
Dunbridge Mill Arms Inn
East Buckland Lower Pitt
East Grinstead Gravetye Manor
Egham La Bonne Franquette
Elcot Elcot Park Resort Hotel, Orangery
Restaurant
Ely Old Fire Engine House
Emsworth 36 On The Quay
Erpingham Ark
Evershot Summer Lodge
Eversley New Mill Restaurant
Evesham Riverside Hotel
Eyton Marsh Country Hotel
Faversham Read's
Felsted Rumbles Cottage
Flitwick Flitwick Manor
Folkestone Paul's
Folkestone La Tavernetta
Gillingham Stock Hill House
Glastonbury No. 3 Restaurant & Hotel
Gloucester Hatton Court
Goring-on-Thames The Leatherne Bottel
Grasmere Michael's Nook
Grasmere White Moss House
Grasmere Wordsworth Hotel
Great Dunmow The Starr
Great Milton Le Manoir aux Quat'Saisons
Grimsthorpe Black Horse Inn
Grimston Congham Hall
Guist Tollbridge
Gulworthy Horn of Plenty
Handforth Belfry Hotel
Harrogate Old Swan Hotel
Haslemere Morel's
Hastings Röser's
Hayfield Bridge End Restaurant
Hersham The Dining Room
Hintlesham Hintlesham Hall
Hockley Heath Nuthurst Grange
Horndon on the Hill Hill House
Horton French Partridge
Hunstrete Hunstrete House
Huntingdon Old Bridge Hotel
Hurstbourne Tarrant Esseborne Manor
Ixworth Theobalds
Kendal Posh Nosh
Kington Penrhos Court
Kintbury Dundas Arms
Kinver Berkleys
Knutsford La Belle Epoque
Knutsford David's Place
Lacock At The Sign of The Angel
Langho Northcote Manor
Lavenham The Swan
Leamington Spa Mallory Court
Ledbury Hope End
Leeds La Grillade
Leeds Haley's Hotel
Lewdown Lewtrenchard Manor
Leeds Low Hall
Lincoln Harvey's Cathedral Restaurant
Linton Wood Hall
Liskeard Well House

Long Melford Chimneys
Longridge Heathcote's
Lower Beeding South Lodge
Lymington Gordleton Mill
Macclesfield Topo's
Maiden Newton Maiden Newton House
Malvern Cottage in the Wood
Malvern Croque-en-Bouche
Manchester Market Restaurant
Manchester That Café
Manchester Woodlands
Manchester Airport Etrop Grange
Manchester Airport Moss Nook
Mawnan Smith Nansidwell
Medmenham Danesfield House
Melbourn Pink Geranium
Melmerby Village Bakery
Moulsford-on-Thames Beetle & Wedge
Nantwich Rookery Hall
New Alresford Hunters
New Milton Chewton Glen
North Huish Brookdale House
Northleach Wickens
Norwich Adlard's
Norwich Brasted's
Norwich Marco's
Nottingham Sonny's
Oakham Hambleton Hall
Old Burghclere Dew Pond
Oxford Bath Place Hotel & Restaurant
Oxford Cherwell Boathouse
Oxford Restaurant Elizabeth
Padstow Seafood Restaurant
Pangbourne Copper Inn Restaurant
Paulerspury Vine House
Penkridge William Harding's House
Pitton Silver Plough
Plumtree Perkins Bar Bistro
Pool-in-Wharfedale Pool Court
Poole Mansion House
Porlock Oaks Hotel
Puckrup Puckrup Hall
Puddington Craxton Wood
Purton Pear Tree
Quorn Quorn Grange
Ramsbottom Village Restaurant
Richmond Petersham Hotel
Ridgeway Old Vicarage
Ripley Michel's
Roade Roadhouse
Romsey Old Manor House
Rotherwick Tylney Hall
Rowde George & Dragon
St Martin's St Martin's Hotel
St Mawes Idle Rocks Hotel
Salcombe Soar Mill Cove
Salcombe Spinnakers
Sandiway Nunsmere Hall
Seaview Seaview Hotel
Sevenoaks Royal Oak
Shanklin Old Village The Cottage
Shepton Mallet Blostin's Restaurant
Sissinghurst Rankins
Sourton Collaven Manor
South Godstone La Bonne Auberge
South Molton Whitechapel Manor
Southampton Browns Brasserie
Staddle Bridge McCoy's

Stamford The George of Stamford
Stapleford Stapleford Park
Stilton Bell Inn
Ston Easton Ston Easton Park
Stonham Mr Underhill's
Stonor Stonor Arms
Storrington Abingworth Hall
Storrington Little Thakeham
Storrington Manley's
Storrington Old Forge
Streatley-on-Thames Swan Diplomat
Stretton Ram Jam Inn
Stroud Oakes
Sutton Partners Brasserie
Sutton Coldfield New Hall
Taplow Cliveden & Waldo's Restaurant
Taunton Castle Hotel
Telford Madeley Court
Tetbury Calcot Manor
Tetbury The Close
Thornbury Thornbury Castle
Thundridge Hanbury Manor
Tiverton Lowman Restaurant
Torquay Table Restaurant
Tresco Island Hotel
Tunbridge Wells Cheevers
Tunbridge Wells Downstairs at
    Thackeray's
Tunbridge Wells Eglantine
Tunbridge Wells Spa Hotel
Tunbridge Wells Thackeray's House
Turners Hill Alexander House
Twickenham McClements
Uckfield Horsted Place
Ullswater Leeming House
Ullswater Old Church Hotel
Ullswater Rampsbeck Country House
    Hotel
Ullswater Sharrow Bay
Ulverston Bay Horse Inn & Bistro
Upper Slaughter Lords of the Manor
Uppingham The Lake Isle
Walkington Manor House
Warminster Bishopstrow House
Wath-in-Nidderdale Sportsman's Arms
Weston-under-Penyard Wharton Lodge
Weybourne Gasche's
Whimple Woodhayes Hotel
Wilmslow Stanneylands
Windermere Holbeck Ghyll
Windermere Roger's Restaurant
Windsor Oakley Court
Winteringham Winteringham Fields
Witherslack Old Vicarage
Wiveliscombe Langley House
Woburn Paris House
Woodstock Bear Hotel
Woodstock Feathers Hotel
Worcester Brown's
Worfield Old Vicarage
Wylam Laburnum House
Wymondham Number Twenty Four
Yattendon Royal Oak
Yeovil Little Barwick House
York Melton's
York Middlethorpe Hall

Scotland

Aberdeen Faraday's
Aberfeldy Farleyer House
Alexandria Cameron House
Alyth Drumnacree House
Arisaig Arisaig House
Auchterarder Auchterarder House
Auchterhouse Old Mansion House
Ayr The Stables
Ballater Tullich Lodge
Banchory Invery House
Banchory Raemoir House
Blairgowrie Kinloch House
Cairndow Loch Fyne Oyster Bar
Canonbie Riverside Inn
Crinan Crinan Hotel: Westward Room
Crinan Crinan Hotel
Cumbernauld Westerwood Hotel
Dalguise Kinnaird
Drumnadrochit Polmaily House
Dulnain Bridge Auchendean Lodge
Edinburgh L'Auberge
Edinburgh The Balmoral, Grill Room
Edinburgh Caledonian Hotel
Edinburgh Kelly's
Edinburgh Martin's
Edinburgh Pierre Victoire
Edinburgh Ristorante Raffaelli
Edinburgh Vintners Room, The Vaults
Eriska Isle of Eriska
Glasgow Buttery
Glasgow One Devonshire Gardens
Glasgow Ubiquitous Chip
Kilfinan Kilfinan Hotel
Kilmore Glenfeochan House
Kinclaven by Stanley Ballathie House
Kingussie The Cross
Kirknewton Dalmahoy Hotel
Linlithgow Champany Inn Chop & Ale
House
Linlithgow Champany Inn
Nairn Clifton Hotel
Newmill-on-Teviot Old Forge Restaurant
Newton Stewart Kirroughtree Hotel
Newtown St Boswells Le Provençale
Onich Allt-nan-Ros Hotel
Peat Inn Peat Inn
Portpatrick Knockinaam Lodge
Scone Murrayshall House
Tiroran Tiroran House
Turnberry Turnberry Hotel
Ullapool Altnaharrie Inn

Wales

Abergavenny Walnut Tree Inn
Abersoch Porth Tocyn Hotel
Chirk Starlings Castle
Coychurch Coed-y-Mwstwr Hotel
East Aberthaw Blue Anchor Inn
Harlech The Cemlyn
Llanberis Y Bistro
Llandrillo Tyddyn Llan
Llandudno Bodysgallen Hall
Llandudno St Tudno Hotel
Llangammarch Wells Lake Country
House Hotel

Llangefni Tre-Ysgawen Hall
Llanrwst Meadowsweet
Llansanffraid Glan Conwy Old Rectory
Llyswen Llangoed Hall
Northop Soughton Hall
Pwllheli Plas Bodegroes
Swansea Keenan's & Brayley's Bistro
Swansea Norton House
Swansea Number One
Talsarnau Maes-y-Neaudd

Channel Islands

Gorey Jersey Pottery
Rozel Bay Chateau la Chaire
Rozel Bay Granite Corner
St Anne Inchalla Hotel
St Brelade Sea Crest
St Lawrence Little Grove
St Peter Port Le Nautique
St Saviour Longueville Manor
Sark Aval Du Creux
Sark Stocks Hotel

Isle of Man

Ballasalla La Rosette
Ramsey Harbour Bistro

Republic of Ireland

Adare Adare Manor
Adare Mustard Seed
Athy Tonlegee House
Ballina Mount Falcon Castle
Cashel Chez Hans
Castledermot Doyle's School House
Country Inn
Cong Ashford Castle
Cork Clifford's
Cork Isaac's
Dingle Doyle's Seafood Bar & Townhouse
Dublin Al Fresco
Dublin Chapter One
Dublin Il Primo
Dublin 101 Talbot
Dunderry Dunderry Lodge Restaurant
Enniskerry Curtleston House
Gorey Marlfield House
Kenmare Park Hotel
Kenmare Sheen Falls Lodge
Killarney Cahernane Hotel
Killarney Gaby's Seafood Restaurant
Killorglin Nick's Restaurant
Kinsale Max's Wine Bar
Leighlinbridge The Lord Bagenal Inn
Maynooth Moyglare Manor
Moycullen Cloonabinnia House Hotel
Mullinger Crookedwood House
Newport Newport House
Oysterhaven The Oystercatcher
Riverstown Coopershill House
Skerries Red Bank Restaurant
Straffan Kildare Hotel
Swords Le Chateau
Thomastown Mount Juliet Hotel
Waterford Dwyer's Restaurant
Waterford Prendiville's Restaurant

Restaurants with Outstanding Wine Lists

England

Alderley Edge Alderley Edge Hotel
Aston Clinton Bell
Aylesbury Hartwell House
Bath Priory Hotel
Battle Netherfield Place
Birmingham Norton Place
Bray-on-Thames The Waterside Inn
Bristol Harvey's
Broxted Whitehall
Buckland Buckland Manor
Bury Normandie Hotel & Restaurant
Calstock Danescombe Valley Hotel
Chadlington The Manor
Chagford Gidleigh Park
Chedington Chedington Court
Cheltenham Redmond's
Chester Chester Grosvenor
Chester Crabwall Manor
Chilgrove White Horse Inn
Chinnor Sir Charles Napier Inn
Colerne Lucknam Park
Corse Lawn Corse Lawn House
Dartmouth Carved Angel
Dedham Fountain House & Dedham Hall
Dedham Le Talbooth
East Grinstead Gravetye Manor
Evershot Summer Lodge
Eversley New Mill Restaurant
Faversham Read's
Fressingfield Fox and Goose
Grasmere White Moss House
Great Dunmow The Starr
Great Milton Le Manoir aux Quat'Saisons
Harrogate Tannin Level
Hastings Roser's
Herstmonceux Sundial Restaurant
Hintlesham Hintlesham Hall
Hunstrete Hunstrete House
Huntingdon Old Bridge Hotel
Keyston Pheasant Inn
Kintbury Dundas Arms
Ledbury Hope End
Malvern Croque-en-Bouche
Nantwich Rookery Hall
New Milton Chewton Glen
North Huish Brookdale House
Norwich Adlard's
Oakham Hambleton Hall
Oxford Cherwell Boathouse
Oxford Restaurant Elizabeth
Pool-in-Wharfedale Pool Court
Ramsbottom Village Restaurant
Ridgeway Old Vicarage
Romsey Old Manor House
Ross-on-Wye Pheasants
Shinfield L'Ortolan
Southwold The Crown
Staddle Bridge McCoy's
Stamford The George of Stamford
Stapleford Stapleford Park
Ston Easton Ston Easton Park
Sutton Coldfield New Hall
Taplow Cliveden
Taunton Castle Hotel
Tetbury The Close
Thornbury Thornbury Castle
Ullswater Sharrow Bay
Uppingham The Lake Isle
Walkington Manor House
Waterhouses Old Beams
Wath-in-Nidderdale Sportsman's Arms
Wilmslow Stanneylands
Windsor Oakley Court
Winteringham Winteringham Fields
Worfield Old Vicarage

Scotland

Aberfoyle Braeval Old Mill
Anstruther Cellar
Auchterarder Auchterarder House
Banchory Invery House
Crinan Crinan Hotel & Westward Room
Dunblane Cromlix House
Edinburgh L'Auberge
Glasgow Ubiquitous Chip
Gullane Greywalls Hotel
Gullane La Potinière
Kingussie The Cross
Linlithgow Champany Inn
Newtonmore Ard-na-Coille
Oban Knipoch Hotel
Peat Inn Peat Inn
Port Appin Airds Hotel

Wales

Abergavenny Walnut Tree Inn
Llandudno Bodysgallen Hall
Llandudno St Tudno Hotel
Llanrwst Meadowsweet
Llyswen Llangoed Hall
Pwllheli Plas Bodegroes

Republic of Ireland

Bray Tree of Idleness
Cork Arbutus Lodge
Dublin Le Coq Hardi
Greystones The Hungry Monk
Howth King Sitric
Kenmare Park Hotel
Kenmare Sheen Falls Lodge

Restaurants with a good list of California wines

England

Alderley Edge Alderley Edge Hotel
Ambleside Rothay Manor
Ashford Eastwell Manor
Aylesbury Hartwell House
Barnsley Armstrong's
Basingstoke Audleys Wood
Bath Bath Spa Hotel
Bath Garlands
Bath Priory Hotel
Bath Royal Crescent Hotel
Birmingham Hyatt Regency
Birmingham Norton Place
Bradford Restaurant 19
Brampton Farlam Hall
Brighton Hospitality Inn
Bristol Harvey's
Bristol Markwick's
Bristol Swallow Royal Hotel
Broadway Lygon Arms
Brockenhurst Le Poussin
Bromsgrove Grafton Manor
Broughton Broughton Park
Broxted Whitehall
Buckland Buckland Manor
Burnham-on-Crouch Contented Sole
Cambridge Midsummer House
Campsea Ashe Old Rectory
Castle Combe Manor House
Chagford Gidleigh Park
Charingworth Charingworth Manor
Chedington Chedington Court
Cheltenham Le Champignon Sauvage
Cheltenham Epicurean
Cheltenham Greenway
Chester Chester Grosvenor
Chester Crabwall Manor
Chilgrove White Horse Inn
Chinnor Sir Charles Napier Inn
Chobham Quails Restaurant
Colerne Lucknam Park
Corse Lawn Corse Lawn House
Cowan Bridge Cobwebs
Dartmouth Carved Angel
Dedham Fountain House
Dedham Le Talbooth
Dorking Partners West Street
East Grinstead Gravetye Manor
Evershot Summer Lodge
Eversley New Mill Restaurant
Evesham Riverside Hotel
Faversham Read's
Freshford Homewood Park
Fressingfield Fox and Goose
Gloucester Hatton Court
Grasmere White Moss House
Great Milton Le Manoir aux Quat'Saisons
Great Yarmouth Seafood Restaurant
Gulworthy Horn of Plenty
Handforth Belfry Hotel

Harrogate Tannin Level
Harwich Pier at Harwich
Hastings Rösers
Helford Riverside
Herstmonceux Sundial Restaurant
Hintlesham Hintlesham Hall
Hockley Heath Nuthurst Grange
Horton French Partridge
Hull Ceruttis
Huntingdon Old Bridge Hotel
Huntsham Huntsham Court
Ixworth Theobalds
Keyston Pheasant Inn
Kintbury Dundas Arms
Leamington Spa Mallory Court
Linton Wood Hall
Longridge Heathcote's
Lower Beeding South Lodge
Lymington Gordleton Mill
Madingley Three Horseshoes
Maiden Newton Maiden Newton House
Malvern Cottage in the Wood
Malvern Croque-en-Bouche
Medmenham Danesfield House
Moulsford-on-Thames Beetle & Wedge
Nantwich Rookery Hall
New Milton Chewton Glen
North Huish Brookdale House
Northleach Wickens
Norwich Adlard's
Oakham Hambleton Hall
Old Burghclere Dewpond Restaurant
Oxford Bath Place Hotel & Restaurant
Oxford Cherwell Boathouse
Oxford 15 North Parade
Padstow Seafood Restaurant
Pool-in-Wharfedale Pool Court
Ramsbottom Village Restaurant
Romsey Old Manor House
Salcombe Soar Mill Cove
Sandiway Nunsmere Hall
Sevenoaks Royal Oak
Solihull Liaison
South Molton Whitechapel Manor
Southwold The Crown
Spark Bridge Bridgefield House
Staddle Bridge McCoy's
Stamford The George of Stamford
Stapleford Stapleford Park
Ston Easton Ston Easton Park
Stonham Mr Underhill's
Stonor Stonor Arms
Stow-on-the-Wold Wyck Hill House
Stratford-upon-Avon Billesley Manor
Streatley-on-Thames Swan Diplomat
Sutton Coldfield New Hall
Taplow Cliveden
Taunton Castle Hotel
Teffont Evias Howard's House
Tetbury The Close
Thundridge Hanbury Manor
Tunbridge Wells Thackeray's House

Twickenham McClements
Uckfield Horsted Place
Ullswater Leeming House
Ullswater Rampsbeck Country House
 Hotel
Ullswater Sharrow Bay
Upper Slaughter Lords of the Manor
Uppingham The Lake Isle
Walkington Manor House
Waterhouses Old Beams
Wilmslow Stanneylands
Windermere Miller Howe
Windermere Roger's Restaurant
Windsor Oakley Court
Winteringham Winteringham Fields
Witherslack Old Vicarage
Woburn Paris House
Worfield Old Vicarage
York Middlethorpe Hall

Scotland

Aberfoyle Braeval Old Mill
Achiltibuie Summer Isles
Alloa Gean House
Anstruther Cellar
Auchterarder Auchterarder House
Auchterhouse Old Mansion House
Banchory Invery House
Banchory Raemoir House
Blairgowrie Kinloch House
Colbost Three Chimneys Restaurant
Cumbernauld Westerwood Hotel
Dalguise Kinnaird
Drumnadrochit Polmaily House
Dunblane Cromlix House
Edinburgh Martin's
Edinburgh Vintners Room, The Vaults
Fort William Inverlochy Castle
Glasgow One Devonshire Gardens
Glasgow Ubiquitous Chip
Gullane Greywalls Hotel
Gullane La Potiniere
Inverness Dunain Park
Kentallen of Appin Ardsheal House
Kilchrenan Ardanaiseig

Kingussie The Cross
Linlithgow Champanay Inn
Nairn Clifton Hotel
Newtonmore Ard-na-Coille
Peat Inn Peat Inn
Port Appin Airds Hotel
Quothquan Shieldhill
Scone Murrayshall House
Ullapool Altnaharrie Inn

Wales

Abergavenny Walnut Tree Inn
Llandudno Bodysgallen Hall
Llandudno St Tudno Hotel
Llanrwst Meadowsweet
Llyswen Llangoed Hall
Northop Soughton Hall
Pwllheli Plas Bodegroes

Northern Ireland

Belfast Roscoff
Holywood Culloden Hotel
Portrush Ramore

Republic of Ireland

Adare Adare Manor
Ballyvaughan Gregans Castle
Cong Ashford Castle
Cork Arbutus Lodge
Cork Lovetts
Dublin Le Coq Hardi
Dublin Patrick Guilbaud
Greystones The Hungry Monk
Kenmare Park Hotel
Kenmare Sheen Falls Lodge
Killarney Cahernane Hotel
Killorglin Nick's Restaurant
Newmarket-on-Fergus Dromoland
 Castle
Rathnew Tinakilly House
Waterford Waterford Castle

Restaurants offering a good range of wines by the glass

England

Ambleside Wateredge Hotel
Barnstaple Lynwood House
Bath Bath Spa Hotel
Bath Royal Crescent Hotel
Brighton Hospitality Inn
Brockenhurst Le Poussin
Burnham-on-Crouch Contented Sole
Cambridge Midsummer House
Chagford Gidleigh Park
Cheltenham Le Champignon Sauvage
Cheltenham Epicurean

Chester Crabwall Manor
Chilgrove White Horse Inn
Chobham Quails Restaurant
Clitheroe Browns Bistro
Colerne Lucknam Park
Corse Lawn Corse Lawn House
Cowan Bridge Cobwebs
Darlington Victor's Restaurant
Dartmouth Carved Angel
Dedham Le Talbooth
Dorking Partners West Street
Eastbourne Grand Hotel
Easton Clarke's
Eversley New Mill Restaurant

Fressingfield Fox & Goose
Grimston Congham Hall
Harrogate Tannin Level
Hintlesham Hintlesham Hall
Horndon on the Hill Hill House
Keyston Pheasant Inn
Lavenham Great House
Leeds Haley's
Longridge Heathcote's
Lower Beeding South Lodge
Lymington Gordleton Mill
Madingley Three Horseshoes
Morston Morston Hall
New Alresford Hunters
Northleach Wickens
Ramsbottom Village Restaurant
Ross-on-Wye Pheasants
Rowde George & Dragon
Sevenoaks Royal Oak
Southwold The Crown
Spark Bridge Bridgefield House
Stroud Oakes
Sutton Coldfield New Hall
Taunton Castle Hotel
Teffont Evias Howard's House
Tetbury The Close
Thundridge Hanbury Manor
Ullswater Leeming House
Ullswater Old Church Hotel
Ullswater Rampsbeck Country House
   Hotel
Ulverston Bay Horse Inn & Bistro
Warminster Bishopstrow House
Waterhouses Old Beams
Williton White House
Wilmslow Stanneylands
Winchester Wykeham Arms
Windermere Miller Howe
Windsor Oakley Court
Winteringham Winteringham Fields
Witherslack Old Vicarage
Woodstock Feathers
Worfield Old Vicarage

Scotland

Anstruther Cellar
Ayr The Stables
Banchory Invery House
Canonbie Riverside Inn
Cupar Ostlers Close
Edinburgh Vintners Room, The Vaults
Kingussie The Cross
Nairn Clifton Hotel
Newtonmore Ard-na-Coille Hotel

Wales

Llandudno St Tudno Hotel
Mumbles PA's Winebar

Channel Islands

St Lawrence Little Grove

Northern Ireland

Annalong Glassdrumman House
Belfast Roscoff

Republic of Ireland

Ballyvaughan Gregans Castle
Enniskerry Enniscree Lodge Inn
Newmarket-on-Fergus Dromoland
   Castle
Oughterard Currarevagh House
Roundwood Roundwood Inn

Hotel Groups
and Hotels with Conference
and Banqueting Facilities

Overleaf is a listing of major hotel groups each of which has to a
lesser or greater extent a definable corporate identity. We have
included budget hotel chains (some coming under the banner of the
major groups) which, while not given our normal percentage grading in
the main gazetteer section of the Guide, nevertheless offer the
businessman or overnight traveller a convenient stop-over.
A brief description of the main characteristics of each group is given
as well as head office addresses, and phone and fax numbers for
general enquiries and central reservations.
In the subsequent tables we list those hotels (in groups or privately
owned) which offer conference and banqueting facilities. The numbers
quoted are for the maximum number of delegates for a theatre-style
conference or diners at a banquet in one room. Leisure centres are
listed if they are part of the hotel and feature at least
an indoor heated swimming pool, sauna, solarium, whirlpool bath
and keep-fit equipment.
These conference and banqueting facilities have not been researched
by our inspectors.

Campanile Hotels

Head Office:
Unit 8 Red Lion Court
Alexandra Road
Hounslow
Middlesex TW3 1JS
Tel 081-569 5757

Central Reservations (from UK):
Tel 010 33 1 64 62 46 46
Fax 010 33 1 64 62 46 61
Weekdays 8am-7pm, Saturdays 9am-12pm
French time.

A relatively new chain of modern,
purpose-built, functional hotels. All are
open 365 days. Liverpool has 24hr
reception and an earlier (6.30am) start to
breakfast.
    All bedrooms are either twin or double,
have remote-control colour TV, fully
fitted bathrooms, radio-alarms. Each hotel
has rooms designed for the disabled. A
standard tariff of £35.75 per room applies
though there is a third person supplement
of £7.50. Each has conference facilities for
30.

Copthorne Hotels

Head Office:
Victoria House
Horley
Surrey RH6 7AF
Tel 0293 772288
Fax 0293 772345

Reservations: Freephone 0800 41 47 41

Standard rooms (Classics) offer good-sized
bedrooms each with a double bed, colour
TV with movie and/or satellite channel,
en-suite bath and shower as well as the
other usual facilities that are expected of a
modern hotel. Executive rooms
(Connoisseur) have larger more
comfortable bedrooms and, usually, a
better outlook. Extras include fresh fruit
and magazines and bathrooms have
bathrobes and better quality toiletries.

De Vere Hotels

Head Office:
De Vere House
Chester Road
Daresbury
Warrington
Cheshire WA4 4BN

Central Enquiries and Conference Desk
North:
Tel 0925 265050
Fax 0925 601264
Conference Desk South:
Tel 0753 64505

On the whole, these are quite distinctive
hotels, some grand, others not so, each
with its own style and character based on
comfort and tradition. Standards of service
are generally high. Leisure clubs are free
to guests.

Edwardian Hotels

Head Office:
140 Bath Road
Hayes, Middlesex UB3 5AW

Central Reservations:
Tel 081-564 8888
Fax 081-759 8422
Conference Line: 081-564 7474
Groups Line: 081-564 7464

A London-based group of hotels ranging
from the Hampshire in Leicester Square
and the Edwardian International at
London Heathrow to the more modest
but still comfortable Kenilworth and
Grafton Hotels.

Forte Hotels

Head Office:
Forte UK Ltd
St Martin's House
20 Queensmere
Slough, Berkshire SL1 1YY
Tel 0753 573266
Fax 0753 577227
Administration 0753 573266

Sales Office:
Forte House
80 Gatehouse Road
Aylesbury
Buckinghamshire HP19 3EB
Tel 0296 393939
Fax 0296 395419
Reservations (local call cost): 0345 40 40 40

Trusthouse Forte has been rebranded and
this vast network of hotels offers six
categories of hotels ranging from the
Exclusive brand to the budget
Travelodges. We feel that the brands Forte
Crest and Forte Posthouse are the two
primarily aimed at the businessman as
theseoffer the best deals in terms of value.
    However, we also list the other hotels
in the group as these often have good

conference facilities, though the package can be more expensive. Heritage hotels are mid-priced and of mixed appeal; they are generally situated in small towns and more rural locations and are suitable for smaller meetings.

Forte Exclusive, Grand & Heritage

Reservations: (local call cost) 0345 40 40 40

Forte Crest

Reservations: (local call cost) 0345 40 40 40

Incorporating some of the best former Posthouses and most of the original Crests, this is a chain of modern business-orientated hotels. Over half have fully equipped business centres. All offer 24hr room service for both executive and standard rooms.

Forte Posthouse

Reservations: Freephone 0800 40 40 40

A leading UK chain of mostly purpose-built modern hotels. Many have health and fitness centres. Rooms have lost the starkness of the early 80s but currently the chief attribute of this chain is the room rate - from Sunday to Thursday the daily 'room only' rate is £53.50, dropping to £39.50 for Friday and Saturday. The midweek room price including cooked breakfast for two people is £67.40.

Forte Travelodge

Reservations: Freephone 0800 850 950

Roadside budget accommodation offering simple but modern rooms in locations conveniently sited along major routes. Room rates, payable in advance, are currently £31.95 per room. All have en-suite bathrooms with shower, colour television, radio/alarms and tea and coffee-making facilities. Rooms sleep three adults, a child under 12 and a baby in a cot. Every Travelodge has a room equipped for the disabled. The lodges have either 27 or 56 bedrooms.

Granada Lodges

Head Office:
Toddington Service Area
MI Service Area Southbound
Toddington
Near Dunstable
Bedfordshire LU5 6HR
Tel 0525 873881
Fax 0525 875358

Central Reservations: Freephone 0800 555 300

A chain of budget hotels located close to major routes. All rooms have private bath and shower, colour TV, radio/alarm and tea and coffee making facilities. In-room continental breakfast is available, otherwise there's a 10% discount on meals taken in the adjacent service area restaurant. Family rooms are available and 2 children under 16 sharing with 2 adults are accommodated free (excluding breakfast). Every lodge has rooms for the disabled.

   Prices are from £34.95 for single, twin and double or family rooms with the exception of Heston (London Heathrow) and Thurrock (Dartford Crossing) which are £43.95. Payment is on arrival.

Hilton Hotels

Head Office:
Hilton International Hotels (UK) Ltd
Chancel House
Neasden Lane
London NW10 2XE

Hilton UK Reservations
PO Box 137
Watford, Herts WD1 1DN
Tel 0923 238877
Fax 0923 249271
Conference Reservations Tel 0923 50222

Hilton International hotels have Executive rooms which are to a higher specification than the Plaza rooms at Hilton National hotels. They include large teletext TVs, a welcome tray with miniature spirits, chocolates, bathrobes, additional toiletries and lounge seating.

   Apart from all but one of the London hotels (the London Hilton on Park Lane), the majority of Hilton hotels have leisure centres that include swimming pools, fitness rooms and saunas.

Holiday Inns

European Head Office:
Woluwe Office Park 1
Rue Neerveld 101
1200 Brussels
Belgium
Tel (02) 773 5511
Fax (02) 772 0772

International Reservations: (moving mid-1993)
10-12 New Lower Parade
Finchley Road, London NW3 5EP
Tel 071-722 7755
Fax 071-722 5483

After starting off in the 70s and early 80s as a leader in the field of luxury business hotels, Holiday Inns haven't kept up the momentum and so some of the newer hotel groups have now caught up and even overtaken them. Under Bass plc the original concept has been expanded to include Holiday Inn Garden Courts, an economy version. Large beds and good bathrooms are a feature as well as the free accommodation of children (including teenagers) when sharing with parents. All have good leisure facilities and well-equipped conference rooms.

Jarvis Hotels

Head Office:
Wye House
London Road
High Wycombe
Buckinghamshire HP11 1LH
Tel 0494 473800
Fax 0494 471666

Linkline Reservations: (local call cost) Tel
0345 581 237
Fax 071-589 8193
Conference Reservations: Tel 071-581 3466
Fax 071-589 8193

A nationwide network of 38 dependable middle-range hotels. A few have leisure clubs (free to guests) and 24 have purpose-built Summit meeting rooms. Trouser presses and hair dryers are standard to all rooms, Executive bedrooms having a better standard of decor and additional amenities such as fruit and chocolates plus extra toiletries in the bathrooms.

Mount Charlotte Thistle Hotels

Head Office:
Mount Charlotte Investments plc
2 The Calls, Leeds
West Yorkshire LS2 7JU
Tel 0532 439111
Fax 0532 445555

National Sales:
Tel 071-937 6423
Central Reservations:
London Tel 071-937 8033
Highlife Shortbreaks
Freephone 0800 700 400
London Conference Sales:
Tel 071-938 1755

Next to the Forte Hotels group, Mount Charlotte Thistle hotels are the most widespread throughout the country with hotels from Plymouth to Wick, and including twenty in London. Overall, the quality of bedroom accommodation is good and many of the hotels appear in the main gazetteer. Most hotels have a main meeting room with capacity for at least 100 delegates. Selected hotels have boardrooms that seat between 10 to 15 people for small meetings and senior management gatherings. The majority of hotels offer Executive bedrooms: these are larger rooms, more recently decorated and each having a number of useful extras. Lady guests have specially designated rooms.

Novotel

Head Office:
Novotel UK
1 Shortlands
Hammersmith
London W6 8DR
Tel 081-748 4580
Fax 081-741 0672

Resinter Reservations: 071-724 1000

A multinational hotel chain with properties located on the outskirts of cities and close to motorway junctions. Rooms, if somewhat plainly decorated, are large and functional. The standard is identical in all and is designed for practical comfort and rest. Each has a bed/settee as well as a double bed. There is ample writing space among the usual modern facilities offered. Accommodation and breakfast are free for two children under 16 sharing their parents' room. Food and efficient room service are available at any time from 6am to midnight and the bar follows the same hours.

Principal Hotels

Head Office:
8th floor
Principal House
11 Ripon Road
Harrogate
North Yorkshire HG1 2JA
Tel 0423 530797
Fax 0423 500086

A group of 19 hotels, most located in town or city centres, that are characterised by an attractive, traditional style and decor. Standard rooms are well equipped, with all the usual amenities. Executive rooms have bathrobes and a trouser press.

Queens Moat Houses

Head Office:
Queens Court
9 Eastern Road
Romford
Essex RM1 3NG
Tel 0708 730522
Fax 0708 762691

Reservations:
Tel 0708 766677
Fax 0708 761033
Freephone (UK only): 0800 289 330

Currently, with properties as diverse as the Royal Crescent in Bath, Eastwell Manor in Ashford, the Rose and Crown in Salisbury and the Newmarket Moat House there is no longer a characteristic pattern to the 102 UK hotels currently in the Queens Moat Houses directory. It was only a relatively short time ago that the group name was synonymous with pleasant enough but, on the whole, rather lacklustre hotels offering acceptable standards of accommodation. With its newest acquisitions Queens Moat Houses has moved firmly into the luxury hotel league as well.

Resort Hotels

Head Office:
Resort House
Edward Street
Brighton
East Sussex BN2 2HW
Tel 0273 676717

Central Reservations (local call charge):
Tel 0345 313 213

Currently based in the South of England

there are now 42 hotels in this group. They vary from a 12th-century coaching inn near Maidenhead to modern purpose-built hotels, some with leisure clubs. These clubs are free to overnight guests.

Stakis Hotels

Head Office:
3 Atlantic Quay
York Street, Glasgow
Tel 041-221 0000
Fax 041-304 1111

Hotel Reservations: Freephone 0800 262 626
Conference Call: Freephone 0800 833 900

Located close to major business centres and trunk routes as well as in country settings; hotels offer spacious, comfortable accommodation and a self-contained business centre. Guests have free use of the sports and leisure facilities. Originally based in Scotland but now with over 30 hotels scattered throughout the UK.

Swallow Hotels

Head Office:
Swallow House
Seaburn Terrace
Sunderland SR1 3AN
Tel 091-529 4595
Fax 091-529 4829

Central Reservations:
Tel 091-529 4666
Fax 091-529 5062

Based in the North East but with new hotels and acquisitions in the south this is a chain of hotels that is striving hard to improve its image. Hotels of the standing of the Birmingham Swallow are to be much admired (although it is still the only hotel in the group with a restaurant that we recommend). 28 of the 34 current hotels have leisure clubs; most include an indoor heated swimming pool, sauna and/or steam room, solarium and spa bath. Mini-gyms also feature in many. The facilities are free to overnight guests.

Children of 14 years and under sharing a room with two adults are accommodated and served a cooked breakfast free of charge.

Whitbread Plc

Head Office:
Whitbread House
Luton
Bedfordshire LU1 3BG
Tel 0582 424200
Fax 0582 400024

Country Club Hotels

Reservations:
Tel 0582 396969
Fax 0582 400024

A feature of the hotels currently in this
group is that all but two have at least one
18-hole golf course. Additionally, all
feature a comprehensive range of leisure
and sports facilities including swimming
pools, saunas, solarium, tennis and squash
courts and fitness studios.

Lansbury Hotels

Reservations:
Tel 0582 400158
Fax 0582 400024

A chain of 43 small hotels with a
maximum of about 60 bedrooms. The
character is fairly formal and traditional.
All differ in style ranging from a mock-
Georgian folly to up-to-date, purpose-built
hotels.

Travel Inns

Reservations:
Tel 0582 482224
Fax 0582 405680

The 31 Travel Inns are all located next to
separate popular themed eating chains all
rooms have bath and shower, always a
double bed with duvet, remote control
TV, tea and coffee making facilities,
radio/alarm and adequate writing/work
space.

They currently operate a price of
£32.50 per room irrespective of whether
taken as a single, double or for family
occupancy. Two children under 16 are
accommodated free when sharing with
adults. Payment is on arrival and reception
closes at 11pm. Every Travel Inn has a
specially adapted room for the disabled.
At some, adjacent meeting rooms are
available.

HOTELS WITH CONFERENCE & BANQUETING FACILITIES

ENGLAND

Key: QMH (Queens Moat Houses), MtCT (Mount Charlotte Thistle).

Avon

Location	Hotel	Tel	Fax	Group	Rooms	Conf	Banq	Leisure Centre
Alveston	Alveston House	0454 415050	0454 415425		30	100	100	
Alveston	Forte Posthouse	0454 412521	0454 413920	Forte	74	100	120	
Bath	Bath Hotel	0225 338855	0225 28941		93	60	60	
Bath	Bath Spa Hotel	0225 444424	0225 444006	Forte	100	120	120	yes
Bath	Combe Grove Manor	0225 834644	0225 834961		41	40		yes
Bath	Francis Hotel	0225 324257	0225 319715	Forte	94	80	60	
Bath	Hilton National	0225 463411	0225 464393	Hilton	150	240	240	yes
Bath	Lansdown Grove	0225 315891	0225 448092		45	100	80	
Bath	Priory Hotel	0225 331922	0225 448276	Select	21	18		
Bath	Queensberry Hotel	0225 447928	0225 446065		22	18		
Bath	Royal Crescent Hotel	0225 319090	0225 339401	QMH	42	60	80	
Bristol	Aztec Hotel	0454 301090	0454 201593	Shire Inns	88	200	250	yes
Bristol	Berkeley Square Hotel	0272 254000	0272 252970		43	12		
Bristol	Bristol Marriott Hotel	0272 294281	0272 225838	Marriott	284	170	170	
Bristol	Forte Crest	0272 564242	0272 569735	Forte	197	500	425	yes
Bristol	Grand Hotel	0272 291645	0272 227619	MtCT	178	500	500	
Bristol	Hilton Hotel	0272 260041	0272 230089	Hilton	201	400	400	yes
Bristol	Moat House	0272 255010	0272 255040	QMH	132	200	170	
Bristol	Redwood Lodge	0275 393901	0275 392104	Country Club	112	175	100	yes
Bristol	Stakis Bristol Hotel	0454 201144	0454 612022	Stakis	111	80	100	yes
Bristol	Swallow Royal Hotel	0272 255100	0272 251515	Swallow	242	250	250	yes

Location	Hotel	Tel	Fax	Group	Rooms	Conf	Banq	Leisure Centre
Bristol	Unicorn Hotel	0272 230333	0272 230300	Rank	245	36		
Chelwood	Chelwood House	0761 490730	0761 490730		8	8		
Dunkirk	Petty France Hotel	045 423 361	045 423 768		20	16		
Freshford	Homewood Park	0225 723731	0225 723820		15	12	70	
Hinton	Hinton Grange	0275 822916	0275 823285		17	25		
Hunstrete	Hunstrete House	0761 490578	0761 490732	Clipper	24	70	50	
Ston Easton	Ston Easton Park	0761 241631	0761 241377		21	24		
Weston-super-Mare	Grand Atlantic	0934 626543	0934 415048	Forte	76	250	250	
Winterbourne	Grange Resort Hotel	0454 777333	0454 777447	Resort	52	150	150	

Bedfordshire

Location	Hotel	Tel	Fax	Group	Rooms	Conf	Banq	Leisure Centre
Aspley Guise	Moore Place	0908 282000	0908 281888		54	60	40	
Bedford	Moat House	0234 355131	0234 340447	QMH	100	320	390	
Bedford	Woodlands Manor	0234 363281	0234 272390		25	50	85	
Dunstable	Old Palace Lodge	0582 662201	0582 696422		49	30	50	
Flitwick	Flitwick Manor	0525 712242	0525 712242		15	50	65	
Leighton Buzzard	The Swan	0525 372148	0525 370444	Resort	38	50	30	
Luton	Forte Posthouse	0582 575955	0582 490065	Forte	117	80		
Luton	Forte Crest	0582 575911	0582 581859	Forte	93	250	220	
Luton	Hotel Ibis	0582 424488	0582 455511		98	200	60	
Luton	Leaside Hotel	0582 417643	0582 419676		13	15		
Luton	Strathmore Thistle	0582 34199	0582 402528	MtCT	150	300	250	
Woburn	Bedford Arms	0525 290441	0525 290432	MtCT	55	90	60	
Woburn	Bell Inn	0525 290280	0525 290017		27	35		

Berkshire

Location	Hotel	Tel	Fax	Group	Rooms	Conf	Banq	Leisure Centre
Ascot	Berystede Hotel	0344 23311	0344 872301	Forte	91	120	120	
Ascot	Royal Berkshire	0344 23322	0344 874240	Hilton	81	75	70	yes

Location	Hotel	Chain						
Bracknell	Hilton National	Hilton	0344 424801	0344 487454	167	300	220	
Elcot	Elcot Park Resort Hotel	Resort	0488 58100	0488 58288	75	200	192	yes
Hungerford	Bear Hotel	Resort	0488 682512	0488 684357	41	80	60	
Hurley	Ye Olde Bell	Resort	0628 825881	0628 825939	36	150	120	
Maidenhead	Fredrick's		0628 35934	0628 771054	38	70	140	
Maidenhead	Holiday Inn	Holiday Inns	0628 23444	0628 770035	189	400	350	
Newbury	Chequers Hotel	Forte	0635 38000	0635 37170	56	65	120	
Newbury	Foley Lodge		0635 528770	0635 528398	69	250	220	
Newbury	Hilton National	Hilton	0635 529000	0635 529337	104	200	180	yes
Newbury	Millwaters		0635 528838	0635 523406	32	25	90	
Newbury	Regency Park Hotel		0635 871555	0635 871571	50	65	60	
Newbury	Stakis Newbury Hotel	Stakis	0635 247010	0635 247077	112	60	40	yes
Reading	Caversham Hotel	QMH	0734 391818	0734 391665	114	180	180	
Reading	Forte Posthouse	Forte	0734 875485	0734 311958	138	100	100	yes
Reading	Ramada Hotel		0734 586222	0734 597842	196	220	160	yes
Sindlesham	Reading Moat House	QMH	0734 351035	0734 666530	96	80	80	
Slough	Copthorne Hotel	Copthorne	0753 516222	0753 516237	219	200	200	yes
Slough	Heathrow/Slough Marriott	Marriott	0753 544244	0753 540272	352	300	350	yes
Streatley-on-Thames	Swan Diplomat		0491 873737	0491 872554	45	130	100	
Windsor	Oakley Court	QMH	0628 74141	0628 37011	92	160	200	
Wokingham	Stakis St Anne's Manor	Stakis	0734 772550	0734 772526	130	250	300	

Buckinghamshire

Location	Hotel	Chain						
Aston Clinton	Bell Inn	Forte	0296 630252	0296 631250	21	250	300	
Aylesbury	Forte Crest		0296 393388	0296 392211	94	100	80	
Aylesbury	Hartwell House	Historic House	0296 747444	0296 747450	48	100	66	
Beaconsfield	Bellhouse Hotel	De Vere	0753 887211	0753 888231	136	400	400	yes
Burnham	Burnham Beeches Moat House	QMH	0628 603333	0628 603994	75	180	150	
Burnham	Grovefield Hotel		0628 603131	0628 668078	38	50	120	
Chenies	Bedford Arms Thistle	MtCT	0923 283301	0923 284825	10	30	65	
Gerrards Cross	Bull Hotel	De Vere	0753 885995	0753 847747	95	220	144	
High Wycombe	Forte Posthouse	Forte	0494 442100	0494 474031	106	100	90	

Location	Hotel	Tel	Fax	Group	Rooms	Conf	Banq	Leisure Centre
Marlow	Compleat Angler Hotel	0628 484444	0628 486388	Forte	64	120	120	
Medmenham	Danesfield House	0628 891010	0628 890408		93	100	100	
Milton Keynes	Forte Crest	0908 667722	0908 674714	Forte	163	150	110	yes
Stoke Mandeville	Belmore Hotel	0296 612022	0296 612174		13	30		
Taplow	Cliveden	0628 668561	0628 661837		31	36	30	yes

Cambridgeshire

Location	Hotel	Tel	Fax	Group	Rooms	Conf	Banq	Leisure Centre
Cambridge	Arundel House	0223 67701	0223 67721		88	35	100	
Cambridge	Cambridgeshire Moat House	0954 780555	0954 780010	QMT	100	180	300	
Cambridge	Cambridge Lodge	0223 352833	0223 355166		11	16		
Cambridge	Forte Posthouse	0223 237000	0223 233426	Forte	118	60	60	yes
Cambridge	Garden House	0223 63421	0223 316605	QMT	118	200	250	
Cambridge	Gonville Hotel	0223 66611	0223 315470		62	200	130	
Cambridge	Holiday Inn	0223 464466	0223 464440	Holiday Inns	199	150	150	
Cambridge	University Arms	0223 351241		De Vere	117	300	300	
Duxford	Duxford Lodge	0223 836444	0223 832271		15	36	36	
Ely	Lamb Hotel	0353 663574	0353 666350	QMT	32	60	60	
Huntingdon	Old Bridge Hotel	0480 52681	0480 411017	Poste Hotels	26	50	100	
Peterborough	Butterfly Hotel	0733 64240	0733 65538		70	80	60	
Peterborough	Forte Posthouse	0733 240209	0733 244455	Forte	93	45	40	
Peterborough	Moat House	0733 260000	0733 262737	QMT	129	400	360	yes
Peterborough	Swallow Hotel	0733 371111	0733 236725	Swallow	163	200	250	yes
Six Mile Bottom	Swynford Paddocks	063 870 234	063 870 283		15	30	20	
St Ives	Slepe Hall	0480 63122	0480 300706		16	220	220	
Stilton	Bell Inn	0733 241066	0733 245173		19	100	100	
Wansford-in-England	Haycock Hotel	0780 782223	0780 783031	Poste Hotels	51	150	200	

Cheshire

Town	Hotel							
Alderley Edge	Alderley Edge Hotel	0625 583033	0625 586343		32	150	100	
Alsager	Manor House	0270 884000	0270 882483	Compass	57	250	150	
Bramhall	Moat House	061-439 8116	061-440 8071	QMH	65	140	150	
Bucklow Hill	The Swan	0565 830295	0565 830614	De Vere	70	40	70	
Bunbury	Wild Boar	0829 260309	0829 261081		37	65	75	
Chester	Abbots Well	0244 332121	0244 335287	Jarvis	127	230	180	yes
Chester	Blossoms Hotel	0244 323186	0244 46433	Forte	64	100	50	
Chester	Chester Resort Hotel	0244 851551	0244 851089	Resort	113	230	200	
Chester	Chester International	0244 322330	0244 316118	QMH	152	420	400	
Chester	Chester Grosvenor	0244 324024	0244 313246		78	250	220	
Chester	Crabwall Manor	0244 851666	0244 851400		48	100	100	
Chester	Forte Posthouse	0244 680111	0244 674100	Forte	107	115	80	yes
Chester	Mollington Banastre	0244 851471	0244 851165	Ambassador	66	250	250	yes
Chester	Rowton Hall	0244 335262	0244 335464		42	200	160	yes
Handforth	Belfry Hotel	061-437 0511	061-499 0597	77	81	120	180	yes
Knutsford	Cottons Hotel	0565 650333	0565 755351	Shire Inns	86	200	200	
Mottram St Andrew	Mottram Hall	0625 828135	0625 829284	De Vere	133	200	200	
Nantwich	Rookery Hall	0270 610016	0270 626027	Select	45	80	80	
Northwich	Hartford Hall	0606 75711	0606 782285		20	30		
Prestbury	Bridge Hotel	0625 829326	0625 827557		23	100	100	
Puddington	Craxton Wood	051-339 4717	051-339 1740		14	20	20	
Runcorn	Forte Crest	0928 714000	0928 714611	Forte	134	500	450	
Sandbach	Chimney House	0270 764141	0270 768916	Lansbury	48	90	90	
Sandiway	Nunsmere Hall	0606 889100	0606 889055		32	48	60	
Warrington	Lord Daresbury Hotel	0925 267331	0925 265615	De Vere	141	400	350	yes
Wilmslow	Moat House	0625 529201	0625 531876	QMH	125	350	300	yes
Wilmslow	Stanneylands	0625 525225	0625 537282		33	80	100	

Cleveland

Town	Hotel							
Crathorne	Crathorne Hall	0642 700398	0642 700814		37	160	120	
Hartlepool	Grand Hotel	0429 266345	0429 265217		41	200	160	

Location	Hotel	Tel	Fax	Group	Rooms	Conf	Banq	Leisure Centre
Middlesbrough	Hotel Baltimore	0642 224111	0642 226156	MtCT	31	60	90	
Middlesbrough	Hospitality Inn	0642 232000	0642 232655		180	400	400	
Stockton-on-Tees	Swallow Hotel	0642 679721	0642 601714	Swallow	124	300	250	
Thornaby-on-Tees	Forte Posthouse	0642 591213	0642 594989	Forte	135	120	80	

Cornwall

Location	Hotel	Tel	Fax	Group	Rooms	Conf	Banq	Leisure Centre
Carlyon Bay	Carlyon Bay Hotel	0726 812304	0726 814938		73	200	250	
Carlyon Bay	Porth Avallen Hotel	0726 812802	0726 817097		24	40	100	
Falmouth	Falmouth Hotel	0326 312671	0326 319533		72	200	190	yes
Falmouth	Greenbank Hotel	0326 312440	0326 211362		61	80	120	
Falmouth	St Michael's Hotel	0326 312707	0326 211772		73	150	200	
Golant	Cormorant Hotel	0726 833426	same		11	36	36	
Helland Bridge	Tredethy Country Hotel	020 884 262	020 884 707		11	40	40	
Land's End	State House	0736 871844	0736 871812		34	240	200	
Looe	Talland Bay Hotel	0503 72667	0503 72940		23	30		
Mawnan Smith	Budock Vean Hotel	0326 250288	0326 250892		58	30		
Newlyn	Higher Faugan Country House	0736 62076	0736 51648		12	20	30	
Newquay	Hotel Bristol	0637 875181	0637 879347		76	180	265	
Newquay	Hotel Riviera	0637 874251	0637 850823		50	150	180	
St Ives	Garrack Hotel	0736 796199	0736 798955		18	20	40	
Truro	Alverton Manor	0872 76633	0872 222989		25	200	150	
Veryan	Nare Hotel	0872 501279	0872 501856		39	80	100	

Cumbria

Location	Hotel	Tel	Fax	Group	Rooms	Conf	Banq	Leisure Centre
Alston	Lovelady Shield	0434 381203	0434 381515		12	12	50	

Location	Hotel	Tel 1	Tel 2	Group				
Ambleside	Nanny Brow	053 94 32036	053 94 32450		19	36	40	
Ambleside	Rothay Manor	053 94 33605	053 94 33607		18	20	85	
Appleby-in-Westmorland	Tufton Arms	076 83 51593	076 83 52761		19	50	40	
Appleby-in-Westmorland	Appleby Manor	076 83 51571	076 83 52888		30		60	
Applethwaite	Underscar Manor	076 87 75000	076 87 74904		11	16	120	
Bassenthwaite	Armathwaite Hall	076 87 76551	076 87 76220		42	120		yes
Borrowdale	Borrowdale Hotel	076 87 77224	076 87 77338		34	30	70	
Borrowdale	Stakis Lodore Swiss Hotel	076 87 77285	076 87 77343	Stakis	70	80	225	yes
Bowness-on-Windermere	Old England Hotel	053 94 42444	053 94 43432	Forte	79	120	120	
Bowness-on-Windermere	Belsfield Hotel	053 94 42448	053 94 46397	Forte	66	130	22	yes
Bowness-on-Windermere	Linthwaite House	053 94 88600	053 94 88601		18	40		
Carlisle	Swallow Hilltop	0228 29255	0228 25238	Swallow	92	500	500	yes
Cartmel	Aynsome Manor	053 95 36653	053 95 36016		13	12	75	
Coniston	Sun Hotel	053 94 41248			11	20		
Crook	Wild Boar Hotel	0539 445225	0539 442498		36	30	100	
Crooklands	Crooklands Hotel	053 95 67432	053 95 67525		30	120	36	
Grasmere	Michael's Nook	053 94 35496	053 94 35765		14	20	40	
Grasmere	The Swan	053 94 35551	053 94 35741	Forte	36	30	115	
Grasmere	Wordsworth Hotel	053 94 35592	053 94 35765		37	100	30	yes
Hawkshead	Tarn Hows	053 94 36696	053 94 36766		19	120	110	
Kendal	Woolpack Hotel	0539 723852	0539 728608		54	120	150	
Keswick	Keswick Hotel	076 87 72020	076 87 71300	Principal	66	80	70	
Langdale	Langdale Hotel	096 67 302	096 67 694		65	90		yes
Newby Bridge	The Swan	053 95 31681	053 95 31917		36	60	200	
Penrith	North Lakes Gateway Hotel	0768 68111	0768 68291	Shire Inns	85	200	170	
Silloth-on-Solway	Skinburness Hotel	069 73 32332	069 73 32549		25	200		yes
Ullswater	Leeming House	076 84 86622	076 84 86443	Forte	40	20		
Ullswater	Old Church Hotel	076 84 86204	076 84 86368		10	25		
Ullswater	Rampsbeck Country House	076 84 86442	same		21	20		
Ullswater	Sharrow Bay	076 84 86301	076 84 86349		28	15		
Wetheral	The Crown	0228 561888	0228 561637	Shire Inns	49	200		yes
Windermere	Holbeck Ghyll	053 94 32375	053 94 34743		14		200	
Windermere	Merewood Hotel	053 94 46484	053 94 42128		20	200	16	
Windermere	Miller Howe	053 94 42536	053 94 45664		13	10	100	

Location	Hotel	Tel	Fax	Group	Rooms	Conf	Banq	Leisure Centre
Derbyshire								
Ashbourne	Ashbourne Oaks Lodge	0335 46666	0335 46549		51	250	190	
Ashbourne	Callow Hall	0335 43403	0335 43624		12	30	45	
Ashford-in-the-Water	Riverside Hotel	0629 814275	0629 812873		15	16	60	
Bakewell	Hassop Hall	0629 640488	0629 640577		13	50	120	
Baslow	Cavendish Hotel	0246 582311	0246 582312		24	16		
Castle Donington	Donington Thistle	0332 850700	0332 850823	MtCT	110	200	180	yes
Chesterfield	Chesterfield Hotel	0246 271141	0246 220719		73	200	230	
Derby	Forte Posthouse	0332 514933	0332 518668	Forte	62	60	50	
Derby	International Hotel	0332 369321	0332 294430		62	50	150	
Dovedale	Izaak Walton Hotel	033 529 555	033 529 539		34	60		
Dovedale	Peveril of the Peak	033 529 333	033 529 507	Forte	47	95	60	
Matlock	Riber Hall	0629 582795	0629 580475		11	16	34	
Matlock Bath	New Bath Hotel	0629 583275	0629 580268	Forte	55		200	yes
Morley	Breadsall Priory	0332 832235	0332 833509	Country Club	91	150	80	
Newton Solney	Newton Park	0283 703568	0283 703214	Jarvis	51	140	100	
Renishaw	Sitwell Arms	0246 435226	0246 433915		30	100	160	
South Normanton	Swallow Hotel	0773 812000	0773 580032	Swallow	161	250	220	yes
Devon								
Barnstaple	Imperial Hotel	0271 45861	0271 24448	Forte	56	80	80	
Bideford	Yeoldon House	0237 474400	0237 476618		10	60	85	
Bigbury-on-Sea	Burgh Island Hotel	0548 810514	0548 810243		14	100	100	
Bishop's Tawton	Halmpstone Manor	0271 830321	0271 830826		5	15	15	
Brixham	Quayside Hotel	0803 855751	0803 882733		29	30	16	
Chagford	Great Tree Hotel	0647 432491			12	30	35	
Chittlehamholt	Highbullen	0769 540561	0769 540492		35	20	70	

Town	Hotel	Tel	Tel 2	Group				
Clawton	Court Barn	040 927 219			8	30	110	
Dartmouth	Stoke Lodge	0803 770523			24	80	120	yes
Exeter	Buckerell Lodge	0392 52451			54	60	110	
Exeter	Forte Crest	0392 412812	0392 412114	Forte	110	180	208	
Exeter	Rougemont Hotel	0392 54982	0392 413549	MtCT	90	300	120	
Exeter	Royal Clarence	0392 58464	0392 420928	QMH	56	150	60	
Exeter	White Hart	0392 79897	0392 439423		61	70	40	
Exmouth	Imperial Hotel	0395 274761	0392 50159	Forte	57	40	40	
Gittisham	Combe House	0404 42756	0404 46004		15	20	30	
Holbeton	Alston Hall	075 530 555	075 530 494		20	100	40	
Hope Cove	Cottage Hotel	0548 561555			35	50	30	yes
Huntsham	Huntsham Court	039 86 365	039 86 456		17	50	50	
Lewdown	Lewtrenchard Manor	056 683 256	056 683 332		8	50	100	
Lifton	Arundell Arms	0566 784666	0566 784494		29	100	50	
Lynton	Lynton Cottage	0598 52342	0598 52597		17	25	100	
Newton Abbot	Passage House	0626 55515	0626 63336		40	60	20	yes
North Huish	Brookdale House	0548 82402	0548 82699		8	25	40	
Paignton	Palace Hotel	0803 555121	0803 527974	Forte	52	50	200	
Paignton	Redcliffe Hotel	0803 526397	0803 528030		59	150	45	
Parkham	Penhaven Country House	0237 451388	0237 451878		12			
Plymouth	Astor Hotel	0752 225511	0752 851994	MtCT	56	150	110	
Plymouth	Boringdon Hall	0752 344455	0752 346578		40	110	100	
Plymouth	Copthorne Hotel	0752 224161	0752 670688	Copthorne	135	75	80	
Plymouth	Forte Crest	0752 662828	0752 660974		106	100	140	
Plymouth	Moat House	0752 662866	0752 673816	QMH	217	500	500	
Plymouth	Novotel	0752 221422	ext 126	Novotel	101	240	180	
Salcombe	Marine Hotel	0548 844444	0548 843109		51	70	70	yes
Saunton	Saunton Sands	0271 890212	0271 890145		96	200	250	
Sidmouth	Belmont Hotel	0395 512555	0395 579154		54	40	120	
Sidmouth	Fortfield Hotel	0395 512403			55	130	110	
Sidmouth	Hotel Riviera	0395 515201	0395 577775		31	90	90	
Sidmouth	Victoria Hotel	0395 512651	0395 579154		65	100	120	yes
Sourton	Collaven Manor	083 786 522	083 786 570		9	20	20	
South Molton	Whitechapel Manor	0769 573377	0769 573797		10	24	24	
Thurlestone	Thurlestone Hotel	0548 560382	0548 561069		68	100	150	yes

Location	Hotel	Tel	Fax	Group	Rooms	Conf	Banq	Leisure Centre
Torquay	Grand Hotel	0803 296677	0803 213462		101	300	300	yes
Torquay	Homers Hotel	0803 213456	0803 213458		15	50	45	
Torquay	Imperial Hotel	0803 294301	0803 298293	Forte	167	350	350	yes
Torquay	Livermead House	0803 294361	0803 200758		63	100	180	
Torquay	Livermead Cliff Hotel	0803 299666	0803 294496		64	60	80	
Torquay	Osborne Hotel	0803 213311	0803 296788		23	60	110	
Torquay	Palace Hotel	0803 200200	0803 299899		140	350	550	
Woody Bay	Woody Bay Hotel	059 83 264			15	16		
Woolacombe	Woolacombe Bay Hotel	0271 870388	ext 437		61	350	350	yes
Yelverton	Moorland Links	0822 852245	0822 855004		30	120	200	

Dorset

Location	Hotel	Tel	Fax	Group	Rooms	Conf	Banq	Leisure Centre
Bournemouth	Carlton Hotel	0202 552011	0202 299573		70	140	120	
Bournemouth	Forte Posthouse	0202 553262	0202 557698	Forte	98	100	100	
Bournemouth	Langtry Manor	0202 553887	0202 290115		27	70		
Bournemouth	Norfolk Royale	0202 551521	0202 299729		95	80	120	
Bournemouth	Palace Court	0202 557681	0202 554918		108	200	250	
Bournemouth	Royal Bath Hotel	0202 555555	0202 554158	De Vere	131	200	500	yes
Bournemouth	Swallow Highcliff Hotel	0202 557702	0202 292734	Swallow	157	500	350	
Chedington	Chedington Court	0935 891265	0935 891442		10	30		
Corfe Castle	Mortons House Hotel	0929 480988	0929 480820		17	65	45	
East Stoke	Kemps Country House Hotel	0929 462563	0929 405287		15	80	120	
Evershot	Summer Lodge	0935 83424	0935 83005		17	25	20	
Ferndown	Dormy Hotel	0202 872121	0202 895388	De Vere	128	250	275	yes
Longham	Bridge House	0202 578828	0202 572620		37	70	100	
Maiden Newton	Maiden Newton House	0300 20336	0300 21021		6	6		
Mudeford	Avonmouth Hotel	0202 483434	0202 479004	Forte	41	60	120	

Town	Hotel	Phone 1	Phone 2	Chain				
Poole	Haven Hotel	0202 707333	0202 708796		95	180	150	
Poole	Hospitality Inn	0202 666800	0202 684470	MtCT	68	80	50	
Poole	Mansion House	0202 685666	0202 665709		28	30	110	
Poole	Sandbanks Hotel	0202 707377	0202 708885		105	170	200	
Shaftesbury	Grosvenor Hotel	0747 52282	0747 54755	Forte	41	150	120	
Shaftesbury	Royal Chase Hotel	0747 53355	0747 51969		35	190	160	
Sherborne	Eastbury Hotel	0935 813131	0935 817296	Clipper	15	80	80	
Sherborne	Forte Posthouse	0935 813191	0935 816493	Forte	59	100	70	
Wareham	Priory Hotel	0929 551666	0929 554519		19	20	20	
West Bexington	Manor Hotel	0308 897785	0308 897035		13	60	40	

Durham

Town	Hotel	Phone 1	Phone 2	Chain				
Barnard Castle	Jersey Farm Hotel	0833 38223	0833 31988		22	150	200	
Blanchland	Lord Crewe Arms	0434 675251	0434 675337		18	20	65	
Chester-le-Street	Lumley Castle	091-389 1111	091-387 1437		65	150	200	
Coatham Mundeville	Hall Garth	0325 300400	0325 310083		42	300	250	
Darlington	Blackwell Grange Moat House	0325 380888	0325 380899	QMH	99	300	250	
Darlington	St George Thistle	0325 332631	0325 333851	MtCT	59	160	120	
Darlington	Swallow King's Head	0325 380222	0325 382006	Swallow	85	200	250	
Darlington	White Horse	0325 382121	0325 355953		40	45	120	
Durham	Royal County Hotel	091-386 6821	091-386 0704	Swallow	150	150	120	
Neasham	Newbus Arms	0325 721071	0325 721770		15	110	70	yes

Essex

Town	Hotel	Phone 1	Phone 2	Chain			
Basildon	Forte Crest	0268 533955	0268 530119	Forte	110	300	250
Brentwood	Forte Posthouse	0277 260260	0277 264264	Forte	150	120	120
Brentwood	Moat House	0277 225252	0277 262809	QMH	33	60	85
Broxted	Whitehall	0279 850603	0279 850385		25	126	120
Coggeshall	White Hart	0376 561654	0376 561789		18	30	70
Colchester	Butterfly Hotel	0206 230900	0206 231095		50	80	80

Location	Hotel	Tel	Fax	Group	Rooms	Conf	Banq	Leisure Centre
Dedham	Dedham Vale Hotel	0206 322273	0206 322752		6	40	110	
Dedham	Maison Talbooth	0206 322367	0206 322752		10	20		
Epping	Forte Posthouse	0992 573137	0992 560402	Forte	79	100	85	
Great Baddow	Pontlands Park	0245 76444	0245 478393		17	200	100	yes
Great Dunmow	Saracen's Head	0371 873901	0371 875743	Forte	24	60	50	
Harlow	Green Man	0279 442521	0279 626113	Forte	55	75	64	
Harlow	Moat House	0279 422441	0279 635094	QMH	120	220	180	
Ingatestone	Heybridge Moat House	0277 355355	0277 353288	QMH	22	600	500	
Maldon	Blue Boar	0621 852681	0621 856202	Forte	28	100	80	
North Stifford	Moat House	0375 390909	0375 390426	QMH	126	150	120	
Saffron Walden	Saffron Hotel	0799 22676	0799 513979		24	100	80	
Woodford Bridge	Prince Regent Hotel	081-505 9966	081-506 0807		51	300	250	

Gloucestershire

Location	Hotel	Tel	Fax	Group	Rooms	Conf	Banq	Leisure Centre
Amberley	Amberley Inn	0453 872565	0453 872738		14	15	60	
Bibury	The Swan	0285 740204	0285 740473		18	12		
Bourton-on-the-Water	Dial House	0451 22244			10	24	24	
Charingworth	Charingworth Manor	038 678 555	038 678 353		24	38		yes
Cheltenham	Cheltenham Park	0242 222021	0242 226935	Park Hotels	154	350	300	yes
Cheltenham	Golden Valley Thistle	0242 232691	0242 221846	MtCT	124	220	300	
Cheltenham	Greenway	0242 862352	0242 862780		19	18	18	
Cheltenham	Hotel de la Bere	0242 237771	0242 236016	Forte	57	80	80	
Cheltenham	Queen's Hotel	0242 514724	0242 224145	Forte	77	200	180	yes
Chipping Camden	Cotswold House	0386 840330	0386 840310		15	30	40	
Chipping Campden	Noel Arms	0386 840317	0386 841136		26	60	60	
Cirencester	Fleece Hotel	0285 658507	0285 651017	Resort	25	60	60	
Cirencester	Stratton House	0285 651761	0285 640024		41	120	120	
Clearwell	Clearwell Castle	0594 832320	0594 835523		16	40	140	
Corse Lawn	Corse Lawn House	0452 780479	0452 780840		19	30	70	

Town	Hotel	Operator	Tel	Fax				
Fairford	Bull Hotel		0285 712535	0285 713782	20	30	80	
Fairford	Hyperion House		0285 712349	0285 713126	27	14	30	yes
Gloucester	Forte Crest		0452 613311	0452 371036	123	100	100	
Gloucester	Hatherley Manor		0452 730217	0452 731032	55	200	200	
Gloucester	Hatton Court		0452 617412	0452 612945	46	60	50	
Lower Slaughter	Lower Slaughter Manor		0451 20456	0451 22150	19	16		
Mickleton	Three Ways Hotel		0386 438429	0386 438118	40	100	100	
Moreton-in-Marsh	Manor House		0608 50501	0608 51481	37	36	100	
Painswick	Painswick Hotel		0452 812160	0452 812059	15	30		
Stonehouse	Stonehouse Court	Clipper	0453 825155	0453 824611	37	120		
Stow-on-the-Wold	Fosse Manor		0451 30354	0451 32486	20	25	25	
Stow-on-the-Wold	Grapevine Hotel		0451 30344	0451 32278	23	15		
Stow-on-the-Wold	Unicorn Hotel	Forte	0451 30257	0451 31090	20	15		
Tetbury	Calcot Manor		0666 890391	0666 890394	14	25	50	
Tetbury	The Close		0666 502272	0666 504401	15	24	65	
Tewkesbury	Snooty Fox Hotel		0666 502436	0666 503479	12	30		
Tewkesbury	Royal Hop Pole	Forte	0684 293236	0684 296680	29	12		
Tewkesbury	Tewkesbury Park	Country Club	0684 295405	0684 292386	78	150	150	yes
Westonbirt	Hare & Hounds		066 688 233	066 688 241	30	40	150	

Greater Manchester

Town	Hotel	Operator	Tel	Fax				
Altrincham	Bowdon Hotel		061-928 7121	061-927 7560	82	150	150	
Altrincham	Cresta Court		061-927 7272	061-926 9194	139	400	350	
Bolton	Forte Posthouse	Forte	0204 651511	0204 61064	96	120	90	
Bolton	Pack Horse Hotel	De Vere	0204 27261	0204 364352	73	375	230	
Manchester	Britannia Hotel		061-228 2288	061-236 9154	362	300	250	
Manchester	Charterhouse Hotel	Hidden	061-236 9999	061-236 0674	58	150	120	
Manchester	Copthorne Hotel	Copthorne	061-873 7321	061-873 7318	166	150	132	yes
Manchester	Forte Posthouse	Forte	061-998 7090	061-946 0139	190	120	100	
Manchester	Holiday Inn Crowne Plaza	Holiday Inns	061-236 3333	061-228 2241	303	500	600	yes
Manchester	Novotel	Novotel	061-799 3535	061-703 8207	119	220	160	
Manchester	Hotel Piccadilly	Jarvis	061-236 8414	061-236 2533	271	800	700	

Location	Hotel	Tel	Fax	Group	Rooms	Conf	Banq	Leisure Centre
Manchester	Portland Thistle	061-228 3400	061-228 6347	MtCT	205	300	300	yes
Manchester	Ramada Renaissance	061-835 2555	061-835 0731		200	350	400	
Manchester	Sachas Hotel	061-228 1234	061-236 9202		223	600	650	yes
Manchester Airport	Etrop Grange	061-499 0500	061-499 0790		41	100	100	
Manchester Airport	Forte Crest	061-437 5811	061-436 2340	Forte	297	200	200	yes
Manchester Airport	Four Seasons Hotel	061-904 0301	061-980 1787		94	160	140	
Manchester Airport	Hilton International	061-436 4404	061-436 1521	Hilton	223	200	150	yes
Standish	Almond Brook Moat House	0257 425588	0257 427327	QMH	126	150	100	
Stockport	Alma Lodge	061-483 4431	061-483 1983	Jarvis	56	250	225	

Hampshire

Location	Hotel	Tel	Fax	Group	Rooms	Conf	Banq	Leisure Centre
Alton	Grange Hotel	0420 86565	0420 541346		34	40	75	
Alton	The Swan	0420 83777	0420 87975	Forte	36	120	125	
Ampfield	Potters Heron Hotel	0703 266611	0703 251359	Lansbury	54	140	120	
Basingstoke	Audleys Wood	0256 817555	0256 817500	MtCT	71	45	40	
Basingstoke	Forte Posthouse	0256 468181	0256 840081	Forte	85	180	160	
Basingstoke	Hilton National	0256 20212	0256 842835	Hilton	134	160	120	
Basingstoke	Hilton Lodge	0256 460460	0256 840441	Hilton	144	160	120	
Beaulieu	Montagu Arms	0590 612324	0590 612188		24	45	120	
Brockenhurst	Balmer Lawn Hotel	0590 23116	0590 23864		58	90	100	
Brockenhurst	Careys Manor	0590 23551	0590 22799		80	100	150	yes
Burley	Burley Manor	0425 403522	0425 403227		30	80	75	
Eastleigh	Forte Crest Southampton	0703 619700	0703 643945	Forte	120	300	250	
Fareham	Red Lion	0329 822640	0329 823579	Lansbury	44	120	90	
Fareham	Solent Hotel	0489 880000	0489 880007	Shire Inns	90	200	250	yes
Farnborough	Forte Crest	0252 545051	0252 377210	Forte	110	200	180	yes
Havant	Bear Hotel	0705 486501	0705 470551	Lansbury	42	120	100	

Location	Hotel	Chain	Phone	Phone				
Havant	Forte Posthouse	Forte	0705 465011	0705 466468	92	180	120	yes
Hurstbourne Tarrant	Esseborne Manor		0264 76444	0264 76473	12	12	28	
Lymington	Gordleton Mill		0590 682219	0590 683073	7		50	
Lymington	Passford House		0590 682398	0590 683494	56	100	150	yes
Lymington	Stanwell House	Clipper	0590 677123	0590 677756	35	20	70	
Lyndhurst	The Crown		0703 282922	0703 282751	40	70	50	
Lyndhurst	Lyndhurst Park		0703 283923	0703 283019	59	200	300	
Lyndhurst	Parkhill Hotel		0703 282944	0703 283268	20	40	80	
Middle Wallop	Fifehead Manor		0264 781565	0264 781400	16	30	40	
Milford-on-Sea	South Lawn		0590 643911	0590 644820	24		75	
New Milton	Chewton Glen		0425 275341	0425 272310	58	110	120	yes
Petersfield	Langrish House		0730 66941	0730 60543	18	60	100	
Portsmouth	Forte Crest	Forte	0705 827651	0705 756715	163	220	180	
Portsmouth	Hilton National	Hilton	0705 219111	0705 210762	122	230	200	
Portsmouth	Hospitality Inn	MtCT	0705 731281	0705 817572	115	280	250	
Portsmouth	Pendragon Hotel	Forte	0705 823201	0705 750283	49	60	90	
Portsmouth	Portsmouth Marriott Hotel	Marriott	0705 383151	0705 388701	170	280	250	yes
Romsey	White Horse Hotel	Forte	0794 512431	0794 517485	33	40	90	
Rotherwick	Tylney Hall		0256 764881	0256 768141	91	100	110	
Silchester	Romans Hotel		0734 700421	0734 700691	23	60	44	
Southampton	Dolphin Hotel	Forte	0703 339955	0703 333650	73	75	120	yes
Southampton	Forte Posthouse	Forte	0703 330777	0703 332510	128	200	200	
Southampton	Hilton National	Hilton	0703 702700	0703 767233	135	180	140	
Southampton	Novotel	Novotel	0703 330550	0703 222158	121	450	350	
Southampton	Polygon Hotel	Forte	0703 330055	0703 332435	119	500	400	yes
Southampton	Southampton Park Hotel		0703 223467	0703 332538	71	200	150	
Stockbridge	Grosvenor Hotel	Lansbury	0264 810606	0264 810747	25	80	70	
Wickham	Old House Hotel		0329 833049	0329 833672	12	10	35	
Winchester	Forte Crest	Forte	0962 861611	0962 841503	94	100	85	
Winchester	Lainston House		0962 863588	0962 72672	32	80	80	
Winchester	Royal Hotel		0962 840840	0962 841582	75	120	100	

see also under **Isle of Wight**

Hereford & Worcester

Location	Hotel	Tel	Fax	Group	Rooms	Conf	Banq	Leisure Centre
Abberley	Elms Hotel	0299 896666	0299 896804	QMH	25	60	44	
Abbot's Salford	Salford Hall	0386 871300	0386 871301		33	50	50	
Broadway	Broadway Hotel	0386 852401	0386 853879		20	25		
Broadway	Dormy House	0386 852711	0386 858636		49	200	120	
Broadway	Lygon Arms	0386 852255	0386 858611	Savoy Group	66	80	85	
Bromsgrove	Country Court	021-447 7888	021-447 7273	Stakis	141	80	60	yes
Bromsgrove	Grafton Manor	0527 579007	0527 575221		9	8		
Bromsgrove	Perry Hall	0527 579976	0572 575998	Jarvis	58	70	95	
Buckland	Buckland Manor	0386 852626	0386 853557		11	24	38	
Chaddesley Corbett	Brockencote Hall	0562 777876	0562 777872		8	30	50	
Droitwich Spa	Chateau Impney	0905 774411	0905 772371		114	300	400	
Droitwich Spa	Raven Hotel	0905 772224	0905 772371		72	150	250	
Evesham	Evesham Hotel	0386 765566	0386 765443		40	12		
Evesham	Riverside Hotel	0386 446200	0386 40021		7	25	48	
Eyton	Marsh Country Hotel	0568 613952			5	36	24	
Harvington	The Mill	0386 870688	0386 870688		15	30	40	
Hereford	Moat House	0432 354301	0432 275114	QMH	60	150	400	
Kidderminster	Stone Manor	0562 777555	0562 777834		52	150	250	
Malvern	Abbey Hotel	0684 892332	0684 892662	De Vere	107	150	200	
Malvern	Colwall Park Hotel	0684 40206	0684 40847		20	100	100	
Malvern	Cottage in the Wood	0684 573487	0684 560662		20	20	65	
Malvern	Foley Arms	0684 573397	0684 569665		28	50	80	
Much Birch	Pilgrim Hotel	0981 540742	0981 540620		20	50	40	
Ross-on-Wye	Chase Hotel	0989 763161	0989 768330		39	250	250	
Ross-on-Wye	Pengethley Manor	098 987 211	098 987 238		24	60	85	
Stourport-on-Severn	Moat House	0299 827733	0299 878520	QMH	68	350	300	

Location	Hotel	Tel 1	Tel 2	Group				
Weston-under-Penyard	Wharton Lodge	0989 750795	0989 750700		9	14	60	
Worcester	Fownes Resort Hotel	0905 613151	0905 23742	Resort	61	120	100	
Worcester	Giffard Hotel	0905 726262	0905 723458	Forte	103	130	180	

Hertfordshire

Location	Hotel	Tel 1	Tel 2	Group				
Dane End	Green End Park	0920 438344	0920 438523		10	120	90	
Hadley Wood	West Lodge Park	081-440 8311	081-449 3698		50	80	63	
Harpenden	Glen Eagle Hotel	0582 760271	0582 460819		50	60	150	
Harpenden	Moat House	0582 764111	0582 769858	QMH	53	150	120	
Hatfield Heath	Down Hall	0279 731441	0279 730416		103	200	180	
Hertingfordbury	White Horse Hotel	0992 586791	0992 550809	Forte	42	60	20	
Letchworth	Broadway Toby Hotel	0462 480111			35	180	180	
Sawbridgeworth	Manor of Groves	0279 600777	0279 600374		39	35	150	
South Mimms	Forte Posthouse	0707 43311	0707 46728	Forte	123	170	120	
St Albans	Noke Thistle	0727 54252	0727 41906	MtCT	111	70	60	yes
St Albans	St Michael's Manor	0727 864444	0727 48909		26	35	35	
St Albans	Sopwell House	0727 864477	0727 44741		84	300	250	
Stanstead Abbots	Briggens House	0279 792416	0279 793685	QMH	54	100	100	yes
Stevenage	Novotel	0438 742299	0438 723872	Novotel	100	150	110	
Thundridge	Hanbury Manor	0920 487722	0920 487692		98	138	112	yes
Watford	Hilton National	0923 35881	0923 220836	Hilton	198	350	350	yes

Humberside

Location	Hotel	Tel 1	Tel 2	Group				
Beverley	Beverley Arms	0482 869241	0482 870907	Forte	57	80	65	
Bridlington	Expanse Hotel	0262 675347	0262 604928		48	50	120	
Cleethorpes	Kingsway Hotel	0472 601122	0472 601381		50	16	24	
Grimsby	Forte Crest	0472 350295	0472 241354	Forte	52	250	200	
Hull	Forte Posthouse	0482 645212	0482 643332	Forte	97	100	100	
Hull	Forte Crest	0482 225221	0482 213299	Forte	99	140	120	
Tickton	Tickton Grange	0964 543666	0964 542556		16	86	86	
Walkington	Manor House	0482 881645	0482 866501		6	24	24	

Location	Hotel	Tel	Fax	Group	Rooms	Conf	Banq	Leisure Centre
Willerby	Grange Park	0482 656488	0482 655848		109	550	500	yes
Willerby	Willerby Manor	0482 652616	0482 653901		36	450	400	

Isle of Wight

Location	Hotel	Tel	Fax	Group	Rooms	Conf	Banq	Leisure Centre
Calbourne	Swainston Manor	0983 521121	0983 521406		17	150	120	
Ryde	Hotel Ryde Castle	0983 63755	0983 68925		17	230	200	
Seaview	Seaview Hotel	0983 612711	0983 613729		16	14		
Shanklin	Cliff Tops Hotel	0983 863262	0983 867139		88	350	300	yes
Ventnor	Royal Hotel	0983 852186	0983 855395	Forte	54	36	120	

Kent

Location	Hotel	Tel	Fax	Group	Rooms	Conf	Banq	Leisure Centre
Ashford	Ashford International	0233 611444	0233 627708	QMH	200	400	400	yes
Ashford	Eastwell Manor	0233 635751	0233 635530	QMH	23	60	80	
Ashford	Holiday Inn Garden Court	0233 713333	0233 712082	Holiday Inns	104	25		
Bearsted	Tudor Park	0622 34334	0622 735360	Country Club	120	275	216	yes
Brands Hatch	Brands Hatch Thistle	0474 854900	0474 853220	MtCT	137	300	250	
Bromley	Bromley Court	081-464 5011	081-460 0899		119	170	250	
Canterbury	Canterbury Hotel	0227 450551	0277 450873		27	40	70	
Canterbury	Chaucer Hotel	0227 464427	0227 450397	Forte	42	120	120	
Canterbury	County Hotel	0227 766266	0227 451512		73	100	150	
Canterbury	Howfield Manor	0227 738294	0227 731535		13	30	85	
Canterbury	Slatters Hotel	0227 463271	0227 764117	QMH	31	100	100	
Cranbrook	Hartley Mount	0580 712230	0580 712588		7	65		
Cranbrook	Kennel Holt Hotel	0580 712032	0580 712931		10	20		
Dover	Forte Posthouse	0304 821222	0304 825576	Forte	67	40	20	
Dover	Moat House	0304 203270	0304 213230	QMH	79	150	120	yes
Dover	White Cliffs Hotel	0304 203633	0304 216320		56	100	70	

Location	Hotel	Phone	Phone	Chain				
Fawkham	Brandshatch Place	0474 872239	0474 879652	Hidden	29	120	150	yes
Hawkhurst	Tudor Court	0580 752312	0580 753966		18	60	85	yes
Hollingbourne	Great Danes	0622 30022	0622 735290	Jarvis	126	600	425	yes
Hythe	Hythe Imperial	0303 267441	0303 264610		100	200	200	
Hythe	Stade Court	0303 268263	0303 261803		42	80	100	
Lenham	Chilston Park	0622 859803	0622 858588		40	120	80	
Maidstone	Larkfield Priory	0732 846858	0732 846786	Forte	52	70	70	
Maidstone	Stakis Country Court Hotel	0622 34322	0622 34600	Stakis	139	90	60	yes
Rochester	Forte Crest	0634 687111	0634 684512	Forte	105	40	80	
Sevenoaks	Royal Oak	0732 451109	0732 740187		39	45		
Shorne	Inn on the Lake	0474 823333	0474 823175		78	500	400	
St Margaret's	Wallet's Court	0304 852424			7	20		
Tonbridge	Rose & Crown	0732 357966	0732 357194	Forte	50	110	80	
Tunbridge Wells	Royal Wells Inn	0892 511188	0892 511908		22	100	90	
Tunbridge Wells	Spa Hotel	0892 520331	0892 510575		76	350	180	yes
Wateringbury	Wateringbury Hotel	0622 812632	0622 812720		40	80	100	
Wrotham Heath	Forte Posthouse Maidstone	0732 883311	0732 885850	Forte	118	60	60	yes

Lancashire

Location	Hotel	Phone	Phone	Chain				
Blackburn	Moat House	0254 264441	0254 682435	QMH	98	350	300	
Blackpool	Imperial Hotel	0253 23971	0253 751784	Forte	183	500	450	yes
Blackpool	Pembroke Hotel	0253 23434	0253 27864		274	900	600	
Bolton	Egerton House	0204 307171	0204 593030	Rank	32	150	150	
Bolton	Last Drop Village Hotel	0204 591131	0204 304122	Rank	83	220	220	yes
Broughton	Broughton Park	0772 864087	0772 861728	Country Club	98	220	180	
Clayton-le-Woods	Pines Hotel	0772 38551	ext 302		39	100	164	
Lancaster	Forte Posthouse	0524 65999	0524 841265	Forte	110	120	100	yes
Leyland	Leyland Resort Hotel	0772 422922	0772 622282	Resort	93	220	180	
Lytham	Clifton Arms	0253 739898	0253 730657	Lansbury	41	300	200	
Preston	Forte Crest	0772 59411	0772 882955	Forte	126	120	100	
Preston	Novotel	0772 313331	0772 627868	Novotel	100	200	150	
Samlesbury	Swallow Trafalgar	0772 877351	0772 877424	Swallow	78	150	200	yes

Location	Hotel	Tel	Fax	Group	Rooms	Conf	Banq	Leisure Centre
Samlesbury	Tickled Trout	0772 877671	0772 847463		72	120	80	
Worthington	Kilbey Court	0257 472100	0257 422401	Denley Court	54	150	200	
Leicestershire								
Hinckley	Hinckley Island Hotel	0455 631122	0455 634536		253	400	400	
Leicester	Belmont Hotel	0533 544773	0533 470804		68	150	140	yes
Leicester	Country Court	0533 630066	0533 630627	Stakis	141	90	70	
Leicester	Forte Posthouse	0533 630500	0533 823623	Forte	172	80	80	yes
Leicester	Grand Hotel	0533 555599	0533 544736	Jarvis	92	450	410	
Leicester	Holiday Inn	0533 531161	0533 513169	Holiday Inns	188	300	280	yes
Leicester	Leicester Forest Moat House	0533 394661		QMH	34	65	60	
Leicester	Park International	0533 620471	0533 514211	Park Hotels	209	400	220	
Lockington	Hilton Nat. E.Mid Airport	0509 674000	0509 672412	Hilton	151	250	200	yes
Loughborough	King's Head	0509 233222	0509 262911	Jarvis	78	120	120	
Lutterworth	Denbigh Arms	0455 553537	0455 556627	Resort	34	60	50	
Market Harborough	Three Swans Hotel	0858 466644	0858 433101		37	75	95	
Melton Mowbray	George Hotel	0664 62112	0664 410457		22	35	78	
Oakham	Barnsdale Lodge	0572 724678	0572 724961		17	250	250	
Oakham	Hambleton Hall	0572 756991	0572 724721		15	30	60	
Oakham	Whipper-In Hotel	0572 756971	0572 757759		25	50	120	
Quorn	The Quorn	0509 415050	0509 415557		19	80	120	
Quorn	Quorn Grange	0509 412167	0509 415621		17	120	130	
Rothley	Rothley Court	0533 374141	0533 374483	Forte	36	100	100	
Stapleford	Stapleford Park	057 284 522	057 284 651		35	200	150	
Stretton	Ram Jam Inn	0780 410776	0780 410361		10	40		

Lincolnshire

Location	Hotel	Telephone	Fax	Group				
Belton	Belton Woods Hotel	0476 593200	0476 74547	Forte	96	275	240	yes
Lincoln	Forte Crest	0522 520341	0522 510780	Forte	70	80	80	
Lincoln	White Hart	0522 526222	0522 531798	Poste Hotels	50	160	110	
Stamford	The George of Stamford	0780 55171	0780 57070		47	50	90	

London

Location	Hotel	Telephone	Fax	Group				
	Tower Thistle	071-481 2575			808	210	150	
EC1	New Barbican Hotel	071-251 1565	071-538 3199	MtCT	470	100	600	
E14	London International	071-515 1551		MtCT	44	800	100	
N1	Great Northern Hotel	071-837 5454	071-278 5270	Compass	89	100	85	
NW1	Kennedy Hotel	071-387 4400	071-387 5122	MtCT	360	330	100	
NW1	London Wilshire	071-631 8000	071-631 8080		309	50	100	
NW1	White House	071-387 1200	071-388 0091	Rank	576	25	200	
NW3	Clive Hotel	071-586 2233	071-586 1659	Hilton	96	400	25	
NW3	Forte Posthouse	071-794 8121	071-435 5586	Forte	138	60	270	
NW3	Regent's Park Marriott	071-722 7711	071-586 5822	Marriott	303	300	75	yes
NW3	Swiss Cottage Hotel	071-722 2281	071-483 4588		82	150	240	
NW4	Hendon Hall	081-203 3341	081-203 9709	MtCT	52	25	130	
NW8	Hilton Int. Regent's Park	081-722 7722	081-483 2408	Hilton	377			
SE3	Bardon Lodge	081-853 4051	081-858 7387		37			
SE16	Scandic Crown Nelson Dock	071-231 1001	071-231 0599		390	410	300	yes
SW1	The Berkeley	071-235 6000	071-235 4330	Savoy Group	160	220	200	
SW1	Cadogan Hotel	071-235 7141	071-245 0994	Historic House	75	40	40	
SW1	Chelsea Hotel	071-235 4377	071-235 3705		225	120	180	
SW1	Dukes Hotel	071-491 4840	071-493 1264		64	36		
SW1	Ebury Court	071-730 8147	071-823 5966		46	20		
SW1	Forte Crest St James's	071-930 2111	071-839 2125	Forte	256	90	75	
SW1	The Goring	071-834 8211	071-834 4393		82	70	52	
SW1	Grosvenor Hotel	071-834 9494	071-630 1978	MtCT	366	200	150	
SW1	Halkin Hotel	071-333 1000	071-333 1100		41	30	30	
SW1	Hyatt Carlton Tower	071-235 5411	071-245 6570		224	150	300	

Location	Hotel	Tel	Fax	Group	Rooms	Conf	Banq	Leisure Centre
SW1	Hyde Park Hotel	071-235 2000	071-235 4552	Forte	185	250	250	
SW1	The Lanesborough	071-259 5599	071-259 5606		95	70	50	
SW1	The Lowndes	071-235 6020	071-235 1154		78	25	24	
SW1	Royal Westminster Thistle	071-834 1821	071-828 8933	MtCT	134	250	130	
SW1	Royal Court Hotel	071-730 9191	071-824 8381	QMH	102	40	40	
SW1	Royal Horseguards Thistle	071-839 3400	071-925 2263	MtCT	376	750	700	
SW1	Rubens Hotel	071-834 6600	071-828 5401	189	75	50		
SW1	St James Court	071-821 1899	071-630 7587		390	250	200	
SW1	Scandic Crown Victoria	071-834 8123	071-828 1099		210	200	210	yes
SW1	Sheraton Park Tower	071-235 8050	071-235 8231		295	80	200	
SW1	Sheraton Belgravia	071-235 6040	071-259 6243		89	30	45	
SW1	The Stafford	071-493 0111	071-493 7121		74	20	30	
SW1	Stakis St Ermin's	071-222 7888	071-222 6914	Stakis	290	200	250	
SW1	22 Jermyn Street	071-734 2353	071-734 0750		18	12	30	
SW3	Basil Street Hotel	071-581 3311	071-581 3693		92	55	80	
SW3	The Capital	071-589 5171	071-225 0011		48	20	24	
SW3	Egerton House	071-589 2412	071-584 6540		30	18		
SW3	Hogarth Hotel	071-370 6831	071-373 6179		86	50	60	
SW5	Swallow International	071-370 4200	071-244 8194	Swallow	417	200	200	yes
SW6	Earls Court Park Inn Int	071-385 1255	071-381 4450		501	1,750	1,750	
SW7	Adelphi Hotel	071-373 7177	071-373 7720		68	80		
SW7	The Gloucester	071-373 6030	071-373 0409	Rank	550	400	350	
SW7	The Gore	071-584 6601	071-589 8127		58	12		
SW7	Holiday Inn Kensington	071-373 2222	071-373 0559	Holiday Inns	162	150	200	
SW7	Norfolk Hotel	071-589 8191	071-581 1874	QMH	96	60	80	
SW7	Regency Hotel	071-370 4595	071-370 5555		210	100	60	
SW7	Rembrandt Hotel	071-589 8100	071-225 3363		195	250	180	yes
SW10	Hotel Conrad	071-823 3000	071-351 6525		160	150	200	yes
SW19	Cannizaro House	081-879 1464	081-879 7338	MtCT	45	50	80	

W1	The Athenaeum	071-499 3464	071-493 1860	Rank	144	44	40	
W1	Berkshire Hotel	071-629 7474	071-629 8156	Edwardian	147	45	26	
W1	Berners Park Plaza	071-636 1629	071-580 3972		235	160	200	
W1	Britannia Inter-Continental	071-629 9400	071-629 7736	Inter-Continental	317	100	80	
W1	Brown's Hotel	071-493 6020	071-493 9381	Forte	133	35	70	
W1	Chesterfield Hotel	071-491 2622	071-491 4793		113	60	100	
W1	Churchill Hotel	071-486 5800	071-486 1255		448	40	250	
W1	Claridge's	071-629 8860	071-499 2210	Savoy Group	190	450	220	
W1	The Clifton-Ford	071-486 6600	071-486 7492	Doyle	212	180	180	
W1	Cumberland Hotel	071-262 1234	071-724 4621	Forte	894	475	560	
W1	The Dorchester	071-629 8888	071-409 0114		197	550	550	yes
W1	Durrants Hotel	071-935 8131	071-487 3510		96	50	50	
W1	Forte Crest Regent's Park	071-388 2300	071-387 2806	Forte	320	650	300	
W1	Grafton Hotel	071-388 4131	071-387 7394	Edwardian	323	110		
W1	Green Park Hotel	071-629 7522	071-491 8971		161	66	80	
W1	Grosvenor House	071-499 6363	071-493 3341	Forte	454	1,500	1,500	yes
W1	Holiday Inn Mayfair	071-493 8282	071-629 2827	Holiday Inns	185	70	50	
W1	Holiday Inn Marble Arch	071-723 1277	071-402 0666	Holiday Inns	241	100	160	
W1	Hospitality Inn Piccadilly	071-930 4033	071-925 2586	MtCT	92	16		
W1	Inn on the Park Hotel	071-499 0888	071-493 1895		228	300		
W1	Inter-Continental Hotel	071-409 3131	071-409 7460	Inter-Continental	467	800	800	
W1	The Langham	071-636 1000	071-323 2340	Hilton	411	320	280	
W1	London Mews Hilton	071-493 7222	071-629 9423	Hilton	72	35	25	
W1	London Hilton on Park Lane	071-493 8000	071-493 4957	Hilton	448	1,200	1,000	
W1	London Marriott Hotel	071-493 1232	071-491 3201	Marriott	223	800	550	
W1	May Fair Inter-Continental	071-629 7777	071-629 1459	Inter-Continental	293	308	350	
W1	Le Meridien	071-734 8000	071-437 3574		263	250	250	yes
W1	Montcalm Hotel	071-402 4288	071-724 9180		116	80	60	
W1	Mostyn Hotel	071-935 2361	071-487 2759		122	150	100	
W1	Park Lane Hotel	071-499 6321	071-499 1965		330	500	1,000	
W1	Rathbone Hotel	071-636 2001	071-636 3882		72	12		
W1	The Ritz	071-493 8181	071-493 2687		129	110	80	
W1	St George's Hotel	071-580 0111	071-436 7997	Forte	86	50	50	

Location	Hotel	Tel	Fax	Group	Rooms	Conf	Banq	Leisure Centre
W1	SAS Portman Hotel	071-486 5844	071-935 0537		272	400	400	
W1	The Selfridge	071-408 2080	071-629 8849	MtCT	296	250	276	
W1	Washington Hotel	071-499 7000	071-495 6172		173	70	60	
W1	The Westbury	071-629 7755	071-495 1163	Forte	243	120	100	
W2	London Metropole	071-402 4141	071-724 8866		747	1000	1000	
W2	Columbia Hotel	071-402 0021	071-706 4691		102	200	300	
W2	Hospitality Inn Bayswater	071-262 4461	071-706 4560	MtCT	175	40	25	
W2	London Embassy	071-229 1212	071-229 2623	Jarvis	193	70	120	
W2	Royal Lancaster Hotel	071-262 6737	071-724 3191	Rank	418	1,400	1,200	
W2	Whites Hotel	071-262 2711	071-262 2147	MtCT	54	30		
W6	Novotel	081-741 1555	081-741 2120	Novotel	640	900	750	
W8	Apollo Hotel	071-835 1133	071-370 4853		59	30		
W8	Copthorne Tara	071-937 7211	071-937 7100	Copthorne	829	600	600	
W8	Kensington Park Hotel	071-937 8080	071-937 7616	MtCT	323	125	110	
W8	Kensington Palace Thistle	071-937 8121	071-937 2816	MtCT	298	250	160	
W8	Hotel Lexham	071-373 6471	071-244 7827		66	25		
W8	Royal Garden Hotel	071-937 8000	071-938 4532	Rank	398	900	640	
W11	The Halcyon	071-727 7288	071-229 8516		43	40	80	
W11	Hilton Int. Kensington	071-603 3355	071-602 9397	Hilton	603	250	250	
W14	Hilton Int. Olympia	071-603 3333	071-603 4846	Hilton	406	90	60	
WC1	Bonnington Hotel	071-242 2828	071-831 9170		215	100	150	
WC1	Forte Crest Bloomsbury	071-837 1200	071-833 2290	Forte	284	550	700	
WC1	Holiday Inn King's Cross	071-833 3900	071-917 6163	Holiday Inns	405	250	180	yes
WC1	Kenilworth Hotel	071-637 3477	071-631 3133	Edwardian	192	120	150	
WC1	The Marlborough	071-636 5601	071-636 0532	Edwardian	169	200	150	
WC1	Hotel Russell	071-837 6470	071-837 2857	Forte	326	450	350	
WC1	St Giles Hotel	071-636 8616	071-631 1031		600	45	110	yes
WC1	Scandic Crown Euston	071-383 4105	071-383 4106		150	120	100	
WC2	Hampshire Hotel	071-839 9399	071-930 8122	Edwardian	124	120	100	

Location	Hotel			Group				
WC2	The Howard	071-836 3555	071-379 4547		137	120	120	
WC2	Moat House	071-836 6666	071-831 1548	QMH	153	100	100	
WC2	Mountbatten Hotel	071-836 4300	071-240 3540	Edwardian	127	70	100	
WC2	Royal Trafalgar Thistle	071-930 4477	071-925 2149	MtCT	108	8		
WC2	The Savoy	071-836 4343	071-240 6040	Savoy Group	202	500	500	
WC2	The Waldorf	071-836 2400	071-836 7244	Forte	292	600	400	

London Airport Heathrow

Location	Hotel			Group				
Heathrow Airport	Berkeley Arms Hotel	081-897 2121	081-897 7014	Jarvis	56	150	140	
Heathrow Airport	Edwardian International	081-759 6311	081-759 4559	Edwardian	462	520	380	yes
Heathrow Airport	Excelsior Hotel	081-759 6611	081-759 3421	Forte	839	800	800	yes
Heathrow Airport	Forte Crest	081-759 2323	081-897 6130	Forte	572	200	150	
Heathrow Airport	Forte Posthouse Ariel	081-759 2552	081-564 9265	Forte	180	50	30	
Heathrow Airport	Heathrow Penta Hotel	081-897 6363	081-897 1113		636	500	500	
Heathrow Airport	Heathrow Hilton Hotel	081-759 7755	081-759 7579	Hilton	400	140	200	
Heathrow Airport	Holiday Inn Heathrow	0895 445555	0895 445122	Holiday Inns	384	90	120	yes
Heathrow Airport	Park Hotel	081-759 2400	081-759 5278	MtCT	306	600	400	
Heathrow Airport	Sheraton Skyline	081-759 2535	081-750 9150		352	500	450	
Heathrow Airport	Sheraton Heathrow Hotel	081-759 2424	081-759 2091		415	80	80	

London Airport Gatwick

Location	Hotel			Group				
Gatwick Airport	Chequers Thistle	0293 786992	0293 820625	MtCT	78	85	60	
Gatwick Airport	Forte Posthouse	0293 771621	0293 771054	Forte	216	150	120	
Gatwick Airport	Gatwick Penta Hotel	0293 820169	0293 820259		260	150	150	yes
Gatwick Airport	Moat House	0293 785599	0293 785991	QMH	121	180	180	
Gatwick Airport	Copthorne Effingham Park	0342 714994	0342 716039	Copthorne	122	500	500	
Gatwick Airport	Copthorne London Gatwick	0342 714971	0342 717375	Copthorne	227	110	130	yes
Gatwick Airport	Europa Gatwick	0293 886666	0293 886680		211	150	120	
Gatwick Airport	Forte Crest Gatwick	0293 567070	0293 567739	Forte	474	550	500	yes
Gatwick Airport	Gatwick Hilton Internatiol	0293 518080	0293 28980	Hilton	550	500	400	yes

Location	Hotel	Tel	Fax	Group	Rooms	Conf	Banq	Leisure Centre
Gatwick Airport	Gatwick Concorde Hotel	0293 533441	0293 535369	QMH	116	60	120	
Gatwick Airport	Holiday Inn Gatwick	0293 529991	0293 515913	Holiday Inns	223	300	200	yes
Merseyside								
Birkenhead	Bowler Hat Hotel	051-652 4931	051-653 8127		29	80	120	
Haydock	Forte Posthouse	0942 717878	0942 718419	Forte	136	170	130	yes
Haydock	Haydock Thistle	0942 272000	0942 711092	MtCT	139	200	180	yes
Liverpool	Atlantic Tower	051-227 4444	051-236 3973	MtCT	226	140	120	
Liverpool	Britannia Adelphi Hotel	051-709 7200	051-708 8326		391	900	750	yes
Liverpool	Forte Crest	051-709 7050	051-709 2193	Forte	154	600	500	
Liverpool	Moat House	051-709 0181	051-709 2706	QMH	251	400	200	yes
Liverpool	St George's Hotel	051-709 7090	051-709 0137	Forte	155	300	280	
Southport	Prince of Wales Hotel	0704 536688	0704 543488	Forte	104	450	350	
Middlesex								
Heathrow Airport - *see under* **London Airports**								
Shepperton	Moat House	0932 241404	0932 245231	QMH	180	300	280	
Wembley	Hilton National	081-902 8839	081-900 2201	Hilton	300	250	300	
Norfolk								
Barnham Broom	Barnham Broom Hotel	060 545 393	060 545 8224		52	200	250	
Blakeney	Blakeney Hotel	0263 740797	0263 740795		60	200	200	
Blakeney	Manor Hotel	0263 740376	0263 741116		36	15		
East Dereham	Phoenix Hotel	0362 692276		Forte	23	160	160	
Great Yarmouth	Carlton Hotel	0493 855234	0493 852220	Waveney	90	150	120	

Town	Hotel	Phone 1	Phone 2	Chain				
Grimston	Congham Hall	0485 600250	0485 601191		14	12	10	
Hethersett	Park Farm	0603 810264	0603 812104		38	100	120	
King's Lynn	Butterfly Hotel	0553 771707	0553 768027		50	50	15	
King's Lynn	Duke's Head	0553 774996	0553 763556	Forte	71	240	230	
King's Lynn	Knights Hill Hotel	0533 675566	0533 675568		58	400	400	
Knapton	Knapton Hall	0263 720405	0263 721692		9	20	30	
Northwich	Sprowston Manor	0603 41 0871	0603 42.3911		97	90	100	
Norwich	Airport Ambassador Hotel	0603 410544	0603 789935		108	450	350	
Norwich	Forte Posthouse	0603 56431	0603 506400	Forte	113	100	60	yes
Norwich	Friendly Hotel	0603 741161	0603 741500		80	200	200	
Norwich	Hotel Nelson	0603 760260	0603 620008		121	90	90	
Norwich	Norwich Sport Village	0603 788898	0603 406845		55	2,000	2,000	yes
Norwich	Hotel Norwich	0603 787260	0603 400466		108	340	300	yes
Ormesby St Margaret	Ormesby Lodge	0493 730910	0493 733103		9	40	100	
Shipdham	Shipdham Place	0362 820303			8	20	20	
Thetford	The Bell	0842 754455	0842 755552	Forte	47	90	65	
West Runton	The Links	0263 838383	0263 838265		40	200	200	

Northamptonshire

Town	Hotel	Phone 1	Phone 2	Chain				
Crick	Forte Posthouse Northampton	0788 822101	0788 823955	Forte	88	185	120	yes
Northampton	Holiday Inn Garden Court	0604 22777	0604 35454	Holiday Inns	104	30		
Northampton	Moat House	0604 22441	0604 230614	QMH	138	800	600	
Northampton	Stakis Country Court	0604 700666	0604 702850	Stakis	144	80	75	
Northampton	Swallow Hotel	0604 768700	0604 769011	Swallow	122	250	210	yes
Northampton	Westone Moat House	0604 406262	0604 415023	QMH	66	100	180	
Oundle	Talbot Hotel	0832 273621	0832 274545	Forte	40	100	100	
Weedon	Crossroads Hotel	0327 40354	0327 40849		48	50	120	

Northumberland

Town	Hotel	Phone 1	Phone 2	Chain				
Allendale	Bishop Field	0434 683248	0434 683830		11	20		
Alnwick	White Swan	0665 602109	0665 510400	Williamson	43	160	120	

Location	Hotel	Tel	Fax	Group	Rooms	Conf	Banq	Leisure Centre
Belford	Blue Bell Hotel	0668 213543	0668 213787		17	120	85	
Berwick-upon-Tweed	Kings Arms	0289 307454	0289 308867		36	200	150	
Chollerford	George Hotel	0434 681611	0434 681727	Swallow	50	65	98	
Hexham	Beaumont Hotel	0434 602331	0434 602331		23	80	100	
Langley-on-Tyne	Langley Castle	0434 688888	0434 684019		8	160	120	
Longhorsley	Linden Hall	0670 516611	0670 88544		45	200	300	

Nottinghamshire

Location	Hotel	Tel	Fax	Group	Rooms	Conf	Banq	Leisure Centre
Barnby Moor	Ye Olde Bell	0777 705121	0777 860242	Principal	55	250	200	
Newark-on-Trent	Grange Hotel	0636 703399	0636 702328		15	20	44	
Nottingham	Forte Crest	0602 470131	0602 484366	Forte	130	450	500	
Nottingham	Forte Posthouse	0602 397800	0602 490469	Forte	91	70	50	
Nottingham	Holiday Inn Garden Court	0602 500600	0602 500433	Holiday Inns	100	40		
Nottingham	Moat House	0602 602621	0602 691506	QMH	172	200	200	
Nottingham	Novotel	0602 720106	0602 720106	Novotel	112	200	200	
Nottingham	Royal Moat House	0602 414444	0602 475667	QMH	201	600	500	
Nottingham	Rutland Square Hotel	0602 411114	0602 410014		104	200	140	
Nottingham	Stakis Victoria Hotel	0602 419561	0602 484736	Stakis	166	200	200	
Nottingham	Strathdon Thistle	0602 418501	0602 483725	MtCT	69	650	150	
Southwell	Saracen's Head	0636 812701	0636 815408	Forte	27	120	120	

Oxfordshire

Location	Hotel	Tel	Fax	Group	Rooms	Conf	Banq	Leisure Centre
Abingdon	Abingdon Lodge	0235 553456	0235 554117	Four Pillars	63	180	140	
Abingdon	Upper Reaches	0235 522311	0235 555182	Forte	25	100	65	

Banbury	Moat House	0295 259361	0295 270954	QMH	48	100	80	
Banbury	Whately Hall	0295 263451	0295 271736	Forte	74	130	90	
Chadlington	The Manor	0608 76711			7	12		yes
Clanfield	The Plough at Clanfield	036 781 222	036 781 596		6		12	
Great Milton	Le Manoir aux Quat'Saisons	0844 278881	0844 278847		19	36	45	
Henley-on-Thames	Red Lion	0491 572161	0491 410039		26	75	50	
Horton-cum-Studley	Studley Priory	086 735 203	086 735 613		19	50	55	
Kingham	Mill House	0608 658188	0608 658492		24	50	50	
Moulsford-on-Thames	Beetle & Wedge	0491 651381	0491 651376		10	50		
Oxford	Eastgate Hotel	0865 248244	0865 791681	Forte	43	100	80	
Oxford	Moat House	0865 59933	0865 310259	QMH	155	120	100	
Oxford	Randolph Hotel	0865 247481	0865 791678	Forte	109	300	250	
Steeple Aston	Hopcrofts Holt Hotel	0869 40259	0869 40865		85	150	250	
Thame	Spread Eagle	0844 213661	0844 261380		33	250	250	
Wallingford	George Hotel	0491 36665	0491 25359	MtCT	39	120	100	
Wallingford	Shillingford Bridge Hotel	086 732 8567	086 732 8636		31	120	150	
Wantage	Bear Hotel	023 57 66366	023 57 68826		38	80	60	
Weston-on-the-Green	Weston Manor	0869 50621	0869 50901	Hidden	37	40	80	
Witney	Witney Lodge	0993 779777	0993 703467		74	130	130	
Woodstock	Bear Hotel	0993 811511	0993 813380	Forte	45	150	80	
Woodstock	Feathers Hotel	0993 812291	0993 813158		17	35	60	
Wroxton St Mary	Wroxton House	0295 730482	0295 730800		32	45	70	

Shropshire

All Stretton	Stretton Hall Hotel	0694 723224	0746 780850		14	20	
Alveley	Mill Hotel	0746 780437	0584 876019		21	200	250
Ludlow	Dinham Hall	0584 876464	0584 876030		13	50	
Ludlow	Feathers Hotel	0584 875261	063 086 585		40	80	80
Market Drayton	Goldstone Hall	063 086 202	0691 670606		8	70	100
Oswestry	Wynnstay Hotel	0691 655261	0952 461658		27	180	150
Shifnal	Park House	0952 460128	0743 352744	Rank	54	250	250
Shrewsbury	Lion Hotel	0743 353107		Forte	59	200	140

Location	Hotel	Tel	Fax	Group	Rooms	Conf	Banq	Leisure Centre
Shrewsbury	Prince Rupert Hotel	0743 236000	0743 357306	QMH	65	100	80	
Telford	Holiday Inn	0952 292500	0952 291949	Holiday Inns	100	240	180	
Telford	Madeley Court	0952 680068	0952 684275		32	80	60	
Telford	Moat House	0952 291291	0952 292012	QMH	148	400	350	yes
Telford	Telford Hotel	0952 585642	0952 586602		86	300	240	yes
Weston-under-Redcastle	Hawkstone Park	0939 200611	0939 200311		59	200	180	

Somerset

Location	Hotel	Tel	Fax	Group	Rooms	Conf	Banq	Leisure Centre
Dulverton	Carnarvon Arms	0398 23302	0398 24022		25	120	120	
Middlecombe	Periton Park	0643 706885	0643 702698		8	25	30	
North Petherton	Walnut Tree Inn	0278 662255	0278 663946		28	90	70	
Street	Bear Hotel	0458 42021	0458 840007		15	80	110	
Taunton	Castle Hotel	0823 272671	0823 336066		35	90	90	
Taunton	County Hotel	0823 337651	0823 334517	Forte	66	400	350	
Taunton	Forte Posthouse	0823 332222	0823 332266	Forte	97	200	170	
Yeovil	The Manor	0935 231161	0935 706607	Forte	41	60	70	

Staffordshire

Location	Hotel	Tel	Fax	Group	Rooms	Conf	Banq	Leisure Centre
Hanchurch	Hanchurch Manor	0782 643030	0782 643035		12	12		
Lichfield	George Hotel	0543 414822	0543 415817	Jarvis	38	100	100	
Newcastle-under-Lyme	Clayton Lodge	0782 613093	0782 711893	Jarvis	50	270	250	
Newcastle-under-Lyme	Forte Posthouse	0782 717171	0782 717138	Forte	126	70	100	yes
Rolleston-on-Dove	Brookhouse Hotel	0283 814188	0282 813644		19	14		
Stafford	Tillington Hall	0785 53531	0785 59223	De Vere	90	200	174	
Stoke-on-Trent	Haydon House Hotel	0752 711311	0752 717470		30	80	80	yes
Stoke-on-Trent	Moat House	0782 219000	0782 284500		147	500	350	

Location	Hotel							
Stoke-on-Trent	North Stafford Hotel	0782 744477	0782 744580	Principal	69	450	475	
Stoke-on-Trent	Stakis Grand Hotel	0782 202361	0782 286464	Stakis	128	300	250	
Swinfen	Swinfen Hall	0543 481494	0543 480341		19	200	150	yes

Suffolk

Location	Hotel							
Aldeburgh	Brudenell Hotel	0728 452071	0728 454082	Forte	47	50	80	
Aldeburgh	Wentworth Hotel	0728 452312			31	30	100	
Beccles	Waveney House	0502 712270	0502 712660		13	100	120	
Bury St Edmunds	Angel Hotel	0284 753926	0284 750092		40	180	150	
Bury St Edmunds	Butterfly Hotel	0284 760884	0284 755476		66	40	40	
Bury St Edmunds	Suffolk Hotel	0284 753995	0284 753097	Forte	33	35	35	
Copdock	Ipswich Moat House	0473 86444	0473 86801	QMH	74	500	40	yes
Felixstowe	Orwell Moat House	0394 285511	0394 670687	QMH	58	200	180	
Hintlesham	Hintlesham Hall	047 387 334	047 387 463		33	80	120	
Ipswich	Belstead Brook Hotel	0473 684241	0473 681249		92	80	120	
Ipswich	Forte Posthouse	0473 690313	0473 690412	Forte	112	60	65	
Ipswich	Marlborough Hotel	0473 257677	0473 226927		22	120	90	
Ipswich	Novotel	0473 232400	0473 232414	Novotel	101	180	74	
Long Melford	Black Lion	0787 312356	0787 74557		9	16	200	
Long Melford	Bull Hotel	0787 78494	0787 880307	Forte	25	60	25	
Needham Market	Pipps Ford	044 979 208	044 979 561		6	20	100	
Newmarket	Moat House	0638 667171	0638 666533	QMH	47	150	30	
Newmarket	White Hart	0638 663051	0638 667284		23	120	150	
Southwold	The Crown	0502 722275	0502 722740		12	40	200	
Southwold	The Swan	0502 722186	0502 724800		45	50	25	
Sudbury	Mill Hotel	0787 75544	0787 73027		50	80	85	
Woodbridge	Seckford Hall	0394 385678	0394 380610		35	100	80	
Yoxford	Satis House	072 877 418			7	20	30	

Surrey

Location	Hotel							
Bagshot	Pennyhill Park	0276 71774	0276 73217		76	60	80	
Bramley	Bramley Grange	0483 893434	0483 893835		45	150	120	

Location	Hotel	Tel	Fax	Group	Rooms	Conf	Banq	Leisure Centre
Camberley	Frimley Hall	0276 28321	0276 691253	Forte	67	60	130	
Churt	Frensham Pond Hotel	025 125 516	1 025 125 263	1	53	130	150	yes
Cobham	Hilton National	0932 864471	0932 868017	Hilton	152		250	
Cobham	Woodlands Park	0372 843933	0372 842704	Select	58	300	280	yes
Croydon	Croydon Park	081-680 9200	081-760 0426		214	300	200	
Croydon	Forte Posthouse	081-688 5185	081-681 6438	Forte	83	170	170	
Croydon	Selsdon Park	081-657 8811	081-651 6171		170	150	220	yes
East Horsley	Thatchers Resort Hotel	048 65 4291	048 65 4222	Resort	59	100	100	
Egham	Great Fosters	0784 433822	0784 472455		45		200	
Egham	Runnymede Hotel	0784 436171	0784 436340		172	400	350	
Farnham	Bishop's Table Hotel	0252 710222	0252 733494		18	30	80	
Farnham	Bush Hotel	0252 715237	0252 733530	Forte	68	60	90	
Farnham	Trevena House	0252 716908	0252 722583		20	14		
Guildford	The Angel	0483 64555	0483 33770		11	80	100	
Guildford	Forte Crest	0483 574444	0483 302960	Forte	111	150		
Haslemere	Lythe Hill Hotel	0428 651251	0428 644131		40	60	130	
Horley, Gatwick Airport - *see under* **London Airports**								
Nutfield	Nutfield Priory	0737 822072	0737 823321	Hidden	52	60	110	yes
Richmond	Petersham Hotel	081-940 7471	081-940 9998		54	30	70	
Richmond	Richmond Gate Hotel	081-940 0061	081-332 0354		53	70	70	
Seale	Hog's Back Hotel	025 18 2345	025 18 3113	Jarvis	75	120	120	yes
Sutton	Holiday Inn	081-770 1311	081-770 1539		116	200	180	yes
Weybridge	Oatlands Park	0932 847242	0932 842252		131	300	300	
Weybridge	Ship Thistle	0932 848364	0932 857153	MtCT	39	120	120	

Sussex
Sussex, East

Battle	Netherfield Place	042 46 4455	042 46 4024		14	50	70	

Boreham Street	White Friars Hotel	0323 832355	0323 833882		21	30	60	
Brighton	Bedford Hotel	0273 29744	0273 775877		129	450	350	
Brighton	Brighton Metropole	0273 775432	0273 207764		328	1,000	1,000	yes
Brighton	Grand Hotel	0273 21188	0273 202694	De Vere	200	820	600	yes
Brighton	Hospitality Inn	0273 206700	0273 820692	MtCT	204	300	200	
Brighton	Old Ship Hotel	0273 29001	0273 820718		152	350	250	
Brighton (Hove)	Sackville Hotel	0273 736292	0273 205759		45	80	110	
Brighton (Hove)	Whitehaven Hotel	0273 778355	0273 731177		17	45	45	
Cooden	Cooden Resort Hotel	042 43 2281	042 43 6142	Resort	41	200	150	yes
Eastbourne	Cavendish Hotel	0323 410222	0323 410941	De Vere	112	150	350	
Eastbourne	Grand Hotel	0323 412345	0323 412233	De Vere	164	400	400	yes
Eastbourne	Queen's Hotel	0323 22822	0323 31056	De Vere	108	300	250	
Eastbourne	Wish Tower Hotel	0323 22676	0323 21474	Principal	65	60	120	
Hastings	Cinque Ports Hotel	0424 439222	0424 437277		40	320	250	
Lewes	Shelleys Hotel	0273 472361	0273 483152	MtCT	21	50	40	
Rye	George Hotel	0797 222114	0797 224065	Forte	22	80	100	
Uckfield	Horsted Place	0825 75581	0835 75459		17	35	24	
Wadhurst*	Spindlewood	0580 200430	0580 201132		9	20		

Sussex, West

Amberley	Amberley Castle	0798 831992	0798 831998		13	45	38	
Arundel	Norfolk Arms	0903 882101	0903 884275		34	100	100	
Bognor Regis	Royal Norfolk	0243 826222	0243 826325	Forte	51	65	65	
Bosham	Millstream Hotel	0243 573234	0243 573459		29	500		
Chichester	Dolphin & Anchor	0243 785121	0243 533408	Forte	49	180	180	
Climping	Bailiffscourt	0903 723511	0903 723107		20	36	80	
Crawley	George Hotel	0293 524215	0293 548565	Forte	86	40	30	
Cuckfield	Ockenden Manor	0444 416111	0444 415549		22	50	75	
East Grinstead	Gravetye Manor	0342 810567	0342 810080		18	15	18	
East Grinstead	Woodbury House	0342 313657	0342 314801		14		20	
Findon	Findon Manor	0903 872733			10	50	30	

Gatwick Airport - *see under* **London Airports**

Location	Hotel	Tel	Fax	Group	Rooms	Conf	Banq	Leisure Centre
Goodwood	Goodwood Park	0243 775537	0243 533802	Country Club	89	100	120	
Lower Beeding	Cisswood House	0403 891216	0403 891621		34	200	150	
Lower Beeding	South Lodge	0403 891711	0403 891766		39	80	85	
Midhurst	Spread Eagle	0730 816911	0730 815668		41	130	100	
Pulborough	Chequers Hotel	0798 872486	0798 872715		11	20		
Rusper	Ghyll Manor	0293 871571	0293 871419	Forte	27	110	110	
Storrington	Abingworth Hall	0798 813636	0798 813914		21	25	54	
Storrington	Little Thakeham	0903 744416	0903 745022		9	16		
Turners Hill	Alexander House	0342 714914	0342 717328	International	14	55	300	
Walberton	Avisford Park	0243 551215	0243 552485		126	250	300	yes
West Chiltington	Roundabout Hotel	0798 813838	0798 812962		24	40	78	
Worthing	Beach Hotel	0903 234001	0903 234567		82	200	200	
Worthing	Chatsworth Hotel	0903 236103	0903 823726		105	150	150	

Tyne & Wear

Location	Hotel	Tel	Fax	Group	Rooms	Conf	Banq	Leisure Centre
Gateshead	Springfield Hotel	091-477 4121	091-477 7213	Jarvis	60	120	100	
Gateshead	Swallow Hotel	091-477 1105	091-478 7214	Swallow	103	350	350	yes
Newcastle-upon-Tyne	County Thistle	091-232 2471	091-232 1285	MtCT	115	200	220	
Newcastle-upon-Tyne	Forte Crest	091-232 6191	091-261 8529	Forte	166	400	350	
Newcastle-upon-Tyne	Holiday Inn	091-236 5432	091-236 8091	Holiday Inns	150	400	280	yes
Newcastle-upon-Tyne	Moat House	091-262 8989	091-263 4172	QMH	147	400	360	yes
Newcastle-upon-Tyne	Novotel	091-214 0303	091-214 0633	Novotel	126	180	150	
Newcastle-upon-Tyne	Swallow Hotel	091-232 5025	091-232 8428	Swallow	94	120	100	
Newcastle-upon-Tyne	Swallow Gosforth Park	091-236 4111	091-236 8192	Swallow	178	600	500	
Newcastle-upon-Tyne	Airport Moat House	0661 24911	0661 860157	QMH	100	400	350	
Washington	Forte Posthouse	091-416 2264	091-415 3371	Forte	138	80	80	
Washington	Moat House	091-417 2626	091-415 1166	QMH	106	200	180	

Warwickshire

Location	Hotel	Tel	Fax	Chain				
Ansty	Ansty Hall	0203 612222	0203 602155	Hidden	31	70	80	
Bodymoor Heath	Marston Farm	0827 872133	0827 87543		38	45	95	
Brandon	Brandon Hall	0203 542571	0203 544909	Forte	60	100	120	
Charlecote	Charlecote Pheasant	0789 470333	0789 470222	QMH	67	120	120	
Hockley Heath	Nuthurst Grange	0564 783972	0564 783919		15	80	80	
Kenilworth	Clarendon House	0926 57668	0926 50669		31	200	130	
Kenilworth	De Montfort Hotel	0926 55944	0926 57830	De Vere	96	350	200	
Leamington Spa	Holiday Inn Garden Court	0926 425522	0926 881322	Holiday Inns	97	50	50	
Leamington Spa	Inchfield Hotel	0926 883777	0926 330467		22	35	60	
Leamington Spa	Mallory Court	0926 330214	0926 451714		10	-	30	
Leamington Spa	Regent Hotel	0926 427231	0926 450728		83	100	250	
Leamington Spa	Tuscany Hotel	0926 332233	0926 332232		10	20	20	
Stratford-upon-Avon	Alveston Manor	0789 204581	0789 414095	Forte	108	180	120	
Stratford-upon-Avon	Billesley Manor	0789 400888	0789 764145	QMH	41	100	80	
Stratford-upon-Avon	Ettington Park	0789 450123	0789 450472		48	60	56	
Stratford-upon-Avon	Falcon Hotel	0789 205777	0789 414260	QMH	73	200	160	
Stratford-upon-Avon	Forte Posthouse	0789 266761	0789 414547	Forte	60	120	100	
Stratford-upon-Avon	Moat House International	0789 414411	0789 298589	QMH	247	450	450	yes
Stratford-upon-Avon	Shakespeare Hotel	0789 294771	0789 415111	Forte	63	120	120	
Stratford-upon-Avon	Welcombe Hotel	0789 295252	0789 414666		76	120	180	
Stratford-upon-Avon	White Swan	0789 297022	0789 268773	Forte	42	40	20	
Stratford-upon-Avon	Windmill Park	0789 731173	0789 731131	Hilton	100	350	300	yes
Warwick	Hilton National	0926 499555	0926 410020		181	500	350	yes
Wishaw	Belfry Hotel	0675 470301	0675 470178	De Vere	219	300	300	yes

West Midlands

Location	Hotel	Tel	Fax	Chain				
Birmingham	Birmingham Metropole	021-780 4242	021-780 3923		806	2,000	1,440	
Birmingham	Copthorne Hotel	021-200 2727	021-200 1197	Copthorne	212	200	150	yes
Birmingham	Forte Crest	021-643 8171	021-631 2528	Forte	254	630	480	yes
Birmingham	Forte Posthouse	021-357 7444	021-357 7503	Forte	192	150	150	yes

Location	Hotel	Tel	Fax	Group	Rooms	Conf	Banq	Leisure Centre
Birmingham	Holiday Inn	021-631 2000	021-643 9018	Holiday Inns	288	160	200	yes
Birmingham	Hyatt Regency	021-643 1234	021-616 2323		319	240	170	yes
Birmingham	Midland Hotel	021-643 2601	021-643 5075		111	200	185	
Birmingham	Norton Place	021-433-5656	021-433-3048		10	140	140	
Birmingham	Novotel	021-643 2000	021-643 9796	Novotel	148	300	250	
Birmingham	Plough & Harrow	021-454 4111	021-454 1868	Forte	44	70	80	
Birmingham	Royal Angus Thistle	021-236 4211	021-233 2195	MtCT	133	180	180	
Birmingham	Strathallan Thistle	021-455 9777	021-454 9432	MtCT	167		120	
Birmingham	Swallow Hotel	021-452 1144	021-456 3442	Swallow	98	28	21	
Birmingham Airport	Forte Posthouse	021-782 8141	021-782 2476	Forte	136	150	150	
Birmingham Airport	Novotel	021-782 7000	021-782 0445	Novotel	195	35	40	
Coventry	Chace Hotel	0203 303398	0203 301816		67	100	120	
Coventry	De Vere Hotel	0203 633733	0203 225299	De Vere	190	270	300	
Coventry	Forte Posthouse	0203 402151	0203 402235	Forte	184	135	150	
Coventry	Forte Crest	0203 613261	0203 614318	Forte	147	450	450	yes
Coventry	Novotel	0203 365000	0203 362422	Novotel	100	200	100	
Meriden	Forest of Arden Hotel	0676 22335	0676 23711	Country Club	152	150	180	yes
Meriden	Manor Hotel	0676 22735	0676 22186	De Vere	74	275	220	
Solihull	George Hotel	021-711 2121	021-711 3374	Jarvis	78	200	200	
Solihull	Moat House	021-711 4700	021-711 2696	QMH	115	200	200	yes
Solihull	Regency Hotel	021-745 6119	021-733 3801		112	150	120	
Solihull	St John's Swallow Hotel	021-711 3000	021-705 6629	Swallow	206	900	700	yes
Stourbridge	Talbot Hotel	0384 394350	0384 371318		25	650	120	
Sutton Coldfield	Moor Hall	021-308 3751	021-308 8974		75	200	250	
Sutton Coldfield	New Hall	021-378 2442	021-378 4637	MtCT	60	40	40	
Sutton Coldfield	Penns Hall	021-351 3111	021-313 1297	Jarvis	114	650	600	yes
Walsall	Forte Posthouse	0922 33555	0922 612034	Forte	101	45	25	
Walsall Wood	Baron's Court	0543 452020	0543 361276		100	110	90	yes
West Bromwich	Moat House	021-553 6111	021-525 7403	QMH	172	250	200	yes

Location	Hotel	Tel 1	Tel 2	Group				
Wolverhampton	Goldthorn Hotel	0902 29216	0902 710419	Jarvis	93	130	112	
Wolverhampton	Mount Hotel	0902 752055		Park Hotels	56	200	160	
Wolverhampton	Victoria Park	0902 29922	0902 29923		118	200	150	

Wiltshire

Location	Hotel	Tel 1	Tel 2	Group				
Beanacre	Beechfield House	0225 703700	0225 790118	Hidden	20	50	50	
Bradford-on-Avon	Woolley Grange	022 16 4705	022 16 4059		20	40	40	
Castle Combe	Manor House	0249 782206	0249 782159		36	60	100	
Chiseldon	Chiseldon House	0793 741010	0793 741059		21		20	
Colerne	Lucknam Park	0225 742777	0225 743536		42	60	100	yes
Corsham	Rudloe Park	0225 810555	0225 811412		11	90	90	
Easton Grey	Whatley Manor	0666 822888	0666 826120		29	65	80	
Malmesbury	Old Bell Hotel	0666 822344	0666 825145	Clipper	37	30	90	
Marlborough	Ivy House	0672 515333	0672 515338		32	50	70	
Purton	Pear Tree	0793 772100	0793 772369		18	60	48	
Salisbury	Rose & Crown	0722 327908	0722 339816	QMH	28	60	120	
Salisbury	White Hart	0722 327476	0722 412761	Forte	68	50	60	
Stanton St Quintin	Stanton Manor	0666 837552	0666 837022		8		20	
Swindon	Blunsdon House	0793 721701	0793 721056		88	300	250	yes
Swindon	De Vere Hotel	0793 878785	0793 877822		154	290	320	
Swindon	Forte Posthouse	0793 524601	0793 512887	Forte	100	80	60	yes
Swindon	Forte Crest	0793 831333	0793 831401	Forte	97	80	80	
Swindon	Swindon Marriott Hotel	0793 512121	0793 513114	Marriott	153	280	280	yes
Swindon	Wiltshire Hotel	0793 528282	0793 541283	MtCT	95	230	200	
Teffont Evias	Howard's House	0722 716392	0722 716820		8		600	
Warminster	Bishopstrow House	0985 212312	0985 216769		32	70	75	

Yorkshire
Yorkshire, North

Location	Hotel	Tel 1	Tel 2	Group				
Bilbrough	Bilbrough Manor	0937 834002	0937 834724		12	30	30	
Bolton Abbey	Devonshire Arms	0756 710441	0756 710564		40	150	120	

Location	Hotel	Tel	Fax	Group	Rooms	Conf	Banq	Leisure Centre
Boroughbridge	The Crown	0423 322328	0423 324512		42	200	140	
Goathland	Mallyan Spout	0947 86206			24	70	70	
Great Ayton	Ayton Hall	0642 723595	0642 722149		11	30	60	
Hackness	Hackness Grange	0723 882345	0723 882391		28	12		
Harrogate	The Crown	0423 567755	0423 502284	Forte	121	450	300	
Harrogate	Hospitality Inn	0423 564601	0423 507508	MtCT	71	120	120	
Harrogate	Imperial Hotel	0423 565071	0423 500082	Principal	85	200	120	
Harrogate	Majestic Hotel	0423 568972	0423 502283	Forte	156	450	700	yes
Harrogate	Moat House	0423 500000	0423 524435	QMH	214	400	250	
Harrogate	Old Swan Hotel	0423 500055	0423 501154		135	500	600	
Harrogate	Hotel St George	0423 561431	0423 530037	Swallow	93	300	180	yes
Harrogate	Studley Hotel	0423 560425	0423 530967		36	15		
Helmsley	Black Swan	0439 70466	0439 70174	Forte	44	40	30	
Helmsley	Feversham Arms	0439 70766	0439 70346		18	30	30	
Knaresborough	Dower House	0423 863302	0423 867665		32	60	110	
Markington	Hob Green	0423 770031	0423 771589		12	12		
Newby Wiske	Solberge Hall	0609 779191	0609 780472		25	80	100	
Nidd	Nidd Hall	0423 771598	0423 770931		59	250	180	
Reeth	Burgoyne Hotel	0748 84292			8	20	30	
Ripon	Ripon Spa Hotel	0765 602172	0765 690770		40	250	180	
Rosedale Abbey	Milburn Arms	075 15 312	same		11	12		
Scalby	Wrea Head	0723 378211	0723 371780		21	60		
Scarborough	The Crown	0723 373491	0723 362271	Forte	78	200	100	
Scarborough	Holbeck Hall	0723 374374	0723 351114		30	160	140	
Skipton	Randell's Hotel	0756 700100	0756 700107		61	400	330	
South Milford	Posthouse Leeds/Selby	0977 682711	0977 685462		105	300	175	
Staddle Bridge	McCoy's	060 982 671	060 982 660		6	25	25	
Stokesley	Chapters	0642 711888	ext 223		13	54	54	
Whitwell-on-the-Hill	Whitwell Hall	065 381 551	065 381 554		23	70	100	
York	Abbey Park Resort Hotel	0904 658301	0904 621224	Resort	85	140	120	

Location	Hotel	Tel 1	Tel 2				Operator	
York	Dean Court	0904 625082	0904 620305	40	15	35		
York	Forte Posthouse	0904 707921	0904 702804	139	120	65	Forte	
York	Grange Hotel	0904 644744	0904 612453	29	35	80		
York	Hill Hotel	0904 790777		10	20			
York	Holiday Inn	0904 648111	0904 610317	128	150	140	Holiday Inns	
York	Judges Lodging	0904 638733	0904 679947	13	20	30		
York	Middlethorpe Hall	0904 641241	0904 620176	29	68	50		
York	Mount Royale	0904 628856	0904 611171	23	20			
York	Novotel	0904 611660	0904 610925	124	200	150	Novotel	
York	Royal York Hotel	0904 653681	0904 623503	148	180	250	Principal	
York	Swallow Hotel	0904 701000	0904 702308	113	150	120	Swallow	
York	Viking Hotel	0904 659822	0904 641793	188	300	300	QMH	yes

Yorkshire, South

Location	Hotel	Tel 1	Tel 2				Operator	
Barnsley	Ardsley Moat House	0226 289401	0226 205374	73	300	300	QMH	
Dinnington	Dinnington Hall	0909 569661	0909 569661	10	60	60		
Doncaster	Danum Swallow Hotel	0302 342261	0202 329034	66	300	300	Swallow	yes
Doncaster	Grand St Leger	0302 364111	0302 329865	13	70	70		
Doncaster	Moat House	0302 310331	0202 310197	100	400	360	QMH	
Rotherham	Moat House	0709 364902	0709 368960	83	250	175	QMH	
Sheffield	Charnwood Hotel	0742 589411	0742 555107	21	80	120		
Sheffield	Forte Crest	0742 670067	0742 682620	136	300	200	Forte	
Sheffield	Grosvenor House	0742 720041	0742 757199	103	500	450	Forte	yes
Sheffield	Holiday Inn Royal Victoria	0742 768822	0742 724519	100	300	300	Holiday Inns	
Sheffield	Moat House	0742 375376	0742 378140	95	500	300	QMH	
Sheffield	St George Swallow Hotel	0742 583811	0742 500138	141	250	250	Swallow	yes

Yorkshire, West

Location	Hotel	Tel 1	Tel 2				Operator	
Bingley	Bankfield Hotel	0274 567123	0274 551331	103	250	250	Jarvis	
Bradford	Novotel	0274 683683	0274 651342	132	300	250	Novotel	

Location	Hotel	Tel	Fax	Group	Rooms	Conf	Banq	Leisure Centre
Bradford	Stakis Norfolk Gardens	0274 734734	0274 306146	Stakis	120	700	700	
Bradford	Victoria Hotel	0274 728706	0274 736358	Forte	59	150	200	
Bramhope	Forte Crest	0532 842911	0532 843451	Forte	126	150	100	yes
Bramhope	Parkway Hotel	0532 672551	0532 674410	Jarvis	103	250	300	
Garforth	Hilton National	0532 866556		Hilton	144	350	300	yes
Halifax	Holdsworth House	0422 240024	0422 245174		40	100	100	
Huddersfield	George Hotel	0484 515444	0484 535056	Principal	60	200	150	
Huddersfield	Pennine Hilton National	0422 375431	0422 310067	Hilton	118	450	400	yes
Ilkley	Rombalds Hotel	0943 603201	0943 816586		15	80	50	
Leeds	42 The Calls	0532 440099	0532 344100		39	55	125	
Leeds	Haley's Hotel	0532 784446	0532 753342		22	30	24	
Leeds	Hilton International	0532 442000	0532 433577	Hilton	210	400	290	yes
Leeds	Leeds Marriott Hotel	0532 442200	0532 440460	Marriott	125	200	250	
Leeds	Queen's Hotel	0532 431323	0532 425154	Forte	188	650	650	
Linton	Wood Hall	0937 587271	0937 584353		44	140	100	
Monk Fryston	Monk Fryston Hall	0977 682369	0977 683544		28	40	80	
Otley	Chevin Lodge	0943 467818	0943 850335		52	150	120	
Wakefield	Cedar Court	0924 276310	0924 280221		151	350	300	
Wakefield	Forte Posthouse	0924 276388	0924 276437	Forte	99	150	120	
Wakefield	Swallow Hotel	0924 372111	0924 383648	Swallow	64	230	200	
Wentbridge	Wentbridge House	0977 620444	0977 620148	Select	12	120	120	

SCOTLAND

Key: QMH (Queens Moat Houses), MtCT (Mount Charlotte Thistle).

Borders

Location	Hotel	Tel	Fax	Group	Rooms	Conf	Banq	Leisure Centre
Dryburgh	Dryburgh Abbey	0835 22261	0835 23945		30	200	120	
Kelso	Ednam House	0573 224168	0573 226319		32	160	120	
Kelso	Sunlaws House	057 35 331	057 35 611		22	25	20	
Melrose	George & Abbotsford Hotel	089 682 2308	089 682 3363		31	160	140	
Peebles	Park Hotel	0721 20451			24	80	120	
Peebles	Peebles Hotel Hydro	0721 20602	0721 22999		137	400	350	yes
Peebles	Tontine Hotel	0721 20892	0721 29732	Forte	37	40	90	
Selkirk	Philipburn House	0750 20747	0750 21690		16	40		

Central

Location	Hotel	Tel	Fax	Group	Rooms	Conf	Banq	Leisure Centre
Airth	Airth Castle	032 483 411	032 483 419		74	400	280	
Alloa	Gean House	0259 219275	0259 213827		10	80	50	
Bridge of Allan	Royal Hotel	0786 832284	0786 834377		32	150	130	
Drymen	Buchanan Highland Hotel	0360 60588	0360 60943		50	200	130	
Dunblane	Cromlix House	0786 822125	0786 825450		14	36	30	
Dunblane	Stakis Dunblane Hydro	0786 822551	0786 825403	Stakis	240	500	400	yes
Falkirk	Hotel Cladhan	0324 27421	0324 611436		37	250	250	

Location	Hotel	Group	Tel	Fax	Rooms	Conf	Banq	Leisure Centre
Dumfries & Galloway								
Beattock	Auchen Castle		068 33 407	068 33 667	25	25	80	
Gatehouse of Fleet	Cally Palace		0557 814341	0557 814522	54	80		
Newton Stewart	Kirroughtree Hotel		0671 2141	0671 2425	22	30		
Rockcliffe	Baron's Craig		055 663 225		27	100		
Stranraer	North West Castle		0776 4413	0776 2646	74	180	180	yes
Fife								
Dunfermline	King Malcolm Thistle	MtCT	0383 722611	0383 730865	48	150	120	
Glenrothes	Balgeddie House		0592 742511	0592 621702	18	70	70	
Letham	Fernie Castle		033 781 381	033 781 422	16	160	140	
Markinch	Balbirnie House		0592 610066	0592 610529	30	150	120	
St Andrews	Ruffets Hotel		0334 72594	0334 78703	20	45	100	
St Andrews	Rusack's Hotel		0334 74321	0334 77896	50	150	150	
St Andrews	St Andrews Old Course	Forte	0334 74371	0334 77668	125	300	300	yes
Grampian								
Aberdeen	Ardoe House		0224 867355	0224 861283	71	150	200	
Aberdeen	Bucksburn Moat House	QMH	0224 713911	0224 714020	144	540	420	yes
Aberdeen	Caledonian Thistle	MtCT	0224 640233	0224 641627	80	45	30	
Aberdeen	Copthorne Hotel	Copthorne	0224 630404	0224 640573	89	220	200	
Aberdeen	Stakis Tree Tops	Stakis	0224 313377	0224 312028	112	620	500	yes
Aberdeen Airport	Aberdeen Marriott Hotel	Marriott	0224 770011	0224 722347	154	400	380	yes
Aberdeen Airport	Skean Dhu Hotel	MtCT	0224 725252	0224 723745	148	600	460	
Ballater	Craigendarroch Hotel		033 97 55858	033 97 55447	50	100	100	
Banchory	Invery House		033 02 4782	033 02 4712	14	40	30	

Location	Hotel	Phone 1	Phone 2	Chain				
Banchory	Raemoir House	033 02 4884	033 02 2171		25	50	30	
Banchory	Tor-na-Coille Hotel	033 02 2242	033 02 4012		25	80	90	
Craigellachie	Craigellachie Hotel	0340 881204	0340 881253		30	30	30	yes
Elgin	Mansion House	0343 548811	0343 547916		23	180	200	
Maryculter	Maryculter House	0224 732124	0224 733510		11	20	20	
Newburgh	Udny Arms Hotel	035 86 89444	035 86 89012		26	125	100	yes
Peterhead	Waterside Inn	0779 71121	0779 70670		110	250	230	yes

Highland

Location	Hotel	Phone 1	Phone 2	Chain				
Appin	Invercreran Hotel	063 173 414	063 173 532		9	25	30	
Aviemore	Aviemore Highlands Hotel	0479 810771	0479 811473	Principal	103	175	220	
Aviemore	Stakis Coylumbridge Resort	0479 810661	0479 810862	Stakis	175	750	600	yes
Aviemore	Stakis Four Seas	0479 810681	0479 810534	Stakis	89	120	100	yes
Chapel of Garioch	Pittodrie House	046 681 444	046 681 648		27	130	130	
Dulnain Bridge	Muckrach Lodge	047 985 257	047 985 325		12	70	80	
Gairloch	Creag Mor	0445 2068	0445 2044		17	30	110	
Inverness	Caledonian Hotel	0463 235181	0463 711206	Jarvis	100	300	220	yes
Inverness	Culloden House	0463 790461	0463 792181		23	30	30	
Inverness	Kingsmills Hotel	0463 237166	0463 225208	Swallow	84	70	40	yes
Inverness	Mercury Hotel	0463 239666	0463 711145	MtCT	118	300	160	
Isle of Raasay	Isle of Raasay Hotel	047 862 222			12	23		
Kentallen of Appin	Holly Tree	063 174 292	063 174 345		11	12		
Nairn	Carnach House	0667 52094			14	22	40	
Nairn	Golf View Hotel	0667 52301	0667 55267	Rank	48	100	120	
Nairn	Newton Hotel	0667 53144	0667 54026		44	40	80	
Uig	Uig Hotel	047 042 205	047 042 308		17	12		
Whitebridge	Knockie Lodge	045 63 276	045 63 389		10	10		

Lothian

Location	Hotel	Phone 1	Phone 2	Chain				
Dirleton	Open Arms Hotel	0620 85241	0620 85570		7	80	80	
Edinburgh	The Balmoral	031-556 2414	031-557 3747	Forte	189	300	430	yes

Location	Hotel	Tel	Fax	Group	Rooms	Conf	Banq	Leisure Centre
Edinburgh	Barnton Thistle	031-339 1144	031-339 5521	MtCT	50	130	100	
Edinburgh	Braid Hills Hotel	031-447 8888	031-452 8477		69	200	120	
Edinburgh	Caledonian Hotel	031-225 2433	031-225 6632	QMH	240	400	220	
Edinburgh	Carlton Highland	031-556 7277	031-556 2691		199	350	280	yes
Edinburgh	Forte Posthouse	031-334 0390	031-334 9237	Forte	208	120	100	
Edinburgh	George Inter-Continental	031-225 1251	031-226 5644		195	200	250	
Edinburgh	Hilton National	031-332 2545	031-332 3805	Hilton	144	115	90	
Edinburgh	Holiday Inn Garden Court	031-332 2442	031-332 3408	Holiday Inns	119	70		
Edinburgh	Howard Hotel	031-557 3500	031-557 6515	Select	16	40	30	
Edinburgh	King James Thistle	031-556 0111	031-557 5333	MtCT	147	250	250	
Edinburgh	Roxburghe Hotel	031-225 3921	031-220 2518		75	180	200	
Edinburgh	Royal Terrace Hotel	031-557 3222	031-557 5334		95	40	70	yes
Edinburgh	Scandic Crown	031-557 9797	031-557 9789		238	160	120	
Edinburgh	Sheraton Hotel	031-229 9131	031-228 4510		263	485	485	yes
Edinburgh	Stakis Grosvenor Hotel	031-226 6001	031-220 2387	Stakis	136	300	450	
Edinburgh	Swallow Royal Scot	031-334 9191	031-316 4507	Swallow	259	350	250	yes
Gullane	Greywalls Hotel	0620 842144	0620 842241		23	20	20	
Ingliston	Norton House	031-333 1275	031-333 5305		47	300	150	
Kirknewton	Dalmahoy Hotel	031-333 1845	031-335 3203	Country Club	115	220	160	yes
North Berwick	Marine Hotel	0620 2406	0620 4480	Forte	84	350	250	
North Middleton	Borthwick Castle	0875 20514	0875 21702		10	60	60	
North Queensferry	Queensferry Lodge	0383 410000	0383 419708		32	200	200	
South Queensferry	Forth Bridges Moat House	031-331 1199	031-319 1733	QMH	108	250	200	
Uphall	Houstoun House	0506 853831	0506 854220		30	50	40	

Orkney

Location	Hotel	Tel	Fax	Group	Rooms	Conf	Banq	Leisure Centre
Harray Loch	Merkister Hotel	085 677 366			15	30	80	

Shetland

Location	Hotel							
Lerwick	Shetland Hotel	0595 5515	0595 5828		66	350	200	yes

Strathclyde

Location	Hotel							
Alexandria	Cameron House	0389 55565	0389 59522		68	300	168	yes
Ayr	Caledonian Hotel	0292 269331	0292 610722	Jarvis	114	200	175	
Crinan	Crinan Hotel	054 683 261	054 683 292		22	60		
Cumbernauld	Westerwood Hotel	0236 457171	0236 738478		47	150	170	
East Kilbride	Stuart Hotel	035 52 21161	035 52 64410		39	200	150	
Erskine	Forte Posthouse	041-812 0123	041-812 7642	Forte	166	600	450	yes
Giffnock	Macdonald Thistle	041-638 2225	041-638 6231	MtCT	58	150	100	
Glasgow	Copthorne Hotel	041-332 6711	041-332 4264	Copthorne	140	100	100	
Glasgow	Devonshire Hotel	041-339 7878	041-339 3980		15	50	25	
Glasgow	Forte Crest	041-248 2656	041-221 8986	Forte	254	850	750	yes
Glasgow	Glasgow Marriott Hotel	041-226 5577	041-221 9202	Marriott	298	720	640	
Glasgow	Hospitality Inn	041-332 3311	041-332 4050	MtCT	307	1,500	1,000	
Glasgow	Jurys Pond Hotel	041-334 8161	041-334 3846	Jurys	137	150	100	yes
Glasgow	Kelvin Park Lorne Hotel	041-334 4891	041-334 1659	QMH	99	250	180	
Glasgow	Moat House International	041-204 0733	041-221 2022	QMH	300	1,000	1,000	yes
Glasgow	One Devonshire Gardens	041-339 2001	041-337 1663		27	50	32	
Glasgow	Stakis Grosvenor	041-339 8811	041-334 0710	Stakis	95	400	400	
Glasgow	Swallow Hotel	041-427 3146	041-427 4059	Swallow	119	300	300	yes
Glasgow	Tinto Firs Hotel	041-637 2353	041-633 1340	MtCT	30	200	130	
Glasgow	Town House	041-332 3320	041-332 9756	Hidden	34	140	140	
Glasgow Airport	Forte Crest	041-887 1212	041-887 3738	Forte	300	500	300	
Glasgow Airport	Stakis Normandy	041-886 4100	041-885 2366	Stakis	141	1,000	1,000	
Gourock	Stakis Gantock Hotel	0475 34671	0475 32490	Stakis	101	200	136	
Irvine	Hospitality Inn	0294 74272	0294 77287	MtCT	128	300	200	yes
Kilfinan	Kilfinan Hotel	070 082 201	070 082 205		11	50	40	
Kilmelford	Culfail Hotel	085 22 274	085 22 264		12	40	30	
Kilwinning	Montgreenan Mansion	0294 57733	0294 85397		21	100	100	
Langbank	Gleddoch House	047 554 711	047 554 201		33	80	120	

Location	Hotel	Tel	Fax	Group	Rooms	Conf	Banq	Leisure Centre
Milngavie	Black Bull Thistle	041-956 2291	041-956 1896	MtCT	27	120	120	
Oban	Columba Hotel	0631 62183	0631 64683		49	400	400	
Quothquan	Shieldhill	0899 20035	0899 21092		11	16	32	
Stewarton	Chapeltoun House	0560 82696	0560 85100		8	60	50	
Strachur	Creggans Inn	036 986 279	036 986 637		21	100	100	
Tarbert	Stonefield Castle	0880 820836	0880 820929		33	70		
Troon	Marine Highland Hotel	0292 314444	0292 316922		72	220	160	yes
Troon	Piersland House	0292 314747	0292 315613		19	80		
Turnberry	Turnberry Hotel	0655 31000	0655 31706		132	150	150	yes

Tayside

Location	Hotel	Tel	Fax	Group	Rooms	Conf	Banq	Leisure Centre
Aberfeldy	Farleyer House	0887 820332	0887 829430		11	20		
Alyth	Lands of Loyal Hotel	082 83 3151	082 83 3313		11	35		
Auchterarder	Auchterarder House	0764 63646/7	0764 62939		15	50	70	
Auchterarder	Gleneagles Hotel	0764 62231	0764 62134		236	345	260	yes
Auchterhouse	Old Mansion House	082 626 366	082 626 400		6	20		
Blairgowrie	Kinloch House	0250 884237	0250 884333		21	15	30	
Callander	Roman Camp	0877 30003	0877 31533		14	30	50	
Cleish	Nivingstone House	0577 850216	0577 850238		17	40	80	
Crieff	Crieff Hydro	0764 2401	0764 3087		199	400	350	yes
Dalguise	Kinnaird	0796 482440	0796 482289		9	45		
Dundee	Angus Thistle	0382 26874	0382 22564	MtCT	58	500	400	
Dundee	Invercarse Hotel	0382 69231	0382 644112		39	200	280	
Forfar	Royal Hotel	0307 62691	same		19	220	160	yes
Kenmore	Kenmore Hotel	0887 830205	0887 830262		38	100	80	
Kinross	Windlestrae Hotel	0577 63217	0577 64733		45	250	250	yes
Perth	Royal George Hotel	0738 24455	0738 30345	Forte	42	100	80	
Perth	Stakis City Mills Hotel	0738 28281	0738 43423	Stakis	76	120	130	
Pitlochry	Green Park Hotel	0796 473248	0796 473520		37	40	40	
Scone	Murrayshall House	0738 51171	0738 52595		19	60	80	

WALES

Key: QMH (Queens Moat Houses), MtCT (Mount Charlotte Thistle).

Location	Hotel	Tel	Fax	Group	Rooms	Conf	Banq	Leisure Centre
Clwyd								
Ewloe	St David's Park Hotel	0244 520800	0244 520930		121	270	220	
Llandrillo	Tyddyn Llan	049 084 264	049 084 264		10	50		yes
Northop	Soughton Hall	0352 86811	0352 86382		12	40	90	
Ruthin	Ruthin Castle	082 42 2664	082 42 5978		58	200	140	
Dyfed								
Brechfa	Ty Mawr	0267 202332	0267 202437		5	10		
Carmarthen	Ivy Bush Royal	0267 235111	0267 234914	Forte	80	200	200	
Fishguard	Fishguard Bay Hotel	0348 873571	0348 873030		62	200	300	
Gwbert-on-Sea	Cliff Hotel	0239 613241	0239 615391		73	200	200	
Lamphey	Court Hotel	0646 672273	0646 672480		31	90	90	
Llandeilo	Cawdor Arms	0558 823500			17	80	125	
Penally	Penally Abbey	0834 3033			11	20	45	
St David's	Warpool Court	0437 720300	0437 720676		25	25	70	
Gwent								
Chepstow	St Pierre Hotel	0291 625261	0291 629975		147	220	200	yes
Llangybi	Cwrt Bleddyn Hotel	0633 49521	0633 49220		36	200	170	yes
Llanvihangel Gobion	Llansantffraed Court	0873 840678	0873 840674		21	80	120	
Monmouth	King's Head	0600 712177	0600 713545		29	200	180	

Location	Hotel	Tel	Fax	Group	Rooms	Conf	Banq	Leisure Centre
Newport	Celtic Manor	0633 413000	0633 412910		75	350	200	
Newport	Country Court Hotel	0633 413733	0633 413713	Stakis	141	95	72	yes
Newport	Hilton National	0633 412777	0633 413087	Hilton	119	500	400	yes
Newport	Kings Hotel	0633 842020	0633 244667		47	200	220	
Tintern	Beaufort Hotel	0291 689777	0291 689727	Jarvis	24	50	100	
Tintern Abbey	Royal George	0291 689205	0291 689448		19	80	120	

Gwynedd

Location	Hotel	Tel	Fax	Group	Rooms	Conf	Banq	Leisure Centre
Aberdovey	Plas Penhelig	0654 767676	0654 767783		11	20	35	
Abersoch	Riverside Hotel	075 881 2419			12	20		
Beaumaris	Bulkeley Arms	0248 810415	0248 810146		43	160	135	
Beddgelert	Royal Goat Hotel	076 686 224	076 686 422		34	150	150	
Betws-y-Coed	Royal Oak	0690 710219	0690 710603		27	25	90	
Bontddu	Bontddu Hall	0341 49661	0341 49284		20	100	120	
Criccieth	Bron Eifion Hotel	0766 522385	0766 522003		19	120	90	
Llandderfel	Palé Hall	067 83 285			17	55	30	
Llandudno	Bodysgallen Hall	0492 584466	0492 582519	Historic House	28	50	4	
Llandudno	Empire Hotel	0492 860555	0492 860791		51	48	48	
Llandudno	St Tudno Hotel	0492 874411	0492 860407		24	10	50	
Llandudno	St George's Hotel	0492 877544	0492 878477		87	250	250	
Llangefni	Tre-Ysgawen Hall	0248 750750	0248 750035		19	120	130	
Llanrug	Seiont Manor	0286 673366	0286 2840		28	100	100	
Llanwnda	Stables Hotel	0286 830711	0286 830413		14	100	120	
Portmeirion	Hotel Portmeirion	0766 770228	0766 771331		34	100	100	
Talsarnau	Maes-y-Neuadd	0766 780200	0766 780211		16	20	50	
Talyllyn	Tynycornel Hotel	0654 782282	0654 782679		15	25		

Powys

Location	Hotel	Tel	Fax	Group				
Crickhowell	Gliffaes Country House	0874 730371	0874 730463		22	20	30	
Eglwysfach	Ynyshir Hall	0654 781209	0654 781366		9	35	120	
Lake Vyrnwy	Lake Vyrnwy Hotel	069 173 692	069 173 289		30	120	120	
Llangammarch Wells	Lake Country House Hotel	059 12 202	059 12 457		19	80		
Llyswen	Llangoed Hall	0874 754525	0874 754545		23	45	150	
Machynlleth	Wynnstay Arms	0654 702941	0654 703884		20	30	98	
Presteigne	Radnorshire Arms	0544 267406	0544 260418	Forte	16	25		

South Glamorgan

Location	Hotel	Tel	Fax	Group				
Barry	Mount Sorrel Hotel	0446 740069	0446 746600		50	200	150	
Cardiff	Angel Hotel	0222 232633	0222 396212	QMH	91	350	300	
Cardiff	Cardiff International	0222 341441	0222 223742		143	40	120	
Cardiff	Cardiff Marriott Hotel	0222 399944	0222 395578	Marriott	182	300	300	yes
Cardiff	Forte Posthouse	0222 731212	0222 549147	Forte	136	140	120	yes
Cardiff	Forte Crest	0222 388681	0222 371495	Forte	157	150	180	
Cardiff	Moat House	0222 732520	0222 549092	QMH	135	220	250	yes
Cardiff	Park Hotel	0222 383471	0222 399309	MtCT	119	300	200	
Porthkerry	Egerton Grey	0446 711666	0446 711690		10	30	40	

West Glamorgan

Location	Hotel	Tel	Fax	Group				
Gowerton	Cefn Goleu Park	0792 873099	0792 391358		6	20	20	
Reynoldston	Fairyhill	0792 390139	0792 456044		15	20	40	
Swansea	Forte Crest	0792 651074	0792 797535	Forte	99	230	180	yes
Swansea	Hilton National	0792 310330	0792 403210	Hilton	120	200	120	
Swansea	Norton House	0792 404891	0792 650345		15	25	18	
Swansea	Swansea Marriott Hotel	0792 642020		Marriott	118	250	175	yyes

CHANNEL ISLANDS

Key: QMH (Queens Moat Houses), MtCT (Mount Charlotte Thistle).

Guernsey

Location	Hotel	Tel	Fax	Group	Rooms	Conf	Banq	Leisure Centre
St Martin	St Margaret's Lodge	0481 35757	0481 37594		47	120	120	
St Martin	La Trelade Hotel	0481 35454	0481 37855		45	65	200	
St Peter Port	Braye Lodge	0481 723787	0481 712876		26	250	120	
St Peter Port	Duke of Richmond	0481 726221	0481 728945		74	100	200	
St Peter Port	Old Government House	0481 724921	0481 724429		72	150	150	
St Peter Port	St Pierre Park	0481 728282	0481 712041		135	200	200	yes

Jersey

Location	Hotel	Tel	Fax	Group	Rooms	Conf	Banq	Leisure Centre
Bouley Bay	Water's Edge Hotel	0534 62777	0534 63645		51	120		
Gorey	Moorings Hotel	0534 53633	0534 56660		16	25	65	
Havre des Pas	Hotel de la Plage	0534 23474	0534 68642		78	15		
Portelet Bay	Portelet Hotel	0534 41204	0534 46625		86	50	130	
St Aubin	La Haule Manor	0534 41426			20	200	60	
St Brelade	Atlantic Hotel	0534 44101	0534 44102		50	60	60	
St Brelade	Hotel Chateau Valeuse	0534 46281	0534 47110		33	70		yes
St Brelade's Bay	Hotel L'Horizon	0534 43101	0534 46269	Clipper	104	200	250	
St Helier	Beaufort Hotel	0534 32471	0534 20371		54	130	140	
St Helier	Grand Hotel	0534 22301	0534 37815	De Vere	115	180	250	yes
St Helier	Pomme d'Or Hotel	0534 78644	0534 37781		150	300	300	
St Lawrence	Little Grove	0534 25321	0534 25325		13	20	20	
St Peter	Mermaid Hotel	0534 41255	0534 45826		68	120	120	
St Saviour	Longueville Manor	0534 25501	0534 31613		32	70		

Isle of Man

Location	Hotel	Tel	Fax	Group	Rooms	Conf	Banq	Leisure Centre
Douglas	Palace Hotel	0624 662662	0624 625535		135	320	350	yes
Douglas	Sefton Hotel	0624 626011	0624 676004		80	100	100	yes
Ramsey	Grand Island Hotel	0624 812455	0624 815291		54	500	250	yes

NORTHERN IRELAND

Location	Hotel	Tel	Fax	Group	Rooms	Conf	Banq	Leisure Centre

Key: QMH (Queens Moat Houses), MtCT (Mount Charlotte Thistle).

Co Antrim

Location	Hotel	Tel	Fax	Group	Rooms	Conf	Banq	Leisure Centre
Belfast	Dukes Hotel	0232 236666	0232 237177		21	130	160	
Belfast	Plaza Hotel	0232 333555	0232 232999		83	100	60	
Belfast	Wellington Park	0232 381111	0232 665410		56	150	150	
Dunadry	Dunadry Inn	084 94 32474	084 94 33389		67	350	300	yes
Dunmurry	Forte Crest Belfast	0232 612101	0232 626546	Forte	82	450	300	
Larne	Magheramorne House	0574 279444	0574 260138		22	200		
Portballintrae	Bayview Hotel	026 57 31453	026 57 32360		16	150	180	
Templepatrick	Templeton Hotel	084 94 32984	084 94 33406		20	400	320	

Co Down

Location	Hotel	Tel	Fax	Group	Rooms	Conf	Banq	Leisure Centre
Annalong	Glassdrumman House	039 67 68451	039 67 67041		9	16	60	
Comber	La Mon House	0232 448631	0232 448026		46	600	450	yes
Holywood	Culloden Hotel	023 17 5223	023 17 6777		91	500	300	
Newtownards	Strangford Arms	0247 814141	0247 818846		40	280	200	

Location	Hotel	Tel	Fax	Group	Rooms	Conf	Banq	Leisure Centre
Co Londonderry								
Londonderry	Everglades Hotel	0504 46722	0504 49200		52	400	250	

REPUBLIC OF IRELAND

Location	Hotel	Tel	Fax	Group	Rooms	Conf	Banq	Leisure Centre

Key: QMH (Queens Moat Houses), MtCT (Mount Charlotte Thistle).

Co Clare

Location	Hotel	Tel	Fax	Group	Rooms	Conf	Banq	Leisure Centre
Bunratty	Fpatricks Shannon Shamrock	061 361177	061 61252		115	200	200	yes
Ennis	Auburn Lodge	065 21247	065 21202		100	400		
Ennis	Old Ground Hotel	065 28127	065 28112	Forte	58	250	180	
Ennis	West County Inn	065 28421	065 28801	Lynch	100	200	500	
Newmarket-on-Fergus	Clare Inn	061 368161	061 368622		121	400	350	
Newmarket-on-Fergus	Dromoland Castle	061 368144	061 363355		73	350	450	
Shannon	Great Southern	061 61122	061 61982	Great Southern	115	160	150	

Co Cork

Location	Hotel	Tel	Fax	Group	Rooms	Conf	Banq	Leisure Centre
Ballylickey	Sea View House	027 50462	027 51555		17	30		
Cork	Arbutus Lodge	021 501237	021 502893		19	150	180	
Cork	Fitzpatrick Silver Spring	021 507533	021 507641		110	800	700	yes

Location	Hotel			Group				
Cork	Imperial Hotel	021 274040	021 274040		101	350	250	
Cork	Jurys Hotel	021 276622	021 274477	Jurys	185	600	500	yes
Cork	Morrisons Island Hotel	021 275858	021 275833		40	15		
Cork	Rochestown Park Hotel	021 892233	021 892178		39	300	200	
Kanturk	Assolas Country House	029 50015	029 50795		9	20		
Kinsale	Actons Hotel	021 772135	021 772231	Forte	57	400	300	yes
Mallow	Longueville House	022 47156	022 47459		16	20		

Co Donegal

Location	Hotel			Group				
Rathmullan	Rathmullan House	074 58188	074 58200		23	12		
Rossnowlagh	Sand House	072 51777	072 52100		40	75		

Co Dublin

Location	Hotel			Group				
Dublin	Berkeley Court	01 601711	01 617238	Doyle	207	225	275	
Dublin	Burlington Hotel	01 605222	01 608496	Doyle	500	1,000	1,000	
Dublin	Hotel Conrad	01 765555	01 765424		190	250	250	
Dublin	Gresham Hotel	01 746881	01 787175	Ryan	200	325	250	
Dublin	Jurys Hotel	01 605000	01 605540	Jurys	400	800	650	
Dublin	Mont Clare Hotel	01 616799	01 615663		74	175	200	
Dublin	Montrose Hotel	01 269 3311	01 269 1164	Doyle	180	80		
Dublin	New Royal Dublin Hotel	01 733666	01 733120		117	200	250	
Dublin	Sachs Hotel	01 680995	01 686147		20	150	120	
Dublin	Shelbourne Hotel	01 766471	01 616006	Forte	164	400	300	
Dublin	The Westbury	01 679 1122	01 679 7078	Doyle	205	200	200	
Dublin Airport	Forte Crest	01 379211	01 425874	Forte	192	150	130	
Dun Laoghaire	Royal Marine Hotel	01 280 1911	01 280 1089	Ryan	104	600	400	
Killiney	Court Hotel	01 285 1622	01 285 2085		86	300	300	
Killiney	Fitzpatrick's Castle	01 285 1533	01 285 0207		85	270	400	yes

Location	Hotel	Tel	Fax	Group	Rooms	Conf	Banq	Leisure Centre
Co Galway								
Clifden	Abbeyglen Castle	095 21201	095 21797		40	230	200	
Galway	Ardilaun House	091 21433	091 21546		90	500	250	
Galway	Corrib Great Southern	091 55281	091 51390	Great Southern	185	1,000	800	
Galway	Great Southern	091 64041	091 66704	Great Southern	116	400	350	
Oughterard	Connemara Gateway Hotel	091 82328	091 82332		62	300	200	
Renvyle	Renvyle House	095 43511	095 43515		74	70	160	
Co Kerry								
Beaufort	Dunloe Castle	064 44111	064 44583		140	800	400	
Kenmare	Park Hotel	064 41200	064 41402		50	35	50	
Kenmare	Sheen Falls Lodge	064 41600	064 41386		40	120		
Killarney	Aghadoe Heights Hotel	064 31766	064 31345		61	50	70	yes
Killarney	Cahernane Hotel	064 31895	064 34340		52	20		
Killarney	Hotel Europe	064 31900	064 32118		210	500	650	
Killarney	Great Southern	064 31262	064 31642	Great Southern	183	1,000	700	yes
Parknasilla	Great Southern	064 45122	064 45323	Great Southern	84	80		yes
Co Kildare								
Maynooth	Moyglare Manor	01 628 6351	01 628 5405		17	40	70	
Newbridge	Hotel Keadeen	045 31666	045 34402		37	700	500	
Straffan	Kildare Hotel	01 6273333	01 6273312		45	600	600	yes

Co Limerick

Location	Hotel	Phone	Phone	Chain				
Adare	Adare Manor	061 396566	061 396124		64	90	220	
Adare	Dunraven Arms	061 396209	061 396541		47	400	400	
Limerick	Greenhills Hotel	061 53033	061 53307		60	300	400	yes
Limerick	Jurys Hotel	061 327777	061 326400	Jurys	96	180	130	yes
Limerick	Limerick Inn	061 51544	061 326281	Ryan	153	800	800	yes
Limerick	Two Mile Inn	061 53122	061 53783		125	250	300	

Co Louth

Location	Hotel	Phone	Phone				
Dundalk	Ballymascanlon House	042 71124	042 71598	36	250	300	yes

Co Mayo

Location	Hotel	Phone	Phone				
Ballina	Downhill Hotel	096 21033	096 21338	52	300	400	yes
Cong	Ashford Castle	092 46003	092 46260	83	40	140	

Co Meath

Location	Hotel	Phone	Phone			
Navan	Ardboyne Hotel	046 23119	046 22355	27	700	400

Co Monaghan

Location	Hotel	Phone	Phone				
Carrickmacross	Nuremore Hotel	042 61438	042 61853	69	200	400	yes

Location	Hotel	Tel	Fax	Group	Rooms	Conf	Banq	Leisure Centre
Co Tipperary								
Clonmel	Clonmel Arms	052 21233	052 21526		35	450	400	
Dundrum	Dundrum House	062 71116	062 71366		55	400	350	yes
Glen of Aherlow	Aherlow House	062 56153	061 355405	Waveney	10	160	220	
Kilcoran	Kilcoran Lodge	052 41288	052 41994		23	300	220	yes
Co Waterford								
Waterford	Granville Hotel	051 55111	051 70307		74	300	200	
Waterford	Jurys Waterford Hotel	051 32111	051 32863	Jurys	99	550	600	
Waterford	Tower Hotel	051 75801	051 70129		125	600	500	yes
Waterford	Waterford Castle	051 78203	051 79316		19	16		
Co Wexford								
Ferrycarrig Bridge	Ferrycarrig Hotel	053 22999	053 41982		40	400	400	yes
Gorey	Marlfield House	055 21124	055 21572		19	20	30	
Newbawn	Cedar Lodge	051 28386	051 28222		18	100	80	
Rosslare	Great Southern	053 33233	053 33543	Great Southern	99	150	180	yes
Wexford	White's Hotel	053 22311	053 45000		82	600	350	

Co Wicklow

Blessington	Downshire House	045 65199	045 65335	25	100	250
Delgany	Glenview Hotel	01 287 3399	01 287 7511	26	150	110
Dunlavin	Rathsallagh House	045 53112	045 53343	14	50	
Rathnew	Hunter's Hotel	0404 40106	0404 40338	17	10	
Rathnew	Tinakilly House	0404 69274	0404 67806	29	150	100

Special Features

lifetime™

*"It's knowing you can
always keep in touch."*

Whatever life holds in store.

BRITISH PORK

FOREWORD

*B*ritish Meat Catering is once again delighted to be associated with Egon Ronay's Cellnet Guide 1993 Hotels & Restaurants in sponsoring such a prestigious competition.

British pork is now firmly established on the menus of the country's leading hotels and restaurants as chefs and the dining public alike become more aware of the versatility and superb eating quality of lean British pork.

Consumption of meat in Britain is very stable and independent research shows that 97% of the population eat meat, furthermore, nearly a third of consumption is now out of the home. In support of this, British Meat Catering works year round with all sectors of the catering industry providing advice, guidance and develops new British pork dishes to satisfy the demand for a varied menu of consistent quality.

Brian Kilkenny
Head of Home Marketing
Meat and Livestock Commission

THE
BRITISH PORK
COMPETITION

THE
BRITISH PORK
COMPETITION

$\mathcal{O}$nce again, British Meat Catering and the Guide set chefs the ultimate challenge. A competition to find who could create and cook an original British pork dish as part of a three-course menu. Hundreds entered, though we were only able to select 24 to cook-off in four regional finals, culminating in a grand final. Each of the three runners-up received £500, third place £750, second place £1,000 and the winner walked away with £7,500 of travel vouchers for the holiday of a lifetime.

Andrew Eliel, Managing Editor, Egon Ronay's Guides, and Derek Andrews, Catering Development and Promotions Manager, MLC, acted as chief judges throughout the regionals with a guest judge joining them at each stage.

Winning Chef, Peter Auer,
The Dorchester

CENTRAL LONDON HEAT
Westminster College
18th May 1992

Competing chefs

William Fitzgerald, sous-chef,

previously Hilaire, now Whites Club.

Timothy Muehlbauer,

sous-chef, Claridges.

Peter Auer, senior sous-chef,

The Dorchester.

Loic Le Pape, sous-chef, Le Mesurier.

Andrew Bunn, sous-chef,

The Lanesborough.

Timothy Meuhlbauer, right,
Claridges

Joint winners

(both through to final)

Peter Auer

Andrew Bunn

The first of the regional heats set the standard for other chefs to follow. The judges were unable to separate the two winners, and decided that both deserved to go through to the final. Peter's dish of marinated pork neck was the simplest main course and undoubtedly the best, though Andrew's trio of British pork scored high marks for originality and execution. His rhubarb blancmange was unquestionably the dessert of the day.

William Fitzgerald,
Whites Club

SOUTHERN HEAT
Polytechnic of West London
Slough
20th May 1992

Competing chefs

David Everitt-Matthias, chef-patron,

Le Champignon Sauvage, Cheltenham.

Karl-Heinz Nagler, executive chef, Haven Hotel, Poole.

Ronald Maxfield, head chef, Cliveden, Taplow.

Jean-Christophe Novelli, chef-patron, Provence, Lymington.

Nigel Marriage, sous-chef, L'Ortolan, Shinfield.

Mauro Bregoli, chef-patron, Old Manor House, Romsey.

Winner

(through to the final)

David Everitt-Matthias

Runner-up

(through to the final)

Ronald Maxfield

Ronald Maxfield,
Cliveden

An extraordinarily competitive heat with several chefs almost collapsing from their efforts. Some dishes suffered from over complication, whereas David's Chump of Wiltshire Free Range Pork with a Black Pudding Purée, was well balanced and easily the best on the day.

Mignons de porc rotis au curry et sa marinière de moules, Jean-Christophe Novelli

David Everitt-Matthias and commis chef, Derek Baker, receiving their award

WALES/MIDLANDS HEAT
Henley College, Coventry
21st May 1992

Competing chefs

*S*teven Morris, head chef, Tre-Ysgawen Hotel, Llangefni.

Andrew Price, sous-chef, Plas Bodegroes, Pwllheli.

Christopher Dawson, commis chef,

Hotel Maes-y-Neuadd, Talsarnau.

Robert Slater, sous-chef, Swallow Hotel, Birmingham.

Aaron Patterson, head chef, Hambleton Hall, Oakham.

Winner

(through to final)

Aaron Patterson

A close heat, with several highlights. A strong line-up
of British pork dishes, with Aaron receiving the judges
verdict. His roast suckling pig with caramelised apples was a
masterpiece of understatement, since it used every cut
including cutlet, kidney, liver and trotter. Overall, the'
balance of the dishes was somewhat heavy, confirming that
guests who dine at these establishments
expect a lot on the plate!

**A crispy Mille Feuille of British Pork,
Aaron Patterson**

NORTH/SCOTLAND HEAT
University College of Salford
Manchester,
4th June 1992

Competing chefs

*D*erek Smith, head chef, Raemoir House, Banchory.

Peter Leggat, head chef, Wincham Hall, Wincham.

Bruce Sangster, executive chef, Murrayshall, Scone.

Germain Schwab, chef-patron,

Winteringham Fields, Winteringham.

Stuart McLeod, head chef, Nidd Hall, Nidd.

Malcolm Warham, senior sous-chef, Westerwood Hotel,

Cumbernauld.

Winner

(through to final)

Germain Schwab

**Loin of pork crowned with a mousse
of maize fed chicken,
Bruce Sangster**

*B*ruce, winner of the British Lamb competition two years ago, again competed strongly with loin of Scotch pork crowned with a mousse of maize-fed chicken, but had to give way on this occasion to Germain, whose robust country-style British pork dish contrasted with the other chefs' more modern approach. Schwab's tasty British pork cheeks in Calvados and crispy crackling, served with a compote of red cabbage, was both original and unpretentious.

An informal dinner for chefs and judges was held at
Dell'Ugo, one of London's newest and most fashionable
restaurants the night before the final, so the competitors
were nicely relaxed for the big day.

THE FINAL
Westminster College
25th June 1992

Competing chefs

Peter Auer, senior sous-chef, The Dorchester, London.

Andrew Bunn, sous-chef, The Lanesborough, London.

David Everitt-Matthias, chef patron, Le Champignon
Sauvage, Cheltenham.

Ronald Maxfield, head chef, Cliveden, Taplow.

Aaron Patterson, head chef, Hambleton Hall, Oakham.

Germain Schwab, chef-patron,
Winteringham Fields, Winteringham.

Judges

Egon Ronay

Brian Kilkenny, Head of Home Marketing,
Meat and Livestock Commission.

Derek Andrews, Catering Development & Promotions
Manager, Home Marketing, MLC.

Lorna Pettipher, Editor, Chef Magazine.

Jacques Schneider, Managing Director, Profile.

Andrew Eliel, Managing Editor.

Peter Auer,
The Dorchester

A close-run affair with Peter Auer edging out Andrew Bunn. Ron Maxfield, runner-up in the southern heat, claimed third spot. Peter's main course, marinated pork neck (see recipe), was unanimously voted the best British pork dish, but Egon was able to comment favourably on specific dishes from each contestant. So much effort, excellent camaraderie, the chefs

Brian Kilkenny, Peter Auer, Egon Ronay

Competing chefs and judges

and their assistants all deserve praise - it was a terrific competition and thanks are due to all who participated: the judges, the chefs, the colleges who provided the venues, and of course, the organisers, namely British Meat Catering.

THE BRITISH PORK COMPETITION

MARINATED BRITISH PORK NECK, ROASTED WITH THYME JUS

Ingredients: serves 4

1kg British Pork neck with skin

For the marinade:

$1/2$ ltr pork jus, 30g Celeriac, peeled and cubed, 30g Carrots,
peeled and cubed, 50g Onions, peeled and cubed,
15g Parsley stems, Rosemary, Thyme, 1 Clove garlic,
1 Bay leaf, 5 Juniper berries, crushed, 2g Caraway seed,
3g White peppercorn, crushed, 2g Coriander seed.

For the cooking:

20 Button mushrooms, 50ml Madeira, 25ml Pork glaze,
2g Thyme, $1/2$ White cabbage, 10g Chopped shallots,
100g Smoked bacon, Salt, Pepper, Vinegar, Sugar,
Caraway seed, 200g Cooked, cold potatoes passed
through a sieve, 50g Flour, 1 Egg, 20g Melted butter,
Nutmeg, 20g Clarified butter.

Recipe

Prepared the day before:

1. Trim the neck, take off skin and remove
some fat if necessary.

2. Tie the neck with a string.

3. Mix all ingredients for the marinade and put in a container
together with the neck and cover with
the pork skin. Leave in the fridge overnight.

Prepared on the day:

4. Seal the neck on all sides, sweat the celeriac,
carrots and onion. Add the rest of the marinade to the neck
and put in the oven. Add some water.

5. Slightly sweat the button onions, brown and add the
thyme. Cook in the oven.

6. Blanch 8 leaves from the outside of the cabbage.
Cut them into squares of 10cm.

7. Cut 200g of cabbage into julienne.

8. Sweat the shallots and bacon in butter. Add the cabbage,
vinegar, chopped caraway seed, sugar, salt and pepper.

9. Deglaze with water and cook gently at the side
of the stove.

10. When cooked, stuff the cabbage leaves with julienne.
Roll into a roulade and braise gently
in the oven for 30 minutes.

11. Slice the pork skin into julienne and roast in the oven
until very crispy.

12. Mix all the ingredients for the potatoes together
and season.

13. Roll the potatoes into the shape of a sausage.
Blanch them in boiling water for 2 minutes.
Then put them in cold water, dry on a tray.
Finish by pan frying until golden brown in clarified butter.

14. Cook for $2^{1/2}$ hours until meat is tender.
Take out of the oven,
remove the string and cut into 12 slices.

15. Drain the sauce and add chopped thyme.

16. Dress on the plate as shown.

HIGH LEVEL SPEC

The Saab 900SE has everything
you'd expect and a whole lot
more. All for a lot less than
you'd think.

Price £15,495*

- Anti Lock Brakes (ABS)
- Sunroof
- Alloy Wheels
- Electric Windows
- Metallic Paint
- Central Locking

GROUND LEVEL CHEQUE

- Heated Front Seats
- Audio with CD Autochanger
- 16 Valves, Injection
- Catalyst
- Power Assisted Steering

For further information

please ring

0800 626556

The Lowdown on Mark-ups

By Robin Young

Many years ago I won an instant of journalistic notoriety by pointing out that it was possible to save hundreds of pounds simply by buying a bottle of wine in one central London restaurant rather than another. Sir James Goldsmith's now defunct *Now!* magazine paid me £220, I remember, for this revelatory scoop, and I became consumer columnist of *Decanter*, the wine buff's magazine, on the strength of it. It was a post I held for a decade or so thereafter. What other difference did the revelation make? Such is the power of the press that I would venture to suggest that it made absolutely no difference at all.

Neither of the restaurants involved in my exposé, Le Gavroche at the top end of the price scale and Au Jardin des Gourmets at the bottom, altered their pricing policy one iota. Interestingly, Albert Roux at Le Gavroche in Mayfair had been trying to buy extra supplies of Chateau Lafite 1945, the wine concerned in the amazing price difference, from Joseph Berkmann, the proprietor of Au Jardin des Gourmets. Roux, charging about £1,000 a bottle more for the stuff than Berkmann's restaurant did, had almost sold out and was down to his last couple of bottles, while Berkmann catering in Soho to less well-flushed punters had comparatively plentiful supplies and found turnover steady but slow.

I do not even imagine that it was the appearance of my article which stopped Mr Berkmann supplying Monsieur Roux with more bottles to which he could apply his meaty surcharge. As I recall, the owner of Au Jardin had already made it clear he would not be selling his stocks to the rival restaurateur anyway.

The anomalous price differentials on the restaurant wine lists continued undisturbed, and so they have done to this day.

Buy, for example, Chateau Lafite 1970 at Le Gavroche now and it will cost you £560. Drink it at Ard-na-Coille hotel near Inverness and it is a quarter of the price. Flying to Scotland and taking a taxi to the hotel would still leave enough change in your pocket to pay for the dinner.

If your choice is Chateau Mouton Rothschild 1961, the cost including service at Le Gavroche is £865. At Crabwall Manor outside Chester it is only £350.

Yet do not think that Le Gavroche always tops the league. Why, at the Old Manor House in Romsey (a firm favourite of mine in other ways) the same wine is £950, and at Le Gavroche's Mayfair neighbour, the re-opened Mirabelle, the price tag has climbed to £1,050.

With Chateau Latour '61 the differentials are even more extreme. The Manor Hotel and Restaurant at Chadlington sets the low marker of just £290 a bottle. The same wine is £330 at Netherfield Place in Sussex, £435 at Le Talbooth in Constable country, £470 at Alderley Edge, £475 with the fanatical Barry Philips at the White Horse, Chilgrove, and £720 at Chewton Glen in Hampshire. The Waterside Inn at Bray wants £880 including service, the Old Manor House is ambitious again with a price of £900. The Inn on the Park has recently reduced its price for this bottle from a staggering £1,150 to £602 – did they get a sneak preview of this piece?

The difference between the Manor Hotel and the Old Manor House, an appreciable £600, is enough to pay for a decent holiday. More modestly, if you just fancy saving a quick couple of hundred quid on a bottle, Chateau Latour 1970 is £110 at the Croque-en-Bouche in Malvern, but £310 at the Inn on the Park.

Naturally, I am glad to know that the Guide is taking up the cudgels on this issue once more, and delighted to have the benefit of their researches to expose the examples quoted here. They leave no room for doubt that Andrew Eliel, the Guide's managing editor, is absolutely right when he says that many restaurants are overcharging for their wines in a quite diabolical fashion.

In the end, though, only the customer's refusal to pay ridiculous prices can persuade greedy and avaricious restaurateurs to stop demanding them. One mug willing to part with a thousand smackers over the odds makes up for quite a lot of parsimonious persons fastidiously sticking to tap water in powerless protest.

It is not only classic clarets which are subjected to massive mark-ups. Even for commonplace wines in common consumption and freely available from supermarket shelves, the mark-up can be four or even five times the wine's current wholesale price.

An everyday, Australian red such as Penfold's Bin 28 Kalimna Shiraz is, at the time of writing, under £5 wholesale from Lay & Wheeler of Colchester. It sells for £10 at La Truffe Noire in Tooley Street, London, SE1. At the Ritz Hotel in Piccadilly the price is £21.

A bottle of Lanson Black Label non-vintage champagne can be as little as £19.75 at Hill House, Horndon-on-the-Hill, in Essex, £21 at Grizedale Lodge in Cumbria, or £22.95 at the Black Bull, Moulton, in Yorkshire. Yet it is £36.50 with 15 per cent service charge still to pay at both the Connaught and Mr Kai in London, £37 at La Bonne Auberge, £37.25 at the Cottage in the Woods, £37.50 at the Swan Diplomat, £38 at Gravetye Manor, £38.50 at the Savoy, and £39 at the Langham. Customers at Le Meridien in Piccadilly though, are apparently quite happy to pay double the lowest restaurant prices, and three times shop price, forking out £44 a bottle for the identical champagne.

Similarly you can have 1983 Veuve Clicquot for under £30 (£29.50 at Stane St Hollow) or substantially over £60 (£65, in fact, including service, at the Waterside Inn).

With 1983 Louis Roederer Cristal Brut the difference stretches from £57 at the new La Sémillante in London and £64.50 at Roscoff to £175 at Le Gavroche, while for Dom Perignon of the same vintage Paul Henderson at Gidleigh Park, Chagford, Devon, wants a modest £66 compared to £120 at Raymond Blanc's Le Manoir aux Quat Saisons in Great Milton, Oxfordshire, and £151.90 at La Tante Claire in Chelsea.

Paul Henderson says he is delighted that the Guide is taking up the question of wine pricing. "It does annoy me", he says, "to eat in restaurants where the food is good but the wine prices rapacious. Many of these places have no stock to speak of, taking deliveries from merchants on a weekly basis and paying a month in arrears, then collecting cash from the punters. Here our current stock is worth about £150,000, which will cost about £18,000 in interest this year."

Mr Henderson's pricing policy is designed to encourage his customers to drink better wines. "We mark up the cheapest wines by £10 plus VAT, and the most expensive wines a maximum of £25. This makes wines over £30 good value in restaurant terms – for a wine costing us £15 ex VAT our mark up is less than 100 per cent. Incidentally, I also buy well, spending a lot of time checking out prices; I buy from about 25 merchants each year, getting as close to the importer as possible."

How restaurateurs price their wines is, of course, finally their own business. A few adopt policies even more generous and progressive than Mr Henderson's. Appleby Manor, for instance, mark up every wine by £4.50, except for four value-for-money fine wines and champagnes (the latter carry a £6 increase). As owner Nick Swinscoe says: "it means I can recommend any wine I want to customers without being accused of pushing the most profitable, since I'm making the same profit on every bottle". Some buying *en primeur* or opportunistically and applying modest or flat-rate mark-ups end up charging less for their fine wines served in the restaurant than the bottles would command in the London auction rooms, which makes them bargains indeed.

One can expect that restaurants which employ large numbers of staff to cater for relatively few customers will have to charge more to cover their significantly increased overheads. Fair enough, but isn't that what the customers are paying service charge for? And does it explain the high prices in places that frankly have no wine service expertise at all?

How much more enterprising and enjoyable it would be, though, if restaurants generally tried to promote and encourage wine drinking by offering discounts on their bin ends, and lower prices on new introductions, slow sellers, or wines appropriate for the particular season. Instead of trying to sell more, they seem intent only on taking larger profit from what they sell already. It is the customers' fault if they let them continue in this lazy attitude.

If customers pay too much for their wine it is, ultimately, their own fault. The way to ensure that you do not join in this folly is by doing at least some homework on wine prices before you go dining out. If you know what sort of price the wines you are likely to be drinking sell at retail, you can judge what sort of value you are being offered in the restaurant.

Compendious details of wine prices are difficult to carry in your head, but it is easy enough to remember a few commonly encountered markers that you can go by: Cordier clarets of appropriate vintages, for example, Duboeuf Beaujolais, Hugel Alsace wines, Rosemount Estate Australians, or the Torres range from Penedes. In more modest establishments, have an idea what price you should expect to pay for Mouton Cadet, Blue Nun and Mateus Rosé.

Some restaurants will let you view a copy of the wine list in advance, or you can ask for some sample prices when ringing up to make your reservation.

If you go in without the faintest idea what wines should reasonably be expected to cost, you are asking to be ripped off – and all the evidence suggests that you probably will be, on rather a grand scale.

Prices quoted were taken from wine lists provided by restaurants between March and August 1992.

Maps

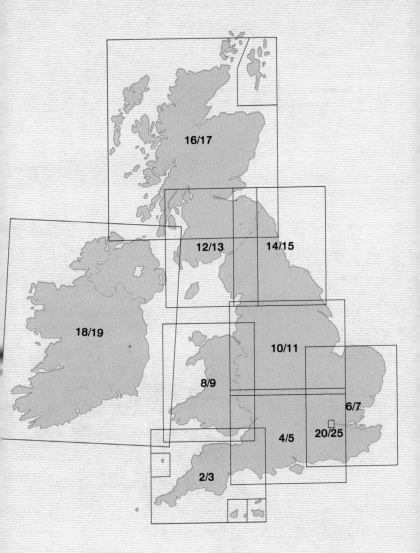

16/17

12/13 14/15

18/19

10/11

8/9 20/25 6/7

4/5

2/3

	Motorways	☐	Hotel
	Primary Routes	●	Restaurant
	Other Roads	◉	Hotel and Restaurant
	County Boundaries	■	London hotels

Designed and Produced by
Euromap Ltd, Pangbourne, Berkshire.

ading Guides Ltd.

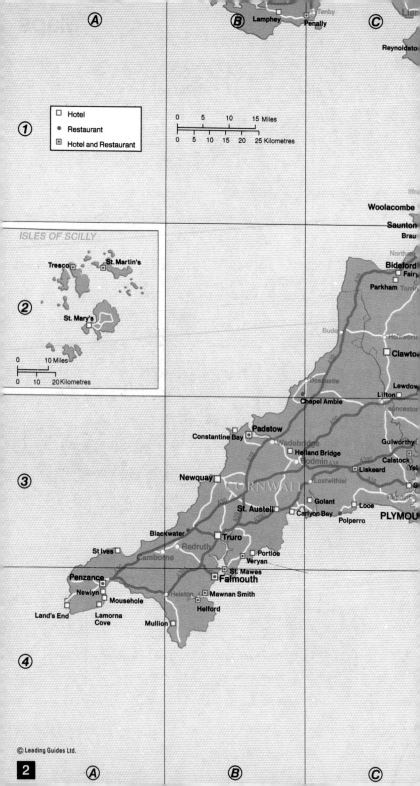

Ⓐ

Ⓑ Lamphey Penally Tenby Llar

Ⓒ Reynoldsto

Legend:
- ☐ Hotel
- ● Restaurant
- ☒ Hotel and Restaurant

Ⓐ①

0   5   10   15 Miles
0   5   10 15 20   25 Kilometres

Ilfra
Woolacombe
Saunton
Brau
Northam
Bideford
Fairy
Parkham Torn

ISLES OF SCILLY

Tresco St. Martin's

Ⓐ②

St. Mary's

0   10 Miles
0   10   20 Kilometres

Bude
Holsworu
Clawto
Boscastle
Lewdow
Lifton
Launceston
Chapel Amble
Padstow
Constantine Bay
Wadebridge
Gulworthy
Helland Bridge
Bodmin
Calstock
Yel
Liskeard
Newquay
CORNWALL
Lostwithiel
S
Ⓐ③
Golant
St. Austell
Looe
Carlyon Bay
Polperro
PLYMOU
Blackwater
Truro
Redruth
Portloe
St Ives
Camborne
Veryan
Penzance
St. Mawes
Newlyn
Falmouth
Mousehole
Helston
Mawnan Smith
Land's End
Lamorna
Cove
Helford
Mullion

Ⓐ④

© Leading Guides Ltd.

2

Ⓐ   Ⓑ   Ⓒ

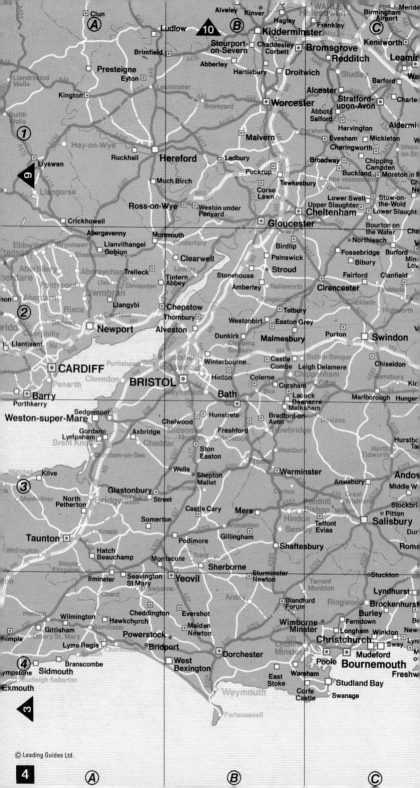

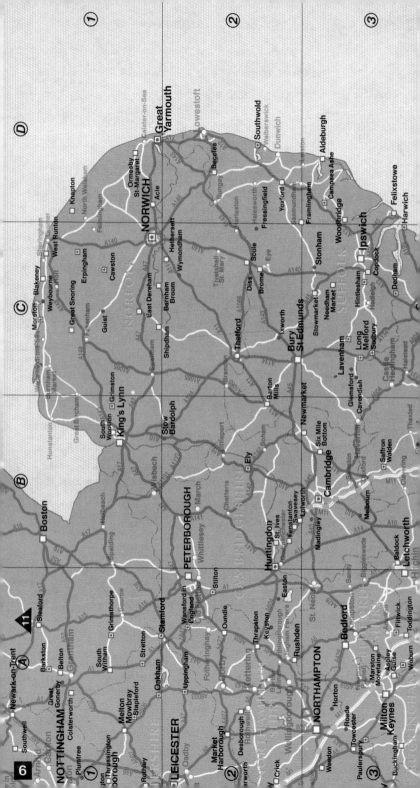

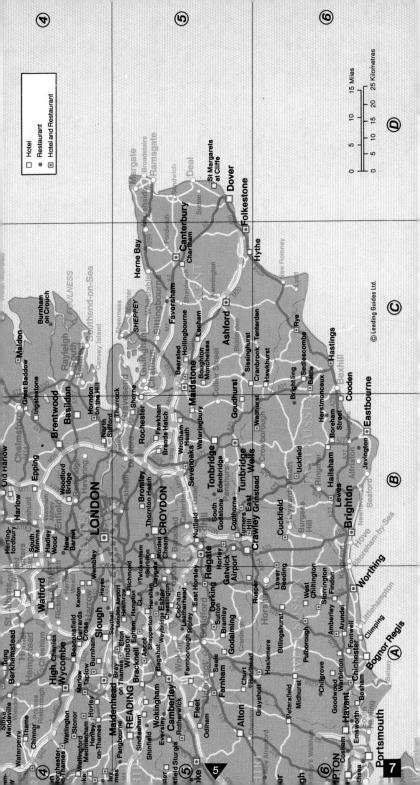

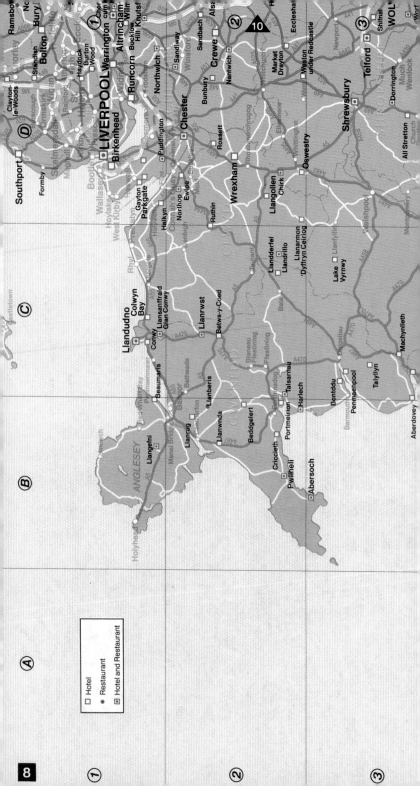

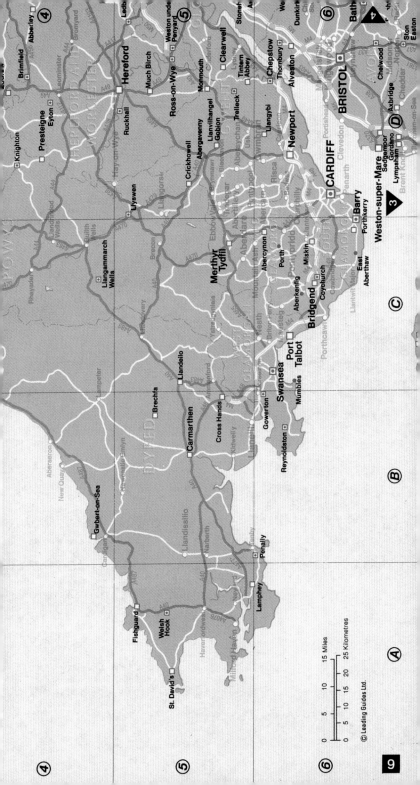

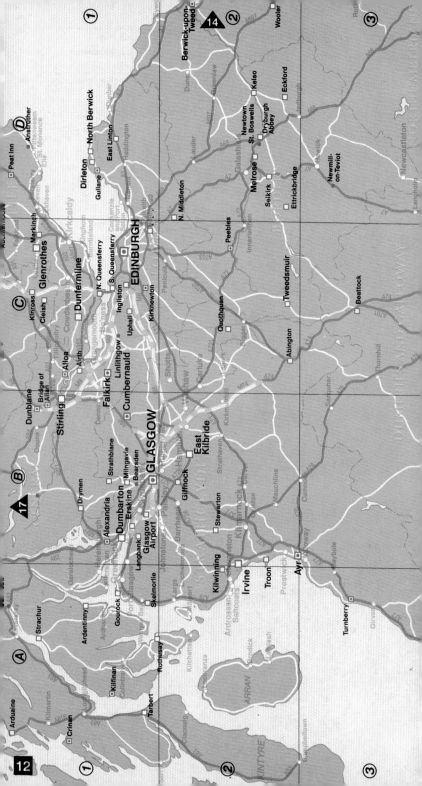

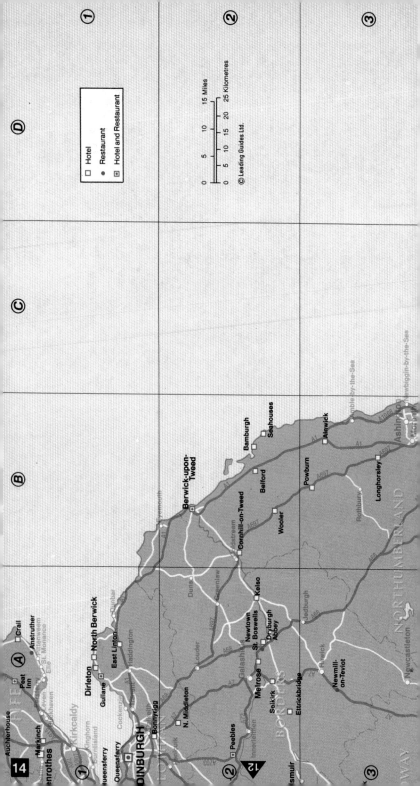

14

① ② ③

Ⓐ Ⓑ Ⓒ Ⓓ ①

Hotel
Restaurant
Hotel and Restaurant

0 5 10 15 Miles
0 5 10 15 20 25 Kilometres
© Leading Guides Ltd.

②

③

FIFE

Crail
Peat Inn
Anstruther
St. Monance
Pittenweem
Elie
Leven
Markinch
Kirkcaldy
Kinghorn
Burntisland
Auchterhouse
nrothes
Queensferry

EDINBURGH
Bonnyrigg

North Berwick
Dirleton
Gullane
East Linton
Haddington
Dunbar

N. Middleton

Peebles
Innerleithen

Galashiels
Lauder

Melrose
Newtown
St. Boswells
Dryburgh Abbey
Kelso

Selkirk
Ettrickbridge

Newmill-on-Teviot
Jedburgh

BORDERS

smuir

12

Coldstream
Eyemouth
Duns
Greenlaw

Berwick-upon-Tweed
Cornhill-on-Tweed

Wooler
Belford
Bamburgh
Seahouses

Powburn
Alnwick

Rothbury
Longhorsley

NORTHUMBERLAND
Newcastleton
Newbiggin-by-the-Sea
Amble-by-the-Sea
Ashington

WAY

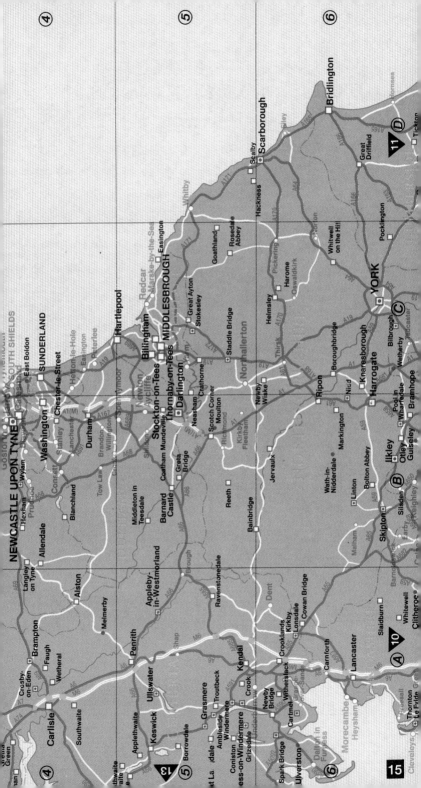

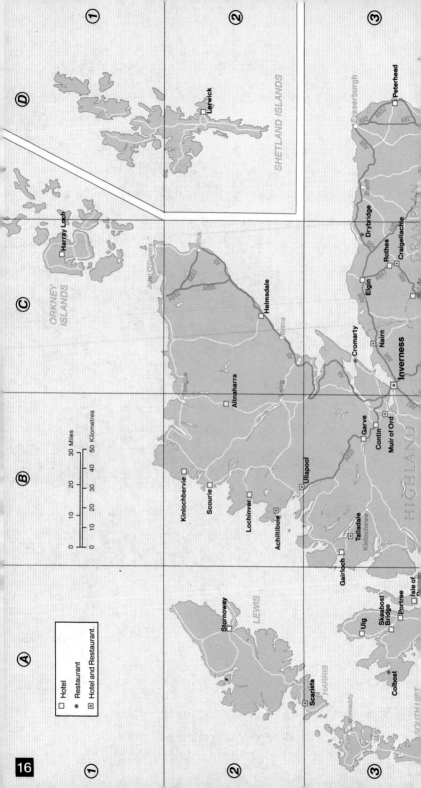

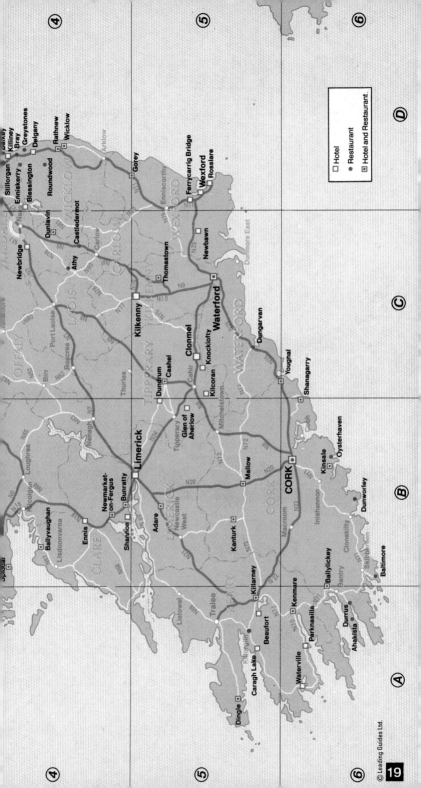

Hotel
Restaurant
Hotel and Restaurant.

© Leading Guides Ltd.

19

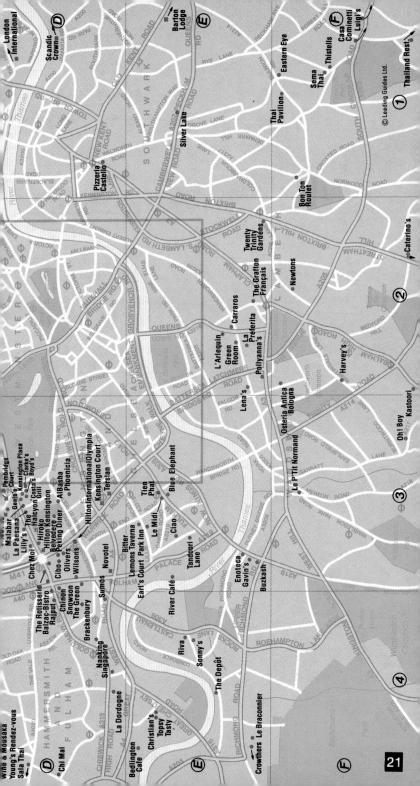

© Leading Guides Ltd.

23

Wedgwood®

for fine Hotels and Restaurants

Wedgwood Hotel & Restaurant Division
Park Street · Fenton · Stoke-on-Trent · ST4 3JB
Telephone: 0782 744221 Fax: 0782 744491

977

Index

Aagrah *Bradford* **276**
Aagrah *Shipley* **543**
Aagrah *Skipton* **545**
Abbey Court *W2* **50**
Abbey Hotel *Malvern* **454**
Abbey Hotel *Penzance* **505**
Abbey Park Resort Hotel *York* **630**
Abbeyglen Castle *Clifden* **780**
Abbots Well *Chester* **321**
Aberdeen Marriott Hotel *Aberdeen Airport* **642**
Abingdon Lodge *Abingdon* **226**
Abingworth Hall *Storrington* **563**
Absolute End *St Peter Port* **753**
L'Accento Italiano *W2* **50**
Actons Hotel *Kinsale* **805**
Adam's Café *W12* **50**
Adare Manor *Adare* **772**
Adelphi Hotel *SW7* **50**
Adlard's *Norwich* **489**
Adrian's *Howth* **800**
Aghadoe Heights Hotel *Killarney* **803**
Aherlow House *Glen of Aherlow* **799**
Aherne's Seafood Restaurant *Youghal* **821**
Airds Hotel *Port Appin* **705**
Airport Ambassador Hotel *Norwich* **489**
Airport Moat House *Newcastle-upon-Tyne* **481**
Airth Castle *Airth* **644**
Ajimura *WC2* **51**
Al Basha *W8* **51**
Al Bustan *SW1* **51**
Al Fresco *Dublin* **786**
Al Hamra *W1* **51**
Al San Vincenzo *W2* **51**
Al-Shami *Oxford* **499**
Alastair Little *W1* **52**
Alba *EC1* **52**
Alderley Edge Hotel *Alderley Edge* **227**
Alexander Hotel *SW7* **52**
Alexander House *Turners Hill* **592**
Alexandra Hotel *Lyme Regis* **447**
Alexandra Hotel *Oban* **701**
Alfonso's *Cavendish* **312**
Allt-nan-Ros Hotel *Onich* **702**
Alma Lodge *Stockport* **559**
Almond Brook Moat House *Standish* **556**
Les Alouettes *Claygate* **329**
Alp-Horn *Edinburgh* **663**
Alston Hall *Holbeton* **410**
Altnaharra Hotel *Altnaharra* **645**
Altnaharrie Inn *Ullapool* **716**
L'Altro *W11* **52**
Alverton Manor *Truro* **589**
Alveston House *Alveston* **231**
Alveston Manor *Stratford-upon-Avon* **567**
Hotel Ambassadeur *St Clement's Bay* **759**
Amber *Glasgow* **677**
Amberley Castle *Amberley* **231**
Amberley Inn *Amberley* **231**
Ancient Camp Inn *Ruckhall* **525**
The Angel *Guildford* **389**
Angel Hotel *Bury St Edmunds* **302**
Angel Hotel *Cardiff* **724**
Angus Thistle *Dundee* **662**

Anna's Place *N1* **53**
Annie's *Moreton-in-Marsh* **472**
Ansty Hall *Ansty* **233**
Antico *Eton* **362**
Anupam *Malvern* **454**
Apollo Hotel *St Helier* **759**
Apollo Hotel *W8* **53**
Appleby Manor Hotel *Appleby-in-Westmorland* **233**
Apsley House *Bath* **248**
Arbutus Lodge *Cork* **781**
Ard-na-Coille Hotel *Newtonmore* **699**
Hotel Ard-na-Sidhe *Caragh Lake* **777**
Ardagh Hotel *Clifden* **780**
Ardanaiseig *Kilchrenan* **689**
Ardboyne Hotel *Navan* **810**
Ardentinny Hotel *Ardentinny* **647**
Ardilaun House *Galway* **798**
Ardoe House *Aberdeen* **640**
Ardsheal House *Kentallen of Appin* **689**
Ardsley Moat House *Barnsley* **243**
The Argyll *SW3* **53**
Arirang Korean Restaurant *W1* **53**
Arisaig House *Arisaig* **647**
Arisugawa *W1* **54**
Ark *Erpingham* **361**
L'Arlequin *SW8* **54**
Armadillo *Liverpool* **440**
Armathwaite Hall *Bassenthwaite* **248**
Armless Dragon *Cardiff* **724**
Armstrong's *Barnsley* **243**
Arrow Mill *Alcester* **226**
Arts Theatre Café *WC2* **54**
Arundel House *Cambridge* **304**
Arundell Arms *Lifton* **438**
Ashbourne Oaks Lodge *Ashbourne* **236**
Ashford Castle *Cong* **781**
Ashford International *Ashford* **236**
Ashoka West End *Glasgow* **677**
Ashwick House *Dulverton* **351**
Asian Tandoori Centre *Southall* **551**
Assolas Country House *Kanturk* **801**
Aster House *SW7* **54**
Astor Hotel *Plymouth* **507**
Asuka *NW1* **55**
At The Sign of The Angel *Lacock* **425**
The Athenaeum *W1* **55**
Atlantic Hotel *St Brelade* **757**
Atlantic Tower *Liverpool* **440**
Atlantis *Aberdeen* **640**
Atlas Hotel *W8* **55**
Au Bon Accueil *SW3* **55**
Au Jardin des Gourmets *W1* **56**
L'Auberge *Edinburgh* **663**
Auburn Lodge *Ennis* **797**
Auchen Castle *Beattock* **652**
Auchendean Lodge *Dulnain Bridge* **660**
Auchterarder House *Auchterarder* **648**
Audleys Wood *Basingstoke* **245**
Aval Du Creux *Sark* **761**
L'Aventure *NW8* **56**
Aviemore Highlands Hotel *Aviemore* **649**
Avisford Park *Walberton* **600**
Avonmouth Hotel *Mudeford* **475**
Aynsome Manor *Cartmel* **310**
Ayton Hall *Great Ayton* **383**

Ayumi-Ya *Blackrock* **776**
Ayumi-Ya Japanese Steakhouse *Dublin* **786**
Aztec Hotel *Bristol* **288**
Bacco *SW7* **56**
Bahn Thai *W1* **56**
Bailiffscourt *Climping* **330**
Balbirnie House *Markinch* **696**
Balgeddie House *Glenrothes* **684**
Ballachulish Hotel *Ballachulish* **650**
Ballathie House *Kinclaven by Stanley* **692**
Ballylickey Manor House *Ballylickey* **774**
Ballymaloe House *Shanagarry* **815**
Ballymascanlon House *Dundalk* **795**
Ballynahinch Castle *Ballynahinch* **775**
Balmer Lawn Hotel *Brockenhurst* **296**
The Balmoral *Edinburgh* **664**
Hotel Baltimore *Middlesbrough* **469**
Balzac Restaurant *W12* **56**
Bangkok *SW7* **57**
Bankfield Hotel *Bingley* **259**
La Barbe *Reigate* **518**
Bardon Lodge *SE3* **57**
Barnard's *Cosham* **336**
Barnham Broom Hotel *Barnham Broom* **242**
Barnsdale Lodge *Oakham* **496**
Barnton Thistle *Edinburgh* **664**
Baron's Court *Walsall Wood* **601**
Baron's Craig *Rockcliffe* **707**
Barrett's Restaurant *Glemsford* **378**
Basil Street Hotel *SW3* **57**
Batch Farm *Lympsham* **448**
Bath Hotel *Bath* **249**
Bath Place Hotel & Restaurant *Oxford* **499**
Bath Spa Hotel *Bath* **248**
Baverstock Hotel *Merthyr Tydfil* **739**
Bay Horse Inn & Bistro *Ulverston* **596**
Bay Tree *Burford* **299**
Bay Tree *Sheffield* **538**
Bayview Hotel *Portballintrae* **769**
Beach Hotel *Worthing* **626**
Bear Hotel *Crickhowell* **729**
Bear Hotel *Havant* **399**
Bear Hotel *Hungerford* **414**
Bear Hotel *Street* **570**
Bear Hotel *Wantage* **602**
Bear Hotel *Woodstock* **622**
Beaufort Hotel *St Helier* **759**
Beaufort Hotel *Tintern* **748**
The Beaufort *SW3* **57**
Beaumont Hotel *Hexham* **408**
Beckfords *Chepstow* **726**
Bedford Arms Thistle *Chenies* **321**
Bedford Arms *Woburn* **620**
Bedford Hotel *Brighton* **284**
Bedlington Café *W4* **57**
Beechfield House *Beanacre* **253**
Beetle & Wedge *Moulsford-on-Thames* **474**
Bel Alp House *Haytor* **402**
Belfry Hotel *Handforth* **392**
Belfry Hotel *Wishaw* **619**
Belgo *NW1* **58**
Bell Hotel *Charlbury* **315**
Bell Hotel *Driffield* **350**
Bell Hotel *Tewkesbury* **582**
Bell Inn *Aston Clinton* **238**
Bell Inn *Stilton* **558**

Bell Inn *Woburn* **620**
The Bell *Thetford* **583**
La Belle Alliance *Blandford Forum* **268**
La Belle Epoque *Knutsford* **424**
Bellhouse Hotel *Beaconsfield* **253**
Belmont Hotel *Leicester* **434**
Belmont Hotel *Sidmouth* **543**
Belmore Hotel *Stoke Mandeville* **559**
Belsfield Hotel *Bowness-on-Windermere* **275**
Belstead Brook Hotel *Ipswich* **418**
Belton Woods Hotel *Belton* **256**
Belvedere in Holland Park *W8* **58**
Bengal Brasserie *Belfast* **764**
Benihana *NW3* **58**
Bentley's *W1* **58**
Berkeley Arms Hotel *Heathrow Airport* **402**
Berkeley Court *Dublin* **786**
Berkeley Restaurant *Penzance* **505**
Berkeley Square Hotel *Bristol* **289**
The Berkeley *SW1* **59**
Berkleys *Kinver* **424**
Berkshire Hotel *W1* **59**
Berners Park Plaza *W1* **59**
Berystede Hotel *Ascot* **235**
Beverley Arms *Beverley* **257**
Bharat *Bradford* **276**
Bhatti *WC2* **60**
Bhavani Junction *Leeds* **430**
Bibendum Oyster Bar *SW3* **60**
Bibendum *SW3* **60**
Bilbrough Manor *Bilbrough* **258**
Billesley Manor *Stratford-upon-Avon* **567**
Birmingham Metropole *Birmingham* **259**
Bishop Field *Allendale* **228**
Bishop's Table Hotel *Farnham* **368**
Bishopstrow House *Warminster* **603**
Bistro Montparnasse *Southsea* **553**
Bistrot 190 *SW7* **60**
Bitter Lemons Taverna *SW6* **61**
Black Bull *Moulton* **475**
Black Bull Thistle *Milngavie* **697**
Black Chapati *Brighton* **284**
Black Horse Inn *Grimsthorpe* **387**
Black Lion *Long Melford* **442**
Black Swan *Beckingham* **255**
Black Swan *Helmsley* **405**
Black Swan Inn *Ravenstonedale* **517**
Blackheath House & MacDuff's Restaurant *Garvagh* **767**
Blackwell Grange Moat House *Darlington* **342**
Blairs Cove House Restaurant *Durrus* **797**
Blakeney Hotel *Blakeney* **267**
Blakes Hotel *SW7* **61**
Bloom's *E1* **62**
Bloom's *NW11* **61**
Blooms Hotel *Dublin* **787**
Blossoms Hotel *Chester* **321**
Blostin's Restaurant *Shepton Mallet* **541**
Blue Anchor Inn *East Aberthaw* **729**
Blue Bell Hotel *Belford* **256**
Blue Boar *Maldon* **453**
Blue Elephant *SW6* **62**
Blue Goose *Bristol* **289**
Blue Haven Hotel *Kinsale* **805**
Blueprint Café *SE1* **62**
Blunsdon House *Swindon* **575**
Bodysgallen Hall *Llandudno* **734**

Boluisce Seafood Bar *Spiddal* **816**
Bombay Brasserie *Bradford* **276**
Bombay Brasserie *SW7* **62**
Bon Appétit *Malahide* **807**
Bon Ton Roulet *SE24* **63**
Bond's *Castle Cary* **310**
La Bonne Auberge *South Godstone* **549**
La Bonne Franquette *Egham* **359**
Restaurant Bonnet *Cranleigh* **338**
Bonnington Hotel *WC1* **63**
Bontddu Hall *Bontddu* **723**
Boringdon Hall *Plymouth* **507**
Borrowdale Hotel *Borrowdale* **271**
Borthwick Castle *North Middleton* **700**
Boscundle Manor *St Austell* **528**
Restaurant Bosquet *Kenilworth* **420**
Boulestin *WC2* **63**
Les Bouviers *Wimborne* **613**
Bowdon Hotel *Altrincham* **230**
Bowler Hat Hotel *Birkenhead* **259**
Box Tree *Ilkley* **417**
Boyd's *W8* **63**
The Brackenbury *W6* **64**
Le Braconnier *SW14* **64**
Braeval Old Mill *Aberfoyle* **643**
Braid Hills Hotel *Edinburgh* **665**
Bramley Grange *Bramley* **280**
Brandon Hall *Brandon* **281**
Brands Hatch Thistle *Brands Hatch* **281**
Brandshatch Place *Fawkham* **370**
Brasserie du Marché aux Puces *W10* **65**
Brasserie Faubourg *SW8* **64**
Brasserie Forty Four *Leeds* **431**
Brasserie Lott *SW3* **65**
Brasserie on West Regent Street *Glasgow*
   677
La Brasserie *SW3* **64**
Brasted's *Norwich* **490**
Braye Lodge *St Peter Port* **753**
Breadsall Priory *Morley* **473**
Breamish House *Powburn* **513**
Brickwall Hotel *Sedlescombe* **537**
Bridge End Restaurant *Hayfield* **401**
Bridge Hotel *Prestbury* **513**
Bridge House Inn *Spiddal* **817**
Bridge House *Longham* **443**
Bridge House *Reigate* **519**
Bridgefield House *Spark Bridge* **554**
Briggens House *Stanstead Abbots* **556**
Brighton Metropole *Brighton* **285**
Bristol Marriott *Bristol* **289**
Hotel Bristol *Newquay* **484**
Britannia Adelphi Hotel *Liverpool* **441**
Britannia Hotel *Manchester* **456**
Britannia Inter-Continental Hotel *W1* **65**
Broadway Hotel *Broadway* **294**
Broadway Toby Hotel *Letchworth* **437**
Brockencote Hall *Chaddesley Corbett* **312**
Bromley Court *Bromley* **297**
Bron Eifion Hotel *Criccieth* **729**
Brookdale House *North Huish* **486**
Brookhouse Hotel *Rolleston-on-Dove* **521**
Brothers at the Chantry *Dronfield* **351**
Broughton Park *Broughton* **298**
Browns Bistro *Clitheroe* **330**
Browns Brasserie *Southampton* **551**
Browns *Brighton* **285**
Browns *Cambridge* **304**
Browns *Oxford* **499**
Brown's Hotel *W1* **65**

Brown's *Worcester* **624**
Bruce Swallow Hotel *East Kilbride* **663**
Brudenell Hotel *Aldeburgh* **227**
Bryanston Court *W1* **66**
Bubb's *EC1* **66**
Buchan's *SW11* **66**
Buchanan Highland Hotel *Drymen* **660**
Buckerell Lodge *Exeter* **364**
Buckland Manor *Buckland* **298**
Bucksburn Moat House *Aberdeen* **640**
Budock Vean Hotel *Mawnan Smith* **465**
Bulkeley Arms *Beaumaris* **722**
The Bull at Charlbury *Charlbury* **316**
Bull Hotel *Fairford* **365**
Bull Hotel *Gerrards Cross* **377**
Bull Hotel *Long Melford* **442**
Bully's *Cork* **782**
Bunbury's *Barry* **722**
Bunchrew House *Inverness* **686**
Burgh Island Hotel *Bigbury-on-Sea* **258**
Burgoyne Hotel *Reeth* **518**
Burley Manor *Burley* **300**
Burlington Hotel *Dublin* **787**
Burnham Beeches Moat House *Burnham*
   300
Burts Hotel *Melrose* **696**
Bush Hotel *Farnham* **368**
Bushmills Inn *Bushmills* **766**
Butterfly Hotel *Bury St Edmunds* **302**
Butterfly Hotel *Colchester* **332**
Butterfly Hotel *King's Lynn* **422**
Butterfly Hotel *Peterborough* **506**
Buttery *Glasgow* **677**
Buzkash *SW15* **66**
Cabarfeidh Hotel *Stornoway* **712**
Cadogan Hotel *SW1* **66**
Café Cézanne *Twickenham* **592**
Café Delancey *NW1* **66**
Café du Marché *EC1* **67**
Café Fish *SW1* **67**
Café Fleur *Harrogate* **393**
Café Gandolfi *Glasgow* **678**
Café Pelican *WC2* **67**
Café Royal Grill Room *W1* **67**
Cahernane Hotel *Killarney* **803**
Calcot Manor *Tetbury* **581**
Caledonian Hotel *Ayr* **649**
Caledonian Hotel *Edinburgh* **665**
Caledonian Hotel *Inverness* **686**
Caledonian Thistle *Aberdeen* **640**
California Pizza Company *W1* **67**
Callow Hall *Ashbourne* **236**
Cally Palace *Gatehouse of Fleet* **676**
Cambridge Lodge *Cambridge* **304**
Cambridgeshire Moat House *Cambridge*
   304
Camden Brasserie *NW1* **68**
Cameron House *Alexandria* **644**
Campanile Hotel *Basildon* **245**
Campanile Hotel *Birmingham* **260**
Campanile Hotel *Cardiff* **724**
Campanile Hotel *Coventry (North)* **337**
Campanile Hotel *Coventry (South)* **337**
Campanile Hotel *Doncaster* **346**
Campanile Hotel *Hull* **413**
Campanile Hotel *Liverpool* **441**
Campanile Hotel *Newcastle-upon-Tyne*
   481
Campanile Hotel *Plymouth* **508**
Campanile Hotel *Redditch* **518**

Campanile Hotel *Rotherham* **523**
Campanile Hotel *Runcorn* **525**
Campanile Hotel *Wakefield* **599**
Canal Brasserie *W10* **68**
Cannizaro House *SW19* **68**
Canterbury Hotel *Canterbury* **307**
La Capannina *St Helier* **759**
The Capital *SW3* **68**
Le Caprice *SW1* **69**
Caragh Lodge *Caragh Lake* **778**
Caravan Serai *W1* **69**
Cardiff International *Cardiff* **724**
Cardiff Marriott Hotel *Cardiff* **724**
Careys Manor *Brockenhurst* **296**
Carlton Highland *Edinburgh* **665**
Carlton Hotel *Bournemouth* **272**
Carlton Hotel *Great Yarmouth* **386**
Carlyon Bay Hotel *Carlyon Bay* **309**
Carnach House *Nairn* **697**
Carnarvon Arms *Dulverton* **352**
Carraro's *SW8* **69**
Carved Angel *Dartmouth* **343**
Casa Cominetti *SE6* **70**
Casa Romana *Weybridge* **610**
Casale Franco *N1* **70**
Cashel House *Cashel* **778**
Cashel Palace *Cashel* **779**
Castle Hotel *Taunton* **578**
Castle Hotel *Windsor* **617**
Castle Inn *Castle Combe* **311**
Castle View Hotel *Chepstow* **727**
Castleton House *Glamis* **676**
Caterino's *SW16* **70**
Cavendish Hotel *Baslow* **247**
Cavendish Hotel *Eastbourne* **356**
Caversham Hotel *Reading* **517**
Cawdor Arms *Llandeilo* **733**
Cedar Court *Wakefield* **599**
Cedar Lodge *Newbawn* **810**
Cefn Goleu Park *Gowerton* **730**
Ceilidh Place *Ullapool* **717**
Cellar *Anstruther* **646**
Celtic Manor *Newport* **740**
The Cemlyn *Harlech* **731**
Ceruttis *Hull* **413**
Chace Hotel *Coventry* **336**
Champany Inn Chop & Ale House
  Linlithgow **695**
Champany Inn *Linlithgow* **695**
Le Champignon Sauvage *Cheltenham*
  317
Channings *Edinburgh* **666**
Chapeltoun House *Stewarton* **712**
Chapter 11 *SW10* **70**
Chapters *Stokesley* **561**
Charingworth Manor *Charingworth* **315**
Charlecote Pheasant *Charlecote* **316**
Charles Bernard Hotel *NW3* **70**
Charlie Chan *Cambridge* **305**
Charlotte's Place *W5* **71**
Charnwood Hotel *Sheffield* **539**
Charterhouse Hotel *Manchester* **456**
Chase Hotel *Ross-on-Wye* **522**
Chateau Impney *Droitwich Spa* **350**
Le Chateau *Swords* **818**
Hotel Chateau Valeuse *St Brelade* **758**
Chatsworth Hotel *Worthing* **626**
Chaucer Hotel *Canterbury* **307**
Chedington Court *Chedington* **316**
Cheevers *Tunbridge Wells* **590**

Chelsea Hotel *SW1* **71**
Cheltenham Park *Cheltenham* **318**
Chelwood House *Chelwood* **320**
Cheng-Du *NW1* **71**
Chequers Hotel *Newbury* **479**
Chequers Hotel *Pulborough* **515**
Chequers Thistle *Gatwick Airport* **375**
Cherwell Boathouse *Oxford* **499**
Chester Grosvenor *Chester* **321**
Chester International *Chester* **322**
Chester Resort Hotel *Chester* **322**
Chesterfield Hotel *Chesterfield* **324**
Chesterfield Hotel *W1* **71**
Chevin Lodge *Otley* **498**
Chewton Glen *New Milton* **477**
Chez Hans *Cashel* **779**
Chez Liline *N4* **71**
Chez Max *Surbiton* **573**
Chez Moi *W11* **72**
Chez Nous *Plymouth* **508**
Chi Mai *W3* **72**
Chiang Mai *W1* **72**
Chicago Pizza Pie Factory *W1* **72**
Chicago Rib Shack *SW7* **72**
Chilston Park *Lenham* **437**
Chimney House *Sandbach* **533**
Chimneys *Long Melford* **442**
China Garden *Brighton* **285**
China Jazz *NW1* **72**
China-Sichuan Restaurant *Stillorgan* **817**
Chinon *W14* **73**
Chiseldon House *Chiseldon* **327**
Christian's *W4* **73**
Christopher Hotel *Eton* **362**
Christopher's *WC2* **73**
Chuen Cheng Ku *W1* **73**
Chung Ying *Birmingham* **260**
Chung Ying Garden *Birmingham* **260**
Churchill Hotel *W1* **74**
Chutney Mary *SW10* **74**
Château la Chaire *Rozel Bay* **756**
Ciao *SW6* **75**
Cibo *W14* **75**
Cinque Ports Hotel *Hastings* **397**
Circus Restaurant *Bath* **249**
Cisswood House *Lower Beeding* **444**
Hotel Cladhan *Falkirk* **673**
Clare Inn *Newmarket-on-Fergus* **810**
Clarendon House *Kenilworth* **421**
Clarets *Blackrock* **776**
Claridge's *W1* **75**
Clarke's *Easton* **358**
Clarke's *W8* **76**
Clayton Lodge *Newcastle-under-Lyme*
  481
Clearwell Castle *Clearwell* **330**
Cliff Hotel *Gwbert-on-Sea* **731**
Cliff Tops Hotel *Shanklin* **538**
Clifford's *Cork* **782**
Clifton Arms *Lytham* **450**
Clifton Hotel *Nairn* **698**
The Clifton-Ford *W1* **76**
Clive Hotel *NW3* **77**
Cliveden *Taplow* **577**
Clonmel Arms *Clonmel* **781**
The Close *Tetbury* **581**
Cobbett's *Botley* **271**
Coburg Hotel *W2* **77**
Cobwebs *Cowan Bridge* **337**
Coed-y-Mwstwr Hotel *Coychurch* **728**

Collaven Manor *Sourton* **548**
Collin House *Broadway* **294**
Collin House *SW1* **77**
Colonnade Hotel *W9* **77**
Columba Hotel *Oban* **701**
Columbia Hotel *W2* **77**
Colwall Park Hotel *Malvern* **454**
Combe Grove Manor *Bath* **249**
Combe House *Gittisham* **378**
Comme Ça *Chichester* **324**
Compleat Angler Hotel *Marlow* **464**
Concord Hotel *SW5* **77**
Congham Hall *Grimston* **388**
The Connaught *W1* **78**
Connemara Gateway Hotel *Oughterard* **811**
Hotel Conrad *Dublin* **787**
Hotel Conrad *SW10* **78**
Conrah Country Hotel *Aberystwyth* **721**
Contented Sole *Burnham-on-Crouch* **300**
Cooden Resort Hotel *Cooden* **334**
Coopershill House *Riverstown* **814**
Copper Inn Restaurant *Pangbourne* **503**
Copthorne Effingham Park *Gatwick Airport* **375**
Copthorne Hotel *Aberdeen* **640**
Copthorne Hotel *Birmingham* **260**
Copthorne Hotel *Glasgow* **678**
Copthorne Hotel *Manchester* **456**
Copthorne Hotel *Plymouth* **508**
Copthorne Hotel *Slough* **546**
Copthorne London Gatwick *Gatwick Airport* **375**
Copthorne Tara *W8* **79**
Le Coq Hardi *Dublin* **787**
Corbet Arms *Market Drayton* **462**
Cormorant Hotel *Golant* **380**
Corner Café *Leeds* **431**
Corney & Barrow *EC2* **79**
Corrib Great Southern Hotel *Galway* **798**
Corse Lawn House *Corse Lawn* **335**
Corsemalzie House *Port William* **706**
Costa's Grill *W8* **79**
Cotswold House *Chipping Camden* **326**
Cottage Hotel *Hope Cove* **411**
Cottage in the Wood *Malvern* **455**
The Cottage *Shanklin Old Village* **538**
Cottons Hotel *Knutsford* **425**
Country Court *Bromsgrove* **297**
Country Court Hotel *Newport* **741**
Country Court *Leicester* **434**
Country Friends *Dorrington* **349**
County Hotel *Canterbury* **307**
County Hotel *Taunton* **579**
County Thistle *Newcastle-upon-Tyne* **481**
Court Barn *Clawton* **329**
Court Hotel *Killiney* **804**
Court Hotel *Lamphey* **732**
Crabwall Manor *Chester* **322**
Craigdarroch Lodge *Contin* **656**
Craigellachie Hotel *Craigellachie* **656**
Craigendarroch Hotel *Ballater* **650**
Crannog Seafood Restaurant *Fort William* **673**
Crathorne Hall *Crathorne* **339**
Craven Gardens Hotel *W2* **79**
Crawford Gallery Café *Cork* **782**
Craxton Wood *Puddington* **514**
Creag Mor *Gairloch* **675**
Creggans Inn *Strachur* **712**

Cresta Court *Altrincham* **230**
Crieff Hydro *Crieff* **656**
Crinan Hotel *Crinan* **657**
Cringletie House *Peebles* **703**
La Croisette *SW10* **80**
Cromleach Lodge *Boyle* **776**
Cromlix House *Dunblane* **661**
Crook Inn *Tweedsmuir* **716**
Crookedwood House *Mullingar* **809**
Crooklands Hotel *Crooklands* **340**
Croque-en-Bouche *Malvern* **455**
Crosby Lodge *Crosby-on-Eden* **340**
The Cross *Kingussie* **692**
Crossroads Hotel *Weedon* **606**
Crown & Cushion *Chipping Norton* **327**
The Crown *Bawtry* **253**
The Crown *Boroughbridge* **270**
The Crown *Framlingham* **373**
The Crown *Harrogate* **393**
Crown Inn *Chiddingfold* **325**
The Crown *Lyndhurst* **449**
The Crown *Scarborough* **535**
The Crown *Southwold* **553**
The Crown *Wetheral* **609**
Crowthers *SW14* **80**
Croydon Park *Croydon* **340**
Cuilfail Hotel *Kilmelford* **691**
Culloden Hotel *Holywood* **767**
Culloden House *Inverness* **686**
Cumberland Hotel *W1* **80**
Currarevagh House *Oughterard* **812**
Curry Pot *Leicester* **435**
Curtlestown House *Enniskerry* **797**
Cwrt Bleddyn Hotel *Llangybi* **736**
D'Arcy's *Glasgow* **678**
D'Isney Place *Lincoln* **439**
Dalhousie Castle *Bonnyrigg* **653**
Dalmahoy Hotel *Kirknewton* **694**
Dan's *SW3* **80**
Danescombe Valley Hotel *Calstock* **303**
Danesfield House *Medmenham* **466**
Danum Swallow Hotel *Doncaster* **347**
Daphne *NW1* **81**
David's Place *Knutsford* **425**
Dawat *Leeds* **431**
Hotel de la Bere *Cheltenham* **317**
De Montfort Hotel *Kenilworth* **421**
De Vere Hotel *Coventry* **336**
Dean Court *York* **630**
Dedham Vale Hotel *Dedham* **344**
Defune *W1* **81**
Dell'Ugo *W1* **81**
Denbigh Arms *Lutterworth* **447**
The Depot *SW14* **81**
Devonshire Arms *Bolton Abbey* **270**
Devonshire Hotel *Glasgow* **678**
Dew Pond *Old Burghclere* **497**
Dial House *Bourton-on-the-Water* **274**
Digby's *Dun Laoghaire* **794**
Dinham Hall *Ludlow* **446**
The Dining Room *Hersham* **407**
Dinnington Hall *Dinnington* **346**
Dog House Hotel *Frilford Heath* **374**
Dolphin & Anchor *Chichester* **325**
Dolphin Hotel *Southampton* **551**
Don Pepe *NW8* **82**
Donington Thistle *Castle Donington* **311**
The Dorchester *W1* **82**
La Dordogne *W4* **83**
Dormy Hotel *Ferndown* **371**

Dormy House *Broadway* **294**
Dorset Square Hotel *NW1* **84**
Dovecliffe Hall *Burton-on-Trent* **301**
Dower House *Knaresborough* **424**
Dower House *Muir-of-Ord* **697**
Dower House *Woodhall Spa* **622**
Down Hall *Hatfield Heath* **398**
Downshire House *Blessington* **776**
Downstairs at Thackeray's *Tunbridge Wells* **590**
Doyle's School House Country Inn *Castledermot* **779**
Doyle's Seafood Bar & Townhouse *Dingle* **785**
Dragon & Phoenix *Manchester* **456**
Dragon Inn *W1* **84**
Dragon's Nest *W1* **84**
The Draycott *SW3* **84**
Drimcong House Restaurant *Moycullen* **809**
Dromoland Castle *Newmarket-on-Fergus* **811**
Drum & Monkey *Harrogate* **394**
Drumnacree House *Alyth* **645**
Dryburgh Abbey *Dryburgh* **660**
Duke of Richmond *St Peter Port* **753**
Duke's Head *King's Lynn* **422**
Dukes Hotel *Belfast* **764**
Dukes Hotel *Stratford-upon-Avon* **567**
Dukes Hotel *SW1* **85**
Dun Cow *Dunchurch* **352**
Dunadry Inn *Dunadry* **767**
Dunain Park *Inverness* **687**
Dundas Arms *Kintbury* **423**
Dunderry Lodge Restaurant *Dunderry* **795**
Dundrum House *Dundrum* **796**
Dunloe Castle *Beaufort* **775**
Dunraven Arms *Adare* **772**
Dunworley Cottage *Dunworley* **796**
Durley House *SW1* **85**
Durrants Hotel *W1* **85**
Dwyer's Restaurant *Waterford* **819**
The Eagle *EC1* **86**
Earls Court Park Inn International *SW6* **86**
Eastbury Hotel *Sherborne* **541**
Eastern Eye *SE22* **86**
Eastgate Hotel *Oxford* **500**
Eastwell Manor *Ashford* **236**
Ebury Court *SW1* **86**
Ebury Hotel *Canterbury* **308**
Eddrachilles Hotel *Scourie* **710**
Eden Plaza Hotel *SW7* **86**
Ednam House *Kelso* **688**
Edwardian International *Heathrow Airport* **402**
Efes Kebab House *W1* **87**
Egerton Grey *Porthkerry* **743**
Egerton House *Bolton* **269**
Egerton House *SW3* **87**
Eglantine *Tunbridge Wells* **590**
Elcot Park *Elcot* **360**
Eleven Park Walk *SW10* **87**
Elizabeth Hotel *SW1* **87**
Restaurant Elizabeth *Oxford* **500**
Elms Hotel *Abberley* **226**
Elysée Restaurant *Bournemouth* **272**
Embassy House Hotel *SW7* **87**
Empire Hotel *Llandudno* **734**
English Garden *SW3* **88**
English House *SW3* **88**

Enniscoe House *Crossmolina* **785**
Enniscree Lodge Inn *Enniskerry* **798**
Enoteca *SW15* **88**
Epicurean *Cheltenham* **318**
Ernie's *Dublin* **788**
L'Escargot Doré *W8* **88**
L'Escargot *Herne Bay* **407**
L'Escargot *W1* **88**
Esseborne Manor *Hurstbourne Tarrant* **416**
Est *W1* **89**
L'Estaminet *WC2* **89**
L'Etoile *W1* **89**
Etrop Grange *Manchester Airport* **461**
Ettington Park *Stratford-upon-Avon* **567**
Ettrickshaws Hotel *Ettrickbridge* **673**
Europa Gatwick *Gatwick Airport* **375**
Hotel Europe *Killarney* **803**
Everglades Hotel *Londonderry* **768**
Evesham Hotel *Evesham* **363**
Excelsior Hotel *Heathrow Airport* **402**
Expanse Hotel *Bridlington* **283**
The Factor's House *Fort William* **674**
Fairlawns *Aldridge* **228**
Fairwater Head Hotel *Hawkchurch* **399**
Fairyhill *Reynoldston* **744**
Falcon Hotel *Stratford-upon-Avon* **568**
Falmouth Hotel *Falmouth* **366**
Falstaff Hotel *Canterbury* **308**
La Famiglia *SW10* **89**
Fanari *NW1* **89**
Faraday's *Aberdeen* **640**
Farlam Hall *Brampton* **280**
Farleyer House *Aberfeldy* **642**
Farringford Hotel *Freshwater* **373**
Farthings Hotel *Hatch Beauchamp* **398**
Faulkners *E8* **89**
Feathers Hotel *Ludlow* **446**
Feathers Hotel *Pocklington* **509**
Feathers Hotel *Woodstock* **623**
The Feathers *Ledbury* **430**
The Fenja *SW3* **90**
Fernie Castle *Letham* **695**
Ferrycarrig Hotel *Ferrycarrig Bridge* **798**
Feversham Arms *Helmsley* **405**
La Fiesta *Dublin* **788**
Fifehead Manor *Middle Wallop* **468**
15 North Parade *Oxford* **500**
La Fin de la Chasse *N16* **90**
Findon Manor *Findon* **371**
Fischer's Baslow Hall *Baslow* **247**
Fisherman's Haunt Inn *Winkton* **618**
Fisherman's Lodge *Newcastle-upon-Tyne* **481**
Fishguard Bay Hotel *Fishguard* **730**
Fitzpatrick Silver Springs *Cork* **783**
Fitzpatrick's Castle *Killiney* **804**
Fitzpatricks Shannon Shamrock *Bunratty* **777**
Fleece Hotel *Cirencester* **328**
Flitwick Manor *Flitwick* **371**
Florians *N8* **90**
Foley Arms *Malvern* **455**
Foley Lodge *Newbury* **479**
Forest of Arden Hotel *Meriden* **468**
Forsters *East Boldon* **354**
Forte Crest *Aylesbury* **239**
Forte Crest *Basildon* **245**
Forte Crest Belfast *Dunmurry* **767**
Forte Crest *Birmingham* **260**

Forte Crest Bloomsbury *WC1* **90**
Forte Crest *Bramhope* **279**
Forte Crest *Brighouse* **284**
Forte Crest *Bristol* **289**
Forte Crest *Cardiff* **725**
Forte Crest *Coventry* **337**
Forte Crest *Dublin Airport* **793**
Forte Crest *Exeter* **364**
Forte Crest *Farnborough* **368**
Forte Crest *Gatwick Gatwick Airport* **376**
Forte Crest *Glasgow* **678**
Forte Crest *Glasgow Airport* **683**
Forte Crest *Gloucester* **378**
Forte Crest *Grimsby* **387**
Forte Crest *Guildford* **389**
Forte Crest *Heathrow Airport* **403**
Forte Crest *Hull* **413**
Forte Crest *Lincoln* **439**
Forte Crest *Liverpool* **441**
Forte Crest *Luton* **446**
Forte Crest *Manchester Airport* **462**
Forte Crest *Milton Keynes* **471**
Forte Crest *Newcastle-upon-Tyne* **482**
Forte Crest *Nottingham* **492**
Forte Crest *Plymouth* **508**
Forte Crest *Portsmouth* **512**
Forte Crest *Preston* **513**
Forte Crest Regent's Park *W1* **90**
Forte Crest *Rochester* **521**
Forte Crest *Runcorn* **525**
Forte Crest *Sheffield* **539**
Forte Crest Southampton *Eastleigh* **358**
Forte Crest St James's *SW1* **90**
Forte Crest *Swansea* **746**
Forte Crest *Swindon* **576**
Forte Crest *Winchester* **614**
Forte Posthouse (Ariel) *Heathrow Airport* **403**
Forte Posthouse *Alveston* **231**
Forte Posthouse *Ashford* **237**
Forte Posthouse *Basingstoke* **246**
Forte Posthouse *Birmingham* **261**
Forte Posthouse *Birmingham Airport* **265**
Forte Posthouse *Bolton* **269**
Forte Posthouse *Bournemouth* **272**
Forte Posthouse *Brentwood* **283**
Forte Posthouse *Cambridge* **305**
Forte Posthouse *Cardiff* **725**
Forte Posthouse *Chester* **323**
Forte Posthouse *Coventry* **337**
Forte Posthouse *Croydon* **340**
Forte Posthouse *Derby* **345**
Forte Posthouse *Dover* **349**
Forte Posthouse *Edinburgh* **666**
Forte Posthouse *Epping* **361**
Forte Posthouse *Erskine* **672**
Forte Posthouse Gatwick *Gatwick Airport* **376**
Forte Posthouse *Havant* **399**
Forte Posthouse *Haydock* **401**
Forte Posthouse *High Wycombe* **408**
Forte Posthouse *Hull* **414**
Forte Posthouse *Ipswich* **418**
Forte Posthouse *Lancaster* **426**
Forte Posthouse Leeds/Selby *South Milford* **549**
Forte Posthouse *Leicester* **435**
Forte Posthouse *Luton* **446**
Forte Posthouse *Manchester* **457**

Forte Posthouse *Newcastle-under-Lyme* **481**
Forte Posthouse Northampton/Rugby *Crick* **339**
Forte Posthouse *Norwich* **490**
Forte Posthouse *Nottingham* **492**
Forte Posthouse *NW3* **91**
Forte Posthouse *Peterborough* **506**
Forte Posthouse *Reading* **517**
Forte Posthouse *Sherborne* **541**
Forte Posthouse *South Mimms* **549**
Forte Posthouse *Southampton* **551**
Forte Posthouse *Stratford-upon-Avon* **568**
Forte Posthouse *Swindon* **576**
Forte Posthouse *Taunton* **579**
Forte Posthouse *Thornaby-on-Tees* **583**
Forte Posthouse *Wakefield* **599**
Forte Posthouse *Walsall* **601**
Forte Posthouse *Washington* **604**
Forte Posthouse *York* **630**
Forte Travelodge *Abington* **643**
Forte Travelodge *Acle* **226**
Forte Travelodge *Alton* **229**
Forte Travelodge *Amesbury* **233**
Forte Travelodge *Baldock* **241**
Forte Travelodge *Barnsley* **243**
Forte Travelodge *Barton Mills* **244**
Forte Travelodge *Barton Stacey* **244**
Forte Travelodge *Barton-under-Needwood* **245**
Forte Travelodge *Barton-under-Needwood* **245**
Forte Travelodge *Basingstoke* **246**
Forte Travelodge *Bebington* **254**
Forte Travelodge *Billingshurst* **259**
Forte Travelodge *Blyth* **268**
Forte Travelodge *Brentwood* **283**
Forte Travelodge *Bridgend* **724**
Forte Travelodge *Burnley* **301**
Forte Travelodge *Burtonwood* **301**
Forte Travelodge *Carcroft* **309**
Forte Travelodge *Cardiff* **725**
Forte Travelodge *Chesterfield* **324**
Forte Travelodge *Colsterworth* **333**
Forte Travelodge *Cork* **781**
Forte Travelodge *Crewe* **339**
Forte Travelodge *Cross Hands* **729**
Forte Travelodge *Desborough* **346**
Forte Travelodge *Dorking* **348**
Forte Travelodge *Droitwich* **350**
Forte Travelodge *Dudley* **351**
Forte Travelodge *Dumbarton* **661**
Forte Travelodge *Dunchurch* **353**
Forte Travelodge *Dunstable* **353**
Forte Travelodge *Eastleigh* **358**
Forte Travelodge *Edinburgh* **666**
Forte Travelodge *Ely* **360**
Forte Travelodge *Fenstanton* **370**
Forte Travelodge *Fleet* **371**
Forte Travelodge *Fontwell* **372**
Forte Travelodge *Gateshead* **374**
Forte Travelodge *Gordano* **381**
Forte Travelodge *Grantham* **381**
Forte Travelodge *Gretna Green* **684**
Forte Travelodge *Hailsham* **391**
Forte Travelodge *Halkyn* **731**
Forte Travelodge *Hartlebury* **396**
Forte Travelodge *Hartshead Moor* **396**
Forte Travelodge *Haydock* **401**
Forte Travelodge *Ilminster* **418**

Forte Travelodge *King's Lynn* **423**
Forte Travelodge *Knutsford* **425**
Forte Travelodge *Lolworth* **442**
Forte Travelodge *Ludlow* **446**
Forte Travelodge *Marston* **464**
Forte Travelodge *Morden* **472**
Forte Travelodge *Newark* **478**
Forte Travelodge *Northampton* **487**
Forte Travelodge *Nuneaton* **495**
Forte Travelodge *Okehampton* **497**
Forte Travelodge *Oldbury* **498**
Forte Travelodge *Oswestry* **498**
Forte Travelodge *Oxford* **500**
Forte Travelodge *Penrith* **504**
Forte Travelodge *Peterborough* **506**
Forte Travelodge *Podimore* **509**
Forte Travelodge *Reading* **517**
Forte Travelodge *Retford* **519**
Forte Travelodge *Rugeley* **525**
Forte Travelodge *Rushden* **526**
Forte Travelodge *Scotch Corner* **536**
Forte Travelodge *Sedgemoor* **537**
Forte Travelodge *Skipton* **546**
Forte Travelodge *Sleaford* **546**
Forte Travelodge *South Cave* **549**
Forte Travelodge *South Mimms* **549**
Forte Travelodge *South Witham* **550**
Forte Travelodge *Stockport* **559**
Forte Travelodge *Stowmarket* **566**
Forte Travelodge *Sutton Coldfield* **574**
Forte Travelodge *Sutton Scotney North*
    575
Forte Travelodge *Sutton Scotney South*
    575
Forte Travelodge *Swavesey* **575**
Forte Travelodge *Swords* **818**
Forte Travelodge *Telford* **580**
Forte Travelodge *Thrapston* **584**
Forte Travelodge *Thrussington* **584**
Forte Travelodge *Tiverton* **586**
Forte Travelodge *Towcester* **588**
Forte Travelodge *Uppingham* **597**
Forte Travelodge *Uttoxeter* **597**
Forte Travelodge *Wentbridge* **607**
Forte Travelodge *Worksop* **626**
Forte Travelodge *York* **630**
Fortfield Hotel *Sidmouth* **544**
Forth Bridges Moat House *South
    Queensferry* **711**
42 The Calls *Leeds* **431**
47 Park Street *W1* **91**
Fosse Manor *Stow-on-the-Wold* **565**
Fossebridge Inn *Fossebridge* **372**
Fountain House & Dedham Hall *Dedham*
    344
Fountain House *Bath* **250**
Four Seasons Hotel *Manchester Airport*
    462
Four Seasons Hotel *St Fillans* **709**
Four Seasons *W2* **92**
Fouters Bistro *Ayr* **649**
Fownes Resort Hotel *Worcester* **625**
Fox & Goose *Fressingfield* **374**
Foxtrot Oscar *SW3* **92**
Franc's *Chester* **323**
Francine's *Maldon* **454**
Francis Hotel *Bath* **250**
Francs *Altrincham* **230**
Frederick's *N1* **92**
Fredrick's *Maidenhead* **452**

French Partridge *Horton* **412**
Frensham Pond Hotel *Churt* **328**
Friendly Hotel *Norwich* **490**
Frimley Hall *Camberley* **303**
La Frégate *St Peter Port* **753**
Les Frères Jacques *Dublin* **788**
Fuji *W1* **93**
Fung Shing *WC2* **93**
Funnywayt'mekalivin *Berwick-upon-Tweed*
    256
G & T's Village Bistro *Porth* **743**
Gaby's Seafood Restaurant *Killarney* **804**
Garden House *Cambridge* **305**
Garlands *Bath* **250**
Garrack Hotel *St Ives* **529**
Gasché's *Weybourne* **609**
Gatwick Concorde Hotel *Gatwick Airport*
    376
Gatwick Hilton International *Gatwick
    Airport* **376**
Gatwick Penta Hotel *Gatwick Airport* **376**
La Gaulette *W1* **93**
Gavin's *SW15* **93**
Gavver's *SW1* **93**
Gay Hussar *W1* **94**
Gaylord *Manchester* **457**
Geale's *W8* **94**
Gean House *Alloa* **645**
George & Abbotsford Hotel *Melrose* **697**
George & Dragon *Altrincham* **230**
George & Dragon *Rowde* **524**
George Hotel *Chollerford* **328**
George Hotel *Crawley* **339**
George Hotel *Dorchester-on-Thames* **348**
George Hotel *Hatherleigh* **399**
George Hotel *Huddersfield* **413**
George Hotel *Lichfield* **438**
George Hotel *Melton Mowbray* **467**
George Hotel *Odiham* **497**
George Hotel *Rye* **526**
George Hotel *Solihull* **547**
George Hotel *Wallingford* **601**
George Hotel *WC1* **94**
George III Hotel *Penmaenpool* **742**
George Inter-Continental Hotel *Edinburgh*
    666
The George of Stamford *Stamford* **555**
George's Bistro & Piano Bar *Dublin* **789**
Gerard's *Aberdeen* **641**
Ghyll Manor *Rusper* **526**
Gidleigh Park *Chagford* **313**
Giffard Hotel *Worcester* **625**
Gilbert's *SW7* **94**
Gilpin Lodge *Bowness-on-Windermere*
    275
Giovanni's *WC2* **94**
Glaister's *SW10* **95**
Glansevern Arms *Pantmawr* **742**
Glassdrumman House *Annalong* **764**
Glebe Hotel *Barford* **242**
Gleddoch House *Langbank* **694**
Glen Eagle Hotel *Harpenden* **393**
Glenborrodale Castle *Glenborrodale* **683**
Gleneagles Hotel *Auchterarder* **648**
Glenfeochan House *Kilmore* **691**
Glenview Hotel *Delgany* **785**
Gliffaes Country House Hotel *Crickhowell*
    729
The Gloucester *SW7* **95**
Hotel Godolphin *St Mary's* **529**

Golden Cock *Farnley Tyas* **369**
Golden Valley Thistle *Cheltenham* **318**
Goldstone Hall *Market Drayton* **463**
Goldthorn Hotel *Wolverhampton* **621**
Golf View Hotel *Nairn* **698**
Gonbei *WC1* **95**
Gonville Hotel *Cambridge* **305**
Good Earth *Esher* **361**
Good Earth *NW7* **95**
Good Friends *E14* **95**
Goodwood Park *Goodwood* **380**
Gopal's of Soho *W1* **96**
Gordleton Mill *Lymington* **447**
The Gore *SW7* **96**
The Goring *SW1* **96**
Grafton Français *SW4* **97**
Grafton Hotel *W1* **97**
Grafton Manor *Bromsgrove* **297**
Grahame's Seafare *W1* **97**
Granada Lodge *Birmingham* **261**
Granada Lodge *Blyth* **268**
Granada Lodge *Carlisle* **309**
Granada Lodge *Chippenham* **326**
Granada Lodge *Edinburgh* **666**
Granada Lodge *Ferrybridge* **371**
Granada Lodge *Grantham* **382**
Granada Lodge *Heathrow Airport* **403**
Granada Lodge *Kinross* **693**
Granada Lodge *Leicester* **435**
Granada Lodge *Manchester* **457**
Granada Lodge *Saltash* **533**
Granada Lodge *Tamworth* **577**
Granada Lodge *Thurrock* **585**
Granada Lodge *Toddington* **586**
Granada Lodge *Wakefield* **599**
Granada Lodge *Warminster* **603**
Granada Lodge *Washington* **604**
Grand Atlantic *Weston-super-Mare* **608**
Grand Hotel *Brighton* **285**
Grand Hotel *Bristol* **289**
Grand Hotel *Eastbourne* **357**
Grand Hotel *Hartlepool* **396**
Grand Hotel *Leicester* **435**
Grand Hotel *St Helier* **759**
Grand Hotel *Torquay* **586**
Grand Island Hotel *Ramsey* **762**
Grand St Leger *Doncaster* **347**
Grange Hotel *Alton* **229**
Grange Hotel *Newark-on-Trent* **478**
Grange Hotel *York* **630**
Grange Park *Willerby* **611**
Grange Resort Hotel *Winterbourne* **618**
Granite Corner *Rozel Bay* **757**
Granville Hotel *Waterford* **819**
Grapevine Hotel *Stow-on-the-Wold* **565**
Gravetye Manor *East Grinstead* **355**
Great Danes *Hollingbourne* **411**
Great Fosters *Egham* **359**
Great House *Lavenham* **427**
Great Nepalese *NW1* **97**
Great Northern Hotel *N1* **97**
Great Southern *Galway* **799**
Great Southern *Killarney* **804**
Great Southern *Parknasilla* **812**
Great Southern *Rosslare* **814**
Great Southern *Shannon* **816**
Great Tree Hotel *Chagford* **314**
Greek Valley *NW8* **97**
Green Cottage *NW3* **98**
Green End Park *Dane End* **342**

Green Man *Harlow* **392**
Green Park Hotel *Pitlochry* **705**
Green Park Hotel *W1* **98**
The Green Room *SW11* **98**
Green's Restaurant & Oyster Bar *SW1* **98**
Greenbank Hotel *Falmouth* **366**
Greenhead House *Chapeltown* **315**
Greenhills Hotel *Limerick* **807**
Greenhouse *W1* **99**
Greens Seafood Restaurant *Norwich* **490**
Greenway *Cheltenham* **318**
Gregans Castle *Ballyvaughan* **775**
Gresham Hotel *Dublin* **789**
Grey Door *Dublin* **789**
Grey Gables *Cawston* **312**
Greywalls Hotel *Gullane* **684**
Grill St Quentin *SW3* **99**
La Grillade *Leeds* **431**
Grinkle Park *Easington* **354**
Grizedale Lodge *Grizedale* **388**
Grosvenor Hotel *Shaftesbury* **538**
Grosvenor Hotel *Stockbridge* **558**
Grosvenor House *Sheffield* **539**
Grosvenor House *W1* **99**
Grosvenor Thistle Hotel *SW1* **100**
Grovefield Hotel *Burnham* **300**
Hackness Grange *Hackness* **390**
The Halcyon *W11* **100**
Halepi *W2* **100**
Haley's Hotel *Leeds* **432**
Halkin Hotel *SW1* **100**
Hall Forte Travelodge *Northop* **741**
Hall Garth *Coatham Mundeville* **331**
Halmpstone Manor *Bishop's Tawton* **265**
Hambleton Hall *Oakham* **496**
Hamiltons *Twickenham* **593**
Hampshire Hotel *WC2* **101**
Hanbury Manor *Thundridge* **585**
Hanchurch Manor *Hanchurch* **391**
Hand Hotel *Llanarmon Dyffryn Ceiriog* **732**
Hand Hotel *Llangollen* **736**
Handforth Chinese Restaurant *Handforth* **392**
Harbour Bistro *Ramsey* **763**
Hare & Hounds *Westonbirt* **609**
Hare Arms *Stow Bardolph* **565**
Hark to Bounty Inn *Slaidburn* **546**
Harris's *Penzance* **505**
Harry's Place *Great Gonerby* **385**
Harry's *Wilmslow* **612**
Hartford Hall *Northwich* **489**
Hartley Mount *Cranbrook* **338**
Hartwell House *Aylesbury* **239**
Harveys Café *SW10* **102**
Harveys Restaurant *Bristol* **289**
Harveys *SW17* **102**
Hassop Hall *Bakewell* **241**
Hatherley Manor *Gloucester* **379**
Hathersage Inn *Hathersage* **399**
Hatton Court *Gloucester* **379**
La Haule Manor *St Aubin* **757**
Haven Hotel *Poole* **510**
Hawkstone Park *Weston-under-Redcastle* **609**
Haycock Hotel *Wansford-in-England* **601**
Haydock Thistle *Haydock* **401**
Haydon House Hotel *Stoke-on-Trent* **560**
Hazel Barton *Chedington* **317**
Heathcote's *Longridge* **443**

Heathrow Hilton *Heathrow Airport* **403**
Heathrow Penta Hotel *Heathrow Airport* **403**
Heathrow/Slough Marriott Hotel *Slough* **546**
Hee's *Basingstoke* **246**
Hellas *NW1* **102**
Hendon Hall *NW4* **102**
Henry Wong *Birmingham* **261**
Henry's *Birmingham* **261**
Henry's *Bournemouth* **273**
Heybridge Moat House *Ingatestone* **418**
Highbullen *Chittlehamholt* **327**
Higher Faugan Country House Hotel *Newlyn* **484**
Higoi *Nottingham* **492**
Hilaire *SW7* **103**
Hill Hotel *York* **631**
Hill House *Horndon on the Hill* **412**
Hilton Hotel *Bristol* **290**
Hilton International Kensington *W11* **103**
Hilton International *Leeds* **432**
Hilton International *Manchester Airport* **462**
Hilton International Olympia *W14* **103**
Hilton International Regent's Park *NW8* **103**
Hilton Lodge *Basingstoke* **246**
Hilton National *Basingstoke* **246**
Hilton National *Bath* **250**
Hilton National *Bracknell* **276**
Hilton National *Cobham* **331**
Hilton National E Midlands Airport *Lockington* **442**
Hilton National *Edinburgh* **666**
Hilton National *Garforth* **374**
Hilton National *Newbury* **479**
Hilton National *Newport* **741**
Hilton National *Portsmouth* **512**
Hilton National *Southampton* **551**
Hilton National *Swansea* **746**
Hilton National *Warwick* **604**
Hilton National *Watford* **605**
Hilton National *Wembley* **606**
Hilton Park *Scotshouse* **815**
Hinckley Island Hotel *Hinckley* **408**
Hintlesham Hall *Hintlesham* **409**
Hinton Grange *Hinton* **409**
Hipping Hall *Cowan Bridge* **338**
L'Hippocampe *W1* **104**
Hob Green *Markington* **463**
Hog's Back Hotel *Seale* **536**
Hogarth Hotel *SW5* **104**
Holbeck Ghyll *Windermere* **615**
Holbeck Hall *Scarborough* **535**
Holdsworth House *Halifax* **391**
Holiday Inn *Birmingham* **261**
Holiday Inn *Cambridge* **305**
Holiday Inn Crowne Plaza *Manchester* **457**
Holiday Inn Garden Court *Ashford* **237**
Holiday Inn Garden Court *Edinburgh* **667**
Holiday Inn Garden Court *Leamington Spa* **428**
Holiday Inn Garden Court *Northampton* **487**
Holiday Inn Garden Court *Nottingham* **492**
Holiday Inn Garden Court *Warrington* **603**
Holiday Inn Gatwick *Gatwick Airport* **377**
Holiday Inn *Glasgow* **678**
Holiday Inn Heathrow *Heathrow Airport* **403**
Holiday Inn Kensington *SW7* **104**
Holiday Inn Kings Cross/Bloomsbury *WC1* **104**
Holiday Inn *Leeds* **432**
Holiday Inn *Leicester* **435**
Holiday Inn *Maidenhead* **452**
Holiday Inn Marble Arch *W1* **105**
Holiday Inn Mayfair *W1* **105**
Holiday Inn *Newcastle-upon-Tyne* **482**
Holiday Inn *Portsmouth* **512**
Holiday Inn Royal Victoria *Sheffield* **539**
Holiday Inn *Sutton* **573**
Holiday Inn *Telford* **580**
Holiday Inn *York* **631**
Holly Tree *Kentallen of Appin* **689**
Home Farm *Wilmington* **612**
Homers Hotel *Torquay* **586**
Homewood Park *Freshford* **373**
Hong Kong *WC2* **105**
Honours Mill Restaurant *Edenbridge* **359**
Hopcrofts Holt Hotel *Steeple Aston* **558**
Hope End *Ledbury* **430**
Hotel L'Horizon *St Brelade's Bay* **758**
Horn of Plenty *Gulworthy* **390**
Horsted Place *Uckfield* **593**
Hospitality Inn Bayswater *W2* **105**
Hospitality Inn *Brighton* **286**
Hospitality Inn *Glasgow* **679**
Hospitality Inn *Harrogate* **394**
Hospitality Inn *Irvine* **688**
Hospitality Inn *Middlesbrough* **469**
Hospitality Inn Piccadilly *W1* **105**
Hospitality Inn *Poole* **510**
Hospitality Inn *Portsmouth* **512**
L'Hotel *SW3* **105**
Houstoun House *Uphall* **717**
Howard Hotel *Edinburgh* **667**
The Howard *WC2* **106**
Howard's *Bristol* **290**
Howard's House *Teffont Evias* **579**
Howfield Manor *Canterbury* **308**
Hsing *W2* **106**
Huguenot *Cork* **783**
The Hungry Monk *Greystones* **800**
Hungry Monk Restaurant *Jevington* **419**
Hunstrete House *Hunstrete* **414**
Hunt's *Bristol* **290**
Hunter's Hotel *Rathnew* **813**
Hunters Lodge *Broadway* **295**
Hunters *New Alresford* **477**
Huntsham Court *Huntsham* **415**
Hyatt Carlton Tower *SW1* **106**
Hyatt Regency *Birmingham* **261**
Hyde Park Hotel *SW1* **107**
Hyn's *Ascot* **235**
Hyperion House *Fairford* **366**
Hythe Imperial *Hythe* **417**
I Sardi *SW10* **107**
Hotel Ibis *Luton* **446**
Idle Rocks Hotel *St Mawes* **530**
Ikeda *W1* **108**
Ikkyu *W1* **108**
Imperial Hotel *Barnstaple* **244**
Imperial Hotel *Blackpool* **266**
Imperial Hotel *Cork* **783**
Imperial Hotel *Exmouth* **365**
Imperial Hotel *Harrogate* **394**

Imperial Hotel *Pleinmont* **752**
Imperial Hotel *Torquay* **587**
Inchalla Hotel *St Anne* **752**
Inchbae Lodge *Garve* **675**
Inchfield Hotel *Leamington Spa* **428**
L'Incontro *SW1* **108**
Indian Cavalry Club *Edinburgh* **667**
Inn at Whitewell *Whitewell* **611**
Inn on the Lake *Godalming* **380**
Inn on the Lake *Shorne* **543**
Inn on the Park Hotel *W1* **108**
Inter-Continental Hotel *W1* **110**
International Hotel *Derby* **345**
Inver Lodge Hotel *Lochinver* **696**
Invercarse Hotel *Dundee* **662**
Invercreran Hotel *Appin* **646**
Inverlochy Castle *Fort William* **674**
Invery House *Banchory* **651**
Ipswich Moat House *Copdock* **334**
Isaacs *Cork* **783**
Island Hotel *Tresco* **588**
Isle of Eriska *Eriska* **672**
Isle of Mull Hotel *Craignure* **656**
Isle of Raasay Hotel *Isle of Raasay* **688**
Isohama *SW1* **110**
Istanbul Iskembecisi *N16* **110**
Ivy Bush Royal *Carmarthen* **726**
Ivy House *Braithwaite* **279**
Ivy House *Marlborough* **463**
The Ivy *WC2* **110**
Izaak Walton Hotel *Dovedale* **349**
Jack Fuller's *Brightling* **284**
Jacques *Cork* **783**
Jade Garden *W1* **111**
Jameson's Restaurant *Bristol* **290**
Jersey Arms *Middleton Stoney* **469**
Jersey Farm Hotel *Barnard Castle* **242**
Jersey Pottery *Gorey* **755**
Jervaulx Hall *Jervaulx* **419**
Joe Allen *WC2* **111**
Joe's Café *SW3* **111**
Judges Lodging *York* **631**
Jurys Hotel & Towers *Dublin* **789**
Jurys Hotel *Cork* **784**
Jurys Hotel *Limerick* **807**
Jurys Pond Hotel *Glasgow* **679**
Jurys Waterford Hotel *Waterford* **819**
Kalamaras *W2* **111**
Kalpna *Edinburgh* **667**
Kam's *W2* **112**
Kapriol *Dublin* **790**
Kaya *W1* **112**
Hotel Keadeen *Newbridge* **810**
Keenan's & Brayley's Bistro *Swansea* **746**
Kelly's *Edinburgh* **667**
Kelly's Strand Hotel *Rosslare* **814**
Kelvin Park Lorne Hotel *Glasgow* **679**
Kemps Country House Hotel *East Stoke* **356**
Ken Lo's Memories of China *SW1* **112**
Ken Lo's Memories of China *SW10* **112**
Kenilworth Hotel *WC1* **112**
Kenmore Hotel *Kenmore* **689**
Kennedy Hotel *NW1* **113**
Kennel Holt Hotel *Cranbrook* **338**
Kensington Court Hotel *SW5* **113**
Kensington Manor *SW7* **113**
Kensington Palace Thistle *W8* **113**
Kensington Park Hotel *W8* **113**
Kensington Place *W8* **113**

Keswick Hotel *Keswick* **421**
Khan's of Kensington *SW7* **114**
Khyber Pass *SW7* **114**
Kilcoran Lodge *Kilcoran* **802**
Kildare Hotel *Straffan* **817**
Kildrummy Castle *Kildrummy* **690**
Kilfinan Hotel *Kilfinan* **691**
Kilhey Court *Worthington* **626**
Kilkea Castle *Castledermot* **779**
Killiecrankie Hotel *Killiecrankie* **691**
King James Thistle *Edinburgh* **668**
King Malcolm Thistle *Dunfermline* **662**
King Neptune *Newcastle-upon-Tyne* **482**
King Sitric *Howth* **800**
King's Arms Inn *Montacute* **471**
King's Arms *Melksham* **467**
King's Head *East Dereham* **355**
King's Head *Loughborough* **444**
King's Head *Monmouth* **739**
Kings Arms *Berwick-upon-Tweed* **257**
Kings Hotel *Newport* **741**
Kingshead House *Birdlip* **259**
Kingsmills Hotel *Inverness* **687**
Kingsway Hotel *Cleethorpes* **330**
Kinloch House *Blairgowrie* **653**
Kinloch Lodge *Sleat* **711**
Kinlochbervie Hotel *Kinlochbervie* **693**
Kinnaird *Dalguise* **658**
Kipling's *Bridge of Allan* **654**
Kirkhouse Inn *Strathblane* **713**
Kirkstone Foot *Ambleside* **232**
Kirroughtree Hotel *Newton Stewart* **699**
Kitchen at Polperro *Polperro* **509**
Knapton Hall *Knapton* **424**
Knights Hill Hotel *South Wootton* **551**
Knightsbridge Green Hotel *SW1* **114**
Knipoch Hotel *Oban* **701**
Knockie Lodge *Whitebridge* **717**
Knockinaam Lodge *Portpatrick* **706**
Knocklofty House *Knocklofty* **806**
Knoll House *Studland Bay* **571**
Koto *NW1* **114**
Krug's *Farnham* **368**
K2 *Bradford* **277**
Kundan *SW1* **114**
Kuti's *Southampton* **552**
Laburnum House *Wylam* **627**
Lainston House *Winchester* **614**
Lake Country House Hotel *Llangammarch Wells* **735**
The Lake Isle *Uppingham* **597**
Lake Vyrnwy Hotel *Lake Vyrnwy* **731**
Lal Qila *W1* **115**
Lamb Hotel *Ely* **360**
Lamorna Cove Hotel *Lamorna Cove* **426**
Landgate Bistro *Rye* **527**
Lands of Loyal Hotel *Alyth* **646**
The Lanesborough *SW1* **115**
Langan's Bistro *Brighton* **286**
Langan's Bistro *W1* **116**
Langan's Brasserie *W1* **116**
Langdale Hotel *Langdale* **426**
The Langham *W1* **116**
Langland Court Hotel *Swansea* **746**
Langley Castle *Langley-on-Tyne* **427**
Langley House *Wiveliscombe* **620**
Langrish House *Petersfield* **507**
Langshott Manor *Horley* **411**
Langtry Manor *Bournemouth* **273**
Lansdown Grove *Bath* **250**

Lantern Lodge *Hope Cove* **411**
Lanterna *Scarborough* **535**
Larkfield Priory *Maidstone* **453**
Last Drop Village Hotel *Bolton* **269**
Launceston Place *W8* **117**
Laurent *NW2* **117**
Leadon's Brasserie *Chepstow* **727**
Leaside Hotel *Luton* **447**
The Leatherne Bottel *Goring-on-Thames* **381**
Leeming House *Ullswater* **594**
Leicester Forest Moat House *Leicester* **435**
Leith's *W11* **118**
Lemonia *NW1* **118**
Lena's *SW11* **118**
Letterfinlay Lodge *Spean Bridge* **712**
Lettonie *Bristol* **291**
Lewtrenchard Manor *Lewdown* **437**
Hotel Lexham *W8* **118**
Leyland Resort Hotel *Leyland* **438**
Liaison *Solihull* **547**
Lido *W1* **119**
Lilly's *W11* **119**
Limerick Inn *Limerick* **807**
Linden Hall *Longhorsley* **443**
Lindsay House *W1* **119**
The Links *West Runton* **608**
Linthwaite House *Bowness-on-Windermere* **275**
Lion Hotel *Shrewsbury* **543**
Little Akropolis *W1* **119**
Little Barwick House *Yeovil* **629**
Little Grove *St Lawrence* **760**
Little Thakeham *Storrington* **563**
Little Yang Sing *Manchester* **457**
Livermead Cliff Hotel *Torquay* **587**
Livermead House *Torquay* **587**
Llangoed Hall *Llyswen* **738**
Llansantffraed Court *Llanvihangel Gobion* **738**
Llechwen Hall *Abercynon* **720**
Llyndir Hall *Rossett* **745**
Lobster Pot *Mousehole* **475**
Loch Fyne Oyster Bar *Cairndow* **654**
Loch Fyne Oyster Bar *Nottingham* **493**
Loch Maree Hotel *Talladale* **713**
Loch Melfort Hotel *Arduaine* **647**
Lochalsh Hotel *Kyle of Lochalsh* **694**
Locks *Dublin* **790**
Lodge on the Loch *Onich* **702**
Log Cabin Hotel *Kirkmichael* **693**
Lok Ho Fook *W1* **119**
London Embassy *W2* **120**
London Hilton on Park Lane *W1* **120**
London International *E14* **120**
London Marriott *W1* **120**
London Metropole Hotel *W2* **121**
London Mews Hilton on Park Lane *W1* **121**
London Wilshire *NW1* **121**
Long's *Blackwater* **267**
Longueville House *Mallow* **808**
Loon Fung *Glasgow* **679**
The Lord Bagenal Inn *Leighlinbridge* **806**
Lord Crewe Arms *Bamburgh* **241**
Lord Crewe Arms *Blanchland* **268**
Lord Daresbury Hotel *Warrington* **603**
Lords of the Manor *Upper Slaughter* **596**
Lou Pescadou *SW5* **121**

Louisiana *St Peter Port* **753**
Lovelady Shield *Alston* **229**
Lovetts *Cork* **784**
Low Hall *Leeds* **433**
Lower Pitt *East Buckland* **354**
Lower Slaughter Manor *Lower Slaughter* **445**
Lowman Restaurant *Tiverton* **586**
The Lowndes *SW1* **121**
Luc's Restaurant & Brasserie *EC3* **122**
Lucknam Park *Colerne* **333**
Lugger Hotel *Portloe* **511**
Lugleys *Wootton Common* **624**
Luigi's *SE19* **122**
Lumley Castle *Chester-le-Street* **324**
Luttrell Arms *Dunster* **353**
Lygon Arms *Broadway* **295**
Lynch Country House Hotel *Somerton* **548**
Lyndhurst Park *Lyndhurst* **449**
Lynton Cottage *Lynton* **450**
Lynwood House *Barnstaple* **244**
Lythe Hill Hotel *Haslemere* **397**
Mabey's Brasserie *Sudbury* **572**
MacCloskey's *Bunratty* **777**
Macdonald Thistle *Giffnock* **676**
Madeley Court *Telford* **580**
Maes-y-Neaudd *Talsarnau* **747**
Magheramorne House *Larne* **768**
Maiden Newton House *Maiden Newton* **451**
Maison Talbooth *Dedham* **344**
Majestic Hotel *Harrogate* **394**
Majlis *SW7* **122**
Malabar *W8* **122**
Mallory Court *Leamington Spa* **428**
Mallyan Spout *Goathland* **380**
Malt House Restaurant *Galway* **799**
Maltsters Arms *Chapel Amble* **314**
Maltsters Arms *Tuckenhay* **589**
Mamma Adele *Thornton Heath* **584**
Man Ho *Leicester* **436**
Mandarin Chef *Maidstone* **453**
Mandarin *Guildford* **389**
Mandarin Kitchen *W2* **123**
Mandeer *W1* **123**
Mandeville Hotel *W1* **123**
Manley's *Storrington* **564**
Le Manoir aux Quat'Saisons *Great Milton* **385**
The Manor *Chadlington* **312**
Manor Hotel *Blakeney* **267**
Manor Hotel *Meriden* **468**
Manor Hotel *West Bexington* **607**
Manor House *Alsager* **229**
Manor House *Belfast* **764**
Manor House *Castle Combe* **311**
Manor House *Moreton-in-Marsh* **472**
Manor House *Walkington* **600**
Manor of Groves *Sawbridgeworth* **534**
Manor Park *Skelmorlie* **711**
The Manor *Yeovil* **629**
Mansion House *Elgin* **672**
Mansion House *Poole* **510**
Manzi's *E14* **123**
Manzi's *WC2* **123**
Marco's *Norwich* **490**
La Marinade *Brighton* **286**
Marine Highland Hotel *Troon* **715**
Marine Hotel *North Berwick* **700**

Marine Hotel *Salcombe* **531**
Market Restaurant *Manchester* **458**
Markwick's *Bristol* **291**
Marlborough Hotel *Ipswich* **418**
The Marlborough *WC1* **123**
Marlfield House *Gorey* **799**
Maroush *W2* **124**
Marsh Country Hotel *Eyton* **365**
Marsh Goose *Moreton-in-Marsh* **472**
Marston Farm *Bodymoor Heath* **268**
Martin's *Edinburgh* **668**
Maryculter House *Maryculter* **696**
Masako *W1* **124**
Masons Arms *Branscombe* **281**
Master Builder's House *Buckler's Hard*
   299
Mata Hari *Glasgow* **679**
Mauro's *Bollington* **269**
Max's Wine Bar *Kinsale* **805**
Maxi's Chinese Restaurant *Leeds* **433**
May Fair Inter-Continental *W1* **124**
Maynard Arms *Grindleford* **388**
McClements *Twickenham* **593**
McCoy's *Staddle Bridge* **555**
Meadow House *Kilve* **422**
Meadowsweet *Llanrwst* **737**
Melton's *York* **631**
Memories of India *SW7* **125**
Mercury Hotel *Fort William* **675**
Mercury Hotel *Inverness* **687**
Le Meridien *W1* **125**
Merkister Hotel *Harray Loch* **685**
Mermaid Hotel *St Peter* **761**
Mermaid Inn *Rye* **526**
Merrion Hotel *Leeds* **433**
Merryfield House *W1* **126**
Le Mesurier *EC1* **126**
Methuen Arms *Corsham* **335**
Meudon Hotel *Mawnan Smith* **465**
Michael's Nook *Grasmere* **382**
Michael's Restaurant *Bristol* **291**
Michels' *Ripley* **520**
Middlethorpe Hall *York* **631**
Le Midi *SW6* **126**
Midland Hotel *Birmingham* **262**
Midsummer House *Cambridge* **306**
Mijanou *SW1* **126**
Milburn Arms *Rosedale Abbey* **522**
The Milestone *W8* **127**
Mill Arms Inn *Dunbridge* **352**
Mill End *Chagford* **314**
The Mill *Harvington* **396**
Mill Hotel *Alveley* **230**
Mill Hotel *Sudbury* **572**
Mill House Inn *Ashington* **238**
Mill House *Kingham* **422**
Miller Howe *Windermere* **616**
Miller's *Harrogate* **394**
Millstone Hotel *Mellor* **467**
Millstream Hotel *Bosham* **271**
Millwaters *Newbury* **479**
Mimmo d'Ischia *SW1* **127**
Mims Restaurant *New Barnet* **477**
Ming *W1* **127**
Mirabelle *W1* **127**
Miskin Manor *Miskin* **739**
Mr Hung's *Monkstown* **809**
Mr Hung's Sawadee Thai Restaurant
   Stillorgan **817**
Mr Kai *W1* **128**

Mr Ke *NW3* **128**
Mr Underhill's *Stonham* **562**
Mitsukoshi *SW1* **128**
Miyama *EC4* **129**
Miyama *W1* **129**
Moat House *Banbury* **241**
Moat House *Bedford* **255**
Moat House *Blackburn* **266**
Moat House *Bramhall* **279**
Moat House *Brentwood* **283**
Moat House *Bristol* **292**
Moat House *Cardiff* **725**
Moat House *Doncaster* **347**
Moat House *Dover* **350**
Moat House *Gatwick Airport* **377**
Moat House *Harlow* **392**
Moat House *Harpenden* **393**
Moat House *Harrogate* **394**
Moat House *Hereford* **406**
Moat House International *Stratford-upon-
   Avon* **568**
Moat House International *Glasgow* **680**
Moat House *Liverpool* **441**
Moat House *Newcastle-upon-Tyne* **482**
Moat House *Newmarket* **484**
Moat House *North Stifford* **486**
Moat House *Northampton* **487**
Moat House *Nottingham* **493**
Moat House *Oxford* **500**
Moat House *Peterborough* **506**
Moat House *Plymouth* **508**
Moat House *Rotherham* **523**
Moat House *Sheffield* **539**
Moat House *Shepperton* **540**
Moat House *Solihull* **547**
Moat House *Stoke-on-Trent* **560**
Moat House *Stourport-on-Severn* **565**
Moat House *Telford* **581**
Moat House *Washington* **604**
Moat House *WC2* **129**
Moat House *West Bromwich* **607**
Moat House *Wilmslow* **613**
Mollington Banastre *Chester* **323**
Momo *W5* **129**
La Mon House *Comber* **766**
Mon Plaisir *WC2* **129**
Monk Fryston Hall *Monk Fryston* **471**
Monkeys *SW3* **130**
Mont Clare Hotel *Dublin* **790**
Montagu Arms *Beaulieu* **254**
Montcalm Hotel *W1* **130**
Montgreenan Mansion *Kilwinning* **692**
Montrose Hotel *Dublin* **790**
Moon *Kendal* **420**
Moor Hall *Sutton Coldfield* **574**
Moore Place *Aspley Guise* **238**
Moorings Hotel *Gorey* **755**
Moorland Links *Yelverton* **629**
Morel's *Haslemere* **397**
Mornington Hotel *W2* **130**
Morrisons Island Hotel *Cork* **784**
Morritt Arms *Greta Bridge* **387**
Morston Hall *Morston* **473**
Mortal Man Inn *Troutbeck* **589**
Mortons House Hotel *Corfe Castle* **334**
Moss Nook *Manchester Airport* **462**
Mostyn Hotel *W1* **130**
Motcomb's *SW1* **130**
Mottram Hall *Mottram St Andrew* **474**
Mount Falcon Castle *Ballina* **773**

Mount Hotel *Wolverhampton* **621**
Mount Juliet Hotel *Thomastown* **818**
Mount Royale *York* **632**
Mount Sorrel Hotel *Barry* **722**
Mountbatten Hotel *WC2* **131**
Moyglare Manor *Maynooth* **808**
Muckrach Lodge *Dulnain Bridge* **661**
Mulligans of Mayfair *W1* **131**
Munchy Munchy *Oxford* **501**
Murray Arms Inn *Gatehouse of Fleet* **676**
Murray's *Cuckfield* **341**
Murrayshall House *Scone* **709**
Le Muscadet *W1* **131**
Museum Street Café *WC1* **131**
Mustard Seed *Adare* **772**
Restaurant Na Mara *Dun Laoghaire* **795**
Nakamura *W1* **132**
Nakano *SW1* **132**
Nanking *W6* **132**
Nanny Brow *Ambleside* **232**
Nansidwell *Mawnan Smith* **465**
Nare Hotel *Veryan* **598**
Le Nautique *St Peter Port* **754**
Navidale House *Helmsdale* **685**
Nawaab *Bradford* **277**
Neal Street Restaurant *WC2* **132**
Hotel Nelson *Norwich* **491**
Neptune Restaurant *Ballyhack* **774**
Neshiko *N1* **133**
Netherfield Place *Battle* **252**
New Asia *Leeds* **433**
New Barbican Hotel *EC1* **133**
New Bath Hotel *Matlock Bath* **465**
New Bold Hotel *Southport* **552**
New England Hotel *Boston* **271**
New Fook Lam Moon *W1* **133**
New Garden *Aberkenfig* **721**
New Hall *Sutton Coldfield* **574**
New Happy Gathering *Birmingham* **262**
New Kam Tong *W2* **133**
New Mill Restaurant *Eversley* **363**
New Royal Dublin Hotel *Dublin* **790**
New World *W1* **134**
Newbridge House *Bath* **251**
Newbus Arms *Neasham* **476**
Newpark Hotel *Kilkenny* **802**
Newport House *Newport* **811**
Newton Hotel *Nairn* **698**
Newton Park *Newton Solney* **485**
Newtons *SW4* **134**
Nick's Restaurant *Killorglin* **805**
Nick's Warehouse *Belfast* **764**
Nico at Ninety *W1* **135**
Nico Central *W1* **134**
Nidd Hall *Nidd* **485**
Nikita's *SW10* **135**
Restaurant 19 *Bradford* **277**
19 Grape Lane *York* **632**
Ninjin *W1* **136**
Nirmal's *Sheffield* **540**
Nivingstone House *Cleish* **655**
Noble House *Nottingham* **493**
Noel Arms *Chipping Campden* **326**
Noke Thistle *St Albans* **527**
Nontas *NW1* **136**
Noor Jahan *SW5* **136**
Norfolk Arms *Arundel* **234**
Norfolk Hotel *SW7* **136**
Norfolk Royale *Bournemouth* **273**

Normandie Hotel *Bury* **301**
North Lakes Gateway Hotel *Penrith* **504**
North Stafford Hotel *Stoke-on-Trent* **560**
North West Castle *Stranraer* **713**
Northcote Manor *Langho* **427**
Norton House *Ingliston* **686**
Norton House *Mumbles* **740**
Norton Place *Birmingham* **262**
Hotel Norwich *Norwich* **491**
Norwich Sport Village Hotel *Norwich* **491**
Novotel *Birmingham* **263**
Novotel *Birmingham Airport* **265**
Novotel *Bradford* **277**
Novotel *Coventry* **337**
Novotel *Manchester* **458**
Novotel *Newcastle-upon-Tyne* **482**
Novotel *Nottingham* **493**
Novotel *Plymouth* **509**
Novotel *Preston* **513**
Novotel *Southampton* **552**
Novotel *Stevenage* **558**
Novotel *W6* **136**
Novotel *York* **632**
Now & Zen *WC2* **137**
Number One *Swansea* **746**
Number Sixteen *SW7* **137**
Number Thirty Three *Perth* **704**
No. 3 Restaurant & Hotel *Glastonbury* **378**
Number Twenty Four *Wymondham* **628**
Nunsmere Hall *Sandiway* **533**
Nuremore Hotel *Carrickmacross* **778**
Nusa Dua *W1* **137**
Nutfield Priory *Nutfield* **495**
Nuthurst Grange *Hockley Heath* **410**
O'Keeffe's *Cork* **784**
Oak House *Axbridge* **239**
Oakes *Stroud* **571**
Oakley Court *Windsor* **617**
Oaks Hotel *Porlock* **511**
Oaksmere *Brome* **296**
Oatlands Park *Weybridge* **610**
Ocean City *Nottingham* **493**
Ocean Palace *Bournemouth* **273**
Ockenden Manor *Cuckfield* **341**
October Café *Glasgow* **680**
October Restaurant *Bearsden* **652**
Odette's *NW1* **137**
Odin's Restaurant *W1* **137**
Ognisko Polskie *SW7* **138**
Oh'Boy *SW17* **138**
Oisins *Dublin* **791**
Old Beams *Waterhouses* **605**
Old Bell Hotel *Malmesbury* **454**
Old Bridge Hotel *Huntingdon* **415**
Old Church Hotel *Ullswater* **594**
Old Court House *Gorey* **755**
Old Court House Inn *St Aubin* **757**
Old England Hotel *Bowness-on-
    Windermere* **276**
Old Farmhouse *Lower Swell* **445**
Old Fire Engine House *Ely* **360**
Old Forge Restaurant *Newmill-on-Teviot*
    699
Old Forge *Storrington* **564**
Old Government House *St Peter Port* **754**
Old Ground Hotel *Ennis* **797**
Old House Hotel *Wickham* **611**
Old Inn *Crawfordsburn* **767**
Old Manor House *Romsey* **522**
Old Mansion House *Auchterhouse* **648**

Old Mill *Ide* **417**
Old Monastery Restaurant *Drybridge* **659**
Old Palace Lodge *Dunstable* **353**
Old Parsonage *Oxford* **501**
Old Post Office *Clun* **331**
Old Presbytery *Kinsale* **805**
Old Rectory *Campsea Ashe* **306**
Old Rectory *Great Snoring* **386**
Old Rectory *Llansanffraid Glan Conwy*
 737
Old Rectory *Wicklow* **821**
Old Ship Hotel *Brighton* **287**
Old Ship Hotel *Mere* **468**
Old Swan Hotel *Harrogate* **395**
Old Swan *Minster Lovell* **471**
Old Vicarage *Ridgeway* **520**
Old Vicarage *Witherslack* **619**
Old Vicarage *Worfield* **625**
Old Woolhouse *Northleach* **488**
Olde Ship Hotel *Seahouses* **536**
Oliver's *W14* **138**
Olivo *SW1* **138**
Ommaroo Hotel *Havre des Pas* **756**
On The Park *Cheltenham* **319**
One Devonshire Gardens *Glasgow* **680**
101 Talbot *Dublin* **790**
192 *W11* **139**
1789 *E3* **139**
Hotel 167 *SW5* **139**
Onich Hotel *Onich* **702**
Open Arms Hotel *Dirleton* **659**
Ormesby Lodge *Ormesby St Margaret*
 498
Orso *WC2* **139**
L'Ortolan *Shinfield* **542**
Orwell Moat House *Felixstowe* **370**
Osborne Hotel *Torquay* **587**
Osteria Antica Bologna *SW11* **139**
Ostlers Close *Cupar* **658**
Otters Restaurant *Braunton* **281**
The Oystercatcher *Oysterhaven* **812**
Le P'tit Normand *SW18* **140**
PA's Winebar *Mumbles* **740**
Pack Horse Hotel *Bolton* **270**
La Paesana *W8* **140**
Painswick Hotel *Painswick* **503**
Palace Court *Bournemouth* **273**
Palace Hotel *Douglas* **762**
Palace Hotel *Paignton* **502**
Palace Hotel *Torquay* **587**
Palé Hall *Llandderfel* **733**
Panda *W1* **140**
Pandora Inn *Falmouth* **366**
Paris House *Woburn* **620**
Park Farm *Hethersett* **408**
Park Hotel *Cardiff* **725**
Park Hotel *Heathrow Airport* **404**
Park Hotel *Kenmare* **801**
Park Hotel *Peebles* **703**
Park House *Shifnal* **541**
Park International *Leicester* **436**
Park Lane Hotel *W1* **140**
Parkhill Hotel *Lyndhurst* **449**
Parkway Hotel *Bramhope* **279**
Parkwood Hotel *W2* **141**
La Parmigiana *Glasgow* **680**
Partners Brasserie *Sutton* **573**
Partners West Street *Dorking* **348**
Passage House *Newton Abbot* **485**
Passford House *Lymington* **448**

Pasta Fresca *Dublin* **791**
Patrick Guilbaud *Dublin* **791**
Paul's *Folkestone* **372**
Peacock Hotel *Rowsley* **525**
Restaurant Peano *Barnsley* **243**
Pear Tree *Purton* **515**
Pearl of Knightsbridge *SW1* **141**
Peat Inn *Peat Inn* **702**
Peebles Hotel Hydro *Peebles* **703**
Peking Garden *W14* **141**
Pelham Hotel *SW7* **141**
Pembridge Court Hotel *W2* **142**
Pembroke Hotel *Blackpool* **266**
Penally Abbey *Penally* **742**
Penang Village *Manchester* **458**
Pendragon Hotel *Portsmouth* **512**
Pengethley Manor *Ross-on-Wye* **523**
Penhaven Country House *Parkham* **503**
Pennine Hilton National *Huddersfield* **413**
Penns Hall *Sutton Coldfield* **574**
Pennyhill Park *Bagshot* **240**
Penrhos Court *Kington* **423**
Periquito Hotel *Rugby* **525**
Periton Park *Middlecombe* **469**
Perkins Bar Bistro *Plumtree* **507**
Perry Hall *Bromsgrove* **298**
Peter's *NW6* **142**
Petersham Hotel *Richmond* **519**
Le Petit Canard *Maiden Newton* **452**
Hotel Petit Champ *Sark* **761**
Le Petit Prince *NW5* **142**
Petty France Hotel *Dunkirk* **352**
Peveril of the Peak *Dovedale* **349**
Pheasant Hotel *Harome* **393**
Pheasant Inn *Bassenthwaite Lake* **248**
Pheasant Inn *Keyston* **421**
The Pheasant *Seavington St Mary* **537**
Pheasants *Ross-on-Wye* **523**
Philipburn House *Selkirk* **710**
Phoenicia *W8* **142**
Phoenix Hotel *East Dereham* **355**
Hotel Piccadilly *Manchester* **458**
Pied à Terre *W1* **142**
Pier at Harwich *Harwich* **397**
Pierre Victoire *Edinburgh* **668**
Pierre's *Falkirk* **673**
Piersland House *Troon* **715**
Pilgrim Hotel *Much Birch* **475**
Pines Hotel *Clayton-le-Woods* **330**
Pink Geranium *Melbourn* **466**
Pinocchio's *NW1* **143**
Pipps Ford *Needham Market* **477**
Pitlochry Hydro *Pitlochry* **705**
Pittodrie House *Chapel of Garioch* **655**
Pizzeria Castello *SE1* **143**
La Place Hotel *St Brelade* **758**
Places of Interest *Andover* **233**
Hotel de la Plage *Havre des Pas* **756**
Plas Bodegroes *Pwllheli* **744**
Plas Penhelig *Aberdovey* **720**
Plaza Hotel *Belfast* **765**
Plough & Harrow *Birmingham* **263**
The Plough at Clanfield *Clanfield* **329**
PLS Gujrati Pure Vegetarian *Bradford* **278**
Plumber Manor *Sturminster Newton* **572**
Poissonnerie de l'Avenue *SW3* **143**
Pollyanna's *SW11* **143**
Polmaily House *Drumnadrochit* **659**
Polo One *Dublin* **791**
Polurrian Hotel *Mullion* **476**

Polygon Hotel *Southampton* **552**
Pomegranates *SW1* **144**
Pomme d'Or Hotel *St Helier* **760**
Le Pont de la Tour *SE1* **144**
Pontlands Park *Great Baddow* **384**
Pool Court *Pool-in-Wharfedale* **509**
Poons *W2* **145**
Poons *WC1* **145**
Poons *WC2* **144**
Poons *WC2* **145**
Poons *WC2* **145**
Poppies Restaurant *Brimfield* **288**
Port-an-Eilean Hotel *Strathtummel* **713**
Portelet Hotel *Portelet Bay* **756**
Porters Wine Bar *Taunton* **579**
Porth Avallen Hotel *Carlyon Bay* **309**
Porth Tocyn Hotel *Abersoch* **721**
Portland Thistle *Manchester* **459**
Portledge Hotel *Fairy Cross* **366**
Hotel Portmeirion *Portmeirion* **743**
Portobello Hotel *W11* **146**
Posh Nosh *Kendal* **420**
La Potinière *Gullane* **685**
Potters Heron Hotel *Ampfield* **233**
Le Poulbot *EC2* **146**
Le Poussin *Brockenhurst* **296**
Prachee *Guiseley* **390**
La Preferita *SW11* **146**
Prendiville's Restaurant *Waterford* **820**
President Hotel *WC1* **146**
Il Primo *Dublin* **791**
Prince Hotel *SW7* **146**
Prince of Wales Hotel *Southport* **553**
Prince Regent Hotel *Woodford Bridge* **622**
Prince Rupert Hotel *Shrewsbury* **543**
Priory Hotel *Bath* **251**
Priory Hotel *Wareham* **602**
Le Provençale *Newtown St Boswells* **700**
Puckrup Hall *Puckrup* **514**
Puerto Bella *Dublin* **792**
Pun *SW7* **147**
Purple Rooms *Birmingham* **263**
Qinggis *NW3* **147**
Le Quai *St Pierre W8* **147**
Quails Restaurant *Chobham* **328**
Quality Chop House *EC1* **147**
Quan Ju De *Manchester* **459**
Quayles *Cardiff* **725**
Quayside Hotel *Brixham* **294**
Queen's Hotel *Cheltenham* **319**
Queen's Hotel *Eastbourne* **357**
Queen's Hotel *Leeds* **433**
Queensberry Hotel *Bath* **251**
Queensferry Lodge *North Queensferry* **701**
Quince & Medlar *Cockermouth* **332**
Quincy's *NW2* **148**
Quorn Grange *Quorn* **516**
The Quorn *Quorn* **516**
Radnorshire Arms *Presteigne* **744**
Raemoir House *Banchory* **651**
Ragam *W1* **148**
Rajdoot *Birmingham* **263**
Rajdoot *Dublin* **792**
Rajdoot *Manchester* **459**
Rajput *W12* **148**
Ram Jam Inn *Stretton* **570**
Ramada Hotel *Reading* **518**
Ramada Renaissance *Manchester* **459**

Ramore *Portrush* **769**
Rampsbeck Country House Hotel *Ullswater* **595**
Randell's Hotel *Skipton* **546**
Randolph Hotel *Oxford* **501**
Rani *N3* **149**
Rankins *Sissinghurst* **545**
Rasa Sayang *W1* **149**
Rathbone Hotel *W1* **149**
Rathmullan House *Rathmullan* **813**
Rathsallagh House *Dunlavin* **796**
Raven Hotel *Droitwich Spa* **351**
Ravi Shankar *NW1* **149**
Read's *Faversham* **369**
Reading Moat House *Sindlesham* **545**
La Reash *W1* **149**
Red Bank Restaurant *Skerries* **816**
Red Fort *W1* **150**
Red Lion *Fareham* **367**
Red Lion *Henley-on-Thames* **405**
Redcliffe Hotel *Paignton* **502**
Redesdale Arms *Moreton-in-Marsh* **473**
Redmond's *Cheltenham* **319**
Redwood Lodge *Bristol* **292**
Regency Hotel *Solihull* **547**
Regency Hotel *SW7* **150**
Regency Park Hotel *Newbury* **480**
Regent Hotel *Leamington Spa* **429**
Regent's Park Marriott *NW3* **150**
Rembrandt Hotel *SW7* **150**
Renvyle House *Renvyle* **814**
Riber Hall *Matlock* **464**
Richmond Gate Hotel *Richmond* **520**
Ripon Spa Hotel *Ripon* **521**
Rise of the Raj *Leicester* **436**
Rising Sun Inn *Lynmouth* **450**
Rising Sun Inn *Umberleigh* **596**
Rising Sun *St Mawes* **530**
Ristorante Caprese *Glasgow* **681**
Il Ristorante *Dalkey* **785**
Ristorante Raffaelli *Edinburgh* **669**
Ristorante Tinelli *Edinburgh* **669**
Ritcher's *Wells* **606**
The Ritz *W1* **151**
Riva *SW13* **151**
River Café *W6* **151**
River House *Lympstone* **449**
River House *Thornton-le-Fylde* **584**
River Kwai *Canterbury* **308**
River Kwai *Worthing* **626**
Riverside *Helford* **404**
Riverside Hotel *Abersoch* **721**
Riverside Hotel *Ashford-in-the-Water* **237**
Riverside Hotel *Evesham* **363**
Riverside Inn *Burton-on-Trent* **301**
Riverside Inn *Canonbie* **654**
Riverside Restaurant *Bridport* **283**
Hotel Riviera *Newquay* **484**
Hotel Riviera *Sidmouth* **544**
Roadhouse *Roade* **521**
Rocher's *Milford-on-Sea* **470**
Roches Bistro *Malahide* **808**
Rochestown Park Hotel *Cork* **784**
Rock Glen Manor Hotel *Clifden* **780**
Rodney Hotel *Bristol* **292**
Rogano *Glasgow* **681**
Roger's Restaurant *Windermere* **616**
Roman Camp *Callander* **654**
Romans Hotel *Silchester* **544**
Romantica Taverna *W2* **152**

Rombalds Hotel *Ilkley* **418**
Rookery Hall *Nantwich* **476**
Roscoff *Belfast* **765**
Rose & Crown Inn *Bainbridge* **240**
Rose & Crown *Salisbury* **532**
Rose & Crown *Tonbridge* **586**
Rosedale Hotel *Portree* **706**
La Rosette *Ballasalla* **762**
Rosleague Manor *Letterfrack* **806**
Rothay Manor *Ambleside* **232**
Rothes Glen Hotel *Rothes* **708**
Rothley Court *Rothley* **524**
The Rotisserie *W12* **152**
Rougemont Hotel *Exeter* **364**
Roundabout Hotel *West Chiltington* **607**
Roundwood House *Mountrath* **809**
Roundwood Inn *Roundwood* **815**
Rowton Hall *Chester* **323**
Roxburghe Hotel *Edinburgh* **669**
Royal Angus Thistle *Birmingham* **263**
Royal Bath Hotel *Bournemouth* **274**
Royal Berkshire *Ascot* **235**
Royal Castle Hotel *Dartmouth* **344**
Royal Chase Hotel *Shaftesbury* **538**
Royal China *W2* **152**
Royal Clarence *Exeter* **364**
Royal County Hotel *Durham* **353**
Royal Court Hotel *SW1* **152**
Royal Crescent Hotel *Bath* **252**
Royal Garden Hotel *W8* **152**
Royal George Hotel *Perth* **704**
Royal George *Tintern Abbey* **748**
Royal Goat Hotel *Beddgelert* **723**
Royal Hop Pole *Tewkesbury* **582**
Royal Horseguards Thistle *SW1* **153**
Royal Hotel *Bridge of Allan* **654**
Royal Hotel *Forfar* **673**
Royal Hotel *Llangollen* **736**
Royal Hotel *Ventnor* **598**
Royal Hotel *Winchester* **614**
Royal Lancaster Hotel *W2* **153**
Royal Marine Hotel *Dun Laoghaire* **795**
Royal Moat House *Nottingham* **493**
Royal Norfolk *Bognor Regis* **269**
Royal Oak *Betws-y-Coed* **723**
Royal Oak Inn *Winsford* **618**
Royal Oak *Sevenoaks* **537**
Royal Oak *Yattendon* **628**
Royal Terrace Hotel *Edinburgh* **669**
Royal Trafalgar Thistle *WC2* **153**
Royal Victoria Hotel *Hastings* **398**
Royal Wells Inn *Tunbridge Wells* **590**
Royal Westminster Thistle *SW1* **153**
Royal York Hotel *York* **632**
RSJ *SE1* **148**
Rubens Hotel *SW1* **154**
Rudloe Park *Corsham* **336**
Rue St Jacques *W1* **154**
Rufflets Hotel *St Andrews* **708**
Rules *WC2* **154**
Rumbles Cottage *Felsted* **370**
Runnymede Hotel *Egham* **359**
Rusack's Hotel *St Andrews* **708**
Hotel Russell *WC1* **154**
Ruthin Castle *Ruthin* **745**
Rutland Square Hotel *Nottingham* **494**
Hotel Ryde Castle *Ryde* **526**
Ryecroft Hotel *Wooler* **624**
La Réserve *SW10* **150**
Röser's *Hastings* **398**

Sabras *NW10* **155**
Sachas Hotel *Manchester* **459**
Sachs Hotel *Dublin* **792**
Sackville Hotel *Brighton (Hove)* **288**
Saffron Hotel *Saffron Walden* **527**
Saga *W1* **155**
St Andrews Old Course Hotel *St Andrews* **708**
St Brelade's Bay Hotel *St Brelade's Bay* **759**
St David's Park Hotel *Ewloe* **730**
Hotel St George *Harrogate* **395**
St George Hotel *Eccleshall* **358**
St George Swallow Hotel *Sheffield* **540**
St George Thistle *Darlington* **342**
St George's Hotel *Liverpool* **441**
St George's Hotel *Llandudno* **734**
St George's Hotel *W1* **155**
St Giles Hotel *WC1* **155**
St James Court *SW1* **155**
St John's Swallow Hotel *Solihull* **548**
St Margaret's Lodge *St Martin* **752**
St Martin's Hotel *St Martin's* **529**
St Michael's *Falmouth* **367**
St Michael's Manor *St Albans* **528**
St Moritz *W1* **156**
St Non's Hotel *St David's* **745**
St Pierre Hotel *Chepstow* **727**
St Pierre Park *St Peter Port* **754**
St Quentin *SW3* **156**
St Tudno Hotel *Llandudno* **735**
Sala Thai *W5* **156**
Salford Hall *Abbot's Salford* **226**
Salloos *SW1* **156**
Sambuca *SW3* **157**
San Frediano *SW3* **157**
San Lorenzo *SW3* **157**
San Martino *SW3* **157**
Sand House *Rossnowlagh* **815**
Sandbanks Hotel *Poole* **511**
Sandrini *SW3* **158**
Sang Sang *Leeds* **433**
Santini *SW1* **158**
Saracen's Head *Great Dunmow* **384**
Saracen's Head *Southwell* **553**
Sardis *Darlington* **342**
SAS Portman *W1* **155**
Satay Hut *N1* **158**
Satis House *Yoxford* **633**
Saunton Sands *Saunton* **534**
Les Saveurs *W1* **158**
The Savoy *WC2* **159**
Scandic Crown *Edinburgh* **669**
Scandic Crown Euston *WC1* **160**
Scandic Crown Nelson Dock *SE16* **160**
Scandic Crown Victoria *SW1* **160**
Scarista House *Scarista* **709**
Scole Inn *Scole* **535**
Scourie Hotel *Scourie* **710**
Sea Crest *St Brelade* **758**
Sea View House *Ballylickey* **774**
Seafood Bar *Falmouth* **367**
Seafood Restaurant *Great Yarmouth* **387**
Seafood Restaurant *Padstow* **502**
Seaview Hotel *Seaview* **536**
Seckford Hall *Woodbridge* **622**
Sefton Hotel *Douglas* **762**
Seiont Manor *Llanrug* **737**
The Selfridge *W1* **160**
Selsdon Park *Croydon* **341**

Sema *SE22* **161**
September Brasserie *Blackpool* **266**
Hotel Seventy Degrees *Colwyn Bay* **728**
Seymour House *Chipping Campden* **327**
Shakespeare Hotel *Stratford-upon-Avon* **568**
Shalimar *Dublin* **792**
Shamiana *Edinburgh* **670**
Shampers *W1* **162**
Shanghai *W8* **162**
Sharrow Bay *Ullswater* **595**
Sheba *Wetherby* **609**
Sheekey's Restaurant *WC2* **162**
Sheen Falls Lodge *Kenmare* **801**
Shelbourne Hotel *Dublin* **792**
Shelleys Hotel *Lewes* **438**
Sheraton Belgravia *SW1* **162**
Sheraton Heathrow Hotel *Heathrow Airport* **404**
Sheraton Hotel *Edinburgh* **670**
Sheraton Park Tower *SW1* **163**
Sheraton Skyline *Heathrow Airport* **404**
Sherlock Holmes Hotel *W1* **163**
Shetland Hotel *Lerwick* **694**
Shieldhill *Quothquan* **707**
Shillingford Bridge Hotel *Wallingford* **601**
Ship Hotel *Parkgate* **503**
Ship Thistle *Weybridge* **610**
Shipdham Place *Shipdham* **542**
Shiro *Ahakista* **772**
Shogun *W1* **163**
Siam Orchid *Manchester* **460**
Signor Sassi *SW1* **164**
Silver Darling *Aberdeen* **641**
Silver Lake *SE5* **164**
Silver Plough *Pitton* **507**
Simonsbath House *Simonsbath* **545**
Simply Nico *SW1* **164**
Simpson's-in-the-Strand *WC2* **164**
Singapore Garden *NW6* **165**
Singapore *W4* **164**
Sir Charles Napier Inn *Chinnor* **326**
Sitwell Arms *Renishaw* **519**
Skeabost House *Skeabost Bridge* **710**
Skean Dhu Hotel *Aberdeen Airport* **642**
Skinburness Hotel *Silloth-on-Solway* **544**
Slatters Hotel *Canterbury* **308**
Slepe Hall *St Ives* **528**
Slieve Russell Hotel *Ballyconnell* **774**
Sligo Park *Sligo* **816**
Sloans *Birmingham* **264**
Snooty Fox Hotel *Tetbury* **582**
Snows on the Green *W6* **165**
Soar Mill Cove *Salcombe* **531**
Soho Soho *W1* **165**
Solberge Hall *Newby Wiske* **480**
Solent Hotel *Fareham* **367**
Sonarga *Manchester* **460**
Sonargaon *N1* **165**
Sonny's *Nottingham* **494**
Sonny's *SW13* **165**
Sopwell House *St Albans* **527**
Soufflé *Bearsted* **254**
Soughton Hall *Northop* **741**
Soulard Restaurant *N1* **166**
Sous le Nez en Ville *Leeds* **434**
South Lawn *Milford-on-Sea* **470**
South Lodge *Lower Beeding* **444**
South Sands *Salcombe* **531**

Southampton Park Hotel *Southampton* **552**
Spa Hotel *Tunbridge Wells* **591**
Spindlewood *Wadhurst* **599**
Spinnakers *Salcombe* **532**
Sportsman's Arms *Wath-in-Nidderdale* **605**
Spread Eagle *Midhurst* **470**
Spread Eagle Restaurant *SE10* **166**
Spread Eagle *Thame* **583**
Springfield Country Hotel *Wareham* **602**
Springfield Hotel *Gateshead* **374**
Springs Hotel *North Stoke* **486**
Sprowston Manor *Norwich* **491**
The Square *SW1* **167**
Sri Siam *W1* **167**
The Stables *Ayr* **650**
Stables Hotel *Llanwnda* **738**
Stade Court *Hythe* **417**
The Stafford *SW1* **167**
Staithes *Cheltenham* **320**
Stakis Aviemore Four Seasons *Aviemore* **649**
Stakis Bristol Hotel *Bristol* **292**
Stakis City Mills Hotel *Perth* **704**
Stakis Country Court Hotel *Maidstone* **453**
Stakis Country Court *Northampton* **487**
Stakis Coylumbridge Resort Hotel *Aviemore* **649**
Stakis Dunblane Hydro *Dunblane* **661**
Stakis Gantock Hotel *Gourock* **684**
Stakis Grand Hotel *Stoke-on-Trent* **560**
Stakis Grosvenor *Glasgow* **681**
Stakis Grosvenor Hotel *Edinburgh* **670**
Stakis Lodore Swiss Hotel *Borrowdale* **271**
Stakis Newbury Hotel *Newbury* **480**
Stakis Norfolk Gardens *Bradford* **278**
Stakis Normandy *Glasgow Airport* **683**
Stakis St Anne's Manor *Wokingham* **621**
Stakis St Ermin's *SW1* **167**
Stakis Tree Tops *Aberdeen* **641**
Stakis Victoria Hotel *Nottingham* **494**
Stane Street Hollow *Pulborough* **515**
Stanneylands *Wilmslow* **613**
Stanton Manor *Stanton St Quintin* **557**
Stanwell House *Lymington* **448**
Stapleford Park *Stapleford* **557**
Star & Eagle Inn *Goudhurst* **381**
Starlings Castle *Chirk* **727**
The Starr *Great Dunmow* **384**
State House *Land's End* **426**
Stephen Bull Bistro *EC1* **168**
Stephen Bull *W1* **168**
Stewart Hotel *Duror* **663**
Stock Hill House *Gillingham* **377**
Stocks Hotel *Sark* **761**
Stoke Lodge *Dartmouth* **344**
Ston Easton Park *Ston Easton* **561**
Stone Hall *Welsh Hook* **749**
Stone Manor *Kidderminster* **422**
Stonefield Castle *Tarbert* **714**
Stonehouse Court *Stonehouse* **562**
Stonor Arms *Stonor* **562**
Strand Restaurant *Belfast* **765**
Strangford Arms *Newtownards* **768**
Stratford House *Stratford-upon-Avon* **568**
Strathallan Thistle *Birmingham* **264**
Strathdon Thistle *Nottingham* **494**

Strathmore Thistle *Luton* **447**
Stratton House *Cirencester* **329**
Stretton Hall Hotel *All Stretton* **228**
String of Horses Inn *Faugh* **369**
Stuart Hotel *East Kilbride* **663**
Studley Hotel *Harrogate* **395**
Studley Priory *Horton-cum-Studley* **412**
Suffolk Hotel *Bury St Edmunds* **302**
Summer Isles *Achiltibuie* **643**
Summer Lodge *Evershot* **362**
Sumos *W6* **168**
Sun Hotel *Coniston* **333**
Sundial Restaurant *Herstmonceux* **407**
Sunlaws House *Kelso* **688**
Suntory *SW1* **169**
Supan *W9* **169**
Le Suquet *SW3* **169**
Sutton Hall *Macclesfield* **450**
Swainston Manor *Calbourne* **303**
Swallow Gosforth Park *Newcastle-upon-Tyne* **483**
Swallow Highcliff Hotel *Bournemouth* **274**
Swallow Hilltop *Carlisle* **309**
Swallow Hotel *Birmingham* **264**
Swallow Hotel *Gateshead* **374**
Swallow Hotel *Glasgow* **681**
Swallow Hotel *Newcastle-upon-Tyne* **483**
Swallow Hotel *Northampton* **487**
Swallow Hotel *Peterborough* **506**
Swallow Hotel *South Normanton* **550**
Swallow Hotel *Stockton-on-Tees* **559**
Swallow Hotel *Sunderland* **572**
Swallow Hotel *Wakefield* **599**
Swallow Hotel *York* **633**
Swallow International Hotel *SW5* **169**
Swallow King's Head *Darlington* **342**
Swallow Royal Hotel *Bristol* **293**
Swallow Royal Scot *Edinburgh* **670**
Swallow Trafalgar *Samlesbury* **533**
The Swan *Alton* **229**
The Swan *Bibury* **257**
The Swan *Bucklow Hill* **299**
Swan Diplomat *Streatley-on-Thames* **569**
The Swan *Grasmere* **382**
The Swan *Lavenham* **428**
The Swan *Leighton Buzzard* **436**
The Swan *Newby Bridge* **480**
The Swan *Southwold* **554**
Swansea Marriott *Swansea* **747**
Sweeny's Oughterard House *Oughterard* **812**
Swindon Marriott *Swindon* **576**
Swinfen Hall *Swinfen* **577**
Swiss Cottage Hotel *NW3* **169**
Swynford Paddocks *Six Mile Bottom* **545**
Sychnant Pass Hotel *Conwy* **728**
Sydney Street *SW3* **170**
Szechuan House *Edinburgh* **670**
La Sémillante *W1* **161**
Ta Se Mohogani Gaspipes *Dublin* **793**
Table Restaurant *Torquay* **588**
The Tageen *WC2* **170**
Le Talbooth *Dedham* **345**
Talbot Hotel *Oundle* **498**
Talbot Hotel *Stourbridge* **564**
Talland Bay Hotel *Looe* **444**
Tandoori Lane *SW6* **170**
Tannin Level *Harrogate* **395**
La Tante Claire *SW3* **170**
Tanyard Hotel *Boughton Monchelsea* **272**

Tarn End *Brampton* **280**
Tarn Hows Hotel *Hawkshead* **400**
Tate Gallery Restaurant *SW1* **171**
Tatsuso *EC2* **171**
Tatyan's *Cirencester* **329**
La Tavernetta *Folkestone* **372**
Taychreggan Hotel *Kilchrenan* **690**
Teesdale Hotel *Middleton-in-Teesdale* **470**
Telford Hotel *Telford* **581**
Templeton Hotel *Templepatrick* **769**
Terstan Hotel *SW5* **171**
Tewkesbury Park *Tewkesbury* **582**
Thackeray's House *Tunbridge Wells* **591**
Thai Siam *Leeds* **434**
Thailand Restaurant *SE14* **171**
That Café *Manchester* **460**
Thatchers Resort Hotel *East Horsley* **356**
Theobalds *Ixworth* **419**
Thierry's *SW3* **172**
36 On The Quay *Emsworth* **361**
Thistells *SE22* **172**
Thistles *Cromarty* **657**
Thomas Luny House *Teignmouth* **580**
Thompson's *Chichester* **325**
Thornbury Castle *Thornbury* **583**
Three Chimneys Restaurant *Colbost* **655**
Three Horseshoes Inn *Powerstock* **513**
Three Horseshoes *Madingley* **451**
The Three Lions *Stuckton* **571**
Three Swans Hotel *Market Harborough* **463**
Three Ways Hotel *Mickleton* **468**
Thruxted Oast *Chartham* **316**
Thurlestone Hotel *Thurlestone* **585**
Tickled Trout *Samlesbury* **533**
Tickton Grange *Tickton* **585**
Tides Reach *Salcombe* **532**
Tien Phat *SW6* **172**
Tiger Lee *SW5* **172**
Tiger under the Table *NW11* **172**
Tillington Hall *Stafford* **555**
Tillmouth Park *Cornhill-on-Tweed* **335**
Tinakilly House *Rathnew* **813**
Tinto Firs Hotel *Glasgow* **681**
Tiroran House *Tiroran* **714**
Tithas *Camberley* **304**
Tobermory Hotel *Tobermory* **715**
Tollbridge *Guist* **390**
Tonlegee House *Athy* **773**
Tontine Hotel *Peebles* **704**
Topkapi *W1* **173**
Topo's *Macclesfield* **451**
Topps Hotel *Brighton* **287**
Topsy Tasty *W4* **173**
Tor-na-Coille Hotel *Banchory* **652**
Torc Great Southern *Killarney* **804**
Tower Hotel *Waterford* **820**
The Tower *Sway* **575**
Tower Thistle *E1* **173**
Town House *Glasgow* **682**
Trattoria Lucca *NW1* **173**
Travel Inn *Aberdeen* **641**
Travel Inn *Ashford* **237**
Travel Inn *Basildon* **245**
Travel Inn *Basingstoke* **247**
Travel Inn *Cannock* **307**
Travel Inn *Cardiff* **726**
Travel Inn *Cheltenham* **320**
Travel Inn *Chessington* **321**

Travel Inn *Christchurch* **328**
Travel Inn *Croydon* **341**
Travel Inn *Cumbernauld* **657**
Travel Inn *Dover* **350**
Travel Inn *Dundee* **662**
Travel Inn *Gayton* **377**
Travel Inn *Gloucester* **379**
Travel Inn *Gloucester* **379**
Travel Inn *Hagley* **391**
Travel Inn *Hayes* **401**
Travel Inn *Hereford* **406**
Travel Inn *Horsham* **412**
Travel Inn *Kenton* **421**
Travel Inn *Newhouse* **699**
Travel Inn *Northampton* **488**
Travel Inn *Nuneaton* **495**
Travel Inn *Old Harlow* **498**
Travel Inn *Preston* **514**
Travel Inn *Rotherham* **524**
Travel Inn *Solihull* **548**
Travel Inn *Stockport* **559**
Travel Inn *Taunton* **579**
Travel Inn *Tring* **589**
Travel Inn *Warrington* **604**
Travel Inn *Wrotham Heath* **627**
Tre-Ysgawen Hall *Llangefni* **736**
Tredethy Country Hotel *Helland Bridge* **405**
Tree of Idleness *Bray* **777**
Trefeddian Hotel *Aberdovey* **720**
Tregarthen's Hotel *St Mary's* **530**
Treglos Hotel *Constantine Bay* **334**
La Trelade Hotel *St Martin* **752**
Hotel Tresanton *St Mawes* **530**
Trevena House *Farnham* **368**
La Truffe Noire *SE1* **173**
Tudor Court *Hawkhurst* **399**
Tudor Park *Bearsted* **254**
Tufton Arms *Appleby-in-Westmorland* **234**
Tui *SW7* **174**
Tuk Tuk Restaurant *N1* **174**
Tulchan Lodge *Advie* **644**
Tullich Lodge *Ballater* **650**
Turnberry Hotel *Turnberry* **715**
Turner's *SW3* **174**
Tuscany Hotel *Leamington Spa* **429**
Twenty Trinity Gardens *SW9* **174**
21 Queen Street   *Newcastle-upon-Tyne* **483**
22 Jermyn Street *SW1* **175**
Two Fat Ladies *Glasgow* **682**
Two Mile Inn *Limerick* **807**
Ty Mawr *Brechfa* **723**
Tyddyn Llan *Llandrillo* **733**
Tylney Hall *Rotherwick* **524**
Tynycornel Hotel *Talyllyn* **748**
Ubiquitous Chip *Glasgow* **682**
Udny Arms Hotel *Newburgh* **698**
Uig Hotel *Uig* **716**
Underscar Manor *Applethwaite* **234**
Unicorn Hotel *Bristol* **293**
Unicorn Hotel *Stow-on-the-Wold* **566**
University Arms *Cambridge* **306**
Uplands *Aldeburgh* **227**
Uplands *Cartmel* **310**
Upper Reaches *Abingdon* **226**
Veronica's *W2* **175**
Victor's Restaurant *Darlington* **343**
Victoria Hotel *Bradford* **278**
Victoria Hotel *Sidmouth* **544**

Victoria Park *Wolverhampton* **621**
Vijay *NW6* **175**
Viking Hotel *York* **633**
Village Bakery *Melmerby* **467**
Village Green *Trellech* **748**
Village Restaurant *Ramsbottom* **517**
Villandry Dining Room *W1* **175**
Vin Santo *SW10* **176**
Vine House *Paulerspury* **504**
Vintners Room, The Vaults *Edinburgh* **670**
Wakaba *NW3* **176**
The Waldorf *WC2* **176**
Wallett's Court *St Margaret's* **529**
Walnut Tree Inn *Abergavenny* **720**
Walnut Tree Inn *North Petherton* **486**
Walton's *SW3* **176**
Warmanbie Hotel *Annan* **646**
Warpool Court *St David's* **745**
Warren Lodge *Shepperton* **540**
Washington Hotel *W1* **176**
Water's Edge Hotel *Bouley Bay* **755**
Wateredge Hotel *Ambleside* **232**
Waterford Castle *Waterford* **820**
Wateringbury Hotel *Wateringbury* **605**
The Waterside Inn *Bray-on-Thames* **282**
Waterside Inn *Peterhead* **705**
Waveney House *Beccles* **255**
Weavers *Diss* **346**
Weavers *Haworth* **400**
Welcombe Hotel *Stratford-upon-Avon* **569**
Welcome Restaurant *Belfast* **765**
Well House *Liskeard* **440**
Well House *Watlington* **606**
Wellington Arms *Stratfield Turgis* **566**
Wellington Park *Belfast* **766**
Wentbridge House *Wentbridge* **607**
Wentworth Hotel *Aldeburgh* **227**
West Arms Hotel *Llanarmon Dyffryn Ceiriog* **732**
West County Inn *Ennis* **797**
West Lodge Park *Hadley Wood* **391**
The Westbury *Dublin* **793**
The Westbury *W1* **177**
Westerwood Hotel *Cumbernauld* **658**
Weston Manor *Weston-on-the-Green* **608**
Westone Moat House *Northampton* **488**
Wharton Lodge *Weston-under-Penyard* **608**
Whately Hall *Banbury* **241**
Whatley Manor *Easton Grey* **358**
Whipper-In Hotel *Oakham* **497**
White Cliffs Hotel *Dover* **350**
White Friars Hotel *Boreham Street* **270**
White Hart *Coggeshall* **332**
White Hart *Exeter* **364**
White Hart Inn *Andover* **233**
White Hart Inn *Moretonhampstead* **472**
White Hart *Lincoln* **439**
White Hart *Newmarket* **484**
White Hart *Salisbury* **532**
White Hart *St Austell* **528**
White Hart *Uttoxeter* **598**
White Horse *Darlington* **343**
White Horse *Dorking* **348**
White Horse Hotel *Hertingfordbury* **408**
White Horse Hotel *Romsey* **522**
White Horse Inn *Chilgrove* **325**
White House *Herm* **754**
White House *NW1* **177**
White House *Williton* **612**

White Moss House *Grasmere* **382**
White Swan *Alnwick* **228**
White Swan *Stratford-upon-Avon* **569**
White Tower *W1* **177**
White's Hotel *Wexford* **821**
Whitechapel Manor *South Molton* **549**
Whitehall *Broxted* **298**
Whitehaven Hotel *Brighton (Hove)* **288**
Whites Hotel *W2* **177**
Whittington's *EC4* **178**
Whitwell Hall *Whitwell-on-the-Hill* **611**
Wickens *Northleach* **488**
Wilbraham Hotel *SW1* **178**
Wild Boar *Bunbury* **299**
Wild Boar Hotel *Crook* **339**
Willerby Manor *Willerby* **612**
Willett Hotel *SW1* **178**
William Harding's House *Penkridge* **504**
The Willows *Ashington* **238**
Wilson's *W14* **178**
Wilton's *SW1* **178**
Wiltshire Hotel *Swindon* **576**
Wincham Hall *Northwich* **489**
Windlestrae Hotel *Kinross* **693**
Windmill Park *Stratford-upon-Avon* **569**
Wine & Mousaka *Richmond* **520**
Wine & Mousaka *W5* **179**
Winterbourne Hotel *Bonchurch* **270**
Winteringham Fields *Winteringham* **618**
Wish Tower Hotel *Eastbourne* **357**
Witney Lodge *Witney* **619**
Wodka *W8* **179**
Wood Hall *Linton* **439**

Woodbury House *East Grinstead* **356**
Woodhayes Hotel *Whimple* **610**
Woodlands *Manchester* **460**
Woodlands Manor *Bedford* **255**
Woodlands Park *Cobham* **331**
Woods Place *Grayshott* **383**
Woody Bay Hotel *Woody Bay* **623**
Woolacombe Bay Hotel *Woolacombe* **623**
Woolley Grange *Bradford-on-Avon* **278**
Woolpack Hotel *Kendal* **420**
Wordsworth Hotel *Grasmere* **383**
Wrea Head *Scalby* **534**
Wroxton House *Wroxton St Mary* **627**
Wyck Hill House *Stow-on-the-Wold* **566**
Wykeham Arms *Winchester* **614**
Wynnstay Arms *Machynlleth* **739**
Wynnstay Hotel *Oswestry* **498**
Xian *Hindhead* **409**
Y Bistro *Llanberis* **732**
Yalbury Cottage *Dorchester* **347**
Yang Sing *Manchester* **461**
Yardley Court *SE9* **179**
Ye Olde Bell *Barnby Moor* **242**
Ye Olde Bell *Hurley* **416**
Ye Olde Dog & Partridge Inn *Tutbury* **592**
Yeoldon House *Bideford* **258**
Ynyshir Hall *Eglwysfach* **730**
Young's Rendezvous *W5* **179**
Yumi *W1* **179**
Zen *SW3* **180**
Zetland House *Cashel* **778**
Ziani *SW3* **180**

BRITANNIA FOOD SAFETY SERVICE LTD

NEW RECIPE FOR HYGIENE

Eating out is one of life's pleasures but not if it damages your health. Over the last few years, there has been an unfortunate and unprecedented increase in food – borne illnesses. In 1990, the Government brought in The Food Safety Act with the aim of providing greater controls through the food chain, from source to ultimate consumption.

The Act also strengthens the powers of enforcement and toughens up the penalties for offences.

However, the Government does not – and could not – tell the food industry in detail how to do the job. The responsibility for ensuring the safety of food rests with those who prepare, handle, serve or sell it.

The Britannia Food Safety and Hygiene Award Scheme provides clear, practical guidance, on complying with the Food Safety Act and on all matters relating to food safety and hygiene. It is open to restaurants, hotels, pubs, bars, cafes – anywhere food is prepared and sold.

The aim is to raise consumer confidence in eating out.

THE SCHEME WORKS LIKE THIS.

When a catering establishment joins, a Britannia environmental health specialist visits the premises and carries out a comprehensive inspection. The objective is to highlight areas where hygiene practices or the condition of premises or equipment fall below optimum standards.

The establishment is then provided with a customised manual – a food safety Bible – which sets out, step by step, the routines that need to be followed to ensure compliance with the Act. Food storage arrangements, for example, monitoring of temperatures in chiller cabinets and display counters, cleaning routines, pest control and basic training in staff hygiene, are just some of the elements covered. It adds up to a complete food safety and hygiene management system including documentation and record keeping.

At the end of three months the inspector returns and if the changes needed to bring the premises and procedures up to standard have been implemented, a Britannia Food Safety and Hygiene Award Certificate is issued. The first establishment to apply for membership of the scheme and receive its certificate was the Dorchester Hotel in London.

Return visits are made at six monthly or quarterly intervals to confirm that standards are being maintained.

24 HOUR HOTLINE

Besides the Award Certificate, members of the scheme have other benefits too. There is a 24 hour hot line for legal or technical information on any Food Safety Act query. In an emergency a Britannia specialist will be on site within hours. Any changes to the law are notified and explained, and, in the unlikely event of a prosecution being served, Britannia backs its service with a legal expenses guarantee up to £25,000 per claim providing the standards set out in the manual have been maintained.

The Food Safety Act is where the Britannia Food Safety and Hygiene Award Scheme starts. Many establishments move on, under Britannia's guidance, to bring in improvements which take them above the minimum required standards.

People eat out now more than ever before and are acutely aware of food related illnesses. The public needs assurance that the food they eat is safe and prepared in premises which conform to high standards of hygiene. The Britannia Food Safety and Hygiene Award Scheme gives people that confidence.

When you see the Britannia Food Safety and Hygiene Award certificate in your favourite eating place, you know it is operating to high standards of hygiene and food safety.

Egon Ronay's Guides Information Lines

As an additional service to our readers we offer the following round-the-clock recorded information lines.

New restaurants in London **0891 334300**
Places to stay with children in London **0891 334301**
Dining and Dancing in London **0891 334302**
Restaurants for theatre-goers in London **0891 334303**
Sunday eating in London **0891 334304**

New restaurants in England **0891 334305**
New restaurants in Scotland **0891 334306**
New restaurants in Wales **0891 334307**

Sunday eating in England **0891 334308**
Sunday eating in Scotland **0891 334309**
Sunday eating in Wales **0891 334310**

Paris hotels **0891 334313**
Paris restaurants **0891 334314**

Brussels hotels **0891 334315**
Brussels restaurants **0891 334316**

New de luxe hotels with recommended restaurants **0891 334317**

Restaurants avec chambres, some restaurants with outstanding bedrooms **0891 334320**

Places to stay with children out of London **0891 334325**

Our inspectors choose **0891 334326**

Broadsystem Ltd. The Elephant House Hawley Crescent London NW1 8NP

Calls are charged at 36p per minute at cheap rate and 48p per minute at other times.
These charges do not apply to calls from cellphones, for details contact your cellular Service Provider/Dealer.

READERS' COMMENTS

Please use this sheet, and the continuation overleaf, to recommend hotels or restaurants of **really outstanding quality.**

Complaints about any of the Guide's entries will be treated seriously and passed on to our inspectorate, but we would like to remind you always to take up your complaint with the management at the time.

We regret that owing to the volume of readers' communications received each year, we will be unable to acknowledge these forms, but they will certainly be seriously considered.

Please post to: **Egon Ronay's Guides, 73 Uverdale Road, London SW10 0SW**

Please use an up-to-date Guide. We publish annually. (1993)

Name and address of establishment	Your recommendation or complaint

1002

Readers' Comments continued

Name and address of establishment	Your recommendation or complaint

Your Name (BLOCK LETTERS PLEASE)

Address

READERS' COMMENTS

Please use this sheet, and the continuation overleaf, to recommend hotels or restaurants of **really outstanding quality.**

   Complaints about any of the Guide's entries will be treated seriously and passed on to our inspectorate, but we would like to remind you always to take up your complaint with the management at the time.

   We regret that owing to the volume of readers' communications received each year, we will be unable to acknowledge these forms, but they will certainly be seriously considered.

Please post to: **Egon Ronay's Guides, 73 Uverdale Road, London SW10 0SW**

Please use an up-to-date Guide. We publish annually. (1993)

Name and address of establishment	Your recommendation or complaint

1004

Readers' Comments continued

Name and address of establishment	Your recommendation or complaint

Your Name (BLOCK LETTERS PLEASE)

Address

READERS' COMMENTS

Please use this sheet, and the continuation overleaf, to recommend hotels or restaurants of **really outstanding quality.**

Complaints about any of the Guide's entries will be treated seriously and passed on to our inspectorate, but we would like to remind you always to take up your complaint with the management at the time.

We regret that owing to the volume of readers' communications received each year, we will be unable to acknowledge these forms, but they will certainly be seriously considered.

Please post to: **Egon Ronay's Guides, 73 Uverdale Road, London SW10 0SW**

Please use an up-to-date Guide. We publish annually. (1993)

Name and address of establishment	Your recommendation or complaint

Readers' Comments continued

Name and address of establishment	Your recommendation or complaint

Your Name (BLOCK LETTERS PLEASE)

Address

READERS' COMMENTS

Please use this sheet, and the continuation overleaf, to recommend hotels or restaurants of **really outstanding quality.**

Complaints about any of the Guide's entries will be treated seriously and passed on to our inspectorate, but we would like to remind you always to take up your complaint with the management at the time.

We regret that owing to the volume of readers' communications received each year, we will be unable to acknowledge these forms, but they will certainly be seriously considered.

Please post to: **Egon Ronay's Guides, 73 Uverdale Road, London SW10 0SW**

Please use an up-to-date Guide. We publish annually. (1993)

Name and address of establishment	Your recommendation or complaint

Name and address of establishment	Your recommendation or complaint

Your Name (BLOCK LETTERS PLEASE)

Address